A RECIPE FOR
H·E·A·L·T·H

A RECIPE FOR

H·E·A·L·T·H

• Building a strong immune system •

Dr Ian Brighthope & Ruth Maier
with Peter Fitzgerald

McCulloch Publishing

The publishers would like to thank Villeroy & Boch for their assistance in providing the crockery for the colour photographs in this book.

First published 1989 by McCulloch Publishing Pty Ltd
348 Drummond Street, Carlton, Vic. 3053

© Ian Brighthope, Ruth Maier, Peter Fitzgerald, 1989

Designed by Sandra Nobes
Food stylist Ann Creber
Photography Philip Wymant
Typeset by Meredith Typesetters, Richmond, Vic.
Printed by Griffin Press Limited, Netley, South Australia

Cataloguing-in-publication

Brighthope, Ian, 1946–
   A recipe for health, building a strong immune system.

   Includes index
   ISBN 0 949646 26 1

   1. Cookery. 2. Immunity — Nutritional aspects. I. Maier,
   Ruth, 1939– . II. Fitzgerald, Peter, 1940– . III. Title
   641.5'63

FRONT COVER: Barbecued Chicken Dinner

C·O·N·T·E·N·T·S

1 Introduction 7

2 How to Get the Most From This Book 23

3 Getting Organised 25

4 Tonics & Juices 30

5 Breakfast 40

6 Soups 53

7 Salads 59

8 Main Dishes 69

9 Side Dishes 97

10 Desserts 112

11 Breads & Loaves 131

12 Selecting Your Own Menu Plan 147

References & Further Reading 173

Index 174

IAN BRIGHTHOPE specialises in nutritional and orthomolecular medicine, particularly in the treatment of cancer, psychiatric disorders, heart disease, allergies, arthritis, skin disease, asthma and auto-immune diseases.

A graduate in both agricultural science and medicine, Ian Brighthope became interested in the implications of human nutrition and disease. His concern about the effects on the food chain of the increasing use of chemicals in agricultural production and food processing led him to investigate the consequences for the human nervous and immune systems.

Dr Brighthope is President of the Australian College of Nutritional Medicine, was a founding director of the Orthomolecular Medical Association of Australia, is a Fellow of both the International College of Applied Nutrition and the New York based Academy of Orthomolecular Psychiatry and is principal lecturer for Australia's first post-graduate medical course in nutrition which he pioneered. His many publications include *The Aids Fighters*, *You Can Knock Out Aids* and *Sleep Soundly*.

■   ■   ■

RUTH MAIER has been involved in nutrition education for over 26 years. During this time she has taught in both state and private high schools, lectured for 12 years at Rusden State College, undertaken a range of consultancies and conducted over 20 public lectures in both Australia and New Zealand. Areas of particular interest to Ruth Maier include nutrition for adolescents, the elderly, the overweight and those with specific health problems. She is a member of the Nutrition Society of Australia, the Australian Public Health Association and the International Federation of Home Economics.

■   ■   ■

PETER FITZGERALD is a Melbourne freelance journalist and writer. Previously medical writer for *The Herald*, Peter Fitzgerald is interested in consumer affairs generally and health issues in particular. Previous publications in which Peter Fitzgerald has been involved include *Manage Your Pain – New Hope for Chronic Pain Sufferers* and *Mirrors of the Mind – The Creative Powers of your Imagination*, both with Dr Leonard Rose and, with Dr Ian Brighthope, *The Aids Fighters*, *You Can Knock Out Aids* and *Sleep Soundly*.

· 1 ·
INTRODUCTION –
IMPROVING · IMMUNITY

Throughout history famine and pestilence have taken their toll with disastrous consequences for various cultures. The Black Plague of the 14th century which killed more than 25 million in Western Europe is a good example. However, many societies have recognised that there is an association between malnutrition and lowered resistance to various diseases – in particular infectious disease.

All living things including animals, plants and humans suffer from infectious and degenerative diseases specific to their species. In humans, such illness and death is frequently the direct result of various nutrient deficiencies which impair proper working function of the body's systems – especially the immune system.

In our society, which is typical of western, industrialised nations, we see many malnourished individuals. This malnourishment actually results from the over-consumption of refined carbohydrates which include sugar and sugar-containing products, white flour products and alcohol. Also, the excessive intake of fats in take-away foods, animal flesh and dairy products contributes to this malnourishment.

Extra salt and the enormous quantity of chemical additives in our food supply aggravate poor nourishment and add excessively high toxic loads on to the body's biochemistry. These poisonous substances can, of course, put a strain on our body's tissues and organs, including the immune defence system. The result is often damage to the immune system followed by its failure to work properly.

The consumption of poor quality food, together with a relative lack of important vitamins, minerals and other essential nutritional factors, normally present in our foods, contributes to the production of many diseases including recurrent infections, inflammatory disorders such as arthritis and eczema, allergies and even cancer.

• THE DESTRUCTION OF NUTRIENTS •

In many illnesses and disease states, there are on-going processes which adversely affect the sufferer's nutritional status. The persistence of a chronic viral infection, for example, will somehow adversely affect the nutritional status of a person in a way which is not completely understood.

The presence of a disease, or illness, causes the body to be less efficient in managing the nutrients which it obtains from the diet. Also, disease changes the need for various nutrients. For example, zinc and amino acids are required in greater amounts during times of infection, inflammation and stress. Certain diseases may interfere with the functioning of internal organs with subsequent loss of nutrients from the gut or from the kidneys via the urine.

Most degenerative diseases have an effect on the absorptive capacity of the intestines. We find that the intestine doesn't take up the nutrients that it should – a form of malabsorption. This of course is aggravated by the presence of various parasites in the gut. These parasites often over-grow in people with severe disease, especially if they are taking antibiotics or other drugs. An example is the overgrowth of the yeast organism *Candida*, which causes thrush, after the use of antibiotics or the contraceptive pill.

The presence of severe illness often produces such a malnourished state that the body has no way of naturally healing itself. The immune system, in particular, becomes over-worked resulting in a progressive downhill spiral.

Various combinations of poor nutrition can co-exist. These include deficiencies of proteins, calories, or specific nutrients, for example, vitamins, minerals, trace elements or essential fatty acids. These deficiencies, or imbalances, may result in far-reaching changes to the immune system. Imbalances in nutrients can also cause changes in a person's psychological and mental state resulting in anxiety, depression and of course chronic fatigue, lethargy and physical weakness.

The changes to the immune system which occur as a result of nutritional deficiencies and imbalances include:

- A reduction in the number of white cells needed to fight infections.
- A decrease in the number of antibodies produced by certain white cells which inactivate bacteria and viruses.
- A reduction in the concentration of special messenger chemicals produced by the immune system including such things as 'interferon' and 'complement'. These are chemicals in the blood which improve the action of antibodies and white cells and which carry messages and information from one part of the immune system to another.

• PREVENTION – NEVER TOO LATE •

Careful nutritional assessment is very important for people who have developed a disorder of the immune system. It's also very important for those who have a family history of disease and who are at risk of developing a weakened immune system. Their diet and lifestyle should be assessed very early and changes made as quickly as possible in order that they can live free of the disease.

Super-optimal performance of the immune system can be achieved with diet. There have been many scientific studies done which show that poor nutrition can alter the competence of the immune system. Even people who think they have a good, well-balanced diet may suffer from one or more nutrient deficiencies, thus putting them at a slight disadvantage. The help of a doctor, or dietitian, suitably experienced in nutritional medicine should be sought if you have doubts about your diet and nutrient intake.

▪ VIRAL INFECTIONS AND DIET ▪

A viral infection can take a number of different forms. For example, the common cold can affect some people very severely. Others will only experience a few minor symptoms. A similar situation also occurs with hepatitis, glandular fever and meningitis-causing viruses. The difference isn't so much in the infective agent but rather it is in the patient's response to that particular virus. Individuals who are run down, poorly nourished and who are under chronic stress suffer more frequently and severely from simple viral infections than those who are optimally nourished and who control their stress levels.

Millions of people world-wide now know the value of good diet and vitamin C in the prevention of viral infections such as the common cold and influenza. If they are unfortunate enough to contract a viral infection, they know that its severity will be minimised because of their improved eating patterns. Others choose to add food like garlic or cod-liver oil to their diet knowing increased resistance to infection results.

Poor nutrition, on the other hand, will suppress the immune response. Resistance to disease is thereby reduced. By impairing the production of antibodies, suppressing the immune cells and reducing the ability of the body's surfaces such as the skin and the mucous membranes to stop viral invasion, poor diet and substandard nutrition pave the way for more infections, allergies, immune diseases and perhaps even cancer.

▪ NUTRIENTS IMPORTANT FOR 'IMMUNE FUNCTION' ▪

The competence of the immune system is reduced in individuals who have a deficiency of a single nutrient, for example, a vitamin or trace mineral. Usually, however, multiple deficiencies are more common, particularly in the very ill and the aged.

It appears that the most important nutrients for the proper and adequate functioning of the immune system are proteins, essential fatty acids, and vitamins A,

E, B2, B5, B6, folic acid, vitamin B12 – and most importantly, ascorbic acid (vitamin C).

The most important minerals required for the proper functioning of the immune system include zinc, iron, manganese, magnesium, copper and the trace elements selenium and germanium.

Also important are accessory food factors which may play an important role in indirectly supporting the nutrients for the immune system. These include such things as the bioflavonoids. Bioflavonoids are substances found in nature which are closely associated with vitamin C. They are responsible for the red, yellow and orange colourings in various fruits and vegetables. Lemon bioflavonoids are present in the skin of the lemon fruit. They support the function of vitamin C and help prevent its metabolic destruction in the body. Some of the bioflavonoids themselves also play a role in suppressing viral growth.

▪ WHY DO I NEED A NUTRIENT-RICH DIET? ▪

There are many reasons why you may need to increase the nutritional value of your diet. Many people believe that by eating a well-balanced diet, they can obtain all of the important nutrients from food, including vitamins and minerals necessary for good health. The problem is the definition of a well-balanced diet. Some regard a well-balanced diet as one which consists of a take-away meal from a different fast food outlet every night of the week. Others believe that they can balance their diet by adding a few fruits and vegetables while consuming huge quantities of meat, white bread and carbonated soft drinks.

Even if one is consuming a very well-balanced diet by selecting foods from the five major food groups, the nutrient values within the foods of those groups may be low.

Nutrition in fact plays a very important role in many illnesses and therefore should never be ignored. This book is of value to both hospitals and other institutions caring for the sick and injured and for anyone interested in increasing the intake of nutrients essential for improving the body's defences. Improving your diet is a safe method of creating an immune system which can fight infections and prevent the onset of degenerative diseases.

▪ WHY WE SHOULD INCREASE OUR INTAKE OF ▪ NUTRIENT-RICH FOODS

STRESS

Physical and emotional stresses can increase the body's requirements for certain nutrients including the water-soluble B-group vitamins and ascorbic acid. Supplementation of the diet with these nutrients can increase one's resistance to the ravaging effects of most stresses.

POLLUTION

Environmental pollutants interfere with the body's biochemistry. These pollutants can poison the body's enzymes and increase the production of harmful so-called 'free radicals'. Free radicals are chemicals which destroy the highly complex large molecules such as proteins and nucleic acids in our cells which may result in mutations, or cancer. The presence of these free radicals increases the body's requirements for nutrients such as vitamin E and beta-carotene.

DISEASE AND ACCIDENTS

At the first sign of an infection, the body's defence system responds to the challenge by consuming greater than usual quantities of amino acids, zinc, magnesium and vitamins B5 and B6. These nutrients are used to produce antibodies and increase white cells to attack and destroy the invading germs.

There are many diseases and illnesses in which nutrients are required in greater quantities than usual. These diseases include arthritis, diabetes, auto-immune disorders, cancer, leukaemia, lymphoma, skin diseases, allergies, asthma, bowel diseases and AIDS.

Even trauma such as an emotional crisis, motor car accident causing broken bones and lacerations, head injuries, near drownings, burns or even exposure to toxic chemical spills, increases the need for specific nutrients. For example, if the diet is low in calcium and vitamin C, the repair of fractured bones is retarded. People undergoing surgery also have an increased requirement for zinc, vitamin E and proteins which are necessary for cellular repair and regeneration.

Victims of burns suffer large losses of protein and trace elements from the fluid which leaks out of the burns' site. Accident victims who have lost blood will certainly require nutritional replenishment and, in some cases, even a blood transfusion.

CONVENIENCE AND JUNK FOODS

These foods are usually very highly processed and contain unnecessarily high concentrations of sugar, salt, refined carbohydrates such as white flour and added fats which also are usually used in the cooking process.

During the processing of these foods many nutrients are either destroyed or lost. For example, excessive cooking destroys the B complex vitamins and vitamin C. The processing of white flour results in the removal of over 90 per cent of the important vitamins and minerals in the wheat grain. It also removes fibre. Fibre is important for healthy bowel function and deficiencies of fibre are associated with diseases such as constipation, hemorrhoids, diverticulitis, high cholesterol, diabetes, varicose veins, gall stones and even cancer of the large bowel.

An unbalanced diet, resulting from the consumption of convenience foods, will very quickly result in such conditions as lethargy, irritability, anxiety, depression, a feeling of unwellness and in some cases sleep disorders and severe psychological and behavioural problems.

These highly processed foods also create an increased demand on the body's digestive and metabolic resources. These demands in themselves can result in the body's depletion of essential nutrients.

In other words, junk foods place unusual stresses on the body's metabolic machinery which in the short term may not have any drastic noticeable effect but in the long-term will cause damage of one form or another.

CAFFEINE, COLA AND HOT SPICES

The habitual drinking of beverages containing caffeine and cola, including tea and coffee, can act as irritants to the stomach and intestines resulting in reduced efficiency. Very hot, spicy foods can also cause inflammation of the linings of these organs. This results in a reduction of the absorption of food and nutrients from the bowel into the body.

The secretion of important digestive fluids may also be inhibited as a consequence of the consumption of these beverages. Caffeine, for example, has been shown to increase the loss of calcium in the urine and this loss is sufficient to explain the development of osteoporosis (or bone-loss) in middle-aged women.

ALCOHOL

Alcohol can damage the lining of the intestinal tract resulting in poor absorption of nutrients. This leads to mild to severe forms of malnutrition. The regular, heavy use of alcohol not only damages the brain, liver and pancreas – which are vital organs for organisation, digestion and metabolism – but heavy alcohol use increases the body's need for certain of the B group vitamins and a number of minerals including zinc and magnesium.

Alcohol not only kills the body's cells, but it also affects the availability, absorption and use of many nutrients in the diet. This is why many people who have alcohol-related problems are frequently ill from a wide variety of disorders, many of which are the result of a nutritionally-depleted immune system.

SMOKING

Smoking greatly increases the requirements for vitamin C. Vitamin C is essential for the normal functioning of the immune system. The immune system suffers in smokers. In fact important 'helper' cells of the immune system are actually destroyed or reduced in numbers in people who smoke.

Medical evidence has also shown that smokers who are low in vitamins A and E have a greater risk of developing lung cancer. Smokers, and even ex-smokers, would be wise to follow the recommendations concerning diet outlined in this book.

Fresh fruit, vegetables and sprouted seeds, such as alfalfa sprouts, are high in vitamin C, and these foods are important especially for smokers and those who have to live or work in a smoky environment.

FOOD PROCESSING AND COOKING METHODS

The thawing of meats results in the loss of juices containing many important nutrients. Lengthy cooking of many foodstuffs can destroy or oxidise essential vitamins, such as the B group complex, vitamins C and E. Microwave cooking can destroy some nutrients, and may even produce harmful by-products. (Vitamin B6, for example, is destroyed by microwave irradiation.)

Over-heating or boiling vegetables in excessive quantities of water can not only destroy nutrients but leaches out very important minerals; the minerals are thrown out in the waste cooking water while the vegetables are eaten depleted of valuable mineral content. The best method of preparing vegetables is by light steaming or rapid stir frying as in the Chinese technique of cooking. In fact, eating many raw vegetables in the form of salads is one way of ensuring a minimum loss of nutrients from preparation.

FOOD STORAGE

Although home freezing and short-term food storage may not adversely affect food quality greatly, prolonged food storage results in changes to the taste and texture of food. In many cases, there is an obvious loss of that 'freshness' quality. However, probably the most important effect of food storage is the change to the levels of vitamin E. Vitamin E is a naturally occurring anti-oxidant or preservative which helps to protect food from losing its freshness and becoming rancid. To improve the storage life of breads, the oil content of flour is removed to prevent it becoming rancid. But the removal of oils from the flour also results in the removal of vitamin E. As a result, white flour products are devoid of the oils and vitamin E usually present, both of which are important for health.

Food storage and preservation involve the addition of synthetic anti-oxidant chemicals. Some of these chemicals can interfere with our metabolism. For example, the preservatives, sulphites and sulphates in soft drinks, sausages, manufactured meats and dried fruits such as dried apricots may interfere with the metabolism of the B complex vitamins. Nitrites from foods grown with artificial nitrogenous fertilisers can be converted in the intestine to nitrosamines which are cancer producing chemicals. This conversion to cancer-causing chemicals can be prevented by increasing the intake of ascorbic acid (vitamin C).

It is however important that any food that has been processed or stored and has had chemicals added to it be used only if the rest of the diet can be shown to be adequate and sufficient in many of these protective nutrients.

Other challenges to the human immune system are chemical additives to which many people develop sensitivities or allergies. Again, the well-nourished immune system can help to protect against these problems.

AGRICULTURAL PROCEDURES

Over many years of crop production, soils which have been over-worked become depleted of minerals and essential trace elements. They can also lose their normal physical structure with the result that poor quality crops are grown. Many soils around the world are known to be deficient in certain trace elements. Crops can still be grown on these soils but the food produced may be deficient in trace elements. For example, certain forms of cancer and heart disease are more common in areas of the world where selenium deficient soils exist.

In America, the levels of essential minerals in crops declined by nearly 70 per cent over a four year period. It's also been estimated that some soils in America and Australia have only another 25 to 30 years of productive life left in them.

These soils are already in a poor condition. With such poor quality soils, we cannot expect to obtain the best quality foods. Therefore, following a nutrient-concentrated diet from time to time as outlined in this book would be a wise thing to do if you wish to maintain a healthy immune system.

ANTIBIOTICS AND OTHER MEDICATIONS

Many medications interfere with the digestion and absorption of nutrients from the foods we eat. Antibiotics in particular can do this. In fact, many people with a mild to moderate weakness of the immune system, and who suffer from recurring infections throughout the winter, take antibiotics as a matter of course. The anti-biotics they take not only kill the disease-producing bacteria but also the friendly bacteria that are normally present in the gut. These friendly bacteria normally produce B group vitamins which are absorbed through the intestinal wall. For people who are on long-term medications or antibiotics, the high nutrient intake of the recipes in this book will not only benefit their general condition but also help to overcome some of the problems caused by drug-nutrient interactions.

▪ INDIVIDUAL REQUIREMENTS ▪

We are all individuals and have different and distinct requirements for specific nutrients from our diets. No two people have exactly the same requirements. Wide fluctuations from the official recommended nutritional intakes are common. This is especially so for pregnant women, athletes, hard manual labourers and those of us who are at risk of developing a disease which runs in families, for example, diabetes, arthritis and heart disease. A menopausal woman has greater requirements of calcium than a man of the same age. Higher intakes of vitamin B6 are recommended for people on relatively high protein diets, for example, those who eat a lot of meat and fish.

Manual labourers who consume extra calories for energy require more thiamine (vitamin B1) than sedentary workers who eat a lower energy diet.

It's been suggested that people who, because of a strong family history, are at risk of developing certain diseases such as cancer, diabetes, heart disease, asthma and some immune-based disorders should increase their intake of nutritionally dense foods in order to prevent these disorders developing. For example, the National Cancer Institute in the United States now recommends an increased intake of green and yellow vegetables to reduce the incidence of certain cancers such as bowel cancer.

These foods either contain anti-cancer factors or factors which aid the immune system in eliminating cancer growth. Medical experts are also recommending the consumption of oily, cold water fish such as sardines, herring and mackerel to protect against heart disease.

Oat bran and some other plant foods are helpful in reducing cholesterol. A complex carbohydrate diet containing plenty of unprocessed plant food can greatly help in the management and control of blood sugar levels in diabetic patients. Individuality is a crucial factor in optimum nutrition. This individuality is determined by both genetic and environmental influences.

FOOD ALLERGIES AND SENSITIVITIES

These are more common than once suspected and many people who suffer from mild to moderate symptoms may have food sensitivities.

Symptoms may include headaches and migraines, rashes, joint pains, muscle weakness and fatigue, sore throats and swollen glands, undiagnosed abdominal pains and cramps, recurrent infections (inflammations), loose bowels, burning or frequency of urination and even psychological problems such as anxiety and depression.

There are a number of approaches to the treatment of these food allergies and sensitivities – the most common being the avoidance of the offending foods. However, quite often people with allergies are taken off a large number of foods in an attempt to improve their health. Sometimes this works but more often than not it is prone to failure. The failure occurs because very restricted diets are almost impossible for the average person to comply with.

Another more satisfactory approach is to eliminate one or two of the major offending foods and place the allergy sufferer on a rotation diet in which food and food groups are not eaten regularly. This means that a particular food may be eaten only once in every three to four days. The use of an immune-boosting diet program, with meal planners as outlined in this book, is an ideal way of strengthening the immune system in people with allergies.

The families of allergy sufferers can also benefit from the dietary approach in this book. From time to time, a short interval of five to 10 days on the immune-boosting diet may help to protect against the development, or progression, of allergies in your family.

It's not always necessary, for example, to totally remove from your diet grains containing gluten or dairy products containing lactose with the consequent loss of significant dietary sources of nutrients including vitamins B2, B1, calcium, protein and good quality fibre. Sensitivities to these foods can be modified with a nutritionally-concentrated diet – combined with moderate reductions in the quantities of these foods and the frequency with which they are consumed.

PICKY EATERS

Some people eat very small quantities of food. Providing they have sedentary occupations and do very little or no exercise, they are able to maintain their normal weight. Because of their lower than average food intake, the important nutrients they require for optimum health may also be low. This puts them at risk of obtaining lower than optimum intakes of some essential micro-nutrients.

In cases of anorexia nervosa, severe dieting and purging with laxatives results in gross body wasting. Zinc deficiency is common in anorexics. Zinc deficiency causes a loss of the sensation of taste (hypogeusia). This loss of taste sensation results in a diminished appreciation of food and further aggravates the anorexia. Zinc supplementation, with improved diet, plus the removal of food allergies or intolerances in anorectics, is essential for recovery. The psychological problems become much easier to resolve as well.

LOWERED BODY RESERVES

Our bodies are marvellous machines which can function under many different forms of stress. We can store many important nutrients and vitamins such as A and E.

Despite the ability of our bodies to conserve vitamin A, Canadian autopsy data has shown that up to 30 per cent of the population has reserves of vitamin A so low as to be judged 'at risk'. Vitamin A is an essential nutrient for healthy skin and mucous membranes, including the linings of the lungs, intestines and sinuses. Vitamin A also plays a vital role in proper immune function. A low, or deficient, level of vitamin A has been associated with increased infection rates, especially in children and increased rates of cancer, especially in smokers.

ATHLETES

In general, athletes tend to consume large amounts of food, often processed and containing lowered concentrations of essential nutrients. They also experience considerable psychological and physical stresses.

The excessive consumption of protein-rich foods and protein powder supplements which some athletes consume may increase requirements for B complex vitamins, especially vitamin B6.

All these factors definitely effect their needs for iron, magnesium, zinc, the B complex vitamins and vitamin C. It's been shown by tests on Australian Olympic athletes and by tests on A-grade footballers that wide-ranging vitamin deficiencies occur in these groups.

Also, while still controversial, it appears that supplementation of an athlete's diet with these essential nutrients can improve their performance. The use of the high calorie, high-nutrient dense menus in this book are an ideal way of improving an athlete's nutritional status without necessarily having to resort to high-dose supplementation.

WOMEN OF REPRODUCTIVE AGE, PREGNANT AND LACTATING WOMEN

An average woman maintains her weight on 7,560 kilojoules per day. At this level, her diet is likely to be low in a number of nutrients, including thiamine, iron and calcium.

Iron is particularly important in women of reproductive age. It's lost in the blood with each monthly period. If she is a light eater, consuming only small quantities of iron in her diet, she may be at risk of either an iron deficiency anaemia or an iron-deficiency without anemia but with chronic fatigue and lethargy.

A woman in this category would do very well to adopt the program in this book for a week or two every few months. Of course, it would be better to look at the social and psychological factors behind the low intake of food, and correct these with professional help.

When pregnant or breast-feeding, a woman has increased requirements for dietary nutrients. In fact, food intake in pregnancy increases by approximately 20 per cent. But the requirements for certain nutrients including calcium and folic acid increases by up to 30 to 100 per cent.

There's no guarantee that a woman eating a sensible well-balanced diet will receive these nutrients. In fact, the 10-State Nutritional Survey in the United States from 1968 to 1970, showed that as many as 80 per cent of the pregnant women surveyed had dietary intakes below two-thirds of the recommended daily allowances.

This is a disturbing figure and the implications for poor health apply not only to the mother but to the unborn child. Quite apart from the increased requirements for good quality protein and calories during pregnancy is the increased requirement for essential fatty acids, the B complex vitamins, folic acid, vitamin B12, vitamins A, D, E and the minerals calcium, iron, magnesium, zinc and phosphorous.

A pregnant woman who is run down, or suffering from infections, would do well to consider using the dietary guidelines in this book for one to two weeks at a time. However, it would be prudent to consult with your own doctor first as supplementation may be required.

THE PREMENSTRUAL SYNDROME

The premenstrual syndrome is a collection of symptoms which occur typically the week prior to a woman's menstrual period. These symptoms include depression, anxiety, irritability, headaches, abdominal bloating, breast tenderness, lethargy and fluid retention.

A large percentage of women who suffer from the premenstrual syndrome consume a diet high in sugar, salt, refined carbohydrates and dairy foods.

It's also been shown that they can benefit from the addition of magnesium, vitamin B6 and Evening Primrose Oil (a herbal medicine with a high concentration of the essential fatty acid, gamma-linolenic acid which has widespread actions on nearly every cell and has been found to be extremely uselful in alleviating the symptoms of PMT, arthritis and eczema.) Sometimes a simple change of diet to one which is nutrient-dense can greatly improve the symptoms of the premenstrual syndrome. The simple avoidance of sugar offers dramatic improvement to a fortunate few.

ORAL CONTRACEPTIVES

Approximately 22 per cent of Australian women between the ages of 15 to 44 are taking the oral contraceptive pill at any one time. It has been shown that the oral contraceptive pill can decrease the absorption of folic acid. It's also been shown to increase the need for vitamin B6, vitamin C, zinc and vitamin B2.

The Pill has been shown to have metabolic affects on the liver, pancreas, gall bladder and other vital organs and it has an influence on protein and carbohydrate metabolism.

For the woman who has been on the oral contraceptive pill for some time and who is suffering from allergies, infections or other symptoms suggestive of a run-down immune system, the use of the menus and diet plans in this book would be of great benefit.

Other supplementation may also be necessary.

ADOLESCENTS

Teenagers are another group who may require extra nutrients in their diet. This is particularly so during the rapid growth spurts which occur in teenage years. It's at these times that extra nutrients are required for growth and development. At these times, there's also an increased level of physical activity which in itself places greater demands on biochemical physiology.

It is illogical and unscientific to assume that eating a standard Australian diet provides all of the nutrients essential for health. For example, data from the United States 10-State Nutrition Survey from 1968 to 1970 covering 24,000 families and 86,000 individuals showed that between 30 to 50 per cent of adolescents aged 12 to 16 had dietary intakes below two-thirds of the Recommended Daily Allowances for vitamins A, C, calcium and iron.

Calcium, of course, is essential for bone growth and development and iron is lost in adolescent females during their menstrual cycle. Inadequate intakes of iron have been associated with behavioural and learning disorders.

Just at the stage when teenagers are under extra pressure to perform at school, the risks of nutritional disorders and deficiencies contributing to learning problems could be devastating. The high-nutrient foods and menus in this book may prove to be of great benefit to them during times of added stress.

FAD DIETS

These include a whole range of diets including lower cholesterol and high protein diets for body builders and athletes with the most common being aimed at weight loss. Some of these diets can be so bizarre that whole groups of food are excluded from them. The Pritikin diet, for example, is very high in fibre found in plant food but it excludes animal fats and significant animal protein. The risk with this diet is that an excessive consumption of grains may result in a food sensitivity to grain. Also the Pritikin diet lacks essential fatty acids. Low fat diets may be deficient in fat-soluble vitamins, such as vitamins A, D and E.

Even well-balanced diets created by dietitians may be unsuitable because of individual requirements for certain nutrients and intolerances to particular foods. People on fad diets are at risk of nutritional imbalances and deficiencies and sooner or later will suffer some degree of unwellness. The foods recommended in this book are particularly helpful for someone who has been following a fad diet for sometime.

VEGETARIANS

Strict vegan diets, which exclude all animal products, (including eggs and dairy foods) must be very carefully planned to avoid a vitamin B12 deficiency which may lead to anaemia. Low vitamin B12 in the diet may also contribute to weakness, fatigue and psychological disorders without causing an associated anaemia.

LAXATIVES

Constipation, which is defined as straining to pass a stool, is one of the most common symptoms in modern western society. Several factors may contribute to constipation, the most important being a lack of dietary fibre. Dietary fibre can be defined as simply being unprocessed plant food.

A sedentary lifestyle, or a lifestyle lacking exercise, will also contribute to constipation. One of the most common medications used today are laxatives. The overuse of these laxatives may result in rushing the food through the intestines. As a result, there's a reduced time for nutrients to be absorbed from food. Oil-based laxatives contribute to a loss of fat-soluble vitamins.

Most laxatives, used to excess, can result in large losses of important minerals including sodium, potassium and magnesium. Millions of people throughout the world are unnecessarily spending billions of dollars on laxatives annually when the simple solution is a change in lifestyle and eating habits. The increased bulk, and fibre, provided by the recipes in this book should help to overcome the problem of constipation suffered by any individual.

OLDER PEOPLE

Older people have been shown to have a very low intake of protein, certain vitamins and minerals – in particular iron, calcium and zinc. Vitamin C and folic acid deficiencies have also been found in elderly populations. Fibre intake is often low, possibly as a result of the inability to chew fruit and vegetables because of dentures or loss of teeth.

Other important B complex vitamins shown to be deficient in the elderly and the infirm include riboflavine and pyridoxine. High quality protein intake is also a problem in this group. Several reasons may co-exist for the nutritional impairment in our elderly people. One of these is, of course, economic.

High quality protein foods and nutrient dense foods are generally more expensive than the tea, toast and snacks on which many elderly people seem to survive. Another reason is the lack of ability to prepare good meals due to physical handicaps. Also with aging, there's an impairment in the senses of taste and smell which reduces the elderly person's desire for good quality food.

Deficiencies of nutrients may occur despite a reasonable intake of high quality food because of the aging process itself. This happens because of a reduction in the secretion of digestive enzymes or the presence of chronic disease, especially of the gastro-intestinal system.

A high-nutrient content eating program, as outlined in this book, would be ideal for many people in nursing homes or other institutions who may have a chronic disease of some type, or who are also on long-term medication and whose general health may be slowly deteriorating.

THE 'INDOORS' SYNDROME

Despite the fact that we supposedly have an increasing number of leisure hours, many people still remain indoors for most of the time. As a consequence, they may lack exposure to an adequate amount of sunlight. This particularly applies to shift workers, invalids and the chronically institutionalised. Sunlight is essential for health. When the skin is exposed to sunlight, vitamin D is produced in the skin itself. Vitamin D has been shown to act more like a hormone than a vitamin.

It's not only responsible for maintaining calcium levels in the body and thus preventing ricketts and osteoporosis (thinning of the bones with increased risk of fractures) but it has been shown to play a vital role in the prevention of certain cancers, including breast cancer.

Natural sunlight also effects the central nervous system through the eyes, having what is believed to be some anti-depressant action on the central nervous system.

For those who are unable to expose themselves to sunlight, the best food sources rich in vitamin D are fatty fish, cod liver oil, eggs, milk, butter and cheese. The recipes in this book contain sufficient quantities to provide very good levels of vitamin D in the diet.

Excessive exposure to sunlight has been shown to be immuno-suppressive and causes skin cancer. The best approach is to take everything in moderation, and use adequate protection from the sun's harmful rays.

DIGESTIVE DISORDERS

Disorders of digestion can occur in a wide variety of illnesses, even in people who are reasonably healthy. Extremely common in our society is the problem of eating too fast and not chewing one's food sufficiently.

This results in large chunks of food entering the stomach and intestine and passing through to the large bowel without being properly digested and absorbed into the bloodstream.

This is symptomatic of our fast lifestyle. In fact, the fast eating syndrome has been facilitated to some degree by the junk food industry. For example, most fast food take-away hamburgers literally melt in the mouth and require very little chewing. Despite the fact that these foods are easily broken up mechanically, they don't contain optimum quantities of essential nutrients and contain unnecessary quantities of sugar, salt and fat.

▪ HOW TO GAIN THE MOST FROM THIS BOOK ▪

The recipes and menu plans in this book are designed to be used by people who suspect they may have an inadequate intake of certain nutrients in their diet. They may include people who are in relatively good health or those who have a chronic disease or illness. It also applies to family members who are at risk of developing chronic illnesses.

In fact, the use of the recipes and menu plans in this book by the general population, from time to time, is highly advisable. However, you should remember that to ensure the intake of reasonably high levels of essential nutrients, it's also necessary to increase the number of kilojoules eaten.

Therefore, people who are of normal weight may gain weight if they use the menu planners for anything longer than two weeks at a time.

For individuals of normal weight who suffer from recurrent infections, mild allergies or a feeling of general unwellness, the use of the recipes and menu plans of the normal energy menu (10,000 kilojoules daily) should give a real boost to their nutritional status and immune systems.

The high energy menu (13,000 kilojoules daily) is ideal for those people who are of low weight, or low normal weight. For over-weight individuals, the normal energy menu plans are recommended for two weeks at a time. For the severely overweight person, a suitable nutritionist should be consulted for help. This book is of special value to those who suffer from chronic long-term illnesses, including arthritis, auto-immune diseases, allergies, leukaemia, cancer, AIDS, alcoholism, nutritional anemias, psychiatric disorders, skin complaints, chronic fatigue syndrome, recurring infections, infertility and those who are under chronic stress or who have suffered from injury, surgery or other trauma. It is also of great value to athletes whose nutritional requirements are increased when training and competing.

We recommend the help of a qualified medical nutritionist or dietitian for people with illnesses.

A change in eating behaviour and proper food planning can result in not only an improved feeling of well-being but the reduction of the risk of many nutritionally-related degenerative diseases.

This is not a medical reference book. Rather, it is recommended for those who are either at risk of, or who suffer from, a disease related to a weakened immune system. This is also a book recommended for urban dwellers who are exposed to the ravaging effects of air, water and food pollution.

Bon Appetit!

Ian Brighthope, D.D.A., M.A.T.A., M.B., B.S.

· 2 ·
HOW · TO · GET · THE MOST · FROM · THIS BOOK

This is no ordinary cookbook. Rather, it is a book of specifically designed recipes, menu plans and nutrition advice aimed to either help people with a specific health problem or to assist apparently 'well' people who want to protect themselves from disease by boosting their immune system.

· WHY AND HOW ·

The recipes in this book have been carefully designed to provide high densities of nutrients essential for an effective immune system.

In fact, the criteria for each recipe and menu plan in this book were the provision of high nutrient density food *plus* an optimal daily intake of food energy in a ratio from the basic food groups.

Chapter 12 includes two tables which show the nutrient density and the daily energy intake for the foods used in the recipes in this book. The information provided in these tables is essential if you wish to modify the recipes and menu plans to suit your own individual requirements.

Whilst following the menu plans in this book it is still possible, with a little thought, to eat out and maintain the necessary nutrient and energy intakes that we recommend. These days there are plenty of good salad bars and health shops where you can buy the type of foods we suggest for lunches. Healthy eating places and vegetarian restaurants now exist which offer appropriate dinner menus. Where necessary, staff in such establishments are generally happy to provide alternative foods or dishes.

· NUTRIENT INTAKE ·

Obviously, not every recipe can have high levels of *all* the nutrients we require.

Therefore, Chapter 12 contains menu plans designed to ensure a daily and weekly balance of nutrients necessary for a healthy immune system.

■ ENERGY INTAKE ■

An energy analysis is provided with every recipe in this book.

Since not all people need the same level of energy, menu plans are also provided for those who do have a particular need for a high energy intake. People who could benefit from the high energy menu plans may include athletes, adolescents or young adults with an active sporting life, pregnant or nursing mothers, those involved in strenuous occupations or under stress, and people suffering from some diseases associated with weight loss. With such diseases, including many cancers and AIDS, there is often a problem with the body's ability to absorb nutrients. Therefore not only is a high density nutrient diet required to boost the immune system but a high energy menu is also required to ensure that sufficient food is absorbed to prevent further weight loss.

■ HOW THE RECIPES WERE COMPILED ■

In designing the recipes and menu plans in this book, food composition tables were used to select foods high in the nutrient types known to boost the immune system, such as:

Vitamins – C, beta carotene and E

Minerals – magnesium, manganese, selenium, zinc and copper

Amino acids – methionine and cysteine, and

Fats – linolenic

Foods meeting these criteria were fed into a data base and sorted to isolate those with the highest density of desired nutrients.

Then the optimal daily energy intake for the menu plans was set at: energy – 3,200 cal. (13,500 Kj), protein – 20%, fats - 30% and carbohydrate – 50%.

Isolated foods were then analysed on this basis and corrections made to the recipes and menu plans until a balance was achieved that met the criteria for both nutrient density and energy intake.

Also included in the design of menu plans were 'allergy free' days – days on which one of the following was omitted: cows' milk, eggs, corn/soy, orange/tomato and wheat.

In addition to the specific menu plans in Chapter 12, tables are also provided to show both the nutrient density and the energy level of a wide range of foods from which it is possible to design your own menus. If you are unsure about which menu plan is best for *you*, talking with your doctor or a trained dietitian will help you decide.

However, by following the recipes and foods recommended in this book you can certainly help to dramatically boost your immune system and contribute to a greater sense of well-being.

· 3 ·
GETTING · ORGANISED

The high nutrient recipes in this book allow you to quickly prepare attractive and appetising meals – whether for yourself, your guests or members of your household – with a minimum of fuss. The following guidelines will help to streamline your time in the kitchen even further.

· SHOPPING GUIDE ·

To maximise your nutrient intake, follow these simple shopping guidelines:

- buy fresh food and, where possible, purchase organically grown or biodynamic items
- use frozen food sparingly
- limit purchases of tinned and packet foods
- reduce intake of food additives
- buy whole grain cereals and cereal products
- buy free-range poultry and eggs
- eliminate, or minimise, intake of caffeine and alcohol

The following food items are used in the high nutrient recipes and menu plans. Once your cupboard is stocked with these items you will only need to buy fresh food such as fruit, vegetables, milk and meat.

· BASIC PANTRY ITEMS ·

DRY FOOD

Wholemeal flour
Rice flour or cornmeal or arrowroot
Buckwheat flour
Rolled oats
All-Bran breakfast cereal
Wheatgerm

Bran (oat or rice)
Baking powder (bicarbonate)
Baking soda
Skim milk powder
Brown rice
Brown lentils

Dried or tinned lima beans, soy beans,
   chick peas, red kidney beans
Wholemeal pasta, such as spaghetti
Pearl barley

Brown sugar
Gelatine
Wholemeal crackers

TINNED AND/OR BOTTLED FOOD

Tuna
Salmon
Crab
Sardines in SILD oil

Baked beans
Evaporated skim milk
Coconut cream
Honey or golden syrup

Olive oil
Apple cider vinegar
Peanut butter

NUTS AND DRIED FRUIT

Almonds
Brazil
Walnuts

Coconut
Prunes
Dates

Dried apricots
Sultanas
Raisins

REFRIGERATED ITEMS

Butter – low salt
Plain yoghurt*
Milk*
Eggs
Meat

Cheddar cheese
Parmesan cheese
Tofu (firm Chinese variety works best
   for recipes in this book)
*Check if your menu calls for low fat or skim milk

SPICES

Allspice
Black pepper
Cardamom
Cayenne pepper
Chilli powder

Cinnamon
Cinnamon sticks
Cummin
Curry powder
Ginger powder

Mixed spices
Mustard powder
Nutmeg
Paprika
Peppercorns

HERBS

Basil
Chives
Dill

Mint
Oregano
Parsley

Tarragon
Bay leaves

OTHER

Carraway seeds	Sunflower seeds	Horseradish sauce
Celery seeds	Pumpkin seeds	Worcestershire sauce
Sesame seeds	Soy sauce – low salt	Vanilla essence

■ EQUIPMENT CHECK LIST ■

Whilst the high nutrient recipes in this book are simple to make, the following basic kitchen equipment will make preparation even easier.

- Blender
- Kettle
- Measuring spoons, cups, jug
- Scales
- Saucepans (preferably stainless steel)
- Frying pan
- Steamer
- Ovenproof casserole
- Baking tins and trays
- Cutting board
- Large cutting knife
- Small vegetable knife
- Grater
- Sieve or strainer
- Metal serving spoon
- Mixing bowls
- Orange juicer
- Oven mitt
- Foil

SERVING

Appetising meals are even more appealing when they are presented in an attractive and interesting way. Help to achieve this effect by giving some thought to accessories such as tablecloths, place mats, serviettes, cutlery, crockery, glassware and low floral decorations.

■ GLOSSARY ■

Bake: to cook by dry heat in an oven.
Barbecue: to cook food slowly covered in aluminium foil.
Blend: to mix together.
Boiling point: surface of the liquid bubbles briskly.
Breadcrumbs: stale bread, dried in a low oven and rolled into crumbs.
Brown: to brown food in a small amount of fat.
Chill: to cool food in a refrigerator – not the freezer.
Chop: a small cut of meat with a bone.
Chicken stock: liquid obtained from cooking chicken in water with herbs.

Coat a spoon: when sauce, or liquid, is thick enough to form a film on the back of the cooking spoon.

Coconut cream: combination of ground coconut meat and coconut milk.

Dice: small cubes of food.

Garnish: a decoration for food.

Glaze: a liquid brushed over food to improve its appearance, e.g. milk brushed over pastry before baking.

Grate: to form fine particles by pressing food across a grater.

Grill: cooking directly under heat.

Kebabs: small pieces of food threaded on a skewer.

Knead: to work a flour mixture until the dough is soft and pliable.

Mousse: a light dessert.

Sago: a starch product obtained from the trunk of the sago tree.

Score: to cut narrow strips in the surface of food often to prevent splitting during cooking, e.g. apples and potatoes

Shred: to cut into long, narrow pieces.

Simmer: to bring liquid just below boiling point, i.e. bubbles only rising occasionally.

Soy sauce: sauce obtained from fermenting soy beans.

Stew: to simmer food gently in a liquid which just covers it.

Tofu: a soy bean curd made by cooking, pureeing and pressing soy beans.

Water bath: a way of protecting ingredients from extreme heat whilst cooking – the dish containing the food sits in a larger container of water.

▪ OVEN TEMPERATURES ▪

	Degrees Celsius	Degrees Fahrenheit
Cool	100	200
	110	225
Very slow	120	250
	140	275
Slow	150	300
Moderately slow	160	325
Moderate	180	350
Moderately hot	190	375
Hot	200	400
	220	425
Very hot	230	450
	240	475
	250	500

MEASUREMENTS AND EQUIVALENTS

Metric measurements have been used throughout this book. All spoon measurements are level.

LIQUIDS

1 cup = 250 mls
1 tbls = 30 mls

1 tsp = 5 mls
1 litre = 1000 mls

DRY PRODUCTS

1 tbls = 4 tsp
3 tbls = 1/4 cup
6 tbls = 1/2 cup
9 tbls = 3/4 cup

12 tbls = 1 cup
1000g = 1 kilogram

1 cal. = 4.2 Kj

ABBREVIATIONS

tsp = teaspoon
tbls = tablespoon
ml = millilitre
g = gram
kg = kilogram
Cal. = calorie

Pro. = protein
Fat = fat
CHO = carbohydrate
Kj = kilojoule
En. = energy

T·O·N·I·C·S &
J·U·I·C·E·S

Freshly extracted tonics and juices are powerful nutritive foods, rich in vitamins and minerals, which are readily absorbed into the body.

Juices also offer fruit acids which stimulate digestion and help in the absorption of nutrients thereby increasing the efficiency of other nutrients in the drink. Fruit acids also prevent the drinks from discolouring.

It is quite common for tonics and juices to contain a variety of fresh foods. Suitable foods include:

- High quality fruits and vegetables
- Milk, coconut milk and yoghurt
- Flavourings such as vanilla, Worcestershire sauce

Consume these beverages as a snack, as a dessert or as a nightcap.

Dilute using:
- Filtered tap water
- Mineral water
- Distilled water
- Ice cubes

SERENDIPITY JUICES

Serendipity was the term coined by Horace Walpole after 'The Three Princes of Serendip', a fairytale, and means the ability to make happy and unexpected discoveries.

You can do this by experimenting with the following food combinations in your blender. As a first guide, use the quantities in brackets.

Preparation time: 10 minutes.

Serves: 2.

- Spinach (1 cup), celery (1/2 cup), cucumber (1/4 cup), parsley (1/4 cup) or apple (1).
- Carrot (1 cup), beet (1/2 cup), celery (1/2 cup), onion (1/4).
- Buttermilk (1 cup), banana (1), almonds (6).
- Carrot (1 cup), low fat yoghurt (1/2 cup), banana (1), milk (1/2 cup), mint.
- Milk (1 cup), egg (1), wheatgerm (1 tsp), honey (1 tsp), vanilla essence (1 tsp), nutmeg (1/4 tsp).
- Lettuce (1 cup), spinach (1/2 cup), carrot (1/2 cup).
- Apple (1) and mixed vegetables (1 cup).
- Carrot (1 cup), tomato (1), celery (1/2 cup), Worcestershire sauce (2 tsp).
- Cantaloupe (1 cup), and orange (1).

- Prepare foods and place in blender.
- Blend and correct consistency using water.

HOT MULLED BERRY JUICE

Preparation time: 10 minutes.
Serves: 2.

2 cups berries (i.e. cranberry, raspberry, loganberry)
2 whole cloves
1/4 tsp nutmeg
1 cinnamon stick
Garnish: Lemon slices

- Wash berries 3 times in cold water.
- Blend berries.
- Place berry juice in saucepan with spices.
- Heat without boiling. Let stand for 3 minutes.
- Strain.
- Serve and garnish with lemon slice.

Energy per serve:
Cal: 81 from Protein 4, Fat 10, CHO 67.
Kj: 339 from Protein 17, Fat 41, CHO 282.

STRAWBERRY ROYALE

Preparation time: 5 minutes.
Serves: 1.

1 cup strawberries
1/2 orange, peeled
1 tsp honey
Garnish: Whole strawberries

- Wash strawberries 3 times in water.
- Blend strawberries, orange and honey.
- Serve in tall glass and garnish with whole or sliced strawberries.

Energy per serve:
Cal: 98 from Protein 6, Fat 9, CHO 83.
Kj: 412 from Protein 26, Fat 37, CHO 349.

KOALA MAUVE

Preparation time: 5 minutes.
Serves: 1.

1 cup blueberries or blue grapes
1/2 orange
2 ice cubes

- Wash blueberries 3 times in cold water.
- Peel orange.
- Place blueberries and orange in blender.
- Blend until smooth.
- Add 2 ice cubes and blend just to break up ice slightly.
- Serve in a tall glass, perhaps with a blue serviette wrapped around the base.

Energy per serve:
Cal: 120 from Protein 6, Fat 9, CHO 105.
Kj: 503 from Protein 26, Fat 37, CHO 440.

■ *Greenacres Tonique (p. 33), Strawberry Royale (p. 32), Cantaloupe Supreme (p. 34).* ▶

MELON SPARKLE

Preparation time: 8 minutes.
Serves: 2.

2 cups diced cantaloupe or papaya
1 lime
4 fresh mint leaves
2 ice cubes
Garnish: Mint

- Blend all ingredients together.
- Serve in glass and decorate with a mint sprig.

Energy per serve:
Cal: 65 from Protein 5, Fat 4, CHO 56.
Kj: 272 from Protein 20, Fat 19, CHO 234.

GREENACRES TONIQUE

Preparation time: 20 minutes.
Serves: 2.

1/4 cup celery chopped
1/4 cup lettuce
1/4 cup spinach
1/4 cup asparagus chopped
1/4 cup green pepper chopped
1 cup water
Onion salt
Garnish: 1 tbls Parmesan cheese

- Blend all ingredients together until smooth.
- Pour into tall glasses and sprinkle with cheese.

Energy per serve:
Cal: 15 from Protein 5, Fat 1, CHO 10.
Kj: 63 from Protein 19, Fat 4, CHO 40.

◀ *Muesli (p. 44), Buckwheat Pancakes (p. 43) with Spiced Apple (p. 41).* ■

AVOCADO SMOOTHIE

Preparation time: 5 minutes.
Serves: 3.

1/4 avocado
1/2 cup asparagus
1/4 cup plain yoghurt
1 cup water
Garnish: Black pepper

- Blend all ingredients until smooth.
- Pour into low, wide glasses and sprinkle with black pepper.

Energy per serve:
Cal: 47 from Protein 7, Fat 27 CHO 13.
Kj: 196 from Protein 28, Fat 115, CHO 53.

SWEET LYCHEE

Preparation time: 5 minutes.
Serves: 1.

5 lychees
1/2 cup coconut milk
1 tbls almonds

- Grind almonds in blender. Add lychees and milk. Blend.
- Pour into glasses.

Energy per serve:
Cal: 333 from Protein 20, Fat 184, CHO 128.
Kj: 1391 from Protein 85, Fat 770, CHO 536.

CANTALOUPE SUPREME

Preparation time: 5 minutes.
Serves: 2.

1 cup cantaloupe diced
1 fresh orange peeled
2 tbls coconut milk (optional)
Garnish: Orange peel

- Blend ingredients.
- Garnish with strips of orange peel.

Energy per serve:
Cal: 56 from Protein 4, Fat 3 CHO 50.
Kj: 236 from Protein 17, Fat 11, CHO 208.

JUNGLE JUICE

Preparation time: 5 minutes.
Serves: 3.

2 celery sticks chopped
1 apple chopped
2 tsp peanut butter or nuts
2 cups milk

- Blend ingredients.
- Pour into glasses.

Energy per serve:
Cal: 145 from Protein 26 , Fat 60, CHO 59.
Kj: 607 from Protein 108, Fat 252, CHO 248.

3 BETA TONIQUE

Preparation time: 10 minutes.
Serves: 2.

1 cup cantaloupe diced
1 cup orange diced
1 cup yellow peach diced
1/2 cup water (optional)
Garnish: Orange circles

- Slice 2 orange circles and set aside for garnish.
- Place ingredients in blender and blend until smooth.
- Pour into glasses and garnish with orange slices.

Energy per serve:
Cal: 88 from Protein 7, Fat 3, CHO 78.
Kj: 369 from Protein 30, Fat 11, CHO 328.

TOMATO ZIP

Preparation time: 10 minutes.
Serves: 2.

2 tomatoes
1/2 cup spinach
1 tsp Worcestershire sauce
1/8 tsp garlic
1/2 cup water

- Take 2 thin slices from the tomato for the garnish.
- Blend all ingredients.
- Pour into glasses.
- Cut from centre to edge of tomato slices and use as garnish by placing on the side of the glass, cocktail fashion.

Energy per serve:
Cal: 30 from Protein 6, Fat 1, CHO 23.
Kj: 127 from Protein 26, Fat 4, CHO 98.

CORNY THICK SHAKE

Preparation time: 10 minutes.
Serves: 2.

1 1/2 cups corn
2 tomatoes
1 slice wholemeal bread
1 tsp diced onion
1/2 green pepper
1/2 cup water
Garnish: Parsley

- Place all ingredients in the blender and blend until smooth.
- Pour into glass and garnish with parsley.

Energy per serve:
Cal: 175 from Protein 24, Fat 6, CHO 144.
Kj: 731 from Protein 102, Fat 26, CHO 603.

GOLDEN JUICE

Preparation time: 10 minutes.
Serves: 3.

1 cup papaya chopped
1 cup orange chopped
1 tbls peanut butter or nuts
2 tsp lemon juice
1 cup milk or orange juice
Garnish: Egg white and dessicated or shredded coconut

- Blend ingredients.
- Dip the rim of the glass in egg white and then into coconut.
- Pour blended ingredients into glasses.

Energy per serve:
Cal: 128 from Protein 20, Fat 48, CHO 60.
Kj: 535 from Protein 85, Fat 200, CHO 250.

BEETROOT TONIQUE

Preparation time: 5 minutes.
Serves: 2.

1/2 cup beetroot, cooked or raw
2 tsp horseradish
1 tbls yoghurt
1 cup water
Garnish: Yoghurt

- Blend all ingredients.
- Pour into glasses and garnish with a dollop of yoghurt.

Energy per serve:
Cal: 19 from Protein 3, Fat 3, CHO 13.
Kj: 81 from Protein 14, Fat 11, CHO 56.

MALTED ORANGE

Preparation time: 5 minutes.
Serves: 1.

1 cup milk
1/2 orange flesh and orange peel
1 to 2 tsp malted milk or malt extract

- Place all ingredients in blender and blend until smooth.
- Serve.

Energy per serve:
Cal: 207 from Protein 35, Fat 71, CHO 101.
Kj: 865 from Protein 145, Fat 296, CHO 424.

BARLEY WATER

Preparation time: 10 minutes.
Cooking time: 20 minutes.
Serves: 6

This drink is an excellent thirst quencher during hot weather. Serve cold with a slice of lemon or as a hot toddy for a late night drink.

3 tbls pearl barley
6 cups cold water
2 lemons juice and peel
2 oranges juice and peel
1 tbls honey

- Place barley in a sieve and wash under running water.
- Put barley and water in a saucepan and bring to the boil.
- Simmer 20 minutes and remove from heat.
- Add flavorings and leave to cool.
- Strain into a jug.
- Discard barley and the peel.
- Cover and store in refrigerator.
- Serve cold or hot as desired.

Energy per serve:
Cal: 83 from Protein 6, Fat 1, CHO 77.
Kj: 349 from Protein 24, Fat 4, CHO 322.

ORIENTAL DRIFT

Preparation time: 10 minutes.
Serves: 2.

5 lychees

1/2 cup mango

1/2 cup yellow peach

1/2 cup water

- Blend all ingredients.
- Pour into glasses.
- Perhaps serve on a bamboo mat.

Energy per serve:
Cal: 113 from Protein 5, Fat 7, CHO 101.
Kj: 472 from Protein 21, Fat 30, CHO 421.

PINK FANCY

Preparation time: 5 minutes.
Serves: 2.

1 cup yellow peach

1/2 cup beetroot, cooked or raw

1 cup coconut milk

- Blend ingredients, adjusting the consistency with water.
- Pour into delicate glasses.

Energy per serve:
Cal: 130 from Protein 9, Fat 60, CHO 60.
Kj: 543 from Protein 38, Fat 252, CHO 253.

B·R·E·A·K·F·A·S·T

Breakfast is the most important meal of the day as it replenishes nutrients used during sleeping. A good breakfast should offer a selection of foods which, in turn, gives the body a wider range of available nutrients. As the day progresses, more demands are made on the body and it's still expected to operate at peak performance. People who don't eat breakfast become easily fatigued, are less able to concentrate and tend to develop irregular eating patterns.

Breakfast, lunch and dinner should be spaced to keep the body's blood glucose level elevated sufficiently to prevent periods of fatigue. The possibilities for wonderful breakfasts are endless.
We suggest:

- Juices, fresh fruit, stewed fruits, avocado.
- Muesli, porridge, pancakes, waffles, wholemeal toast.
- Poached egg, scrambled egg, omelette.
- Sardines, smoked kippers, grilled meat.
- Left-over vegetables.

STEWED FRUIT

Fruits such as apples, pears, rhubarb and cherries can be cooked with flavourings and served with cereals or yoghurt. These fruits can be cooked and stored in the freezer or refrigerator.

SPICED APPLE OR RHUBARB

Preparation time: 5 minutes.
Cooking time: 5 minutes.
Storage: 3 days
Serves: 1

---

1 apple or 1 cup rhubarb

1 cup Lo-cal ginger ale

- Wash fruit, slice and place in a saucepan.
- Add enough ginger ale to 1/4 cover fruit.
- Stew gently with lid on saucepan.

Energy per serve:
Cal: 82 from Protein 0, Fat 2, CHO 80.
Kj: 344 from Protein 0, Fat 7, CHO 336.

SPICED PRUNES

Preparation time: 10 minutes.
Cooking time: 15 minutes.
Storage: 3 days
Serves: 2
This can be eaten hot with porridge or muesli or stored in the refrigerator and eaten as a snack.

---

1 cup of prunes

1 apple cored

1 cup water

1/2 to 1 tsp cardamom

1/4 tsp allspice

- Wash prunes in cold water and place in a saucepan.
- Blend all other ingredients together until smooth.
- Pour over prunes and gently bring to the boil.
- Simmer 10 minutes.
- Let stand for 5 minutes.

Energy per serve:
Cal: 164 from Protein 4, Fat 4, CHO 156.
Kj: 685 from Protein 17, Fat 15, CHO 653.

PEARS OR CHERRIES

Preparation time: 5 minutes
Cooking time: 5 minutes.
Storage: 3 days
Serves: 1

---

1 pear or 1/2 cup cherries

Apple juice

Cinnamon sticks or 1/2 tsp of powdered cinnamon

- Wash fruit. Slice the pears, core and halve and place in a saucepan.
- Pour over apple juice and spice.
- Place the lid on the saucepan and stew until the fruit is soft.

Energy per serve:
Cal: 195 from Protein 8, Fat 18, CHO 170.
Kj: 817 from Protein 34, Fat 74, CHO 709.

APRICOT ORANGE

Preparation time: 10 minutes.
Storage time: 12 hours to 3 days
Serves: 2
This fruit can be served cold with breakfast cereal or with yoghurt or ice cream.

1/2 cup dried apricots

2 cups orange juice

1/2 to 1 tsp cinnamon

- Wash apricots three times in cold water.
- Place all ingredients together in a large bowl and cover.
- Refrigerate overnight.

Energy per serve:
Cal: 197 from Protein 12, Fat 5, CHO 180.
Kj: 825 from Protein 51, Fat 22, CHO 752.

NOV 2006,
We liked!

BUCKWHEAT PANCAKES

Preparation time: 40 minutes.
Serving time: 5 minutes.
Serves: 4.

These thin pancakes have a lovely flavour and can be served with savoury or sweet fillings. Hot spiced apple is a suggestion for breakfast. Extra pancakes can be cooked and frozen or stored in the refrigerator for up to a week. Place plastic food wrap between the pancakes and put in a plastic bag.

1 cup milk
1/2 cup buckwheat flour
1/2 cup rice flour or cornflour
1 tbls olive oil
Pinch salt
1 tsp baking powder
2 tsp butter or oil for cooking

- Place all ingredients in the blender except the baking powder.
- Whisk until blended. Let stand for 30 minutes.
- Add baking powder and blend in.
- Heat 2 tsp butter or oil in frying pan and quickly pour in enough batter to 3/4 coat frying pan base.
- Tilt pan to make sure batter runs evenly over the pan base. Cook over moderate heat.
- When upper surface begins to dry, carefully slide the pancake over using a large flat lifter.
- Brown other side. Place hot, spiced apple on the pancake and roll up or fold over and serve.

Energy per serve:
Cal: 127 from Protein 12, Fat 67, CHO 48.
Kj: 530 from Protein 49, Fat 281, CHO 200.

MUESLI

Preparation time: 20 minutes.
Storage time: up to 6 months.
Muesli has many uses apart from being a breakfast cereal since it can be served with yoghurt, used to top cooked fruits or as a base for muesli cookies. Make a large quantity and store in an airtight container.

6 cups of rolled oats
2 cups wheatgerm
2 cups bran
1 cup coconut, dessicated or shredded
1 cup skimmed milk powder
1 cup sultanas
1 cup dried chopped apricots
1 cup dried chopped peaches
1/2 cup sunflower seeds

- Combine all ingredients.
- Store in airtight container.
- Serve 1/2 cup muesli with 3/4 cup of milk for breakfast.
- Top with sliced fresh fruit.

Energy per serve:
Cal: 127 from Protein 19, Fat 26, CHO 82.
Kj: 532 from Protein 81, Fat 107, CHO 344.

TOAST 'N SPREAD

Wholemeal toast with a nutritious spread offers a quick hassle-free approach to breakfast. Below are some ideas from which to choose.

BAKED BEANS

Heat 1/2 cup of beans, place on toast and top with 2 slices of tomato.

Energy per serve:
Cal: 166 from Protein 25, Fat 47, CHO 94.
Kj: 694 from Protein 106, Fat 196, CHO 392.

AVOCADO

Peel 1/4 avocado and mash with a fork on to 2 slices of un-buttered toast; sprinkle with lemon juice and black pepper.

Energy per serve:
Cal: 210 from Protein 20, Fat 84, CHO 106.
Kj: 878 from Protein 85, Fat 352, CHO 442.

SARDINES IN FISH OIL

Mash 2 tbls sardines on to 1 slice of un-buttered toast. Sprinkle with 1/2 tsp lemon juice.

Energy per serve:
Cal: 145 from Protein 49, Fat 49, CHO 47.
Kj: 493 from Protein 147, Fat 148, CHO 198.

TUNA

Flake 2 tbls tuna with a fork, add one tsp mayonnaise and spread on to 1 slice of toast.

Energy per serve:
Cal: 131 from Protein 48, Fat 36, CHO 46.
Kj: 546 from Protein 202, Fat 152, CHO 192.

COTTAGE CHEESE

Place 1 slice of bread on an oiled tray, spread on 3 tbls cottage cheese, top with 2 slices of tomato and toast in an oven for 15 minutes until the cheese begins to melt.

Energy per serve:
Cal: 145 from Protein 47, Fat 38, CHO 60.
Kj: 605 from Protein 197, Fat 159, CHO 250.

SPREADS

These spreads take 5-10 minutes to prepare in a blender. Placed in containers and stored in the refrigerator, they can last up to a week. Spreads can be used on wholemeal breads, toast, pancakes or crackers.

TOFU SPREAD

1 cup tofu sliced
2 tsp low-salt soy sauce
1/2 tsp mustard powder
1 tbls diced onion
1/2 tomato

- Place all ingredients in the blender.
- Blend until smooth.
- Refrigerate.

Energy per serve:
Cal: 29 from Protein 9, Fat 12, CHO 9.
Kj: 123 from Protein 38, Fat 48, CHO 37.

ALMOND SPREAD

1/2 cup almonds
1/2 cup tofu sliced
2 tbls apple or pear juice
1 tbls lemon juice

- Grind almonds in blender.
- Add all ingredients, blend until smooth.
- Refrigerate.

Energy per serve:
Cal: 32 from Protein 5, Fat 21, CHO 5.
Kj: 132 from Protein 22, Fat 89, CHO 21.

JAMS (COOKED)

2 cups fruit (peach, pineapple, apricot)
1 tsp lemon juice
2 tsp gelatine or arrowroot
1 to 2 tsp honey (optional)

- Stew fruits without water until soft.
- Mix gelatine with 1 tbsp water and add to fruit mixture.
- Boil for 2 minutes and add lemon juice and honey.
- Cool and refrigerate.

Energy per serve:
Cal: 8 from Protein 1, Fat 0, CHO 7.
Kj: 34 from Protein 3, Fat 0, CHO 30.

JAMS (UNCOOKED)

1 cup fresh fruit (papaya, peach, plum or apricot)

1/2 cup dates or sultanas

orange juice

- Place all fruits in the blender.
- Blend and adjust consistency with orange juice.
- Refrigerate.

Energy per serve:
Cal: 16 from Protein 1, Fat 0, CHO 15.
Kj: 65 from Protein 3, Fat 0, CHO 62.

FRENCH TOAST

Preparation time: 10 minutes.
Cooking time: 6 minutes.
Serves: 1.

1 egg beaten

1 tbls milk

1 tsp butter

1 slice wholemeal bread

Garnish: 1 tsp chopped herbs

- Melt butter in frying pan.
- Beat egg and milk together in a basin.
- Cut bread in half and dip into the egg mixture until the mixture is soaked up.
- Cook bread in buttered frying pan turning until each side is golden brown.
- Garnish with fresh herbs and serve immediately.

Energy per serve:
Cal: 192 from Protein 35, Fat 104, CHO 53.
Kj: 803 from Protein 147, Fat 433, CHO 222.

SCRAMBLED EGGS

Preparation time: 10 minutes.
Cooking time: 4 minutes.
Serves: 1.

1 spring onion chopped
1 tsp butter
1 tbls milk
1 egg beaten
1 tbls parsley chopped
Garnish: Wholemeal toast

- Fry spring onion and butter in frying pan.
- Mix milk, egg and parsley together and add to the saucepan.
- Cook over low heat stirring with a wooden spoon. Remove from heat when mixture begins to thicken.
- Serve hot on wholemeal toast.

Energy per serve:
Cal: 182 from Protein 33, Fat 97, CHO 51.
Kj: 760 from Protein 139, Fat 407, CHO 214.

OMELETTE

Preparation time: 15 minutes.
Cooking time: 5 minutes.
Serves: 1.

This is a high protein dish which is excellent for breakfast, lunch or dinner. One of the fillings below can be selected to add flavour and texture.

2 eggs whole or 1 whole egg plus 1 egg white
1 tbls water
1 tbls chopped parsley
1 tsp butter
Pepper

- Melt butter in frying pan.
- Blend all ingredients together.

■ *Omelette (p. 48).* ▶

- Pour into heated frying pan and cook on LOW heat for 3 minutes. Loosen sides and bottom of mixture to allow uncooked mixture to run underneath.
- When set, place selected filling on half of the omelette and fold over the other half forming a crescent shape.
- Slide the filled omelette on to a plate and serve immediately with wholemeal toast.

SUGGESTED FILLINGS:
- Chopped asparagus
- Fish, e.g. tuna or salmon
- Cheese with chives
- Hot spiced apple

Energy per serve:
Cal: 276 from Protein 62, Fat 151, CHO 64.
Kj: 1156 from Protein 257, Fat 633, CHO 266.

SCRAMBLED FISH

Preparation time: 10 minutes.
Cooking time: 5 minutes.
Serves: 1.

1/2 cup cooked fish
1 1/2 tbls milk
1 egg
1 tbls chopped parsley
1 tsp butter
Pepper
Garnish: Wholemeal toast

- Melt butter in frying pan.
- Mix all ingredients together in a basin and add it to the butter.
- Stir gently as ingredients are heated.
- Serve hot with wholemeal toast.

Energy per serve:
Cal: 329 from Protein 158, Fat 115, CHO 55.
Kj: 1374 from Protein 662, Fat 481, CHO 230.

◄ *Vegetable Minestrone (p. 57).* ■

CORN HASH

Preparation time: 15 minutes.
Cooking time: 10 minutes.
Serves: 2.

1 cup cooked corn kernels
1 cup grated or chopped carrot
1 cup milk
1 tbls plain flour
1/2 onion sliced
1/4 tsp sesame seeds
1 tbls parsley chopped
Pepper
Garnish: Wholemeal toast

- Place corn and carrot in saucepan.
- Place all other ingredients in the blender and blend until smooth.
- Place blended ingredients into saucepan with corn and carrot.
- Stir and bring the mixture to the boil. Cook for 5 minutes. Serve with wholemeal toast.

Energy per serve:
Cal: 235 from Protein 34, Fat 46, CHO 155.
Kj: 984 from Protein 144, Fat 192, CHO 648.

VEGETABLE SCRAMBLE

Preparation time: 5 minutes.
Cooking time: 5 minutes.
Serves: 1.

1 cup left-over vegetables
2 tsp butter
1 egg
1 tbls milk

---

1 tbls parsley chopped

Pepper

Garnish: Wholemeal toast

- Fry vegetables lightly in butter.
- Beat egg, milk, pepper and chopped parsley together.
- Pour over vegetables, stirring until the scrambled mixture sticks together.
- Serve.

Energy per serve:
Cal: 342 from Protein 56, Fat 141, CHO 145.
Kj: 1429 from Protein 232, Fat 588, CHO 608.

PORRIDGE

Preparation time: 5 minutes.
Cooking time: 5 minutes.
Serves: 1.
Porridge is a term used to describe cooked cereals which may be oatmeal, corn-meal, millet, cracked wheat, rice, rolled rye or rolled wheat. The cereal is cooked with water and served with milk and fresh fruit.

1/2 cup rolled oats or other cereal

2 tbls bran

1 1/2 cups cold water

1 tbls mixed orange and lemon peel

1/2 tsp cinnamon

- Place oats, bran and water in saucepan.
- Bring to boil, add peel and cinnamon.
- Simmer for 5 minutes.
- Serve with milk.

Energy per serve:
Cal: 109 from Protein 18, Fat 9, CHO 82.
Kj: 454 from Protein 75, Fat 37, CHO 342.

ALTERNATIVE PORRIDGE INGREDIENTS

Preparation time: 10 minutes.
Cooking time: 30 minutes.
Serves: 1.

1/4 cup buckwheat grain or millet
1/4 cup brown rice
1 1/2 cups water
2 tbls dried apricots chopped
2 tbls dried peaches chopped
1 tbls honey (optional)

- Cook grains together in cold water and bring to boil until soft.
- Mix with chopped fruit and honey.
- Serve with milk.

Energy per serve:
Cal: 352 from Protein 20, Fat 8, CHO 324.
Kj: 1471 from Protein 84, Fat 33, CHO 1354.

TOSSED TOFU

Preparation time: 5 minutes.
Cooking time: 5 minutes.
Serves: 1.
A delightful dish served with wholemeal toast, sliced tomato, papaya or grated carrot.

1/2 cup tofu drained and sliced
1 tsp olive oil
1 tsp herbs
1 clove garlic crushed

- Heat the oil in frying pan. Add tofu.
- Add seasonings and toss tofu in pan to heat.
- Serve.

Energy per serve:
Cal: 86 from Protein 18, Fat 60, CHO 7.
Kj: 349 from Protein 77, Fat 252, CHO 30.

S·O·U·P·S

Soups offer great taste and high nutritional value. With home-made soups, you are in control of the ingredients used and the development of flavour.

A food blender helps make quick and easy soups. To make your soups extra special, select any of the following to decorate the soup when serving:

- Crushed whole grain crackers.

- Chopped fresh herbs such as parsley, chives, dill.

- Fresh sprouts.

- Diced vegetables.

- Sesame seeds.

If all the soup isn't eaten in one meal, the remainder can be stored in airtight containers labelled and frozen for six to nine months.

AVOCADO VELVET

Preparation time: 15 minutes.
Chilling time: 15 minutes.
Serves: 4.

---

1 avocado

2 spring onions chopped

2 tsp lime juice

2 cups chicken broth

1 cup plain yoghurt

1 tsp chopped ginger OR 1/2 tsp ginger powder

Garnish: Chopped chives or fresh sprouts

- Remove avocado flesh and place in blender.
- Add all ingredients to blender. Blend to a creamy consistency.
- Refrigerate.
- Serve with garnish.

Energy per serve:
Cal: 135 from Protein 18, Fat 89, CHO 28.
Kj: 563 from Protein 74, Fat 374, CHO 115.

GAZPACHO CREME

Preparation time: 10 minutes.
Chilling time: 15 minutes.
Serves: 2.

---

2 cups tomatoes chopped

1 cup cucumber chopped

1/2 cup green pepper chopped

1 tbls onion chopped

2 mint leaves

1 cup buttermilk or yoghurt

Paprika or black pepper to taste

Garnish: Yoghurt, tomato, chives

- Place all ingredients in blender and blend to a rough consistency; this may require addition of some cold water.
- Chill and serve.
- Garnish with yoghurt, chopped tomato and chives.

Energy per serve:
Cal: 96 from Protein 24, Fat 11, CHO 61.
Kj: 400 from Protein 100, Fat 44, CHO 256.

THICK BEAN SOUP

Preparation time: Overnight soaking of beans PLUS 20 minutes.
Cooking time: 1 1/2 hours.
Serves: 6.

1 cup lima beans soaked overnight
1 onion chopped
1/2 cup chopped turnip
1 cup chopped carrot
1 potato chopped
3 cups sliced cabbage
3 tomatoes chopped
1/4 tsp oregano or cummin
6 cups chicken stock

- Cover beans with cold water and soak overnight.
- Drain beans and place in a large saucepan with all ingredients.
- Cover with chicken stock, bring to boil, then simmer for 1 1/2 hours.

Energy per serve:
Cal: 172 from Protein 37, Fat 19, CHO 115.
Kj: 720 from Protein 157, Fat 81, CHO 482.

CABBAGE AND EGG WHIRL

Preparation time: 10 minutes.
Cooking time: 10 minutes.
Serves: 4.

2 cups sliced cabbage (White Mustard, Bokchoy or Pakchoy)
1 onion sliced
2 tsp unsalted butter
4 cups chicken stock
1 egg beaten
Garnish: 1 tbls chopped parsley and pepper

- Melt butter in large saucepan and fry onion. Add cabbage and stir-fry for 2 minutes.
- Add chicken stock and bring soup to boil. Cook 5 minutes.
- Remove saucepan from heat, stir in beaten egg. Add pepper to taste.
- Serve and garnish with chopped parsley.

Energy per serve:
Cal: 84 from Protein 18, Fat 45, CHO 21.
Kj: 352 from Protein 77, Fat 189, CHO 86.

PUMPKIN AND CARROT

Preparation time: 15 minutes.
Cooking time: 20 minutes.
Serves: 4.

2 cups chopped pumpkin
1 cup chopped carrot
1 chopped onion
2 cloves of garlic, chopped
1 tsp celery seeds
Garnish: Yoghurt, chopped parsley

- Place ingredients in saucepan and just cover with water.
- Cook until vegetables are soft.

What can we, as parents, do to help? Lots!

Use your school's P&C meetings to discuss the present quality and policies of the school canteen with other parents. Voice your concerns if you feel the canteen is offering too limited a selection of nutritious food. Individually, or as a group, approach or petition the school principal and/or canteen manager with suggestions, ideas and offers of help.

Here are a few simple suggestions put forward by the NHF which your school canteen could very easily adopt and which would make little or no difference to running costs:

• provide chilled water with mint or lemon (as one alternative to soft drinks)
• make the change to wholegrain bread
• change to low-fat cheese, yoghurt and milk
• as alternatives to hot dogs and pies, prepare and supply simple rice and vegetable meals, spaghetti bolognaise and so on
• as alternatives to chocolate bars, ice-blocks and lollies, offer fresh fruit salad, frozen fruit pieces and fruit slices (made with wholemeal pastry and with no added sugar).

School canteens should be offering our children food that is good for them!

continued from page 93

had from a sandwich, made with two slices of fresh, lightly-buttered wholegrain bread filled with lean meat, cheese or canned fish with fresh salad, and a piece of fresh fruit. Protein is particularly important during the growing years. Children's rapid growth and development means that they need twice as much protein per kilogram of body weight as does an adult.

Many children need to be stimulated to eat; this can be done by using your imagination and making food interesting with the use of colour, shape, texture and, finally, flavour. Discuss your child's likes and dislikes with her. You may discover she has been swapping that sandwich you usually make with a friend! Chat with other mums to find out what they are packing in their children's lunch boxes. Perhaps there is a trend or fad at school that your child is missing out on (eg sprout sandwiches).

Ensure your child's packed lunch will 'go the distance' by wrapping individual portions of food securely.

Lunch boxes are now available which have a frozen water-bottle insert to keep the lunch cool. This idea may be well worth considering during hot weather.

Combine commonsense and creativity when preparing lunches. Try cutting bread in different shapes; vary the fillings from day to day, avoiding those that discolour or go soggy; combine different ingredients for interest and eye appeal — or perhaps use a theme, eg Italian; use a variety of breads, like Lebanese flat bread, french sticks, wholegrain slices, pocket bread and sesame rolls.

Try these suggestions for tasty, healthy sandwich fillings:

red salmon, cream cheese and shredded lettuce

leg ham, pineapple, cheese and tomato

walnuts, celery, mayonnaise and shredded lettuce

roast beef, grated carrot and zucchini

cheese, asparagus, sprouts and chopped capsicum

chicken, celery, sliced mushrooms and coleslaw

red salmon, sprouts and tasty cheese

ham, shallots and mayonnaise

grated carrot, sultanas and nuts

peanut butter, honey and sprouts

baked beans, cheese and lettuce

cucumber, ham, pineapple and sprouts

cream cheese, grated carrot, sliced raw button mushrooms and lettuce

spicy cooked mince, cheese and tomato

roast pork, apple sauce and shredded red cabbage

boiled egg, sprouts, cheese and capsicum

chicken, tomato, sunflower seeds and cottage cheese.

Include snack items in the form of canned snack fruit, cheese sticks, fresh fruit, vegetable sticks or homemade wholegrain cookies and cakes.

Here are two snack recipes which freeze successfully.

- Place vegetables and liquid in blender and blend until smooth.
- Return to saucepan and heat.
- Serve and garnish with yoghurt and chopped parsley.

Energy per serve:
Cal: 47 from Protein 6, Fat 1, CHO 40.
Kj: 197 from Protein 26, Fat 4, CHO 168.

VEGETABLE MINESTRONE

Preparation time: Overnight soaking of beans PLUS 30 minutes.
Cooking time: 1 hour.
Serves: 4.

1/4 cup lima beans soaked overnight
1/2 tbls olive oil
1 onion, chopped
1 clove garlic, crushed
5 cups water
1 large carrot, diced
1 stick celery, sliced
1 potato, diced
1/2 cup green beans, sliced
2 tomatoes, chopped
1/4 cup wholemeal pasta
2 tbls parsley
Pepper to taste

- Soak lima beans in plenty of cold water overnight.
- Next day, drain beans.
- Place oil in a large saucepan, heat, add onion and garlic. Fry gently for 2 minutes. Add water and drained lima beans.
- Boil, then simmer with lid on saucepan until beans are tender (about 30 minutes).
- Add all ingredients, cover and simmer 20 minutes.

Energy per serve:
Cal: 198 from Protein 28, Fat 25, CHO 145.
Kj: 829 from Protein 117, Fat 104, CHO 608.

CORN AND CELERY

Preparation time: 10 minutes.
Cooking time: 5 minutes.
Serves: 4.

2 cups cooked corn
4 sticks celery, washed, chopped
2 cups whole milk
1/2 tsp caraway seeds
Pepper to taste
Garnish: Whole grain crackers and parsley

- Place all ingredients in blender and blend.
- Pour into saucepan and heat bringing to the boil.
- Garnish with crushed whole grain crackers and chopped parsley.

Energy per serve:
Cal: 155 from Protein 28, Fat 36, CHO 91.
Kj: 647 from Protein 116, Fat 152, CHO 379.

S·A·L·A·D·S

Salads are sophisticated combinations of wholesome foods of endless variety which can be eaten for breakfast, lunch or dinner. The nutritional value of salads depends on the combination of foods used and fibre is well represented.

Basic to most salads are the greens and there is a wide range to select from including endive, lettuce, cabbage, escarole, parsley, chard, and watercress.

The following points are recommended when preparing salad greens:

- Wash them thoroughly in cold running water.
- Shake off water.
- Drain on a cloth and 'wipe' dry.
- Place in a plastic bag and store in crisper section of refrigerator.

The dark leafy salad greens provide Vitamin A and C, folacin and B vitamins. These nutrients can be added to by combining the following to salads generally:

- Chopped parsley and chives for vitamin A & C.
- Chopped or sliced red pepper for vitamin C.
- Seeds, nuts, whole grain crisps for protein, iron, B vitamins and fibre.
- Cheese, meats, eggs, marinated beans for protein.
- Salad dressings.

SALAD DRESSINGS

These add nutrients as well as zing and interest to salads. Dressings can be made in quantity and stored in the refrigerator as a standard food item.

ALL-PURPOSE DRESSING

Preparation time: 10 minutes.
Storage time: 6 months.

1/2 cup olive oil
1/4 cup vinegar
1 clove garlic mashed
1 tsp mixed dried herbs e.g chives, tarragon and parsley
1 tsp mustard paste OR 1/2 tsp mustard powder
2 tsp sesame seeds
2 tsp black pepper

- Place all ingredients in a blender and blend until smooth.
- Place in jar.
- Store in refrigerator.

Energy per serve:
Cal: 85 from Protein 1, Fat 81, CHO 3.
Kj: 355 from Protein 2, Fat 340, CHO 13 .

SESAME DRESSING

Preparation time: 5 minutes.
Storage time: 1 month.

1/2 cup lemon juice
1/2 cup sesame or olive oil
1/2 cup sesame seeds toasted
1/4 cup sunflower seeds

Note: To toast sesame seeds, place in frying pan and stir over heat for 4 minutes.

- Place all ingredients in blender and blend.
- Store in refrigerator.

Energy per serve:
Cal: 55 from Protein 4, Fat 47, CHO 5.
Kj: 231 from Protein 15, Fat 196, CHO 19.

MAYONNAISE-STYLE DRESSING

Preparation time: 10 minutes.
Storage time: 1 month.

200 g tofu
2 tbls olive oil
2 tsp low-salt soy sauce
2 tbls parsley chopped
2 tbls lemon juice

- Slice tofu and blend all ingredients together in blender.
- Store in refrigerator.
- Serve combined with salad or as a dip for vegetable/salad platter.

Energy per serve:
Cal: 21 from Protein 3, Fat 16, CHO 2.
Kj: 88 from Protein 13, Fat 67, CHO 8.

WATERMELON COOLER

Preparation time: 20 minutes.
Chilling time: 20 minutes.
Serves: 2.
A lovely, light salad served with grilled fish and greens.

2 cups diced or balled watermelon
4 spring onions cut into circles
4 tbls chopped parsley
2 tbls chopped mint

- Place all ingredients together in serving bowl.
- Mix thoroughly using a spoon and fork.
- Cover bowl and refrigerate.
- Serve with green salad and hot or cold meat.

Energy per serve:
Cal: 62 from Protein 5, Fat 9, CHO 48.
Kj: 258 from Protein 21, Fat 37, CHO 200.

CHINESE CABBAGE SLAW

Preparation time: 20 minutes.
Chilling time: 10 minutes.
Serves: 4.

1/4 cabbage shredded
1 onion chopped
2 sticks celery chopped
2 tsp low-salt soy sauce
2 tsp preserved ginger chopped
Sesame dressing to taste
Garnish: Chopped parsley

- Combine above ingredients in a salad bowl.
- Refrigerate before serving.
- Garnish.

Energy per serve:
Cal: 68 from Protein 7, Fat 42, CHO 20.
Kj: 285 from Protein 30, Fat 174, CHO 82.

SPRING SALAD

Preparation time: 30 minutes.
Chilling time: 10 minutes.
Serves: 4.

2 cups cauliflower steamed
1 cup carrot grated
1 cup asparagus chopped
1/2 cup spring onions chopped
1 tbls chopped parsley
2 tbls raisins

Garnish: Mayonnaise-style dressing and 1 tbls
chopped walnuts

- Break cauliflower into small flowerettes.
- Combine all ingredients.
- Refrigerate.

Energy per serve:
Cal: 149 from Protein 13, Fat 74, CHO 61.
Kj: 621 from Protein 55, Fat 311, CHO 256.

TUNA-BEANS ON RYE

Preparation time: 40 minutes.
Chilling time: 10 minutes.
Serves: 4.

1 cup tuna drained
1 cup green beans cooked
1 cup celery chopped
4 slices rye or other bread
Mayonnaise-style dressing
2 hard boiled eggs cut into wedges
2 tsp capers
Salad greens

- Combine tuna, green beans and celery in a bowl.
- Spread rye bread with Mayonnaise-style dressing.
- Place tuna mix on bread.
- Place rye bread on serving plates.
- Decorate each plate with salad greens, egg and capers. Extra mayonnaise may also be served.
- Refrigerate.

Energy per serve:
Cal: 251 from Protein 86, Fat 86, CHO 79.
Kj: 1048 from Protein 358, Fat 359, CHO 331.

GREENS WITH CHEESE

Preparation time: 15 minutes.
Chilling time: 10 minutes.
Serves: 4.
This salad can be served as a starter or with the main meal.

4 cups mixed salad greens
1 cup diced cheese
1 tbls chopped parsley
1 tbls chopped chives
All-purpose dressing to taste
Garnish: Crushed whole wheat crackers

- Combine all the above ingredients in a salad bowl.
- Refrigerate.
- Garnish.

Energy per serve:
Cal: 247 from Protein 54, Fat 154, CHO 39.
Kj: 1034 from Protein 225, Fat 644, CHO 165.

DAME CHARMANTE

Preparation time: 45 minutes.
Chilling time: 15 minutes.
Serves: 2.
This charming lady is a meal in herself – just cool it.

1 cantaloupe
2 cups cooked chicken meat diced
1 1/2 oranges segmented
1 tomato diced
2 tbls Mayonnaise-style dressing
1 tsp tomato sauce
1/2 orange juiced

■ *Chick Peas Catalonian Style (p. 68)* ▶

1/2 tsp mustard powder

Garnish: 1/4 red pepper cut into slivers and paprika

- Cut cantaloupe in half, scoop out seeds.
- Place all ingredients in a large bowl and mix using salad servers.
- Fill mixture into cantaloupe halves, piling it high to form a peak.
- Decorate with red pepper strips and paprika.
- Chill.
- Serve on a doily on a plate.

Energy per serve:
Cal: 513 from Protein 232, Fat 108, CHO 173.
Kj: 2143 from Protein 970, Fat 451, CHO 722.

RICE-BEAN MIX

Preparation time: 30 minutes.
Cooking time: 40 minutes.
Chilling time: 10 minutes.
Serves: 2.
This crunchy salad is good served with mixed greens.

1 cup brown rice cooked (1/3 cup uncooked)
1 cup soya or lima beans cooked (1/3 cup uncooked)
1 cup carrot grated
1 cup red bell pepper diced
1 cup spring onions sliced
1 tbls fresh ginger grated
Curry powder to taste
Sesame dressing

- Cook rice and beans separately. Drain.
- Mix all ingredients together.
- Use Sesame dressing to moisten salad.
- Chill.

Energy per serve:
Cal: 265 from Protein 36, Fat 33, CHO 196.
Kj: 1107 from Protein 150, Fat 137, CHO 821.

◀ *Avocado Buckwheat Pasta and Rice-Bean Mix (pp. 74 & 65).* ■

SALAD CARMEN

Preparation time: 15 minutes.
Cooking time: 45 minutes.
Chilling time: 15 minutes.
Serves: 6.

3 cups brown rice cooked (1 cup uncooked)
2 cups cooked meat diced
1 cup green peas cooked
1 red bell pepper sliced
1/2 cup All-purpose dressing

■ Combine all ingredients together in salad bowl.

Energy per serve:
Cal: 254 from Protein 89, Fat 45, CHO 121.
Kj: 1063 from Protein 371, Fat 189, CHO 504.

BEETROOT SALAD

Preparation time: 10 minutes.
Cooking time: 60 minutes.
Serves: 2.
This salad can be made in advance and stored in the refrigerator for two weeks;
serve with alfalfa and wholemeal bread.

2 medium beetroots
1 tsp caraway seeds
2 cups vinegar
2 to 3 tsp grated horseradish, fresh or prepared

■ Wash beets, cover with cold, unsalted water.
■ Cook until tender, approx. 30 minutes.
■ Remove skin and slice.
■ Placed in a dish and sprinkle horseradish over the beets.
■ Boil vinegar and caraway seeds and pour over the beets.
■ Cool and store in refrigerator.

Energy per serve:
Cal: 103 from Protein 9, Fat 2, CHO 92.
Kj: 429 from Protein 37, Fat 7, CHO 384.

GOLDEN SALAD

Preparation time: 25 minutes.
Chilling time: 25 minutes.
Serves: 4.

2 cups carrot grated
2 oranges diced
1/2 cup raisins
1/2 cup coconut
1 lime, juiced

- Combine all ingredients.
- Chill.

Energy per serve:
Cal: 156 from Protein 8, Fat 32, CHO 116.
Kj: 653 from Protein 35, Fat 133, CHO 485.

CRAB AVOCADO

Preparation time: 45 minutes.
Chilling time: 2 hours.
Serves: 2.

1 ripe avocado
1 cup crab meat
1 tbls lemon juice
1 tomato diced
2 spring onions chopped
1/4 cup Mayonnaise-style dressing
1/2 tsp mustard powder OR 1 tsp chilli sauce
Garnish: Parsley sprigs and lemon slices

- Cut avocado in half and remove kernel.
- Sprinkle avocado with lemon juice to prevent discoloration.
- Mix all the other ingredients together and pile onto avocado. Garnish.
- Chill.

Energy per serve:
Cal: 337 from Protein 58, Fat 213, CHO 65.
Kj: 1409 from Protein 243, Fat 892, CHO 274.

SALADE LOUISE

Preparation time: 15 minutes.
Chilling time: 10 minutes.
Serves: 2.
Jaffa grapefruits – sweet and juicy – are a must for this salad.

Lettuce
1 grapefruit segmented
1/4 cup raisins
1/4 cup walnuts chopped

- Line small plate with lettuce.
- Fan out segmented grapefruit.
- Sprinkle raisins and walnuts together at the base of the grapefruit fan.

Energy per serve:
Cal: 208 from Protein 17, Fat 83, CHO 108.
Kj: 870 from Protein 72, Fat 348, CHO 450.

CHICK PEAS CATALONIAN STYLE

not bad
Sept 2012

Preparation time: 10 minutes.
Cooking time: 20 minutes.
Serves: 2.

1 cup chick peas (garbanzo beans) cooked
3 tomatoes chopped
2 cloves garlic chopped
2 tsp mixed fresh herbs
1 tbls Mayonnaise-style dressing

- Mix all ingredients together.
- Chill.
- Serve with green salad.

Energy per serve:
Cal: 168 from Protein 33, Fat 28, CHO 107.
Kj: 702 from Protein 136, Fat 118, CHO 448.

M·A·I·N D·I·S·H·E·S

■ LEGUMES: DRIED BEANS, PEAS AND LENTILS ■

These offer a wide variety of tastes and are important sources of protein, carbo-hydrate, fibre, B vitamins and minerals such as zinc, magnesium and iron. Where possible, purchase organically grown or biodynamic grains and legumes. Legumes require pre-soaking and 1 cup of dried legumes yields approximately 2 cups of cooked legumes.

Basic cooking method:

- Place legumes in a sieve and wash under running tap water.

- Place legumes in a bowl, cover with 5 to 8 cm (2 to 3 inches) of water and soak overnight. Refrigerate soya beans to prevent fermentation or, if time doesn't permit overnight soaking, bring legumes and water to boil for 5 minutes. Allow to stand for 1 1/2 hours.

- Cook legumes in soaking water the following day until soft.

COOKING CHART LEGUMES

Blackeye peas (cow peas)	1 hour
Garbanzo beans (chick peas)	3 hours
Kidney beans	1 1/2 hours
Lentils	1 hour
Lima beans	1 1/2 hours
Navy beans	1 1/2 hours
Red beans	1 1/2 hours
Soy beans	3 1/2 hours
Split peas	1 hour

Whole grain cereals supply valuable nutrients such as vitamins, minerals, protein, carbohydrate and fibre.
Basic cooking method:

- Place grain in a sieve and wash under running water.

- Boil water in large saucepan and add grain. The ratio of grain to water is 1: 6.

- Leave lid off saucepan and boil rapidly.

- Test grain between fingers to see if it's cooked.

- Drain through a sieve.

COOKING CHART FOR WHOLE GRAIN CEREALS

GRAIN	DRY	YIELD	COOKING TIME
Buckwheat kernels	1 cup	3 1/2 cups	1 hour
Barley	1 cup	3 1/2 cups	1 hour
Corn	1 cup	3 cups	1 1/2 hours
Millet	1 cup	3 1/4 cups	30 mins.
Rice	1 cup	3 cups	45-50 mins.

■ FISH ■

Fish is an excellent source of protein, essential fatty acids, B vitamins and minerals such as copper, zinc (oysters), fluoride, iodine (seafood), phosphorous and calcium from oysters and fish eaten with bones such as salmon.
Fish meat has a delicate flavour so don't add too much spice. The cooking time is short compared with other meat types. Cooking techniques recommended are:

- Steam
- Bake
- Poach
- Stir-fry

■ MEATS ■

These provide high quality protein, vitamins and minerals but also contain a lot of calories, saturated fats and cholesterol. Fats should be cut off meats before cooking and you should buy free-range poultry.
Recommended cooking techniques:

- Grill
- Steam
- Stir-fry
- Stew
- Bake

• SUGGESTED WEEKLY MAIN DINNER DISHES •

FISH: 2 serves.
LEGUMES: 2 serves.
BEEF: 1 serve.
PORK: 1 serve.
CHICKEN: 1 serve.
EGGS: 3 to 4 per week. This also includes baked items containing eggs.

SAVOURY GROUND BEEF

Preparation time: 30 minutes.
Cooking time: 30 minutes.
Serves: 4.

500 g lean ground beef
1 onion sliced
1 garlic clove sliced
1 carrot diced
2 tomatoes chopped
1 tsp caraway seeds
1 cup chicken stock
1 tsp olive oil
Garnish: 1/2 cup fresh parsley chopped or 1 tbls dried parsley

- Fry onion and garlic in olive oil.
- Place all ingredients in saucepan and bring to boil.
- Place the lid on saucepan and simmer for 25 minutes.
- Serve with plain pasta or on whole wheat toast.

Energy per serve:
Cal: 512 from Protein 178, Fat 297, CHO 37.
Kj: 2142 from Protein 743, Fat 1243, CHO 155.

STIR-FRY PORK AND VEGETABLES

Preparation time: 40 minutes.
Cooking time: 40 minutes.
Serves: 2.
This is a tasty, colorful meal served in Chinese bowls and eaten with chopsticks.

PORK:
2 cups raw pork sliced
1 tbls green ginger sliced
2 tbls cornflour
1 tbls low-salt soy sauce
1/2 onion diced
1 tbls olive oil
1 cup chicken stock

- Mix pork, ginger, flour and soy sauce in a basin. Let it stand while preparing vegetables.
- Fry onion in frying pan, add pork and stir fry for 5 minutes.
- Add chicken stock and simmer for 20 minutes.
- Serve in serving dish for table.

VEGETABLES:
1/2 onion sliced
1 clove garlic pressed
1 cup celery sliced
1 cup carrot chopped
1 cup broccoli pieces
1/2 cup green beans
2 tsp olive oil
1 cup water

- Fry the onion and garlic in oil in a frying pan.
- Add vegetables and stir fry for 5 minutes.
- Add water and cook on LOW heat for 8 minutes covering the frying pan with the lid.
- Serve in a serving dish for the table.

RICE:

1/2 cup whole grain rice

4 cups boiling water

- Wash rice in a sieve under running tap.
- Bring water to the boil and cook rice for 35 minutes.
- Drain rice.
- Place in serving dish for the table.

Energy per serve:
Cal: 849 from Protein 213, Fat 345, CHO 291.
Kj: 3547 from Protein 889, Fat 1443, CHO 1214.

PASTA

Preparation time: 20 minutes.
Cooking time: 10 minutes.
Serves: 4.
This pasta is a good accompaniment to Savoury Mince. It can also be used to make Macaroni Cheese.

1 1/2 cups wholemeal flour

2 tsp baking powder

2 eggs

1/4 tsp nutmeg

1/4 cup water

- Bring a large saucepan of water to the boil and add 1/2 tsp of salt.
- Place flour and baking powder in a basin.
- In a blender, mix eggs, nutmeg and water. Then add to the flour. Mix for 3 minutes using a wooden spoon.
- When water reaches boiling point add the mixture a 1/4 of a teaspoon at a time. These small portions will sink, then rise when cooked. Cook for 10 minutes.
- Drain.
- Place pasta in a buttered casserole and sprinkle with breadcrumbs.

Energy per serve:
Cal: 198 from Protein 37, Fat 35, CHO 126.
Kj: 827 from Protein 153, Fat 148, CHO 526.

AVOCADO BUCKWHEAT PASTA

Preparation time: 20 minutes.
Cooking time: 10 minutes.
Serves: 4.
This nutritious pasta can be served in place of potatoes sprinkled with cheese or served with a meat or fish sauce.

1/2 cup buckwheat flour
1/2 cup finely ground whole wheat flour or cornflour
1 tsp baking powder
1/4 tsp nutmeg
1 egg
1/2 avocado
1/4 cup water

- Place the water in a large saucepan and bring to the boil and add 1 tsp salt.
- Sift the first 4 ingredients together.
- Blend the egg and avocado in the water until smooth.
- Add blended ingredients to flours and stir with a wooden spoon until a smooth pasta results.
- When the water reaches boiling point add the mixture a 1/4 of a teaspoon at a time. These small portions will sink, then rise when cooked. Cook for 10 minutes, then drain the pasta.

Energy per serve:
Cal: 156 from Protein 19, Fat 50, CHO 86.
Kj: 650 from Protein 81, Fat 211, CHO 358.

SPINACH RICE

Preparation time: 30 minutes.
Cooking time: 30 minutes.
Serves: 4.

1 cup brown rice cooked
1/2 cup cheddar cheese grated
2 eggs beaten
2 tbls parsley chopped

Black pepper to taste

1 tsp oregano chopped

3 cups spinach washed and chopped

Garnish: 2 tbls wheatgerm and 2 tbls almonds chopped

- Combine the rice, cheese, eggs, parsley, pepper, oregano and spinach.
- Pack into a greased casserole.
- Top with garnish.
- Bake at 180 deg C or 350 deg F for 30 minutes.

Energy per serve:
Cal: 216 from Protein 45, Fat 104, CHO 66.
Kj: 901 from Protein 189, Fat 437, CHO 275.

KANGAROO RED

Preparation time: 20 minutes.
Cooking time: 20 minutes.
Serves: 2.

1 1/2 cups red kidney beans cooked

3 tomatoes chopped

2 cups carrots chopped

1 onion sliced

2 cloves garlic minced

1 tbls olive oil

1/2 to 1 tsp chilli powder

Garnish: Chopped parsley

- Fry onions and garlic in oil.
- Add kidney beans, tomatoes, carrots and 1/4 cup water.
- Add chilli powder to taste.
- Simmer on low heat for 20 minutes.
- Serve and garnish with parsley.

Energy per serve:
Cal: 378 from Protein 60, Fat 90, CHO 228.
Kj: 1580 from Protein 251, Fat 377, CHO 952.

LENTIL BURGERS

Preparation time: 15 minutes.
Cooking time: 25 minutes.
Serves: 3.

3 cups brown lentils cooked
1 cup mashed potato
1 cup bran
1 tsp sesame seeds
1/2 cup chopped brazil nuts or walnuts
1/2 cup parsley chopped
2 tsp each of oregano and basil
Black pepper

- Combine all ingredients and divide into 6.
- Coat burgers with extra bran.
- Place on a greased baking tray and bake at 220 deg C or 440 deg F for 25 minutes.

Energy per serve:
Cal: 454 from Protein 88, Fat 126, CHO 240.
Kj: 1896 from Protein 369, Fat 525, CHO 1002.

BARBECUED CHICKEN DINNER

Preparation time: 20 minutes.
Cooking time: 60 minutes.
Serves: 1.

1 chicken leg and breast
2 tbls brown rice cooked
3 dried apricots washed
2 slices tomato
1 spring onion sliced
Pepper
1 tsp olive oil
8 inch x 8 inch (20 cm. by 20 cm.) aluminum foil

- Remove fat from the chicken.
- Grease foil with oil.
- Place rice, chicken, apricots, tomato, spring onion and pepper on to the foil.
- Fold the top and ends of Alfoil to seal contents.
- Place in centre of charcoal grill or bake on a tray in the oven for 60 minutes at 180 deg C or 400 deg F.

Energy per serve:
Cal: 766 from Protein 314, Fat 335, CHO 116.
Kj: 3201 from Protein 1314, Fat 1402, CHO 485.

SOYA BEAN NUTLOAF

Preparation time: 45 minutes.
Cooking time: 60 minutes.
Serves: 8.

2 cups soya bean cooked
1 1/2 cups brown rice cooked
1 onion chopped
2 cups carrot chopped
1 cup celery chopped
2 tomatoes chopped
1 clove garlic chopped
1/4 tsp cummin
1/2 tsp dried thyme or 2 tsp fresh thyme
2 tbls parsley chopped
1/2 cup wheatgerm
1 egg
1/2 cup walnuts chopped
1/2 tsp pepper

Garnish: 1 cup grated cheese

- Blend soya beans and the egg until smooth. Water may need to be added.
- Place all ingredients in a basin and add soya bean mixture. Mix well.
- Place mixture into loaf pan and bake at 180 deg C or 350 deg F for 50 minutes.
- Sprinkle with grated cheese 10 minutes before cooking time is completed.
- Serve hot or cold.

Energy per serve:
Cal: 270 from Protein 56, Fat 118, CHO 96.
Kj: 1127 from Protein 233, Fat 492, CHO 402.

BAKED FISH & CHIPS

Preparation time: 15 minutes.
Cooking time: 30 minutes.
Serves: 4.
Served with beetroot and a green salad using kale or similar, this is a very tasty meal.

1 packet frozen haddock (or similar) – 450 g
1 packet frozen chips or freshly made chips – 450 g
Milk
Breadcrumbs
Foil oiled

- Cut frozen fish into 4 blocks and coat with milk and breadcrumbs.
- Place fish at one end of greased aluminum foil on a flat tray. Place the chips at the other end.
- Bake at 180 deg C or 400 deg F for 25 minutes (freshly made chips can be lightly boiled, drained, painted with yoghurt and baked.)

Energy per serve:
Cal: 237 from Protein 53, Fat 115, CHO 69.
Kj: 990 from Protein 221, Fat 481, CHO 288.

LIVER SLICES

Preparation time: 15 minutes.
Cooking time: 6 minutes.
Serves: 2.
This highly nutritious dish is at its best served with hot sliced potatoes and a lettuce salad.

250 g calves or pork liver
1 onion sliced in circles
1 tsp butter
1/2 cup chicken stock
2 tsp plain wholemeal flour
Pepper
Garnish: Chopped parsley or chives.

- Remove skin from the liver and slice thinly.
- Place butter in frying pan and fry onion.
- Add liver and cook over low heat for 3 minutes.
- Blend flour with chicken stock and add to liver. Cook until boiling for 3 minutes.
- Serve and garnish.

Energy per serve:
Cal: 396 from Protein 192, Fat 128, CHO 75.
Kj: 1655 from Protein 805, Fat 537, CHO 314.

BURGERS

Preparation time: 30 minutes.
Cooking time: 25 minutes.
Serves: 4.

250 g lean ground beef
250 g soya beans cooked
2 onions chopped
1 carrot grated
2 tbls parsley chopped
4 tbls bran
2 tbls fresh herbs
Pepper to taste
Wheatgerm for coating
Foil

- Mash soya beans in a basin and add all ingredients.
- Consistency may need to be adjusted using water.
- Mould mixture into oval or round shapes and dip into the wheatgerm.
- Place on greased Alfoil on a flat baking dish.
- Bake in oven for 20 to 25 minutes at 180 deg C or 350 deg F. Alternatively grill or pan fry.

Energy per serve:
Cal: 353 from Protein 119, Fat 161, CHO 73.
Kj: 1476 from Protein 496, Fat 673, CHO 307.

EGG FLORENTINE

Preparation time: 15 minutes.
Cooking time: 10 minutes.
Serves: 1.

---

6 spinach leaves

1 egg

1 slice cheddar cheese

Garnish: 1 slice wholemeal toast

- Steam spinach and place on a serving plate.
- Boil water in saucepan and poach the egg, then drain.
- Place egg on spinach and top with cheese.
- Brown under griller.
- Cut toast into triangles and garnish around the spinach.

Energy per serve:
Cal: 326 from Protein 87, Fat 173, CHO 66.
Kj: 1361 from Protein 363, Fat 722, CHO 277.

SAVOURY FISH PIE

Preparation time: 25 minutes.
Cooking time: 35 minutes.
Serves: 3.

---

2 cups tuna, salmon or flaked fish

1 onion chopped

1 clove garlic minced

2 sticks celery chopped

1 red pepper chopped

2 tomatoes chopped

2 bay leaves

1/2 tsp basil

1/2 tsp dill

Pepper

Garnish: 1/2 cup grated cheese and 1/4 cup parsley

■ *Stir-Fry Pork and Vegetables (p. 72)* ▶

- Mix all ingredients together.
- Pack into oven dish.
- Cook at 180 deg C or 350 deg F for 30 minutes.
- Sprinkle the top with cheese and parsley and return to the oven for 5 minutes.

Energy per serve:
Cal: 247 from Protein 148, Fat 66, CHO 34.
Kj: 1032 from Protein 618, Fat 274, CHO 141.

FISH BURGERS

Preparation time: 35 minutes.
Cooking time: 20 minutes.
Serves: 2.
These burgers are at their best served with a hot tomato sauce.

1 cup salmon, tuna or sardines
1 cup potato cooked and mashed
1 tbls parsley chopped
Cayenne pepper
1/2 tsp cummin or dill
1/2 lemon juiced
1 tsp anchovy paste (if desired)
Garnish: Breadcrumbs and parsley

- Flake fish using a fork and mash in the bones.
- Mix all ingredients together and flavor well.
- Divide into 6 portions and roll in breadcrumbs and extra chopped parsley.
- Grill, pan fry or bake on a foil sheet for 10 minutes.

HOT TOMATO SAUCE
2 tomatoes chopped
1 spring onion chopped
1/2 tsp herbs

- Place all ingredients in blender and blend until consistency is coarse.
- Heat in saucepan.
- Pour over fish burgers.

Energy per serve:
Cal: 312 from Protein 93, Fat 59, CHO 160.
Kj: 1305 from Protein 390, Fat 248, CHO 667.

◀*Kangaroo Red (p. 75).* ■

SOUSED FISH

Preparation time: 15 minutes.
Cooking time: 15 minutes.
Serves: 4.

This is an old-fashioned way of cooking fish. It can be cooked in advance and stored in the refrigerator for up to 14 days. Soused fish may be served hot with mashed or boiled potatoes or cold with a crisp salad.

4 fish fillets
1/4 cup vinegar
1 onion sliced
6 peppercorns
4 cloves
1 chilli chopped or 1/8 tsp chilli powder
1/4 tsp mixed spice
1/4 tsp ginger powder OR 1 tsp fresh or preserved ginger

- Wash and dry fillets. Roll into a turban shape.
- Place into oven dish and add all ingredients.
- Cover dish and cook in oven for 15 minutes at 180 deg C or 350 deg F.
- Allow fish to cool in cooking liquid.
- Refrigerate.

Energy per serve:
Cal: 127 from Protein 103, Fat 11, CHO 14.
Kj: 532 from Protein 430, Fat 44, CHO 58.

FISH IN FOIL

Preparation time: 15 minutes.
Cooking time: 10 to 40 minutes.
Serves: 2.

1 whole fish (450 g to 700 g)
lemon juice
Pepper
Olive oil
Foil

- Grease foil with oil.
- Wash and dry fish. Sprinkle inside and outside with lemon juice and pepper.
- Place on foil and seal the edges encasing the fish.
- Place on tray. Bake in oven at 180 deg C or 350 deg F for 20-30 mins.
- The fish is cooked when the flesh can be separated or flaked with a fork.

VARIATIONS (allow 10 minutes extra cooking time):

- Fill the fish cavity with breadcrumbs, oysters, crab, parsley and lemon.
- Stuff with sliced mushrooms, chopped onion, tomato, parsley, lemon juice and dill seed.
- Stuff with breadcrumbs, butter, anchovies, oysters, egg yolk, milk and spring onion.

Energy per serve of basic recipe:
Cal: 725 from Protein 554, Fat 150, CHO 20.
Kj: 3030 from Protein 2316, Fat 629, CHO 85.

PORK WITH APPLE

Preparation time: 30 minutes.
Cooking time: 40 minutes.
Serves: 2.

250 g of pork
1 tsp olive oil
1 onion sliced
1 green apple, cored and sliced
1 cup chicken stock
2 tsp plain flour
Black pepper

- Trim fat off meat and tenderize meat by hitting it with a meat cleaver or hammer. Cut meat into strips.
- Fry onion with oil in a frying pan, add meat, onion and apple.
- Stir-fry for 5 minutes.
- Mix flour with chicken stock, add to frying pan and bring to the boil.
- Add black pepper, cook gently until the meat is tender.

Energy per serve:
Cal: 441 from Protein 161, Fat 222, CHO 57.
Kj: 1843 from Protein 674, Fat 929, CHO 240.

SPAGHETTI BAKE

Preparation time: 90 minutes.
Cooking time: 40 minutes.
Serves: 4.

BASE
2 cups meat or fish cooked (leftovers work well)
2 cups spaghetti cooked
MEAT SAUCE
2 tomatoes chopped
1 onion chopped
1 carrot chopped
2 tsp olive oil
1 tsp fresh herbs
2 tbls grated Parmesan cheese
Black pepper
WHITE SAUCE
1 cup milk
1 egg
2 tbls plain flour
1/4 cup grated cheddar cheese
TOPPING
1 tbls butter
2 tbls breadcrumbs
4 tbls grated cheddar cheese

- Place meat and spaghetti in a casserole dish. Combine meat sauce ingredients and pour over meat and spaghetti.
- Blend white sauce ingredients, cook until thick and pour over meat and spaghetti.
- Mix topping ingredients and sprinkle over white sauce.
- Bake in oven at 200 deg C or 400 deg F until golden brown.

Energy per serve:
Cal: 668 from Protein 163, Fat 283, CHO 222.
Kj: 2794 from Protein 681, Fat 1184, CHO 930.

CHICKEN WITH ALMONDS

Preparation time: 45 minutes.
Cooking time: 25 minutes.
Serves: 4.

4 chicken breasts
1 cup almonds
1 tbls oil
1 onion sliced
3 cloves garlic chopped
1 tbls ginger chopped
1 tbls arrowroot
1 tbls low-salt soy sauce
1 cup green beans sliced
1 cup mushroom sliced
1 cup celery sliced
1 cup green peppers chopped
1 cup chicken stock
3 cups whole grain rice cooked

- Cut chicken into pieces, add arrowroot, soy sauce and ginger.
- Fry onion, almonds and garlic in oil and then add chicken and stir-fry for 5 minutes.
- Add vegetables and stir-fry for a further 5 minutes. Then add chicken stock.
- Simmer for 10 minutes.
- Serve with rice.

Energy per serve:
Cal: 710 from Protein 267, Fat 238, CHO 205.
Kj: 2967 from Protein 1116, Fat 995, CHO 856.

MACARONI CHEESE

Preparation time: 30 minutes.
Cooking time: 20 minutes.
Serves: 2.
This tasty dish can be served with a plate of steamed carrots and broccoli.

3 tbls of macaroni or 1 cup of cooked pasta
1/2 cup cheese grated
1 cup milk
1 tbls plain flour
1/4 tsp of mustard
Cayenne pepper
Garnish: 2 tbls breadcrumbs and 2 tbls grated cheese

- Wash macaroni. Cook in boiling water. Drain.
- To make sauce, blend milk, flour, mustard, pepper in blender. Pour into saucepan.
- Cook sauce bringing to the boil and stirring constantly with a wooden spoon.
- Combine the cooked macaroni, sauce and cheese.
- Place in an oven-proof dish. Sprinkle with breadcrumbs and cheese.
- Brown under griller or in oven.

Energy per serve:
Cal: 382 from Protein 80, Fat 168, CHO 134.
Kj: 1597 from Protein 334, Fat 703, CHO 560.

BAKED CHOPS

Preparation time: 60 minutes.
Cooking time: 60 minutes.
Serves: 2.
This dish uses the oven to cook the entire meal as Baked Sweet Potato & Stuffed Tomatoes accompany the chops. Baked apples, served with walnut cream, finish off the meal. (See index for these recipes.)

2 lamb or pork chops
1 tbls mayonnaise or All-purpose dressing
3 tbls crumbed wholemeal bread
Foil

- Wash chops and trim off fat. Dry the chops.
- Place mayonnaise in a dish and coat chops, then coat them with breadcrumbs.
- Put chops on oiled foil.
- Place 2 pieces of sweet potato on the foil.
- Prepare stuffed tomatoes and place beside the potatoes.
- Prepare baked apples and place them in a baking dish on a shelf below the cooking chops.
- Bake the entire meal at 180 deg C or 350 deg F for 40-60 minutes. Do not turn the chops.

Energy per serve baked chops only:
Cal: 327 from Protein 96, Fat 189, CHO 42.
Kj: 1367 from Protein 400, Fat 792, CHO 176.

CHICKEN WITH RICE

Preparation time: 15 minutes.
Cooking time: 45 minutes.
Serves: 3.
A colorful dish where all the food value of meat and vegetables is retained as it is cooked in one saucepan with all the contents of the saucepan being served. Serve with green vegetables.

500 g chicken pieces
1 tbls olive oil
1/2 onion chopped
1 clove garlic crushed
2 tomatoes chopped
1/2 cup whole grain rice uncooked
2 cups chicken broth
1/2 tsp pepper
Garnish: 9 asparagus spears and parsley chopped

- Fry onion and garlic in oil, add chicken, tomatoes, rice, broth and pepper.
- Bring to the boil and simmer for 45 minutes.
- Serve and garnish with asparagus spears and chopped parsley.

Energy per serve:
Cal: 477 from Protein 242, Fat 111, CHO 124.
Kj: 1993 from Protein 1010, Fat 463, CHO 520.

SOUSED ORANGE CHICKEN

Preparation time: 30 minutes.
Cooking time: 40 minutes.
Serves: 4-6.
This dish has a delicate flavor and can be served hot or cold.

1 chicken or chicken pieces (450 g to 700 g)
1 lemon quartered
4 oranges juiced
1 cup water
2 stalks celery chopped
1 carrot chopped
2 bay leaves
2 tbls green chopped herbs

- Remove skin and fat from chicken. Wash chicken and place in a saucepan.
- Add all ingredients and place over the chicken.
- Slowly bring to the boil and simmer for 20 minutes with lid on saucepan.
- Remove saucepan from the heat and let the chicken stand for 20 minutes.
- Drain the chicken, wrap in foil or greaseproof paper and refrigerate.
- Discard juice and vegetables.

Energy per serve:
Cal: 534 from Protein 235, Fat 220, CHO 78.
Kj: 2230 from Protein 981, Fat 921, CHO 328.

ACCOMPANIMENTS

The following are good accompaniments to Soused Orange Chicken.

Cold:
- Grapefruit, orange, yoghurt and lettuce.
- Preserved ginger and green salad.
- Mayonnaise, celery, walnuts and beetroot.
- Corn, pineapple, cauliflower and sprouts.
- Apple, radish, almonds, lemon juice and lettuce.

Hot:
- Plum sauce: 6 plums, 2 tsp vinegar, 1 tbls apple or orange juice, 2 tsp flour, 2 red chilli chopped (optional). Blend together and cook until thickened.

- Broccoli, mushroom, rice and almonds.
- Chestnuts and asparagus.
- Lemon sauce: 1/4 cup lemon juice, 1/2 cup orange juice, 2 tsp plain wholemeal flour, lemon and orange peel. Blend and cook until thickened.
- Saute with peanut sauce. Heat 2 tbls crunchy peanut butter and 1 tbls lemon juice.

CHILLI CON CARNE

Preparation time: 30 minutes.
Cooking time: 45 minutes .
Serves: 3.

500 g lean beef sliced
1 tbls olive oil
1 onion chopped
2 cloves garlic chopped
3 tomatoes chopped
1 cup carrot sliced
1 cup chicken stock
1/2 tsp chilli powder
2 bay leaves crushed
1/2 tsp oregano
1/2 tsp cummin
1/2 tsp black pepper
Garnish: 3 cups kidney beans, cooked

- Heat oil and fry onion, garlic and meat until brown.
- Add all ingredients.
- Simmer for 40 minutes. Check flavor.
- Serve on a bed of cooked kidney beans.

Energy per serve:
Cal: 720 from Protein 256, Fat 260, CHO 204.
Kj: 3010 from Protein 1068, Fat 1088, CHO 854.

WHITE STEW

Preparation time: 30 minutes.
Cooking time: 60 minutes.
Serves: 3.

500 g pork or chicken
1 1/2 cups chicken stock
6 peppercorns
1 onion sliced
1 cup turnip diced
1 cup celery thick slices
1 cup carrot large dice
1/2 tsp cayenne pepper
2 tbls wholemeal flour
1/2 cup milk
2 tbls cream
1 cup parsley chopped

- Trim the fat from the meat and cut into pieces.
- Place the stock and peppercorns and meat in a saucepan and bring to the boil. Simmer for 30 minutes with the lid on.
- Add vegetables to the saucepan and cook for 20 minutes.
- Place milk, flour and 1 cup of liquid from the saucepan into a blender and blend.
- Pour into saucepan and bring contents to the boil. Add cream and serve garnished with chopped parsley.
- Serve with a green and a yellow or orange coloured vegetable.

Energy per serve:
Cal: 564 from Protein 212, Fat 275, CHO 77.
Kj: 2359 from Protein 885, Fat 1151, CHO 323.

MEAT CURRY

Preparation time: 60 minutes.
Cooking time: 60 minutes.
Serves: 4.

500 g meat (beef, lamb, pork or chicken)
1 onion sliced
1 tbls curry paste or 2 tsp curry powder
1 tbls olive oil
1 cup carrot diced
1 cup potato diced
1 cup tomato chopped
1 cup chicken stock
RICE
1 cup brown rice
4 cups water

- Trim fat and cut meat into pieces.
- Fry onion, meat and curry paste in oil.
- Add vegetables and chicken stock. Simmer 45 minutes.
- Cook rice in boiling water for 45 minutes. Drain.
- Serve meat, rice and sambal separately.

VARIATIONS:
For a sweet curry, omit carrot, potato and tomato and substitute with banana, apple and 1/4 cup sultanas.

Energy per serve:
Cal: 900 from Protein 221, Fat 412, CHO 266.
Kj: 3761 from Protein 923, Fat 1724, CHO 1114.

SAMBAL

Preparation time: 10 minutes
Sambal is often served with curries, and consists of an assortment of foods placed decoratively on a large platter; for example: coconut, peanuts, raisins, chutney, mango or paw paw, cucumber with yoghurt, hard-boiled egg.

BAKED BEEF ROLL

Preparation time: 35 minutes.
Cooking time: 90 minutes.
Serves: 4.

500 g lean ground beef
1 egg beaten
4 tbls plain flour
1 potato grated
1 carrot grated
1 tomato chopped
1/2 onion chopped
1 tsp dried herbs
1/4 tsp pepper

- Mix meat and egg together.
- Pat out the meat mixture onto a floured board.
- Spread all of the ingredients on to the meat.
- Moisten edges of the meat with water and then roll up.
- Place on an oiled baking dish.
- Bake in oven at 180 deg C or 350 deg F for 90 minutes.
- After the first 45 minutes, vegetables such as pumpkin and sweet potato may be placed around the meat.
- When cooked, place on serving dish.
- Brown gravy can be made with cooking juices from the pan by blending 1/2 cup of cooking liquor and 1/2 cup water with 1 tbls flour. Heat and bring to the boil for 2 minutes. Flavour with pepper.

Energy per serve:
Cal: 476 from Protein 156, Fat 246, CHO 75.
Kj: 1991 from Protein 650, Fat 1029, CHO 312.

SWEET AND SOUR PORK

Preparation time: 35 minutes.
Cooking time: 15 minutes.
Serves: 3.

500 g pork fillet

1 tbls oil

1 onion chopped

2 cloves garlic chopped

2 tsp arrowroot

1 tbls low-salt soy sauce

1 tbls vinegar

2 dates chopped

1 cup pineapple chopped

1 cup carrot sliced

1 cup green beans sliced

1/2 cup red pepper sliced

1 cup chicken stock

Garnish: 3 cups cooked whole grain rice.

- Slice pork thinly, add arrowroot and soy sauce.
- Fry garlic and onion in oil in a frying pan. Add pork and brown.
- Combine all ingredients and simmer for 5 minutes. Check the flavor.
- Serve with rice.

Energy per serve:
Cal: 849 from Protein 239, Fat 330, CHO 281.
Kj: 3550 from Protein 997, Fat 1380, CHO 1173.

BROWN STEW

Preparation time: 30 minutes.
Cooking time: 60 minutes.
Serves: 3.
Served with potatoes and peas, this is a very filling and satisfying meal.

500 g lean steak or chops
1 tbls oil
1 tbls plain flour
1 onion sliced
1 carrot diced
1 1/2 cups chicken stock
1/2 tsp black pepper
Garnish: 1 cup parsley chopped or 1 cup crushed savoury crackers or toast

- Trim fat and bone from meat.
- Fry onion in oil, then add meat. Heat until a rich, brown color.
- Add flour and stir, cooking until brown.
- Add stock slowly and other ingredients. Stir until boiling.
- Simmer for 45 minutes.
- Serve with chopped parsley and crushed crackers and vegetables.

Energy per serve:
Cal: 556 from Protein 204, Fat 261, CHO 91.
Kj: 2323 from Protein 851, Fat 1092, CHO 381.

SAVOURY KEBABS

Preparation time: 30 minutes.
Cooking time: 12-15 minutes.
Serves: 1
These are prepared in advance to allow the marinade to flavour the kebabs. Serve on whole grain rice with a side salad.

8 steak cubes 170 g
4 onion wedges
4 red pepper squares
4 green pepper squares
4 zucchini circles
2 satay sticks
MARINADE
2 tbls lemon juice
1 tbls olive oil
1 tsp garlic crushed
1 tsp sesame seeds
Optional: 1/2 tsp chilli powder OR 1/4 teaspoon ginger
RICE
1 cup cooked whole grain rice.

- Trim fat off the meat and cut the meat into large cubes.
- Wash and prepare vegetables.
- Thread meat and vegetables on to satay sticks
- Place the satay sticks in a sealable container.
- Mix the marinade ingredients together and pour over the kebabs.
- Seal container and refrigerate for two hours or more.
- Cook under griller or bake in the oven. Turn kebabs during cooking.
- Serve on rice. Pour cooking liquor over kebabs.

Energy per serve:
Cal: 745 from Protein 230, Fat 291, CHO 223.
Kj: 3069 from Protein 955, Fat 1189, CHO 925.

FAVOURITE STYLE CHOPS

Preparation time: 30 minutes.
Cooking time: 90 minutes.
Serves: 2.

450 g lamb chops or 500 g round steak
1 tbls plain flour
3 tomatoes chopped
3 tsp Worcestershire sauce
3 tsp vinegar
1 tsp dried mustard powder
3 dates chopped
1 cup water
1 cup carrot sliced
1 onion sliced
Garnish: Parsley or chives

- Remove fat from meat and cut meat into pieces.
- Mix flour, mustard and meat in a basin and place into an oven casserole.
- Mix other ingredients together and pour over the meat.
- Top with carrot and onion.
- Cover casserole and cook at 200 deg C or 400 deg F for 90 minutes. Garnish and serve.

Energy per serve:
Cal: 582 from Protein 195, Fat 288, CHO 99.
Kj: 2432 from Protein 815, Fat 1203, CHO 414.

■ *Barbecued Chicken Dinner (p. 76).*▶

S·I·D·E D·I·S·H·E·S

Vegetables offer a wide range of flavours, nutrients and textures and supply fibre, vitamins A, B and C and minerals such as iron, calcium and potassium. Whilst vegetables may be served raw or cooked, a balance is recommended. Cooking destroys some vitamin B and C although it enhances the absorption of the beta-carotene factor of vitamin A present in spinach and carrot.

KEY POINTS

Purchase:

■ Buy fresh vegetables and, where possible, purchase organically grown or bio-dynamic produce.

■ Use frozen vegetables sparingly

■ Select mature sizes to ensure maximum beta carotene content.

Storage:

■ Place in closed containers in the refrigerator.

■ Potatoes and onions should be stored in a cool, dry cupboard.

Preparation:

■ Wash under running water.

■ Avoid peeling unless the skin is tough or bitter.

■ Don't soak in water.

■ Cut vegetables and cook immediately.

■ Tear green, leafy vegetables rather than slicing them.

◀ *Aussie Gold 'n Green (p. 104).* ■

Cooking:

- Steam
- Stir-fry
- Bake
- Boil using minimal water and cook quickly with a tightly fitting lid.

Eating:

To aid absorption of beta-carotene, serve with a little butter if not included in the recipe.

STIR-FRIED CAULIFLOWER

Preparation time: 10 minutes.
Cooking time: 10 minutes.
Serves: 2.

1 cup cauliflower
3 tsp butter
2 cloves garlic crushed
1 tbls wholemeal dried breadcrumbs OR one slice toast crushed

- Wash cauliflower and break it up into small pieces.
- Melt butter and add garlic and cauliflower.
- Stir-fry for 5 minutes.
- Add breadcrumbs and serve.

Energy per serve:
Cal: 102 from Protein 9, Fat 58, CHO 34.
Kj: 426 from Protein 38, Fat 244, CHO 144.

GREEN BEANS PROVENCALE

Preparation time: 10 minutes.
Cooking time: 12 minutes.
Serves: 2.

2 cups whole green beans
2 tsp butter

1/2 onion sliced
2 cloves garlic crushed
4 tomatoes chopped
1 tsp basil
Garnish: 2 tbls breadcrumbs and 2 tbls parsley chopped

- Wash and trim beans. Steam.
- Fry onion, garlic, tomatoes and basil in butter.
- Combine the beans and tomato mixture and heat.
- Serve sprinkled with breadcrumbs and parsley.

Energy per serve:
Cal: 184 from Protein 23, Fat 46, CHO 115.
Kj: 768 from Protein 95, Fat 192, CHO 480.

SUCCOTASH

Preparation time: Overnight soaking of beans PLUS 5 minutes.
Cooking time: 90 minutes.
Serves: 2.

1 cup corn kernels cooked
1 cup lima beans cooked
2 tsp butter
Paprika to taste
1 tbls of plain wholemeal flour
1 cup milk
Garnish: 2 tbls chives OR parsley chopped

- Place in blender milk, flour, seasoning and butter and blend.
- Place the blended mixture in a saucepan, add the corn and beans.
- Boil and simmer for 5 minutes.
- Add garnish to the mixture and serve.

Energy per serve:
Cal: 292 from Protein 49, Fat 77, CHO 165.
Kj: 1220 from Protein 207, Fat 322, CHO 691.

CABBAGE IN CREAMY HORSERADISH SAUCE

Preparation time: 20 minutes.
Cooking time: 10 minutes.
Serves: 4.

1/4 cabbage (White Mustard, Bokchoy or Pakchoy)
1 tbls butter
2 tbls plain wholemeal flour
1 1/2 cups milk
2 tbls grated horseradish, fresh or prepared
1/4 tsp dill seed or caraway seed
Black pepper
Garnish: 1 cup parsley chopped

- Wash cabbage and remove fibrous centre stalk.
- Slice or tear the cabbage.
- Melt butter in saucepan and lightly fry the cabbage.
- Place milk, flour and seasonings in the blender and blend.
- Add blended sauce to cabbage, stir and bring to the boil. Cook for 4 minutes.
- Add parsley and serve.

Energy per serve:
Cal: 142 from Protein 20, Fat 65, CHO 57.
Kj: 592 from Protein 86, Fat 270, CHO 237.

RED CABBAGE FLEMISH STYLE

Preparation time: 20 minutes.
Cooking time: 30 minutes.
Serves: 4.

This dish is a diner's delight and is usually served with pork and baked potatoes.

1/4 red cabbage
1 tbls butter
3 tbls vinegar
3 tbls water
1/4 tsp cinnamon
1/4 tsp allspice

1 tbls sultanas

2 green apples cored and diced

- Wash cabbage and remove the fibrous centre stalk.
- Slice or tear cabbage.
- Saute lightly in butter, moisten with water and vinegar.
- Season and cook for 20 minutes.
- Add diced apples and sultanas and cook for 10 minutes.
- Taste and adjust seasoning.
- Serve.

Energy per serve:
Cal: 101 from Protein 5, Fat 28, CHO 69.
Kj: 424 from Protein 19, Fat 118, CHO 286.

GOLDEN LATKES

Preparation time: 20 minutes.
Cooking time: 12-25 minutes.
Serves: 6.
Serve these hot with meat dishes, salads or green vegetables.

1 cup pumpkin grated

1 cup sweet potato grated

1 onion grated

1 tbls wholemeal flour

2 eggs beaten

1/2 tsp nutmeg powder

1/4 tsp black pepper

2 tsp olive oil

- Mix all ingredients together in a basin.
- Heat oil in frying pan.
- Drop tablespoons full of the mixture on to the pan, flatten and cook until golden brown on both sides.
- Serve.

Energy per serve:
Cal: 77 from Protein 13, Fat 33, CHO 31.
Kj: 321 from Protein 53, Fat 137, CHO 131.

MASHED MEDLEY

Preparation time: 10 minutes.
Cooking time: 15 minutes.
Serves: 4.

---

1 cup carrot chopped

1 cup sweet potato chopped

1 cup turnip, peeled and chopped (to remove bitter flavour, peel thickly)

2 tsp butter

1 tbls milk

Black pepper

Garnish: 2 tbls grated cheese

- Steam turnip, potato and carrot together.
- Mash vegetables adding butter, milk and pepper.
- Serve hot, sprinkled with grated cheese.

Energy per serve:
Cal: 81 from Protein 9, Fat 34, CHO 38.
Kj: 337 from Protein 38, Fat 141, CHO 158.

BEETROOT IN SPICED SAUCE

Preparation time: 15 minutes.
Cooking time: 40 minutes.
Serves: 4.

---

3 small beetroots or 1 large

2 tsp butter

1 tbls plain wholemeal flour

2 cloves

1/4 tsp caraway seed

1/4 onion chopped

1 cup chicken stock

2 tbls vinegar

Garnish: 2 tbls plain yoghurt and 2 tbls horseradish,
fresh or prepared

- Wash beets, place in cold, unsalted water.
- Bring to the boil and simmer until tender, 25-45 minutes.
- Remove skins and slice.
- Blend all other ingredients in blender.
- Heat and bring sauce to the boil for 2 minutes.
- Add beetroot to sauce.
- Mix yoghurt and horseradish together.
- Serve beetroot hot.
- Garnish with horseradish and yoghurt sauce.

Energy per serve:
Cal: 77 from Protein 11, Fat 25, CHO 42.
Kj: 324 from Protein 44, Fat 104, CHO 176.

BROCCOLI WITH ORANGE

Preparation time: 15 minutes.
Cooking time: 10 minutes.
Serves: 2.

2 cups broccoli
1/2 cup plain yoghurt
2 tbls orange juice and the peel
2 tsp plain wholemeal flour
1/4 tsp nutmeg
1 tsp butter
Garnish: Orange peel spirals

- Wash broccoli and cut into pieces. Steam.
- Place other ingredients in blender and blend.
- Pour blended sauce into saucepan, bring to boil and cook for 2 minutes.
- Place broccoli on serving dish and pour over sauce.
- Garnish with orange peel spirals.

Energy per serve:
Cal: 197 from Protein 44, Fat 52, CHO 100.
Kj: 823 from Protein 186, Fat 218, CHO 419.

AUSSIE GOLD 'N GREEN

Preparation time: 10 minutes.
Cooking time: 7 minutes.
Serves: 1.
This colourful dish can be served as a complete dinner dish, accompanied by wholemeal toast or as a side dish. The vibrant colors of this dish are the Australian national colors – gold and green.

1/2 cup pumpkin (large cut style)
1/2 cup carrot (large cut style)
1 tsp butter
1/4 cup fresh parsley chopped OR 1 tbls dried
Black pepper to taste
Garnish: 1 slice wholemeal toast

- Steam pumpkin and carrot together until soft.
- Place vegetables in a dish and mash with a fork.
- Add butter and pepper and then parsley.
- Serve piled high on plate.
- Garnish with toast triangles.

Energy per serve:
Cal: 189 from Protein 16, Fat 46, CHO 126.
Kj: 788 from Protein 68, Fat 192, CHO 528.

ASPARAGUS GENEVA STYLE

Preparation time: 15 minutes.
Cooking time: 15 minutes.
Serves: 1.

5 asparagus spears
2 tbls cheese grated
2 tbls chives OR parsley chopped

- Wash and steam asparagus spears or tie together and cook them standing upright in boiling water.
- Place in oven dish.

- Sprinkle with cheese and chives.
- Brown under griller or bake in oven.

Energy per serve:
Cal: 98 from Protein 24, Fat 56, CHO 18.
Kj: 409 from Protein 101, Fat 233, CHO 75.

ASPARAGUS SPEARS AMANDINE

Preparation time: 15 minutes.
Cooking time: 15 minutes.
Serves: 1.

5 asparagus spears
1 tsp butter
1/4 tsp tarragon
1 tsp chives chopped
Garnish: 1 tbls almonds sliced and 1 tbls parsley chopped

- Steam asparagus spears or tie together and cook them standing upright in boiling water.
- Drain, add tarragon and chives to the melted butter.
- Place asparagus in serving dish and pour the melted, herbed butter over the asparagus.
- Garnish with almonds and parsley.

Energy per serve:
Cal: 239 from Protein 29, Fat 169, CHO 40.
Kj: 998 from Protein 123, Fat 707, CHO 168.

STUFFED VEGETABLES

The flavour of vegetables takes on a different dimension when cooked whole with stuffing. In the following recipes, the stuffings given are interchangeable. However, the amounts will need to be adjusted according to the vegetable's size. Vegetables suitable for stuffing include all varieties of pumpkin, zucchini, bell peppers, tomatoes, eggplant or aubergine and cabbage.

STUFFED BUTTERNUT

Preparation time: 30 minutes.
Cooking time: 90 minutes.
Serves: 4.

---

1 medium size pumpkin

2 tsp butter

1 onion chopped

1 clove garlic chopped

1/2 cup celery chopped

1/2 cup parsley chopped

1/2 cup walnuts chopped

1/2 cup wholemeal breadcrumbs

1 1/2 cups grated cheese

1 tsp basil

- Cut the butternut lengthwise, remove seeds and bake at 180 deg C or 350 deg F until the flesh is soft.
- Scoop out flesh leaving 2cms around the skin for firmness.
- Mash cooked butternut flesh.
- Heat butter, fry onions and garlic. Add butternut flesh, celery, walnuts, parsley, breadcrumbs and basil.
- Mix well and place into butternut shell.
- Sprinkle with cheese and bake for 15 minutes at 180 deg C or 350 deg F.

Energy per serve:
Cal: 460 from Protein 69, Fat 241, CHO 150.
Kj: 1922 from Protein 290, Fat 1006, CHO 626.

STUFFED PEPPER

Preparation time: 15 minutes.
Cooking time: 40 minutes.
Serves: 1.

---

1 sweet red or green bell pepper

1/4 cup soy beans cooked and mashed

1/2 tomato chopped

1 slice wholemeal bread

1/2 tsp oregano

1/2 tsp basil

- Boil pepper for 3 minutes. Remove the stem and seeds.
- Crumble bread, add mashed beans, tomato and herbs.
- Fill the pepper with this mixture.
- Place in a baking tray with a small amount of water.
- Bake at 180 deg C or 350 deg F.

Energy per serve:
Cal: 161 from Protein 35, Fat 34, CHO 92.
Kj: 674 from Protein 148, Fat 141, CHO 386.

STUFFED TOMATOES

Preparation time: 15 minutes.
Cooking time: 15 minutes.
Serves: 2.

2 medium tomatoes

2 tsp butter

1/4 onion chopped

1 tbls cooked meat or fish chopped

2 tsp wholemeal breadcrumbs

2 tsp parsley chopped

Pepper to taste

- Wash and dry tomatoes.
- Cut a slice from the bottom of each tomato. This slice forms the lid.
- Scoop out the centre of the tomatoes and chop the pulp.
- Fry onions in butter and add all ingredients and stir.
- Fill the tomato cases and top with lids.
- Place tomatoes on an oiled oven tray and bake at 180 deg C or 350 deg F.

Energy per serve:
Cal: 106 from Protein 27, Fat 41, CHO 38.
Kj: 442 from Protein 115, Fat 170, CHO 157.

STUFFED EGGPLANT (AUBERGINE)

Preparation time: 15 minutes.
Cooking time: 15 minutes.
Serves: 2.

1 eggplant
2 tsp olive oil
2 cloves garlic crushed
1 tomato chopped
4 tbls wholemeal rice cooked
1/4 tsp basil
1/4 tsp oregano

Garnish: 6 slices tomato, olive oil, 1 tbls parsley
chopped

- Wash eggplant. Cut in half lengthwise.
- Score the flesh with a sharp knife.
- Heat oil and garlic, then fry the cut face of the eggplant.
- Scoop out the softened flesh and add to the oil and garlic.
- Mix in the chopped tomato, rice and herbs.
- Refill eggplant shells and top decoratively with tomato slices.
- Brush with olive oil and bake in oven at 180 deg C or 350 deg F.

Energy per serve:
Cal: 191 from Protein 17, Fat 64, CHO 110.
Kj: 799 from Protein 72, Fat 266, CHO 461.

STUFFED CABBAGE

Preparation time: 60 minutes.
Cooking time: 90 minutes.
Serves: 2.

4 large cabbage leaves
2 tbls cooked rice
1/2 cup lean ground beef
1 egg beaten
1/4 tsp caraway seed

1/2 cup carrot chopped finely
Black pepper
SAUCE
2 tomatoes chopped
2 cloves garlic mashed
2 tsp plain wholemeal flour
Chilli powder

- Wash cabbage leaves, place in large saucepan with 2 cups boiling water. Cover and steam for 10 minutes. Remove from water.
- Combine rice, beef, egg, carrot and spices.
- Cut the centre rib out of the cabbage leaves and place 1/4 of stuffing mixture on each leaf. Fold the sides of the cabbage over the stuffing and roll up the leaves forming a cylinder shape.
- Place cabbage rolls in a saucepan or oven dish.
- Mix the sauce ingredients together in a small saucepan. Boil for 2 minutes and pour over the cabbage rolls. Cook in the oven at 180 deg C or 350 deg F.

Energy per serve:
Cal: 264 from Protein 72, Fat 103, CHO 90.
Kj: 1103 from Protein 300, Fat 429, CHO 374.

BAKED SWEET POTATO

Preparation time: 15 minutes.
Cooking time: 60 minutes.
Serves: 4.

1 sweet potato
Butter
Pepper for seasoning

- Wash and peel potato. Cut it into even size pieces.
- Rub potato with butter and sprinkle with seasoning.
- Place on baking tray and bake until tender.

Energy per serve:
Cal: 38 from Protein 2, Fat 9, CHO 27.
Kj: 158 from Protein 9, Fat 37, CHO 112.

CORN MIX

Preparation time: 5 minutes.
Cooking time: 5 minutes.
Serves: 2.

---

1 cup corn kernels cooked

1 cup brown rice cooked

1/2 cup parsley chopped

2 tsp butter

- Melt butter. Add rice and corn.
- Cover and heat slowly for 5 minutes.
- Add chopped parsley, stir and serve.

Energy per serve:
Cal: 229 from Protein 20, Fat 41, CHO 168.
Kj: 959 from Protein 85, Fat 170, CHO 704.

BEANS WITH PEPPER

Preparation time: 5 minutes.
Cooking time: 5 minutes.
Serves: 2.

---

1 cup long green beans

1/2 red pepper

- Wash beans, top and tail and steam.
- Wash pepper and slice into 4 circles.
- Place cooked beans through 2 circles of pepper.
- Serve.

Energy per serve:
Cal: 30 from Protein 5, Fat 2, CHO 23.
Kj: 125 from Protein 21, Fat 7, CHO 96.

SCALLOPED VEGETABLES

Preparation time: 20 minutes.
Cooking time: 60 minutes.
Serves: 4.

1 cup turnip peeled thickly
1 cup sweet potato
1 cup carrot
1 tbls plain wholemeal flour
1 cup milk
2 tsp butter
Pepper

- Wash and peel vegetables. Cut into thin circles.
- Place flour and pepper in a bag, add vegetables and shake.
- Place vegetables in a baking dish.
- Heat milk and pour over the vegetables. Add dobs of butter. Cover the baking dish.
- Bake and remove the cover after cooking for 45 minutes. Bake for another 15 minutes at 180 deg C or 400 deg F.

Energy per serve:
Cal: 112 from Protein 14, Fat 37, CHO 61.
Kj: 470 from Protein 60, Fat 155, CHO 254.

D·E·S·S·E·R·T·S

Desserts prepared with a minimum of sugar and fat can be part of a nutritionally balanced meal. These desserts may be served hot or cold although preference should be given to fresh fruits over baked ones.

There's no better dessert than fresh fruit which supplies nutrients such as:

■ Fibre.

■ Vitamin C – papayas, oranges, melons, mangoes and strawberries.

■ Vitamin A – apricots, watermelons, cantaloupes, papayas.

■ Potassium – apricots, cantaloupes, oranges, dried fruit.

Prepare dried fruit by washing three times in water. Then soak it overnight in sufficient orange juice or water to cover the fruit, thus restoring the water volume.

Points to note:

■ All fruits should be washed before using.

■ Use the skin where possible.

■ Tofu can be sliced, frozen and thawed as required.

■ Use the firm Chinese variety of tofu.

■ One cup of dairy milk equals one cup of soybean milk.

■ One cup sugar equals 1/2 cup of golden syrup or honey or 4 dates and 1/2 cup water blended.

■ Spices are used instead of sugar wherever possible.

■ All fruits in the recipes are interchangeable with those on the preferred shopping list.

■ *Stuffed Eggplant and Beans with Pepper (pp. 108 & 110).*▶

TOFU ICE CREAM

Preparation time: 20 minutes.
Freezer time: 6 hours.
Serves: 6.
These recipes can be based on either soy or cow's milk. All tofu ice cream needs to be taken from the freezer half an hour before use as thawing time differs from conventional ice cream.

2 cups water
1/2 cup golden syrup
1 tsp vanilla essence
1 tsp vinegar
1 tbls melted butter
1/2 cup tofu or 1/2 cup whole milk powder
1/2 cup soy milk powder or 1/2 cup whole milk powder
2 tsp gelatine
3 tbls cold water

- Combine gelatine and the 3 tbls cold water in a small bowl. Place the bowl over hot water and stir until the gelatine is dissolved.
- Place the 2 cups water, syrup and butter in the saucepan and bring it to the boil.
- Remove from heat and add mashed tofu. Stir and pour into a blender, adding milk powder.
- Blend for 5 minutes, add the dissolved gelatine while the blending is in progress. Add vanilla and vinegar.
- Cool, stirring occasionally.
- Pour into a container, freeze until mushy. Beat again.
- Place in freezer in a plastic container and re-freeze.

VARIATIONS:

A substitute for water can be 2 cups of milk or 1 cup coconut milk and 1 cup water.

Energy per serve:
Cal: 141 from Protein 22, Fat 36, CHO 82.
Kj: 588 from Protein 92, Fat 152, CHO 344.

◄ *Peach Ginger Whip (p. 127).* ■

ICE CREAM ICE

Preparation time: 15 minutes.
Freezer time: 2 hours.
Serves: 4.

1 cup evaporated skim milk (semi-frozen)
1/2 cup plain yogurt
1/4 cup skim milk
1 tsp vanilla essence
4 to 6 tbls golden syrup or honey

- Place ingredients in blender and blend for 5 minutes.
- Pour into shallow trays and freeze until the texture is grainy with ice crystals.
- Place the mixture back into the blender and blend until thick and creamy.
- Add variations.
- Pour into a container and re-freeze.

VARIATIONS:

- 2 tsp rose water and 1/2 cup of chopped brazil nuts or toasted coconut
- 4 tbls chopped glace ginger
- 1/2 cup fruit puree and 1 tsp cinnamon
- 1/2 cup chopped almonds

Energy per serve:
Cal: 163 from Protein 25, Fat 10, CHO 128.
Kj: 681 from Protein 106, Fat 41, CHO 534.

PAPAYA SNOW

Preparation time: 10 minutes.
Cooking time: 20 minutes.
Serves: 2.
The papaya can be substituted for yellow peach, apricot or plum (prune type).

1 1/2 cups papaya diced
1 large red apple refrigerated
1 tbls orange juice
Garnish: 1 Kiwi fruit

- Blend the papaya, grated cold apple and cold orange juice.
- Pour into serving dishes and garnish with circles of Kiwi fruit.

Energy per serve:
Cal: 120 from Protein 4, Fat 3, CHO 113.
Kj: 500 from Protein 17, Fat 11, CHO 472.

BAKED CEREAL CUSTARD

Preparation time: 15 minutes.
Cooking time: 35 minutes.
Serves: 4.

2 eggs
1 tbls honey
1 1/2 cups milk
1 tsp vanilla
1/4 tsp nutmeg
2 tsp butter
1/2 cup cooked cereal such as rice, millet or buckwheat

- Place cooked cereal in a buttered oven dish.
- Heat milk but don't boil.
- Place the milk and other ingredients in a blender. Blend for 2 minutes.
- Pour over the cereal. Place the oven dish in a shallow pan half-filled with hot water.
- Bake at 180 deg C or 200 deg F until brown. Serve warm.

VARIATIONS:

- Coconut – 1 cup shredded coconut and 1 tsp lemon rind (omit the nutmeg and butter).
- Bread and butter – add 2 slices of buttered bread, 2 tbls sultanas or raisins. Cut bread into squares and place in an oven dish, sprinkle with sultanas (omit cooked cereal).

Energy per serve:
Cal: 157 from Protein 27, Fat 72, CHO 59.
Kj: 657 from Protein 113, Fat 300, CHO 245.

FRUIT ORIENTAL STYLE

Preparation time: 30 minutes.
Cooling time: 30 minutes.
Serves: 4.

---

1 cup lychees

1 cup yellow peaches large diced

1 cup grapes

2 tbls glace ginger or ginger in syrup

2 tbls lychee juice or water

Toothpicks

Garnish: 2 tbls coconut shredded

- Place a toothpick in each piece of fruit and stand these in a shallow serving dish.
- Combine finely chopped ginger and lychee juice and pour this over the fruit.
- Decorate with shredded coconut and refrigerate

Energy per serve:
Cal: 96 from Protein 4, Fat 14, CHO 78.
Kj: 399 from Protein 15, Fat 59, CHO 325.

MELON AND GINGER

Preparation time: 15 minutes.
Cooking time: 60 minutes.
Serves: 2.

---

2 cups honeydew melon or mango

2 tbls chopped glace ginger or ginger in syrup

- Ball or dice melon flesh. Chop ginger and add to melon.
- Refrigerate to develop flavor.
- Serve in clear glass dishes.

Energy per serve:
Cal: 85 from Protein 4, Fat 2, CHO 79.
Kj: 356 from Protein 19, Fat 7, CHO 330.

MELEE OF BERRIES

Preparation time: 20 minutes.
Serves: 4.

1 cup blueberries
1 cup strawberries
1 cup blackberries
1 cup raspberries
1 orange peel and juice
Tofu slices or carrot bread

- Wash and dry berries. Place in a large bowl, moisten with orange juice.
- Place sliced tofu on small serving dish and sprinkle with orange peel.
- Serve dishes separately.

Energy per serve:
Cal: 111 from Protein 14, Fat 20, CHO 77.
Kj: 465 from Protein 60, Fat 85, CHO 320.

WHOLEMEAL PASTRY No.1

Preparation time: 40 minutes
Makes: 2 pie cases.

2 cups plain wholemeal flour
1 cup butter
1/4 tsp salt
Water to mix
Extra flour

- Mix flour and salt and slice in the butter.
- Rub flour and butter together to break up the fat.
- Sprinkle with water and knead to a dough.
- Cover dough and let it stand for 30 minutes.

Energy per pie case:
Cal: 1213 from Protein 53, Fat 823, CHO 337.
Kj: 5070 from Protein 221, Fat 3441, CHO 1408.

WHOLEMEAL PIE CRUST No.2

Preparation time: 10 minutes
Cooking time: 10 minutes
Makes: 2 pie cases.

2 cups plain wholemeal flour
1 cup nuts, finely ground
1 to 1 1/2 cups water

- Grind nuts in blender.
- Place nuts and flour in a basin and add enough water to form a soft dough.
- Press into an oiled pie dish.
- Bake at 200 deg C or 400 deg F for 20 minutes.

Energy per pie case:
Cal: 831 from Protein 120, Fat 331, CHO 380.
Kj: 3473 from Protein 502, Fat 1384, CHO 1587.

WHOLEMEAL PIE CRUST No.3

Preparation time: 10 minutes
Cooking time: 15 minutes
Makes: 2 pie cases.

1 cup wholemeal breadcrumbs
1 cup wheatgerm
1/2 cup dates
1 cup orange juice

- Blend dates and orange juice.
- Add to breadcrumbs and wheatgerm. Mix to a soft, firm dough.
- Oil pie dish, crumble in the dough and press the mixture across the base and sides.
- Bake at 200 deg C or 400 deg F for 15 minutes if a cooked pie shell is required.

Energy per pie case:
Cal: 597 from Protein 130, Fat 92, CHO 374.
Kj: 2494 from Protein 544, Fat 385, CHO 1565.

RICE PASTRY

Makes: 1 pie case.

---

1 cup brown rice, cooked

1 egg

1 tbls butter

- Beat egg, then combine the rice with butter.
- Press into greased pie pan.
- Bake at 200 deg C or 400 deg F for 15 minutes if a cooked pie shell is required.

Energy per pie case:
Cal: 572 from Protein 46, Fat 331, CHO 195.
Kj: 2392 from Protein 193, Fat 1384, CHO 816.

PECAN PIE

Preparation time: 45 minutes.
Cooking time: 45 minutes.
Serves: 6.

---

1 wholemeal pie shell

1 cup pecans

1 cup tofu mashed and firmly packed

1/2 cup golden syrup

1 tsp vanilla

2 tbls melted butter

2 tbls lemon juice

2 tsp lemon rind

- Layer pecans on the uncooked pie crust.
- Blend together all the other ingredients, adding the tofu gradually.
- Pour over pecans.
- Bake at 200 deg C or 400 deg F for 45 minutes. Serve warm.

Energy per serve:
Cal: 400 from Protein 41, Fat 173, CHO 186.
Kj: 1673 from Protein 171, Fat 725, CHO 776.

PUMPKIN PIE

Preparation time: 90 minutes.
Cooking time: 45 minutes.
Serves: 6.

1 wholemeal pie shell uncooked
1 egg
2 tbls honey
2 cups pumpkin steamed
1 cup tofu mashed
1 cup carrot grated
1/2 cup dates chopped
2 tsp cinnamon
1/2 tsp ginger
1/2 tsp allspice

- Blend egg, honey and pumpkin. Gradually add tofu.
- Pour over carrots, dates, spices and stir to mix the ingredients.
- Spoon into pie shell. Sprinkle with cinnamon.
- Bake at 200 deg C or 400 deg F until filling is firm.
- Serve warm.

Energy per serve:
Cal: 431 from Protein 61, Fat 158, CHO 212.
Kj: 1802 from Protein 256, Fat 659, CHO 888.

FRUIT BASKETS

Preparation time: 40 minutes.
Serves: 6.
Whole fruit such as cantaloupe, watermelon and pineapple can have the flesh removed and the shell used as table decoration laden with fresh, colourful fruits.

1 whole fruit (cantaloupe, watermelon or pineapple)
4 Kiwi fruits
2 oranges
2 cups seedless grapes
2 cups strawberries

Mint or preserved ginger

- Cut whole fruit in half and remove seeds.
- Scoop out the flesh, dice and place in a large bowl.
- Peel and slice Kiwi fruits and oranges.
- Wash grapes and strawberries.
- Chop mint or ginger.
- Place all fruits in a large bowl and mix with mint or ginger.
- Pile into fruit shells.
- Serve on doily on a platter and decorate around the base with green leaves.

Energy per serve:
Cal: 120 from Protein 7, Fat 13, CHO 100.
Kj: 500 from Protein 28, Fat 56, CHO 416.

PAPAYA ORANGE MOUSSE

Preparation time: 20 minutes.
Cooking time: 3 minutes.
Setting time: Sets immediately.
Serves: 2.

1 cup papaya diced
1/4 cup orange juice
1/2 cup tofu mashed
1 tbls golden syrup
2 tsp lemon juice
2 tsp gelatine
2 tbls water

- Combine gelatine and water in a small bowl. Place the bowl over hot water and stir until the gelatine is dissolved.
- Cook papaya and orange juice together in a small saucepan for 2 minutes. This deactivates enzymes in the papaya.
- Place papaya mixture in blender, add tofu and flavorings and blend for 5 minutes.
- Add gelatine mixture while blender is processing. Blend for 2 minutes.
- Pour into serving dishes, refrigerate for 1 hour.

Energy per serve:
Cal: 136 from Protein 28, Fat 23, CHO 85.
Kj: 566 from Protein 115, Fat 96, CHO 355.

CREAMS

Any of the following creams are a good nutritious accompaniment to plain ice cream, fruit salad, fruit kebabs or fruit pie.

WALNUT CREAM

Preparation time: 5 minutes.
Serves: 3.

2 tbls walnuts
2 bananas
2 tbls plain yoghurt

- Grind walnuts in blender.
- Add sliced banana and yoghurt.
- Blend until smooth.
- Spoon into serving dish.

Energy per serve:
Cal: 108 from Protein 9, Fat 58, CHO 42.
Kj: 452 from Protein 37, Fat 241, CHO 174.

PAPAYA CREAM

Preparation time: 5 minutes.
Serves: 3.

1 cup papaya chopped
2 tbls almonds
2 tbls plain yoghurt

- Grind almonds in blender.
- Add yoghurt and papaya.
- Blend until smooth and serve in a dish.

Energy per serve:
Cal: 47 from Protein 6, Fat 25, CHO 16.
Kj: 198 from Protein 26, Fat 104, CHO 69.

DATE CREAM

Preparation time: 5 minutes.
Serves: 3.

---

4 dates chopped

3 tbls plain yoghurt

2 tbls commercial coconut cream

- Blend all ingredients in blender. Blend until smooth.
- Pour into small serving jug.

Energy per serve:
Cal: 40 from Protein 3, Fat 13, CHO 24.
Kj: 167 from Protein 13, Fat 56, CHO 99.

FRESH COCONUT CREAM

Preparation time: 15 minutes.
Cooling time: 60 minutes.
Serves: 10.

---

1 coconut

- Drain milk from coconut. Break open coconut and remove flesh.
- Grind flesh in blender and use coconut milk to correct consistency.
- Refrigerate for 1 hour.
- Serve over fruit or as required.

Energy per serve:
Cal: 89 from Protein 2, Fat 73, CHO 15.
Kj: 374 from Protein 10, Fat 303, CHO 61.

SULTANA CREAM

Preparation time: 5 minutes.
Serves: 3.

1/2 cup sultanas

3 tbls plain yoghurt

4 strips lemon peel

- Blend all ingredients in blender. Blend until smooth.
- Pour into small serving jug.

Energy per serve:
Cal: 91 from Protein 6, Fat 5, CHO 79.
Kj: 379 from Protein 26, Fat 22, CHO 331.

PEACH CREAM

Preparation time: 15 minutes.
Serves: 3.

---

1 large yellow peach

2 tbls commercial coconut cream

Orange juice

- Wash peach and cut off flesh.
- Place flesh in blender with coconut cream.
- Blend until smooth.
- Adjust consistency with orange juice.
- Serve in a dish.

Energy per serve:
Cal: 28 from Protein 2, Fat 10, CHO 16.
Kj: 117 from Protein 8, Fat 41, CHO 69.

GRANITA

Frozen ices are hot weather favourites and can also be served between meal courses or as a dessert in themselves.

Preparation time: 30 minutes.
Freezing time: 3 hours.
Serves: Depends on quantity of fruit used.

Suggestions:

Papaya and blackcurrants.

Mangoes.

Cantaloupe and orange.

Strawberries, lime juice and honey.

Apricot, peach and lemon juice.

Garnish: Mint leaves.

- Place fresh fruit or combination of fruit in blender and blend thoroughly to thick consistency. Adjust consistency with orange juice or water.
- Pour into a shallow container, cover and freeze.
- When frozen, remove from freezer. Break-up the mixture and blend again until a slush is obtained.
- Place in a bowl and re-freeze.
- Allow granita to soften slightly before serving.
- Serve in glasses and garnish with mint leaves.

Energy per serve:
Cal: 80 from Protein 4, Fat 5, CHO 71.
Kj: 335 from Protein 17, Fat 22, CHO 296.

APRICOT SAGO

Preparation time: 15 minutes.
Cooking time: 12-15 minutes.
Serves: 2.

4 tbls sago
2 cups water
2 lemons (peel and juice)
4 tbls orange juice
4 apricots
1 tsp honey (optional)

- Wash sago.
- Place sago, water, lemon juice and rind in a saucepan. Boil and simmer until the mixture is clear – approximately 12 minutes.
- Add chopped apricots and orange juice to blender, add sago mixture and blend. Add honey if desired.
- Pour into serving dishes and chill.
- Serve with coconut cream or fresh fruit.

Energy per serve:
Cal: 209 from Protein 11, Fat 3, CHO 196.
Kj: 875 from Protein 47, Fat 11, CHO 818.

STEWED APPLE

Preparation time: 15 minutes.
Cooking time: 15 minutes.
Serves: 1 cup.

---

2 medium red apples

3 dates or apricots or 2 tbls sultanas
1/4 cup water

1/8 tsp cinnamon

3 strips lemon peel

Garnish: 2 tbls orange juice

- Wash apples and cut into quarters, core and slice.
- Don't peel the apples. Place water in the saucepan, chop dates and add with cinnamon, lemon peel and apples.
- Bring to the boil, place lid on saucepan and cook over low heat for 10 minutes or until soft.
- Add 2 tbls orange juice.
- Serve.

Energy per serve:
Cal: 141 from Protein 3, Fat 2, CHO 137.
Kj: 591 from Protein 12, Fat 7, CHO 571.

FRUIT CRUMBLE

Preparation time: 20 minutes.
Cooking time: 45 minutes.
Serves: 4.

---

2 cups stewed peaches, apricots or plums

2 cups muesli

1 tsp cinnamon

2 tsp butter

1 cup orange juice

- Butter a shallow baking dish.
- Place 1 cup fruit in the dish and top with 1 cup of muesli.
- Repeat layering.
- Dot with butter and pour over orange juice.
- Bake at 180 deg C or 350 deg F.

Energy per serve:
Cal: 372 from Protein 33, Fat 106, CHO 233.
Kj: 1556 from Protein 136, Fat 444, CHO 976.

PEACH GINGER WHIP

Preparation time: 20 minutes.
Setting time: 15 minutes.
Serves: 2.
Plums (prune type), cherries or apricots can be substituted for the peach.

2 medium size yellow peaches
4 tbls ginger in syrup OR 1/2 tsp ginger powder AND
1/2 tsp honey
1 cup plain yoghurt
1/2 tsp mixed spice
1 lemon – peel and juice
Honey OR ginger syrup (optional)
2 tsp gelatine
2 tbls water
Garnish: Kiwi fruit or ginger slices

- Combine gelatine and water in a small bowl. Place the bowl over hot water and stir until the gelatine is dissolved.
- Place all ingredients in blender and blend until smooth.
- Pour into glass dishes and refrigerate.
- Garnish with slices of Kiwi fruit or ginger.

Energy per serve:
Cal: 148 from Protein 29, Fat 32, CHO 88.
Kj: 620 from Protein 120, Fat 133, CHO 366.

CHERRY COBBLER

Preparation time: 20 minutes.
Cooking time: 35-40 minutes.
Serves: 4.

1 tbls butter
1/2 cup brown sugar
1 cup plain wholemeal flour
1 tbls baking powder
1/4 tsp cinnamon
1/4 tsp nutmeg
3/4 cup milk
2 cups stewed cherries or blueberries
1 cup cherry juice or orange juice

- Butter a shallow baking dish using the 1 tbls of butter.
- Mix in a basin the sugar, flour, baking powder and spice. Add milk, mix well and pour into the baking dish.
- Top with cherries and pour over the orange juice.
- Cook at 180 deg C or 350 deg F.
- Slice and serve with a cream.

Energy per serve:
Cal: 343 from Protein 28, Fat 56, CHO 260.
Kj: 1435 from Protein 117, Fat 233, CHO 1085.

FRUIT SLICE

Preparation time: 60 minutes.
Cooking time: 35-40 minutes.
Serves: 6.

Pastry:
1 quantity wholemeal pastry
Filling:
3 cups stewed apple, cherries or rhubarb
1/2 cup nuts chopped
Glaze:
1 egg beaten

■ *Fresh Fruit Kebabs (p. 129).*▶

---
1 tbls milk

- Roll out the pastry into an oblong shape. Use extra flour to prevent the dough sticking.
- Cover half with stewed fruit and nuts.
- Fold the uncovered pastry over the fruit and seal the edges with water. Press edges together using a spoon handle.
- Place on greased oven tray and brush with glaze.
- Pierce pastry in several places with a fork.
- Bake at 200 deg C or 400 deg F until the pastry is brown.
- Cool and slice diagonally.

Energy per serve:
Cal: 473 from Protein 32, Fat 289, CHO 152.
Kj: 1977 from Protein 132, Fat 1210, CHO 635.

FRESH FRUIT KEBABS

Preparation time: 60 minutes.
Cooling time: 30 minutes.

Assorted fruits selection:
Cantaloupe
Kiwi fruit
Apricot
Pineapple
Prune
Strawberry
Orange
Wooden satay sticks
Mint chopped

- Prepare fruits and cut into uniform large pieces.
- Mix mint with pineapple or orange.
- Thread fruits on sticks.
- Place sticks on serving dish or in a sealed container and refrigerate.

Energy per serve:
Cal: 97 from Protein 6, Fat 4, CHO 87.
Kj: 405 from Protein 26, Fat 15, CHO 365.

◄*Mexican Roll (p. 136).* ∎

BAKED APPLE

Preparation time: 15 minutes.
Cooking time: 40 minutes.
Serves: 2.

2 apples
2 dates or prunes
2 tsp coconut
1/4 tsp cinnamon
2 tsp butter

- Wash and core apples. Score skin in two places.
- Fill core hole with dates, coconut, cinnamon and butter.
- Place in oven dish and add 2 tbls water.
- Bake at 180 deg C or 350 deg F.

Energy per serve:
Cal: 155 from Protein 1, Fat 47, CHO 107.
Kj: 648 from Protein 5, Fat 196, CHO 446.

FRESH FRUIT MEDLEY

Preparation time: 10 minutes.
Cooking time: 15 minutes.
Serves: 2.

Selection of 3 orange/yellow fruits to yield 2 cups
1/4 cup coconut shredded
2 tsp mint chopped

- Combine all ingredients.
- Refrigerate.

Energy per serve:
Cal: 114 from Protein 8, Fat 32, CHO 75.
Kj: 477 from Protein 32, Fat 133, CHO 312.

B·R·E·A·D·S &
L·O·A·V·E·S

These recipes offer a variety of non-yeast bakery items. Wholemeal products supply a wide range of nutritional requirements such as carbohydrates, fibre, vitamin B, iron, magnesium, zinc and some protein plus other vitamins and minerals.

The breads, which have a chewy texture, are more moist and heavier than the loaves. The bakery items can be served as snacks or to accompany the main meal. Platters of two or three varieties can be served with fresh fruit, cheeses or tofu as a dessert.

RAISING EQUIVALENTS

To make your own wholemeal self-raising flour, mix 1 cup plain wholemeal flour with 2 tsp baking powder.

You can make your own baking powder by sifting two parts cream of tartar with one part baking soda (bicarbonate).

POINTS TO REMEMBER

- Buy small quantities of flour, nuts and dried fruits to ensure freshness.

- Measure honey, treacle and molasses using a spoon which has been dipped in a cup of hot water for 10 seconds to make it easy to remove.

- All baking pans and trays are prepared by painting with melted butter and sprinkling with dried breadcrumbs.

- Milk can be substituted for soy milk or half yoghurt plus half water – or half coconut milk plus half water.

- Date puree can be substituted for granulated sugar.

- Half a cup of tofu plus 2 tbls water equals 2 eggs. Use Chinese-style tofu firmly packed; always slice and add as the last ingredient to the blender.

- Loaf pans used are:
  Oblong 22 cm × 11 cm × 9 cm deep.
  Circular 16 cm diameter × 6 cm deep.
  Tray 30 cm × 23 cm × 1.5 cm deep.

- To economise on energy and time, bake two loaf varieties at the same time. Recipes indicate whether one or two loaves are produced – just halve the ingredients if desired.

- The flavor of fruit breads is improved by wrapping them in plastic and refrigerating them for two to five days.

- All bakery items can be cooked, sliced and wrapped in plastic, frozen and then thawed when required.

CHEESE CORN BREAD

Preparation time: 20 minutes.
Cooking time: 40 minutes.
Yields: 2 loaves (16 slices).
A tasty and moist savoury bread which can be served warm and unbuttered or buttered sprinkled with chopped parsley.

3 cups cornmeal
2 cups cheddar cheese grated
1/2 cup wheatgerm
1 1/2 tsp chilli powder
2 eggs
1 1/2 cups plain yoghurt
1 cup milk
2 tsp baking soda

- Blend eggs, yoghurt, milk and soda.
- Place dry ingredients in a bowl and mix in the blended ingredients. Stir to mix.
- Pour batter into 2 prepared loaf pans.
- Bake at 180 deg C or 350 deg F.

Energy per slice:
Cal: 210 from Protein 41, Fat 70, CHO 99.
Kj: 878 from Protein 171, Fat 292, CHO 414.

SODA BREAD

Preparation time: 20 minutes.
Cooking time: 45 minutes.
Yields: 2 loaves (16 slices).
This bread is best served warm after baking – spread with garlic butter, it tastes great with salads.

2 cups wholemeal plain flour
2 cups barley flour
2 tsp baking soda
1 tsp baking powder
1/4 cup tofu sliced or 1 egg
1 tbls olive oil
2 cups buttermilk or 1 cup yoghurt
1 cup milk
1 tbls lemon juice

- Blend buttermilk, milk, lemon juice, oil and tofu.
- Place dry ingredients in a bowl and pour the blended ingredients over it.
- Mix to form a sticky dough.
- Spread into 2 prepared loaf tins. Stand for 5 minutes.
- Bake at 180 deg C or 350 deg F.

Energy per slice:
Cal: 165 from Protein 23, Fat 19, CHO 123.
Kj: 691 from Protein 95, Fat 81, CHO 515.

WHOLEMEAL BREAD

Preparation time: 25 minutes.
Cooking time: 45 minutes.
Yields: 2 loaves (16 slices).

2 cups wholemeal plain flour
1 cup cornmeal
1/4 cup arrowroot or soy flour
1/4 cup wheatgerm
1 1/2 tsp baking powder
3 1/2 tsp baking soda
1 cup plain yoghurt
1 cup milk
1/2 cup molasses

- Place dry ingredients in a bowl.
- Blend yoghurt, milk and molasses and then add to dry ingredients. Stir and mix well.
- Place in 2 prepared tins.
- Bake at 180 deg C or 350 deg F.

Energy per slice:
Cal: 134 from Protein 20, Fat 15, CHO 99.
Kj: 559 from Protein 82, Fat 63, CHO 414.

BASIC DOUGH RECIPE

Preparation time: 15 minutes.

2 cups wholemeal plain flour
4 tsp baking powder
1 tbls butter chopped
3/4 cup milk
Extra flour

- Place flour and baking powder in basin.
- Add finely chopped butter and mix in milk to form a soft and pliable dough.
- Place dough on a floured surface and knead lightly for 3 minutes.
- Cover until ready to use.

Energy per recipe:
Cal: 1040 from Protein 155, Fat 193, CHO 692.
Kj: 4345 from Protein 646, Fat 807, CHO 2893.

SMALL ROLLS

Preparation time: 40 minutes.
Cooking time: 20 minutes.
Yields: 12.

1 quantity basic dough recipe
2 tbls melted butter
2 tbls milk for glazing

- Roll out dough to 1 cm thickness, rectangular shape.
- Spread with melted butter.
- Mix filling ingredients together and sprinkle over buttered dough.
- Moisten edges of dough with water and roll up.
- Cut up into 12 slices and arrange on a prepared baking tray. Glaze with milk.
- Bake at 200 deg C or 400 deg F.
- Serve with butter if desired.

SUGGESTED FILLINGS:

- Flaked tuna, grated cheese and parsley.
- Sardines, mushroom slices, lemon, parsley and chilli powder.
- Mixed, diced dried fruit, lemon peel, brown sugar, mixed spice.
- Peanut butter, honey, vanilla, wheatgerm.

MEXICAN ROLL

Preparation time: 35 minutes.
Cooking time: 30 minutes.
Serves: 4.
This tasty bread is served hot and makes an excellent meal with salads, fish and meat.

1 quantity basic dough recipe
6 tbls tomato ketchup
2 tbls onions chopped finely
1/4 green pepper chopped
8 stuffed olives sliced
1/8 tsp chilli powder

- Roll out dough to 1 cm thickness, rectangular shape.
- Spread with ingredients.
- Moisten edges with water and roll up Swiss roll style.
- Place on a buttered oven tray. Make a series of cuts 3/4 quarters of the way through the roll and 2 cm apart.
- Shape into a crescent and paint with milk and bake at 200 deg C or 400 deg F.

Energy per serve:
Cal: 293 from Protein 41, Fat 69, CHO 183.
Kj: 1225 from Protein 170, Fat 289, CHO 766.

CHEESE PLAIT

Preparation time: 30 minutes.
Cooking time: 30 minutes.
Serves: 4.

1 quantity basic dough recipe
1 tsp mustard powder
1 tbls chopped parsley
1 tsp onion chopped
1/4 tsp cayenne pepper
1 cup cheese grated
2 tbls milk for glazing

- Add the above ingredients to the basic dry mixture before adding the milk. Add 1 tbls extra milk.
- Divide the dough into 3 portions and roll each out to a 30cm roll. Moisten the edges with milk at one end and press together.
- Plait loosely. Seal edges with milk and press together.
- Place plait on buttered oven tray.
- Glaze with milk.
- Bake at 200 deg C or 400 deg F.

Energy per serve:
Cal: 402 from Protein 67, Fat 159, CHO 175.
Kj: 1679 from Protein 281, Fat 666, CHO 733.

PIZZA

Preparation time: 40 minutes.
Cooking time: 25 minutes.
Serves: 4.

1 buttered baking tray 30 cm × 23 cm × 1.5 cm deep
1 quantity basic dough recipe
1 cup tomato paste or puree

- Roll out the dough to fit the baking tray.
- Place the dough on the baking tray and cover with tomato puree.
- Sprinkle on toppings.
- Bake 200 deg C or 400 deg F.
- Slice into chunky portions.

SUGGESTED TOPPINGS:

- Supremo: Cheese, tomato, asparagus, mushroom, onion, capsicum, sunflower seeds.
- Hawaiian: Cheese, tomato, crab or tuna, pineapple, capsicum, chilli.
- Vegetarian: Cheese, tomato, mushroom, olives, onion, capsicum, basil, parsley, sesame seed.
- Seafood: Cheese, tomato, prawns, oysters, anchovies, garlic, oregano or curry powder.
- Mexican: Cheese, tomato, ground beef, chilli, onion, capsicum.

Energy per serve:
Cal: 426 from Protein 75, Fat 158, CHO 193.
Kj: 1782 from Protein 316, Fat 659, CHO 808.

PEACH NUT BREAD

Preparation time: 40 minutes.
Cooking time: 75 minutes.
Yields: 2 loaves (16 slices).

1/4 cup butter chopped
1/2 cup honey
2 eggs
2 tsp vanilla
2 cups chopped diced peaches
1 cup sunflower seed kernels
2 cups wholemeal plain flour
4 tsp baking powder
1 cup buckwheat flour
1 1/2 tsp mixed spice
1/2 cup wheatgerm
1 cup orange juice

- Blend butter, honey, eggs and vanilla.
- Place all other ingredients in a bowl.
- Mix liquid ingredients with dry ingredients.
- Stir and mix well; adjust the consistency with orange juice until the mixture is of a sticky consistency.
- Place in 2 prepared loaf pans.
- Bake at 150 deg C or 350 deg F.

Energy per slice:
Cal: 239 from Protein 27, Fat 71, CHO 142.
Kj: 999 from Protein 111, Fat 296, CHO 592.

GALA BREAD

Preparation time: 40 minutes.
Cooking time: 75 minutes.
Yields: 2 loaves (16 slices).

2 eggs
1/2 cup olive oil
1/2 cup honey
1 cup orange juice
1 cup papaya mashed
1/2 cup buckwheat or soy flour
1 1/2 cups wholemeal plain flour
4 tsp baking powder
1 cup skimmed milk powder
1/4 cup wheatgerm
1/2 cup granulated brown sugar
1/2 cup dried apricots chopped
1/2 cup brazil nuts chopped
1/4 cup sunflower kernels
1/2 tsp baking soda

- Blend eggs, oil, honey, orange juice and papaya.
- Place all other ingredients in a large bowl and mix in the blended ingredients.
- Pour the mixture into 2 prepared loaf pans.
- Bake at 150 deg C or 300 deg F

Energy per slice:
Cal: 235 from Protein 18, Fat 99, CHO 118.
Kj: 982 from Protein 74, Fat 414, CHO 493.

BRAN LOAF

Preparation time: 15 minutes.
Cooking time: 45 minutes .
Yields: 1 loaf (8 slices).
This is a bland tasting loaf. Slice and serve with butter.

2 cups wholemeal flour
4 tsp baking powder
3/4 cup bran
2 tsp golden syrup
3/4 cup boiling water
3/4 cup milk

- Place flour, baking powder and bran in a basin.
- Add syrup to boiling water and then add milk and pour on to the dry ingredients.
- Mix well. Place in a prepared loaf pan.
- Bake at 180 deg C or 350 deg F.

VARIATIONS:

Add one of the following to the dry ingredients:
- 1 tsp caraway seed
- 1 tbls fresh chopped herbs
- Peel of 1 orange and 1 lemon

Energy per slice:
Cal: 124 from Protein 19, Fat 10, CHO 95.
Kj: 517 from Protein 79, Fat 41, CHO 397.

CARROT BRAZIL NUT BREAD

Preparation time: 20 minutes.
Cooking time: 45-50 minutes.
Yields: 2 loaves (16 slices).
Sliced thinly and served cold this is a good accompaniment to a fruit platter.

2 cups carrot grated
1/2 cup tofu or 1 egg
1/2 cup honey
3/4 cup oil
1/2 tsp vanilla
2 cups wholemeal flour
4 tsp baking powder
1 tsp mixed spice
1 cup brazil nuts
1 cup milk

- Place carrot, honey, oil, vanilla and tofu in a blender then blend.
- Place flour, baking powder, spice and brazil nuts in a bowl.
- Add blended ingredients and mix with milk.
- Place into 2 prepared loaf tins.
- Bake at 180 deg C or 350 deg F.

Energy per slice:
Cal: 262 from Protein 19, Fat 163, CHO 80.
Kj: 1095 from Protein 80, Fat 681, CHO 334.

SUNFLOWER DATE LOAF

Preparation time: 20 minutes.
Cooking time: 50 minutes.
Yields: 1 loaf (8 slices).

2 cups wholemeal flour
4 tsp baking powder
1/2 cup sunflower kernels
1 cup dates chopped
1/2 tsp baking soda
1 cup boiling water
2 tbls butter melted
1 tbls golden syrup
1 egg
1 lemon (juice and peel)

- Place water, soda and dates in a saucepan and boil. Stir to mash the dates; allow to cool.
- Blend butter, syrup, egg, lemon juice and peel. Add the date mixture and blend.
- Pour the blended mixture over the flour, baking powder and sunflower kernels. Mix well.
- Place in a prepared loaf pan. Bake at 180 deg C or 350 deg F.

Energy per slice:
Cal: 269 from Protein 28, Fat 80, CHO 162.
Kj: 1125 from Protein 117, Fat 333, CHO 675.

CARROT AND PEACH LOAF

Preparation time: 40 minutes.
Cooking time: 50 minutes .
Yields: 1 loaf (8 slices).
This basic recipe can be adapted to give a range of variations of flavour and texture.

1 cup wholemeal flour
2 tsp baking powder
1 cup carrot grated
1 cup yellow peach chopped
1/4 cup dates chopped
2 tbls golden syrup
1 tsp baking soda
1 tsp mixed spice
1/2 cup oil
2 eggs

- Place flour, baking powder, carrot and peach in a basin.
- Blend dates, syrup, baking soda, spice, oil and eggs in a blender.
- Add the blended mixture to the flour mixture. Mix well and spread into 1 prepared loaf pan.
- Bake at 180 deg C or 350 deg F.

VARIATIONS:

The carrot and peach may be replaced by either:
- 1 cup papaya and 1 cup pineapple.
- 1 cup sour cherries.
- 1 cup apple and 1/2 cup muesli and 2 tbls of milk.
- 1 cup sour cherries and 1 cup coconut.

Energy per slice:
Cal: 236 from Protein 16, Fat 136, CHO 84.
Kj: 988 from Protein 66, Fat 570, CHO 352.

APRICOT BREAD

Preparation time: 30 minutes.
Cooking time: 45 minutes .
Yields: 2 loaves (16 slices).
This loaf will keep up to 4 weeks in the refrigerator. Serve cold and buttered.

2 cups dried apricots chopped
2 cups milk
1/2 cup granulated brown sugar
2 cups All-Bran cereal
2 cups wholemeal flour
4 tsp baking powder

- Put apricots, milk and sugar in a saucepan and heat gently for 5 minutes. Allow to cool.
- Add All-Bran, flour and baking powder and mix to a soft consistency using extra milk.
- Pour into 2 prepared loaf pans.
- Bake at 180 deg C or 350 deg F.

VARIATIONS:

Replace apricots with another dried fruit, such as
- Peaches and orange peel.
- Sultanas.
- Raisins.
- Papaya and lemon peel.

Energy per slice:
Cal: 206 from Protein 23, Fat 19, CHO 163.
Kj: 860 from Protein 96, Fat 81, CHO 683.

■ *Apricot Bread (p. 144).*▶

CHERRY STREUSEL

Preparation time: 30 minutes.
Cooking time: 45 minutes .
Yields: 1 loaf (8 slices).

DOUGH
1 1/2 cups wholemeal flour
3 tsp baking powder
2 tbls butter
2 tbls golden syrup
1 egg
3/4 cup milk
FILLING
1 cup cherries
1 tsp cinnamon
TOPPING
1/2 cup muesli
1 tbls butter melted
1/2 tsp cinnamon

- Blend butter, syrup, egg and milk.
- Pour blended mixture over dry dough ingredients and mix to a soft consistency.
- Spread half the dough in a prepared loaf tin.
- Place the filling on top of the dough and place the other half of the dough mixture on top.
- Sprinkle topping over the dough.
- Bake at 200 deg C or 400 deg F.

Energy per slice:
Cal: 210 from Protein 23, Fat 68, CHO 119.
Kj: 878 from Protein 97, Fat 285, CHO 496.

◄ *Cherry Streusel (p. 145).* ■

PUMPKIN LOAF

Preparation time: 30 minutes.
Cooking time: 45 minutes.
Yields: 2 loaves (16 slices).

3 cups wholemeal flour
6 tsp baking powder
1/2 cup sunflower kernels
1/2 cup sultanas
1 egg
1 cup pumpkin cooked and mashed
1 cup milk
1/4 cup brown granulated sugar
1/4 cup honey
1/4 cup butter melted
1 tsp mixed spices
1 tsp nutmeg

- Place flour, baking powder, kernels and sultanas in a bowl.
- Blend rest of the ingredients and add to the dry ingredients.
- Mix well.
- Place in 2 prepared loaf pans.
- Bake at 180 deg C or 350 deg F.

Energy per slice:
Cal: 179 from Protein 20, Fat 53, CHO 105.
Kj: 746 from Protein 84, Fat 222, CHO 440.

· 12 ·
SELECTING · YOUR · OWN
MENU · PLAN

The recipes in this book have been carefully designed to provide high densities of nutrients essential for an effective immune system.

The most critical constituents of high density foods are: vitamin C, beta carotene, vitamin E, magnesium, manganese, selenium, zinc, copper, methionine, cysteine and linolenic acid.

Since not every recipe can have high levels of *all* nutrients required, menu plans have been designed so that daily and weekly balances of nutrients and energy levels can be achieved.

The Nutrient Density Table included in this chapter shows the nutrient densities for a wide variety of foods in the major food groupings; the higher up this table that the food appears, the higher its nutrient density. Whilst other foods can be eaten, three-quarters of your daily intake should come from the foods in this table.

Two separate menus, each covering four weeks, have been designed. The first, which provides a *normal* energy intake, is based on an average daily intake of 10,000 Kj whilst the second, providing a *high* energy intake, is based on an average intake of 13,000 Kj per day.

Remember, with a little planning and by visiting the healthy eating places which exist today, it *is* possible to eat out whilst following any of the menu plans in this book.

· WHICH MENU PLAN SHOULD YOU USE? ·

Everyone has different energy needs.

People who could benefit from the *high* energy menu may include athletes, adolescents, pregnant or nursing mothers, those who lead an active sporting life, are involved in strenuous occupations or are under extreme stress or people suffering from some diseases associated with weight loss. With such diseases, including many cancers and AIDS, there is often a problem with the body's ability to absorb nutrients. Therefore not only is a high density nutrient diet required to boost the immune system but a high energy menu is also required to ensure that sufficient food is absorbed to prevent further weight loss.

Based on the information provided in this book, you should be able to decide which menu plan best suits your needs. If you do not have a need for above normal energy input, use the *normal* energy menu plan; if you are in this category and use the *high* energy menu plan you are likely to put on weight. However, if you are in doubt about which menu plan is best for *you*, talking with your doctor or a trained dietician will help you decide.

If you need to adjust the menu plans to suit your own energy requirements it is important that you *do not omit* any of the suggested foods but, rather, reduce or increase the size of the recommended servings.

For instance, if one member of the family is on a *high* energy menu, others in the family can follow the same menu by adjusting the portions – reducing the portions by about 20% for adult men and adolescents, by about 40% for adult women and yet further for children.

People who have a medical condition accompanied by weight loss may also need to adjust the size of portions in the *high* energy menu depending on the severity of their weight loss problem. It is best to take advice from your doctor in such cases but basically keep a careful eye on your weight and adjust accordingly, i.e. if you put on too much weight while on the menu, cut down the portions but if you do not put on excessive weight stay on the suggested servings.

If you are currently overweight as part of your health problem, these menus are *not recommended* as your weight problem is likely to get worse. The needs of people with overweight problems vary so much from person to person that it is difficult to design a universal menu plan in such cases. However, you could ask a skilled nutritionist to use the principles in this book to design a menu specifically for you. The table of Daily Energy Requirements in this chapter will help as a guide in adjusting portion sizes for your specific needs.

NORMAL ENERGY FOOD PLANS

MENU 1

Meal	Day 1	Day 2	Day 3	Day 4	Day 5	Day 6	Day 7
Breakfast	orange juice 1 cup bread 2 slices sardines 30 g apple 1	*Buckwheat Porridge strawberries 1 cup rice cake 1 butter 1 tsp jam 1 tsp	*Muesli 1 cup skim-milk 1 cup toast 1 slice butter 1 tsp tomato 1 yellow peach 1	toast 2 slices peanut butter 1 tbls asparagus spears 4 strawberries 1 cup	*Muesli 1 cup skim-milk 1 cup toast 2 slices chicken 90 g grapes 1 cup	*Toast 2 slices butter 1 tsp jam 2 tsp	*Rice Porridge honey 1 tsp dates 4 cinnamon 1 tsp skim-milk 1 cup banana 1
Snack	*3 Beta Tonique	*Oriental Drift	*Koala Mauve	*Melon Sparkle	*Pink Fancy wholemeal crackers 2	*Malted Orange (soy milk)	*Greenacres Tonique
Lunch	Salmon 120 g bread 2 slices butter 2 tsp *Spring Salad 1 cup papaya 1 cup	chicken breast 90 g *Golden Salad rice cake 1 butter 1 tsp cherries 1 cup	flaked crab meat 180 g bread 2 slices butter 1 tsp *Beetroot Salad lettuce 2 cups carrot ½ cup	*Tuna-bean On Rye red pepper ½ cup green pepper ½ cup walnuts ¼ cup orange 1	sardines 60 g asparagus spears 4 carrot ½ cup salad greens 1 cup bread 2 slices lo-fat yoghurt ½ cup banana 1	*Pumpkin Soup bread roll 1 green salad 2 cups papaya 1 cup	*Dame Charmante 1 salad greens 1 cup rice cake 1 butter 1 tsp fruit salad 1 cup
Snack	Peanut butter snadwich	rice bread 1 slice fish paste 1 tsp butter 1 tsp	orange 1	salad sandwich apple 1	rice cake 1 dates 4	wholemeal crackers 2 fish paste 1 tbls	lo-fat yoghurt ¾ cup *Muesli ½ cup
Dinner	*Lentil Burger *Tomato Sauce *Red Cabbage *Baked Sweet potatoes 2 *Fruit Kebab *Tofu Ice-cream	*Stir Fry Pork & Vegetables brown rice 1½ cups *Oriental Style Fruit	*Fish In Foil *Baked Sweet Potato 1 *Corn Mix spinach 1 cup *Tofu Ice-cream yellow peach 1	grilled steak 200 g brown rice 1 cup onion 1 carrot ½ cup broccoli ½ cup *Papaya Orange mousse	*Baked Chops 2 baked sweet potato 1 baked onion 1 corn ½ cup *Baked Apple *Tofu Ice-cream	soused orange chicken brown rice ¾ cup mushroom ½ cup *Apricot Sago *Coconut Cream 1 tbls	*Cabbage & Egg Whirl soup *Fish Burgers *Tomato Sauce spinach 1 cup brown rice ½ cup
Snack	*Golden Juice	lo-fat yoghurt 1 cup banana small	wholemeal crackers 2 almond butter 1 tsp	lo-fat yoghurt 1 cup prunes 4	rice cake 1 peanut butter 1 tsp	alfalfa sandwich banana 1	rice cake 1 almond butter 1 tsp orange

*Denotes recipes in this book

NORMAL ENERGY FOOD PLANS

MENU 2

Meal	Day 1	Day 2	Day 3	Day 4	Day 5	Day 6	Day 7
Breakfast	Honeydew melon ¼ toast 2 slices beetroot 4 slices apple 1	*Buckwheat Pancakes *Stewed Apple skim-milk 1 cup banana 1	*Muesli 1 cup skim-milk 1 cup banana 1	salmon 45 g toast 2 slices peach 1	*Porridge skim-milk 1 cup raisins 2 tbls	*Strawberry Royale toast 1 slice peanut butter 1 tsp papaya 1 cup	baked beans ½ cup tomato 1 rice cakes 2 cantaloupe ¼
Snack	Banana small soy milk ½ cup	*Red Beet Tonique	*Cantaloupe Supreme rice cake 1	*Koala Mauve	*Carrot Brazil Nut bread 1 slice	chicken borth 1 cup wholemeal cracker 4	lo-fat yoghurt 1 cup *Muesli 1 cup
Lunch	Chicken meat 120 g carrot, grated 1 cup red pepper ½ cup salad greens 1 cup wholemeal cracker 2 cantaloupe ½	tuna 120 g bean mix ½ cup lettuce 1 cup carrot, grated ½ cup rice cake 1 butter 1 tsp banana 1	*Vegetable minestrone Soup crab meat 120 g spinach salad – spinach 1½ cup – tomato 1 bread roll	*Gazpacho Creme chicken meat 120 g bean salad ½ cup beetroot ½ cup wholemeal crackers 4 pineapple 2 slices	crab meat 120 g beans ½ cup brown rice ½ cup parsley ¼ cup lettuce 1½ cups papaya 1 cup	curried egg sandwich chinese cabbage slaw 1 cup lo-fat yoghurt 1 cup banana 1	*Avocado Velvet Soup salmon 120 g carrot, grated ½ cup raisin ¼ cup mayonnaise 2 tsp lettuce 1 cup pineapple 2 slices
Snack	peanut butter sandwich	cheese 60 g celery 2 sticks	wholemeal crackers 4 chicken broth 1 cup	lo-fat yoghurt 1 cup *Muesli ½ cup	dates 5 wholemeal crackers 4	*Carrot Brazil *Nutbread 1 slice	orange 1
Dinner	*Stir Fry Pork & Vegetables brown rice ½ cup *Melon Sparkle	*Kangaroo Red tortilla shells 4 broccoli 1 cup *Baked Apple *Baked Cereal custard	*Baked Beef Roll gravy 4 tbls *Baked Sweet Potato 2 baked tomato broccoli 1 cup peach 1	*Maccaroni Cheese *Stir Fried Cauliflower pumpkin ¾ cup green beans ½ cup *Cheery Cobbler *Ice Cream Ice	*Pork with Apple *Red Cabbage Flemish sweet potato 1 cup broccoli 1 cup carrot ½ cup	*Savoury Ground Beef wholemeal pasta 1½ cups *Beans with Red Pepper pumpkin 1 cup orange 1	*Baked Fish and Chips spinach 1 cup carrot ½ cup green beans ½ cup *Baked Apple *Baked Cereal custard
Snack	hot soy milk 1 cup honey 1 tsp	dates 4	date sandwich	pumpkin seeds ¼ cup	lo-fat yoghurt 1 cup banana 1	dates 3 celery sticks 2	*Jungle Juice *Rice Bran Loaf

*Denotes recipes in this book

NORMAL ENERGY FOOD PLANS

MENU 3

Meal	Day 1	Day 2	Day 3	Day 4	Day 5	Day 6	Day 7
Breakfast	Orange juice 1 cup baked beans ½ cup tomato 1 slice butter 1 tsp prunes 3	*Serendipity Juice – apple, mixed vegetables rice cake 2 tomatoes 2	*Buckwheat Pancakes berries 1 cup toast 2 slices honey 2 tsp	salmon 45 g green pepper ¼ cup toast 2 slices	*Porridge skim-milk 1 cup raisins 2 tbls	*Strawberry Royale *Corn Hash toast 1 slice	*Serendipity Juice – carrot, tomato *Muesli skim-milk 1 cup
Snack	Strawberries 1 cup soy milk 1 cup	orange 1	cantaloupe ¼	*Peach Nut Bread 1 slice orange 1	*Apricot Bread 2 slices	wholemeal crackers 2 carrot sticks 2	papaya 1 cup
Lunch	*Corny Thick Shake sardine sandwich – bread 2 slices – sardines 4 – parsley 2 tbls – lemon juice	*Crab Avocado rice cakes 2 salad greens 1 cup raisins ¼ cup strawberries 1 cup	*Tomato Zip chicken 120 g rice salad 1 cup green salad 1 cup bread 1 slice butter 1 tsp	Curried Chicken sandwich – bread 2 slices – chicken 120 g – curry powder ¼ tsp – alfalfa sprouts 1 cup – mayonnaise 2 tsp *Malted Orange	*Rice Bean Mix tuna 120 g lettuce 1 cup tofu ice cream cantaloupe 1 cup	*Thick Bean Soup *Mexican Roll *Chinese Cabbage Slaw 1 cup apple 1	*Pumpkin and Carrot Soup chicken 120 g mixed salad 1 cup strawberries 1 cup
Snack	Dates 4	rice cake 1 fish paste 1 tbls	*Apricot Bread 1 slice apple 1	rice cake 2 cheese 1 slice carrot sticks 2	peanut butter sandwich	*Pumpkin Pie	banana and date sandwich – (rice bread)
Dinner	*Brown Stew sweet potato ½ cup peas ½ cup *Pumpkin Pie	*Chicken with Almonds brown rice 1 cup *Fresh Fruit Medley *Tofu Ice Cream	*Chili Con Carne broccoli 1 cup pumpkin ½ cup lo-fat yoghurt ½ cup prunes 4	*Thick Bean Soup *Spinach Rice green salad 1 cup *Pumpkin Pie	*Liver slices toast 1 slice green beans 1 cup carrot 1 cup *Fruit Kebabs lo-fat yoghurt ½ cup	*Fish in Foil *Baked Sweet Potato baked pumpkin spinach 1 cup *Tofu Ice Cream	*Savoury Fish Pie *Stuffed Egg Plant brown rice 1 cup lo-fat yoghurt 1 cup peach 1 apple 1
Snack	*Apricot Bread 2 slices	lo-fat yoghurt ½ cup banana 1	wholemeal crackers 2 fish paste 1 tbls	papaya 1 cup dates 2	*Hot Mulled Juice *Peach Nut Bread 1 slice	dates 3 celery sticks 4	peanuts ¼ cup cheese 1 slice rice bread 2 slices

*Denotes recipes in this book

NORMAL ENERGY FOOD PLANS

MENU 4

Meal	Day 1	Day 2	Day 3	Day 4	Day 5	Day 6	Day 7
Breakfast	*3 Beta Tonique toast 2 slices sardines 30 g lemon juice banana 1	*Buckwheat Porridge *Stewed Peach skim-milk 1 cup	*Muesli skim-milk 1 cup toast 1 slice butter 1 tsp tomato 1	orange 1 toast 3 slices date spread 3 tsp – 3 dates – orange juice	*Muesli skim-milk 1 cup	*Tossed Tofu tomato 1 toast 1 slice *Cantaloupe Supreme	*Rice Porridge dates 2 skim-milk 1 cup rice cake 1 date spread 1 tbls.
Snack	dates 4 soy milk 1 cup	banana 1 lo-fat yoghurt 1 cup	*Golden Juice wholemeal crackers 2	*Red Beet Tonique banana 1	*Jungle Juice	Banana sandwich	orange 1
Lunch	Chicken 120 g pita 1 lemon juice 2 tsp lettuce 1 cup beetroot ½ cup carrot grated ¼ cup asparagus spears 2 cantaloupe ½	salmon 120 g *Rice Bean Mix Salad lettuce 1 cup beetroot ½ cup *Fruit Kebabs *Walnut Cream	*Corn and Celery soup chicken 120 g bean salad ½ cup raisins ¼ cup	cold meat 120 g *Chinese Cabbage Slaw carrot, grated ½ cup pita 1 butter 1 tsp *Ice Cream Ice papaya 1 cup	tuna 120 g green beans 1 cup pita 1 lo-fat yoghurt ½ cup banana 1	*Vegetable Minestrone bread roll butter 1 tsp tuna 120 g lettuce 1 cup *Salad Carmen	*Soused Fish sweet potato ½ cup carrots 1 cup green beans 1 cup
Snack	Peanut butter sandwich	rice bread 2 slices butter 1 tsp carrot sticks 2	orange 1	*Carrot and Peach Loaf 1 slice	celery sticks 2 walnuts 2 tbls	kiwi fruit 1 large	papaya 1 cup
Dinner	oysters natural 6 bread 1 slice butter 1 tsp *Kangaroo Red spinach 1 cup *Melon Sparkle	*Chicken With Rice broccoli 1 cup asparagus spears 6 apple 1 date 1	*White Stew pumpkin ½ cup peas ½ cup spinach 1 cup fruit salad 1 cup *Papaya Cream	*Baked Fish and Chips baked pumpkin ½ cup green beans 1 cup *Cherry Cobbler *Date Cream	*Sweet & Sour Pork brown rice 1 cup broccoli 1 cup asparagus spears 4 *Melee of Berries	Soused Orange Chicken *Corn Mix green beans 1 cup *Fruit Kebabs *Peach Cream	*Curry Sambal brown rice 1 cup *Oriental Style Fruit
Snack	*Carrot and Peach Loaf 1 slice	*Pink Fancy Rice Crackers 2	wholemeal crackers 2 dates 2	lo-fat yoghurt ½ cup mango ½	wholemeal crackers 2 dates 2	soy milk 1 cup	lo-fat yoghurt ½ cup banana small

*Denotes recipes in this book

HIGH ENERGY FOOD PLANS

WEEK 1

Meal	Day 1	Day 2	Day 3	Day 4	Day 5	Day 6	Day 7
Breakfast	orange juice ½ cup boiled egg 1 bread 2 slices butter 2 tsp peanut butter 2 tsp	*Buckwheat Porridge strawberries 1 cup rice cake 2 butter 2 tsp *Jam 1 tbls	*Muesli 1 cup wholemilk 1 cup yellow peach 1 toast 1 slice butter 1 tsp	*French Toast 2 slices peanut butter 1 tbls strawberries 1 cup	puffed millet 1½ cups milk 1 cup toast 2 slices chicken 90 g grapes 1 cup	*Spiced Prunes *Scrambled Fish toast 1 slice butter 1 tsp *Jam 2 tsp	*Rice Porridge honey 1 tsp dates 4 cinnamon 1 tsp milk 1 cup banana 1
Snack	*3 Beta Tonique	*Oriental Drift	*Koala Mauve	*Melon Sparkle	*Pink Fancy wholewheat/ crackers 2	*Malted Orange [soy milk]	*Greenacres tonique
Lunch	salmon 120 g bread 2 slices butter 2 tsp *Spring Salad 1 cup papaya 1 cup	chicken breast 120 g *Golden Salad rice cakes 2 butter 2 tsp cherries 1 cup	flaked crab meat 180 g bread 2 slices butter 2 tsp *Beetroot salad lettuce 2 cups	*Tuna-Bean on Rye red pepper ½ green pepper ½ walnuts ½ cup orange 1	sardines 60 g asparagus spears 4 carrots ½ cup salad greens 1 cup bread 2 slices yoghurt ½ cup banana 1	*Pumpkin Soup bread roll 1 butter 2 tsp peanut butter 1 tbls papaya 1 cup	*Dame Charmante 1½ salad greens 1 cup rice crackers 3 butter 3 tsps fruit salad 1 cup
Snack	peanut butter sandwich	rice bread 2 slices fish paste 1 tsp butter 2 tsp	orange sunflower seeds ¼ cup	salad sandwich apple 1	pumpkin seeds ¼ cup dates 4	wholewheat crackers 2 fish paste 1 tbls	yoghurt ¾ cup *Muesli ½ cup
Dinner	*Lentil Burger 2 tomato sauce *Red Cabbage *Baked Sweet Potatoes 2 *Fruit Kebab	*Stir Fry Pork & Vegetables rice 1½ cups *Oriental style fruit	oysters 6 lemon juice 1 tsp *Fish in foil *Corn mix spinach 1 cup *Tofu Ice Cream yellow peach 1	Grilled steak 80 g rice 1 cup asparagus spears 4 carrot 1 cup *Papaya Orange mousse	*Baked Chops 2 *Baked Sweet potatoes 2 baked onion 1 corn ½ cup *Baked Apple *Tofu Ice Cream	*Soused Orange chicken rice ¾ cup broccoli 1 cup mushroom ½ cup almonds ¼ cup *Apricot Sago *Coconut Cream 1 tbls	*Cabbage & Egg whirl soup *Fish Burgers *Tomato Sauce spinach 1 cup soy beans ¼ cup rice ½ cup
Snack	*Golden Juice pumpkin seeds 1 cup	yoghurt 1 cup banana 1	whole wheat crackers 3 almond butter 1 tsp	yoghurt 1 cup sunflower seeds ¼ cup prunes 4	rice cakes 2 peanut butter 1 tbls	alfalfa sandwich banana 1	rice cake 1 almond butter 1 tsp orange 1

*Denotes recipes in this book

HIGH ENERGY FOOD PLANS

MENU 2

Meal	Day 1	Day 2	Day 3	Day 4	Day 5	Day 6	Day 7
Breakfast	prunes 6 honeydew melon ¼ sardines 60 g bread 2 slices butter 2 tsp	*Buckwheat Pancakes *Stewed Apple milk 1 cup honey 2 tsp	*Muesli ¾ cup milk ¾ cup banana 1 almonds 6	omelete (1 egg) salmon ¼ cup toast 2 slices butter 2 tsp peach 1	*Porridge milk 1 cup raisins 2 tbls poached egg toast 1 slice butter 1 tps	*Strawberry Royale toast 2 slices peanut butter 1 tps papaya 1 cup	*Tomato Zip rice cakes 3 sardines 90 g lemon ½ grapes 1 cup banana 1
Snack	banana 1 soy milk 1 cup	*Red Beet Tonique	*Canteloupe Supreme	*Koala Mauve	*Carrot Brazil Nut bread 1 slice	chicken broth 1 cup wholewheat crackers 2	yoghurt 1 cup *Muesli 1 cup
Lunch	chicken meat 120g potato salad 1 cup red pepper ½ salad greens 1 cup wholewheat/ crackers 4 canteloupe ½	tuna 120 g carrot ½ cup bean mix 1 cup lettuce 1 cup rice cakes 2 butter 2 tsp banana 1	flaked crabmeat 120 g spinach salad – spinach 1½ cup – tomato 1 – feta cheese 60 g bread roll 1 butter 2 tsp peach 1	*Gazpacho Creme wholewheat crackers 4 chicken 90 g bean salad 1 cup beetroot ½ cup pineapple 2 slices	crab 120 g beans ½ cup rice ½ cup lettuce 1½ cups parsley ¼ cup papaya 1 cup	salmon sandwich – bread 2 slices – salmon 30 g *Chinese Cabbage slaw yoghurt 1 cup banana 1	*Avocado Velvet soup rice cakes 2 butter 2 tsp salmon 90 g crab 90 g lettuce 1 cup tomato catchup pineapple 2 slices
Snack	peanut butter sandwich	cheese 60 g celery 2 sticks	*Carrot Brazil Nut bread 1 slice	yoghurt 1 cup *Muesli ½ cup	dates 5 wholewheat crackers 4	*Carrot Brazil Nut bread 1 slice	orange sunflower seeds ¼ cup
Dinner	Crab cocktail – crab 60 g – tomato 1 – lettuce 1 cup *Stir Fry Pork & vegetables rice 1½ cups *Melon Sparkle	*Kangaroo Red 2 tortilla shells 4 broccoli 1 cup *Baked Apple baked cereal custard	*Baked Beef Roll 2 gravy 4 tbls *Baked Sweet Potato 2 baked tomato turnip greens 1 cup	*Macaroni Cheese *Stir Fry Cauliflower pumpkin ¾ cup green beans ½ cup *Cherry Cobbler *Ice Cream Ice	*Pork With Apple *Red Cabbage/flemish potato 1 cup broccoli 1 cup carrot ½ cup *Pumpkin Pie	*Savoury Ground Beef 1½ pasta 2 cups *Beans With Red Pepper pumpkin 1 cup *Pecan Pie	*Baked Fish & Chips 2 spinach 1 cup carrot 1 cup beans 1 cup *Baked Apple *Baked Cereal Custard
Snack	*Carrot Brazil Nut bread 1 slice hot soy milk 1 cup honey 2 tsp	dates 4 brazil nuts ¼ cup	date sandwich with almond butter	pumpkin seeds ¼ cup	yoghurt 1 cup banana 1	dates 6 celery sticks 2	*Jungle Juice *Bran Loaf

*Denotes recipes in this book

MENU 3

HIGH ENERGY FOOD PLANS

Meal	Day 1	Day 2	Day 3	Day 4	Day 5	Day 6	Day 7
Breakfast	orange juice 1 cup baked beans 1 cup toast 2 slices butter 2 tsp prunes 6	*Serendipity Juice [apple, mixed vegetables] baked beans 1 cup toast 2 slices butter 1 tsp	*Buckwheat Pancakes berries 1 cup milk 1 cup honey 2 tsp	Baked beans ½ cup salmon 30 g parsley ¼ cup toast 2 slices orange	*Porridge milk 1 cup raisins 2 tbls banana 1 toast 1 slice butter 1 tsp date spread 1 tbls	*Strawberry Royale *Corn Hash bread roll butter 2 tsp	*Serendipity Juice [egg flip] *Muesli milk ¾ cup rice cakes 2 butter 2 tsp peanut butter 2 tsp
Snack	strawberries 1 cup soy milk 1 cup	orange *Peach Nut Bread 2 slices	cantaloupe ¼	*Peach Nut Bread 2 slices	*Apricot Bread 2 slices butter 2 tsp	savoury crackers 4	papaya 1 cup almonds ¼ cup
Lunch	*Corny Thick Shake sardine sandwich – bread 2 slices – sardines 4 – lemon juice – parsley 2 tbls	*Crab Avocado rice cakes 2 butter 2 tsp strawberries 1 cup	*Jungle Juice chicken 120 g rice salad 1 cup green salad 1 cup bread 2 slices butter 2 tsp	curried chicken sandwich bread 2 slices chicken 90 g curry powder ½ tsp alfalfa sprouts mayonnaise 2 tsp *Malted Orange	*Rice Bean Mix tuna 120 g bread roll 1 butter 2 tsp lettuce 1 cu- *Tofu Ice Cream canteloupe 1 cup	*Thick Bean Soup *Mexican Roll 2 serves coleslaw 1 cup apple	*Pumpkin & Carrot Soup chicken breast 120 g mixed salad 1 cup strawberries 1 cup
Snack	dates 4 sunflower seeds ¼ cup	rice crackers 2 fish paste 1 tbls	*Apricot Bread 2 slices butter 1 tsp	rice cakes 2 peanut butter 1 tbls carrot sticks 2	peanut butter sandwich	*Pumpkin Pie	banana & date sandwich [rice bread]
Dinner	*Brown Stew potato 1 peas ½ cup *Pumpkin Pie	*Chicken With almonds rice 1½ cups *Fresh Fruit Medley	*Chili Con Carne *Asparagus Spears amandine yoghurt ½ cup prunes 4 banana 1	*Thick Bean Soup *Spinach Rice green salad 1 cup *Pumpkin Pie *Ice-cream-ice	*Liver slices toast 1 slice green beans 1 cup carrot 1 cup *Fruit Kebabs yoghurt ½ cup	*Fish In Foil *Baked Sweet Potato baked pumpkin spinach 1 cup *Tofu Ice Cream *Baked Apple	*Savoury Fish Pie *Stuffed Egg Plant rice 1 cup peach 1 yoghurt 1 cup rice cakes prunes 6 apple 1
Snack	*Apricot Bread 2 slices butter 2 tsp	yoghurt 1 cup banana 1	savoury crackers 4 peanut butter 1 tbls	papaya 1 cup dates 4	*Hot Mulled Juice *Peach Nut Bread 2 slices	dates 6 celery sticks 4	peanuts ¼ cup cheese 1 slice rice bread 2 slices

*Denotes recipes in this book

HIGH ENERGY FOOD PLANS

MENU 4

Meal	Day 1	Day 2	Day 3	Day 4	Day 5	Day 6	Day 7
Breakfast	*3 Beta Tonique sardines 90 g toast 3 slices lemon juice 2 tsp banana 1	*Buckwheat Porridge *Stewed Peach milk 1 cup honey 2 tsp	*Muesli 1½ Serves milk 1 cup toast 3 slices butter 2 tsp tomato 1	orange 1 poached egg 1 toast 3 slices honey 3 tsp date spread 3 tbls	*Muesli 1½ Serves milk 1 cup toast 3 slices sardines 90 g black pepper asparagus spears 4	*Tossed Tofu tomato toast 2 slices *Canteloupe Supreme	*Rice Pudding dates 4 milk 1 cup rice cake 2 peanut butter 1 tbls
Snack	dates 4 soy milk 1 cup	banana 1 dates 4 yoghurt 1 cup	*Golden Juice savoury crackers 6	*Red Beet Tonique banana 1	*Jungle Juice	*Carrot & Peach Loaf 1 slice	orange 1 brazil nuts ¼ cup
Lunch	chicken breast 120 g pita 1 lemon juice 2 tsp lettuce 1 cup beetroot ½ cup carrot ¼ cup asparagus spears 2 canteloupe ½	Salmon 120 g *Rice Bean Mix Salad lettuce 1 cup beetroot ½ cup *Fruit Kebabs *Walnut Cream	*Corn & Celery Soup bread roll butter 2 tsp chicken 120 g bean salad 1 cup raisins ¼ cup brazil nuts ¼ cup	cold meat 120 g *Chinese Cabbage slaw beetroot 1 cup pita 1 butter 2 tsp papaya 1 cup *Ice-Cream-Ice	*Golden Latkes tuna 120 g green beans 1 cup mayonnaise 2 tsp pita 1 yoghurt 1 cup banana 1 dates 4	*Vegetable Minestrone bread roll butter 1 tsp tuna 90 g lettuce 1 cup *Salad Carmen	*Soused Fish mashed potato 1 carrots 1 cup green beans 1 cup yoghurt 1 cup banana 1
Snack	Peanut butter sandwich	carrot sticks 2 cheese 60 g rice bread 2 slices butter 1 tsp	orange 1 sunflower seeds ¼ cup	*Carrot & Peach Loaf 2 slices	celery sticks 2 walnuts 2 tbls	peanut butter sandwich	papaya 1 cup
Dinner	oysters natural 6 bread 1 slice butter 1 tsp *Kangaroo Red taco shells 4 greens 1 cup *Melon Sparkle	*Chicken with Rice 1½ serves broccoli 1 cup asparagus spears 6 *Baked Cereal Custard *Baked Apple	*White Stew sweet potato 1 pumpkin ½ cup peas 1 cup spinach 1 cup fruit salad 1½ cups *Papaya Cream	*Baked Fish & Chips *Baked Pumpkin green beans 1 cup bread 2 slices *Cherry Cobbler *Date Cream	*Sweet & Sour Pork brown rice 1 cup broccoli 1 cup asparagus spears 4 *Melee of Berries	*Soused Orange chicken *Corn Mix greens 1 cup *Fruit slice *Peach Cream	*Curry Sambal rice 1 cup *Oriental Style Fruit
Snack	*Carrot & Peach Loaf 2 slices	*Pink Fancy Rice crackers 6	crackers 6 dates 4	yoghurt 1 cup mango ½	crackers 6 dates 4	soy milk 1 cup honey 2 tsp	*Malted Orange rice cake 1 raisins 10

*Denotes recipes in this book

■ DESIGN YOUR OWN MENU? ■

We recommend that, where possible, you should follow the set menu plans since each day's food has been scientifically calculated to meet the objectives of high density nutrients and appropriate energy levels. However, if you wish to change the plans there are two ways of doing so – by substitution or by designing your own menus. The information provided in the latter part of this chapter shows how you can design your own menus using one of these two methods.

■ DESIGNING YOUR OWN MENU ■
SUBSTITUTION METHOD

Using the substitution method, you replace one or more of the suggested foods in a day's menu with others of your choice.

This means that you are basically sticking to the set menu plans but changing some of the foods or recipes perhaps because you want a change, or another recipe looks interesting or maybe you don't like one of the foods in the set menu or because a particular food is not available.

When making changes to the set menu plans using this method we suggest that you:

■ substitute with similar foods, i.e. if you take out a meat dish, replace it with another meat dish; if you remove a grain food, such as one of the breads, replace it with another bread; if you omit a particular fruit or vegetable, replace it with a different fruit or vegetable, and so on.

■ pick your replacement foods from as high up in Nutrient Density Table in this chapter since the higher up the table the food appears, the richer it is in the desired nutrients.

■ keep the energy intake of the day's food as close to the original level as possible.

■ each recipe in this book is accompanied by a simple analysis of the energy intake from *one serve* of that recipe. In addition, there is a table of analyses on p.166 which covers most of the other foods that you may wish to eat. So, it is not too difficult to compare the energy levels of the food you remove from a menu plan with the food you use to replace it. If the two match reasonably closely, go ahead and substitute. If you are out by more than the following, you will need to do some adjusting:

Energy	1,000 Kj
Protein	400 Kj
Fats	500 Kj
Carbohydrate	800 Kj

■ to adjust energy levels either use another recipe or food with a better match or change the quantities; perhaps doubling or halving the quantity of the new recipe or food will bring the total into better balance.

Remember, do replace foods with similar types to maintain a nutrient balance. Here is an example of a substitution in the *normal* energy menu – the set menu is from Menu 1, Day 1 but we want to replace sardines with a boiled egg, Lentil Burgers with Macaroni Cheese and Red Cabbage with Scalloped Vegetables. As you will see, this substitution works well.

Food or Recipe	Energy Kj	Protein Kj	Fats Kj	Carbohydrates Kj
Substitute Sardines 30g	224	113	111	0
With Boiled Egg 1	340	102	222	16
Total difference	+116	-11	+111	+16
Substitute Lentil Burger*	1896	369	525	1002
With Macaroni Cheese*	1597	334	703	560
Total difference	-299	-35	+178	-442
Substitute Red Cabbage*	424	19	118	286
With Scalloped Vegetables*	470	60	155	254
Total difference	+46	+41	+37	-32
Grand Total Difference (Sum of differences)	-137	-5	+326	-458
Are differences less than	1000	400	500	800

*Denotes recipes in this book

Here is an example of a substitution in the *high* energy menu – the set menu is from Menu 1, Day 1 but we want to replace Lentil Burgers with Macaroni Cheese, Red Cabbage with Scalloped Vegetables and Pumpkin Seeds with Almonds. However, as you will see, the changes are low in energy – the biggest problem being in carbohydrates. So, we suggest you review the total day's menu and add a honey sandwich with the Beta Tonique for the first snack of the day.

Food or Recipe	Energy Kj	Protein Kj	Fats Kj	Carbohydrates Kj
Substitute Lentil Burgers 2*	3792	738	1050	2004
With Macaroni Cheese*	1597	334	703	560
Total difference	-2195	-404	-347	-1444
Substitute Red Cabbage*	424	19	118	286
With Scalloped Vegetables*	470	60	155	254
Total difference	+46	+41	+37	-32
Substitute Pumpkin Seeds ½ cup	1360	238	962	160
With Almonds ½ cup	1506	204	1110	192
Total difference	+146	-34	+148	+32
Grand Total Difference (Sum of differences)	-2003	-397	-162	+1444
Are differences less than	1000	600	600	800

*Denotes recipes in this book

At the end of this chapter we have provided blank forms to assist in designing your own menus in either the *high* or *normal* energy categories – use these forms to calculate the day's energy intake.

YOUR OWN MENUS

Designing your own menus will entail changing all or most of the recommended foods with ones of your own choice. To do this and achieve all the correct attributes is not easy and requires considerable knowledge since the more you move from the recommended plans the more likely it will be that your basic needs may not be met. However, if you decide that you want to have the occasional day with meals you design yourself, go ahead using the principles below. Ideally, you should only use your own menus once every three or four days, the remaining days staying on the planned menus.

When designing your own menus we recommend that you follow the basic menu plan layout. Therefore, you should have:

Breakfast:
a piece of fruit or a fruit drink
a cereal, some bread and perhaps some butter
preferably some milk (skim for *high* energy, full milk for *normal* energy)
try some jam or peanut butter

Morning snack:
fruit or fruit drink (if the energy content is low, add a couple of rice crackers)

Lunch:
a meat or fish dish
plenty of green or orange vegetables
bread or rice cakes or crackers and butter
fruit – one or two pieces
if energy content is low, try adding milk or nuts or yoghurt

Afternoon snack:
bread or crackers with butter and nuts or yoghurt

Dinner:
a meat or fish dish
plenty of green and orange vegetables
a cereal – rice is best but spaghetti or macaroni will do
perhaps a slice or two of bread
fruit and/or a dessert

Evening snack:
fruit
if more energy is needed, add some nuts, milk or crackers and butter

When designing your own menus use the blank forms provided on the next pages. Then look up the analysis of each food and each recipe in the nutrient and energy level charts on pages 164–9.

If a food you want to use is not included in this book, use the analysis for a similar food. Remember to select foods from as high up on the tables as possible since these contain more of the special nutrients you need.

Try to get the foods in each section to meet the criteria above. Then juggle food types and quantities to meet the energy requirements and the ratios between protein, fats and carbohydrates stated in the table. Provided you have selected your foods from those in this book and you have achieved a balance of the three energy sources you should have a reasonably well-designed menu for the day. As a guide, two examples of 'design your own' menus are included in this chapter – one for a *normal* energy menu and one for a *high* energy menu.

At first you may find it difficult to design a menu that meets all the requirements. If you cannot get close to the desired result, then try again or go back to one of the menus in the book and try substituting some of the foods. However, with practice and by using the tables supplied, the process will become easier.

Without turning you into a nutrition specialist, the following tips will help if you want to either use the substitution method or design your own menus.

- If you like the foods in the set menus, stick as closely to them as you can.

- Try substituting a few foods of your choice – this will probably be all you want and will give you the best chance of meeting your nutritional requirements.

- If you want to design your own menus, do so on the occasional day and use the set menus on all the other days. Your own menu every third or fourth day is not unreasonable.

- Do follow the calculations supplied in this chapter and consult the tables giving nutritional densities and energy values and don't guess.

As far as possible stick to the recipes and foods recommended in this book – they have been carefully selected because they supply the high nutrient densities *you* need.

Here is an example of how to design your own **NORMAL ENERGY** menu.

Food or Recipe	Energy Kj	Protein Kj	Fats Kj	Carbohydrates Kj
Orange	257	17	0	240
Muesli 1 cup*	532	81	107	344
Skim Milk 1 cup	343	136	15	192
Toast 2 pieces	592	102	74	416
Sardines 60g	448	226	222	0
Total for breakfast	2172	562	418	1192
Does it meet these?	2000-3000	400-600	600-900	1000-1500
Koala Mauve*	503	26	97	440
Wholemeal Crackers 2	150	15	65	70
Total for morning snack	653	41	102	510
Does it meet these?	0-1000	0-200	0-300	0-500
Chicken 90g	610	425	185	0
Asparagus Spears 4	86	34	4	48
Carrot ½ cup	98	8	2	88
Lettuce 1 cup	37	17	4	16
Bread 2 pieces	592	102	74	416
Lo-fat Yoghurt ½ cup	304	102	74	128
Banana 1	486	17	37	432
Total for lunch	2213	705	380	1128
Does it meet these?	2000-3500	400-700	600-1000	1000-1250
Rice Cake 1	137	14	11	112
Dates 5	517	17	4	496
Total for afternoon snack	654	31	15	608
Does it meet these?	0-1000	0-200	0-300	0-500
Baked Chops 2*	2734	800	1584	352
Baked Sweet Potato*	158	9	37	112
Baked Onion	120	17	8	96
Corn ½ cup	392	51	37	304
Baked Apple*	648	5	196	446
Tofu Ice-cream*	588	92	152	344
Total for dinner	4640	974	2014	1654
Does it meet these?	2500-5000	500-1000	750-1500	1200-2500
Rice Cake 1	137	14	11	112
Peanut Butter 1 tsp.	102	21	74	12
Total for evening snack	239	35	85	124
Does it meet these?	0-1000	0-200	0-300	0-500
Grand Total for the Day	10571	2348	3014	5216
Does it meet these?	9000-11000	1800-2200	2500-3300	4500-5500

*Denotes recipes in this book

Here is an example of how to design your own **HIGH ENERGY** menu.

Food or Recipe	Energy Kj	Protein Kj	Fats Kj	Carbohydrates Kj
Buckwheat Pancakes*	530	49	281	200
Stewed Pear*	817	34	74	709
Milk 1 cup	608	136	296	176
Raisins 1 tsp	196	8	3	184
Total for breakfast	2151	227	654	1269
Does it meet these?	2000-3000	400-600	600-900	1000-1500
Beetroot Tonique*	81	14	11	56
Total for morning snack	81	14	11	56
Does it meet these?	0-1500	0-300	0-450	0-750
Tuna 90g	547	510	37	0
Soybeans ½ cup	502	170	185	152
Carrot ½ cup	99	8	2	88
Lettuce 1 cup	37	17	4	16
Rice Cakes 2	274	28	22	224
Butter 2 tsp.	296	0	296	0
Banana 1	486	17	37	432
Total for lunch	2241	750	583	882
Does it meet these?	2500-4000	500-800	750-1200	1200-2000
Cheese 60g	904	238	666	0
Celery 2 sticks	32	0	0	32
Total for afternoon snack	936	238	666	32
Does it meet these?	0-1500	0-300	0-450	0-750
Kangaroo Red*	1580	251	377	952
Tortilla Shells 4	1116	136	148	832
Broccoli 1 cup	240	85	11	144
Baked Apple*	648	5	196	446
Baked Cereal Custard*	657	113	300	245
Total for dinner	4241	590	1032	2619
Does it meet these?	3500-6000	700-1200	1000-1800	1700-3000
Dates 5	517	17	4	496
Brazil Nuts ¼ cup	835	68	703	64
Total for evening snack	1352	85	707	560
Does it meet these?	0-1500	0-300	0-450	0-750
Grand Total for the Day	11002	1904	3653	5448
Does it meet these?	11500-14000	2200-2600	3400-4200	5700-7000

*Denotes recipes in this book

The foods in this table have been placed in their order of nutrient densities with the highest being first in each column. While you can use other foods, three-quarters of your daily intake should come from the food in the table below.

TABLE OF NUTRIENT DENSITIES

Cereal & Cereal Products	Fruit	Vegetables	Meat & Meat Equivalent	Milk & Milk Products	Fats & Oils
Soybean	Cantaloupe	Carrot	Beef	Whole milk	Olive oil
Buckwheat	Papaya	Sweet potato	Pork	Buttermilk	Coconut
Wheat	Peach	Spinach	Pork Liver	Cheese	Seeds
Wheatgerm	Orange	Silverbeet	Fish	Yoghurt	sunflower
Corn	Mandarin	Pumpkin	Lamb		sesame
Rice	Blackcurrant	Zucchini	Crab		pumpkin
Barley	Lemon	Endive	Oyster		Butter
	Strawberries	Cabbage	Egg		Nuts
	Redcurrants	Broccoli	Tofu		brazil
	Lychee	Asparagus	Soy beans		walnuts
	Apricot	Peppers	Lima beans		peanuts
	Plums (prune)	Peas	Chick peas		almonds
	Cherries	Tomato	or		
		Celery	Garbanzo beans		
			Black eyed peas		

DAILY ENERGY REQUIREMENTS

These are the Australian daily recommeded energy intakes for typical people.

Person	Age	Energy Needs Kj	Adjust portions in the NORMAL ENERGY menu by
Men	18–25	11,600	Increase portion size by about 15%
	35–55	10,400	No adjustment needed
	55–75	8,800	Reduce portion size by about 10%
Women	18–35	8,400	Reduce portion size by about 15%
	35–55	7,600	Reduce portion size by about 25%
	55–75	6,400	Reduce portion size to about 2/3
pregnant		9,000	Reduce portion size by about 10%
lactating		10,900	Increase portion size by about 10%
Boys	3–7	7,200	Reduce portion size to about 3/4
	7–11	9,200	Reduce portion size by about 10%
	11–15	12,200	Increase portion size by about 20%
	15–18	12,600	Increase portion size by about 1/4
Girls	3–7	7,200	Reduce portion size to about 3/4
	7–11	9,200	Reduce portion size by about 10%
	11–15	10,400	No adjustment necessary
	15–18	9,200	Reduce portion size by about 10%

Ref: Recommended Dietary Intakes for use in Australia, 1986, NHMRC

FOODS   ENERGY ANALYSES

Food Name	Quantity	Energy Kj	Protein Kj	Fats Kj	C/H Kj
Cereal and cereal products					
All-Bran cereal	30 g	441	68	37	336
Barley pearled uncooked	1 cup	2,874	272	74	2,528
Buckwheat flour	1 cup	1,387	102	37	1,248
Crackers wholemeal	2 crackers	150	15	65	70
Cornmeal enriched	1 cup	1,989	187	74	1,728
Flour wheat whole	1 cup	1,724	272	89	1,363
Flour cake or pastry	1 cup	1,372	119	37	1,216
Granola Nature Valley	1 roll	593	34	111	448
Macaroni	1 cup	467	68	15	384
Mixed grain bread	1 slice	263	34	37	192
Oatmeal cooked	1 cup	576	102	74	400
Rice brown cooked	1 cup	922	85	37	800
Rice cake	1 cake	137	14	11	112
Rye bread	1 slice	263	34	37	192
Spaghetti whole wheat	1 cup	780	119	37	624
Tortilla corn	1 tortilla	279	34	37	208
Wheat bran	1 tbls	15	3	0	11
Wheat bread whole	1 slice	296	51	37	208
Wheatgerm	30 g	472	153	111	208
Fruit					
Apple	1 apple	343	0	7	336
Apricots dried cooked	1 cup	942	51	11	880
Apricots fresh	3 apricots	220	17	11	192
Banana	1 banana	486	17	37	432
Blackberries	1 cup	342	17	37	288
Blueberries	1 cup	374	17	37	320
Cantaloupe	½ melon	423	34	37	352
Cherries sweet	10 cherries	230	17	37	176
Currants black	1 cup	121	14	2	105
Currants red	1 cup	112	12	4	97
Dates	5 dates	517	17	4	496
Grapefruit	1 fruit	354	34	0	320
Grapes	60 g	167	0	7	160
Kiwifruit	1 fruit	200	17	7	176
Lemon	1 lemon	101	17	4	80
Lychee	1 cup	392	20	15	357
Mandarin	1 fruit	161	17	0	144
Mango	1 fruit	614	17	37	560
Melon honeydew	¼ melon	532	43	9	480
Orange fresh	1 fruit	257	17	0	240

Food Name	Quantity	Energy Kj	Protein Kj	Fats Kj	C/H Kj
Orange juice canned	1 cup	424	17	7	400
Papaya	1 cup	296	17	7	272
Peach	1 fruit	177	17	0	160
Pears	1 fruit	454	17	37	400
Pineapple	1 cup	358	17	37	304
Prunes dried cooked	1 cup	1,009	34	15	960
Raisins	1 cup	1,962	85	37	1,840
Raspberries	1 cup	278	17	37	224
Strawberries	1 cup	214	17	37	160
Watermelon diced	1 cup	230	17	37	176

Vegetables

Food Name	Quantity	Energy Kj	Protein Kj	Fats Kj	C/H Kj
Asparagus	4 spears	86	34	4	48
Avocado	1 avocado	1,370	68	1,110	192
Beans green cooked	1 cup	204	43	10	151
Beets cooked	1 cup	210	34	0	176
Broccoli	1 cup	240	85	11	144
Cabbage	1 cup	136	17	7	112
Carrot grated	1 cup	197	17	4	176
Cauliflower	1 cup	118	34	4	80
Celery	1 stalk	16	0	0	16
Corn cooked	1 ear	392	51	37	304
Cucumber	6 slices	16	0	0	16
Eggplant cooked	1 cup	117	17	4	96
Endive	1 cup	49	17	0	32
Jerusalem artichoke	1 cup	467	51	0	416
Kale cooked	1 cup	183	34	37	112
Lettuce	1 cup	37	17	4	16
Mixed frozen vegetables	1 cup	319	68	11	240
Mushrooms cooked	1 cup	216	51	37	128
Olive green canned	4	74	0	74	0
Onion chopped	1 cup	241	34	15	192
Onion spring	6 onion	49	17	0	32
Peas green cooked	1 cup	515	136	11	368
Pepper red sweet	1 pepper	88	17	7	64
Potato boiled	1 potato	487	51	4	432
Pumpkin	1 cup	230	34	4	192
Radish	4 radish	16	0	0	16
Silverbeet	1 cup	137	34	7	96
Spinach cooked	1 cup	208	85	11	112
Tomato	1 tomato	101	17	4	80
Turnips cooked	1 cup	149	17	4	128
Zucchini	1 cup	359	34	37	288

Food Name	Quantity	Energy Kj	Protein Kj	Fats Kj	C/H Kj
Meat and meat equivalents					
Beef chuck blade lean	90 g	886	442	444	0
Beef ground lean	90 g	949	357	592	0
Beef liver	90 g	762	391	259	112
Chicken breast roasted	1 breast	1,541	986	555	0
Chicken drumstick	90 g	610	425	185	0
Cod boiled	120 g	471	430	41	0
Crabmeat canned	1 cup	518	391	111	16
Fish sticks	30 g	277	102	111	64
Flounder baked no fat	90 g	326	289	37	0
Lamb chops lean	90 g	954	510	444	0
Oyster	1 cup	616	340	148	128
Pork chop	90 g	1,094	391	703	0
Pork liver	120 g	600	397	155	47
Salmon pink canned	90 g	474	289	185	0
Sardines canned, in oil	90 g	673	340	333	0
Tuna canned, in water	90 g	547	510	37	0
Beans lima cooked	1 cup	1,093	272	37	784
Egg	1 egg	340	102	222	16
Lentils cooked	1 cup	917	272	37	608
Peas chick or garbanzo	1 cup	1,361	316	161	883
Soybeans cooked	1 cup	1,014	340	370	304
Tofu	1 piece	386	153	185	48
Milk and milk products					
Buttermilk	1 cup	402	136	74	192
Cheese cheddar	30 g	452	119	333	0
Cheese parmesan	1 tbls	108	34	74	0
Milk evaporated skim	1 cup	824	323	37	464
Milk skim	1 cup	343	136	15	192
Milk whole	1 cup	608	136	296	176
Yoghurt whole milk	1 cup	571	136	259	176
Yoghurt Lo-fat	1 cup	608	204	148	256
Fats and oils					
Almonds	30 g	753	102	555	96
Brazil nuts	30 g	835	68	703	64
Butter	1 tsp	148	0	148	0
Coconut raw shredded	1 cup	1,242	51	999	192
Cream whipping	1 tbls	185	0	185	0
Mayonnaise	1 tbls	407	0	407	0
Olive oil	1 tbls	518	0	518	0

Food Name	Quantity	Energy Kj	Protein Kj	Fats Kj	C/H Kj
Peanut butter	1 tbls	429	85	296	48
Peanuts	1 cup	3,722	663	2,627	432
Pecans halves	30 g	817	34	703	80
Pumpkin seeds	30 g	680	119	481	80
Sunflower seeds	30 g	700	102	518	80
Walnuts	30 g	814	68	666	80
Extras					
Chicken broth	1 cup	114	37	54	23
Honey	1 tbls	272	0	0	272
Molasses cane	1 tbls	176	0	0	176
Sugar brown	1 cup	3,392	0	0	3,392
Table syrup, corn, maple	1 tbls	256	0	0	256
Tomato sauce	1 cup	354	51	15	288

Use a form like this to design your own **NORMAL ENERGY** menu.

Food or Recipe	Energy Kj	Protein Kj	Fats Kj	Carbohydrates Kj
Total for breakfast Does it meet these?	2000-3000	400-600	600-900	1000-1500
Total for morning snack Does it meet these?	0-1000	0-200	0-300	0-500
Total for lunch Does it meet these?	2000-3500	400-700	600-1000	1000-1250
Total for afternoon snack Does it meet these?	0-1000	0-200	0-300	0-500
Total for dinner Does it meet these?	2500-5000	500-1000	750-1500	1200-2500
Total for evening snack Does it meet these?	0-1000	0-200	0-300	0-500
Grand Total for the Day Does it meet these?	9000-11000	1800-2200	2500-3300	4500-5500

Use a form like this to design your own **HIGH ENERGY** menu.

Food or Recipe	Energy Kj	Protein Kj	Fats Kj	Carbohydrates Kj
Total for breakfast Does it meet these?	2000-3000	400-600	600-900	1000-1500
Total for morning snack Does it meet these?	0-1500	0-300	0-450	0-750
Total for lunch Does it meet these?	2500-4000	500-800	750-1200	1200-2000
Total for afternoon snack Does it meet these?	0-1500	0-300	0-450	0-750
Total for dinner Does it meet these?	3500-6000	700-1200	1000-1800	1700-3000
Total for evening snack Does it meet these?	0-1500	0-300	0-450	0-750
Grand Total for the Day Does it meet these?	11500-14000	2200-2600	3400-4200	5700-7000

Use a form like this to calculate the day's energy level when using the substitution method.

Food or Recipe	Energy Kj	Protein Kj	Fats Kj	Carbohydrates Kj
Substitute				
With				
Total difference				
Substitute				
With				
Total difference				
Substitute				
With				
Total difference				
Substitute				
With				
Total difference				
Substitute				
With				
Total difference				
Grand Total Difference (Sum of differences)				
Are differences less than	1000	400	500	800

REFERENCES · &
FURTHER · READING

1. Davies, Dr Stephen & Stewart, Dr Alan, *Nutritional Medicine*, 1987, Pan Books, London.
2. Whitney, Eleanor N. & Hamilton, Eva M.N., *Understanding Nutrition*, 1981, West Publishing Co., U.S.A.
3. Penington, Jean A.T. & Church, Helen N., *Food Values*, 1985, Harper & Row Publishers, New York.
4. United States Department of Agriculture, *Handbook of the Nutritional Contents of Food*, Dover Publications Inc., New York.
5. Jacobsen, Michael, *Nutritional Wizard*, Centre for Science in the Public Interest, 1986.

I·N·D·E·X

Almond Spread, 46
Apple
  with Pork, 83
  Baked, 130
  Spiced, 41
  Stewed, 126
Apricot
  Bread, 145
  Orange, 42
  Sago, 125
Asparagus
  Amandine, 105
  Geneva Style, 104
Avocado
  in Crab and Avocado Salad,
    67
  Smoothie, 34
  Spread, 45
  Velvet, 54

Baked Beans, 44
Baked Beef Roll, 92
Baked Chops, 86
Barley Water, 38
Beans
  and Rice Mix, 65
  in Kangaroo Red, 75
  in Succotash, 99
  with Pepper, 110
  Provencale, 98
  Soup, 55
  Soya Nutloaf, 77
Beetroot
  in Spiced Sauce, 102
  Salad, 66
  Tonique, 37
Berries
  in Koala Mauve, 32
  Hot Mulled Juice, 31
  Melee of, 117
Bran Loaf, 140

Breads
  Apricot, 145
  Basic Dough, 134
  Carrot and Brazil Nut, 141
  Cheese and Corn, 132
  Cheese Plait, 136
  Gala, 139
  Mexican Roll, 136
  Peach and Nut, 138
  Pizza, 137
  Small Rolls, 135
  Soda, 133
  Wholemeal, 134
Broccoli,
  with Orange, 103
Brown Stew, 94
Buckwheat Pancakes, 43
Burgers, 79

Cabbage
  and Egg Whirl, 56
  in Creamy Horseradish Sauce,
    100
  Chinese Slaw, 62
  Red, Flemish Style, 100
  Stuffed, 108
Cantaloupe
  and Melon Sparkle, 33
  in Dame Charmante, 64
  in Golden Juice, 37
  in 3 Beta Tonique, 35
  Supreme, 34
Carrot
  and Brazil Nut Bread, 141
  and Peach Loaf, 143
Cauliflower
  Stir-Fried, 98
Cereals
  Use of, 70
  Baked Custard, 115

Cheese
  and Corn Bread, 132
  Plait, 136
Cherry
  Cobbler, 128
  Streusel, 144
Chick Peas Catalonian Style,
  68
Chicken
  with Almonds, 85
  with Rice, 87
  Barbecued, 76
  Soused Orange, 88
Chilli Con Carne, 89
Coconut Cream, 123
Corn
  and Celery Soup, 58
  and Cheese Bread, 132
  in Corny Thick Shake, 36
  in Succotash, 99
  Hash, 50
  Mix, 110
Cottage Cheese Spread, 45
Creams
  Coconut, 123
  Date, 123
  Papaya, 122
  Peach, 124
  Sultana, 123
  Walnut, 122
Curry, 91

Dame Charmante, 64
Date
  in Sunflower and Date Loaf,
    142
  Cream, 123

Eggplant
  Stuffed, 108

INDEX

Eggs
Florentine, 80
Omelette, 48
Scrambled, 48

Favourite Style Chops, 96
Fish
in Foil, 82
Baked, 78
Burgers, 81
Crab and Avocado Salad, 67
Properties of, 70
Sardine Spread, 45
Savoury Pie, 80
Scrambled, 49
Soused, 82
Tuna-Beans on Rye Salad, 63
Tuna Spread, 45
French Toast, 47
Fruit
Baskets, 120
Crumble, 126
Kebabs, 129
Medley, 130
Oriental Style, 116
Slice, 128

Gala Bread, 139
Gazpacho Creme, 54
Golden Juice, 37
Golden Latkes, 101
Granita, 124
Greenacres Tonique, 33

Hot Mulled Berry Juice, 31

Ice Cream Ice, 114

Jams
Cooked, 46
Uncooked, 47
Juices
Avocado Smoothie, 34
Barley Water, 38
Beetroot Tonique, 37
Cantaloupe Supreme, 34
Corny Thick Shake, 36
Golden, 37
Greenacres Tonique, 33
Hot Mulled Berry, 31
Jungle, 35
Koala Mauve, 32
Malted Orange, 38
Melon Sparkle, 33
Oriental Drift, 39
Pink Fancy, 39
3 Beta Tonique, 35
Tomato Zip, 36
Strawberry Royale, 32
Sweet Lychee, 34
Jungle Juice, 35

Kangaroo Red, 75
Koala Mauve, 32

Legumes, 69
Lentil Burgers, 76
Liver Slices, 78
Loaf
Bran, 140
Carrot and Peach, 143
Pumpkin, 146
Sunflower and Date, 142
Lychee
in Oriental Drift, 39
Sweet Lychee, 34

Macaroni Cheese, 86
Malted Orange, 38
Mashed Medley, 102
Meat
Baked Beef Roll, 92
Baked Chops, 86
Brown Stew, 94
Burgers, 79
Chilli Con Carne, 89
Curry, 91
Favourite Style Chops, 96
Liver Slices, 78
Pork with Apple, 83
Savoury Ground Beef, 71
Savoury Kebabs, 95
Spaghetti Bake, 84
Stir-Fry Pork and Vegetables, 72
Sweet and Sour Pork, 93
White Stew, 90
Melon
and Ginger, 116
Sparkle, 33
Mexican Roll, 136
Muesli, 44

Orange Malted, 38
Oriental Drift, 39

Pancakes
Buckwheat, 43
Papaya
Cream, 122
Orange Mousse, 121
Snow, 114
Pasta
Avocado Buckwheat, 74
Macaroni Cheese, 86
Spaghetti Bake, 84
Wholemeal, 73
Pastry
Pie Crust, 118
Rice, 119
Wholemeal, 117
Peach
and Ginger Whip, 127
and Nut Bread, 138
Cream, 124
Pears, 42
Pecan Pie, 119
Pepper Stuffed, 106

Pies
Pecan, 119
Pumpkin, 120
Pink Fancy, 39
Pizza, 137
Pork
with Apple, 83
Stir-Fry and Vegetables, 72
Sweet and Sour, 93
Porridge, 51, 52
Potato
Baked Sweet, 109
Prunes
Spiced, 41
Pumpkin
and Carrot Soup, 56
in Aussie Gold 'n Green, 104
Loaf, 146
Pie, 120
Stuffed, 106

Rhubarb
Spiced, 41
Rice and Bean Mix, 65

Soda Bread, 133
Salad
Beetroot, 66
Carmen, 66
Chick Peas Catalonian Style, 68
Chinese Cabbage Slaw, 62
Crab Avocado, 67
Dame Charmante, 64
Golden, 67
Greens with Cheese, 64
Louise, 68
Rice-Bean Mix, 65
Spring, 62
Tuna-Beans on Rye, 63
Watermelon Cooler, 61
Salad Dressings
All-Purpose, 60
Mayonnaise-Style, 61
Sesame, 60
Sambal, 91
Savoury Ground Beef, 71
Savoury Kebabs, 95
Serendipity Juices, 30
Soups
Avocado Velvet, 54
Cabbage and Egg Whirl, 56
Corn and Celery, 58
Gazpacho Creme, 54
Pumpkin and Carrot, 56
Thick Bean, 55
Vegetable Minestrone, 57
Soya Bean Nutloaf, 77
Spaghetti Bake, 84
Spinach
and Rice, 74
Spreads
Almond, 46
Tofu, 46

Strawberry Royale, 32
Succotash, 99
Sultana Cream, 123
Sunflower and Date Loaf,
142
Sweet Lychee, 34

3 Beta Tonique, 35
Tofu
Ice Cream, 113

Spread, 46
Tossed, 52
Tomato
Sauce, 81
Stuffed, 107
Zip, 36

Vegetable
Mashed Medley, 102
Minestrone, 57

Properties and preparation,
97
Scalloped, 111
Scramble, 50
Stuffed, 105

Walnut Cream, 122
Watermelon Cooler, 61
White Stew, 90

Reappraisals in Canadian History
Pre-Confederation

A. D. Gilbert
C. M. Wallace
R. M. Bray

Laurentian University

Prentice Hall Canada Inc., Scarborough, Ontario

Canadian Cataloguing in Publication Data

Main entry under title:

Reappraisals in Canadian history, pre-confederation

ISBN 0-13-767237-3

1. Canada - History - To 1763 (New France).
2. Canada - History - 1763-1867. 3. Canada -
History - To 1763 (New France) - Historiography.
4. Canada - History - 1763-1867 - Historiography.
I. Gilbert, Angus Duncan, 1941- . II. Wallace,
Carl Murray. III. Bray, Robert Matthew.

FC161.R42 1993   971   C92-094435-3
F1026.R42 1993

Prentice Hall, Inc., Englewood Cliffs, New Jersey
Prentice-Hall International, Inc., London
Prentice-Hall of Australia, Pty., Ltd., Sydney
Prentice-Hall of India Pvt., Ltd., New Delhi
Prentice-Hall of Japan, Inc., Tokyo
Prentice-Hall of Southeast Asia (Pte.) Ltd., Singapore
Editora Prentice-Hall do Brasil Ltda., Rio de Janeiro
Prentice-Hall Hispanoamericana, S.A., Mexico

ISBN: 0-13-767237-3

Acquisitions Editor: Michael Bickerstaff
Developmental Editor: Linda Gorman
Production Editors: William Booth and Norman Bernard
Production Coordinator: Anna Orodi
Cover Design: Monica Kompter
Cover Image Credit: Fish market (957.96.7), Royal Ontario
Museum Canadiana Dept. 1992.
Page Layout: Anita Macklin

1 2 3 4 5   RRD   97 96 95 94 93

Printed and bound in the U.S.A. by R.R. Donnelley & Sons.

Table of Contents

Preface   *vii*
Introduction: Canadian History and Historians   *viii*

1   Native-Newcomer Interaction   1

The Problem of the Iroquois   2
GEORGE T. HUNT

The European Impact on the Culture of a Northeastern Algonquin Tribe:
An Ecological Interpretation   10
CALVIN MARTIN

Conclusion   31
CORNELIUS J. JAENAN

2   Society in New France   39

The Society of New France, 1680's–1760   40
W.J. ECCLES

The Growth of Montreal in the 18th Century 48
LOUISE DECHÊNE

New France: Les Femmes Favorisées   63
JAN NOEL

3   Business and Private Enterprise in New France   91

Canada's Place in the French Imperial Economy: An Eighteenth-Century
Overview   93
DALE MIQUELON

Doing Business in New France   103
MICHAEL BLISS

4   The Expulsion of the Acadians   124

The Expulsion of the Acadians   125
C. BRUCE FERGUSSON

Foundations of British Policy in the Acadian Expulsion: A Discussion of Land Tenure and the Oath of Allegiance   133
DESMOND BROWN

Prologue to Disaster, 1749–1755   149
NAOMI GRIFFITHS

5   The French Military in New France During the Seven Years' War   160

The French Forces in North America During the Seven Years' War   162
W.J. ECCLES

A Different Kind of Courage: The French Military and the Canadian Irregular Soldier During the Seven Years' War   174
MARTIN L. NICOLAI

6   The Meaning of the Conquest   197

The British Conquest and the Decline of the French-Canadian Bourgeoisie   198
M. BRUNET

What Middle Class?   215
J. HAMELIN

The Conquest of 1760 and the Problem of the Transition to Capitalism   223
CLAUDE COUTURE

7   The Loyalist Experience   239

Victorious in Defeat: The American Loyalists in Canada   241
WALLACE BROWN

Patriarchy and Paternalism: The Case of the Eastern Ontario Loyalist Women   250
JANICE POTTER

8   The War of 1812   271

On to Canada: Manifest Destiny and United States Strategy in the War of 1812   272
REGINALD HORSMAN

Introduction   291
ARTHUR BOWLER

9   The Fur Trade and the Northwest   310

The North West Company: Pedlars Extraordinary   311
W.L. MORTON

The Middleman Role in the Fur Trade: Its Influence on Interethnic Relations in the Saskatchewan-Missouri Plains   321
SUSAN GIANNETTINO

Wage-Labour in the Northwest Fur Trade Economy, 1760–1849 332
GLEN MAKAHONUK

10   The Rebellions of 1837–1838 in Lower Canada   355

The 1837/8 Rebellions in Lower Canada as a Social Phenomenon   356
FERNAND OUELLET

For Whom the Bell Tolls   380
S. TROFIMENKOFF

11   The Maritime Era of Sail   393

Atlantic Canada and the Age of Sail Revisited   394
ERIC SAGER AND LEWIS FISCHER

The Decline of the Sailor as a Ship Labourer in the 19th Century Timber Ports   419
JUDITH FINGARD

12   Responsible Government, The Empire and Canada   435

The Influence of the Durham Report   437
GED MARTIN

French-Canadian Nationalism and the Challenge of Ultramontanism   449
JACQUES MONET

Brokerage and the Politics of Power Sharing 465
S.J.R. NOEL

13   Family Life in Mid-Nineteenth Century British North America   475

The Victorian Family in Canada in Historical Perspective: The Ross Family of Red River and the Jarvis Family of Prince Edward Island   477
J.M. BUMSTED AND WENDY OWEN

Education and the Metaphor of the Family: The Upper Canadian Example   488
ALISON PRENTICE

Childhood and Charity in Nineteenth-Century British North America 506
PATRICIA ROOKE AND R.L. SCHNELL

14 Confederation 530

The United States and Canadian Confederation 531
DONALD CREIGHTON

History as Science or Literature: Explaining Canadian Confederation, 1857–67 543
GED MARTIN

Preface

Reappraisals in Canadian History is designed for use in university-level survey courses. It is, however, neither a textbook nor a traditional reader. Each of the units in the two volumes focuses on differing or complementary interpretations of a particular historical problem. A brief introduction to each unit establishes the context for the selected readings, and suggestions for relevant additional sources are included.

The vitality in Canadian historical studies over the past two decades has been outstanding, resulting in a profusion of new periodicals and monographs. Few organizations, groups, or regions are now without a journal. This has created both opportunities and challenges in fashioning a collection such as this. Although much recent historical writing is included, we have not neglected the important contributions of the previous generation of historians. In assembling these volumes we have consciously rejected the popular trend of trying to satisfy every region and province, every interest group, every minority, everybody. Instead we attempted to find common threads pointing to the integration of the exploding body of literature and interests. This topical approach demanded that all interests, including such disparate ones as regions, women, politics, the underclasses, and minorities, be part of the total fabric rather than segregated ghettoes.

In assembling this collection we have incurred a number of obligations. Faye Kennedy, formerly of Prentice Hall Canada, first persuaded us that there was a need for such a collection. We wish also to thank the Dean of the Faculty of Social Science and the Institute of Northern Ontario Research and Development at Laurentian University for financial assistance. Two of our students, Ross Danaher and Michael Stevenson, gave us logistical support. The students in HIST 1406/1407 participated cheerfully as we experimented with the classroom use of these materials in tutorials. Leo Larivière created the maps. Rose-May Demoré, our departmental secretary, responded to every call for help.

Finally we must thank the dozens of historians, editors and publishers who have generously given us permission to reprint this material. It is both ironic and troubling that the only rebuff we encountered was at the hands of an agency of the federal government, the Canadian War Museum, whose refusal to allow us to reprint material by George F.G. Stanley resulted in a unit on the War of 1812 representing two American but no Canadian historians.

A.D. Gilbert
C.M. Wallace
R.M. Bray

Laurentian University   Sudbury, Ontario

Introduction

Canadian History and Historians

History is misunderstood more often than not. At a superficial level it appears to be one of the few immutables in an ever-changing world. That the past itself can never be altered is irrefutable, and students frequently choose history as an option at university believing that at least one subject will provide security when others mystify with unique concepts, vocabulary and content. That cozy view of history never lasts long, for as a discipline history is complex, malleable, and imprecise, subject to changing conditions and perspectives. Far from being set in cement, history is continuously being recast by each generations's need to find its own past. If R.G. Collingwood was correct, then "every new generation must rewrite history in its own way." The past that he, Winston Churchill and others found meaningful differs dramatically from that of today's leaders and their societies.

This charactersitic of history causes much confusion for students and academics alike. A psychology professor at lunch with several historians recently declared that, after she had taken world history in grade eight, further study was irrelevant. The subject, like Napoleon, was dead. One of the historians ventured the opinion that history had possibly changed more in the past twenty years than psychology. At that point she threw up her hands and left, unable to entertain such a ludicrous proposition. Yet it may be true.

That dynamic nature of the discipline of history, when compared to the permanence of past events such as the death of Napoleon, is the apparent paradox the psychology professor never unravelled. Over the past three decades a revolution has taken place in historical scholarship. In the era after the Second World War a sort of plateau, encompassing a broad consensus about the nature of the discipline, was reached. The traditional scholar worked for months or years in archives, poring over primary sources, and producing "revisionist" books or articles published in the handful of journals that all historians of Canada read. Triumphs were achieved with the discovery of new source material or a new angle on a known subject. Politics and biography were favoured, though economic, religious, military and international topics found their specialists. The overall nature of history as the study of the activities and ideas of elites, however, was rarely questioned. This view from the "court," or top-down, became the textbook version of the Canadian past, and while there were divisions over some interpretations based on ideology, religion, or even personal hostility, there was no division on what history itself was.

In Canada the small coterie of academics dominating the field included Marcel Trudel, Donald Creighton, A.R.M. Lower, W.L. Morton, Hilda Neatby, C.P. Stacey, W.S. MacNutt, Frank Underhill, Guy Frégault, and Margaret Ormsby. A younger generation of "revisionists" from the same mold was expanding the content without challenging the structures. Among them were J.M.S. Careless, Peter Waite, Margaret Prang, W.J. Eccles, Ramsay Cook, Jean Hamelin, Ken McNaught, Blair Neatby, and Jacques Monet. These people all knew each other personally, frequently comparing notes at the Public Archives of Canada, then located on Sussex Drive beside the Royal Mint in Ottawa. At the annual meetings of the Canadian Historical Association they read papers to each other, and were never short of advice. The *Canadian Historical Review*, published by the University of Toronto Press, was the final authority in English Canada, while Abbé Groulx reigned over French Canada with the *Revue d'histoire de l'Amérique française*. It was from this more or less homogeneous group that the dominant view of Canada, as presented in school textbooks, emerged. The comfortable unity of this well-written version of Canada's past permitted it to survive its generation, which many regard as the "Golden Age" of Canadian historical scholarship.

By the late 1960s, however, several younger scholars reacted against that veneration of the images of a previous generation. To them the historical imagination had been crippled by consistency. More than that, the consensus version of the past, in their view, had no relevance for the current generation. One may admire a Rolls Royce Silver Ghost, a 1955 Chevrolet, or even a Model T, the argument goes, but one must not confuse an abacus with a computer, a museum piece with modern needs.

It is the nature of history that the status quo does not survive long, and in the upheaval that characterized the whole mentality of the 1960s, several academics began to search for a more "usable past," one that abandoned the impressionistic views from the "court," and aimed at the reconstruction of a more meaningful society. The "New Social History" was the umbrella under which most of the innovations may be grouped. The dissatisfaction with a Canadian past dominated by political and economic factors led to a renovation with new methodologies, different approaches and alternate subject matter muscling in on the old-school-tie network. Subjects once ignored moved to centre stage, including work on classes and class relations, demography, literacy, the family, leisure, mobility, immigration, religion and education, though there was little cohesion among the disparate activities. Quantification and the computer found their place in the historian's baggage. *Histoire sociale/Social History*, co-sponsored by the University of Ottawa and Carleton University in 1968, eventually provided a focus and emerged as an alternate journal, though its lack of coherent editorial policy was simply a reflection of the diversity of opinion within the discipline. In a sense each historian could become a different school. The *Annales* of France, for example, were the source of inspiration for many French Canadians, while most English Canadians turned to American sociology for their models. Although there was considerable resentment over this "invasion of the barbarians" among the traditional historians, their own anecdotal approach invited criticism from those who asked different questions of sources and approached the past from new perspectives.

By the 1970s a veritable floodgate had opened. The annual meetings of the Canadian Historical Association became not one but a dozen or more fragments meeting separately. There was the ethnic group, the labour, the Atlantic, the Western, the Arctic, the Native, the women, the urban, the local, the material, the oral—the divisions were endless. Each of these had the capacity to subdivide. Labour quickly separated into the "old-fashioned" and the "New Left," with the latter winning the day and mounting its own journal, *Labour/Le Travailleur*. Each segment, in fact, launched one or more journals, such as *Urban History Review, Canadian Ethnic Studies, Polyphony, Canadian Woman Studies, Journal of Canadian Studies, B C Studies,* and *The American Review of Canadian Studies*. The range of topics and quality of scholarship were like the rainbow. Some, like *Acadiensis: Journal of the History of the Atlantic Region*, founded in 1971 at the University of New Brunswick, established and maintained an enviable reputation. Others have been less successful.

As a consequence of this fragmentation over recent decades, a student is faced with not one but many versions of Canadian history. This confusion may be considered an unnecessary encumbrance to those who are content with the "good old stuff," but that implies the study of a dead subject. The reappraisal is never-ending, and the challenge for the student is not to learn a few facts and dates but to sample the literature and to recognize what the authors are doing with the subject and trying to do to the reader. This requires an agile and a critical mind.

Reappraisals in Canadian History is intended to reflect this diversity of interpretation in Canadian history and to present it in such a way as to enable a student to make sense of it. This is not a "textbook" history of Canada, and makes no attempt to survey all of the main developments in that history. Nor is it simply a collection of readings, randomly selected and with little or no relationship one to another. Rather, each of the chapters is devoted to a particular historical problem and the different ways in which historians have approached that problem. In some cases their conclusions stand in sharp contradiction to each other; in others they are complementary. In every case students should attempt not merely to grasp the author's conclusions, but, of even greater importance, to understand how they were reached.

In order to do this it is useful to understand the variety of reasons that may lead different historians to reach different conclusions about what appears to be the same historical problem. In one sense, of course, there is nothing new about this. The debate over "historical relativism" is an old one, and it is now a truism that historians are influenced by the context in which they themselves live. It is, after all, hardly surprising that their view of the past is, to some degree at least, relative to their own time and place and circumstance, to their own preferences and prejudices. This may mean that they view historical evidence in a new light, or that they pose different questions of the past. It has long been accepted, therefore, that there will be differences of emphasis and interpretation, not only between different generations of historians, but also between historians of the same era.

The present fragmentation of the discipline, however, goes far beyond the traditional recognition of the relativity of historical knowledge. Implicit in it is fundamental disagreement over content and methodology, the meaning of history and its purpose. The one point on which historians do agree, however, is that not all historical interpretations are of equal validity. Certainly historians are less inclined than scholars in other disciplines to claim to have discovered any final "truths." This is understandable, given the nature of the evidence with which they deal and the problems with which they are concerned. The readings in this volume are in themselves testimony to the elusiveness of any final answers in history. Despite these limitations, historians do insist that historical scholarship can and must be subjected to critical scrutiny, that historical evidence and the use to which that evidence is put can be evaluated. The study of history at any kind of advanced level requires the development of these analytical skills, and never more so than with its current fragmentation. It is this, rather than the mastery of voluminous detail, that distinguishes the historian from the mere antiquarian. One of the purposes of this collection of readings is to assist students to develop their critical skills. Within each chapter, therefore, students should attempt to identify the interpretative thrust of each author, how the interpretation of one author differs from or complements that of another, what sources and methodologies have been employed, and, finally, how convincingly each author has based his or her interpretation on the historical evidence.

There are a number of fairly obvious points to look for. Has an author found new evidence which calls into question previous work on the subject? Is a new methodology being applied? Is anecdotal evidence, for example, being challenged by statistical analysis? Is a new type of historical evidence being brought to bear on an old problem? Is the historical problem itself being defined in an entirely new way? A very good example by way of illustration can be found in the different ways in which historians have approached the question of the nature of society in New France. In chapter 2, students will find three quite different, although complementary, portraits of that society. In one a description has been developed from the observations of contemporary observers. In another a demographic analysis of an urban area has yielded an entirely different perspective. In the third, an attempt to evaluate the position of a particular group within that society—the women of New France—the reader finds yet another focus. These three readings reflect the use of different sources, different methodologies and different questions to throw light on the same historical problem, the nature of society. In reading these articles, students must first identify these differences in approach if they are to understand and evaluate the differences in the conclusions reached by the authors.

In the pre-Confederation period of Canadian history, the student is confronted not only with conflicting interpretations but with a fragmented subject. While there is a certain unity to the history of New France, even in that era geographic barriers and differences, as well as imperial policies, meant that the St. Lawrence colony and Acadia developed in very different ways. After the Conquest, a somewhat amorphous entity labelled "British North America" contained a sometimes bewildering variety of separate colonies and territories, held together only by their common allegiance to the British Crown and their distrust of the republican experiment in the new United States of America.

The fourteen chapters in this volume are a selection from the history of New France and British North America. An attempt has been made to strike a balance between the various subjects and approaches. Although there are exceptions, generally speaking historical writing on the pre-Confederation period is more traditional and has been less influenced by the New Social History than that on the national period, perhaps because the historical sources are more intractable. The first six chapters of this volume are concerned with the history of New France. Within these chapters, however, students will encounter a wide variety of subjects. Chapters 2 and 3 deal with the social and economic development of the St. Lawrence colony, while chapter 5 contains two very contrasting views of the French military in New France. Chapter 4, on the other hand, is concerned with the tragic history of Acadia, which ended in the expulsion of most of its population. The difficult problem of the nature of the cultural interaction between Amerindian and European is considered in chapter 1, and this theme is picked up again for a later period in chapter 9, "The Fur Trade and the North West." Students should note that in both instances historians have something to learn from anthropologists, who approach this question of cultural interaction from somewhat different perspectives and employ somewhat different methodologies.

In the post-Conquest period there is even more diversity. Two chapters, 7 and 8, are concerned with interaction with the United States. The economic and geographic diversity of British North America are reflected in chapters on the North West, Lower Canada, and the outward-looking Atlantic colonies. In the final three chapters, British North America is interpreted in a less fragmented fashion, through an examination of the imperial relationship, society, and, finally, Confederation itself.

Any rigid categorization of the chapters is bound to be misleading since politics, economics, social dynamics and regional aspects pervade most studies about Canada in one way or another. The student must learn to stride through the variety, identifying the interpretations, the mind-sets, the methodologies, and the mythologies. Each chapter in this collection offers a variety of interpretations which are frequently contradictory. At the same time, each chapter has a coherence which explains something about Canada, its history and its historians. Since history is what historians say it is, the student has both the opportunity and the responsibility to identify those views and the objectives of the historians. History will continue to be misunderstood, and the student must know why.

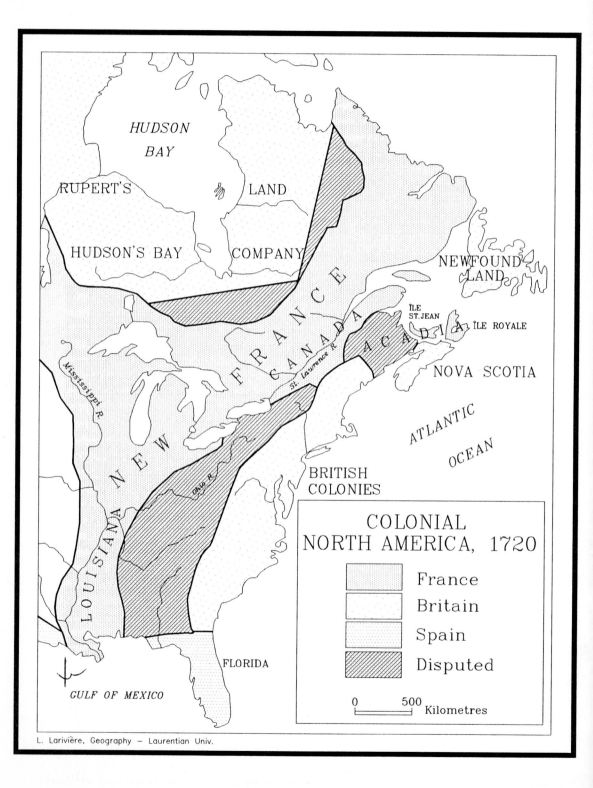

HUDSON
BAY

RUPERT'S   LAND

HUDSON'S BAY   COMPANY

NEWFOUND
LAND

Mississippi R.

St. Laurence R.

CANADA

ÎLE
ST.JEAN

ÎLE ROYALE

NOVA SCOTIA

NEW   FRANCE

ACADIA

ATLANTIC

OCEAN

Ohio R.

BRITISH
COLONIES

LOUISIANA

FLORIDA

GULF OF MEXICO

COLONIAL
NORTH AMERICA, 1720

France
Britain
Spain
Disputed

0   500   Kilometres

L. Larivière, Geography — Laurentian Univ.

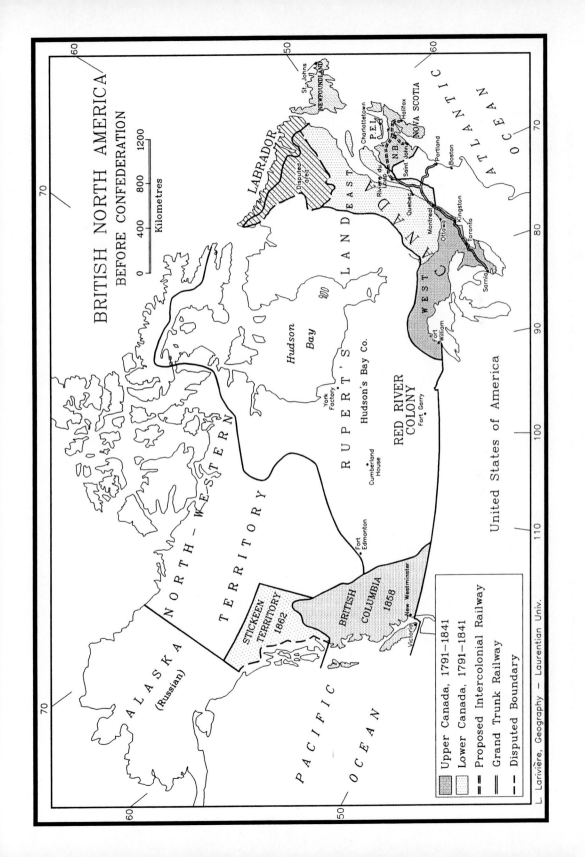

BRITISH NORTH AMERICA
BEFORE CONFEDERATION

Kilometres

0   400   800   1200

ALASKA
(Russian)

NORTH-WESTERN TERRITORY

STICKEEN TERRITORY 1862

BRITISH COLUMBIA 1858

New Westminster
Victoria

PACIFIC OCEAN

Fort Edmonton

RUPERT'S LAND

Hudson's Bay Co.

Cumberland House

RED RIVER COLONY

Fort Garry

York Factory

Hudson Bay

900

LABRADOR

Disputed Area

St. Johns

NEWFOUNDLAND

CANADA EAST

Rivière du Loup

Quebec

Montreal

Ottawa

CANADA WEST

Kingston

Toronto

Sarnia

Fort William

Charlottetown

P.E.I.

N.B.

Saint John

NOVA SCOTIA

Halifax

Portland

Boston

ATLANTIC OCEAN

United States of America

Upper Canada, 1791-1841
Lower Canada, 1791-1841
Proposed Intercolonial Railway
Grand Trunk Railway
Disputed Boundary

L. Larivière, Geography — Laurentian Univ.

60   50   60   70

70

70   80

90

100

110

60   50

CHAPTER

1 NATIVE-NEWCOMER INTERACTION

The "new world" that Europeans discovered in North America was one that was already inhabited. One major theme, therefore, in the early history of Canada is the interaction between Amerindian and European. Not surprisingly, older historical writing on this subject reflected a Eurocentric perspective, describing a process in which a barbarous and inferior culture was inevitably overwhelmed by one much more civilized and technologically advanced. This view of the Amerindian as "Savage" permeated the work of the influential nineteenth-century American historian, Francis Parkman.

The first reading in this unit, "The Problem of the Iroquois," by George T. Hunt, also reflects this Eurocentric approach. When first published in 1940, however, it was hailed as a major reinterpretation of the subject. Completely rejecting Parkman's attribution of the seventeeth-century inter-tribal wars to the "homicidal frenzy" of the Iroquois, Hunt suggested instead that the wars were a direct result of European-Amerindian contact and, in particular, of the relationship of the Amerindians to the fur trade. Having become totally dependent on European technology in the form of trade goods, the Iroquois had no option other than war, once their supply of beaver fur became dangerously depleted by the 1640s.

Although this emphasis on the economic importance of the fur trade to the Amerindians has been influential, more recent historical writing on early Amerindian-European contact suggests that the subject is a much more complex one than Hunt's work would indicate. In the second reading in this unit, Calvin Martin investigates the phenomenon of wildlife depletion. Posing the question of why native "traditional safeguards" against this catastrophe failed so quickly, he concludes that the answer is to be found in the disintegration of the Amerindian culture, in particular their spiritual beliefs, under the European onslaught.

1

In the final reading, the Conclusion from his *Friend and Foe: Aspects of French-Amerindian Cultural Contact in the Sixteenth and Seventeenth Centuries*, Cornelius Jaenan examines the more general question of Amerindian-European cultural interaction. Acknowledging that this interaction had a powerful effect in both directions, he suggests that the process was one in which Europeans gained but natives lost. Amerindian culture was disastrously weakened, but the native peoples remained unintegrated in the developing society of New France.

Suggestions for Further Reading

Axtel, James, *The Invasion Within: The Contest of Cultures in Colonial North America*. New York: Oxford University Press, 1985.

Bailey, A.G., *The Conflict of European and Eastern Algonkian Cultures, 1504-1700* (2nd ed.). Toronto: University of Toronto Press, 1969.

Dickason, Olive, "The Concept of *l'homme sauvage* and Early French Colonialism in the Americas," *Revue française d'histoire d'outre-mer*, 64, no. 234 (1977), 5-32.

————, *The Myth of the Savage and the Beginnings of French Colonialism in the Americas*. Edmonton: University of Alberta Press, 1984.

Krech, S., *Indians, Animals and the Fur Trade: A Critique of Keepers of the Game*. Athens, Georgia: University of Georgia Press, 1981.

Johnston, Susan, "Epidemics: the Forgotten Factor in Seventeenth Century Native Warfare in the St. Lawrence Region," in *Native People, Native Lands: Canadian Indians, Inuit and Metis*, ed. B.A. Cox. Ottawa: Carleton University Press, 1987, 14-31.

Martin, C., *Keepers of the Game: Indian-Animal Relationships and the Fur Trade*. Berkeley, California: University of California Press, 1978.

Schlieser, K.H., "Epidemics and Indian Middlemen: Rethinking the Wars of the Iroquois, 1609-1653," *Ethnohistory*, 23, no. 2 (Spring 1976), 129-145.

Trigger, Bruce, "The French Presence in Huronia: The Structure of Franco-Huron Relations in the First Half of the Seventeenth Century," *Canadian Historical Review*, XLIX, no. 2 (June 1968), 107-141.

————, *Natives and Newcomers: Canada's 'Heroic Age' Reconsidered*. Kingston and Montreal: McGill-Queen's University Press, 1985.

THE PROBLEM OF THE IROQUOIS

George T. Hunt

In most respects the circumstances of the contact between white man and native in North America are unique in the history of such relationships. In other

From *The Wars of the Iroquois: A Study in Intertribal Relations* (Madison: University of Wisconsin Press, 1967), 3–12. Reprinted by permission of The University of Wisconsin Press.

centuries and in other regions, where the frontiers of superior civilizations had long been in contact with the periphera of inferior civilizations, the conditions of these frontier-peripheral areas were well established and relatively familiar, and the process of infiltration and conquest was comparatively gradual. The Russian advance into Siberia, the French and English movement into and beyond India, the penetration of the Orient by the peddling shipmasters of the West, all these were conditioned by the fact that each civilization had already considerable knowledge of the other. In Africa the Nile Valley and the Mediterranean shore had constituted a frontier area before historic times, and even in the southern part of the African continent contacts had been more or less continuous for nearly four hundred years before actual colonization and exploitation were begun.

In North America, on the other hand, a well advanced civilization, in which the mechanism of exploitation was already highly developed, met the Stone Age face to face, in an invasion almost simultaneously continental in extent. There had been a few premonitory invasions along the St. Lawrence River, Coronado's horsemen had retreated from the far Southwest, a few mailed footmen had floundered through southern swamps to the Great River, a few Englishmen had died at Croatan, but these tentative ventures of the sixteenth century had come to nothing. The Wars of Religion cut short the beginning made by Cartier; Texas remained virtually uninhabited; and one hundred and thirty years passed before another white man glimpsed the Mississippi.

In the thirty years following 1603 the whole Atlantic seaboard swarmed with settlement. Champlain established New France at Quebec and Three Rivers; Holland built forts far up the Hudson; England was at Plymouth, in Massachusetts Bay, Virginia, and Maryland, and struggling for a foothold in Maine. The entire coast was explored and mapped. The Stone Age faced the insistent seventeenth century on a fifteen-hundred-mile front which moved swiftly and relentlessly forward. This advance was no matter of slave raids, ivory, or gold. What these white men wanted was what every native had or could get, furs or land, and the trade that was opened was a trade in which every native could take part. As a matter of fact, he was usually frantically eager to take part in it.

The abundance of furs and the inexhaustible market for them made North America a unique theater of interracial contacts. On other continents the desire of traders had been for materials or products considerably less plentiful and less easily obtained by individuals, but here the ease of acquisition, the apparently limitless supply, the ready market, and the permanence of the white settlements permitted the constant participation of every native, expanded the business of trade to unprecedented proportions, and changed, almost overnight, the fundamental conditions of aboriginal economy.

If it is true that "the relations into which the Europeans entered with the aborigines were decided almost wholly by the relations which they found to exist among the tribes on their arrival,"[1] it is certainly equally true that the intertribal relations of the aborigines were in the future to be decided almost wholly by the relations existing between them and the Europeans, especially in those areas in which the fur trade was the chief factor in those relations. On the question of land, the tribes could, and often did, cooperate, and yield or resist together, but the fur trade divided them immediately into groups—those who had fur and those who had none. The great desirability of the trade goods to the Indian who had once known them became shortly a necessity, a very urgent necessity that permitted no renunciation of the trade. As new desires wakened and old skills vanished, the Indian who had fur, or could get it, survived; he who could not get it died or moved away. But whatever he did, life for him could never again be what it had been: old institutions and economies had profoundly altered or disappeared completely at the electrifying touch of the white man's trade, which swept along the inland trails and rivers with bewildering speed and wrought social revolution a thousand miles beyond the white man's habitations, and years before he himself appeared on the scene. English powder burned on the Mississippi a half century before the English cabins reached Lake Ontario,[2] and the Ottawa tribe had fought a commercial war with the Winnebago of Wisconsin, forcing French trade goods upon them, ten years before the hesitant French settlement had reached Montreal.[3] In truth, the Indian world had in many respects already vanished before the white man saw it, and it is not strange that in his great hurry he formed opinions of it that were somewhat wide of the truth. Those who wonder at the foolishness of the Indians who fought each other to extinction instead of combining to stay the white man's advance are usually the same who attribute their intertribal wars to "insensate fury" and "homicidal frenzy."[4] Tribal motives must necessarily be mysterious to the historian who ignores the social and economic metamorphosis brought about by the trade.

The area in which the fur trade was most significant was the northeastern quarter of the continent, where two great waterways led through inhospitable mountains and highlands into a region which in the seventeenth century and long thereafter teemed with furbearers. The St. Lawrence-Ottawa and the Hudson-Mohawk routes led to the Great Lakes and the Mississippi-Ohio country, with their innumerable tributary streams where were to be found more beaver than in any similar area in the world. Commanding both these routes lay the Huron Iroquois, composed of a half dozen consanguine tribes which with the Algonquins of the upper St. Lawrence must have represented a population of nearly one hundred thousand. Yet after only thirty years of intermittent warfare the Iroquois proper, probably the least numerous of the tribes, never numbering more than twelve thousand, were in sole possession of the region east of Lake Michigan, having dispersed, incorporated, or exterminated all their neighbors; they were even credited, though somewhat mistakenly, with a shadowy empire extending west to the Mississippi, and from Carolina to Hudson Bay. As to the importance of the Iroquois, it has been said that their steady alliance with the Dutch and English of the Hudson River colony was "the pivotal fact of early American history."[5]

With intertribal relations and activities centering as they did about the tribe most active in intertribal affairs, the Iroquois, the question, why did the Iroquois do the things that they did, becomes not only pertinent but vital to an understanding of colonial history. The answers thus far given by historians are three, none of which is in the least convincing.[6] The first of these is the theory that they were possessed of an "insensate fury" and "homicidal frenzy," a theory advanced by Parkman. The second is that a superior political organization, the League of the Iroquois, produced by a superior Iroquois intellect, rendered the Five Nations invincible. This thesis was propounded by Lewis H. Morgan, who even ascribed to the Iroquois the paradoxical motive of exterminating their enemies in order to establish universal intertribal peace.[7] To these may be added a third theory, that a great supply of firearms, furnished by the greedy Dutch West India Company and unavailable to their enemies, gave rein to a natural passion for conquest and butchery, which they indulged at random but with almost unimaginable enthusiasm.

Even a cursory contemplation of the generally known facts, however, will raise further questions. If a natural superiority or an innate fury was responsible, it is curious that neither of these traits was manifest in the very closely consanguine tribes, such as the Hurons, the Erie, the Neutrals, and others which the Iroquois conquered. Neither does this thesis explain why the naturally superior and ferocious Iroquois had fled from the Algonquins of the St. Lawrence in the years preceding the coming of Champlain, and were on the defensive, stockaded in invaded territory until after 1620. Even if there had been some virtues inherent in the Iroquois blood stream, that stream had changed very early and very completely, for as early as 1656 a priest found that there were more foreigners than natives in Iroquoia, eleven different nations being represented in the country of the Seneca.[8] In 1660 it would have been hard to find twelve hundred Iroquois of pure blood, according to Lalemant, who anticipated Parkman by remarking, "It may be said that, if the Iroquois have any power, it is only because they are knavish and cruel."[9] Even the casual reader feels, after reviewing the achievements of the Iroquois, that knavery and cruelty could hardly have been the mainspring of their mighty and significant labors.

With respect to the great efficiency claimed for the League, a re-examination of only a few sources leads to the conclusion that in the period of Iroquois conquest the League was little if any more effectual in achieving unanimity of action than were the loose Powhatanic and Cherokee leagues, or even the Algonquin confederacy or the Choctaw republic. Despite the bluster of Mohawk orators, there is not a single recorded instance of unanimous or anywhere near unanimous action by the League prior to 1653, and none save in peace treaties thereafter. The Mohawk orators had a way, confusing to their enemies, as they well knew, of pretending, when on their own business, to speak for the League.[10] The habit has confused historians no less. Osgood, however, has recognized that the League could at best only prevent fratricidal strife among its members.[11] In any event, that result was achieved by the other, less celebrated, confederacies with more marked success than by the League of the Iroquois. The Hurons, for instance, kept peace with their Algonquin neighbors with no organization whatever, no ties of consanguinity, no common tongue or social institutions[12]—in fact, with nothing more in common than an economic interest—while throughout a series of five wars there was no such thing as unanimity among the Five Nations. Rarely did two of the cantons combine in an attack, and then only because their commercial interests were for the time identical. Never did two cantons combine for defense. Mohawks and Onondaga both cheered the French attack upon the Seneca, and Seneca and Onondaga were steadily antipathetic to the Mohawks, who, as the eastern canton, held the Hudson River country and the Dutch trade. The Mohawks sought ceaselessly to exploit their brothers, and were at swords' points with them half the time. All that prevented a vicious intra-Iroquois war was the fact that the common interest of all three in opposing the French and the French Indians was ever greater than their conflicting interests. At that, much Iroquois blood was spilled by Iroquois, and perhaps more embassies of peace traveled within Iroquoia than from Iroquoia to foreign tribes.

If all this is true, one may ask, why has the League been so celebrated by historians, and why has it for seventy-five years been given credit for accomplishing things it did not accomplish? The most important single reason is probably Lewis H. Morgan's book *The League of the Iroquois.* Morgan was a true scholar in spirit, a conscientious observer, and a tireless worker, but he was not a historian, and he had access to few or none of the sources which could have informed him on the history of the League he so carefully observed.[13] It is perhaps not strange that when he viewed the perfected League of 1850, knowing little of Iroquois history except tradition,[14] he should have assumed that the perfection of political organization he saw then was more than two centuries old. The League as he saw it in the nineteenth century offered a plausible explanation for a hitherto unexplained phenomenon of the seventeenth century, and without critical investigation it was temptingly easy to interchange result and cause. The very excellence of his general work unfortunately perpetuated this specific error, which was widely adopted by historians.[15] To those who read the sources, however, it becomes quite clear that the League as Morgan saw it did not wage the wars of the Iroquois nor make them possible, but that in a very real sense it was the wars that made the League which he and others were privileged to examine two hundred years later. The League, then, cannot be an answer to the Iroquois problem.

In the matter of armament also, the assets of the Iroquois have been over-stated. The two thousand muskets which they are credited with having possessed in 1640[16] shrink upon investigation to a possible four hundred, and even this is probably too generous an estimate. In that year a French prisoner testified that a "heavily armed" war band of five hundred Iroquois had exactly thirty-six arquebuses.[17] The supposed greed of the Dutch West India Company is called into serious question when it is discovered that they tried desperately to stop what trade in guns there was, and that both the Company and the settlement at Beverwyck passed and attempted to enforce ordinances against it, even going so far as to ordain the penalty of death. Among the Dutch on the Hudson and Connecticut the French were as bitterly accused of trading arms to Indians as were the Dutch in the French settlements on the St. Lawrence, and the justi-fication was as ample in the one case as in the other. Moreover, the Susquehannah, whom the Iroquois conquered, were far better provided with arms than the Iroquois, possessing even artillery in their forts.[18]

There is no denying that these conditions, to which is attributed the Iroquois phenomenon, existed in some measure and undoubtedly had an aggregate im-portance, but the fact still remains that although they were paralleled elsewhere, in fact were paralleled again and again all over the continent, the phenomenon itself was unparalleled. No other tribe ever did what the Iroquois did, and yet the three theories of inherent qualities, superior organization, and superior ar-mament fail to explain their achievements or to suggest a motive which could have driven them so far and down so hard a road.

The explanation must lie in some fundamental condition which thus far has not received the attention of the relatively few students of Iroquois history. The search should be not for the ineluctable ultimate origin, but for a general condition of Indian life, readily ascertained and recognized, from which the motivation of the Iroquois should appear to proceed inevitably. Since this general condition was peculiar in its effect upon the Iroquois, it follows that unless the Iroquois were themselves peculiar, it must have some connection with geography or climate; and when it is recalled that the rise of the Iroquois to power coincided with the spread of the white trade throughout their region and the regions beyond them, a second inference follows, namely that some peculiarity of the Iroquois posi-tion and the spread of the white trade may well have combined to produce a motivation sufficiently powerful to drive the Iroquois through a half century of bloody intertribal conflict with their brother tribesmen, the closely related peo-ples that almost surrounded them. The inference gains in strength when it is recalled that throughout the wars there runs ceaselessly the theme of trade and commercial arrangement, and that even the merciless Indian oratory, punctuated by gifts made in frank expectation of counter-gifts, is wound tightly about a core of commercial negotiation—of proposal and counter-proposal.

Such wars as those of the Iroquois must have had not only an insistent mo-tivation, but also a disastrous alternative, or at least an alternative that was regarded as disastrous by those who waged them. It is quite likely that if the white trade had become a social and economic necessity to them, their position had life and death as alternatives. That position would have permitted neither compromise nor inactivity, and would explain why their wars were the first truly national intertribal wars on the continent, there being now for the first time a truly national motive. It is possible that William C. Macleod may have struck the lost chord in intertribal relations when he wrote that "the same principles of economic science apply alike to the economy of modern Germany and of the Shoshone Digger Indians, or any like economic group."[19] If the Iroquois were either facing disaster or thought that they were, they may well have turned, as do "enlightened" nations, to war. What is true is never so important, historically, as what people think is true, and while it may be convincingly reasoned, with that keen hindsight which historians often call insight, that the Iroquois would have been better off economically had they done anything other than what they did, this reasoning need not mean that the ultimate facts were clear to the Iroquois or that their motive was not (perhaps mistakenly) economic.

The thesis that when the Iroquois made war on a national scale they did so with somewhat the same ends in view as have their Christian brothers, is admittedly attractive. Such a thesis, however, requires abundant and indisputable documentary evidence, if it aspires to solve the Iroquois problem.

Notes

1. George E. Ellis, "Indians of North America," in Justin Winsor, ed., *Narrative and Critical History of America* (8 vols., Boston and New York, 1884-89), 1:283.

2. The powder was burned by the Iroquois in their assault upon the Illinois in 1680. Oswego, the first English settlement on Lake Ontario, was founded in 1726.

3. Nicolas Perrot, *Memoir on the Manners, Customs, and Religion of the Savages of North America*, translated from the French by Emma H. Blair, in her *Indian Tribes of the Upper Mississippi Valley and Region of the Great Lakes*, 1:293 (Cleveland, 1911). The date is not exact.

4. Francis Parkman, *The Jesuits in North America in the Seventeenth Century (France and England in North America*, pt. 2, Boston, 1867), 434, 444, 447; John A. Doyle, *Virginia, Maryland, and the Carolinas (English Colonies in America*, vol. 1, New York, 1882), 13-14. Doyle merely remarks upon the suicidal feuds and what the Indians could have done if they had united; he does not comment on the reason for the disunity. Parkman, in his *La Salle and the Discovery of the Great West* (12th ed., Boston, 1892), 204, again ascribes their actions to "homicidal fury," though he admits that once, in 1680, "strange as it may seem," there appeared to be another motive.

5. John Fiske, *The Dutch and Quaker Colonies in America* (2 vols., Boston, 1899), 2:172. For representative opinions see Frederic L. Paxson, *History of the American Frontier* (New York, 1924), 52; Herbert L. Osgood, *The American Colonies in the Seventeenth Century* (3 vols., New York, 1907), 1:420-421; Lewis H. Morgan, *League of the Ho-dé-no-sau-nee, or Iroquois* (new edition, edited by Herbert M. Lloyd, New York, 1904), II; Parkman, *Jesuits in North America*, 447; "Governor Dongan's Report on the State of the Province," in Edmund B. O'Callaghan, ed., *Documents Relative to the Colonial History of the State of New York* (15 vols., Albany, 1853-87), 3:393; "M. Du Chesneau's Memoir on the Western Indians," *ibid.*, 9:165; Andrew M. Davis, "Canada and Louisiana," in Winsor, *Narrative and Critical History*, 5:2.

6. For a critical estimate of the literature on the subject see page 185.

7. *League of the Iroquois,* 72.

8. Reuben G. Thwaites, ed., *The Jesuit Relations and Allied Documents* (73 vols., Cleveland, 1896-1901), 43:265.

9. *Ibid.*, 45:207, 211.

10. See, for example, Kiotsaeton to the Governor, in *Jesuit Relations*, 17:253: "Onontio, lend me ear. I am the mouth for the whole of my country; thou listeneth to all the Iroquois in hearing my words"; this when he had to return to his own country to get ratification for a peace concerning only his own people. See also Grangula to La Barre, in Louis A. Lahontan, *New Voyages to North-America*, edited by Reuben G. Thwaites (2 vols., Chicago, 1905), 1:82-83, 85. There are many more examples.

11. Osgood, *American Colonies*, 2:420-422; Parkman, *Jesuits in North America*, 344; John A. Doyle, *The Middle Colonies (English Colonies in America*, vol. 4, New York, 1907), 119.

12. See below, Chapters 3 and 4.

13. When Morgan wrote his *League of the Iroquois*, the *New York Colonial Documents* were only in the process of publication, and the *Jesuit Relations* were also as yet unpublished, so he took his background from Cadwallader Colden, who probably knew less about the subject than Morgan himself. For a discussion of Colden's work see below, page 185.

14. A great deal of nonsense has been written about the reliability of Indian tradition in factual matters. Charles Eastman was a full-blood Sioux, and his *Indian Heroes and Great Chieftains* is written mainly from information obtained directly from the older people of his tribe, but George E. Hyde, after checking it with known facts, says that "it presents a spectacle of poor and distorted memory that is appalling, as nearly every date and statement of fact is incorrect." *Red Cloud's Folk* (Norman, Oklahoma, 1937), 54. See also pages viii, ix, and 60 for other cases in point. Mr. Hyde is one of the regrettably few writers in the field of Indian history who has his feet on the ground, and who deals with source material in a scientific manner.

15. It was adopted by both Parkman and Fiske, and it influenced Channing, Doyle, and Turner. The youthful Turner writes, in his doctoral dissertation, that "thus by priority in securing firearms, as well as by their remarkable civil organization," did the Iroquois rise to power, citing Morgan directly. *The Early Writings of Frederick Jackson Turner* (University of Wisconsin Press, 1938), 97.

16. Louise P. Kellogg, *The French Régime in Wisconsin and the Northwest* (Madison, 1925), 85.

17. Testimony of Marguerie, transcribed by Le Jeune, in the *Jesuit Relations,* 21:37.

18. For a full discussion of the Dutch trade with the Iroquois in firearms, see below, Appendix A.

19. *The Origin of the State Reconsidered in the Light of the Data of Aboriginal North America* (Philadelphia, 1924), 41-42.

THE EUROPEAN IMPACT ON THE CULTURE OF A NORTHEASTERN ALGONQUIN TRIBE: AN ECOLOGICAL INTERPRETATION

Calvin Martin

As the drive for furs, known prosaically as the fur trade, expanded and became more intense in seventeenth-century Canada, complaints of beaver extermination became more frequent and alarming. By 1635, for example, the Huron had reduced their stock of beaver to the point where the Jesuit Father Paul Le Jeune could declare that they had none.[1] In 1684 Baron Lahontan recorded a speech made before the French governor-general by an Iroquois spokesman, who explained that his people had made war on the Illinois and Miami because these Algonquians had trespassed on Iroquois territory and overkilled their beaver, "and contrary to the Custom of all the Savages, have carried off whole Stocks, both Male and Female."[2] This exploitation of beaver and other furbearers seems to have been most intense in the vicinity of major trading posts and among the native tribes most affected by the trade (the Montagnais, Huron, League Iroquois, Micmac, and others[3]), while those tribes which remained beyond European influence and the trade, such as the Bersimis of northeastern Quebec, enjoyed an abundance of beaver in their territories.[4]

Even before the establishment of trading posts, the Micmac of the extreme eastern tip of Canada were engaged in lively trade with European fishermen. Thus areas that were important in the fishing industry, such as Prince Edward Island, the Gaspé Peninsula, and Cape Breton Island, were cleaned out of moose and other furbearers by the mid-seventeenth century.[5] Reviewing this grim situation, Nicolas Denys observed that game was less abundant in his time than formerly; as for the beaver, "few in a house are saved; they [the Micmac] would take all. The disposition of the Indians is not to spare the little

From *William and Mary Quarterly,* 3d ser., XXI (January 1974), 3-26. Reprinted by permission of the author.

ones any more than the big ones. They killed all of each kind of animal that there was when they could capture it."[6]

In short, the game which by all accounts had been so plentiful was now being systematically overkilled by the Indians themselves. A traditional explanation for this ecological catastrophe is neatly summarized by Peter Farb, who conceives of it in mechanistic terms: "If the Northern Athabaskan and Northern Algonkian Indians husbanded the land and its wildlife in primeval times, it was only because they lacked both the technology to kill very many animals and the market for so many furs. But once white traders entered the picture, supplying the Indians with efficient guns and an apparently limitless market for furs beyond the seas, the Indians went on an orgy of destruction." The Indian, in other words, was "economically seduced" to exploit the wildlife requisite to the fur trade.[7]

Such a cavalier dismissal of northeastern Algonquian culture, especially its spiritual component, renders this explanation superficial and inadequate. One can argue that economic determinism was crucial to the course of Algonquian cultural development (including religious perception) over a long period of time. Yet from this perspective European contact was but a moment in the cultural history of the Indians, and it is difficult to imagine that ideals and a life-style that had taken centuries to evolve would have been so easily and quickly discarded merely for the sake of improved technological convenience. As we shall see, the entire Indian-land relationship was suffused with religious considerations which profoundly influenced the economic (subsistence) activities and beliefs of these people. The subsistence cycle was regulated by centuries of spiritual tradition which, if it had been in a healthy state, would have countered the revolutionizing impact of European influence. Tradition would doubtless have succumbed eventually, but why did the end come so soon? Why did the traditional safeguards of the northeastern Algonquian economic system offer such weak resistance to its replacement by the exploitive, European-induced regime?

When the problem is posed in these more comprehensive terms, the usual economic explanation seems misdirected, for which reason the present article will seek to offer an alternative interpretation. The methodology of cultural ecology will be brought to bear on the protohistoric and early contact phases of Micmac cultural history in order to examine the Indian-land relationship under aboriginal and postcontact conditions and to probe for an explanation to the problem of wildlife overkill.[8]

Cultural ecology seeks to explain the interaction of environment and culture, taking the ecosystem and the local human population as the basic units of analysis.[9] An ecosystem is a discrete community of plants and animals, together with the nonliving environment, occupying a certain space and time, having a flow-through of energy and raw materials in its operation, and composed of subsystems.[10] For convenience of analysis, an ecosystem can be separated into its physical and biological components, although one should bear in mind that in nature the two are completely intermeshed in complex interactions. And from the standpoint of cultural ecology, there is a third component: the metaphysical or spiritual.

The ecosystem model of plant and animal ecologists is somewhat strained when applied to a human population, although, as Roy A. Rappaport has demonstrated in his *Pigs for the Ancestors,* the attempt can be very useful.[11] The difficulties encountered include the assignment of definite territorial limits to the area under consideration (resulting in a fairly arbitrary delimitation of an ecosystem), the quantification of the system's energy budget and the carrying capacity of the land, and the identification of subsystem interrelations. Assigning values to variables becomes, in many instances, quite impossible.

The transposition of the ecosystem approach from cultural anthropology to historical inquiry complicates these problems even further, for the relationships between a human population and its environment are seldom amenable to rigorous quantitative analysis using historical documents as sources. Yet this is certainly not always so. In the case of the fur trade, for example, one may in fact be able to measure some of its effects on the environment from merchants' records—showing numbers of pelts obtained from a region over a certain time period—and also from lists of goods given to the Indians at trading posts and by treaties. Even when available, such records are too incomplete to satisfy the rigorous demands of the ecologist, but to say that they are of limited value is not to say that they are useless.

Few historians have used the ecological model in their work.[12] Recognizing the need for the environmental perspective in historiography, Wilbur R. Jacobs recently observed that "those who hope to write about such significant historical events [as the despoiling of the American west] ... will need a sort of knowledge not ordinarily possessed by historians. To study the impact of the fur trade upon America and her native people, for instance, there must be more than a beginning acquaintance with ethnology, plant and animal ecology, paleoecology, and indeed much of the physical sciences."[13]

In the case of the northeastern Algonquian, and the Micmac in particular, the fur trade was but one factor—albeit an important one—in the process of acculturation. Long before they felt the lure of European technology, these littoral Indians must have been infected with Old World diseases carried by European fishermen, with catastrophic effects. Later, the Christian missionaries exerted a disintegrative influence on the Indians' view of and relation to their environment. All three of these factors—disease, Christianity, and technology—which may be labeled "trigger" factors, must be assessed in terms of their impact on the Indians' ecosystem.[14]

Among the first North American Indians to be encountered by Europeans were the Micmacs who occupied present-day Nova Scotia, northern New

Brunswick and the Gaspé Peninsula, Prince Edward Island, and Cape Breton Island. According to the Sieur de Dièreville, they also lived along the lower St. John River with the Malecites, who outnumbered them.[15] For our present purposes, the Micmac territory will be considered an ecosystem, and the Micmac occupying it will be regarded as a local population. These designations are not entirely arbitrary, for the Micmac occupied and exploited the area in a systematic way; they had a certain psychological unity or similarity in their ideas about the cosmos; they spoke a language distinct from those of their neighbors; and they generally married within their own population. There were, as might be expected, many external factors impinging on the ecosystem which should also be evaluated, although space permits them only to be mentioned here. Some of these "supralocal" relations involved trade and hostilities with other tribes; the exchange of genetic material and personnel with neighboring tribes through intermarriage and adoption; the exchange of folklore and customs; and the movements of such migratory game as moose and woodland caribou. The Micmac ecosystem thus participated in a regional system, and the Micmac population was part of a regional population.[16]

The hunting, gathering, and fishing Micmac who lived within this Acadian forest, especially along its rivers and by the sea, were omnivores (so to speak) in the trophic system of the community. At the first trophic level, the plants eaten were wild potato tubers, wild fruits and berries, acorns and nuts, and the like. Trees and shrubs provided a wealth of materials used in the fashioning of tools, utensils, and other equipment.[17] At the time of contact, none of the Indians living north of the Saco River cultivated food crops. Although legend credits the Micmac with having grown maize and tobacco "for the space of several years,"[18] these cultigens, as well as beans, pumpkins, and wampum (which they greatly prized), were obtained from the New England Algonquians of the Saco River area (Abnakis) and perhaps from other tribes to the south.[19]

Herbivores and carnivores occupy the second and third trophic levels respectively, with top carnivores in the fourth level. The Micmac hunter tapped all three levels in his seasonal hunting and fishing activities, and these sources of food were "to them like fixed rations assigned to every moon."[20] In January, seals were hunted when they bred on islands off the coast; the fat was reduced to oil for food and body grease, and the women made clothing from the fur.[21] The principal hunting season lasted from February till mid-March, since there were enough marine resources, especially fish and mollusks, available during the other three seasons to satisfy most of the Micmacs' dietary needs. For a month and a half, then, the Indians withdrew from the seashore to the banks of rivers and lakes and into the woods to hunt the caribou, moose, black bear, and small furbearers. At no other time of the year were they so dependent on the caprice of the weather: a feast was as likely as a famine. A heavy rain could ruin the beaver and caribou hunt, and a deep, crustless snow would doom the moose hunt.[22]

Since beaver were easier to hunt on the ice than in the water, and since their fur was better during the winter, this was the chief season for taking them.[23] Hunters would work in teams or groups, demolishing the lodge or cutting the dam with stone axes. Dogs were sometimes used to track the beaver which took refuge in air pockets along the edge of the pond, or the beaver might be harpooned at air holes. In the summer hunt, beaver were shot with the bow or trapped in deadfalls using poplar as bait, but the commonest way to take them was to cut the dam in the middle and drain the pond, killing the animals with bows and spears.[24]

Next to fish, moose was the most important item in the Micmac diet, and it was their staple during the winter months when these large mammals were hunted with dogs on the hard-crusted snow. In the summer and spring, moose were tracked, stalked, and shot with the bow; in the fall, during the rutting season, the bull was enticed by a clever imitation of the sound of a female urinating. Another technique was to ensnare the animal with a noose.[25]

Moose was the Micmacs' favorite meat. The entrails, which were considered a great delicacy, and the "most delicious fat" were carried by the triumphant hunter to the campsite, and the women were sent after the carcass. The mistress of the wigwam decided what was to be done with each portion of the body, every part of which was used. Grease was boiled out of the bones and either drunk pure (with "much gusto") or stored as loaves of moose-butter;[26] the leg and thigh bones were crushed and the marrow eaten; the hides were used for robes, leggings, moccasins, and tent coverings;[27] tools, ornaments, and game pieces were made from antlers, teeth, and toe bones, respectively.[28] According to contemporary French observers, the Micmac usually consumed the moose meat immediately, without storing any, although the fact that some of the meat was preserved rather effectively by smoking it on racks, so that it would even last the year, demonstrates that Micmac existence was not as hand-to-mouth as is commonly believed of the northeastern Algonquian.[29] Black bear were also taken during the season from February till mid-March, but such hunting was merely coincidental. If a hunter stumbled upon a hibernating bear, he could count himself lucky.[30]

As the lean months of winter passed into the abundance of spring, the fish began to spawn, swimming up rivers and streams in such numbers that "everything swarms with them."[31] In mid-March came the smelt, and at the end of April the herring. Soon there were sturgeon and salmon, and numerous waterfowl made nests out on the islands—which meant there were eggs to be gathered. Mute evidence from seashore middens and early written testimony reveal that these Indians also relied heavily on various mollusks, which they harvested in great quantity.[32] Fish was a staple for the Micmac, who knew the spawning habits of each type of fish and where it was to be found. Weirs were erected across streams to trap the fish on their way downstream on a falling tide, while larger fish, such as sturgeon and salmon, might be speared or trapped.[33]

The salmon run marked the beginning of summer, when the wild geese shed their plumage. Most wildfowl were hunted at their island rookeries; waterfowl were often hunted by canoe and struck down as they took to flight; others, such as the Canadian geese which grazed in the meadows, were shot with the bow.[34]

In autumn, when the waterfowl migrated southward, the eels spawned up the many small rivers along the coast. From mid-September to October the Micmac left the ocean and followed the eels, "of which they lay in a supply; they are good and fat." Caribou and beaver were hunted during October and November, and with December came the "tom cod" (which were said to have spawned under the ice) and turtles bearing their young.[35] In January the subsistence cycle began again with the seal hunt.

As he surveyed the seasonal cycle of these Indians, Father Pierre Biard was impressed by nature's bounty and Micmac resourcefulness: "These then, but in a still greater number, are the revenues and incomes of our Savages; such, their table and living, all prepared and assigned, everything to its proper place and quarter."[36] Although we have omitted mention of many other types of forest, marine, and aquatic life which were also exploited by the Micmac, those listed above were certainly the most significant in the Micmacs' food quest and ecosystem.[37]

Frank G. Speck, perhaps the foremost student of northeastern Algonquian culture, has emphasized that hunting to the Micmacs was not a "war upon the animals, not a slaughter for food or profit."[38] Denys's observations confirm Speck's point: "Their greatest task was to feed well and to go a hunting. They did not lack animals, which they killed only in proportion as they had need of them."[39] From this, and the above description of their effective hunting techniques, it would appear that the Micmac were not limited by their hunting technology in the taking of game. As Denys pointed out, "the hunting by the Indians in old times was easy for them.... When they were tired of eating one sort, they killed some of another. If they did not wish longer to eat meat, they caught some fish. They never made an accumulation of skins of Moose, Beaver, Otter, or others, but only so far as they needed them for personal use. They left the remainder [of the carcass] where the animals had been killed, not taking the trouble to bring them to their camps."[40] Need, not technology, was the ruling factor, and need was determined by the great primal necessities of life and regulated by spiritual considerations. Hunting, as Speck remarks, was "a *holy occupation*";[41] it was conducted and controlled by spiritual rules.

The bond which united these physical and biological components of the Micmac ecosystem, and indeed gave them definition and comprehensibility, was the world view of the Indian. The foregoing discussion has dealt mainly with the empirical, objective, physical ("operational") environmental model of the observer; what it lacks is the "cognized" model of the Micmac.[42]

Anthropologists regard the pre-Columbian North American Indian as a sensitive member of his environment, who merged sympathetically with its living and nonliving components.[43] The Indian's world was filled with super-human and magical powers which controlled man's destiny and nature's course of events.[44] Murray Wax explains:

> To those who inhabit it, the magical world is a "society," not a "mechanism," that is, it is composed of "beings" rather than "objects." Whether human or nonhu-man, these beings are associated with and related to one another socially and sociably, that is, in the same ways as human beings to one another. These patterns of association and relationship may be structured in terms of kinship, empathy, sympathy, reciprocity, sexuality, dependency, or any other of the ways that human beings interact with and affect or afflict one another. Plants, animals, rocks, and stars are thus seen not as "objects" governed by laws of nature, but as "fellows" with whom the individual or band may have a more or less advantageous relationship.[45]

For the Micmac, together with all the other eastern subarctic Algonquians, the power of these mysterious forces was apprehended as "manitou"—trans-lated "magic power"—much in the same way that we might use the slang word "vibrations" to register the emotional feelings emanating (so we say) from an ob-ject, person, or situation.[46]

The world of the Micmac was thus filled with superhuman forces and beings (such as dwarfs, giants, and magicians), and animals that could talk to man and had spirits akin to his own, and the magic of mystical and medicinal herbs—a world where even inanimate objects possessed spirits.[47] Micmac subsistence activities were inextricably bound up within this spiritual matrix, which, we are suggesting, acted as a kind of control mechanism on Micmac land-use, main-taining the environment within an optimum range of conditions.

In order to understand the role of the Micmac in the fur trading enterprise of the colonial period, it is useful to investigate the role of the Micmac hunter in the spiritual world of precontact times. Hunting was governed by spiritual rules and considerations which were manifest to the early French observers in the form of seemingly innumerable taboos. These taboos connoted a sense of cautious reverence for a conscious fellow-member of the same ecosystem who, in the view of the Indian, allowed itself to be taken for food and clothing. The Indian felt that "both he and his victim understood the roles which they played in the hunt; the animal was resigned to its fate."[48]

That such a resignation on the part of the game was not to be interpreted as an unlimited license to kill should be evident from an examination of some of the more prominent taboos. Beaver, for example, were greatly admired by the Micmac for their industry and "abounding genius"; for them, the beaver had "sense" and formed a "separate nation."[49] Hence there were various regula-tions associated with the disposal of their remains: trapped beaver were drawn in public and made into soup, extreme care being taken to prevent the soup from spilling into the fire; beaver bones were carefully preserved, never being given to the dogs—lest they lose their sense of smell for the animal—or thrown into the fire—lest misfortune come upon "all the nation"—or thrown into rivers—"because the Indians fear lest the spirit of the bones ... would promptly carry the news to the other beavers, which would desert the country in order to escape the same misfortune." Likewise, menstruating women were forbidden to eat beaver, "for the Indians are convinced, they say, that the beaver, which has sense, would no longer allow itself to be taken by the Indians if it had been eaten by their unclean daughters." The fetus of the beaver, as well as that of the bear, moose, otter, and porcupine, was reserved for the old men, since it was believed that a youth who ate such food would experience intense foot pains while hunting.[50]

Taboos similarly governed the disposal of the remains of the moose—what few there were. The bones of a moose fawn (and of the marten) were never given to the dogs nor were they burned, "for they [the Micmac] would not be able any longer to capture any of these animals in hunting if the spirits of the martens and of the fawns of the moose were to inform their own kind of the bad treatment they had received among the Indians."[51] Fear of such reprisal also prohibited menstruating women from drinking out of the common kettles or bark dishes.[52] Such regulations imply cautious respect for the animal hunted. The moose not only provided food and clothing, but was firmly tied up with the Micmac spirit-world—as were the other game animals.

Bear ceremonialism was also practiced by the Micmac. Esteem for the bear is in fact common among boreal hunting peoples of northern Eurasia and North America, and has the following characteristics: the beast is typically hunted in the early spring, while still in hibernation. It is addressed, when either dead or alive, with honorific names; a conciliatory speech is made to the animal, either before or after killing it, by which the hunter apologizes for his act and perhaps explains why it is necessary; and the carcass is respectfully treated, those parts not used (especially the skull) being ceremonially disposed of and the flesh consumed in accordance with taboos. Such rituals are intended to propitiate the spiritual controller of the bears so that he will continue to furnish game to the hunter.[53] Among the Micmac the bear's heart was not eaten by young men lest they get out of breath while traveling and lose courage in danger. The bear carcass could be brought into the wigwam only through a special door made specifically for that purpose, either in the left or right side of the structure. This ritual was based on the Micmac belief that their women did not "deserve" to enter the wigwam through the same door as the animal. In fact, we are told that childless women actually left the wigwam at the approach of the body and did not return until it had been entirely consumed.[54] By means of such rituals the hunter satisfied the soul-spirit of the slain animal. Of the present-day Mistassini (Montagnais) hunter, Speck writes that "should he fail to observe these formalities an unfavorable reaction would also ensue with his own soul-spirit, his 'great man' ... as it is called. In such a case the 'great man' would fail to advise him when and where he would find his game. Incidentally the hunter resorts to drinking bear's grease to nourish his 'great man.'"[55] Perhaps it was for a similar reason that the Micmac customarily forced newborn infants to swallow bear or seal oil before eating anything else.[56]

If taboo was associated with fishing, we have little record of it; the only explicit evidence is a prohibition against the roasting of eels, which, if violated, would prevent the Indians from catching others. From this and from the fact that the Restigouche division of the Micmac wore the figure of a salmon as a totem around their neck, we may surmise that fish, too, shared in the sacred and symbolic world of the Indian.[57]

Control over these supernatural forces and communication with them were the principal functions of the shaman, who served in Micmac society as an intermediary between the spirit realm and the physical. The lives and destinies of the natives were profoundly affected by the ability of the shaman to supplicate, cajole, and otherwise manipulate the magical beings and powers. The seventeenth-century French, who typically labeled the shamans (or *buowin*) frauds and jugglers in league with the devil, were repeatedly amazed at the respect accorded them by the natives.[58] By working himself into a dreamlike state, the shaman would invoke the manitou of his animal helper and so predict future events.[59] He also healed by means of conjuring. The Micmac availed themselves of a rather large pharmacopia of roots and herbs and other plant parts, but when these failed they would summon the healing arts of the most noted shaman in the district. The illness was often diagnosed by the *buowin* as a failure on the patient's part to perform a prescribed ritual; hence an offended supernatural power had visited the offender with sickness. At such times the shaman functioned as a psychotherapist, diagnosing the illness and symbolically (at least) removing its immediate cause from the patient's body.[60]

It is important to understand that an ecosystem is holocoenotic in nature: there are no "walls" between the components of the system, for "the ecosystem reacts as a whole."[61] Such was the case in the Micmac ecosystem of precontact times, where the spiritual served as a link connecting man with all the various subsystems of the environment. Largely through the mediation of the shaman, these spiritual obligations and restrictions acted as a kind of control device to maintain the ecosystem in a well-balanced condition.[62] Under these circumstances the exploitation of game for subsistence appears to have been regulated by the hunter's respect for the continued welfare of his prey—both living and dead—as is evident from the numerous taboos associated with the proper disposal of animal remains. Violation of taboo desecrated the remains of the slain animal and offended its soul-spirit. The offended spirit would then retaliate in either of several ways, depending on the nature of the broken taboo: it could render the guilty hunter's (or the entire band's) means of hunting ineffective, or it could encourage its living fellows to remove themselves from the vicinity. In both cases the end result was the same—the hunt was rendered unsuccessful—and in both it was mediated by the same power—the spirit of the slain animal. Either of these catastrophes could usually be reversed through the magical arts of the shaman. In the Micmac cosmology, the overkill of wildlife would have been resented by the animal kingdom as an act comparable to genocide, and would have been resisted by means of the sanctions outlined above. The threat of retaliation thus had the effect of placing an upper limit on the number of animals slain, while the practical result was the conservation of wildlife.

The injection of European civilization into this balanced system initiated a series of chain reactions which, within a little over a century, resulted in the replacement of the aboriginal ecosystem by another. From at least the beginning of the sixteenth century, and perhaps well before that date, fishing fleets from England, France, and Portugal visited the Grand Banks off Newfoundland every spring for the cod, and hunted whale and walrus in the Gulf of St. Lawrence.[63] Year after year, while other, more flamboyant men were advancing the geopolitical ambitions of their emerging dynastic states as they searched for precious minerals or a passage to the Orient, these unassuming fishermen visited Canada's east coast and made the first effective European contact with the Indians there. For the natives' furs they bartered knives, beads, brass kettles, assorted ship fittings, and the like,[64] thus initiating the subversion and replacement of Micmac material culture by European technology. Far more important, the fishermen unwittingly infected the Indians with European diseases, against which the natives had no immunity. Commenting on what may be called the microbial phase of European conquest, John Witthoft has written:

> All of the microscopic parasites of humans, which had been collected together from all parts of the known world into Europe, were brought to these [American] shores, and new diseases stalked faster than man could walk into the interior of the continent. Typhoid, diphtheria, colds, influenza, measles, chicken pox, whooping cough, tuberculosis, yellow fever, scarlet fever, and other strep infections, gonorrhea, pox [syphilis], and smallpox were diseases that had never been in the New World before. They were new among populations which had no immunity to them.... Great epidemics and pandemics of these diseases are believed to have destroyed whole communities, depopulated whole regions, and vastly decreased the native population everywhere in the yet unexplored interior of the continent. The early pandemics are believed to have run their course prior to 1600 A.D.[65]

Disease did more than decimate the native population; it effectively prepared the way for subsequent phases of European contact by breaking native morale and, perhaps even more significantly, by cracking their spiritual edifice. It is reasonable to suggest that European disease rendered the Indian's (particularly the shaman's) ability to control and otherwise influence the supernatural realm dysfunctional—because his magic and other traditional cures were now ineffective—thereby causing the Indian to apostatize (in effect), which in turn subverted the "retaliation" principle of taboo and opened the way to a corruption of the Indian-land relationship under the influence of the fur trade.

Much of this microbial phase was of course protohistoric, although it continued well into and no doubt beyond the seventeenth century—the time period covered by the earliest French sources. Recognizing the limitations of tradition as it conveys historical fact, it may nevertheless be instructive to examine a myth concerning the Cross-bearing Micmac of the Miramichi River which, as recorded by Father Chrestien Le Clercq, seems to illustrate the demoralizing effect of disease. According to tradition, there was once a time when these Indians were gravely threatened by a severe sickness; as was their custom, they looked to the sun for help. In their extreme need a "beautiful" man, holding a cross, appeared before several of them in a dream. He instructed them to make similar crosses, for, as he told them, in this symbol lay their protection. For a time thereafter these Indians, who believed in dreams "even to the extent of superstition," were very religious and devoted in their veneration of this symbol. Later, however, they apostatized:

> Since the Gaspesian [Micmac] nation of the Cross-bearers has been almost wholly destroyed, as much by the war which they have waged with the Iroquois as by the maladies which have infected this land, and which, in three or four visitations, have caused the deaths of a very great number, these Indians have gradually relapsed from this first devotion of their ancestors. So true is it, that even the holiest and most religious practices, by a certain fatality attending human affairs, suffer always much alteration if they are not animated and conserved by the same spirit which gave them birth. In brief, when I went into their country to commence my mission, I found some persons who had preserved only the shadow of the customs of their ancestors.[66]

Their rituals had failed to save these Indians when threatened by European diseases and intergroup hostilities; hence their old religious practices were abandoned, no doubt because of their ineffectiveness.

Several other observers also commented on the new diseases that afflicted the Micmac. In precontact times, declared Denys, "they were not subject to diseases, and knew nothing of fevers."[67] By about 1700, however, Dièreville noted that the Micmac population was in sharp decline.[68] The Indians themselves frequently complained to Father Biard and other Frenchmen that, since contact with the French, they had been dying off in great numbers. "For they assert that, before this association and intercourse [with the French], all their countries were very populous, and they tell how one by one the different coasts, according as they have begun to traffic with us, have been more reduced by disease." The Indians accused the French of trying to poison them or charged that the food supplied by the French was somehow adulterated. Whatever the reasons for the catastrophe, warned Biard, the Indians were very angry about it and "upon the point of breaking with us, and making war upon us."[69]

To the Jesuit fathers, the solution to this sorry state of affairs lay in the civilizing power of the Gospel. To Biard, his mission was clear:

> For, if our Souriquois [Micmac] are few, they may become numerous; if they are savages, it is to domesticate and civilize them that we have come here; if they are rude, that is no reason that we should be idle; if they have until now profited little, it is no wonder, for it would be too much to expect fruit from this grafting, and to demand reason and maturity from a child.
>
> In conclusion, we hope in time to make them susceptible of receiving the doctrines of the faith and of the christian and catholic religion, and later, to penetrate further into the regions beyond.[70]

The message was simple and straightforward: the black-robes would enlighten the Indians by ridiculing their animism and related taboos, discrediting their shamans, and urging them to accept the Christian gospel. But to their chagrin the Indians proved stubborn in their ancient ways, no matter how unsuited to changing circumstances.[71]

Since the advent of European diseases and the consequent disillusionment with native spiritual beliefs and customs, some Indians appear to have repudiated their traditional world view altogether, while others clung desperately to what had become a moribund body of ritual. We would suppose that the Christian message was more readily accepted by the former, while the latter group, which included the shamans and those too old to change, would have fought bitterly against the missionary teachings.[72] But they resisted in vain for, with time, old people died and shamans whose magic was less potent than that of the missionaries were discredited.[73] The missionary was successful only to the degree that his power exceeded that of the shaman. The nonliterate Indian, for example, was awed by the magic of handwriting as a means of communication.[74] Even more significant was the fact that Christianity was the religion of the white man, who, with his superior technology and greater success at manipulating life to his advantage, was believed to have recourse to a greater power (manitou) than did the Indian. Material goods, such as the trading articles offered the Indians by the French, were believed by the native to have a spirit within, in accord with their belief that all animate and inanimate objects housed such a spirit or power.[75] Furthermore, there were degrees of power in such objects, which were determined and calibrated in the Indian mind by the degree of functionalism associated with a particular object.[76] For example, the Micmac believed that there was a spirit of his canoe, of his snowshoes, of his bow, and so on. It was for this reason that a man's material goods were either buried with him or burned, so that their spirits would accompany his to the spirit world, where he would have need of them. Just as he had hunted game in this physical world, so his spirit would again hunt the game spirits with the spirits of his weapons in the land of the dead.[77] Denys described an incident which emphasized the fact that even European trading goods had spirits, when he related how the brass kettle was known to have lost its spirit (or died) when it no longer rang when tapped.[78] Thus Christianity, which to the Indians was the ritual harnessing all of this power, was a potent force among them. Nevertheless, the priests who worked among the Indians frequently complained of their relapsing into paganism, largely because the Micmac came to associate Christianity and civilization in general with their numerous misfortunes, together with the fact that they never clearly understood the Christian message anyway, but always saw it in terms of their own cosmology.[79]

As all religious systems reflect their cultural milieux, so did seventeenth-century Christianity. Polygamy was condemned by the French missionaries as immoral, the consultation of shamans was discouraged, the custom of interring material goods was criticized, eat-all feasts were denounced as gluttonous and shortsighted, and the Indians were disabused of many of their so-called superstitions (taboos).[80] The priests attacked the Micmac culture with a marvelous fervor and some success.[81] Although they could not have appreciated it, they were aided in this endeavor by an obsolescent system of taboo and spiritual awareness; Christianity merely delivered the coup de grace.

The result of this Christian onslaught on a decaying Micmac cosmology was, of course, the despiritualization of the material world. Commenting on the process of despiritualization, Denys (who was a spectator to this transformation in the mid-seventeenth century) remarked that it was accomplished with "much difficulty"; for some of the Indians it was achieved by religious means, while others were influenced by the French customs, but nearly all were affected "by the need for the things which come from us, the use of which has become to them an indispensable necessity. They have abandoned all their own utensils, whether because of the trouble they had as well to make as to use them, or because of the facility of obtaining from us, in exchange for skins which cost them almost nothing, the things which seemed to them invaluable, not so much for their novelty as for the convenience they derived therefrom."[82]

In the early years of the fur trade, before the establishment of permanent posts among the natives, trading was done with the coastwise fishermen from May to early fall.[83] In return for skins of beaver, otter, marten, moose, and other furbearers, the Indians received a variety of fairly cheap commodities, principally tobacco, liquor, powder and shot (in later years), biscuit, peas, beans, flour, assorted clothing, wampum, kettles, and hunting tools.[84] The success of this trade in economic terms must be attributed to pressure exerted on a relatively simple society by a complex civilization and, perhaps even more importantly, by the tremendous pull of this simple social organization on the resources of Europe.[85] To the Micmac, who like other Indians measured the worth of a tool or object by the ease of its construction and use, the technology of Europe became indispensable. But as has already been shown, this was not simply an economic issue for the Indian; the Indian was more than just "economically seduced" by the

European's trading goods.[86] One must also consider the metaphysical implications of Indian acceptance of the European material culture.

European technology of the sixteenth and seventeenth centuries was largely incompatible with the spiritual beliefs of the eastern woodland Indians, despite the observation made above that the Micmacs readily invested trading goods with spiritual power akin to that possessed by their own implements. As Denys pointed out, the trade goods which the Micmac so eagerly accepted were accompanied by Christian religious teachings and French custom, both of which gave definition to these alien objects. In accepting the European material culture, the natives were impelled to accept the European abstract culture, especially religion, and so, in effect, their own spiritual beliefs were subverted as they abandoned their implements for those of the white man. Native religion lost not only its practical effectiveness, in part owing to the replacement of the traditional magical and animistic view of nature by the exploitive European view, but it was no longer necessary as a source of definition and theoretical support for the new Europe-derived material culture. Western technology made more "sense" if it was accompanied by Western religion.

Under these circumstances in the early contact period, the Micmac's role within his ecosystem changed radically. No longer was he the sensitive fellow-member of a symbolic world; under pressure from disease, European trade, and Christianity, he had apostatized—he had repudiated his role within the ecosystem. Former attitudes were replaced by a kind of mongrel outlook which combined some native traditions and beliefs with a European rationale and motivation. Our concern here is less to document this transformation than to assess its impact on the Indian-land relationship. In these terms, then, what effect did the trade have on the Micmac ecosystem?

The most obvious change was the unrestrained slaughter of certain game. Lured by European commodities, equipped with European technology, urged by European traders,[87] deprived of a sense of responsibility and accountability for the land, and no longer inhibited by taboo, the Micmac began to overkill systematically those very wildlife which had now become so profitable and even indispensable to his new way of life. The pathos of this transformation of attitude and behavior is illustrated by an incident recorded by Le Clercq. The Indians, who still believed that the beaver had "sense" and formed a "separate nation," maintained that they "would cease to make war upon these animals if these would speak, howsoever little, in order that they might learn whether the Beavers are among their friends or their enemies."[88] Unfortunately for the beaver, they never communicated their friendliness. The natural world of the Indian was becoming inarticulate.

It is interesting to note that Dièreville, who observed the Micmac culture at the beginning of the eighteenth century, was the only witness to record the native superstition which compelled them to tear out the eyes of all slain animals.

Somehow, perhaps by some sort of symbolic transference, the spirits of surviving animals of the same species were thereby blinded to the irreverent treatment accorded the victim; otherwise, through the mediation of the outraged spirits, the living would no longer have allowed themselves to be taken by the Indians.[89] The failure of the earlier writers to mention this particular superstition suggests that it was of fairly recent origin, a result of the overexploitation of game for the trade. To the Micmac mind, haunted by memories of a former time, the practice may have been intended to hide his guilt and insure his continued success.

Together with this depletion of wildlife went a reduction of dependency on the resources of the local ecosystem. The use of improved hunting equipment, such as fishing line and hooks, axes, knives, muskets, and iron-tipped arrows, spears, and harpoons,[90] exerted heavier pressure on the resources of the area, while the availability of French foodstuffs shifted the position of the Micmac in the trophic system, somewhat reducing his dependency on local food sources as it placed him partly outside of the system. To be sure, a decreasing native population relieved this pressure to a degree, but, according to evidence cited above, not enough to prevent the abuse of the land.

Other less obvious results of the fur trade were the increased incidence of feuding and the modification of the Micmac settlement patterns to meet the demands of the trade. Liquor, in particular brandy, was a favorite item of the trade—one for which the Indians "would go a long way."[91] Its effects were devastating. Both Jean Saint-Vallier (François Laval's successor as bishop of Quebec) and Biard blamed liquor as a cause for the increased death rate of the natives. Moreover, it was observed that drunkenness resulted in social disintegration as the Indians became debauched and violent among themselves, and, at times, spilled over into the French community which they would rob, ravage, and burn. Drunkenness also provided a legitimate excuse to commit crimes, such as murdering their enemies, for which they would otherwise be held accountable.[92]

European contact should thus be viewed as a trigger factor, that is, something which was not present in the Micmac ecosystem before and which initiated a concatenation of reactions leading to the replacement of the aboriginal ecosystem by another.[93] European disease, Christianity, and the fur trade with its accompanying technology—the three often intermeshed—were responsible for the corruption of the Indian-land relationship, in which the native had merged sympathetically with his environment. By a lockstep process European disease rendered the Indian's control over the supernatural and spiritual realm inoperative, and the disillusioned Micmac apostatized, debilitating taboo and preparing the way for the destruction of wildlife which was soon to occur under the stimulation of the fur trade. For those who believed in it, Christianity furnished a new, dualistic world view, which placed man above nature, as well as spiritual support for the fur trade, and as a result the Micmac became dependent on the European marketplace both spiritually and economically. Within his ecosystem the Indian changed from conservator to exploiter. All of this resulted in the intense exploitation of some game animals and the virtual extermination of others. Unfortunately for the Indian and the land, this grim tale was to be repeated many times along the moving Indian-white frontier. Life for the Micmac had indeed become more convenient, but convenience cost dearly in much material and abstract culture loss or modification.

The historiography of Indian-white relations is rendered more comprehensible when the Indian and the land are considered together: "So intimately is all of Indian life tied up with the land and its utilization that to think of Indians is to think of land. The two are inseparable."[94] American Indian history can be seen, then, as a type of environmental history, and perhaps it is from this perspective that the early period of Indian-white relations can best be understood.

Notes

1. Reuben Gold Thwaites, ed., *The Jesuit Relations and Allied Documents: Travels and Explorations of the Jesuit Missionaries in New France, 1610-1791* (New York, 1959 [orig. publ. Cleveland, Ohio, 1896-1901]), VIII, 57.

2. Baron Lahontan, *New Voyages to North-America ... An Account of the Several Nations of that vast Continent ...*, ed. Reuben Gold Thwaites (Chicago, 1905), I, 82.

3. Thwaites, ed., *Jesuit Relations,* V, 25; VI, 297-299; VIII, 57; XL, 151; LXVIII, 47, 109-111; LXIX, 95, 99-113.

4. *Ibid.,* VIII, 41.

5. Nicolas Denys, *The Description and Natural History of the Coasts of North America (Acadia),* ed. and trans. William F. Ganong, II (Toronto, 1908), I, 187, 199, 209, 219-220, hereafter cited as Denys, *Description of North America.*

6. *Ibid.,* 432, 450.

7. Peter Farb, *Man's Rise to Civilization as Shown by the Indians of North America from Primeval Times to the Coming of the Industrial State* (New York, 1968), 82-83.

8. See Wilson D. Wallis and Ruth Sawtell Wallis, *The Micmac Indians of Eastern Canada* (Minneapolis, Minn., 1955), for a thorough ethnographic study of the Micmac. Jacques and Maryvonne Crevel, *Honguedo ou l'Histoire des Premiers Gaspesiens* (Quebec, 1970), give a fairly good general history of the Micmac during the 17th century, together with a description of the fishing industry.

9. Julian H. Steward, "The Concept and Method of Cultural Ecology," in his *Theory of Culture Change: The Methodology of Multilinear Evolution* (Urbana, Ill., 1955), 30-42, and Andrew P. Vayda and Roy A. Rappaport, "Ecology, Cultural and Noncultural," in James A. Clifton, ed., *Introduction to Cultural Anthropology: Essays in the Scope and Methods of the Science of Man* (Boston, 1968), 494.

10. W. D. Billings, *Plants, Man, and the Ecosystem,* 2d ed. (Belmont, Calif., 1970), 4.

11. Roy A. Rappaport, *Pigs for the Ancestors: Ritual in the Ecology of a New Guinea People* (New Haven, Conn., 1968).

12. Among the few who have are William Christie MacLeod, "Conservation Among Primitive Hunting Peoples," *Scientific Monthly,* XLIII (1936), 562-566, and Alfred Goldsworthy Bailey in his little-known book, *The Conflict of European and Eastern Algonkian Cultures, 1504-1700,* 2d ed. (Toronto, 1969).

13. Wilbur R. Jacobs, *Dispossessing the American Indian: Indians and Whites on the Colonial Frontier* (New York, 1972), 25.

14. Billings, *Plants, Man, Ecosystem,* 37-38.

15. Sieur de Dièreville, *Relation of the Voyage to Port Royal in Acadia or New France,* trans. Mrs. Clarence Webster and ed. John Clarence Webster (Toronto, 1933), 184, hereafter cited as Dièreville, *Voyage to Port Royal.* According to the editor, 216, the Malecites later replaced the Micmacs living along the St. John, the latter withdrawing to Nova Scotia. See also Diamond Jenness, *The Indians of Canada,* 3d ed. (Ottawa, 1955), 267.

16. See Rappaport, *Pigs for the Ancestors,* 225-226. If the present article were intended as a more rigorous analysis of the Micmac ecosystem, we would report on the topography of this region, on the soil types, the hydrological characteristics, the climate, the influence of the ocean, and the effects of fires caused by lightning. But since neither the Micmac nor the first Europeans had any appreciable effect on these physical variables—except perhaps that of water relations—we shall pass over the physical environment and go on to the biological. Suffice it to say that the water of numerous rivers and streams was regulated in its flow by beaver dams throughout much of this region, and Indian beaver hunting and trapping certainly upset this control.

17. For a thorough discussion of Micmac plant and animal use see Frank G. Speck and Ralph W. Dexter, "Utilization of Animals and Plants by the Micmac Indians of New Brunswick," *Journal of the Washington Academy of Sciences,* XLI (1951), 250-259.

18. Father Chrestien Le Clercq, *New Relation of Gaspesia, with the Customs and Religion of the Gaspesian Indians,* ed. and trans. William F. Ganong (Toronto, 1910), 212-213, hereafter cited as Le Clercq, *Relation of Gaspesia.* Thwaites, ed., *Jesuit Relations,* III, 77; Marc Lescarbot, *The History of New France,* trans. W. L. Grant (Toronto, 1907), III, 93, 194-195, hereafter cited as Lescarbot, *History of New France.* Lescarbot asserts that the Micmac definitely grew tobacco, most likely the so-called wild tobacco (*Nicotiana rustica*): *ibid.,* 252-253.

19. Lescarbot, *History of New France,* II, 323-325; III, 158.

20. Thwaites, ed., *Jesuit Relations,* III, 77-83.

21. *Ibid.*; Denys, *Description of North America,* II, 403; Lescarbot, *History of New France,* III, 80; Le Clercq, *Relation of Gaspesia,* 88-89, 93; Dièreville, *Voyage to Port Royal,* 146.

22. Lescarbot, *History of New France,* III, 219-220, and Thwaites, ed., *Jesuit Relations,* III, 77-79.

23. Lescarbot, *History of New France,* III, 222-224. See Horace T. Martin, *Castorologia, or the History and Traditions of the Canadian Beaver* (Montreal, 1892), for a good treatise on the beaver.

24. Le Clercq, *Relation of Gaspesia,* 276-280; Dièreville, *Voyage to Port Royal,* 133-134; Denys, *Description of North America,* II, 429-433; Lescarbot, *History of New France,* III, 222-224.

25. Lescarbot, *History of New France,* III, 220-222; Denys, *Description of North America,* II, 426-429; Le Clercq, *Relation of Gaspesia,* 274-276. Speck and Dexter place caribou before moose in order of importance, but they cite no evidence for such ranking. Speck and Dexter, "Utilization of Animals and Plants by Micmacs," *Jour. Wash. Acad. Sci.,* XLI (1951), 255.

26. Le Clercq, *Relation of Gaspesia,* 118-119.

27. *Ibid.,* 93-94; Denys, *Description of North America,* II, 412; Lescarbot, *History of New France,* III, 133; Speck and Dexter, "Utilization of Animals and Plants by Micmacs," *Jour. Wash. Acad. Sci.,* XLI (1951), 255.

28. Speck and Dexter, "Utilization of Animals and Plants by Micmacs," *Jour. Wash. Acad. Sci.,* XLI (1951), 255.

29. Le Clercq, *Relation of Gaspesia,* 116, 119; Dièreville, *Voyage to Port Royal,* 131; Thwaites, ed., *Jesuit Relations,* III, 107-109.

30. Denys, *Description of North America,* II, 433-434.

31. Thwaites, ed., *Jesuit Relations,* III, 79.

32. *Ibid.,* 81, and Speck and Dexter, "Utilization of Animals and Plants by Micmacs," *Jour. Wash. Acad. Sci.,* XLI (1951), 251-254.

33. Lescarbot, *History of New France,* III, 236-237, and Denys, *Description of North America,* II, 436-437.

34. Le Clercq, *Relation of Gaspesia,* 92, 137; Lescarbot, *History of New France,* III, 230-231; Denys, *Description of North America,* II, 435-436.

35. Thwaites, ed., *Jesuit Relations,* III, 83.

36. *Ibid.*

37. Le Clercq, *Relation of Gaspesia,* 109-110, 283, and Denys, *Description of North America,* II, 389, 434.

38. Frank G. Speck, "Aboriginal Conservators," *Audubon Magazine,* XL (1938), 260.

39. Denys, *Description of North America,* II, 402-403.

40. *Ibid.,* 426.

41. Speck, "Aboriginal Conservators," *Audubon Magazine,* XL (1938), 260. Italics in original.

42. Rappaport, *Pigs for the Ancestors,* 237-238, and Vayda and Rappaport, "Ecology, Cultural and Noncultural," in Clifton, ed., *Cultural Anthropology,* 491.

43. See, for example, the writings of Speck, esp. "Aboriginal Conservators," *Audubon Magazine,* XL (1938), 258-261; John Witthoft, "The American Indian as Hunter," *Pennsylvania Game News,* XXIX (Feb.-Apr. 1953); George S. Snyderman, "Concepts

of Land Ownership among the Iroquois and their Neighbors," *Bureau of American Ethnology Bulletin 149*, ed. William N. Fenton (Washington, D. C., 1951), 15-34. Robert F. Heizer, "Primitive Man as an Ecological Factor," Kroeber Anthropological Society, *Papers*, XIII (1955), 1-31. See also William A. Ritchie, "The Indian and His Environment," *Conservationist* (Dec.-Jan. 1955-1956), 23-27; Gordon Day, "The Indian as an Ecological Factor in the Northeastern Forest," *Ecology*, XXIV (1953), 329-346; MacLeod, "Conservation," *Scientific Monthly*, XLIII (1936), 562-566.

44. Witthoft, "American Indian," *Pa. Game News* (Mar. 1953), 17.

45. Murray Wax, "Religion and Magic," in Clifton, ed., *Cultural Anthropology*, 235.

46. See William Jones, "The Algonkin Manitou," *Journal of American Folk-Lore*, XVIII (1905), 183-190, and Frederick Johnson, "Notes on Micmac Shamanism," *Primitive Man*, XVI (1943), 58-59.

47. See Stansbury Hagar, "Micmac Magic and Medicine," *Jour. Am. Folk-Lore*, IX (1896), 170-177, and Johnson, "Shamanism," *Primitive Man*, XVI (1943), 54, 56-57, who report that such beliefs in the supernatural and spiritual survive even in modern times, although in suppressed and attenuated form. Le Clercq, *Relation of Gaspesia*, 187, 209, 212-214, and Denys, *Description of North America*, II, 117, 442.

48. Witthoft, "American Indian," *Pa. Game News* (Feb. 1953), 16.

49. Dièreville, *Voyage to Port Royal*, 139, and Le Clercq, *Relation of Gaspesia*, 225-229, 276-277.

50. Le Clercq, *Relation of Gaspesia*, 225-229.

51. *Ibid.*, 226.

52. *Ibid.*, 227-229.

53. Witthoft, "American Indian," *Pa. Game News* (Mar. 1953), 16-22; A. Irving Hallowell, "Bear Ceremonialism in the Northern Hemisphere," *American Anthropologist*, N.S., XXVIII (1926), 1-175.

54. Le Clercq, *Relation of Gaspesia*, 227.

55. Frank G. Speck, "Mistassini Hunting Territories in the Labrador Peninsula," *Am. Anthropologist*, XXV (1923), 464. Johnson, "Shamanism," *Primitive Man*, XVI (1943), 70-72, distinguishes between the Montagnais, Wabanaki, and Micmac ideas of the "soul."

56. Le Clercq, *Relation of Gaspesia*, 88-89; Dièreville, *Voyage to Port Royal*, 146; Lescarbot, *History of New France*, III, 80.

57. Denys, *Description of North America*, II, 430, 442, and Le Clercq, *Relation of Gaspesia*, 192-193.

58. Denys, *Description of North America*, II, 417-418, and Le Clercq, *Relation of Gaspesia*, 215-218.

59. Thwaites, ed., *Jesuit Relations*, II, 75; Le Clercq, *Relation of Gaspesia*, 215-216; George H. Daugherty, Jr., "Reflections of Environment in North American Indian Literature" (Ph.D. diss., University of Chicago, 1925), 31; Johnson, "Shamanism," *Primitive Man*, XVI (1943), 71-72.

60. Le Clercq, *Relation of Gaspesia,* 215-218, 296-299; Denys, *Description of North America,* II, 415, 417-418; Hagar, "Micmac Magic," *Jour. Am. Folk-Lore,* IX (1896), 170-177. Denys, *Description of North America,* II, 418, observed that most of these ailments were (what we would call today) psychosomatic in origin.

61. Billings, *Plants, Man, Ecosystem,* 36.

62. Thwaites, ed., *Jesuit Relations,* II, 75.

63. H. P. Biggar, *The Early Trading Companies of New France: A Contribution to the History of Commerce and Discovery in North America* (New York, 1965 [orig. publ. Toronto, 1901]), 18-37.

64. John Witthoft, "Archaeology as a Key to the Colonial Fur Trade," *Minnesota History,* XL (1966), 204-205.

65. John Witthoft, *Indian Prehistory of Pennsylvania* (Harrisburg, Pa., 1965), 26-29.

66. Le Clercq, *Relation of Gaspesia,* 146-152. The Recollet fathers, especially Father Emanuel Jumeau, were able to cause a renaissance of the old traditional religion by encouraging these people to look to the cross once more for their salvation, although, of course, this time it was the Christian cross. We should bear in mind that the cross was an art motif common among non-Christian people, and of independent origin from that of the Christian cross. Whether the cross mentioned in this particular tradition was of Christian or aboriginal origin should make little difference, for the story still serves to illustrate the process of apostatization.

67. Denys, *Description of North America,* II, 415. Estimates of the aboriginal population of North America at the time of European contact are constantly being revised upward. Henry F. Dobyns, "Estimating Aboriginal American Population: An Appraisal of Techniques with a New Hemispheric Estimate," *Current Anthropology,* VII (1966), 395-416, has recently placed the figure at a controversial and fantastically high total of 9,800,000 natives.

68. Dièreville, *Voyage to Port Royal,* 116. See Thwaites, ed., *Jesuit Relations,* I, 177-179.

69. Thwaites, ed., *Jesuit Relations,* III, 105-107.

70. *Ibid.,* I, 183.

71. *Ibid.,* II, 75-77; III, 123; and Le Clercq, *Relation of Gaspesia,* 193, 220, 224-225, 227, 239, 253. See also Denys, *Description of North America,* II, 117, 430, 442.

72. Notice that when a custom in any society becomes a mere formality and loses its practical meaning, it is easily discarded when challenged by detractors, who may or may not replace it with something more meaningful. See Le Clercq, *Relation of Gaspesia,* 206, 227, and Lescarbot, *History of New France,* III, 94-95.

73. Jean Baptiste de la Croix Chevrières de Saint-Vallier, *Estat Présent de l'Eglise et de la Colonie Françoise dans la Nouvelle France, par M. l'Evêque de Québec* (Paris, 1688), 36-37, and Thwaites, ed., *Jesuit Relations,* II, 75-77. See Le Clercq, *Relation of Gaspesia,* 220-221, where he speaks of converting a noted shaman to Christianity. André Vachon, "L'Eau-de-Vie dans la Société Indienne," Canadian Historical Association, *Report of the Annual Meeting* (1960), 22-32, has observed that the

priest replaced the shaman and sorcerer in Indian society by virtue of his superior powers. By discrediting his Indian counterparts (and rivals), the priest became the shaman-sorcerer (i.e., a source of both good and evil power).

74. Lescarbot, *History of New France,* III, 128, and Le Clercq, *Relation of Gaspesia,* 133-135.

75. Le Clercq, *Relation of Gaspesia,* 209, 213-214, and Bailey, *Conflict of Cultures,* 47.

76. Denys, *Description of North America,* II, 439.

77. Le Clercq, *Relation of Gaspesia,* 187, 209, 212-214, 238-239, 303; Lescarbot, *History of New France,* III, 279, 285; Thwaites, ed., *Jesuit Relations,* I, 169; Denys, *Description of North America,* II, 437-439; Dièreville, *Voyage to Port Royal,* 161.

78. Denys, *Description of North America,* II, 439-441.

79. Le Clercq, *Relation of Gaspesia,* 125, 193, and Thwaites, ed., *Jesuit Relations,* I, 165. See *ibid.,* II, 89, where baptism was understood by the Micmac (of Port Royal, at least) "as a sort of sacred pledge of friendship and alliance with the French."

80. Lescarbot, *History of New France,* III, 53-54; Denys, *Description of North America,* II, 117, 430, 442; Le Clercq, *Relation of Gaspesia,* 116; Dièreville, *Voyage to Port Royal,* 161; Thwaites, ed., *Jesuit Relations,* III, 131-135. See *ibid.,* II, 75-77, where the shamans complain of having lost much of their power since the coming of the French.

81. Le Clercq observed that since the introduction of Christianity and especially baptism the manitou had not afflicted them to the degree that he did formerly. See Le Clercq, *Relation of Gaspesia,* 225. See also *ibid.,* 229-233, where cases are recorded of native men and women who seemed to feel a divine call and ordination, representing themselves as priests among their fellows.

82. Denys, *Description of North America,* II, 440-441.

83. Samuel de Champlain, *The Voyages of the Sieur de Champlain of Saintoge ...* in H. P. Biggar, ed. and trans., *The Works of Samuel de Champlain,* I (Toronto, 1922), *passim,* and Thwaites, ed., *Jesuit Relations,* III, 81.

84. Lescarbot, *History of New France,* II, 281-282, 323-324; III, 158, 168, 250; Thwaites, ed., *Jesuit Relations,* III, 75-77; Le Clercq, *Relation of Gaspesia,* 93-94, 109; Dièreville, *Voyage to Port Royal,* 132-133, 139-141.

85. Harold A. Innis, *The Fur Trade in Canada: An Introduction to Canadian Economic History,* rev. ed. (Toronto, 1956), 15-17.

86. Farb, *Man's Rise to Civilization,* 82-83.

87. See Thwaites, ed., *Jesuit Relations,* I, 175-177, and Denys, *Description of North America,* II, 439, for mention of the French lust for furs.

88. Le Clercq, *Relation of Gaspesia,* 276-277. See also Dièreville, *Voyage to Port Royal,* 139.

89. Dièreville, *Voyage to Port Royal,* 161.

90. Lescarbot, *History of New France,* III, 191-192, and Denys, *Description of North America,* II, 399, 442-443.

91. Dièreville, *Voyage to Port Royal,* 174, and Denys, *Description of North America,* II, 172, 443-452. If we are to believe Craig MacAndrew and Robert B. Edgerton, *Drunken Comportment: A Social Explanation* (Chicago, 1969), III, the Micmac encountered by Jacques Cartier along the shores of Chaleur Bay in 1534 were the first historically documented North American tribe to receive European liquor.

92. Saint-Vallier, *Estat Présent,* 36-37, 42; Thwaites, ed., *Jesuit Relations,* III, 105-109; Denys, *Description of North America,* II, 443-452; Dièreville, *Voyage to Port Royal,* 166; Le Clercq, *Relation of Gaspesia,* 244-245, 254-257. The subject of North American Indian drinking patterns and problems has been the topic of much debate from the 17th century to the present. The best current scholarship on the subject, which has by no means been exhausted, is contained in MacAndrew and Edgerton, *Drunken Comportment;* Vachon, "L'Eau-de-Vie," Can. Hist. Assn., *Report* (1960), 22-32; Nancy Oestreich Lurie, "The World's Oldest On-Going Protest Demonstration: North American Indian Drinking Patterns," *Pacific Historical Review,* XL (1971), 311-332.

93. Billings, *Plants, Man, Ecosystem,* 37-38.

94. See John Collier's report on Indian affairs, 1938, in the *Annual Report of the Secretary of the Interior* (Washington, D. C., 1938), 209-211, as quoted by Wilcomb Washburn, ed., *The Indian and the White Man* (Garden City, N. Y., 1964), 394.

CONCLUSION

Cornelius J. Jaenan

The French established contact with the Amerindians on a casual basis through the Newfoundland fisheries as early as the fifteenth century, and probably earlier. In the sixteenth century, voyages of so-called discovery and abortive colonization schemes further acquainted the French with the aborigines whom the Spaniards and Portuguese were in the process of subjugating and exploiting. Swarthy American natives were taken as curios of the New World to be displayed in various public spectacles in Western Europe, raising disquieting theological and scientific questions.

In general, the French were less involved than their neighbours in great controversies about the origins of the American aborigines, their nature, and the possible sources of their civilizations. Indeed, Frenchmen did not contact the same highly developed Amerindian civilizations as did the Spaniards in Central and South America. The French judged the Amerindians in terms of their religious beliefs and their degree of civility. Just as there was no doubt that the

From *Friend and Foe: Aspects of French-Amerindian Cultural Contact in the Sixteenth and Seventeenth Centuries* (Toronto: McClelland and Stewart, 1976), 190-197. Reprinted by permission of the author.

tribes were heathen, so there was no doubt that, in terms of the classical distinction between Greeks and barbarians, they were also barbarians. These heathen barbarians were rough and unpolished, to be sure, but views differed as to whether they were men in savage and degenerate form, the prototype of the wild man, or whether they were primitive men without benefit of religion and social institutions. Montaigne observed that "everyone calls barbarian what is his own usage." In whatever way Amerindians were viewed, the consensus was definitely that they were unpolished *sauvages*, and therefore presented a challenge to Frenchmen to civilize them and impart to them the religion, arts and culture of Europe's leading civilization.

One of the early reactions was to equate the Amerindian societies with the lost Paradise of their literary and philosophical tradition. The liberty, equality and fraternity which travellers and missionaries, at least those who tended to be critical of their own society, reported in America provided a very powerful criticism of contemporary France. The Amerindians were apparently proof that Christian Europe did not have a monopoly on goodness and rationality. Those who looked for noble savages or native utopias as a means to criticize and castigate contemporary French manners, morals and government were well served. These precursors of the eighteenth-century deists and rationalists were, however, a minority whose influence must not be exaggerated.

The French discovery of America brought together many threads to form a twisted skein of perceptions of the New World and its peoples. Theories of lost continents and prehistoric migrations, mingled with myths of concurrent creations and cataclysmic displacements of populations, these in turn being overlaid by tales of fabled isles and monstrous lands given over to the devil, fed the imaginative and beckoned the venturesome. Religious revivalism, pious mysticism and eschatological undercurrents in France raised hopes of ushering in the millenial age, of building the spiritual church and New Jerusalem in the New World. From the excitement of early contact in the sixteenth and seventeenth centuries—for the fishermen never revealed their earlier experiences or their fishing grounds—and the contradictory reports of explorers and exploiters, there emerged a dominant French view of the world and of themselves which stood in sharp contrast to the views of the Amerindians.

Although there was a strain of romantic primitivism, the dominant French view of man was that he was a changer and overseer of nature: a husbandman, a builder, an inventor, a domesticator, a civilizer. As a steward of God in his relationship to other forms of life his normal and divinely ordained role was to change and control by his arts and his technology. Frenchmen regarded their intervention in nature as purposive. The Amerindians, on the other hand, saw themselves as having a contractual or symbiotic relationship with the forces of nature. The contractual relationships of the French were to various authorities—to God, to the king, to the seigneur, to the religious superior, to the monopolist. Amerindians saw themselves and their tribal society as a product of nature and they acknowledged this in the names they assigned their tribes and bands. The Amerindians saw themselves as intimately dependent on nature, while the French saw themselves as superior to nature, as destined to dominate it and to bend its forces to their own objectives and aspirations. Progress in French eyes consisted of manipulating, controlling and subordinating nature and society more and more to man's initiative and enterprise. Insofar as religion and nature were intimately related, Amerindian society was more theocentric than was French society in the seventeenth century.

All in all, the French experience differed markedly from the Spanish or English encounters in day-to-day relations with the aborigines. The conceptual frameworks of all Europeans closely resembled each other, whether they classified themselves as Latins or Anglo-Saxons, as Catholics or Protestants. When the contact with Amerindians did not involve displacing the native peoples or extensive European immigration, which was the French experience as contrasted to the English and Spanish experiences, relations remained friendly. Cooperation and intercourse resulted in a certain degree of interdependence and created an impression of successful accommodation and acculturation. Such impressions were superficial observations neglecting the deeper evidences of social disorganization. The fact that the British, who had such a poor reputation in cultural contact in the Anglo-American colonies, assumed and appropriated the apparently friendly French relationship with the tribesmen after the conquest of Canada and the American Revolution suggests the need for an environmental approach to the question of culture clash. The French contact experience with the sedentary agricultural Iroquoian tribes had been less amicable than had their contact with nomadic Algonkian tribes. In the seventeenth century, the Amerindians seem to have stereotyped the Englishman as a farmer or town-dweller whose activities gradually drove the original agriculturalists deeper into the hinterland, whereas the stereotype of the Frenchman was a trader or soldier laden with baubles and brandy who asked only for furs and hospitality.

These comparatively more amicable relations between Frenchmen and Amerindians resulted in more credence being given in France to the good qualities of native life. The view that they were filthy, depraved barbarians never became a dominant and obsessive view with the French, although it was always present as an undercurrent and occasionally surfaced as in the reaction to the so-called Iroquois scourge. When goodness and virtue were accepted as possible in aboriginal societies a number of purposes might be served: those who sought the lost Paradise found in America a hope of restoring it; those who deplored the evils of sophisticated civilization found in America the noble savages; those who chafed at political oppression and bureaucratic corruption saw in America a land of freedom and opportunity; those who wearied of religious turpitude and theological strife caught a vision of the New Israel in the New World and the imminent end of the world. But those who lived and worked in

New France came to believe more in the New World of their own experience than in the America invented by the metropolitan French.

Frenchmen, as a result of contact with primitive peoples, were more convinced that they stood at the pinnacle of civilization. Their society, despite some defects such as religious wars, famines, rural unrest and unemployment, and bureaucratic corruption, was an orderly, rational and Christian one, which all peoples everywhere ought to adopt and emulate if they wished to progress and elevate themselves. Although the French did not discriminate against the Amerindians on strictly racial grounds, they did by their somatic norm image consider them inferior and infantile. Native barbarism and cruelty, which must be seen in the Amerindian religious and social context to be understood, was an important factor in the literature on captivity and the creation of a stereotype of cruel savages. This literary tradition and popular stereotype were largely responsible for later discrimination against the aboriginal peoples in both Canada and the United States.

The Amerindians, for their part, had their own somatic norm image in which Frenchmen were regarded as ugly, effeminate, weak, disorganized, improvident, excitable, domineering, and quite inconsistent in applying their ideals to their everyday living. The French regarded Amerindian societies as devoid of spirituality and basic religious concepts, but it turned out that native society was as religiously oriented as European society. Indeed, many of the aspects of Amerindian life which the French were slow to comprehend—torture of captives, significance of dreams, resistance to conversion—were spiritually based. In the final analysis, it was sometimes French Catholic society that emerged as this-worldly, materialistic and superstitious. True conversion for the Amerindians meant a renunciation of their culture and a loss of their identity, a fact which the French missionaries and civil officials, without realizing the full implications of social disorganization, found quite normal because the French and Catholic qualities of their own civilization were rarely dissociated or conceived as separable.

The fact that the continent was not an empty wilderness but a populated expanse required some accommodation with its inhabitants, and some state policy of occupation. The French response to this challenge came at two levels—the spiritual and the temporal. First, the Amerindians would have to be evangelized and take their place with the Christians of France. Secondly and concurrently, they would have to be assimilated into French society by a process of Frenchification and civilization. As conversion soon proved to be a very disruptive experience in the native communities, religious conversion and cultural assimilation became more closely entwined. Unless the whole community converted and the whole apparatus of French institutions and life-style were adopted, divisions became acrimonious, reversion was likely, and social disorganization always ensued.

In their contacts the French came to sense, although they never fully comprehended or openly acknowledged, that Amerindian societies were well-integrated units. Education, for example, was fully integrated into every-day living. Therefore, French attempts to introduce formal schooling as a means of civilizing and converting the natives cut across traditional belief systems, values, institutional forms and band aspirations. No two societies could have dif-fered more in their conceptual frameworks than did the European and Amerindian. Religion also permeated all aspects of native life, probably to a greater extent than religion permeated French life because the French, unlike the Amerindians, did not always allow their religious convictions to interfere with their economic mores, their warfare, or their personal behaviour. Because the Amerindians sought to live in tune with nature and their religious perceptions, Catholicism as a new religion could only be a disruptive innovation under-mining their spiritual concepts as well as their entire way of life, their value systems, and their moral assumptions.

The French considered the Algonkian nomadic peoples as idlers and vagabonds because they were not sedentary agriculturalists or village craftsmen; conversely, the natives occasionally were only too well informed about poverty and lower-class conditions in France. Amerindian concepts of communal prop-erty, hunting territories and kinship responsibilities found no precise equivalents in French views of property rights, legal jurisdictions, contractual agreements, monopolies and sovereignty. There was no common theoretical ground for ac-commodation. They did not clash, however, because they remained largely isolated and separated from each other. The French towns and seigneuries formed a riparian colony, whereas the majority of the Amerindians, except a small number of domiciled converts resettled on reservations, inhabited the hinterlands. Because of this physical separation, there were few if any con-frontations or contests about property rights or civil jurisdiction.

The French in their contacts with the natives admired their ability to grap-ple with problems in a resourceful manner and often abandoned their abstract speculation to adopt native ways. This utilitarianism, born of a long experi-ence in North America, did not conform to French concepts of artisanal organization, seigneurial subservience, or military logistics, but it gradually became one of the acquired qualities that distinguished a Canadian *habitant* from a metropolitan Frenchman. The superiority of European technology had profound consequences for the Amerindians. As their hunting and warfare be-came more effective and their artifacts became more sophisticated, their demands grew and correspondingly their dependence on the Europeans increased both for supplies and repairs. Inter-dependence developed between native hunter and French trader, between native canoeman and French soldier, between native cat-echist and French missionary.

The French contact experience does suggest that the behavioural patterns routinized and institutionalized among the aborigines were rational, at least in the sense that they applied the best available techniques to the resources at hand in order to obtain the greatest benefit and use from them. There is also another conclusion that clearly emerges. Traditional societies cannot respond so readily to external challenges to their institutional system. Since the French were more adaptable than the Amerindians, the transfer of French institutions to North America also involved a transformation as well as a transplantation. It was the French who gained most from the cultural contacts of the seventeenth century. The French learned new techniques for building, travelling, dressing, fighting, food-gathering and survival in the wilderness. They acquired new foods and medicines. They brought new areas under their domination and new peoples in contact with their trade and religion. French society was sufficiently cohesive and stable to absorb new elements while remaining basically itself. Amerindian societies, on the other hand, often became disorganized as a result of cultural contact and too frequently exhibited the worst elements adopted from French culture.

French culture in New France, however, lacked sufficient men, materials and money to act effectively as a host society for the assimilation of the socially disorganized Amerindians. The great failure of the French in seventeenth-century America was their inability to integrate the native peoples in appreciable numbers into a new social order, thereby overcoming the continuing stresses of cultural clash and the nefarious consequences of social disorganization. As officials of church and state came to realize by 1685, their relatively insignificant and insecure colony could not acculturate the Amerindians. The French were unable to exert the kind of social control necessary to stamp out the brandy traffic or to prevent the exodus of *coureurs-de-bois* each year to the *pays d'en haut*. They could not, therefore, hope to exert much control over the vast territories in which their traders, soldiers and missionaries lived more as guests and dependents of the natives than as representatives of a ruling power.

What was the effect of cultural differences among Amerindian tribes when contact with the French influenced their traditional way of life? All the tribes contacted by the French showed a certain traditional inertia, an adherence to their ancestral beliefs and conceptualization. To live on good terms with the different tribes the French had to accept a degree of coexistence, which meant renouncing any plan of immediate assimilation of the natives. It was essential to accommodate a certain resistance, both conscious and subconscious and rooted in native religion, on the part of the Amerindians. The aborigines developed counter-innovative techniques when they sensed that their traditional society was threatened by the French intrusion. It was in this aspect of contact that the cultural differences emerged between nomadic and sedentary tribes, and between animists and polytheists. The more advanced Amerindian cultures assimilated more rapidly than the less advanced tribes, but they were also better able to preserve their traditional belief system and social organization. It was the less advanced, northern and eastern, nomadic Algonkian-speaking tribes who were most disorganized in the face of contact and who showed the most signs of social disintegration and cultural confusion.

Numerous Amerindians became zealous Catholics, some to the point of demonstrating excessive zeal in their self-mortifications and adorations, and some of them made genuine efforts to take up French agricultural life on the reservations administered for the state by the missionary clergy. But this should not obscure the evidence that the economic and social problems arising out of French competitive pressures, the new religious divisions, the inroads of drunkenness and diseases of epidemic proportions, and the introduction of a new technology were not resolved. The converted and resettled natives were no more immune than those who continued to hold to their traditional beliefs and life-style. Neither conversion nor resettlement seemed to reduce appreciably the cultural conflicts that engulfed their whole society.

Assimilation meant the adoption of a new belief and value system and the setting of new limits for behaviour. It meant that actions and thoughts considered good and moral in their traditional society might be censured in French society, and that sometimes what was formerly censured might now be permissible or approved. The problems attendant on assimilation arose out of the process of change and the admixture of beliefs and values, and often resulted in the confusion of individuals and whole societies. Assimilation efforts seemed essentially to produce dislocation; they were a breaking-down process in order to reconstruct a new order. But by attacking the value system of Amerindian societies in order to replace it with a new value system, the entire integrated way of life was upset, including folklore, religion and occupational patterns. As ambiguities and inconsistencies marked the changes, it was not unusual to find rather bizarre patterns of behaviour. Personal and social demoralization seemed to be reflected in alcohol addiction which became the curse, and often the identifying characteristic, of Amerindian communities.

Acculturation is a two-way process. The French were affected by contact too. When any culture is transplanted it changes and varies, but such adaptations are more marked when the society comes into contact and into conflict with other cultures. There follows an exchange and interaction of cultures which can, theoretically, enrich or impoverish both. Cultural *métissage* results, out of which a new culture can emerge. In a limited way, this is what began to occur in New France in the seventeenth century. The Amerindian societies were undermined and disoriented in several respects, as has been shown, without at the same time being afforded an opportunity to reorganize and consolidate themselves into Euro-Amerindian cultures. The French, on the other hand, did begin to develop a distinctive Canadian culture from a French Renaissance base, which was somewhat changed in both form and spirit by the North American environment and experience, and which was greatly enriched by and made the beneficiary of the centuries-old Amerindian experience in North America.

In the French experience, as in the Amerindian, paradoxes were to be found. The highest aboriginal civilizations were those which assimilated most readily to European society, but were also those best equipped to retain their ancestral beliefs and social structures and so resist losing their identity. In French society, the paradox was that in the seminal development of a distinctive Canadian-French culture, owing much to transplantation and to contact with the Amerindians, the efforts to mould the colony in the image of metropolitan France increased with the passing of time. The optimum condition to assert an independent identity passe d in the early phase of resource exploitation, missionary dominance, and social disorganization, but as the colony grew older and stronger efforts were made to fashion it more and more in the traditional cadres of the absolute monarchy, the Gallican church, mercantilism, and seigneurialism. A result of the important contacts with the indigenous tribes of New France—contacts which absorbed much evangelical zeal, which sustained the economy, and which threatened or assured military and political survival—was a growing Canadian ethnocentrism. The colonists turned to their culture, particularly their religion, as a source of identity. There they found a sense of stability and security. As New France became more like Old France it follows that the cultural gap between French and Amerindian widened rather than closed.

CHAPTER

2 SOCIETY IN NEW FRANCE

The structured society of New France, with the *habitant* toiling under the benign if firm hands of the *seigneur*, the *curé* and the royal officials, remains one of the strongest images in Canadian history. The feudal remnant drawn so vividly by Francis Parkman and George M. Wrong, among others, was transferred to the textbooks and repeated for generations, becoming true by repetition. This concept of a regimented colony became so entrenched in both historical studies and popular literature that forty years of revisionist scholarship have failed to dislodge it. There was little sympathy for the paternalist regime among the Whig historians who created the stereotype, and they found congenial readers. In the 1950s, historians rediscovered the history of New France and, in the process, reconstructed a significantly different *ancien régime*. The pastoral scenes and an official society of orders remained, but its personality was set by its diversity and its irregularity. In the view of some, the typical *canadien* of the era was to be found in the bustling, urban communities, not on the farm.

Among historians, the debate on the nature of society has ranged over the role of the state, the military, the church, the economy, the family and the environment. In the 1950s and 1960s, no individual contributed more to the revision of the history of New France than W.J. Eccles, whose "Society of New France, 1680's - 1760" is included here. With the fervour of a possessed iconoclast, Eccles demolished cherished images about the colony, especially those of the imperious Parkman. Eccles was captivated by the *ancien régime* and its values. The advantages of that aristocratic state, when placed in juxtaposition with the English to the south, became self-evident in Eccles' prose. He did not reject the society of orders, but he did revise the picture, using the traditional methodology of historians.

While Eccles toiled in the court records and travellers' accounts, Louise Dechêne turned to the sources and techniques of *l'Ecole des Annales* of France, especially notarial documents. With Montreal as her model, she examined the economy, demography, occupations, and ways of life in the second article reproduced here: "The Growth of Montreal in the 18th Century." Though Dechêne scrutinizes the same institutions as Eccles, the context in which they are placed gives the colony a different texture.

If Dechêne offered an alternative vision of Montreal, then Jan Noel, in the third selection, "New France: Les femmes favorisées," challenged several assumptions about women, family and, ultimately, society in New France. Noel began with the "pre-private" family of the non-industrial world and showed that, in the "fluid situation" of New France, the demographic and economic circumstances permitted women to play many roles: "Devotés and traders, warriors and landowners, smugglers and politicians, industrialists and financiers."

Suggestions for Further Reading

Dechêne, Louise, *Habitants et Marchands de Montreal au XVIIe* siècle. Paris: Plon, 1974.

Desloges, Yvon and Marc Lafrance, "Dynamique de croissance et société urbaine: Québec au XVIIIe siècle, 1690-1759," *Histoire sociale/Social History, XXI*, no. 42 (novembre 1988), 251-268.

Eccles, W.J., *Canadian Society During the French Regime*. Montreal: Harvest House, 1968.

————, *Essays on New France*. Toronto: Oxford, 1988.

————, "The Social, Economic, and Political Significance of the Military Establishment in New France," *Canadian Historical Review*, LII, no. 1 (March 1971), 1-22.

Gadoury, Lorraine, Yves Landry and Hubert Charbonneau, "Démographie différentielle en Nouvelle-France: villes et campagnes," *Revue d'histoire de l'Amérique française*, 38, no. 3 (hiver 1985), 357-378.

Lachance, André, "Women and Crime in Canada in the Early Eighteenth Century, 1712-1759," in *Crime and Criminal Justice in Europe and Canada*, ed. L.A. Knafla. Waterloo: Wilfrid Laurier University Press, 1981, 157-197.

Miquelon, Dale, *New France 1701-1744*: "A Supplement to Europe". Toronto: McClelland & Stewart, 1987.

THE SOCIETY OF NEW FRANCE, 1680's-1760

W.J. Eccles

In the middle of the 18th Century, a Swedish gentleman named Peter Kalm travelled through the English and French colonies in North America. He wrote an endearing description of the Canadian "habitants" whom he met in the farms, villages and towns along the St. Lawrence River in the year 1749:

From *The Ordeal of New France* (Toronto: Canadian Broadcasting Corporation, 1967), 96-106. Reprinted by permission of the author.

The common man in Canada is more civilized and clever than in any other place of the world that I have visited. On entering one of the peasant's houses, no matter where, and on beginning to talk with their men or women, one is quite amazed at the good breeding and courteous answers which are received, no matter what the question is. One can scarcely find in a city in other parts, people who treat one with such politeness both in word and deed as is true everywhere in the homes of the peasants in Canada.

These people had been living under the direct supervision of the French Kings since the year 1663. That was when Louis XIV turned what had been a struggling colony into a comparatively thriving royal province. Under this French regime, which lasted until 1760, the social and political framework of Canada took on some resemblance to that of today's welfare states.

Although it is true that the people had little say in how they were governed, yet they accepted this as being perfectly natural. At the same time, the officials appointed over them by the King and his ministers were always closely checked to ensure that they did not abuse their authority. The whole structure of society and government was paternalistic, based on responsibilities and duties rather than on freedom and privileges. The people had to obey the royal officials in all things, but these same officials were held responsible for their security and well being.

In 1686, when Jean Bochart de Champigny was appointed intendant of New France, he was given very detailed instructions governing all aspects of his responsibilities:

> His Majesty wishes him to know that his entire conduct must lead to two principal ends; the one to ensure that the French inhabitants established in that country enjoy complete tranquility among themselves, and are maintained in the just possession of all that belongs to them, and the other to conserve the said inhabitants and to increase their numbers by all means possible ...
>
> His Majesty wishes him to visit once a year all the habitations that are situated between the ocean and the island of Montreal, to inform himself of all that goes on, pay heed to all the inhabitants' complaints and their needs, and attend to them as much as he possibly can, and so arrange it that they live together in peace, that they aid each other in their necessities and that they be not diverted from their work.

In other words, the intendant, as the King's representative, was to act as the father of the King's large family of loyal subjects living on the banks of the St. Lawrence River.

That the king would not tolerate the abuse of his subjects by the officials was made plain in 1679. Complaints had been received that the governor of Montreal had imprisoned people arbitrarily. Louis XIV issued an edict forbidding this practice. The officials were ordered on pain of severe penalties not to imprison anyone unless they had been duly charged by a court of law. Oddly enough, that same year, in England, Parliament passed a similar act under rather similar circumstances; the act known as *Habeas Corpus*. In fact, the common people of New France had as much, and likely more, personal freedom than had the people of England at this time, where only some ten per cent of the population had a vote and parliament ruled in the interests of the land-owning class with far less solicitude for the common people than was shown by the appointed officials of New France for the Canadian *habitants*.

Another essential difference between seventeenth century society in Canada and in England was that in Canada it might be described as essentially aristocratic, whereas society in England was coming more and more to be bourgeois in outlook. This may become clearer if we try to see what the chief aims of the people were, what they regarded as constituting the good life.

To the Canadians, as to the French in France, the good life was that of the noble who could appreciate the better things, had the means to enjoy them and made the most of them, without condescending to inquire too closely into the sordid mechanics of their procurement. The main aim was to live well, to enjoy the best available without counting the cost. But in England, as elsewhere in Protestant Europe, bourgeois standards were coming more and more to the fore. In this society work was an end in itself, a sign of virtue; pleasure was suspect, poverty was a mark of sin, and the surplus product of labour was not to be consumed but reinvested to create new wealth.

Before the end of the seventeenth century Canadian society had assumed the pattern that it retained to the end of the French regime. At the top were the royal officials; the governor, the intendant and the senior officers of the military establishment, all men sent out from France and who expected to return to France one day. Beside them were the clergy, but the Crown officials had far more authority over them than the state has today. After 1663, when the colony was taken over by the crown from a private company, there was never any real doubt that the state was supreme in New France. For the most part the clergy of New France were, in comparison with those in France, singularly well educated and many of them were persons of exceptionally strong character. But they had their thoughts and aspirations fixed more on the next world than this; thus they always remained a class apart.

Of the purely Canadian social groups the *seigneurs* ranked highest; some, but not all, were nobles; some had begun active life in the colony as peasants or soldiers and had achieved the rank of seigneur by sheer ability and drive. Many of them got their wealth from the fur trade. In the towns of Quebec, Montreal and Trois Rivières there was a sizeable middle class and urban working class; in fact, between twenty-five and forty percent of the colony's population were town dwellers or lived within easy reach of one or other of the three towns compared to fifteen percent in France. In the country, on the seigneuries, lived the remainder of the population, the *habitants*, who tilled their lands, paid their modest dues to their seigneurs and their tithe of one twenty-sixth of their grain to the church, and were far better off than the peasants of France, or indeed of

England, where a third of the people existed at a bare subsistence level. In 1691 the intendant, Champigny, reported to the minister in France:

> Those who try to make something of their land are rich, or at least live very comfortably, having their fields and fishing close by their homes and a goodly number of cattle in pasture.

In 1749, Peter Kalm, professor of natural history and economy at the University of Abo, toured the English colonies and New France and commented on how civilized the Canadian *habitants* were:

> I travelled in various places during my stay in this country. I frequently happened to take up my abode for several days at the homes of peasants where I had never been seen before, and who had never heard of or seen me, and to whom I had no letters of introduction. Nevertheless they showed me wherever I came a devotion paid ordinarily to a native or a relative. Often when I offered them money they would not accept it. Frenchmen who were born in Paris said themselves that one never finds in France among country people the courtesy and good breeding which one observes everywhere in this land. I heard many native Frenchmen assert this.

Thus the Swedish traveller in 1749. And the Marquis de Denonville, writing earlier in 1686, observed this of the Canadians:

> They are all big, well built and firmly planted on their feet, accustomed whenever necessary to live on little, robust and vigorous, very obstinate and inclined to be dissolute, but quick witted and vivacious.

By the middle of the eighteenth century it appeared to some Frenchmen that the Canadian habitant was, in fact, too affluent. In 1753 a French officer named Franquet, after a trip from Quebec to Montreal, noted in his journal:

> Stopped at Madame Lamothe's at La Chenaye and was very well received, a good dinner, and everything well served. We passed a very comfortable night in clean beds fit for a duchess ... Judging by the furnishings of that house, one would have to say that the country folk are too well off.

This same officer was, however, rather reactionary in his views. He declared that the colony was in danger of being ruined by the excellent education which the girls received from the grey nuns of the Congregation of Notre Dame:

> The bad that results is like a slow poison that tends to depopulate the countryside; once educated, the girls wish to be ladies, they become affected in their manners, they want to live in the town, they will marry no one but a merchant and look down on the condition in which they were born.

The daughters of the seigneurs and more affluent merchant families were educated by the Ursuline nuns whose main aim was to turn out well bred and learned young ladies. They were given the usual religious instruction, Latin and French grammar and literature, good penmanship and mathematics. In addition they were taught something of botany and chemistry in order to be able to prepare simple herbs and drugs; and also such things as drawing and embroidery. But more significantly, they were taught to be good conversationalists, to have charming manners, and to know how to please. Peter Kalm in 1749 was quick to remark on the manners of the Canadian girls:

> The difference between the manner and customs of the French in Montreal and Canada, and those of the English in the American colonies, is as great as that between the manners of those two nations in Europe. The women in general are handsome here; they are well bred and virtuous, with an innocent and becoming freedom. They dress up very fine on Sundays; about the same as our Swedish women, and though on the other days they do not take much pains with other parts of their dress, yet they are very fond of adorning their heads. The hair is always curled, powdered and ornamented with glittering bodkins and aigrettes. Every day but Sunday they wear a little neat jacket, and a short skirt which hardly reaches halfway down the leg, and sometimes not that far. And in this particular they seem to imitate the Indian women ...
>
> The ladies in Canada, and especially at Montreal, are very ready to laugh at any blunders strangers make in speaking, but they are very excusable. People laugh at what appears uncommon and ridiculous. In Canada nobody ever hears the French language spoken by any but Frenchmen, for strangers seldom come there, and the Indians are naturally too proud to learn French, and compel the French to learn their language. Therefore it naturally follows that the sensitive Canadian ladies cannot hear anything uncommon without laughing at it. One of the first questions they put to a stranger is whether he is married; the next, how he likes the ladies in the country, and whether he thinks them handsomer than those of his own country; and the third, whether he will take one home with him ... Nobody can say that they lack either charm or wit.

Although the facilities in the colony were inadequate to give the entire populace an education, in the towns at least the emphasis was always on quality. At the Petit Séminaire in Quebec, at the Jesuit College or the Sulpician's seminary in Montreal, the boys received as good an education as could have been had in any provincial city in France. In 1687 the Abbé Dudouyt in Paris instructed the masters at the Petit Séminaire:

> You must limit yourself to thirty students, select them well and weed out those who do not apply themselves. It is far better to have a few students of high calibre than many indifferent ones.

In addition to education, the clergy were responsible for the hospitals, for alms houses for the poor and aged and indigent. Although the hospital at Quebec, the Hôtel Dieu, had an excellent reputation, its doctors followed the established rules of seventeenth and eighteenth century medicine. One had to be very hale indeed to survive that treatment.

If herbal remedies and a few well known drugs failed to effect a cure, bleeding and purging were invariably inflicted on the patients.

When the superior of the Sulpicians, for example, was stricken with a very severe pain in his side, accompanied by fever and violent headaches, he was bled six times but, it was reported, he only became weaker. He was then thoroughly purged but, to everyone's regret, died two days later.

But the main concern of the clergy was, however, the spiritual and moral well being of the people. It was in this last connexion that, in the seventeenth century, they sometimes came into conflict with the secular authorities. At this time the clergy were very puritanical and tended to regard as sins matters that were accepted as quite normal elsewhere. Ladies' fashions, for example, frequently caused Bishop Laval and his successor, St. Vallier, to thunder denunciations from the pulpit. The ladies of Quebec and Montreal always insisted on dressing according to the latest fashions at the court of Versailles, which dictated very low-cut gowns and elaborate hair styles.

In 1682 Bishop Laval declared in a pastoral letter that women were appearing at mass in very luxurious garments, as though dressed for a ball; and what was far worse, some came dressed in a scandalous manner:

> They come wearing indecent gowns, revealing scandalous views of their nude shoulders and bosoms, or contenting themselves by covering their bare flesh with transparent veils which serve only to heighten the effect of their shameful nakedness. They come with their heads uncovered or with their curled and beribboned coiffures covered only by a piece of lace in a fashion most undignified for a Christian and which detracts from the sanctity of the church.

Such apparel was, the Bishop declared, forbidden. But the ladies appear to have paid no attention, for the complaints continued, and Bishop St. Vallier ordered the priests to refuse absolution to those who so comported themselves, not merely outdoors but also in their homes. To this stricture the ladies protested, and the secular authorities supported them, declaring that the clergy were going too far. The minister at Versailles and the clerical authorities in France quickly ordered the Canadian clergy to cease annoying the people in this fashion, and they had to obey. As any married man could have predicted, in their battle against female vanity the clergy were certain to go down to defeat.

The civil authorities had other more dreary problems to cope with—some of which are still with us today. In Montreal traffic was a continual source of annoyance. Most of the streets were only eighteen feet wide, and pedestrians were frequently run down by wagons or sleighs. The intendant Raudot complained that those on horseback or driving vehicles paid no heed to pedestrians and expected them always to get out of the way. Present-day pedestrians in Montreal might well be incline to remark: "Plus ça change, plus c'est la même chose."

In the country districts the depredations of goblins—the "lutins"—appear to have been a serious problem. They were reputed to sneak into barns at night and get into all kinds of mischief with the live stock. The habitants, however, had a method of curbing their activities which was reputed to be very effective; it consisted of placing a pail of cinders behind the stable door so that any goblin entering could not fail to upset it. The goblin then had to pick up the cinders piece by piece in order to remove all traces of his passage.

This took quite a time, and when the task was completed he, or it, had neither time, energy nor inclination to start tying horses tails together. Very rarely did a goblin return to a stable where he had had this experience.

A more tangible problem in Montreal, Quebec and Trois Rivières was the excessive number of taverns. Any house became a tavern merely by hanging an evergreen branch over the door. In 1726 the intendant Dupuy, limited the number of licenses and issued stringent regulations which are quite revealing:

> It is hereby forbidden for tavern keepers, hotel keepers, and inn keepers to sell soldiers anything to drink in the morning except a little brandy or wine, nor to sell any liquor to lackeys or domestic servants, in or out of livery, at any hour of the day, without the written permission of their masters, on pain of fifty livres fine, and the closing of the establishment for a second offence ...
>
> It is forbidden for tavern keepers, hotel keepers and inn keepers to accept from any youth, valet or soldier, in payment for wine or other drinks, any table ware, cutlery or other utensils, on pain of being named accepters of stolen goods and of being punished as such.

The staple food of the Canadians was white bread. Plenty of it was available, and along with it went quantities of meat and fish. Early in December animals were slaughtered and game was brought in, enough to last the entire winter. The meat and game was then packed in barrels between layers of straw and left in the barns to freeze. If a mid-winter thaw lasted too long everyone went on short rations.

The Swedish visitor Peter Kalm, was favourably impressed with the diet of the Canadians:

> The meals here are in many respects different from those in the English provinces. They breakfast commonly between seven and eight and the governor-general can be seen at seven o'clock, the time when he has his levée. Some of the men dip a piece of bread in brandy and eat it; others take a dram of brandy and eat a piece of bread after it. Chocolate is likewise very common for breakfast, and many of the ladies drink coffee. I have never seen tea used here.
>
> Dinner is exactly at noon. People of quality have a great many dishes and the rest follow their example, when they invite strangers. The loaves are oval and baked of wheat flour. For each person they put a plate, napkin, spoon and fork. (In the English colonies a napkin is seldom or never used.) Sometimes they also provide knives, but they are generally omitted, all the ladies and gentlemen being provided with their own knives. The spoons and forks are of silver, and the plates of Delft ware. The meals begin with a soup with a good deal of bread in it. Then follow fresh meats of various kinds, boiled and roasted, poultry, or game, fricassees, ragouts, etc., of several sorts, together with different kinds of salads. They commonly drink red claret at dinner, either mixed with water or clear; and spruce beer is likewise much in use. Each one has his own

glass and can drink as much as he wishes, for the bottles are put on the table. Butter is seldom served and if it is, it is chiefly for the guest present who likes it. But it is so fresh that one has to salt it at the table. After the main course is finished the table is always cleared. Finally the fruit and sweetmeats are served, which are of many different kinds; walnuts from France or Canada, either ripe or pickled; almonds, raisins, hazelnuts, several kinds of berries, and cranberries preserved in treacle. Cheese is likewise a part of the dessert. Immediately after dinner they drink coffee without cream. They say no grace before or after their meals, but only cross themselves, a custom which is likewise omitted by some.

Peter Kalm, of course, visited the colony in the middle of the eighteenth century, a few years before the British conquest, and at a time when the Canadian economy was flourishing. The fur trade was bringing rich returns to the Montreal merchants; such industries as ship building, mining and smelting, lumbering and fishing were now well established. The population was beginning to grow rapidly, and had the conquest not intervened, New France would have begun to expand in every way. It appears just to have reached what a latter-day American economist has called the "take-off point". In both the towns and the countryside the people were well housed. The churches, and in the older-established seigneuries, both the manor houses and the humbler homes of the *habitants*, were mostly built of stone. Inside they were well enough furnished. The more well-to-do imported their furnishings from France; the *habitants* made do with locally made products. This furniture was generally made of white pine, and frequently of a high order of craftsmanship. The Canadian craftsmen developed great skill in wood carving and wrought iron work, and the pieces that have survived are highly prized today in both Canada and the United States. The churches were adorned with fine carved figures and wood panelling, painted in light blues, terra cotta, creamy white, accented with gilt, giving the interiors a light, spacious and very pleasing—almost gay—appearance. In recent years numerous oil paintings, mainly of religious subjects, have come to light. Although rather primitive, many of them have great charm and some have considerable artistry. All things considered, New France, by the mid-eighteenth century was quite an affluent society. In 1752 the French officer Franquet remarked of Montreal:

> The people there are generally very well off, they never travel on foot, in summer they ride in carriages and in winter use sleighs. They nearly all have horses. Usually they keep as many as there are boys in the family, who use them only for sport and to pay court to their lady friends.

And a few years later an Irish observer had this to say of the river empire's metropolis:

> On the fourteenth of this month I had an opportunity of viewing the interior parts of Montreal; and for delightfulness of situation, I think I never saw any town to equal it ... It stands on the side of a hill sloping down to the river with

the south island of St. Helen, all in front; which forms a most agreeable landscape, the river here being about three miles across ... The streets are regular, the houses well constructed ... and ... there are several pleasant gardens within the walls... Besides these, there are many other gardens and beautiful plantations without the gates ... at an agreeable distance, on the north side of the town... I saw no paintings, or anything remarkably curious, in their churches or other religious houses; everything carried an air of neatness, simplicity, and plainness.

The inhabitants are gay and sprightly, much more attached to dress and finery than those of Quebec, between whom there seems to be an emulation in this respect; and, from the number of silk robes, laced coats, and powdered heads of both sexes, and almost of all ages, that are perambulating the streets from morning to night, a stranger would be induced to believe Montreal is entirely inhabited by people of independent and plentiful fortunes.

That was how Montreal appeared in September 1760 to Captain John Knox of the forty-third Regiment of Foot in General Amherst's invading army.

The calm and prosperity of New France could not last, could not survive untouched by the great struggle for domination between the European powers, chiefly France and Britain. In September of 1760, the Montreal described by Captain Knox had capitulated to victorious British armies. Fifteen years later, under British rule, the colony was to be invaded and partly occupied by a new breed of men from the south, calling themselves "Americans".

But these events, and many more to follow, would only attach the Canadians more firmly than ever to their great sources of strength: their families, their land, their language, their faith and their race.

THE GROWTH OF MONTREAL IN THE 18TH CENTURY

Louise Dechêne

In the middle of the 18th century some 20 percent of the Canadian population lived in towns. This proportion, a high one for the times, suggests at first glance that Quebec and Montreal attracted colonists and grew faster than the rural areas. A few contemporary comments have tended to strengthen this impression.[1] The urban-rural population ratio can be, however, a very deceptive indicator in a colonial context. Trade normally precedes agriculture in a colony and the proportion of urban dwellers decreases as settlement progresses, until it ultimately stabilizes at around 10 percent, an equilibrium point in pre-industrial economies. Because of the slow pace of immigration into New France,

From J.M. Bumsted (ed.), *Canadian History before Confederation: Essays and Interpretations* (Georgetown: Irwin-Dorsey, 1979), 155-67. Reprinted by permission of the author.

the urban proportion of the population declined much more slowly there than in other colonies; thus the ratio of urban to rural population is not very significant.

There is an evident need for a closer study of the demographic evolution of both Quebec and Montreal in the colonial period. This is particularly true for Quebec, the more important of the two towns, which one would expect to show some signs of urban dynamism. This dynamism was clearly absent in the inland post that was Montreal. Despite serious deficiencies in the census, I have attempted through the use of a variety of sources to measure the growth of population in Montreal. Even if my conclusions cannot be extended to other towns, Montreal serves as an example of the sort of inertia that characterizes an economy based on a single staple over a long period.

The figures shown in Table 1 are necessarily approximate. Only 2 of the 23 census returns of the Canadian population made in the 18th century (those of 1707 and 1754), separated the population of Montreal from that of the *banlieue*, an agricultural area included in the same parish. By using the enumerations of dwellings made in 1697, 1731, 1741, and 1781 it is possible to estimate the size of this rural population—a fairly stable group that hovered at a little under 1,000—and subtract it from the figure given for the parish as a whole, leaving only the population of the town and suburbs.

The compilation of census data published in 1871, used as the basis for the 1931 monograph on the urban and rural composition of the Canadian population and for other more recent works, consistently overestimated the population of Montreal. For example, the town is credited with a population of 18,000 in 1790.[2] The figures presented here have been arrived at through the utilization of all available quantitative data, carefully cross-checked. They are, I believe, much closer to reality. Through the 18th century, after as well as before the Conquest, Montreal grew at a very sluggish pace. What follows is a brief analysis of the nature and implications of this slow development.[3]

Urban Land Use

In 1648 an area of 92 acres was reserved for urban occupation and shortly afterwards surrounded by a pallisade. The people who founded and lived in Montreal never called this area anything except *ville*; they felt from the beginning that they were creating a town. Even though the contemporary reality—some fields and a handful of inhabitants clustered around a warehouse—hardly fits any modern definition of the word, this article also uses the term *ville*, or town.

Until about 1665-70, Montreal was a *comptoir*, a centre for exchanges between people from two different civilizations, set in an expanding agricultural area. The operation of the fur trade involved the participation—certainly on

TABLE 1   **Estimates of the Population of Montreal and Comparative Growth Rates**

	Towns and Suburbs				Parish	
Year	Houses	Households	Population	Percent Annual Growth Rate	Population	Percent Annual Growth Rate
1697	152	—	(1,150)[a]	—	(13 200)[b]	—
1707	—	204	1 327	1.4	17 615	2.9
1731	400	—	(2 980)[c]	3.4	(34 850)[c]	2.9
1739	—	—	(3 450)[d]	1.7	43 264	2.7
1741	457	591	(3 575)	—	—	—
1754	—	—	4,000	0.8	55 000	1.6
1781	659	—	5,300	—	—	—
1784	—	—	(5 500)[e]	1.0	113 012	2.5
1831	3 774	—	27 297	3.5	553 134	3.4

Notes:

a. On the basis of seven persons per house, a ratio derived from the 1731 figures. Personnel of religious orders have been added to this figure.

b. Average based on the census returns of 1695 and 1698.

c. Average based on the census returns of 1730 and 1732.

d. Enumerated population of the Parish of Notre-Dame, less 900, the estimated minimum population of the nonurban portion of the parish.

e. The total population of the parish was 6,479. According to the seigneurial enumeration of 1781, there were 120 rural households. Our estimates of the urban population in 1781 and 1784 are maximum figures corresponding to a ratio of eight persons per house, a density that is already a little high for the period. John Hare found a ratio of 7.2 persons in Quebec in 1795 and, at the end of the 19th century, there were no more than eight persons per house in a working class section of Montreal. See "La population de la ville de Quebec, 1795-1805", *Histoire sociale / Social History,* 7 (May 1974), 23-47, and H. B. Ames, *The City Below the Hill* (Toronto, 1972).

SOURCES: Livre des tenanciers de Montreal, 1697, Arch. St-Sulpice; recensements du Canada, AC, GI, 460-1; *1871 Census of Canada,* IV; denombrement seigneurial de 1731, *RAPQ* (1941-1942); perquisition de 1741, *Transactions of the Royal Society of Canada (TRSC),* 111, XV (1921); C. Perrault, *Montreal en 1781;* recensement de 1784 in W. Kingsford, *The History of Canada,* 7:204;*1831 Census, Journals of the Legislative Assembly of Lower Canada,* 41, app. Oo.

very unequal terms, but participation all the same—of the entire population, which by the end of this period amounted to about 200 *habitants.*[4] The area designated for the town was also the site of the first agriculture, carried out on parcels of land ranging in size from a few hundred square feet to two and three acres. Afterward the fields began to overflow into the surrounding *côtes.*[5]

Agricultural and commercial activities were at first closely related. Settlers who obtained land around the town normally lived within the pallisaded area, finding there both protection and easy profits. The latter were in turns applied, with varying degrees of enthusiasm, to clearing their land. At the same time, with the incentive offered by high agricultural prices, most of the fur traders and craftsmen employed indentured labourers to improve their own land.

Initially, the development of an urban concentration was a response to the requirements of defence. By its nature, the fur trade could operate from little more than a warehouse with a very small agricultural base. It would in fact have been to the advantage of the traders to disperse. Had it not been for the military threat constantly hanging over the colony, a more extensive network of trading posts would have been established very quickly. As it was, posts were established above the rapids, at Lachine, Châteauguay, on lake des Deux-Montagnes, as soon as the danger of Iroquois attacks receded.

Montreal's growth was stimulated by the disruption of this initial commercial structure. The recession in the European fur market reducing profit margins, the attempts on the part of Quebec merchants to combine the import trade with fur trading, a part of the business which was eluding them, were among the factors that launched the Canadiens in a century-long march toward the source of the furs.[6] The spread of trading posts within the settled area that had begun was thwarted when the Indians stopped bringing down their furs. It was at this time that the remarkable advantages of Montreal's location came into full play.[7] The town was in effect reborn around a new predominant function: the transshipment of trade articles and furs between Quebec and the interior of the continent. It became the point where both furs and goods changed hands. The new function brought with it some spatial reorganization. The fields in the urban area were parcelled out to accommodate craftsmen and professionals of the trade. The rising land values encouraged many habitants to sell their urban plots and drove out many tenants and squatters. Being from now on excluded from commercial activities, settlers moved out of the town and scattered over the *côtes*.

This new specialization nonetheless produced only a limited degree of urban concentration. It was Montreal's other functions—religious, military, administrative, and as a service centre to the rural community—which sustained its growth. Even so, its population increase remained lower than that of the colony as a whole until the end of the 17th century. There was a period of illusory growth in the last decade, when the town temporarily became a place of refuge. Ruined or frightened by the Anglo-Iroquois raids, settlers from the island and from the seigneuries on the south shore sought safety in the urban enclosure, where they found ample space for the construction of temporary shelters. A list of properties drawn up at the end of this period shows that, despite its 152 houses, Montreal was still a very primitive settlement.

The town experienced its most vigorous period of development in the first quarter of the 18th century. At this time it attracted a substantial proportion of demobilized soldiers[8] and also a number of Canadiens. The latter, however, were not drawn from the rural areas, but were, for the most part, traders, craftsmen, and labourers from Quebec and Trois-Rivières.[9] These arrivals cannot be associated with any expansion of trade. On the contrary, the movement occurred in the midst of a crisis of overproduction and declining beaver prices, and during the very slow recovery that followed. The period did see, however, the beginning of a number of public projects, including the construction of a stone wall around the town. A further factor was the speculation that accompanied the currency crisis and gave rise to an unprecedented interest in real estate investment between 1710 and 1720.[10] The infusion of new blood was of particular benefit to the building trades, and at this point one begins to witness the appearance of specifically urban trades, such as wigmaking or gardening.

The first detailed picture of Montreal dates from 1731. The urban enclosure then held 379 houses, of which 56 percent were wooden and single-storied, similar in appearance to rural dwellings. The rest were of stone, and about one-quarter of all houses had two stories. Families with modest income usually lived in one room or two, including the workshop, unless the latter had been set up in a lean-to; only one room was heated by the fireplace. At a higher income level, the house would be of stone, larger (about 50 by 30 feet), and a great deal more comfortable, with its two chimneys and two or three rooms per floor. Merchants' houses normally included a storage room on the first floor and the shop on the ground floor, while grain and furs were kept in the attic. Very rarely was a separate building used for the trading activities. Four or five rooms remained for the use of the family, which on the basis of 5.5 persons per family plus two servants makes an average of 1.5 person per room, about twice the space available to the common people.[11]

Montreal had five convents and five churches and chapels. Public buildings and private buildings of a commercial or industrial nature included two schools, a law court, a prison, barracks, a *canoterie*, a brewery, and seven warehouses. The walls with their gates and bastions were not yet completed by 1731. Two main thoroughfares, about 24 feet wide, ran parallel to the river, cut at right angles by a dozen narrower streets. This grid pattern was broken by short lanes at the water's edge and on the hill. The market place was bordered by the houses of the principal inhabitants. Here and there were large empty spaces, formed by convent properties and by those belonging to the parish or to the Crown. Their presence, however, did not retard possible housing construction, as is evidenced by the existence of 166 gardens in the town. The unpaved streets were dirty or muddy; and, because the town was small and the surrounding roads rarely passable, the bourgeois did not own carriages and stables were rare. Behind most houses was a shed sheltering a few domestic animals, particularly pigs.[12] To the west of the Récollets' gate stood the suburb of Saint-Joseph, which included 21 houses, two warehouses, and the buildings of the Hôpital Général.

Another enumeration made ten years later gives us an idea of the slow pace of the town's development. Even allowing for a fire that destroyed 46 buildings,[13] it is still surprising to find only 387 houses inside the walls, meaning an average of 5.4 new buildings erected every year in the decade 1731-41. The town seems to have been frozen in its tracks. The three suburbs, to the west, north, and east, had a total of 70 houses. Of the 591 heads of households in the town and its suburbs, some 70 percent owned their dwellings. The large number of rental agreements in the notarial archives added to the presence of 176 tenant households on this 1741 enumeration suggests at first sight some degree of concentration of property. This would be an indicator of urban development, but closer examination reveals the absence of such concentration. Twenty-eight individuals or corporate bodies owned two houses,[14] while 33 owners shared their house with tenants. In all, 66 houses harboured two families or more. The population density within the walls remained at the low figure of 38.8 people per acre. The list of trades, although very incomplete, does show a little island of merchants and other notables clustered in the centre of the town. Moving outwards, we find shopkeepers and officers living next door to craftsmen and unidentified individuals, presumably of very modest status. Saint-Jacques Street was the only one given over principally to craft workers.[15] In short, the impression left by this enumeration is one of rather drab and uniform standard of living.

TABLE 2   **Distribution of Houses in the Town and the Suburbs**

Years	Town	Suburbs	Total
1731	379	21	400
1741	387	70	457
1781	307	352	659

The seigneurial enumeration of 1781 provides an interesting case of urban reorganization. In 1765, the town had been again partially destroyed by fire and it emerged substantially changed after the reconstruction that followed. By 1781, there were only 307 houses inside the walls, about 20 percent less than in 1741. But the houses were now larger, with two and three stories and almost all built of stone. Most of the yards boasted masonry outbuildings, often stables, and those raised storage rooms called *voûtes en plafonds* by the enumerator. The lots, larger than before, still included gardens and were generally enclosed by a wall. Montreal no longer looked like a large village, with rich and poor living side by side. It had been transformed to serve as a business and residential centre for the bourgeoisie.[16] The small craftsmen and the labourers had been pushed outside the walls. To some extent this change was facilitated by the fire, but there were other factors in play: new-found prosperity, rising property values, increasing rents, more unequal income distribution, and so on. More research is needed to reconstitute the mechanism behind this premature segregation.[17] While deconcentration is a normal stage in the process of urbanization, it clearly took place in Montreal in the absence of any demographic pressure, as is evident from the slow development of the suburbs.

The census returns of 1831 have been used as a terminal point in the table of population estimates, but the major transformations that occurred in Lower Canada in the first quarter of the 19th century are beyond the scope of this article.[18] The respective influence of economic progress and of the massive immigration that began after 1815 upon this accelerated urban growth remains to be determined.

The Demographic Pattern

Much of the data necessary to relate the real increase of the population of Montreal to its vital statistics and to the demographic evolution of the whole colony is still lacking. It might be useful, however, to point to some of the methodological difficulties involved in finding and using such data. In 1731, almost a quarter of the population included in the parish of Notre-Dame was rural, making it very difficult to deal separately with the demographic behaviour in the urban area. Setting this problem aside, it would still be pointless to try to calculate crude birth and death rates on the basis of such a small population, subject as it was to the effects of migratory phenomena and resultant short-term variations in the age distribution. Satisfactory results could be obtained only by reconstituting families over a long time. Meanwhile, simple counts in the parish registers might suggest general trends. Counts of this kind for the five parishes on the island of Montreal, in the period prior to 1715, seem to indicate that there was yet no fundamental differences between the urban and the rural demographic patterns. Seasonal variations of marriages and births, for example, were the same, and so was the crude ratio established between these marriages and births.[19] If we exclude soldiers—who were, in any case, never enumerated with the civilian population—epidemics seem to have been no more deadly in the urban parish. These observations are possibly valid for the 18th century as well, because there was little change during this period in the general conditions such as population density and way of life.

It might be thus possible to use our knowledge of the colonial demographic data to grasp the pattern of population growth in the urban area, but this general data is far from complete. There are no immigration statistics for New France. The estimate of net immigration—about 10,000 people spread unevenly over the period 1608-1760—is based on the difference between real increase, as taken from the census returns, and the natural increase, as recorded in the parish registers. The whole problem of emigration remains obscure. We do not know how many Canadiens went to the west, to Louisiana, nor how many newcomers left the colony after a short stay. Departures for France were fairly common among the officers and the merchants and may have been even more so among the common immigrants. For example, depending on the period and the method of recruitment, between 25 and 50 percent of the indentured labourers who came to Montreal in the 17th century returned to France.[20] This two-way migration was certainly more noticeable in the towns than in the rural areas.

Another problem concerns the quality of the statistics from the parish registers. Thanks to the work of Jacques Henripin, we know the nuptiality and fertility rates of the colonial population; but, as yet, we are very uncertain as to the crude mortality rate.[21] The under-registration of burials in the early period has already been well documented by Hubert Charbonneau and his colleagues,[22] and Montreal, apparently, is no exception. For example, the infant mortality rates derived from Montreal's registered burials vary between 10 and 18 percent at the end of the 17th century, when one would expect them to be closer to the 24.6 percent that Henripin arrived at through a careful analysis.[23] It follows that the crude mortality rate before 1740, supposedly under 30 percent, becomes highly suspect. Consequently, an annual rate of natural increase as high as 3 percent, which supposedly prevailed throughout the 18th century, also is very questionable.[24]

What is certain is that, except for a short period, Montreal's rate of growth was much lower than the rest of the colony. It is equally certain that an urban annual rate of real increase of 0.8 to 1.0 percent remained well short of the town's natural increase, even if we adjust the latter to allow for a higher urban mortality and a slightly lower birth rate. Had no immigrants arrived in the town after 1731—which is certainly not the case[25]—it is an inescapable fact that Montreal was undergoing a more or less continuous *loss* of population. While there are still few demographic studies on the French towns of the *ancien Régime,* it seems to be generally accepted that their growth was normally slower than that of the relatively prosperous rural communities.[26] Their lower birth rates combined with higher mortality rates produced chronic population deficits, which were not always completely offset by an inflow from the countryside. Montreal's case, however, was quite different, for it certainly showed a surplus of baptisms over burials; but the town was continuously losing part of that surplus. It seems thus unlikely that Montreal could have exerted any pull on the rural settlements.

The Urban Functions

Slow urban growth can be linked to the colony's economic situation and specifically to the role of the town in this economy. Montreal performed a number of functions, and to give any precise idea of the relative importance of each one would require complete information on the distribution of occupations. My sources unfortunately do not permit that sort of precision. However, on the basis of a general familiarity with this society, based on such relevant material as notarial and judicial records and various tax rolls, I can set out a rough inventory of urban activities around 1731.

The fur trade had been the main incentive behind the creation of Montreal; but once the basic commercial organization had been established, the trade ceased to be a factor of urban growth. After 1731, the pace of development slowed, while the volume of fur exports continued to increase. Fur warehousing and trading expeditions employed relatively little labour. The trade maintained about 30 merchants, while another 20 gained a precarious livelihood from the local market and irregular fur trading ventures. The *voyageurs* were the successors of the more successful *coureurs de bois*. Formerly of rural origin, they gradually attached themselves to the merchants and moved up the social ladder, establishing their families in the town. The group tended to close ranks; the numbers involved did not increase and new members were recruited from within the group or from elements above it. There were perhaps 70 families of *voyageurs* in Montreal in 1731 and by that time a number of them were beginning to move out permanently toward Detroit, Michilimackinac, and other western posts. Each year the merchants and *voyageurs* hired between 250 and 300 of the colony's young men for the seasonal expeditions into the interior. Town-dwellers were proportionally better represented among these *engagés,* but the supply of labourers considerably exceeded the demand. Besides, not every man had the strength to paddle to Lake Superior and to portage with heavy packs. Probably no more than a third of the youth in the town succeeded in getting such jobs. It was this group that displayed the strongest tendency to emigrate. Another 50 individuals—innkeepers, tavern-keepers, teamsters, bakers, and butchers—derived an important part of their clientele from the fur trade. The latter also supported, in a very meagre fashion, a large number of seamstresses, who worked on the putting-out system, making clothes to be used as trade articles. But there again, the merchants' orders were inadequate to support the available feminine labour. In all, about one-third of the work force gained an unequal subsistence from the staple trade.

There were no manufactures in Montreal. Few workshops employed more than two or three apprentices, even if we include the sawmills and tanneries operating at the outskirts of town. About 50 craftsmen produced for the local market, urban, and rural, and there were also gunsmiths, blacksmiths, coopers, and joiners who derived a portion of their income from the fur trade. Complete separation of merchant capital from craft production was the rule; the worker owned his tools and raw material and sold the finished article directly to consumers. Bonds of dependence between producers and merchants occasionally arose from the indebtedness of the former, but the merchants never made use of their advantage to transform production and to establish a permanent capital-labour relationship.[27] During this period, the urban market was scarcely growing and, at the same time, the town craftsmen's rural clientele tended to diminish as elementary rural centres sprang up here and there in the back-country. Once a son had taken over the shop from his father, chances were that his brothers had to fall back on non-skilled trades for a living.[28]

The building trades employed about half of the town's skilled labour as well as a number of navvies. In 1731, however, half of the houses were simple frame structures, which the owners built themselves, and the pace of construction of more elaborate dwellings was slow. Construction of churches and convents, along with public works projects,[29] created better job opportunities, but even these works were interrupted for at least five months of the year. There was thus a situation of chronic unemployment in Montreal, to which the new generations of townsmen, and those immigrants who had momentarily been drawn to the town, responded by emigrating or settling on farms.

Religious, military, administrative, and domestic services probably employed some two-fifths of the work force. Montreal had few administrative jobs to offer; but here, as in all the French towns of the *ancien Régime,* there was a steady expansion in the personnel of religious orders.[30] Convent life in Montreal was a specifically feminine phenomenon that absorbed women of the upper class, an obvious consequence of the emigration of their male counterparts. The missionary impulse had also been a factor of colonial urban foundation in the 17th century. It brought with it important capital inflow,[31] and the sort of determination and perseverence that religious activity involves. The Church was a source of stability during the colony's difficult early years. As time progressed, however, the religious personnel tended to increase more rapidly than did the services it provided.[32]

Montreal was a garrison town. The size of the military population varied according to the period; in 1731 there may have been 200 soldiers quartered in barracks or billeted on the townsfolk.[33] The local consumer market benefitted, no doubt, from their presence, but these soldiers also competed with civilians for part-time employment. Working at lower wages than the latter, they upset the local job market from the end of the 17th century.[34] While the enlisted men were recruited in France, by the 18th century the majority of their officers were Canadiens. About 40 officers had their homes in Montreal, including the Government's general staff and officers who left their families in the town while they served in remote outposts. A majority of them were closely associated with the fur trade and could legitimately be included among the trade's personnel.

Domestic service was an important outlet for a town labour force in pre-industrial times. So it was in Montreal—at least if the situation in 1731 is somewhat similar to that presented by the census of 1784. By this time, servants (presumably including apprentices) formed about one-fifth of the total urban population. The group included 142 slaves, 129 children under 15 years of age, and 913 adults, with males and females about equally represented.[35] These figures illustrate what was by then a familiar situation: under-employment. For, in a period when the practice of putting children into domestic service was everywhere customary, few Montreal children seem to have been parted from their families.[36] Apparently, the bourgeois usually employed adults because the latter were willing to work for very modest wages. The Indian slaves who appeared at the beginning of the 18th century were also inexpensive, but their life expectancy was so short that there was little advantage in substituting them for the abundant local manpower.[37] Such was the distribution of occupations in Montreal for at least a century. The production sector stood in last place.

It is always difficult to determine the nature of the relations between town and countryside, and only a few aspects of the question are dealt with here. Montreal was not in the centre of an agricultural region: it stood on the fringe of the settled seigneurial area, still to a large extent the hinterland of Quebec. Early in the 18th century Canada began to export wheat, but the grain moved directly to port of embarkation without passing through Montreal, so that this tentative orientation to external markets had no effect on the town's development. Only with the opening of lands further upstream, with the settlement of Upper Canada, would Montreal become a transfer point for agricultural products. Until then it maintained a rather tenuous relation with its narrow farm belt, which met the small urban demand and the needs of the western trade. Because external demand had long been non-existent and remained weak and capricious, because of the adverse evolution of the terms of trade resulting from this whole context,[38] the countryside tended to shun unfavourable exchanges, to rely heavily upon itself. But if the peasants rarely prospered, neither did they starve, so that this town did not serve as an asylum for the rural poor. It would be pointless to speculate on the economic diversification prompted by the formation of a large labour pool that might have resulted had a less generous policy been followed towards the settlers.[39] Any increase of their overall burden could only further contract the domestic market. With external circumstances and demographic conditions remaining constant, it is hard to visualize any economic advantages in a heavier taxation of rural production. It could only have spread destitution, without stimulating enterprise.

Merchant capital in New France had no incentive to transform mortgages into rural ownership and to accumulate rents. Town people did not normally invest in the agriculture beyond the limit of one farm, and that only for family needs, not as a means of drawing income. The pattern emerging from these transfers of capital and labour between town and countryside seems, on balance, to run counter to the traditional model.[40] Montreal, for instance, contributed to the growth of the rural population, for, even if the excess urban workers could not easily transform themselves into peasants and generally opt for emigration, one must consider all the town's girls who married discharged soldiers and moved to the land.[41] Furthermore, Montreal did not provide part-time employment for the rural population, if one excepts the hiring for the western trade, an activity incompatible with farming. Making poor use of the ties resulting from the settlers' initial indebtedness, Montreal merchants had little interest in agriculture. The economic dichotomy is certainly not absolute; interactions did take place, but they were not sufficiently important either to dislocate or to consolidate the rural society.

My conclusions are not too far removed from the findings of those who, having reflected upon the weakness of New France, stressed the importance of adverse geographic and demographic conditions, two realities that persisted after 1760. The nature of the initial staple was only a secondary element.[42] The distribution of commercial profits and the social dispersion of capital were derivative from the general historical context and do not explain the failure to diversify the economy. The specific conditions of the development may have, in the long run, forged certain patterns of behaviour, but it goes without saying that psychological factors are not an independent variable.

The accumulation of capital that took place in Montreal was only remotely connected with the regional system of production; this accounts for the continued rigidity of the town's economy.[43] Later on, external factors were to lead Montreal merchants into new speculative ventures. Although also based on monopoly and privilege, these ventures succeeded in establishing closer ties between the distribution centre and its territorial base, which was by then enlarged and more populous. The pace of capital formation was hastened. But another century was already well underway before profits from such trade had dwindled sufficiently to compel the merchants to invest in production.[44] Then Montreal entered another age.

Notes

1. See Guy Frégault, *La Civilisation de la Nouvelle-France 1713-1744* (Montréal, 1969), p. 168, and "La Nouvelle-France, territoire et population," in *Le XVIIIe siècle canadien, Etudes* (Montréal, 1968), pp. 48-49; Louis Trottier, "La genèse du réseau urbain du Québec," in *L'urbanisation de la société canadienne-française* (Québec, 1968), p. 23.

2. *1871 Census of Canada,* IV; *1931 Census of Canada,* Monograph 6, "Rural and Urban Composition of the Canadian Population," by S. A. Cudmore and H. G. Caldwell.

3. This article does not deal with other aspects of Montreal's history, such as institutions and political and social organizations, which are partly discussed in the following works: W. H. Atherton, *Montreal 1535-1914* (Montréal, 1914); C. Bertrand, *Histoire de Montréal* (Montréal, 1935-42); J. I. Cooper, *Montreal, A Brief History* (Montreal, 1969); R. Rumilly, *Histoire de Montréal* (Montréal, 1970), I-II; E. R. Adair, "The Evolution of Montreal under the French Regime," *CHAR* (1942); and others, among which the contributions of O. Maurault and E.-Z. Massicotte must be mentioned.

4. In this early period the term *habitant* designated free individuals holding titles of property in the colony and thus did not include servants or soldiers. The census of 1666 enumerated 659 persons on the island of Montreal, of whom 141 were habitants, heads of households.

5. The *côte* was the elementary unit of rural settlement. See R. C. Harris, *The Seigneural System in Early Canada: A Geographical Study* (Québec and Madison, Wis., 1967).

6. H. A. Innis, *The Fur Trade in Canada: An Introduction to Canadian Economic History* (Toronto, 1956).

7. Raoul Blanchard, *L'Ouest du Canada français. Montréal et sa région* (Montréal, 1953).

8. The island of Montreal received more than 400 demobilized soldiers between 1697 and 1715. A most important inflow of immigrants, part of which benefits the urban area.

9. Based on the marriage registers giving the husband's place of origin: Register of the Parish of Notre Dame.

10. The crisis was catastrophic for the administration, but not for the merchants or the colony as a whole. Jean Hamelin draws a grim picture of it in *Economie et Société en Nouvelle-France* (Québec, 1960), pp. 37-46.

11. In the French towns of this period the average ratio appears to have been one room per family of 4.5 people: F. Braudel and E. Labrousse, *Histoire économique et sociale de la France, 1660-1789* (Paris, 1970), p. 49.

12. See the police ordinances concerning uncleanliness, pigs running at large, or fire hazards in the judiciary records of Montreal. These are characteristics common to many 18th-century towns.

13. The fire of 1734, the second in the town's history. That of 1721 had destroyed about 150 houses, which were quickly rebuilt: M. Mondoux, *L'Hôtel-Dieu premier hôpital de Montréal ...* (Montréal, 1942), pp. 271-72 and 289.

14. The concentration of property was perhaps slightly higher than it appears, as people sometimes built small houses on rented lots which were easily dismantled when their leases were not renewed.

15. On all our lists the inhabitants are very poorly identified, sometimes solely by surname. The work of E.-Z. Massicotte on the enumeration of 1741 was of great assistance on this question: *TRSC*, III, XV (1921), pp. 1-61.

16. There were only 45 proprietors of British or American origin. The remainder, about 82 percent, were Canadiens, the majority of them belonging to families living in the town for two or three generations.

17. In Boston, a town which developed very rapidly, the poor already had been resettled on the outskirts in 1774: S. B. Warner, "A Scaffolding for Urban History," in A. M. Wakestein, ed., *The Urbanization of America, An Historical Anthology* (Boston, 1970), p. 60. On these same problems, at a more advanced stage of urban growth, see L. F. Schnore and P. R. Knight, "Residence and Social Structure, Boston in the Ante Bellum Period," in S. Thernstrom and R. Sennett, eds., *Nineteenth-Century Cities, Essays in the New Urban History* (New Haven, 1969), pp. 247-56.

18. See Fernand Ouellet, *Histoire économique et sociale du Québec, 1760-1850* (Montréal, 1966), and the numerous articles by Jean-Pierre Wallot and Gilles Paquet on the period 1790-1815.

19. This ratio is about five to one in both Notre-Dame and the rural parishes. The rhythm of life, as it appears from the seasonal variations, was strongly conditioned by nature, even in the town.

20. This is still a very positive balance if we compare it, for example, to Maryland, where only 7 percent of the indentured labourers who came between 1670 and 1689 remained in the colony: A. E. Smith, *Colonists in Bondage*, pp. 298-99.

21. Jacques Henripin, *La population canadienne au début du XVIIIe siècle, Nuptialité, fécondité, mortalité infantile* (Paris, 1954).

22. H. Charbonneau, J. Légaré, and Y. Lavoie, "Recensements et registres paroissiaux du Canada durant la période 1665-1668: étude critique," 25, 1 *Population*, (January-February 1970), 97-124.

23. Henripin, *La population canadienne ...*, pp. 103-7.

24. J. Henripin, *Tendances et facteurs de la fécondité au Canada* (Ottawa, 1968), pp. 5-8. The crude mortality rate per decade would vary from 24 to 25 per thousand between 1700 and 1740, and from 32 to 34 per thousand between 1740 and 1790. It did not fall below 27 per thousand until after 1840. But the proportion of young children—the most vulnerable group—was as high in 1700 as in 1800. It is impossible to explain this supposed increase in mortality. It is easier to assume that the burials were more faithfully registered as the century progressed.

25. There was an important movement of immigrants into the colony between 1740 and 1760: P. E. Renaud, *Les origines économiques du Canada, L'oeuvre de la France* (Paris, 1928).

26. This was generally the case for small and medium sized towns but not in the large ports, such as Nantes, Bordeaux, and Marseille: P. Goubert, "Révolution démographique au XVIIIe siècle," in F. Braudel and E. Labrousse, *Histoire économique et sociale,* 72-74.

27. These observations are based on an analysis of the accounts and inventories of Montreal merchants at the beginning of the century. On this question see Maurice Dobb, *Studies in the Development of Capitalism* (New York, 1947).

28. The shortage of Canadian tradesmen was a consequence and not a cause of economic stagnation. Similarly, Montreal long had to go to Quebec to find skilled workers for its large construction projects, precisely because the demand was too irregular to maintain them permanently in the town. See Pierre Harvey, "Stagnation économique en Nouvelle-France," *l'Actualité économique,* 37: 537-48; also J. Mathieu, *La construction navale royale à Québec, 1739-1759* (Québec, 1971).

29. Tradesmen were needed to direct the construction projects but in the case of churches or fortifications, *corvées* or statute labour supplied much of the unskilled labour needed.

30. About 100 nuns and 30 to 40 clerics.

31. French capital and a part of the colonial budget that these pious founders managed to draw in Montreal: L. Gérin, *Aux sources de notre histoire; les conditions économiques et sociales de la colonisation en Nouvelle-France* (Montréal, 1946), pp. 162-91.

32. There is a contrast between the large number of nuns and regulars and the difficulty in finding priests for the rural parishes.

33. The soldiers, recruited in France, were not included in the census and therefore do not appear in our estimates. In peacetime they could obtain a discharge to settle in the colony. Many preferred to complete their service and return to France: Mémoires de R. d'Auteuil, Archives des Colonies, C11A:34; E. Salone, *La Colonisation de la Nouvelle-France. Etude sur les origines de la nation canadienne-française,* (reprint, 1969), pp. 339-42.

34. This was tolerated by the administration and encouraged by the captains who kept their soldiers' pay whenever the latter found employment. I would agree with W. J. Eccles that the soldiers "provided a sorely needed pool of labour" in the early days of the colony, when settlers were few and as yet had no grown children for work on the farms or in the shops. See Eccles, "The Social, Economic and Political Significance of the Military Establishment in New France," *CHR* (March 1971), 5-6. But this was no longer valid at a later period, when soldiers competed with an abundant reserve of unskilled labourers.

35. W. Kingsford, *op. cit.,* 7:204. These figures must be related to the total population of the parish: 6,474 persons.

36. In 1689, in the American colonial town of Bristol one child in five was in domestic service. In Montreal in 1784, the figure was only one in 14. See John Demos, *A Little Commonwealth, Family Life in Plymouth Colony* (New York, 1970), pp. 69-74.

37. See Marcel Trudel, *L'esclavage au Canada français. Histoire et conditions de l'esclavage* (Québec, 1960).

38. Based on the movement of the prices of grain and imported goods from 1650 to 1730. The high agricultural prices at the beginning of the period gave way to a long-term depreciation.

39. L. R. MacDonald, "France and New France: The Internal Contradictions," *CHR* (June 1971), 121-43. The Marxist model of the transition from merchant to industrial capitalism is not pertinent in the case of an 18th-century colonial outpost such as New France. It would be more suitable to use another Marxist concept, that of a primitive accumulation through the expansion of far away markets and regional disequilibrium.

40. G. Friedmann, *Villes et Campagnes* (Paris, 1953); M. Vénard, *Bourgeois et paysans au XVIIe siècle. Recherches sur le rôle des bourgeois parisiens dans la vie agricole au sud de Paris* (Paris, 1957), and other studies.

41. Of 716 marriages contracted between 1680 and 1715 in the parish of Notre Dame, 95 percent of the brides and 47 percent of the grooms were Canadian by birth.

42. M. H. Watkins, "A Staple Theory of Economic Growth," in W. T. Easterbrook and Watkins, eds., *Approaches to Canadian Economic History,* pp. 49-74; P. Harvey, *art. cit.*

43. A point of clarification not in the original article might be relevant here. The lack of integration between the mercantile and the productive sectors described above is not unusual in a precapitalist context, especially in a colony that derives its profits from commodities produced by the Indians rather than by the white colonists. But one should keep in mind that such disarticulation is a local economic phenomenon only, observable with respect to the relationship—or lack of relationship—between the mercantile and productive sectors within the colony itself. On an imperial scale, the disarticulation vanishes. The settlements played crucially important strategic and military roles in furthering imperial objectives. There is no real dualism, but a complex all-integrating pattern of development.

44. For an excellent discussion and illustration of these problems, see Pierre Vilar, *La Catalogue dans l'Espagne moderne. Recherches sur les fondements économiques des structures nationales* (Paris, 1962).

NEW FRANCE: LES FEMMES FAVORISÉES

Jan Noel

You constantly behold, with renewed astonishment, women in the very depths of indigence and want, perfectly instructed in their religion, ignorant of nothing that they should know to employ themselves usefully in their families and who, by their manners, their manner of expressing themselves and their politeness, are not inferior to the most carefully educated among us.[1]

From *Atlantis,* 6, no. 2 (Spring 1981), 80–98. Reprinted by permission of *Atlantis.*

> Les femmes l'emportent sur les hommes par la beauté, la vivacité, la gaité [sic] et l'enjouement; elles sont coquettes et galantes, préfèrent les Européens aux gens du pays. Les manières douces et polies sont communes, même dans les campagnes.[a] [2]
>> ... les femmes y sont fort aimables, mais extrêmement fières.[b] [3]
>> ... elles sont spirituelles, ce qui leur donne de la supériorité sur les hommes dans presque tous les états.[c] [4]

Many a man, observing the women of New France, was struck by the advantages they possessed in education, cultivation and that quality called *esprit* or wit. Even an unsympathetic observer of colonial society, such as the French military officer Franquet, who visited New France in 1752-53, admitted that its women "l'emportent sur les hommes pour l'esprit, généralement elles en ont toutes beaucoup, parlant un français épuré, n'ont pas le moindre accent, aiment aussi la parure, sont jolies, généréuses et même maniérées."[d] [5] He notes, albeit with disapproval, that women very commonly aspired to stations above those to which they were born.[6] The Swedish naturalist Peter Kalm, who deplored the inadequate housekeeping of Canadian women, nevertheless admired their refinement.[7]

Those for whom history is an exercise in statistics have taught us caution in accepting the accounts of travellers, which are often highly subjective. However the consensus (particularly that of seasoned observers such as Charlevoix and Kalm) on the superior education and wit of women in New France suggests that their views are founded on something more than natural male proclivity towards *la différence*. Moreover, historians' accounts of society in New France offer ample evidence that women did indeed enjoy an exceptionally privileged position in that colony. The position was so privileged, in fact, that it contrasts favourably not only with that of their contemporaries in France and in New England, but probably also with twentieth-century Canadian women as far as entrepreneurial activity is concerned.

How did the women of New France acquire a superior education? How did they come to be involved in commerce? What gave rise to their vaunted *esprit*? There is no single answer to these questions. The truth is a compound of three separate factors. First, studies of Western Europe under the *ancien régime,*[e]

---

[a] The women surpass the men in beauty, liveliness, mirth and cleverness; they are flirts and forward, prefer men from Europe to those around them. Pleasant and polite manners are common, even in the countryside.

[b] ...the women are very agreeable but extremely proud.

[c] ...they are witty, which makes them superior to the men in almost every way.

[d] possess greater intelligence then the men, are generally quite intelligent, speak a refined French without the least accent, also like personal adornments, are pretty, generous and even genteel.

[e] the European political and social system before the French Revolution.

indicate that ideas about women's roles were surprisingly flexible and varied. Secondly, the particular demographic configuration of New France gave female immigrants a number of advantages not available to their counterparts in Europe. Thirdly, the colonial economy, with its heavy emphasis on war and the fur trade presented women with a special set of opportunities. Thus, as we shall see, cultural, demographic and economic conditions combined to produce the remarkable women of New France.

Women and the Family Under the *Ancien Régime*

The notion of "woman's place" or "women's role," popular with nineteenth century commentators, suggests a degree of homogeneity inappropriate to the seventeenth century. It is true that on a formal ideological level men enjoyed the dominant position. This can be seen in the marriage laws which everywhere made it a wife's duty to follow her husband to whatever dwelling place he chose.[8] In 1650, the men of Montreal were advised by Governor Maisonneuve that they were in fact responsible for the misdemeanours of their wives since "la loi les établit seigneurs de leurs femmes."[f][9] Under ordinary circumstances the father was captain of the family hierarchy.[10] Yet, it is clear that this formal male authority in both economic and domestic life was not always exercised. Of early seventeenth-century France we are told that

> si la prééminence masculine n'a rien perdu de son prestige, si elle n'a eu à se défendre contre aucune revendication théorique ... elle a dû ... souvent se contenter des apparences et abandonner devant les convenances et les exigences du public l'intérêt positif qu'elle défendait.[g][11]

The idea of separate male and female spheres lacked the clear definition it later acquired. This is in part related to the lack of communication and standardization characteristic of the *ancien régime*—along sexual lines or any others. Generalizations about women are riddled with exceptions. Contradicting the idea of female inferiority, for example, were the semi-matriarchal system in the Basque country, and the linen workers guild, in which a 1645 statute prevented a worker's husband from engaging in occupations unrelated to his wife's business, for which he often served as salesman or partner. More important, because it affected a larger group, was the fact that noblewomen were frequently exempt from legal handicaps affecting other women.[12]

---

[f] the law makes them lords over their wives.

[g] if the male predominance has lost nothing of its authority, if it has not had to struggle against any theoretical claim, it has still had to be satisfied with appearances and make sacrifices to keep up appearances and to fulfil the requirements of the public good that it supports.

One generalization, however, applies to all women of the *ancien régime*. They were not relegated to the private, domestic sphere of human activity because that sphere did not exist. Western Europeans had not yet learned to separate public and private life. As Philippe Ariès points out in his study of childhood, the private home, in which parents and children constitute a distinct unit, is a relatively recent development. In early modern Europe most of domestic life was lived in the company of all sorts of outsiders. Manor houses, where all the rooms interconnect with one another, show the lack of emphasis placed on privacy. Here, as in peasant dwellings, there were often no specialized rooms for sleeping, eating, working or receiving visitors; all were more or less public activities performed with a throng of servants, children, relatives, clerics, apprentices and clients in attendance. Molière's comedies illustrate the familiarity of servants with their masters. Masters, maids and valets slept in the same room and servants discussed their masters' lives quite openly.[13]

Though familiar with their servants, people were less so with their children. They did not dote on infants as parents do today. It may have been, as some writers have suggested, that there was little point in growing attached to a fragile being so very apt, in those centuries, to be borne away by accident or disease. These unsentimental families of all ranks sent their children out to apprentice or serve in other people's homes. This was considered important as a basic education.[14] It has been estimated that the majority of Western European children passed part of their childhood living in some household other than their natal one.[15] Mothers of these children—reaching down, in the town, as far as the artisan class—commonly sent their infants out to nursemaids and in fact had very little to do with their physical maintenance.[16]

This lack of a clearly defined "private" realm relates vitally to the history of women, since this was precisely the sphere which they later were to inhabit.[17] Therefore it is important to focus on their place in the pre-private world. To understand women in New France one first must pass through that antechamber which Peter Laslett appropriately calls "the world we have lost." Its notions of sexuality and of the family apply to France and New France alike.

In this public world people had not yet learned to be private about their bodily functions, especially about their sexuality. For aid with their toilette, noblewomen did not blush to employ *hommes de chambre* [h] rather than maids. The door of the bedchamber stood ajar, if not absolutely open. Its inhabitants, proud of their fecundity, grinned out from under the bedclothes at their visitors. Newlyweds customarily received bedside guests.[18] The mother of Louis XIV held court and chatted with visitors while labouring to bring *le Roi Soleil* [i] into

---

[h] valets

[i] the Sun King

light of day. Humbler village women kept lesser court among the little crowd of neighbours who attended the midwife's efforts.[19] On the other side of the ocean, Franquet, arriving at Trois-Rivières in 1753, enjoyed the hospitality of Madame Rigaud de Vaudreuil who, feeling poorly, apparently received her visitors at bedside; farther west, he shared a bedroom with a married couple at Fort St. Jean.[20] From the seventeenth century to the colony's last days, clerics thundered more or less futilely against the *décolletage* of the *élite*.[j] [21] Lesser folk leaned towards short skirts[22] and boisterous public discussion of impotent husbands.[23] Rape cases also reveal a rather matter-of-fact attitude. Courts stressed monetary compensation for the victim (as if for trespass on private property) rather than wreaking vengeance on the lustful villain.[24] There was not the same uneasiness in relations between the sexes which later, more puritanical, centuries saw, and which, judging by the withdrawal of women from public life in many of these societies, probably worked to their detriment.

Part of the reason these unsqueamish, rather public people were not possessive about their bodies was that they did not see themselves so much as individuals but as part of a larger more important unit—the family. In this world the family was the basic organization for most social and economic purposes.[25] As such it claimed the individual's first loyalty.[26] A much higher proportion of the population married than does today.[27] Studies of peasant societies suggest that, for most, marriage was an economic necessity:

> Le travail, particulièrement en milieu rural, était alors fondé sur une répartition des tâches entre les sexes: les marins et colporteurs sont absents plusieurs mois, leurs femmes font valoir les terres; les pêcheurs des marais vont au marché, les femmes à la pêche; le laboureur travaille aux champs, sa femme à la maison, c'est elle qui va au marché; dans le pays d'Auge, "les hommes s'occupent des bestiaux et les femmes aux fromages". Pour vivre il fallait donc être deux, un homme et une femme.[k] [28]

The family was able to serve as the basic economic unit in pre-industrial societies because the business of earning a living generally occurred at home. Just as public and private life were undifferentiated, so too were home and workplace. Agricultural and commercial pursuits were all generally "domestic" industries. We see this both in France and in New France. Removal of the man from home for most of the working day, an event which Laslett describes

---

[j] necklines of the upper classes

[k] Especially in rural areas, work was then based on the division of labour between the sexes. Since sailors and carters were absent for several months, their wives had to cultivate the land. Freshwater fishermen go to market while their wives go fishing. The ploughman works in the field while his wife works in the house as well as going to market. In the Auge region, "the men tend the animals and the women produce cheese." In order to survive, there had to be two, a man and a woman.

as the single most important event in the history of the modern European family,[29] was only beginning. The idea of man as breadwinner and woman as home-maker was not clearly developed. Women's range of economic activity was still nearly as wide as that of their husbands. Seventeenth-century France saw women working as bonesetters, goldbeaters, bookbinders, doubletmakers, burnishers, laundresses, woolfullers and wigmakers. Aside from their familiar role in the textile and clothing industries, women also entered heavy trades such as stoneworking and bricklaying. A master plumber, Barbe Legueux, maintained the drainage system for the fountains of Paris. In the commercial world, women worked as fishmongers, pedlars, greengrocers, publicans, money-lenders and auctioneers.[30] In New France, wives of artisans took advantage of their urban situation to attract customers into the taverns they set up alongside the workshop.[31] It was in farm work, which occupied most of the population, that male and female tasks differed the least of all. *Habitantes* in New France toiled in the fields alongside the men; and they almost certainly—being better educated than their French sisters—took up the farmwife's customary role of keeping accounts and managing purchases and sales.[32] Studies of Bordeaux commercial families have revealed that women also took a large role in business operations.[33] Marie de l'Incarnation's background as manager of one of France's largest transport companies,[34] shows that the phenomenon existed in other parts of France as well.

Given the economic importance of both spouses, it is not surprising to see marriage taking on some aspects of a business deal, with numerous relatives affixing their signatures to the contract. We see this in the provisions of the law which protected the property rights of both parties contracting a match. The fact that wives often brought considerable family property to the marriage, and retained rights to it, placed them in a better position than their nineteenth-century descendants were to enjoy.[35]

In New France the family's importance was intensified even beyond its usual economic importance in *ancien régime* societies. In the colony's early days, "all roads led to matrimony. The scarcity of women, the economic difficulties of existence, the danger, all tended to produce the same result: all girls became wives, all widows remarried."[36] Throughout the colony's history there was an exceptionally high annual marriage rate of eighteen to twenty-four per thousand.[37] The buildup of the family as a social institution perhaps came about because other social institutions, such as guilds and villages, were underdeveloped.[38] This heightened importance of the family probably enhanced women's position. In the family women tended to serve as equal partners with their husbands, whereas women were gradually losing their position in European guilds and professions.[39] We see this heightened importance of the family in the government's great concern to regulate it. At that time, the state *did* have a place in Canadian bedrooms (whose inhabitants we have already seen to be rather unconcerned about their privacy). Public intervention in domestic life took two major forms: the operation of the legal system and governmental attempts at family planning.

The outstanding characteristic of the legal system in New France—the *Coutume de Paris*[l]—is its concern to protect the rights of all members of the family. The *Coutume de Paris* is considered to have been a particularly benevolent regional variation of French law.[40] It was more egalitarian and less patriarchal than the laws of southern France which were based on Roman tradition. The *Coutume* reinforced the family, for example, by the penalties it levied on those transferring family property to non-kin.[41] It took care to protect the property of children of a first marriage when a widow or widower remarried.[42] It protected a woman's rights by assuring that the husband did not have power to alienate the family property (in contrast to eighteenth-century British law).[43] The Canadians not only adopted the Parisian *coutume* in preference to the Norman *coutume,* which was harsher;[44] they also implemented the law in a way which maximized protection of all family members. Louise Dechêne, after examining the operation of the marriage and inheritance system, concludes that the Canadian application of the law was generous and egalitarian:

> Ces concentions matrimoniales ne nous apparaissent pas comme un marché, un affrontement entre deux lignées, mais comme un accord désintéressé entre les familles, visant à créer une nouvelle communauté, à l'assister si possible, à dresser quelques barrières à l'entour pour la protéger....
> La même simplicité, la même générosité président au partage des successions....[m] [45]

The criminal law, too, served to buttress family life with its harsh punishments for mistreatment of children.[46]

The royal administration, as well as the law, treated the family as a matter of vital public concern. The state often intervened in matters which later generations left to the individual or to the operations of private charity. Most famous, of course, is the policy of encouraging a high birth rate with financial incentives. There were also attempts to withdraw trading privileges from voyageurs who showed reluctance to take immigrant women to wife.[47] Particularly in the seventeenth century, we see the state regulating what modern societies would consider intimate matters. However, in a colony starved for manpower, reproduction was considered a matter of particularly vital public concern—a concern well demonstrated in the extremely harsh punishments

---

[l] the body of customary law in force in the region of Paris.

[m] These marriage agreements do not appear to us to be business arrangements or to turn the two families into adversaries. Rather, they are disinterested agreements between families and are intended to create a new household and, if possible, to help it erect a few defenses to provide protection.
The same simplicity and generosity apply when settling estates.

meted out to women who concealed pregnancy.[48] We see a more positive side of this intervention in the care the Crown took of foundlings, employing nurses at a handsome salary to care for them, and making attempts to prevent children from bearing any stigma because of questionable origins.[49]

State regulation of the family was balanced by family regulation of the state. Families had an input into the political system, playing an important role in the running of the state. Indeed, it might be argued that the family was the basic political unit in New France. In an age when some members of the *noblesse* [n] prided themselves on their illiteracy, attending the right college was hardly the key to political success. Marrying into the right family was much more important. Nepotism, or rewarding one's kin with emoluments, seemed a most acceptable and natural form of patronage for those in power.[50] In this sense, a good marriage was considered a step upward for the whole family, which helps to explain why choice of spouse was so often a family decision.[51] These family lines were particularly tightly drawn among the military élite in New France. Franquet remarked that *"tous les gens d'un certain ordre sont liés de parenté et d'amitié dans ce pays."*[o] [52] In fact, with top military positions passing down from generation to generation, by the eighteenth century this élite became a caste.[53]

In this situation, where the *nom de famille* [p] was vastly more important than that of the individual, it was apparently almost as good for political (though not military) purposes to be an Agathe de Repentigny as a LeGardeur de Repentigny. Moreover, women's political participation was favoured by the large role of entertaining in political life. For the courtier's role, women were as well-trained as men, and there seems to have been no stigma attached to the woman who participated independently of her husband. Six women, Mesdames Daine, Pean, Lotbinière, de Repentigny, Marin, and St. Simon, along with six male officers, were chosen by the Intendant to accompany him to Montreal in 1753.[54] Of the twelve only the de Repentignys were a couple. It is surprising to see women from the colony's first families also getting down to what we would today consider the "business" end of politics. Madame de la Forest, a member of the Juchereau family, took an active role in the political cliques which Guy Frégault describes.[55] Mme. de la Forest's trip to France to plead the cause of Governor de Ramezay was inconsequential, though, in comparison with that of Mme. de Vaudreuil to further Governor Vaudreuil's cause in 1709. *"Douée d'un sens politique trés fin,"*[q] [56] she soon gained the ear of the Minister of Marine. Not

---

[n] nobility

[o] in this country, all the members of a certain class are connected by friendship and family relationships.

[p] family name

[q] Possessing a very subtle political sense

only did she secure the Governor's victory in the long conflict with the Intendants Raudot (father and son) and win promotion for his patrons; she appears to have gone on to upstage her husband by becoming the virtual director of colonial policy at Versailles for a few years. Vaudreuil's biographer discusses the influence Madame de Vaudreuil exerted with the Minster Pontchartrain who so regularly sought her comment on colonial patronage that supplicants began to apply directly to her rather than to the minister.[57] Contemporaries agreed that her influence was vast:

> Pontchartrain, rapporte Ruette d'Auteuil, ne lui refuse rien, "elle dispose de tous les emplois du Canada, elle écrit de toutes parts dans les ports de mer des lettres magnifiques du bien et du mal qu'elle peut faire auprès de lui," et le ministre "fait tout ce qu'il faut pour l'autoriser et justifier ses discours." Riverin confirme que ... "ce n'est plus qu'une femme qui règne tant présente qu'absente."[r] [58]

Governor Frontenac's wife (though not a *Canadienne*) also played an important role at court dispelling some of the thunderclouds which threatened her husband's stormy career.[59]

As for the common folk, we know even less about the political activity of women than that of men. That women participated in a form of popular assembly is hinted at in a report of a meeting held in 1713 (in present-day Boucherville), in which Catherine Guertin was sworn in as midwife after having been elected *"dans l'assemblée des femmes de cette paroisse, à la pluralité des suffrages, pour exercer l'office de sagefemme."*[s] [60] Were these women's assemblies a general practice? If so, what other matters did they decide? This aspect of *habitant* politics remains a mystery, but women, as historians of "crowds" have found, were certainly part of the "pre-industrial crowd."[61] Along with their menfolk, they were full-fledged members of the old "moral economy" whose members rioted, took what was traditionally their rightful share (and no more) when prices were too high or when speculators were hoarding grain.[62] The women of Quebec and Montreal, who rioted against the horsemeat rations and the general hunger of 1757-58, illustrate this aspect of the old polity.[63]

In sum, women's position during the *ancien régime* was open-ended. Although conditions varied, a wide range of roles were available to women, to be taken up or not. This was so because the separate spheres of men and women in *ancien régime* societies were not so clearly developed as they later became.

---

[r] Ruette d'Auteuil reports that Pontchartrain denies her nothing and that "she controls all the postings in Canada. She writes proud letters from every seaport that she can do anything with him," and that the minister "does everything necessary to give her authority and to support what she says." Riverin confirms that "this involves nothing more than a woman who rules whether she is present or not."

[s] in this parish's women's committee, with the majority of the votes, in order to carry out the duties of midwife.

There was as yet no sharp distinction between public and private life: families were for most purposes the basic social, economic and political unit. Owing to the underdevelopment of other institutions (the guild, the seigneurie, the village), this situation was intensified in New France. The activities of bread-winner and home-maker were not yet widely recognized as separate functions belonging to one sex or the other. All members of the family also often shared the same economic functions, or at least roles were interchangeable. Nor had the symbolic, the honorific, the stylistic aspects of government yet been separated from the business end of politics and administration. These conditions, typical of most of pre-industrial France, were also found in New France, where particular demographic and economic conditions would enable the colony's women to develop their freedoms and opportunities to the fullest.

Demographic Advantages

Demography favoured the women of New France in two ways. First, the women who went there were a highly select group of immigrants. Secondly, women were in short supply in the early years of the colony's development, a situation that worked in their favour.

The bulk of the female immigrants to New France fall into one of two categories. The first was a group of extremely well-born, well-endowed and highly dedicated religious figures. They began to arrive in 1639, and a trickle of French nuns continued to cross the ocean over the course of the next century. The second distinct group was the *filles du roi*,[t] government sponsored female migrants who arrived between 1663 and 1673. These immigrants, though not as outstanding as the *dévotes*,[u] were nevertheless privileged compared to the average immigrant to New France, who arrived more or less threadbare.[64] The vast majority of the women (and the men) came from the Ile-de-France and the northwestern parts of France. The women of northern France enjoyed fuller legal rights, were better educated, and more involved in commerce than those in southern France.[65] When they set foot on colonial soil with all this auspicious baggage, the immigrants found that they had yet another advantage. Women constituted a small percentage of the population. As a scarce resource they were highly prized and therefore in an excellent position to gain further advantages.

The first *religieuses*[v] to arrive in New France were the Ursulines and Hospitallers who landed at Quebec in 1639. These were soon followed by women who helped establish Montreal in 1642. Their emigration was inspired by a re-

---

[t] daughters of the King

[u] religious-minded women

[v] nuns

ligious revival in France, which is thought to have arisen in response to the widespread pauperism following the French civil wars of the sixteenth century. The seventeenth-century revival distinguished itself by tapping the energies of women in an unprecedented way.[66] Among its leaders were Anne of Austria and a number of the leading ladies at court.[67] In other parts of France, women of the provincial élite implemented the charity work inspired by Saint Vincent de Paul.[68] Occurring between 1600 and 1660, this religious revival coincided almost exactly with the period when the fledgling Canadian colony, besieged by English privateers and by the Iroquois, was most desperately in need of an injection of immigrants, money and enthusiasm.[69] It was at this moment that the Jesuits in Quebec appealed to the French public for aid. Much to their surprise, they received not a donation but a half-dozen religious zealots, in person. Abandoning the centuries-old cloistered role of female religious figures these nuns undertook missionary work which gave them an active role in the life of the colony.[70] Thus the great religious revival of the seventeenth century endowed New France with several exceptionally capable, well-funded, determined leaders imbued with an activist approach to charity and with that particular mixture of spiritual ardour and worldly *savoir-faire*[w] which typified the mystics of that period.[71] The praises of Marie de l'Incarnation, Jeanne Mance and Marguerite Bourgeoys have been sung so often as to be tiresome. Perhaps, though a useful vantage point is gained if one assesses them neither as saints nor heroines, but simply as leaders. In this capacity, the nuns supplied money, publicity, skills, and settlers, all of which were needed in the colony.

Marie de l'Incarnation, an extremely competent business-woman from Tours, founded the Ursuline Monastery at Quebec in 1639. Turning to the study of Indian languages, she and her colleagues helped implement the policy of assimilating the young Indians. Then, gradually abandoning that futile policy, they turned to the education of the French colonists. Marie de l'Incarnation developed the farm on the Ursuline seigneurie and served as an unofficial adviser to the colonial administrators. She also helped draw attention and money to the colony by writing some twelve thousand letters between 1639 and her death in 1672.[72]

An even more prodigious fund-raiser in those straitened times was Jeanne Mance, who had a remarkable knack for making friends in high places.[73] They enabled her to supply money and colonists for the original French settlement on the island of Montreal, and to take a place beside Maisonneuve as co-founder of the town.[74] The hospital she established there had the legendary wealth of the de Bullion family—and the revenues of three Norman domains—behind it. From this endowment she made the crucial grant to Governor Maisonneuve in 1651 which secured vitally needed French troops—thus saving Montreal.[75]

---

[w] sophistication

Mance and her Montreal colleague Margeurite Bourgeoys both made several voyages to France to recruit settlers. They were particularly successful in securing the female immigrants necessary to establish a permanent colony, recruiting sizeable groups in 1650, 1653 and 1659.[76]

Besides contributing to the colony's sheer physical survival, the nuns materially raised the living standards of the population. They conducted the schools which were attended by girls of all classes, and from both of the colony's races. Bourgeoys provided housing for newly arrived immigrants and served in a capacity perhaps best described as an early social worker.[77] Other nuns established hospitals in each of the three towns. The colonists reaped fringe benefits in the institutions established by this exceptionally dedicated personnel. The hospitals, for example, provided high-quality care to both rich and poor; care which compared favourably with that of similar institutions in France.[78] Thus, the *dévotes* played an important role in supplying leadership, funding, publicity, recruits and social services. They may even have tipped the balance towards survival in the 1650s, when retention of the colony was still in doubt.

In the longer run, they endowed the colony with an educational heritage, which survived and shaped social life long after the initial heroic piety had grown cold. The schools that the *dévotes* founded created a situation very different from that in France, where education of women in the seventeenth century lagged behind that of men.[79] The opinion-setters in France sought to justify this neglect in the eighteenth century and a controversy began over whether girls should be educated outside the home at all.[80] Girls in Montreal escaped all this. Indeed, in 1663 Montrealers had a school for their girls but none for their boys. The result was that for a time Montreal women surpassed men in literacy, a reversal of the usual *ancien régime* pattern.[81] The superior education of women which Charlevoix extolled in 1744 continued until the fall of New France (and beyond)—a tendency heightened by the large percentage of soldiers, generally illiterate, among the male population.[82] The Ursulines conducted schools for the élite at Quebec and Trois-Rivières. This order was traditionally rather weak in teaching housekeeping (which perhaps accounts for Kalm's famous castigation of Canadian housewifery). Nevertheless they specialized in needlework, an important skill since articles of clothing were a major trade good sought by the Indians. Moreover the Ursulines taught the daughters of the élite the requisite skills for administering a house and a fortune—skills which, as we shall see later, many were to exercise.[83]

More remarkable than the Ursuline education, however, was that of the *Soeurs de la Congrégation*,[x] which reached the popular classes in the countryside.[84] Franquet was apparently shocked by the effect of this exceptional education on the colonial girls. He recommended that the *Soeurs'* schools be suppressed because they made it difficult to keep girls down on the farm:

---

[x] Sisters of the Order of the Congregation

Ces Soeurs sont répandues le long des côtes, dans des seigneuries où elles ont été attirées pour l'éducation des jeunes filles; leur utilité semble être démontrée, mais le mal qu'en résulte est comme un poison lent qui tend à dépeupler les campagnes, d'autant qu'une fille instruite fait la demoiselle, qu'elle est maniérée, qu'elle veut prendre un éstablissement à la ville, qu'il lui faut un négociant et qu'elle regarde au dessous d'elle l'état dans lequel elle est née.[y][85]

The second distinct group of female immigrants to New France was the famous *filles du roi*, women sent out by the French government as brides in order to boost the colony's permanent settlement. Over nine hundred arrived between 1663 and 1673.[86] If less impressive than the *dévotes*, they too appear to have arrived with more than the average immigrant's store of education and capital. Like the nuns, they were the product of a particular historical moment which thrust them across the sea. The relevant event here is that brief interlude in the 1660s and 1670s when the King, his Minister Colbert and the Intendant Talon applied an active hand to colonial development.[87]

There has been much historical controversy about whether the *filles du roi* were pure or not.[88] More relevant to our discussion than their morality are their money and their skills. On both these counts, this was a very selective immigration. First of all, the majority of the *filles du roi* (and for that matter, of seventeenth-century female immigrants generally) were urban dwellers, a group which enjoyed better access to education than the peasantry did.[89] Moreover, the *filles du roi* were particularly privileged urbanites. Over one third, some 340 of them, were educated at the Paris Hôpital Général. Students at this institution learned writing and such a wide variety of skills that in France they were much sought after for service in the homes of the wealthy. Six percent were of noble or bourgeois origin. All the *filles* brought with them a 50-100 *livres* [z] dowry provided by the King; most supplemented this with personal funds in the order of 200-300 *livres*.[90] According to Lanctôt, among lay immigrants, these women constituted the immigration *"la plus stricte, la plus saine et la plus recommandable de toute cette époque."*[aa][91] The Parisian origins of many *filles du roi*, and of the nuns who taught their children, probably account for the pure French accent which a number of travellers attributed to the colony's women.[92]

These two major immigrant groups, then, the nuns and the *filles du roi*, largely account for the superior education and "cultivation" attributed to the

---

[y] These nuns can be found all along the river, in the seigneuries where they have been attracted in order to educate the young girls. Their usefulness seems evident but the evil that results from their presence works like a slow poison that tends to reduce the rural population because a girl who has received an education begins to act above her station and to put on airs. She then wants to set herself up in town and to insist on marrying a merchant, eventually deciding that her social class at birth is now beneath her.

[z] pounds

[aa] the most demanding, the healthiest and the most to be recommended for the whole period.

colony's women. Another demographic consideration also favoured the women of New France. As a result of light female emigration, men heavily out-numbered women in the colony's early days; a balance was not attained until 1710.[93] It might be expected that, as a scarce commodity, women would receive favoured treatment. The facility of marriage and remarriage, the salaries women received, and the leniency of the courts and the administrators towards women, suggest that this hypothesis is correct.

Women had a wider choice in marriage than did men in the colony's early days. There were, for example, eight marriageable men for every marriageable woman in Montreal in 1663. Widows grieved, briefly, then remarried within an average of 8.8 months after their bereavement. In those early days the laws of supply and demand operated to women's economic advantage, as well. Rarely did these first Montreal women bother to match their husband's wedding present by offering a dowry.[94] The colony distinguished itself as "the country of the *douaire* not of the *dot*."[bb] [95]

Other economic indicators suggest that scarcity served women well. Observers of women's salaries in the nineteenth and twentieth centuries are used to finding them ranging from one-half to two-thirds those of men. This list of 1744 salaries of New France therefore comes as something of a surprise:

Un professeur de collège	400 livres
Une institutrice	500 livres
Une sage-femme attachée à l'Hôtel-Dieu de Québec	400 livres
le prévot des maréchaux	500 livres
le lieutenant général de Montréal	450 livres
le procureur du roi (Mtl.)	250 livres
un conseiller ordinaire au Conseil Supérieur	300 livres
un Missionnaire au Poste de la mer de l'Ouest	600 livres[cc] [96]

Perhaps the government, as in later centuries, led the way as an "equal opportunity" employer. At any rate, nursemaids hired by the government ac-

---

[bb] "the country of the marriage settlement not of the marriage portion."

[cc]
A male teacher in a college	400 pounds
A female teacher	500 pounds
A midwife working at the Hôtel-Dieu in Quebec City	400 pounds
The provost marshall	500 pounds
The lieutenant-general for Montreal	450 pounds
The royal procurator (Montreal)	250 pounds
An ordinary member on the Superior Council	300 pounds
A missionary stationed at Western Posts	600 pounds

quired not only the civil servant's dignity and job security but were paid, we are told, their salaries in cash, in advance, and at a rate "more than the towns-people were accustomed to pay for the nursing of their own children."[97]

In the social and legal realm we also find privileges which may have been attributable to the shortage of women. Perhaps it is due to the difficulties of replacing battered wives that jealous husbands in New France were willing to forego the luxury of uncontrolled rage. Some of the intendants even charged that there were libertine wives in the colony who got away with taking a second husband while the first was away trading furs.[98] Recent indications that New France conformed rather closely to French traditions make it unlikely that this was common.[99] But the judgements of the Sovereign Council do offer evidence of peaceful reconciliations such as that of Marguerite Leboeuf, charged with adultery in 1667. The charge was dismissed when her husband pleaded before the Sovereign Council on her behalf. Also leaving vengeance largely to the Lord was Antoine Antorche, who withdrew his accusation against his wife even after the Council found her doubly guilty.[100] In this regard the men of New France differed from their Portuguese brothers in Brazil, who perpetrated a number of amorous murders each year; also from their English brethren in Massachusetts, who branded or otherwise mutilated their errant wives and daughters.[101] When such cases reached the courts in New France the judges, too, appear to have been lenient. Their punishments for adulterous women were considerably lighter than those imposed in New England. Other female offenders, such as the whiskey trader captured in 1661, received a much lighter punishment than men convicted of identical offences. A further peculiarity of the legal system in New France, which suggests that women were closer to being on an equal footing with men than in other times and places, was the unusual attempt to arrest not only prostitutes but their clients as well.[102]

Another indication of the lenient treatment Canadian women enjoyed is the level of insubordination the authorities were willing to accept from them. There was a distinct absence of timidity vis-à-vis the political authorities. In 1714, for example, the inhabitants of Côte St. Leonard violently objected to the Bishop's decision to cancel their membership in the familiar church and enroll them in the newly erected parish of Rivière-des-Prairies. A fracas ensued in which the consecrated altar breads were captured by the rebellious parishioners. An officer sent to restore order was assailed by angry women:

> L'huissier chargé d'aller assigner les séditieux, raconte que toutes les femmes l'attendaient "avec des roches et des perches dans leurs mains pour m'assassiner," qu'elles le poursuivirent en jurant: "arrête voleur, nous te voulons tuer et jeter dans le marais."dd [103]

---

dd The officer responsible for apprehending the trouble-makers states that all the women were waiting for him "with rocks and sticks in their hands that they were going to kill me with," and that they chased him, swearing, "Stop, thief, we want to kill you and throw you in the pond."

Other women hurled insults at the Governor himself in the 1670s.[104] An even more outrageous case of insubordination, was that of the two Desaulniers sisters, who by dint of various appeals, deceits and stalling tactics, continued to run an illegal trading post at Caughnawaga for some twenty-five years despite repeated orders from governors, intendants and the ministry itself, to close it down.[105]

A further indication of women's privileged position is the absence of witchcraft persecution in New France. The colony was founded in the seventeenth century when this persecution was at its peak in Western Europe. The New Englanders, too, were burning witches at Salem. Not a single Canadienne died for this offence.[106] It is not—as Marie de l'Incarnation's account of the 1663 earthquake makes clear[107]—that the Canadians were not a superstitious people. A scholar of crime in New France suggests that this surprising absence of witchcraft hysteria relates to the fact that *"depuis le début de la colonie une femme était une rareté trés estimée et de ce fait, protégée de la persécution en masse."*[ee] [108]

Thus, on the marriage market, and in their protection from physical violence, women seem to have achieved a favourable position because of their small numbers. Their relatively high wages and lighter court sentences may also have been related to the demographic imbalance. Moreover, the original female immigrants arrived in the colony with better than average education and capital, attributes which undoubtedly helped them to establish their privileged status.

Economic Opportunities

Even more than demographic forces, the colonial economy served to enhance the position of women. In relation to the varied activities found in many regions of France, New France possessed a primitive economy. Other than subsistence farming, the habitants engaged in two major pursuits. The first was military activity, which included not only actual fighting but building and maintaining the imperial forts, and provisioning the troops. The second activity was the fur trade. Fighting and fur-trading channelled men's ambitions and at times removed them physically from the colony. This helped open up the full range of opportunities to women, whom we have already seen had the possibility of assuming a wide variety of economic roles in *ancien régime* society. Many adapted themselves to life in a military society. A few actually fought. Others made a good living by providing goods and services to the ever-present armies. Still others left military activity aside and concentrated on civilian economic pursuits—pursuits which were often neglected by men. For many this simply meant managing the family farm as best as one could during the trading season, when husbands were away. Other women assumed direction of commercial enterprises, a neglected area in this society which preferred military honours to commercial prizes. Others acted as a sort of

---

[ee] "since the early days of the colony, women have not been numerous and have thus been greatly respected and, as a result, protected from mass persecution."

home-office partner for fur trading husbands working far afield. Still others, having lost husbands to raids, rapids or other hazards of forest life, assumed a widow's position at the helm of the family business.

> New France has been convincingly presented as a military society. The argument is based on the fact that a very large proportion of its population was under arms, its government had a semi-military character, its economy relied heavily on military expenditure and manpower, and a military ethos prevailed among the élite.[109] In some cases, women joined their menfolk in these martial pursuits. The seventeenth century sometimes saw them in direct combat. A number of Montrealers perished during an Iroquois raid in 1661 in which, Charlevoix tells us, "even the women fought to the death, and not one of them surrendered."[110] In Acadia, Madame de la Tour took command of the fort's forty-five soldiers and warded off her husband's arch-enemy, Menou D'Aulnay, for three days before finally capitulating.[111]

The most famous of these seventeenth-century *guerrières* [ff] was, of course, Madeleine de Verchères. At the age of fourteen she escaped from a band of Iroquois attackers, rushed back to the fort on her parents' seigneurie and fired a cannon shot in time to warn all the surrounding settlers of the danger.[112] Legend and history have portrayed Madeleine as a lamb who was able, under siege, to summon up a lion's heart. Powdered and demure in a pink dress, she smiles very sweetly out at the world in a charming vignette in Arthur Doughty's *A Daughter of New France, being a story of the life and times of Magdelaine de Verchères*, published in 1916. Perhaps the late twentieth century is ready for her as she was: a swashbuckling, musket-toting braggart who extended the magnitude of her deeds with each successive telling, who boasted that she never in her life shed a tear; a contentious thorn in the side of the local curé (whom she slandered), and of her *censitaires,*[gg] (whom she constantly battled in the courts).[113] She strutted through life for all the world like the boorish male officers of the *campagnard* [hh] nobility to which her family belonged.[114] One wonders how many more there were like her. Perhaps all trace of them has vanished into the wastebaskets of subsequent generations of historians who, with immovable ideas of female propriety, did not know what on earth to do with them—particularly after what must have been the exhausting effort of pinching Verchères' muscled frame into a corset and getting her to wear the pink dress.

By the eighteenth century, women had withdrawn from hand-to-hand combat, but many remained an integral part of the military élite as it closed in to become a caste. In this system, both sexes shared the responsibility of marrying properly and of maintaining those cohesive family ties which, Corvisier tells us, lay at the heart of military society. Both also appealed to the Ministry for their sons' promotions.[115]

[ff] warrior women

[gg] tenants

[hh] rural

What is more surprising is that a number of women accompanied their husbands to military posts in the wilderness. Wives of officers, particularly of corporals, traditionally helped manage the canteens in the French armies.[116] Almost all Canadian officers were involved in some sort of trading activity, and a wife at the post could mind the store when the husband had to mind the war. Some were overzealous. When Franquet rode into Fort Saint Frédéric in 1752 he discovered a terrific row among its inhabitants. The post was in a virtual state of mutiny because a Madame Lusignan was monopolizing all the trade, both wholesale and retail, at the fort; and her husband, the Commandant, was enforcing the monopoly.[117] In fact, Franquet's inspection tour of the Canadian posts is remarkable for the number of women who greeted him at the military posts, which one might have expected to be a male preserve. Arriving at Fort Sault Saint Louis he was received very politely by M. de Merceau and his two daughters. He noted that Fort Saint Frédéric housed not only the redoubtable Madame Lusignan but also another officer's widow. At Fort Chambly he "spent the whole day with the ladies, and visited Madame de Beaulac, an officer's widow who has been given lodging in this fort."[118]

The nuns, too, marched in step with this military society. They were, quite literally, one of its lifelines, since they cared for its wounded. A majority of the invalids at the Montreal Hôtel Dieu were soldiers, and the Ursuline institution at Trois-Rivières was referred to simply as a *hôpital militaire*.[ii] [119] Hospital service was so vital to the army that Frontenac personally intervened to speed construction of the Montreal Hôtel-Dieu in 1695, when he was planning a campaign against the Iroquois.[120] In the colony's first days, the Ursulines also made great efforts to help the Governor seal Indian alliances by attempting to secure Iroquois students who would serve as hostages, and by giving receptions for Iroquois chiefs.[121]

Humbler folk also played a part in military society. In the towns female publicans conducted a booming business with the thirsty troops. Other women served as laundresses, adjuncts so vital that they accompanied armies even on the campaigns where wives and other camp followers were ordered to stay home.[122] Seemingly indispensable, too, wherever armies march, are prostitutes. At Quebec City they plied their trade as early as 1667. Indian women at the missions also served in this capacity.[123] All told, women had more connections with the military economy than is generally noted.

While warfare provided a number of women with a living, it was in commerce that the *Canadiennes* really flourished. Here a number of women moved beyond supporting roles to occupy centre stage. This happened for several reasons. The first was that the military ethos diverted men from commercial activity. Secondly, many men who entered the woods to fight or trade were gone for years. Others, drowned or killed in battle, obviously never returned.[124] This left many widows who had to earn a livelihood. This happened so often, in fact,

---

[ii] military hospital

that when in 1710 women finally overcame the population imbalance due to their weak immigration, the tables turned quickly; they soon outnumbered the men, and remained a majority through to the Conquest.[125] Generally speaking, life was more hazardous for men than for women[126]—so much so that the next revolution of the historiographic wheel may turn up the men of New France (at least in relation to its women) as an oppressed group.

At any rate, women often stepped in to take the place of their absent husbands or brothers. A surprising number of women traders emerge in the secondary literature on New France. In the colony's earliest days, the mere handful of women included two merchants at Trois-Rivières: Jeanne Enard (mother-in-law of Pierre Boucher) who "by her husband's own admission" was the head of the family as far as fur-trading was concerned; and, Mathurine Poisson, who sold imported goods to the colonists.[127] At Montreal there was the wife of Artus de Sully, whose unspecified (but presumably commercial) activities won her the distinction of being Montreal's biggest debtor.[128] In Quebec City, Eleonore de Grandmaison was a member of a company formed to trade in the Ottawa country. She added to her wealth by renting her lands on the Ile d'Orleans to Huron refugees after Huronia had been destroyed. Farther east, Madame de la Tour involved herself in shipping pelts to France. Another Acadian, Madame Joybert, traded furs on the Saint John River.[129]

With the onset of the less pious eighteenth century, we find several women at the centre of the illegal fur trade. Indian women, including "a cross-eyed squaw named Marie-Magdelaine" regularly carried contraband goods from the Caughnawaga Reserve to Albany.[130] A Madame Couagne received Albany contraband at the other end, in Montreal.[131] But at the heart of this illegal trade were the Desaulniers sisters, who used their trading post on the Caughnawaga reserve as an *entrepô*[jj] for the forbidden English strouds, fine textiles, pipes, boots, lace, gloves, silver tableware, chocolate, sugar and oysters which the Indians brought regularly from Albany.[132] Franquet remarked on the power of these *marchandes*,[kk] who were able to persuade the Indians to refuse the government's request to build fortifications around their village.[133] The Desaulniers did not want the comings and goings of their employees too closely scrutinized.

These *commerçantes*,[ll] honest and otherwise, continued to play their part until the Conquest. Marie-Anne Barbel (*Veuve* [mm] Fornel) farmed the Tadoussac fur trade and was involved in diverse enterprises including retail sales, brickmaking and real estate.[134] On Franquet's tour in the 1750s he encountered other *marchandes* besides the controversial "Madame la Commandante" who had usurped the Fort Saint Frédéric trade. He enjoyed a more restful night closer

---

[jj] warehouse

[kk] women merchants

[ll] dealers

[mm] Widow

to Montreal at the home of Madame de Lemothe, a *marchande* who had prospered so well that she was able to put up her guests in splendid beds which Franquet proclaimed "fit for a duchess."[135]

A number of writers have remarked on the shortage of entrepreneurial talent in New France.[136] This perhaps helps to account for the activities of Agathe de St. Père, who established the textile industry in Canada. She did so after the colonial administrators had repeatedly called for development of spinning and weaving, with no result.[137] Coming from the illustrious Le Moyne family, Agathe St. Père married the ensign Pierre Legardeur de Repentigny, a man who, we are told, had "an easy-going nature." St. Père, of another temperament, pursued the family business interests, investing in fur trade partnerships, real estate and lending operations. Then in 1705, when the vessel bringing the yearly supply of French cloth to the colony was shipwrecked, she saw an opportunity to develop the textile industry in Montreal. She ransomed nine English weavers who had been captured by the Indians, and arranged for apprentices to study the trade. Subsequently these apprentices taught the trade to other Montrealers on home looms which Madame de Repentigny built and distributed. Besides developing the manufacture of linen, drugget and serge, she discovered new chemicals which made use of the native plants to dye and process them.[138]

Upon this foundation Madame Benoist built. Around the time of the Conquest, she was directing an operation in Montreal in which women turned out, among other things, shirts and petticoats for the fur trade.[139] This is a case of woman doing business while man did battle, for Madame Benoist's husband was commanding officer at Lac des Deux Montagnes.

This absence of male entrepreneurs may also explain the operation of a large Richelieu lumbering operation by Louise de Ramezay, the daughter of the Governor of Montreal. Louise, who remained single, lost her father in 1724. Her mother continued to operate the saw-milling operation on the family's Chambly Seigneury, but suffered a disastrous reverse due to a combination of flooding, theft and shipwreck in 1725. The daughter, however, went into partnership with the Seigneuress de Rouville in 1745 and successfully developed the sawmill. She then opened a flour mill, a Montreal tannery and another sawmill. By the 1750s the trade was flourishing: Louise de Ramezay was shipping 20,000 *livres* loads, and one merchant alone owed her 60,000 *livres*. In 1753 she began to expand her leather business, associating with a group of Montreal tanners to open new workshops.[140]

Louise de Ramezay's case is very clearly related to the fact that she lived in a military society. As Louise was growing up, one by one her brothers perished. Claude, an ensign in the French navy, died during an attack on Rio de Janeiro in 1711, Louis died during the 1715 campaign against the Fox Indians, La Gesse died ten years later in a shipwreck off Ile Royale. That left only one son, Jean-Baptiste-Roch, and, almost inevitably, he chose a military career over management of the family business affairs.[141] It may be that similar situations accounted for the female entrepreneurs in ironforging, tilemaking, sturgeon-fishing, sealing and contract building, all of whom operated in New France.[142]

If military society was the warp for this network of trading women, family connections were the woof. Madame Benoist belonged to the Baby family, whose male members were out cultivating the western fur trade. Her production of shirts made to the Indians' specifications was the perfect complement. The secret of the Desaulniers' successful trade network may well be that they were related to so many of Montreal's leading merchants.[143] The fur trade generally required two or more bases of operation. We saw earlier in our discussion that this society not only placed great value on family connections but also accepted female commercial activity. It was therefore quite natural that female relatives would be recruited into business to cover one of the bases. Men who were heading for the west would delegate their powers of attorney and various business responsibilities to their wives, who were remaining in the colony.[144]

We find these husband-wife fur trade partnerships not only among *"Les Grandes Familles"*[nn] but permeating all classes of society. At Trois-Rivières women and girls manufactured the canoes which carried the fur trade provisions westward each summer. This was a large-scale operation which profited from fat government contracts.[145] In Montreal, wives kept the account-books while their husbands traded. Other women spent the winters sewing shirts and petticoats which would be bartered the following summer.[146]

The final reason for women's extensive business activity was the direct result of the hazards men faced in fighting and fur trading. A high proportion of women were widowed; and as widows, they enjoyed special commercial privileges. In traditional French society, these privileges were so extensive that craftsmen's widows sometimes inherited full guild-master's rights. More generally, widows acquired the right to manage the family assets until the children reached the age of twenty-five (and sometimes beyond that time). In some instances they also received the right to choose which child would receive the succession.[147] In New France these rights frequently came into operation; and they had a major impact on the distribution of wealth and power in the society. In 1663, for example, women held the majority of the colony's seigneurial land. The *Veuve* Lemoyne numbered among the twelve Montreal merchants who, between 1642 and 1725, controlled assets of 50,000 *livres*. The *Veuve* Fornel acquired a similar importance later on in the regime. Some of the leading merchants at Louisbourg were also widows. The humbler commerce of tavernkeeping was also frequently a widow's lot.[148]

[nn] The Leading Families

Thus, in New France, both military and commercial activities which required a great deal of travelling over vast distances were usually carried out by men. In their absence, their wives played a large role in the day-to-day economic direction of the colony. Even when the men remained in the colony, military ambitions often absorbed their energies, particularly among the upper class. In these situations, it was not uncommon for a wife to assume direction of the family interests.[149] Others waited to do so until their widowhood, which—given the fact that the average wife was considerably younger than her husband and that his activities were often more dangerous—frequently came early.

Conclusion

New France had been founded at a time in Europe's history in which the roles of women were neither clearly nor rigidly defined. In this fluid situation, the colony received an exceptionally well-endowed group of female immigrants during its formative stage. There, where they long remained in short supply, they secured a number of special privileges at home, at school, in the courts, and in social and political life. They consolidated this favourable position by attaining a major role in the colonial economy, at both the popular and the directive levels. These circumstances enabled the women of New France to play many parts. *Dévotes* and traders, warriors and landowners, smugglers and politicians, industrialists and financiers; they thronged the stage in such numbers that they distinguish themselves as *femmes favorisées*.

Notes

1. F.-X. Charlevoix, *History and General Description of New France* (New York: Harper, 1900), Vol. 3: p. 28.

2. Cited in R.-L. Séguin, "La Canadienne aux XVIIe et XVIIIe siècles," *Revue d'historie de l'Amérique français,* XIII, (mars 1960), p. 492.

3. Séguin, "La Canadienne," p. 500.

4. *Ibid.*

5. L. Franquet, *Voyages et mémoires sur le Canada* (Montréal: Editions Elysee, 1974), p. 57, recording a tour in 1752-53.

6. *Ibid.,* p. 31.

7. Séguin, "La Canadienne," pp. 492, 505.

8. G. Fagniez, *La Femme et la société française dans la première moitié du XVIIe siècle* (Paris: J. Gambler, 1929), p. 154.

9. Marcel Trudel, *Montréal, la formation d'une société* (Montreal: Fides, 1976), p. 216-217.

10. John F. Bosher, "The Family in New France," in *In Search of the Visible Past,* Barry Gough, ed. (Waterloo, Ont.: W.L.U. Press, 1976), p. 7.

11. Fagniez, *Femme et société française,* p. 121.

12. *Ibid.,* pp. 149, 104, 193.

13. Philippe Ariès, *Centuries of Childhood* (New York: Vintage 1962), pp. 392-406.

14. *Ibid.,* pp. 365-66.

15. Peter Laslett, "Characteristics of the Western Family Considered over Time," *Journal of Family History,* 2 (Summer 1977), pp. 89-115.

16. Richard Vann, "Women in Preindustrial Capitalism," in *Becoming Visible: Women in European History,* R. Bridenthal, ed. (Boston: Houghton Mifflin, 1977), p. 206.

17. *Ibid.,* pp. 206-8; Ariès, *Centuries of Childhood,* pp. 397-406.

18. Fagniez, *Femme et société française,* pp. 122-23; 179.

19. Vann, "Women in Preindustrial Capitalism," p. 206.

20. Franquet, *Voyages,* pp. 135 and 61.

21. Séguin, "La Canadienne," pp. 499 and R. Boyer, *Les Crimes et châtiments au Canada française du XVIIIe au XXe siècle* (Montreal: 1966), p. 391.

22. Séguin, "La Canadienne," p. 506.

23. Boyer, *Crimes et châtiments,* p. 351.

24. *Ibid.,* pp. 344-46.

25. Laslett, "Western Family," p. 95.

26. I. Foulché-Delbosc, "Women of Three Rivers, 1651-1663," in *The Neglected Majority,* A. Prentice and S. Trofimenkoff, eds. (Toronto: McClelland and Stewart, 1977), p. 26.

27. Bosher ("The Family," p. 3) found the marriage rate in New France to be about three times that of modern-day Quebec.

28. This information is taken from a study of Normandy, which was the birthplace of many of the Canadian colonists. J.M. Gouesse, "La Formation du couple en Basse-Normandie," *XVIIe Siècle,* Nos. 102-3 (1974), p. 56.

29. Laslett, "Western Family," p. 106.

30. Fagniez, *Femme et société française,* pp. 99-104, 108, 111, 114-16.

31. Louise Dechêne, *Habitants et marchands de Montréal au XVIIe siècle* (Paris: Plon, 1974), p. 393.

32. Fagniez, *Femme et société française,* pp. 101, 1913, Séguin, "La Canadienne," p. 503; also G. Lanctôt, *Filles de joie ou filles du roi* (Montréal, 1952), m pp. 210-13.

33. Cf. Paul Butel, "Comportements familiaux dans le négoce bordelais au XVIIIe siècle," *Annales du Midi,* Vol. 88 (1976): pp. 139-157.

34. M.E. Chabot, "Marie Guyart de L'Incarnation, 1599-1672," in *The Clear Spirit,* M. Innis, ed. (Toronto: University of Toronto Press, 1966), p. 28.

35. Bosher, "The Family," p. 7; H. Neatby, *Quebec, The Revolutionary Age* (Toronto: McClelland and Stewart, 1966), p. 46.

36. Foulché-Delbosc, "Women of Three Rivers," p. 15.

37. Bosher, "The Family," p. 3. I have rounded his figures.

38. Dechêne, *Habitants et marchands,* p. 434, and Bosher, "The Family," p. 5.

39. Vann, "Women in Preindustrial Capitalism," p. 205; cf. also Alice Clark, *Working Life of Women in the Seventeenth Century* (London: Cass, 1968), chs. V, VI; and Fagniez, *Femme et société française,* for the scarcity of women's guilds by the seventeenth century.

40. *Ibid.,* p. 168 ff.

41. Y. Zoltvany, "Esquisse de la Coutume de Paris," *RHAF,* (decembre 1971).

42. Foulché-Delbosc, "Women of Three Rivers," p. 19.

43. Neatby, *Quebec,* p. 46.

44. Fagniez, *Femme et société française,* p. 147.

45. Dechêne, *Habitants et marchands,* pp. 423-24.

46. A. Morel, "Réflexions sur la justice criminelle canadienne au 18e siècle," *RHAF,* 29 (septembre 1975), pp. 241-253.

47. Lanctôt, *Filles de joie,* p. 219.

48. Boyer, *Crimes et châtiments,* pp. 128-29.

49. W.J. Eccles, "Social Welfare Measures and Policies in New France," *Congreso Internacional de Americanistas,* IV, (1966), Seville, pp. 9-19.

50. J. Bosher, "Government and Private Interests in New France," in *Canadian History Before Confederation,* J.M. Bumsted, ed. (Georgetown, Ontario: Irwin-Dorsey, 1972), p. 122.

51. Bosher, "The Family," pp. 5-7; Fagniez, *Femme et société française,* p. 182.

52. Franquet, *Voyages,* p. 148; cf., also Frégault, *Le XVIIIe siècle canadien* (Montréal: Collection Constantes, 1968), pp. 292-293.

53. W.J. Eccles, "The Social, Economic and Political Significance of the Military Establishment in New France," *Canadian Historical Review,* LII (March 1971), pp. 8-10.

54. Franquet, *Voyages,* pp. 129-30. For another, similar trip, *cf.* pp. 140-42.

55. Frégault, *Le XVIIIe Siècle,* pp. 208-9, 216-21.

56. *Ibid.,* pp. 229-30.

57. Y. Zoltvany, *Philippe de Rigaud de Vaudreuil* (Toronto: McClelland and Stewart, 1974), p. 110; also p. 217.

58. Frégault, *Le XVIIIe Siècle,* pp. 228-30.

59. W.J. Eccles, *Frontenac: The Courtier Governor* (Toronto: McClelland and Stewart, 1959), p. 29.

60. *Rapport de l'archiviste de la province de Québec,* 1922-23, p. 151.

61. For example, George Rudé, *The Crowd in the French Revolution* (New York: Oxford, 1959).

62. Superbly described in E.P. Thompson, *The Making of the English Working Class* (London; Penquin, 1976), Ch. Three.

63. Séguin, "La Canadienne," pp. 498-99.

64. Jean Hamelin, "What Middle Class?" *Society and Conquest,* Miquelon, ed. (Toronto, 1977), pp. 109-110; and Dechêne, *Habitants et marchands,* p. 44, who concludes that the largest contingents of male immigrants arriving in seventeenth-century Montreal were *engagés* and soldiers.

65. H. Charbonneau, *Vie et mort de nos ancêtres* (Montréal: Presses de l'université de Montréal, 1975), p. 38; A. Burguière, "Le Rituel du mariage en France: Pratiques ecclésiastiques et pratiques popularies, (XVIᵉ-XVIIIᵉ siècle)," *Annales E. S. C.,* 33ᵉ annee (mai-juin 1978), p. 640; R. Mousnier, *La famille, l'enfant et l'éducation en France et en Grande-Bretagne du XVIᵉ au XVIIIᵉ siècle* (Paris: Sorbonne C.D.U., 1975); Fagneiz, *Femme et société française,* p. 97. Commercial activities, however, also prevailed among the women of Bordeaux, an important port in the Canada trade. (*Ibid.,* p. 196).

66. Fagniez, *Femme et société française,* pp. 267, 273-74, 311-12, 360-61.

67. Claude Lessard, "L'Aide financière de l'Eglise de France à l'Eglise naissante du Canada," in *Mèlanges d'histoire du Canada français offerts au professeur Marcel Trudel.* Pierre Savard, ed. (Ottawa: Editions de l'Université d'Ottawa, 1978), p. 175.

68. Fagniez, *Femme et société française,* pp. 311-321.

69. Marcel Trudel, *The Beginnings of New France,* (Toronto: McClelland and Stewart, 1973). For a gloomy assessment of the neglected colony during this period.

70. G. Brown *et al.,* eds., *Dictionnary of Canadian Biography* (hereafter *DCB*), (Toronto: U. of Toronto Press, 1966-) Vol. 1, p. 118; and J. Marshall, ed., *Word from New France* (Toronto: Oxford, 1967), p. 2.

71. Fagniez, *Femme et société française,* pp. 320-33, 358. Of course, not all *religieuses* were competent as leaders. Madame de la Peltrie, for example, patron of the Urusline convent, appears to have been a rather unreliable benefactress. Despite her firsthand knowledge of the difficulties under which the Ursulines laboured, her "charity" was quixotic. In 1642, she suddenly withdrew her support from the Ursulines in order to join the colonists setting off to found Montreal. Later she again held back her funds in favour of a cherished chapel project, even though the Ursulines' lodgings had just burned to the ground.

72. Chabot, "Marie Guyart de l'Incarnation," pp. 27, 37; *DCB,* 1, p. 353; Lessard, "Aide financière," pp. 169-70.

73. *DCB,* Vol. 1; pp. 483-87; also Lessard, "Aide financière," p. 175.

74. This is the interpretation given by G. Lanctôt in *Montreal under Maisonneuve* (Toronto: Clarke Irwin, 1969), pp. 20-24, 170.

75. *Ibid.,* p. 188.

76. Lanctôt, *Filles de joie,* p. 81 and Trudel, *Montréal,* p. 21. The Hôtel-Dieu de Montréal also sponsored immigrants from 1655 to 1662 (Lanctôt, *Filles de joie,* p. 81.)

77. Trudel, *Montréal,* p. 84.

78. Eccles, "Social Welfare Measures," p. 19; F. Rousseau, "Hôpital et société en Nouvelle-France: l'Hôtel-Dieu de Québec à la fin du XVIIᵉ siècle," *RHAF,* Vol. 31 (juin 1977), p. 47.

79. Mousnier, *La famille l'enfant et l'éducation,* pp. 319-31.

80. Vann, "Women in Preindustrial Capitalism," p. 208.

81. Trudel, *Montréal,* p. 276, 87; P. Goubert, *The Ancien Régime* (New York: Harper, 1974), p. 262.

82. Neatby, *Quebec,* p. 237; French soldiers had a literacy rate of three to four per cent. A. Corvisier, *L'Armée française de la fin du XVIIe siècle au ministére de Choiseul* (Paris: Presses universitaires de France, 1964), p. 862.

83. Fagniez, *Femme et société canadienne,* p. 191.

84. Séguin, "La Canadienne," p. 501, lists nine of these schools in addition to the original one in Montreal.

85. Franquet, *Voyages,* pp. 31-32.

86. According to Lanctôt, (*Filles de joie,* pp. 121-30) there were 961. Silvio Dumas counts only 774 (*Les Filles du roi en Nouvelle France,* Québec, 1972, p. 164). Other estimates have ranged between 713 and 857.

87. J.-N. Fauteux, *Essai sur l'industrie au Canada sous le Régime Francais* (Quebec: Proulx, 1927), "Introduction."

88. For the record, it now seems fairly well established that the females sent to New France, unlike those sent to the West Indies, were carefully screened, and any of questionable morality returned by the authorities to France. Lanctôt (*Filles de joie*) and Dumas, (*Filles du roi*) agree on this. See also Foulché-Delbosc, "Women of Three Rivers," pp. 22-23.

89. Dechêne finds a majority of *Parisiennes* among the Montréal *filles,* (*Habitants et marchands,* p. 96). Lanctôt states that one-half of the 1634-63 emigrants were urbanites and that two-thirds of the *filles* were from Ile-de-France (*Filles de joie,* pp. 76-79 and p. 124). On education in France see Mousnier, *La famille, l'enfant et l'éducation,* pp. 319-25.

90. Lanctôt, *Filles de joie,* pp. 110-130, 207.

91. *Ibid.,* p. 226.

92. Séguin, "La Canadienne," p. 492; Franquet, *Voyages,* p. 57.

93. J. Henripin, *La Population canadienne au début du XVIIIe Siècle* (Paris: Presses universitaires de France, 1954). The overall population was sixty-three percent male in 1663 (Trudel, *Beginnings,* p. 261), an imbalance which gradually declined.

94. Trudel, *Montréal,* pp. 45-47, 108, 113.

95. Foulché-Delbosc, "Women of Three Rivers," p. 19.

96. Frégault, *Le XVIIIe Siècle,* p. 144.

97. Eccles, "Social Welfare Measures," p. 18.

98. Cole Harris, *The Seigneurial System in Early Canada* (Québec: P.U.L., 1968), p. 163.

99. The richest single source for evidence along these lines is Dechêne's *Habitants et marchands.*

100. Boyer, *Crimes et châtiments,* p. 326.

101. Toronto *Globe and Mail,* 29 October 1979, p. 1; Boyer, *Crimes et châtiments,* pp. 329, 340. Cf. also N. Hawthorne's novel, *The Scarlet Letter,* based on an actual occurrence.

102. Boyer, *Crimes et châtiments,* p. 329, 350, 361-62; also Morel, "Justice criminelle canadienne."

103. Dechêne, *Habitants et marchands,* p. 464.

104. Séguin, "La Canadienne," pp. 497-99.

105. Jean Lunn, "The Illegal Fur Trade Out of New France 1713-60," *Canadian Historical Association Report,* (1939), pp. 61-62.

106. Boyer, *Crimes et châtiments,* pp. 286-87.

107. Marshall, *Word from New France,* pp. 287-95.

108. Boyer, *Crimes et châtiments,* p. 306.

109. Eccles, "The Social, Economic and Political Significance of the Military Establishment," *op. cit.*

110. Charlevoix, *New France,* Vol 3, p. 35.

111. Ethel Bennett, "Madame de La Tour, 1602-1645," in *The Clear Spirit,* M. Innis, ed. (Toronto: U. of Toronto Press, 1966), p. 21.

112. *DCB,* Vol. 3, pp. 308-13.

113. *Ibid.,* pp. 308-13; and Boyer, *Crimes et châtiments,* pp. 338-39.

114. For a splendid description of the attitudes and life-style of this class in France, see p. de Vaissière, *Gentilhommes campagnards de l'ancienne France* (Paris, Perin 1903).

115. G. Frégault, *Le Grand Marquis,* (Montréal: Les Etudes de l'Institut d'Histoire de l'Amerique française, 1952), pp. 74-75 and Corvisier, *L'Armée française,* p. 777.

116. *Ibid.,* pp. 762-63, 826.

117. Franquet, *Voyages,* pp. 56, 67-68, 200.

118. *Ibid.,* p. 35, 76, 88.

119. Dechêne, *Habitants et marchands,* p. 398; Franquet, *Voyages,* p. 16.

120. *DCB,* Vol. 2, p. 491.

121. Marshall, *Word from New France,* pp. 27, 213, 222-23, 233.

122. Dechêne, *Habitants et marchands,* p. 393; Franquet, *Voyages,* p. 199; Foulché-Delbosc, "Women of Three Rivers," p. 25; Corvisier, *L'Armée française,* p. 760.

123. Boyer, *Crimes et châtiments,* pp. 349-51; Dechêne, *Habitants et marchands.* p. 41. Dechêne concludes that, considering Montreal was a garrison town with a shortage of marriageable women, the degree of prostitution was normal or, to use her term, *conformiste* (pp. 437-38).

124. Eccles, "The Social, Economic and Political Significance of the Military ...," pp. 11-17; Dechêne, *Habitants et marchands,* p. 121.

125. Séguin, "La Canadienne," pp. 495, 503.

126. Trudel, *Montréal,* pp. 30-33; and Charbonneau, *Vie et mort,* p. 135.

127. Foulché-Delbosc, "Women of Three Rivers," p. 25.

128. Trudel, *Montréal,* p. 163.

129. Bennett, "Madame de la Tour," p. 16; Madame Joybert was the mother of the future Madame de Vaudreuil. *DCB,* Vol. 1, p. 399. For E. de Grandmaison, see *DCB,* Vol. 1, p. 345.

130. Lunn, "Illegal Fur Trade," p. 62.

131. Eccles, *Canadian Society ..., op. cit.,* p. 61.

132. Lunn, "Illegal Fur Trade," pp. 61-75.

133. Franquet, *Voyages,* pp. 120-21.

134. Lilianne Plamondon, "Une femme d'affaires en Nouvelle-France: Marie-Anne Barbel, Veuve Fornel," *RHAF,* 31 (septembre 1977).

135. Franquet, *Voyages,* pp. 156-58.

136. For example, Hamelin in "What Middle Class?" The absence of an indigenous bourgeoisie is also central to the interpretation of Dechêne in *Habitants et marchands.*

137. Séguin, "La Canadienne," p. 494.

138. For accounts of Agathe de Saint-Père, see *DCB,* Vol. III, pp. 580-81; Fauteux, *Industrie au Canada,* p. 464-69; and Massicote, *Bulletin des Recherches historiques* (hereafter BRH), 1944, p. 202-07.

139. Neatby refers to this activity in the early post-Conquest era (*Quebec,* pp. 72-73); Franquet encountered Madame Benoist in 1753 (*Voyages,* p. 150).

140. For a discussion of the de Ramezay's business affairs Cf. Massicote, *BRH,* 1931, p. 530; and Fauteux, *Industrie au Canada,* pp. 158-59, 204-15, 442.

141. *DCB,* Vol. II, p. 548.

142. Fauteux, *Industrie au Canada,* pp. 158; 297, 420-21, 522; and P. Moogk, *Building a House in New France* (Toronto: 1977), pp. 60-64.

143. Lunn, *Illegal Fur Trade,* p. 61.

144. See Moogk (*Building a House,* p. 8) for one case of a husband's transfer of these powers.

145. Franquet, *Voyages,* p. 17.

146. Dechêne, *Habitants et marchands,* pp. 151-53, 187, 391; and Séguin, "La Canadienne," p. 494.

147. Charbonneau, *Vie et mort,* p. 184; Fagniez, *Femme et société française,* pp. 111, 182-84. A recent study by Butel ("Comportements familiaux") has documented the phenomenon of widows taking over the family business in eighteenth-century Bordeaux.

148. Trudel, *Beginnings,* p. 250. This was largely due to the enormous holdings of Jean Lauzon's widow. Dechêne, *Habitants et marchands,* pp. 209 and 204-5, 393; Plamondon, "Femme d'affaires." W.S. MacNutt, *The Atlantic Provinces* (Toronto: McClelland and Stewart, 1965), p. 25.

149. This happened on seigneuries as well as in town, as in the case M. de Lanouguère, "a soldier by preference," whose wife, Marguerite-Renée Denys, directed their seigneury (*DCB,* Vol. 1, p. 418).

CHAPTER

3 BUSINESS AND PRIVATE ENTERPRISE IN NEW FRANCE

For a variety of reasons, the history of business and private enterprise in New France has, until quite recently, been largely ignored. In part this was because, up to about twenty-five years ago, the field of Canadian business history itself was still in its infancy. Historians of New France therefore tended to focus primarily on more traditional issues, such as imperial relations, government policy, institutional structures, the European-Amerindian interaction, the Church and the military.

For many years, too, the study of private enterprise in New France was looked upon almost as a contradiction in terms. From the perspective of Francis Parkman, the nineteenth-century American historian whose works on New France dominated the field well into the twentieth, colonial enterprise was not at all free. In his view, the authoritarian, mercantilistic policies of absolutist France stifled individual business initiative in the colony to the point of suffocation. What barely existed could hardly be analysed.

The re-interpretation of the place of business in New France began in a major way during the 1930s and 1940s, with the emergence of the University of Montreal "nationalist" school of historians led by Maurice Séguin, Guy Frégault, and Michel Brunet. Indebted to their mentor, Abbé Lionel Groulx, the greatest concern of these men was to affirm the existence of a dynamic, locally-based "bourgeoisie" in New France, and that entailed demonstrating the economic vitality, real and potential, of the colony. Far from damning successive French administrations, à la Parkman, for heavy-handed interference in the business affairs of New France, the Montreal school attributed much of the colony's growth to initiatives by the state, and criticized it for not doing more to promote colonial enterprise.

The counter-school of historians from Laval University, headed by Jean Hamelin and Fernand Ouellet, disagreed fundamentally with the idea that the economy of New France was sufficiently strong and diversified to support an indigenous bourgeoisie. Only the fur trade, Hamelin argued, was capable of generating sustained profits, and for most of New France's existence those profits were drained out of the colony to France. On the matter of the impact of the state on business in New France, the Laval historians were closer to their Montreal rivals, agreeing that government initiatives were often responsible for what economic development did take place, although, less sanguine about the economic possibilities of the day, they were also less inclined to blame the state for failing to do more.

The debate over the nature of society and the economy of New France goes on, energized in the last decade by the Marxist analyses of a younger generation of historians and political scientists. For individuals like Gérald Bernier and Vinh Ta Van, the question at issue is the extent to which pre-capitalist and/or capitalist modes of production had penetrated the colony's essentially feudal society by the time of the Conquest.

Contributing to the debate, too, were other historians who examined in detail the business system itself. Two such studies are presented here. Together they demonstrate the complexity of the private-enterprise world of New France. The first, by Dale Miquelon, provides an overview of New France's role in the French imperial, mercantilistic economy in the eighteenth century. The second reading is a chapter from Michael Bliss's history of Canadian business, *Northern Enterprise*. Both of these articles address the three central questions posed about business and private enterprise in New France: What were the strengths and weaknesses of the business system? What impact did the state have on private enterprise, and *vice versa*? To what extent was the business system a creature of France rather than New France?

Suggestions for Further Reading

Bernier, G., "Sur quelques effets de la rupture structurelle engendrée par la Conquête au Québec: 1760-1854," *Revue d'histoire de l'Amérique française*, 35, no. 1 (juin 1981), 69-95.

Bosher, J., "A Quebec Merchant's Trading Circles in France and Canada: Jean-André Lamaletie before 1763," *Histoire sociale/Social History*, IX, no. 19 (May 1977), 24-44.

————, "Government and Private Interests in New France," *Canadian Public Administration*, X, no. 2 (1967), 244-257.

Brunet, Michel, *La présence anglaise et les Canadiens*. Montréal: Beauchemin, 1964.

Frégault, Guy, *La société canadienne sous le régime français*. Ottawa: Société historique du Canada, 1954.

Hamelin, Jean, *Economie et Société en Nouvelle-France*. Québec: Les Presses de l'Université Laval, 1960.

Miquelon, Dale, *Dugard of Rouen: French Trade to Canada and the West Indies, 1729-1770*. Montreal: McGill-Queen's University Press, 1978.

————, "Havy and Lefebvre of Quebec: A Case Study Of Metropolitan Participation in Canadian Trade, 1730-60," *Canadian Historical Review*, LVI, no,1 (March 1975), 1-24.

Nish, Cameron, *Les Bourgeois-gentilshommes de la Nouvelle-France, 1729-1748*. Montréal: Fides, 1968.

Ouellet, Fernand, *Histoire économique et sociale du Québec, 1760-1850*. Montréal: Fides, 1966.

Parkman, Francis, *The Old Regime in Canada*. London: Macmillan, 1899.

Pritchard, J., "Commerce in New France," in *Canadian Business History*, ed. D. Macmillan. Toronto: McClelland & Stewart, 1972.

————, "The Vogage of the *Fier*: An Analysis of a Shipping and Trading Venture to New France, 1724-1728," *Histoire sociale / Social History*, IV, no. 11 (April 1973), 75-97.

Reid, A.G., "General Trade Between Quebec and France During the French Regime," *Canadian Historical Review*, XXXIV, no. 1 (March 1953), 18-32.

Séguin, Maurice, "La Conquête et la vie économique des Canadiens," *L'Action Nationale*, XXVIII, no.4 (1946).

Ta Van, Vinh, "La Nouvelle France et la Conquête: Passage du Féodalisme au Capitalisme," *Cahiers d'histoire de l'Université de Montréal*, II, no. 2 (1982), 3-25.

CANADA'S PLACE IN THE FRENCH IMPERIAL ECONOMY: AN EIGHTEENTH-CENTURY OVERVIEW

Dale Miquelon

In 1702 the French geographer, Guillaume Delisle, wrote of "The utility that the different nations of Europe established in America have drawn from that land." This usefulness made America important and it had become "as it were, a supplement to Europe." This designation, "A Supplement to Europe," seems to me to encapsulate in a true and striking manner the eighteenth-century French response to Canada, or for that matter to Africa or Asia.[1]

Canada was a part of the French Empire from the early seventeenth century until 1763. This imperial connection was the result of the spontaneous and unorchestrated activities of fishermen and merchants and of the directive activity of the French state. Statesmen and businessmen, theoreticians and men of ac-

From *French Historical Studies*, XV, no. 3 (Spring 1988), 432-443. Reprinted by permission of *French Historical Studies*.

tion, all assumed that Canada existed for the benefit of France and not for its own self-realization. The relevant economic theory was mercantilism. The economy was one of primary production, and the engine that drove that economy was imperial trade. The royal manna of expenditures for provisioning, garrison pay, and the building of fortifications was from time to time scattered upon the grateful colony and late in the day came to rival and even surpass the short-run importance of trade. From the voluminous evidence, the following paragraphs tease out three strands that give some idea of "Canada's Place." These are, first, mercantilist thinking within the Ministry of Marine; second, the developing economy of trade and military spending within the Empire; and third, the impact upon Canada of changes in the nature of trade and in levels of military spending.

Jérôme de Pontchartrain, the minister of marine who presided over Canada's destiny from 1699 to 1715, took office as a young man. His youthful openness and desire to do his work well disarm us at the same time as his penchant for solving all questions with mercantilist axioms warns us of his unpromising pedantry. This is especially clear in the letters exchanged between Pontchartrain and his old teacher, Vauban. Upon one of the marshal's letters on Canada, Pontchartrain pencilled what would become the refrain of his administration: "Would cost a lot," "great expense," "expense."[2] To Vauban's lyrical description of "the colonies of Canada" the young minister rejoindered with ill grace: "The worst of all. One gets nothing from them; they cost a lot, etc."[3]

In common with Colbertists before and after him, Pontchartrain encouraged the production of naval stores in Canada and even the building of ships, because these helped to lessen French dependence on the Baltic countries. Nor was he exceptional in worrying about Canada's overdependence upon the failing fur staple and in his desire for Canadian economic diversification. When he writes to Canadian administrators of the "idleness and sloth of the inhabitants that prevent this colony from being peopled," or directs an intendant to encourage trade, "which enriches the people and draws them from an idleness that is often the cause of many misfortunes," we easily recognize the mercantilist faith in the nostrum of trade and the view of the peasantry espoused by mercantilist administrators, confronting and offended by the nonchalance of a preindustrial workforce.[4]

Pontchartrain differed from Colbert and many others by his opposition to the notion of colonial self-sufficiency, which seemed to him contrary to the economic *raison d'être* of empire. But we do find development in Pontchartrain's thought and deviations from theory that are arresting, given the definitive character of his dicta, which sketch out a most doctrinaire mercantilism. During the War of the Spanish Succession, when there was little money to spare in Marine coffers, he sent two potters and a spinner to Canada and authorized an annual gratuity for a Montreal woman who had established a weaving manufacture. Two years running, he warned the Canadian intendant against permitting colonial manufactures, only to add, "This ought to be the general view; however, their establishment in Canada ought not to be absolutely prevented, especially among the poor."[5]

The minister also gave a very limited acceptance to the idea of the multilateral benefits of empire. For him the most important model of empire remained that of a series of bilateral trade relations between the mother country and each colony. His restrictive views on intercolonial trade were challenged by the altered circumstances imposed by the war. Although Pontchartrain had long feared that the colonies if left to their own devices would exchange sugar and flour, cutting into the trade of the French Atlantic ports, he nevertheless, in 1708, in the midst of war, recommended the abolition of duties levied in Martinique on Canadian produce. He had come to see that, as in the case of shipbuilding, colonial supply of flour could prevent dependence upon foreigners. Indeed, in the following year he was even willing to permit foreign ships to carry foreign flour to the West Indies. French merchants, he wrote, would starve the colonists rather than renounce their monopoly or starve the kingdom to make scarcity profits in the West Indies. But a minister had to guarantee the subsistence of both Frenchmen and colonials. Here is the mercantilist dilemma. The colonists, Pontchartrain pointed out, "are not of a more lowly condition than others that they should be so roughly treated."[6] As far as Canada was concerned, he drew attention to the weakness of its agricultural economy, but hoped that the colony could be a point of supply in years of emergency.

The supply problems of the war years (1702-13) had made Canada appear the natural provisioner of the Newfoundland colony of Plaisance (now Placentia, Nfld.), although Pontchartrain had also called Acadia to that role in 1707. At that time he had fretted that the self-sufficiency and surplus production necessary to make his own plan work were "entirely contrary to the general principle of colonies, which is to draw all their needs from the state."[7] Impressed by Canada's ability to feed Plaisance, Pontchartrain, after the war, specifically assigned Canada the task of provisioning the new colony of Ile Royale. The governor and intendant were instructed "to leave navigation between Québec and Ile Royale entirely free."[8] Under the stress of war, Pontchartrain had learned that economic theory was useful only to the extent that it served the needs of the state.

Pontchartrain's son, Frédéric de Maurepas, who was minister of marine from 1723 to 1749, was no less a mercantilist than his father or Colbert. Of the essential continuity of policy, there is no better evidence than the Letters Patent of 1727 that reiterated legislation of 1670, 1698, and 1720 prohibiting foreigners from trading within the Empire. Maurepas' attention was particularly drawn to Canada because in order to enforce the Letters Patent of 1727 some substitute for the illegal trade of the French West Indies with the English colonies had to be found. The department's outward correspondence during the Maurepas years abounds with exhortations that intercolonial trade be stepped up. In particular, Maurepas hoped that the shipment of Canadian wood, flour, peas, and horses to Martinique in return for molasses and rum would replace the illegal trade of the island with New England. Tariff exemptions were provided to encourage the desired traffic. The *pacte coloniale* had become unabashedly multilateral.

Maurepas expressed sympathy with deregulation provided that it was in the framework of the imperial system, as is evident from two of his directives: "Regulation should be occasional, temporary, and only when absolutely needed"; and "Encouragement is the only method that can be used, and success waits upon time and the industry of men."[9] Of course, the Canadian fur trade remained tightly regulated, and antipathy to regulation did not imply any liberal *angst* concerning intervention in general. Canadian shipbuilding and even iron mining and smelting were subsidized. Sealing and fur trading concessions remained the gift of the Crown.

Between 1699 and the early 1720s Canada's place had evolved in official thinking from that of a supplier of furs and a few incidental staples to the mother country to being also an emergency supplier of provisions and wood to Plaisance and the West Indies. Subsequently it was the designated provisioner of Louisbourg and was also much encouraged to maintain a brisk and regular trade to Martinique and St. Domingue, even in peacetime. Certain Canadian manufactures were at first tolerated to sustain the poor, then encouraged to diversify the economy, and (in the case of ships and bar iron) to make up for metropolitan deficiencies. Both Pontchartrain and Maurepas came to understand that the Canadian economy had to be diversified, and Maurepas (by accepting the advice of the Canadian intendant, Gilles Hocquart) thought it also had to be capitalized and given some degree of autonomous direction by the development of colonial entrepreneurs.[10]

In 1701 Louis XIV determined that Canada, with its fur trade, could be useful to the Empire in a political rather than an economic sense by binding the interior tribes to itself and thereby keeping the English out of the North American interior. It was only after the Peace of Utrecht (1713) that the garrisoning of posts in the Great Lakes hinterland and an improving fur trade gave substance to this imperial plan. On Lake Ontario a deficitary trade with strategically important Indians was maintained for *raison d'état*, and after 1744 much money and effort were expended to use Canada as a bulwark against British expansionism—witness Governor de La Galissonière's famous question, "We ask if a country can be abandoned ... when by its position it affords a great advantage over its neighbors?"[11] Yet it is remarkable that the Ministry of Marine persisted in thinking of Canada in mercantilist fashion as a colony that, with the regrettable exception of wartime, ought to pay its way. There are indubitable touches of liberalism in administrative documents (as for example when the Bureau de Commerce in supporting iron mining and smelting suggested that the competition would be good for the French iron industry[12]); nevertheless, in general one can say that the conception of Canada's place in the imperial economy remained always mercantilistic, although this mercantilism became increasingly practical, supple, and even generous.

The link between colonial production and the Empire was shipping, and we can learn much from contractions, expansions, and changes in the general pattern of ship movements. From a plateau in the 1680s and 1690s, Québec-France trade declined sharply in the first two decades of the eighteenth century, recovered to its old level in the 1720s and 1730s, and experienced an abrupt increase in the 1740s. Traffic bottomed out in 1709 to 1713 and peaked in 1729-36 and after 1740. In the 1690s La Rochelle, although sharing the Québec trade with Bordeaux, nevertheless enjoyed an ascendency that it never recovered thereafter. It met stiff competition from other French ports with little previous experience in Canadian trade (notably Rouen) in the 1720s and 1730s and in the 1740s was supplanted by Bordeaux.[13] Québec-France traffic was only part of the story, but it does provide us with a base upon which a total picture can be built. So what is the total picture?

Quite clearly, we are observing a reflection of the fur trade—the staple production that linked colony and metropolis. These statistics mirror the collapse of the beaver market beginning in the later 1690s, compounded by French failure to control the sea in the War of the Spanish Succession, the slow growth after 1710 of a restructured European market absorbing greater quantities of furs other than beaver, and the stabilization of the trade from a point in the 1720s.[14] But there is more to this than a simple return to business as it had been in the "good old days," something which is indicated by the participation of so many new competitors among the French ports after 1720. Canada traditionally suffered from a trade deficit, its growing population demanding a greater value in imports than the fur staple could buy. The result was a chronic pool of debt and the large place among Canadian exports of much capital in the form of bills of exchange founded primarily in the French government's expenditures in Canada. A large part of this fiduciary paper represented the cost of maintaining garrisons and building fortifications. This "invisible export" explains why the imbalance of trade was not invariably disastrous. But in the 1730s and 1740s the trade deficit declined dramatically—1739 and 1741 were in fact years of trade surplus—and bills of exchange constituted an ever smaller part of exports.[15] Behind this was economic diversification and, in fact, a new role in imperial trade.

Canada's new role had its roots in the Empire's wartime difficulties. While traditional trades stagnated and the price of wheat fell steadily, the Empire was unable to supply Plaisance and Martinique with provisions.[16] Canadians were first attracted to the sea by the lure of these two markets and by the promise of even greater profits from privateering. Of the latter, Governor Vaudreuil remarked that there was not "a more glorious nor a more suitable way to occupy youth."[17] In 1704 Canadian private enterprise built its first ship, the *Joybert*. During the war, Canadian ships made several voyages to Martinique, but Plaisance was the ideal market for Canadian entrepreneurs with small ships and little capital. When Plaisance was lost to Great Britain (1713) and replaced by Ile Royale, with its capital of Louisbourg, Canadians continued to play their new role at the new port.[18] At first this trade in provisions and lumber grew slowly, but it abruptly doubled in 1727. In that same year, the trade to Martinique, carried on by both French and Canadian shippers, also burst into life. The triangular trade, idealized by many mercantilists, had become a reality.

Without Louisbourg (for which Plaisance was the model and the miniature), triangular trade would not have been possible. Louisbourg helped by providing *entrepôt* facilities, enabling some Canadian shippers to specialize in bringing cargo to Louisbourg, while other West Indian or French shippers carried it to the Caribbean. But much more important was the new opportunity to sell Canadian cargoes of biscuit and rough flour to the soldier-fisherman population centered at Louisbourg and with the proceeds to buy dried cod. This was added to cargoes of Canadian wood and grain destined for the West Indies, making them more valuable and more saleable than they would otherwise have been. The return for Canadians was not West Indian produce—there was a limit to the amount of rum and molasses Canadians could consume—but rather credits to shore up the deficitary trade with France.[19] The last and most considerable increase of all in Québec-France traffic—the increase after 1740—is possibly a deceptive statistic. To a great extent it reflects a massive import of flour and war *matériel* into Canada and, far from being a healthy sign of an expanding commerce, is an indication of the final submergence of New France's economic role within the Empire by its military and strategic role. The place of fiduciary paper in Canada's exports expanded once again as military spending increased to unprecedented levels and as the new trades suffered from war on the high seas as well as from difficulties of production and marketing.

So far, we have not got much closer to the colony than to observe from an Olympian distance the arrival and departure of vessels from its shores. We have yet to see from the inside how the colony was responding to the exigencies of empire. Fur remained the pre-eminent export and earner of purchasing power. The fur trade, which dovetailed with the military and strategic needs to support far-flung alliances with Indians and to keep Anglo-Americans out of the Great Lakes and Mississippi basins, maintained Canada's link with the forest and the Indian and their imponderable influence.[20] The garrisoning of the western posts and the emoluments of the officer corps that directed them were paid for by the fur trade, which thus was charged with providing economic rents in addition to businessmen's profits. In this instance, then, the military establishment, which is usually seen as making an economic contribution to Canada, absorbed Canadian resources at least commensurate with the protection it afforded the trade. In the final analysis, the Empire failed the fur trade. It either could not absorb all the beaver produced or it could not absorb it at an appropriate price. As a result, countless bundles of beaver made the journey from Montréal to Albany, even after the revival of French demand, and hence to absorption in another imperial market.

As we have seen, in the eighteenth century, Canada was able to profit from the demand for agricultural exports in other parts of the Empire. Census figures for 1723 show a large increase in the area of land under cultivation.[21] One should not squeeze an Old Regime statistic too hard, but we can take this as a symbolic date. More and more land was put to the plough, especially in the 1730s. Prices were better and price swings were more contained. Increasing numbers of sawmills (ten in 1710, seventy in 1739) produced more and more lumber, the invariable companion to provisions in the new trades. New sealing posts along the coast of Labrador, over half of them established in the 1730s, added seal oil to Canada's outbound cargoes. Shipbuilding experienced a "take-off" in 1724, and ships became important items of export to balance imports. In 1738 the blast furnace at the St. Maurice Forges was lighted for the first time. Thus, responding to the needs of empire, Canada was moving beyond its fur-trade base and frontier beginnings. More spending power, more European goods, a more sedentary and Europeanized life style were the results.

Yet the brave new world of the 1720s and 1730s came apart. In 1736 and 1737 there were disastrous crop failures, and the poor crop of 1741 was followed by failures in 1742 and 1743. The new trades collapsed. Indeed, Canada was already being muscled out of the Louisbourg and West Indian markets by Anglo-American shippers with a much more reliable hinterland and shorter ocean crossings. Canadian industries without markets and without food for workers came to a standstill. The Canadian agricultural sector was simply too small, in too tricky a climate, and too distant from its markets to be counted on year after year. As François Havy and Jean Lefebvre, two French merchants resident in Canada, observed, "If provisions are abundant for two or three years running, they become rare and dear for two or three years too."[22] And Canadian farmers were not really cash crop producers; rather, as most farmers in the eighteenth century, they were peasants disposing of modest surpluses. To link them to an export market really placed them on an economic frontier quite out of phase with their traditional outlook and technology. The Empire failed Canada by being unable to protect Canada's markets, whereas Canada failed the Empire by being unequal to the new role it had been called upon to play.

After 1744 Canada became preoccupied with and swallowed up in war. The plethora of military works brought considerable money into the country. Workshops buzzed with activity, and military contractors chalked up fat profits. But war was only profitable if its destruction could be kept at a distance and if trade continued in spite of it. Canada had experienced this good fortune from 1713 to 1744, but would not know it again until after 1815. Knowledgeable merchants were not deceived by glittering wartime profits. As Havy and Lefebvre wrote in the midst of war, "We need a good peace in order to be able to work solidly at increasing the trade of the country."[23]

The impetus for Canadian economic development in the first half of the eighteenth century was external—imperial, but also more than imperial. It finds its origin in what many French historians, following François Simiand, call a "phase A" movement of rising prices and plentiful money. This is the context of prosperity that affected Canada through the revival of French trade in Europe and on many seas and also through the French state's capacity to invest heavily in North America by establishing garrisons and small military works in Canada, and most particularly, by building the fortress of Louisbourg. This phase of Canada's experience is consistent with Canada's history throughout as a primary producer, sensitive—sometimes painfully so—to the vagaries of world markets from which mercantilist devices can provide only modest protection.

Notes

1. This quotation from Guillaume Delisle, "Des descouvertes qui ont été faites dans l'Amérique [1702]" in AN, Archives de la Marine (hereafter AM), Hydrographie, 2 JJ 57 (ex. 115[xi]) 12 E, has provided me with a title for a new general history, *New France, 1701-1744: "A Supplement to Europe"* (Toronto, McClelland and Stewart, "The Canadian Centenary Series," 1987). The series attempts to do for Canadian history what W. L. Langer's "The Rise of Modern Europe" series did for European history, consolidating the extant historiography and enriching it with new documentary research. This essay, read at the Society for French Historical Studies meeting in Minneapolis in March, 1987, presents a theme from the book that the author hopes is of interest to the non-Canadianist. As is evident from the notes, this branch of the history of New France remains indebted to the great strides made in the field in the 1970s. Current work, which still resists generalization, is concentrated to a considerable extent in agricultural history, historical demography, and the social aspects of economic development.

2. Louise Dechêne, ed., *La Correspondance de Vauban relative au Canada* (Québec, 1968), 26-27, marginalia to Vauban à Pontchartrain, Lille, 7 jan. 1699.

3. Ibid.

4. AN, Archives des Colonies (hereafter AC), B, vol. 34 pt. 1, fol. 15, mémoire du roi aux Vaudreuil et Bégon, Marly, 15 juin 1712; ibid. vol. 78, ministre à Bégon, Marly, 27 juin 1712.

5. AN, AC, B, vol 27, pt. 3, fol. 231, ministre à Raudot, Versailles, 9 juin 1706 at fol. 235. On Pontchartrain's ideas on self-sufficiency and interdependence, see ibid., vol. 24, fol. 20. "Mémoire pour servir d'instruction au Comte Denos choisis par le roy pour commander dans les Isles Françoises," Marly, 9 fév. 1701; ibid., fol. 236,

Pontchartrain à Galiffet, Versailles, 7 déc. 1701; ibid., AC, B, vol. 20, fol. 22, Pontchartrain à Villebon, Versailles, 26 mars 1698.

6. AN, AC, B, vol. 31, fol. 515, ministre à D'Aguesseau, 27 sept. 1709, the last of a number of letters from Pontchartrain to Vaucresson, Bégon, d'Aguesseau, and others that illuminate this question. For his original, doctrinaire position, see ibid., vol. 18, fol. 147, "Instruction que le Roy a ordonné estre ez mains du Sr. Robert," Fontainebleau, 12 oct. 1695 and ibid., vol. 23, fol. 62, mémoire du roi à Beauharnois, Versailles, 6 mai 1702.

7. Ibid., vol. 29, pt. 3, fol. 198, ministre à Goutins, Versailles, 30 juin 1707.

8. Ibid., vol. 35, pt. 3, fol. 274v, mémoire du roi aux Vaudreuil et Beauharnois, Versailles, 27 jan. 1713.

9. Ibid., vol. 50, fol. 160, ministre à Beauharnois, Versailles, 5 août 1727; Maurepas à Dupuy, 24 mai 1728. Marine policy during the Maurepas years can be grasped very nicely from the minister's correspondence with the Canadian intendant Gilles Hocquart in AN, AC, B, vols. 53-88 and CIIA, vols. 51-89 (1729-1748). Whereas Jérôme de Pontchartrain's role in policy making is abundantly clear from holograph letters and marginalia, Maurepas' is less certain. It is in the formal sense implying the minister's ultimate responsibility that we state such-and-such a policy to have been Maurepas'. The Letters Patent of 1727 and the earlier legislation they embody are in AN, AD vii 2a.

10. Capitalization is manifest in government grants to develop the Saint-Maurice forges and the government take-over of that industry and in the Crown's considerable investment in shipbuilding and the development of naval stores. A policy of developing a strong Canadian merchant class by government concessions and financial support is attributed to Intendant Hocquart in Donald J. Horton, "Gilles Hocquart, Intendant of New France, 1729-1748" (Ph.D. diss., McGill University, Montréal, 1974).

11. "Memoir on the French Colonies in North America, December, 1750," in *Documents Relative to the Colonial History of the State of New York,* ed. John R. Brodhead and Edward B. O'Callaghan (Albany, N.Y., 1858), X:220-32.

12. Quoted in Cameron Nish, *François-Etienne Cugnet: Entrepreneur et entreprises en Nouvelle-France* (Montréal, 1975), 59.

13. See James Pritchard, "The Pattern of French Colonial Shipping to Canada before 1760," *Revue française d'histoire d'outre-mer* 63 (1976): 189-210. See also Pritchard, "Ships, Men, and Commerce: A Study of Maritime Activity in New France" (Ph.D. diss., University of Toronto, 1971), 488-96.

14. Little work has been done on beaver marketing. It is not clear whether demand for smaller hats in the 1690s reduced the market or whether smaller unit size was compensated for by greater volume. It is also not clear whether improvement in the general market in the 1720s resulted from a radical restructuring of demand, with non-beaver supplanting beaver, or from a more moderate restructuring, with non-beaver adding to a reviving sale of beaver. It is possible that the sale of a good proportion of beaver may have been masked by its being redirected from Paris to London by smuggling through New York.

15. The dramatic reduction in drafts is evident in the accounts of Havy and Lefebvre, merchants of Québec. See my *Dugard of Rouen: French Trade to Canada and the West Indies, 1729-1770* (Montréal, 1978), 81. This microscopic examination of a single firm is complimented by John Bosher's numerous studies in French merchant history, most recently, *The Canada Merchants, 1713-1763* (Oxford, 1987). A table of best estimates of the balance of trade drawn from the correspondence between Hocquart (AC, C11A) and Maurepas (AC, B) has long been conveniently available in A. Jean E. Lunn, "Economic Development in New France, 1713-1760" (Ph.D. diss., McGill University, Montréal, 1942), now published in French as *Développement économique de la Nouvelle-France, 1713-1760* (Montréal, 1986).

16. See the graph of Québec City wheat prices in Jean Hamelin, *Economie et société en Nouvelle-France* (Québec, 1960), 61.

17. AN, AC, C11A, vol. 21, fol. 54V, Vaudreuil à Pontchartrain, 4 nov. 1703.

18. The role of Placentia, easily overlooked, is considered in F. J. Thorpe, "Fish, Forts, and Finance," Canadian Historical Association *Historical Papers* (1971), 52-64, and Pritchard, "Ships, Men, and Commerce."

19. On the importance of the Louisbourg market to Canada, see AN, AC, C11A, vol. 62, fol. 77, Hocquart au ministre, Québec, 11 oct. 1734; ibid., vol. 63, fol. 73, "Réponse au mémoire du roy, Québec, 13 Oct. 1735"; ibid., vol. 65, fol. 28, "Réponse au mémoire du roy, 1736." On the geographical, climatological, and attitudinal difficulties of Canada-West Indies trade, see AN, AC, C8A, vol. 39, fol. 337-372, "Mémoire sur le service des Isles du vent de l'Amérique, 6 xbre 1728," Versailles; ibid., vol. 56, fol. 110, "Eclaircisments données [*sic*] à M. De Ranches par M. de la Croix"; AN, AC, C8B, vol. 3, "Mémoire de Vaucresson, 25 jan. 1713." On the advantages offered by Louisbourg, see AN, AC, C8A, vol. 42, fol. 245, d'Orgeville au ministre, Fort-Royal, 2 sept. 1731; AN, AC, C11A, vol. 69, fol. 243, Hocquart au ministre, Québec, 2 oct. 1738; ibid., vol. 79, fol. 319, idem à idem, Québec, 8 oct. 1743. On purchase of French goods with trade credits, see AN, AC, C11A, vol. 61, fol. 65, "Réponse au mémoire du roy, Québec, 7 oct. 1734"; ibid., vol. 76, fol. 187, "Mémoire sur le commerce de Canada, 1741"; AN, AC, C8A, vol. 53, fol. 411, De La Croix au ministre, 28 déc. 1741.

20. The signal importance of strategic considerations and not just economic ones in explaining the French presence in the North American interior has become a commonplace among New France historians. The thesis is most particularly associated with the works of W. J. Eccles, *The Canadian Frontier, 1534-1760* (New York, 1969; Albequerque, 1974) and *France in America* (New York, 1972). The story of smuggling is told in T. E. Norton, *The Fur Trade in Colonial New York, 1686-1776* (Madison, 1974). The fortunes of the French fur trade can be glimpsed in the problematical records of fur traders going west (see Gratien Allaire, "Les Engagements pour la traite des fourrures—évaluation de la documentation," *Revue d'histoire de l'Amérique française* 34 (1980): 3-26 or of the movement of furs from Canada to France (see Tom Wien, "Castor, peaux, et pelleteries dans le commerce canadien des fourrures, 1720-1790," in *"Le Castor fait tout": Papers of the Fifth North American Fur Trade Conference,* ed. B. Trigger, L. Dechéne, and T. Morantz (Montréal, 1987).

21. AN, AC G¹⋅ Recensements, vols. 460-61. Mercantilist administrators understood the value of statistics, including censuses. Estimates of harvests and of exports, tables of prices, and numerous economic ordinances are to be found in AN, AC C11A-C11G as well as AC G¹ and other series. Canadian historians continue to cite the copious tables in Lunn, *Développement économique,* drawn from this material, which have not been superseded.

22. AN, AC, C8A, vol. 55, fol. 340, Havy et Lefebvre à de La Croix, Québec, 30 mai 1743 (copy).

23. Public Archives of Canada, Collection Baby, fols. 829-833, à Pierre Guy, 19 mai 1746.

DOING BUSINESS IN NEW FRANCE

Michael Bliss

It is sometimes still believed that French colonial policy deliberately retarded the economic development of New France. Suppose that the point of having colonies was to accumulate wealth in the mother country through importing cheap raw materials and exporting expensive manufactured products. Surely, then, colonies existed to export raw resources and import finished products? In such a framework colonial production should remain primitive, lest it compete effectively with the metropolis. In the 1730s Barthélemy Cotton, an enterprising employee of the fur-exporting company in New France (the Compagnie des Indes), began making and selling beaver hats locally. He and a former apprentice, Joseph Huppé, became the principal hatters in Quebec and Montreal respectively, supplying the local market and even exporting semi-finished hats to France. Although the colonials were only making a few hundred hats a year, the Minister of Marine ordered their business closed. At Huppé's Montreal shop, "Au Chapeau Royale," the royal officials smashed his basins and his dyeing and fulling vats and carried off the rest of his equipment to the King's storehouse. The infant hat-making industry of New France, perhaps one of the most "natural" directions in which fur trading could have evolved, was literally destroyed by French fiat. It seems a clear case of French mercantilism stifling the entrepreneurial energies and opportunities of the Canadians.

The crushed hatters were a notorious, but isolated case, in which the real issue was probably the way they diverted furs rightfully belonging to the Compagnie des Indes. The real and constant French policy toward New France, implemented to the point of absurdity, was almost the reverse of doctrinaire

From *Northern Enterprise* by Michael Bliss (Toronto: McClelland and Stewart, 1987), 55-77. Reprinted by permission of the Canadian Publishers, McClelland and Stewart, Toronto.

specialization on primary products. Practical French officials believed the colony had to have a diversified economic base before it could build any kind of export capacity, that without greater exports it would continue to be a drain on the French treasury, and that almost anything it tried to export, other than furs, would obviously compete with the produce of France. They felt they had to try to stimulate growth anyway, and far from suppressing the entrepreneurial instincts of the Canadians, the King's officials in France and Canada did all they could to encourage colonial development. They supported and subsidized all kinds of wealth-creating schemes and complained bitterly when the Canadians failed to develop opportunities which seemed so alluring.

Jean Talon, the first intendant of New France after the royal takeover of the colony in 1663, tried to implement Jean-Baptiste Colbert's aim of diversifying the economy. The officials founded and funded a host of enterprises. Talon tried to stimulate agriculture, shipbuilding, mining, fishing, local manufacturing of leather, beer, shoes, and other consumer goods, and the export of almost everything, both to France and to the French sugar islands in the Caribbean. Talon's intendancy saw a whirlwind of innovation, as the King's money seeded his pet enterprises and the King's storehouses accumulated their products. Talon usually had a direct interest in the projects, functioning as a combined intendant-entrepreneur. After two years of work he reported enthusiastically to Colbert that the colony was rapidly becoming self-sufficient in a variety of its needs and would soon export substantial surpluses. He sent trial shipments of timber and planks, cod, eels, and seal oil to France and the West Indies, and predicted huge volumes of future exports.

The exporting might be done in Canadian-made ships, for Talon dreamed of exploiting the limitless forest to build ocean-going vessels. He sent inspectors to survey the woods and in 1670-71 began regulating the northern forest with ordinances giving the King's carpenters first claim on oak and other wood used in shipbuilding. In a shipyard on the St. Charles River near Quebec, Talon organized the construction of several sizeable hulls. Some were sold to the crown, some to a private syndicate of which Talon was a member. Supported at first by Colbert's enthusiasm and the Department of Marine's largesse. Talon planned to build huge warships on the St. Lawrence: a 450-ton, 42-gun hull was laid down, and wood was cut for a 600 to 800 ton monster. One of the attractions of shipbuilding as an industry was the belief that it could stimulate subsidiary enterprises, such as tar works, hemp production, and forges to make fittings.

Even before Talon left New France in 1672 it was becoming clear that his dreams were wildly impractical. The only resource the colony could contribute to shipbuilding, for example, was wood—and not even a lot of that, for good-quality oak was scarce along the lower St. Lawrence. Most of the carpenters and other artisans who put together the crude Canadian hulls had to be imported from France. So were all their tools and all the fittings and rigging that went into the ships. Huge construction costs led officials to realize that perhaps it would be more economic to export the wood to France and build the ships there. But timber for shipbuilding from Canada could not compete in France with either local supplies or imports from the Baltic countries.

All of Talon's other enterprises were uneconomic and did not survive their sponsor's departure from the colony. The brewery, for example, which had adequate supplies of local grain (as well as hops grown on Talon's seigneury) and for whose product there would seem to have been an obvious demand in the fur-trading colony, had actually only existed because Talon insisted on a quota limiting the import of wine and spirits from France. As soon as Talon left the regulations were eased; the brewery closed, and finally its owner—Talon—sold the building to the Ministry, which converted it into a residence for future intendants. Brewing never became more than a household industry in a colony that imported huge volumes of French wine and brandy.

Colbert and Talon had failed to understand the immense handicaps in New France to almost anything other than the fur business. This was a tiny colony one thousand kilometres up a treacherous river in a harsh northern land whose soil was thin and the climate bitterly cold. The St. Lawrence River is often seen as the bountiful artery of the north in Canadian economic history. In fact, sailing ships had a devil of a time ascending the artery in summer, and in winter the river was frozen for five months and impassable for a sixth. It was much less costly and time-consuming to do business with the West Indian islands or any of the ports on the Atlantic seaboard than it was to get ships up to Quebec. Not that there was much business to be done at Quebec anyway. The colony's total export of furs in most years would fill only one ship, unless the cargo was broken up for security or other purposes. Other than furs there was hardly anything else at Quebec that could not be bought more cheaply elsewhere.

Canadian wood was uneconomic to export, if only because of transportation costs. All Canadian products were uneconomic in open competition with the British colonies to the south. But since imperial policy usually forbade the French to trade with the English, there did seem to be a potential market for Canadian foodstuffs and other products in the French West Indies. The prospect of creating a triangular trade between Canada, the Antilles, and Europe appealed to generations of merchants and officials. It worked well for the British with their England-New England-Caribbean triangle. Aside from the extra length of the sailing voyages, however, the French triangle was hampered by the fact that the habitants who tilled small farms along the St. Lawrence only rarely produced significant surpluses of wheat, oats, peas, or other products. The land was not very good; the farming techniques were primitive; whatever profits there might be in the export trade were too small or irregular to stimulate concerted efforts to improve the situation.

The real breadbasket of the northeastern part of the continent was not a few acres of usually snow-covered soil producing a few thousand bushels of this or that grain; it was the fishing grounds downriver, in the Gulf of St. Lawrence, and out on the Banks in the Atlantic. A major geographical gulf between furs and fish had been created when the fur trade moved up the river to Quebec and beyond. Quebec-based entrepreneurs did try to look back eastward and exploit the fishing possibilities of the north shore and Labrador, but it proved almost impossible for the upriver fur-trading colony to harvest the bounty of the sea. Without a second staple product to export, New France was bound to remain a fur-trading backwater, a couple of towns and a few thousand small farmers up a very long creek.

Talon and Colbert had sensed the limits of the St. Lawrence in the 1670s and had considered trying to create some kind of entrepôt or trading centre somewhere in Acadia, a slumbering, much-neglected land, mostly wilderness, only nominally connected to New France. An eastern port would facilitate Atlantic trading on the one hand and the movement of goods in and out of the St. Lawrence on the other. Most planning of this kind was suspended during the long period of bitter warfare first with the Iroquois and then with the British that ended with the Treaty of Utrecht in 1713—which gave much of Acadia to the British (who renamed it Nova Scotia). Then a French military decision to create a great fortress on Île Royale (Cape Breton Island) had exactly the economic effect that optimists could have hoped for. Within a few years of its foundation, Louisbourg, which included a thriving town on an excellent year-round harbour, was exporting more fish than Canada was exporting furs. Soon Louisbourg had a total maritime trade absolutely greater than Canada's and on a per capita basis many times larger. In the 1720s and 1730s Île Royale was France's busy Atlantic base for legitimate trade with the West Indies, substantial illicit trading with New England and Newfoundland, and, because Louisbourg needed food other than fish, very useful trading with Canada. This later trade declined after the late 1730s, however, because of major crop failures in Canada. From then until the Conquest Canada often had difficulty feeding itself, let alone supplying Louisbourg's needs. New England traders happily filled the gap.[1]

There was always a certain amount of Canadian trade, and New France did became host to a few enterprising Frenchmen hoping to make their fortunes in the New World. In certain periods there were considerable fortunes to be made in the fur trade. The greatest fortune was probably the several hundred thousand livres accumulated by Charles Aubert de la Chesnaye, who came to the colony as a young agent for Rouen merchants in 1655. His early transactions are lost in obscurity, but La Chesnaye soon emerged as a grand merchant trader (*négociant* in the French distinction between general shipping wholesalers and the smaller *marchands* who handled goods in later stages of distribution), importing products for his storehouse in Quebec, maintaining a presence in the fur trade, and, typical of his breed, taking an interest in any other venture that looked reasonably profitable. He became involved in the lumbering activities Talon promoted, tried to develop fishing concessions downriver from Quebec, and was interested in a local brickworks. La Chesnaye also became Canada's first important moneylender, advancing cash to both habitants and seigneurs, including such notables as Bishop Laval, who borrowed 10,600 livres from him to help pay for the seigneury of Beaupré. (La Chesnaye made those investments in return for *contrats du rente,* a kind of bond that paid him 5 to 5é per cent interest, had no maturity date, but was probably negotiable among the handful of other fur traders and merchants making up Quebec's circle of *hommes d' affaires*).

La Chesnaye's enterprises flourished so well and widely that he was able to go home and live for several years in the 1670s in La Rochelle, which had replaced Rouen and St. Malo as the principal source of ships and investors for the Canada trade. Only the death of his Canadian partner obliged La Chesnaye to return to the colony to handle the difficult job of untangling all the estate questions affecting the partnership. He then decided to stay on the spot where so many of his assets were tied up.

La Chesnaye's most frequent investments were in land. He purchased or was granted interests in more of the tracts of land denominated as seigneuries than any one else in the history of New France. Under the semi-feudal seigneurial system a seigneury theoretically generated wealth to its proprietor from the *cens et rentes* and other dues paid by its inhabitants. These "censitaires" benefited reciprocally from some of the obligations incumbent on the seigneur, notably a requirement to help the settlers develop the land by providing such local facilities as a mill for grinding their grain. Historians of New France have concluded that the seigneurial system was close to non-functional, generating little revenue for the seigneurs and having an almost imperceptible effect on the development of farms and settlements. With so much land available for the taking, who would bother with landlords? Canadian seigneurs could not hope to emulate French ancestors whose flourishing estates and letters of nobility meant that they and their children were aloof from the sordid scramble for money. Seigneurial status did not signify much real wealth in the New World.

Upwardly mobile Canadians kept trying. Virtually every successful merchant in New France's history repeated La Chesnaye's progress in becoming seigneur, part seigneur, or multiple seigneur. A few were even able to match his triumph in being granted letters of nobility in 1693, thus becoming a true "gentilhomme." De Chesnaye seems to have aspired to the title, calling himself "noble homme" for years previously. Merchants who chose a path to seigneuries and the aristocracy have sometimes been criticized as following a course of waning entrepreneurial zeal. Perhaps, but the transition was not peculiar to French-Canadian or even French merchants. The passion for landholding and titles affected businessmen from Prussia to New England, and seems to be, as the great French social historian, Fernand Braudel, has argued, a phenomenon of all places and periods.

It was rooted in vague but powerful desires for rest and respectability, and also at many times and places—including even New France—a shrewd sense that land was not a bad investment. Even if the income from a seigneury on the St. Lawrence was slight, it might be a profitable short- or long-term speculation. Trafficking in seigneuries contradicted the feudal notion of grants in perpetuity, but it took place constantly in both New and old France—in other words, a market had developed for real estate. Seigneuries were also a relatively secure investment, in the sense that the land could not easily founder in a storm, be captured by privateers, or be carried off by an invading army. Nor could its value be deliberately debased in the way that gold and silver coinage had been through the centuries and would be many times in the future. Finally, as landed proprietors throughout Europe were beginning to realize in the eighteenth century, improved agricultural and other resource development techniques could produce huge increases in income. Merchants everywhere understood that land was a fundamental source of most wealth.

Aubert de la Chesnaye might have left a greater legacy in Canada if he had limited himself to his seigneuries or a genteel semi-retirement as a noble. At its peak his fortune was estimated at 800,000 livres, about $1.6 million in modern purchasing power, making him easily the richest Canadian businessman of the seventeenth century, perhaps the richest in the history of New France. He appears to have been ruthlessly single-minded in his acquisition of wealth. In 1665 he was fined for having sold shoes from his Quebec store at prices higher than those allowed by the Conseil Souverain in one of its attempts at price-fixing. A trading permit issued to La Chesnaye by the governor of New York in 1684 indicates involvement in the illegal trade with the British. Some of his enemies even accused him, probably falsely, of provoking war with the Iroquois to advance his trading interests.

La Chesnaye's risk-taking was disastrous enough as it was. In the 1680s he was one of the leading spirits in a French challenge to the British fur-trading presence in Hudson Bay. As we see later, the French and Canadian Compagnie du Nord was a strikingly bold and dashing venture—and it failed. The merchants of Quebec had no more success a few years later when they formed the Compagnie du Colonie to take over the European marketing of their furs from French concessionaires who seemed to be garnering poor returns. The venture was a fiasco because of an extreme glut of furs in France, and the Canadians accumulated heavy debts.

Aubert de la Chesnaye died in 1702. The little we know of the personality of the man who was New France's original *brasseur d'affaires* suggests a man of deep contradictions. He owned one of the larger houses in Quebec, but had some of his curtains made from old tablecloths. He owned a wig and shirts trimmed with lace, but commonly dressed in flannel trousers, a serge jacket, and an old beaver hat. In his will he apologized to those he had wronged, though he could not recall any specific offences, stated that his main interest had been in developing the colony rather than acquiring material goods, and asked to be buried in the paupers' cemetery of the Hôtel-Dieu in Quebec. Perhaps this last request was simple realism, for La Chesnaye's liquid assets at his death were only 125,000 livres. His debts totalled 480,000 livres. The sale of his properties did not bring in enough further revenue to cover the obligations. This premier Canadian fortune had been lost by the time of its accumulator's death.

Many of La Chesnaye's generation of Canadian merchants and fur traders lost their wealth more easily than they had accumulated it. François Hazeur, for example, participated in many of the same business endeavours as La Chesnaye, losing money in lumbering, fishing, and the Tadoussac fur-trading concession. When Hazeur died in 1708, Quebec's governor wrote that he was "missed by everyone because of his merit, his virtues, and his uprightness." He was also insolvent. Dennis Riverin, said by contemporaries to possess "an extraordinary spirit of gain," managed to cling to power and influence only through official favouritism after most of his ventures had failed. Charles Guillimin, another of Quebec's richest merchants, tried to entrench himself with a good marriage and a number of acts of military prowess and good citizenship, including loaning 40,000 livres to the government at Quebec during a financial crisis. Unfortunately Guillimin made the loan in Canada's distinctive playing-card money during a period of inflation and took a severe loss when France decided to redeem the card notes at far less than face value. His biographer concludes: "Guillimin's career had followed a pattern that was not untypical of many of New France's merchants: apparent prosperity and increasing social prestige dissipated almost at an instant by administrative decisions taken in France and by the normal vicissitudes of the Canadian economy." By the early 1700s these vicissitudes had included extreme fluctuations in returns from the fur trade, the collapse of the compagnies du Nord and du Colonie, the erratic development policies of the Department of Marine, the fortunes of war, and, as in Guillimin's case, the problem of the currency.

The currency is always a problem. In the eighteenth-century world the basic medium of exchange was specie, that is, gold and silver coins. There never seemed to be enough specie in circulation and it did not circulate easily enough to meet the needs of commerce. The mercantile world had long since developed various sorts of paper—evidences of debt and orders to pay at some future date—which merchants, shippers, buyers and sellers could and did freely create, circulate, and pass from hand to hand. One form of circulating paper was the simple promise to pay (bon from "bon pour"), the ancestor of the notes that Canada's banks would issue during the nineteenth century. Another was the bill of exchange, an order to pay somewhat resembling today's cheque.

Specie was particularly scarce in New France because chronic trade deficits caused it to move back to France (in payment of debts) and because the French government was often reluctant, sometimes unable, to meet its obligations in hard coin. In 1685, one of the years when the Department of Marine had not shipped out money, and with his unpaid soldiers having to hire themselves out to colonists, the intendant Jacques de Meulles issued distinctive notes by cutting up playing cards, assigning denominations, and signing them. Printed paper currency had already been invented in England and Sweden but had yet to appear in France. The first cards were soon redeemed, but the situation repeated itself and the "monnaie de carte" became a useful local circulating medium. Confidence in the card money was probably increased when an enterprising counterfeiter was fined, ordered to make restitution, publicly flogged, and banished.

The value of the paper debt instruments circulating in New France—bills of exchange, notes, card money, and other variants—depended on the likelihood of their being duly redeemed for the promised amount of specie. Merchants lived or died according to their skill and/or luck at not being caught with paper that had lost its value—such as a bill of exchange drawn on a French merchant who had just failed and could not pay. Uncertainties about redemption tainted almost all notes, including those issued by the government. The greater the uncertainty the greater the impediment to trade. Then, as now, trade flourished best in an atmosphere of confidence in the paper currency.

The greatest impediment to confidence was the French government's reluctance to pay its bills. The practice of issuing playing cards or other government notes became an habitual way of meeting local obligations. But the discovery that specie was not immediately needed meant that a fundamental check on government thrift in the colony had been removed. Local administrators developed a tendency to "spend" more than anyone in the Department of Marine had authorized and afterwards urge the case for the mother country redeeming the debt paper they had issued. The mother country was not always willing to oblige. During the War of the Spanish Succession at the beginning of the eighteenth century, for example, the sheer quantity of paper issued by the King's agents in New France led to significant inflation. Then the realization that France might not, probably could not, redeem the notes at face value led to still more deterioration in the currency's value, causing immense hardship for merchants such as Charles Guillimin. The colonials managed to transfer some of the loss to ignorant French exporters who thought they could safely take payment in bills of exchange drawn upon the Department of Marine. When the treasury of France simply did not produce the coin to redeem these bills, the paper-rich merchants of La Rochelle in 1715 sued the Treasurer General of Marine, who was declared personally responsible for the debt. The crown coolly suspended recourse to the courts and promised to pay the bills "le plus promptement qu'il sera possible." After more delays and uncertainties the Canadian card money and other paper was redeemed at about one-half its face value. Soon there were more issues of card money.

By about 1720 economic conditions in New France had stabilized after several decades of war, inflation, fur gluts, and other problems. The second quarter of the eighteenth century saw considerable population growth, substantial expansion of land under cultivation, and the stimulus to trade and production created by the building of the fortress of Louisbourg. During the peaceful 1720s and 1730s it seemed as though the colony might fulfill some of the aspirations of enthusiastic officials by producing a more diversified range of goods and improving its balance of trade. Elaborate and wildly optimistic plans were drawn up to increase agricultural production in the colony, and there was a renewal of official interest in schemes to produce every imaginable vegetable and mineral product—ranging from domesticated buffalo through developing a trade to the West Indies in Amerindian slaves. Some of the ideas were absurdly far-fetched; others, such as attempts to mine copper near Lake Superior or the coal deposits on Île Royale, were several centuries premature. A few, such as the program to foster hemp-growing and the founding of a local iron industry, seemed as though they almost worked.

Hemp was the fibre used to make rope. The Department of Marine thought it could easily become an export crop for the colony. Surely if the habitants could be encouraged to grow hemp the merchants would develop a good trade in it. In 1720 intendant Michel Bégon began applying the stimulus by offering to buy hemp for 60 livres a quintal. Barrels of seed were imported from France and distributed to interested growers. The hemp plan could hardly fail, in a sense, for the government's price was so high (in France hemp sold at 22 to 24 livres per quintal), that habitants filled the King's storehouses with hemp. Local merchants had too much good sense, though, to take over a trade that required paying more than twice the French price for hemp while ignoring normal quality standards. With 234,000 pounds of hemp in storage in 1730, the government finally eliminated the price subsidy, but had no idea what to do with its unexportable fibre.

Why not make the hemp into rope in the colony, thus adding more value on the spot and creating a new industry? But there were no Canadian ropemakers. Intendant Gilles Hocquart, a particularly enthusiastic promoter of diversification, decided to encourage French ropemakers to emigrate, then help set them up in business so they could train Canadian apprentices while creating a new Canadian industry. Several ropemakers came out in the 1730s. The industry failed. Canadian hemp was of poor quality. So was Canadian rope. Local shipowners and shipbuilders met their needs from France whenever possible. As soon as the department stopped paying exorbitant prices for poor-quality hemp, the habitants stopped growing hemp. Nothing came of proposals to import expert hemp-growers from France. No one is known to have tried to smoke the hemp. Considerable amounts of tobacco were grown for smoking in the colony, but elaborate official attempts to stimulate tobacco production for export also bogged down in problems of quality and price.

The most practical of many proposals for mineral development centred on deposits of soft iron in bogs near the St. Maurice River above Trois-Rivières. Why not take advantage of the ore to build a smelter and forge and make iron products for the colony—stoves, kettles, tools, and so on? Local officials who had been promoting state development of the resource for years were delighted when the fur trader and seigneur of St. Maurice, François Poulin de Francheville, came forward with his own scheme in 1729. The founding of Canada's first manufacturing facility included sending a blacksmith to study methods of iron-making in New England and the obtaining of a loan from the government. Several merchants joined the company Francheville formed, work began, and in the early 1730s a few thousand pounds of Canadian bar iron were produced at the St. Maurice forge.

The sudden death of the founder, Francheville, in 1733 led to suspension of operations, reorganization of the company, and a plea for technical help from France. A French expert, Olivier de Vézin, who was lured out at a high salary, declared that Francheville's installations were absurdly primitive and recommended scrapping them. Vézin drew up a plan for iron works capable of producing 600,000 pounds of bar iron a year, two-thirds of which would be exported to France. An investment of about 100,000 livres, Vézin estimated, would yield a profit of about 60,000 livres annually. "This is an enterprise whose success is assured," Intendant Hocquart wrote to the Minister of Marine after receiving Vézin's report. "As, however, it will be necessary to advance much money before drawing a profit, I have every reason to fear that this project will fail if you, My Lord, are not pleased to support and favour it...."

With substantial state aid and participation, a new Compagnie des Forges du St. Maurice was formed in 1737 to undertake the work. Jean Lunn described the venture in a splendid Ph.D. thesis on New France's economy written long before the parallels to modern Canada were apparent:

> Indications of the disaster which was to overtake the enterprise were evident from the beginning.... By October 1737, when the establishment was announced to be complete, the total expenditure was 146,588 livres instead of the 100,000 livres estimated.... In 1737 Hocquart had made over to the company the remainder of the loan of 100,000 livres agreed upon, but the partners declared that they must have an additional 82,642 livres. Their need was so pressing the Hocquart took it upon himself to advance them 25,233 livres to be deducted from the 82,642 livres which he begged the Minister to lend....
>
> The Minister replied in accents of horror and indignation. The King was being gradually more and more deeply involved. First it was only 10,000 livres, then it was 100,000 livres, then delays were proposed in repaying the loan and now it was another 82,000 livres of which 25,000 livres had already been advanced. It seemed clear to the Minister that there had been much waste and extravagance. Nevertheless he did consent to the new loan....
>
> Further shocks were in store for the Minister. In 1738 the company foresaw that it would not be able to meet its first payment due in 1739 and the King had to agree to another year's delay.... De Vézin's estimate had proved completely unreliable, for expenses far exceeded and production fell far short of what had

been anticipated.... Constant breakdowns of the furnace interfered seriously with production.... The Forges were operated by a staff of costly, dilatory, insubordinate and discontented workmen.

According to De Vézin's original estimate the Forges should have manufactured 2,400,000 pounds of iron during the four years from 1737 to 1741. Instead total production for the period was about 1,000,000 pounds.... Up to the end of September 1741 returns from the sale of iron amounted to 114,473 livres. The sale of stock on hand and some other assets later produced 39,184 livres. Total expenditure however was 505,356 livres, leaving the Forges with a deficit of 351,699 livres, less the value of the property at St. Maurice. In October 1741 the partners handed in their resignations and declare the company bankrupt. This was the end of the private exploitation of the mines of St. Maurice.

The enterprise collapsed under a burden of technical, administrative and financial incompetence.

The major private entrepreneur who lost his fortune in the St. Maurice fiasco was François-Etienne Cugnet, the only member of the company with access to funds to advance to the firm. It was not clear that all the funds advanced were rightfully his. The crown took over the forges, which continued to make iron goods for local consumption to the end of the French regime and long afterward. The operations were not profitable.

Intendants like Hocquart often complained that the merchants of the colony lacked the resources to invest in such attractive prospects as the St. Maurice forges. Ten years' residence in the sugar islands would be enough to make a man rich, Hocquart wrote in the prosperous year of 1735, "whereas in this colony the greatest individual fortunes, with a single exception, are of 50 to 60 thousand livres. Of these there may be 4 or 5. Common fortunes are not greater than 20 to 30 thousand livres, and are moreover few in number." Historians have echoed his and other complaints in concluding that a lack of investment capital was a major factor retarding the economic development of New France. And just as capital was in short supply, so was labour, leading to endless complaints about shortages of cheap, skilled labour limiting growth.

These judgments confuse cause and effect. If real opportunities for profitable industrial diversification had existed in New France, both labour and capital would have been attracted from Europe, as they were to all the areas in the Americas, South, Central, and North, where greater opportunities existed than could be found in *cap de nada*. The endless and mostly futile attempts to stimulate the development of every conceivable industry in New France— Joseph-Noël Fauteux's 1927 account of them in his *Essai sur L'Industrie du Canada sous le Régime Français* runs to 555 pages—show that there was no shortage of public and private entrepreneurs trying to exploit opportunities. But there was a shortage of opportunities, a lack of products that could be made in Canada and sold profitably in or outside the colony.

Even the fur trade had settled down by the 1720s into a business with little prospect of great rewards. We see later how the French were extending and rationalizing their trade in constant competition with the English to their north and south. As W. J. Eccles has written, they were also "militarizing" it, subordinating economic considerations to their strategic needs vis-à-vis Englishmen and Indians. The men in the trade were beginning to specialize as operators of inland posts, or as Montreal-based outfitters bringing in goods from Quebec and hiring *engagés* for the trip to the interior. Not many of them accumulated fortunes.

The largest individual investments were made by the import-export merchants moving goods in and out of Quebec, the *négociants* of the Lower Town who were the biggest fish in the small colonial pond. Most were the agents or factors or partners of French *négociants*, big shipping merchants of Rouen, Bordeaux, and particularly La Rochelle, who had dominated business from Canada since taking over from Dutch traders in the 1660s.

A single trading voyage was often an enterprise in itself, with a special partnership having been formed in France to finance it and the profits (or losses) being divided at the end. An eighteenth-century merchant "company" was usually a fixed-term partnership, often of members of a family, with unlimited liability and no provision for share transfers. (In Europe the limited liability partnership had gradually developed out of this situation as a way to mobilize capital and conduct business over longer distances and among members of different families. Allowing a partner to transfer his shares in a firm, with or without his partners' consent, increased flexibility still further. It was one more short step, taken as early as the sixteenth century, to the creation of a joint-stock company in which all shares were fully and publicly transferable. The Hudson's Bay Company was the only such organization to operate in Canada before the nineteenth century.) Most of the Canadian trade was done by merchant partners; some tried a voyage or two and sailed on to a more profitable trade; others found success and increased the length, size, and capital base of their partnership agreements to underwrite more ventures.

The best-known French merchant in the Canada trade was Robert Dugard of Rouen, whose investment in a single ship that traded to Quebec in 1730 led to the formation of the Société du Canada, a long-term partnership under Dugard's management. The Société owned and outfitted a fleet of up to eight ships, maintained a warehouse and very active agents in Quebec, and in handling 10 to 20 per cent of the colony's trade was deeply interested in expansion, particularly to the West Indies.

Dugard and company's ships brought a myriad of consumer goods into Quebec. A single cargo included a wide variety of woollen, linen, and cotton cloth, blankets and garments, shoes, hats, gloves, knives, flat-irons, Dutch stoves, weights, locks, bridal mounts, roasting spits, shoe scrapers, combs, mirrors, window panes, plates, mugs, teapots, spoons, salad bowls, garden vases, foot warmers, paper, writing plumes, penknives, pipes, playing cards, pepper, nutmeg, cloves, cheese, salt, vinegar, dried prunes, almonds, and forty-two barrels of red wine, seven of white, ten of anisette, and ninety half-barrels of brandy. The supplies were for the colonists, for trade with the natives, and for the illicit trade with the English. All trade goods were sold at the firm's warehouses to other merchants or middlemen who shipped them up to Montreal, the centre of both the fur trade and the smuggling trade. Retailers and fur traders often purchased on credit extended by the *négociants*, settling their accounts after the goods had been resold or traded.

The Société's ships left Quebec with cargoes of furs and the occasional surpluses of flour, barrel staves, planks, and fish products that the colony was able to export in the good years. Sometimes the ships came north from or sailed south to the West Indies; Louisbourg was often used as an entrepôt to pick up or exchange cargoes. Even at the best of times trade between Canada and the Indies did not flourish. Canada was not much of a market for rum or molasses or slaves. Worse, as specific studies of individual voyages indicate, it was almost impossible to pick up a cargo in Quebec as valuable as the one brought in: thus the voyage out brought far lower returns than the voyage in. Canadian historians visiting La Rochelle, France, used to be shown streets whose cobblestones were said to have come across the Atlantic as ballast from a country with nothing else to export. Robert Dugard's Société du Canada earned trading profits of about 10 per cent on its investment, not the fabulously high figures of popular and some scholarly belief, but between two and three times as much as could be earned in interest on less risky ventures.

Dugard and his associates, including the young cousins François Havy and Jean Lefebvre who were sent out to be the firm's factors in Quebec, were interested in any kind of enterprise, French or Canadian, that looked particularly profitable. In the late 1730s, for example, they took advantage of a system of royal bounties on ships built in Canada (another department program to stimulate Canadian industry) to launch the first of a total of six major ships they built in the colony. The last three of these were built after the bounties were ended, and were instanced by Hocquart as evidence that significant private shipbuilding really was feasible in Canada after all. In fact Havy and Lefebvre reported to France that the ships were very expensive to build, and the program seems to have been a kind of loss-leader to support the Société's Quebec trade. New France's card money and some of its other paper was not negotiable outside the colony. An importer accepting payment in the local currency needed to convert it into an exportable product. Shipbuilding was one way of turning Canadian card money into a product that could be sold in France.

Shipbuilding continued in New France, on a small scale for local needs, and as a crown venture after the opening of a royal shipyard, largely at Hocquart's urging, in 1739. The private industry disappeared in the war years of the 1740s and 1750s, but there was fairly constant production of naval vessels at the King's shipyard in Quebec. As in Talon's era, all the skilled ship-builders, including the director of the works, were brought from France. One Canadian-born blacksmith at the shipyards determined to quit the job, causing the intendant to comment that "comme il est Canadien il préfère sa liberté a estre assujeti à une cloche." In addition to high labour costs, it turned out that the contractors did not deliver properly selected and seasoned wood for the hulls. Neither cost nor quality justified the operation of the royal shipyard. Significant subsidiary industries, such as tar-making, did not develop. The shipyard's demand for labour and material is thought to have contributed to the demise of the more limited but perhaps more economic private sector of the industry.

Both Havy and Lefebvre had an eye for other opportunities in the colony, and soon came to play an important role as both lenders and investors in attempts to develop fishing and sealing operations downstream from Quebec. Like Havy and Lefebvre, most of the men active in Robert Dugard's Société du Canada were Huguenots, French Protestants whose religion was banned in their homeland and its colonies. A fairly large proportion of the merchants trading to Canada in the eighteenth century had overt or covert Huguenot connections. There is no clear evidence, in this or any other period, that such an incidental correspondence can sustain a view of Protestant businessmen as being more "capitalist" or enterprising in their values than Catholics. The old Weber-Tawney hypothesis of a correlation between the Reformation and the rise of capitalism has led to too many simplistic generalizations implying that a Protestant was bound to be a better businessman than a Catholic or that Protestant countries like England were bound to be more enterprising than Catholic ones like France. There is little hard, statistically sound evidence of significant differences in business behaviour between Huguenots and Catholics, in either France or Canada.

A merchant was a merchant, a man trained by experience to assess opportunities, weighing risk against the possibility of gain. Well before Benjamin Franklin's *Poor Richard's Almanack*, austere European merchants were instilling their sons, clerks, and apprentices with a code of hard work, thrift, and the avoidance of personal indulgence. Success in business was never guaranteed to come easily. The eighteenth-century commercial world was fraught with everyday risks, hazards, and insecurities that would horrify a later age, and there were hardly any institutions (such as commercial intelligence services, effective courts, credit-rating agencies, or corporate structures) to help merchants cope with threats to their livelihood.

They tried to minimize risks by creating or becoming part of information, credit, and agency networks—business systems—making possible long-distance and long-term transactions. A man had to have connections he could trust. No wonder that most pre-modern firms—and a good many even in modern times—began as family affairs, and expanded through the recruitment of a web of offspring, nephews, cousins, and in-laws. The next step was from kin to kind, as trusted fellow-townsmen or churchmen became part of a merchant's network of "correspondents," associates, or agents.

Quebec's trade, then, was handled by groups of merchants with family, regional, and religious ties: men whose contacts had alerted them to opportunities and whose networks made it possible to exploit these opportunities with a minimum of defalcation, dishonesty, or other commercial disaster. Historians have recently concentrated on piecing together the links among what J.R. Bosher calls these "clans" or "swarms" of businessmen, tracing the growth, shifts, and declines in the webs of colonial commerce.

Not many purely Canadian-based merchants were prominent in the transatlantic trade. Men operating from the mother country had too many advantages in access to insurers, credit, ships and outfitters, and profitable cargoes to be easily challenged by enterprising colonials. Nor, as the intendants had pointed out, were there many colonial merchants whose local enterprises had profited enough to finance expansion into more costly and more risky ventures. French merchants and their Quebec agents handled about two-thirds of the colony's external trade. Sometimes the representatives of French firms, or French traders who sailed into Quebec and bought and sold goods on the spot, were criticized as "marchands forains." Locals complained that the outsiders had unfair cost advantages, dumped goods at low prices, competed directly with retailers, and did not have a stake in the colony's well-being. Would the crown please protect them from such unfair competition, they sometimes petitioned.

There were several dozen *négociants* and *marchands* in the towns of Quebec and Montreal, and a larger number of small shopkeepers, traders, tavernkeepers, and artisans, engaged in buying and selling, providing services, and producing domestically crafted goods. Trade was often sleepy and apparently non-competitive, but there could be a fierce struggle for livelihoods, particularly on the margin where farming or labouring shaded into commerce. Carting in Quebec, for example, was so vulnerable to unrestrained competition and rate-cutting that intendants fixed the number of carters at ninety (in a town of about five thousand residents), issuing numbered tin tags to be affixed to their horses' collars. Merchants complained about the carters' fixed high rates. Town shopkeepers complained about competition from countryfolk who persistently refused to limit their selling to designated markets. Country shopkeepers had to compete with pedlars, wandering *marchands forains*, and town merchants who came out to buy directly from habitants, perhaps in hope of cornering the local supply of a product. In a small colony ravaged by periodic crop failures and containing so few producers, markets could so readily produce unattractive prices that intendants issued a host of regulations fixing prices, trying to ensure fair dealing, and otherwise controlling the market.

Accusations of price-gouging, monopoly, and greed were the usual accompaniment of commerce in the eighteenth century and afterwards. Contrapuntally, merchants complained about taxes, customs duties, and all other vexatious regulations. The bourgeoisie of Quebec and Montreal were self-conscious enough to occasionally consider creating a *bourse* or exchange—a meeting place for trading—and they sometimes appointed one of their number to present a petition to the authorities. The most common subject of petitions was the need for the government to maintain merchant confidence and a sound currency by honouring the cards, bills, and notes issued in its name.

Most merchants in the colony were not specialized, and would dabble in any promising venture. As with La Chesnaye and his like, there were no rigid lines between occupations or classes, nobility and bourgeoisie. Merchants became seigneurs, seigneurs engaged in all kinds of trade, all of the elite intermingled in government positions and councils, and marital bonds linked men and families with common tastes in wealth, power, and prestige. Cameron Nish's designation of the successful merchant of New France as a *bourgeois gentilhomme* seems fundamentally sound—so long as it is understood (following Molière) that most eighteenth-century merchants were *bourgeois gentilhommes*. The Canadians differed from type only in being somewhat less prosperous.

Limited opportunities in the colonial economy made it difficult for little men to ascend into the ranks of the merchant bourgeoisie. Of course a few made it: Jean Brunet, a Montreal butcher who was able to retire comfortably after many years in the trade; Jacques Campot, who started as a blacksmith at Detroit and became a substantial general merchant; Ignace-François Delezenne, the most successful of several reasonably prosperous silversmiths in New France, who became a seigneur and in the last years of the colony ran a small industry manufacturing trade silver. Growth at Louisbourg after 1725 probably created more opportunities for mobility there than in Quebec or Montreal. Michel Daccarrette, who began as a small fisherman and sometimes privateer out of Plaisance, Newfoundland, moved to Louisbourg and developed fishing stations on Île Royale that employed as many as 170 men bringing in more than 100,000 livres worth of cod in a season. As the Daccarrette family expanded into shipping, both to France and the West Indies, and to general merchandising, a once-poor fisherman now owned a comfortable Louisbourg house tended by servants and slaves. The *Dictionary of Canadian Biography* memorializes a handful of other men and families who prospered similarly from their skill in capturing the bounty of the New World. Many more tried and fell short, disappearing from history in the mean obscurity of their birth.

Merchants' wives and daughters were sometimes surprisingly active in commerce. With the family unit as the most common basis for a business, in an age of hazardous voyages, long absences, and early death, wives and widows often took an active hand in managing affairs and property. When Francheville of the St. Maurice ironworks died in 1733, for example, his thirty-six-year-old widow, Thérèse, herself the daughter of a prominent Montreal merchant, carried on with his affairs, gradually withdrawing from the forges and investing her inheritance in loans to other merchants. (Her one disastrous mistake was a proposal to sell the family's black slave, Marie-Joseph-Angélique; Marie set fire to the Francheville house in Montreal and fled with her white lover. Forty-six houses and the Hôtel-Dieu were destroyed by the flames; the slave was tortured, hanged, and burned.) Marie-Ann Barbel, mother of fourteen children to Louis Fornel, also managed his businesses during his visits to Labrador sealing stations. After his death Marie-Ann took over the sealing concession, working with his former partners, Havy and Lefebvre, and adding the fur-trading concession at Tadoussac. "Veuve Fornel et compagnie," as she signed her business documents, tried other ventures, such as founding a small pottery when imports from France were interrupted by war. "The country has a resource in Mademoiselle Fornel," Havy and Lefebvre wrote. "She has a very good craftsman and her earth proves good."

Agathe de Saint-Père, Mme de Repentigny, organized a "factory" to make cloth for the colony during a wartime blockade in 1705. Her workers were nine English weavers whom she had ransomed from Indian captors. They taught Canadian apprentices the trade, other Montrealers picked it up, and the little industry came to involve twenty looms on Montreal island producing 120 ells of cloth a day. It survived the departure of the English weavers and operated under Mme de Repentigny's control until 1713. This energetic businesswoman, mother of the Canadian textile industry (the one "manufacturer" listed in the early volumes of the *Dictionary of Canadian Biography*), experimented with new materials ranging from bark fibres to buffalo hair and discovered several new dyes. It seems that neither she nor the widow Fornel, however, could compete with French imports in peacetime.

The grand dame of Canadian lumbering was the "very noble young lady" Louise de Ramezy, unmarried daughter of a governor of Montreal, who took over management of a sawmill on one of her family's properties, ran it for three decades—sometimes through a foreman—and became involved in at least two other sawmills and a tannery in addition to her own seigneury. Another female seigneur, owner of the Île d'Orléans, mother of sixteen, was Charlotte-Françoise Juchereau, who styled herself the Comtesse de Saint-Laurent. "People might perhaps have forgiven her vanity and her usurping the title of countess," an intendant wrote, "if she had at least paid her bills." The three Demoiselles Desaunier kept a notorious trading shop on the Caughnawaga Indian lands outside Montreal. Everyone knew it was the centre for the illegal fur trade with Albany, but the sisters fought off repeated state attempts to dislodge them, and stayed in business for a quarter-century. Of course wives and daughters did not normally engage in either licit or illicit commerce in New France, and when women married, their husbands normally controlled their property. Historians have tended to pay more attention to the strong-minded heroines of the religious communities, Jeanne Mance, Marguerite

Bourgeoys, or Marie de l'Incarnation, than to the equally tough *femmes d'affaires* who occasionally seized opportunities created by the precariousness of life in the little colony.

"We need a good peace," Havy and Lefebvre wrote to a correspondent in France in 1746, "in order to be able to work solidly at increasing the trade of the country. It must be hoped that God will give us the grace soon to see the end of the war." Their hopes were not realized. For most of its history New France was literally embattled, functioning primarily as a military outpost of empire rather than a fur-trading or agricultural colony. The only period of peace and reasonable security in the colony's history ended in the early 1740s; there followed years of war, preparations for war, undeclared war, and war again, culminating in the British conquest of 1759-1760.

For many merchants the wars were disastrous. Robert Dugard's Société du Canada had six ships wrecked or captured during the War of the Austrian Succession in the 1740s. Even through the firm's insurers paid promptly (particularly those based in the enemy capital of London; the Londoners sometimes charged lower rates, some said because they could warn a client of the movements of British fleets), the losses forced the Société to withdraw from Canadian trade. At Louisbourg Michel Daccarrette lost his property and his life during the British siege and capture of Louisbourg in 1745. François Havy's personal fortune and many other merchants' modest accumulations of wealth disappeared in the rubble of Quebec and the destruction of the colony's currency during the Seven Years' War. War destroyed normal trade and many normally conservative traders.

But war also threw up a new breed of risk-takers. It created a huge growth industry servicing the state, supplying troops, provisioning the colony, transporting equipment. The public officials who profited from this opportunity brought the confusion of public and private interests in New France to a climax that finally played itself out in wild inflation, profiteering, scandal, trials and imprisonment, along with military defeat.

Remember that eighteenth-century governments did not expect public officials to set their private interests aside. In an age before the bureaucratization and professionalization of government, part of the compensation for taking the trouble to serve the state was the prospect of using office for private profit. Everyone in Bourbon France did it; every major official in New France was involved in fur trading or other enterprises. Collectors and administrators of the King's revenues kept the accounts in their own name, often investing the money in their own ventures. Consider François Foucault, the King's storekeeper at Quebec from 1715 to 1740. "It was not always clear whether the large credits Foucault extended were from his own or from the king's revenues," his biographer writes. "Consequently, when a creditor proved insolvent, he could shift the loss from his own to the king's ledger." Foucault ran his private store at

Quebec in the same location as the King's store, and had a habit of trading with himself, hiding rake-offs through the use of agents or aliases. This was not particularly unusual in the colony. What was the point of holding an office if you didn't make something out of it?

As military business ballooned during the wars of the 1740s and 1750s so did the opportunities available to the holders of strategic offices. Led by François Bigot, the last intendant of New France, the officials seized their chance. A native of Bordeaux, Bigot had served as financial commissary of Louisbourg, engaging in several commercial ventures and investing in privateering on the side, before being posted to Quebec in 1748. During his twelve years as intendant, Bigot was the centre of an elaborate private operation, in which many military officers and senior officials of the colony participated, to supply profitably the colony's wartime needs. One important partnership included Bigot, Jacques Bréard (the financial controller at Quebec), and the Bordeaux shipping firm of David Gradis et fils. It operated as La Société du Canada, but was very different from Dugard's group of peacetime traders. Gradis, a major outfitter to the King of France, sent ships to Quebec where Bigot and Bréard purchased their cargoes on behalf of the government at prices they set; they then collected half the profits from the voyages. The Bigot group's interests included a small fleet of ships in the Louisbourg-West Indies trade and a company formed secretly to buy furs at interior posts which were supposed to be sold at auction in Quebec.

Bigot routinely awarded contracts and concessions to such friends and associates as Michel Péan (adjutant at Quebec), Louis Pennisseaut, Marie-Ann Barbel, Guillaume Estèbe, and others, taking a personal stake in their ventures. His most enterprising crony was Joseph-Michel Cadet, a Canadian-born merchant butcher, who began to prosper selling meat to the crown and expanded into supplying other foods. Bigot made him purveyor general, responsible for provisioning all the garrisons and eventually the civilian population during the desperate war of the late 1750s. Cadet then organized the Grande Société, a partnership in which all of them had an interest, from which he bought most of the provisions. The gang of purveyors and profiteers was knit together by ties of kin, friendship, avarice, and, at the top, the sexual favours of Angélique "Lélie" Péan, Canada's equivalent of Madame Pompadour.

As the noose of British power tightened around the St. Lawrence in the late 1750s, Quebec and Montreal reeked with defeatism, cynicism, and a scramble for booty. Everyone knew the accounts were crooked; the worst swindles were in Indian presents—goods the officials just redirected into private trade. Citizens had nicknamed the Bigot crowd's stores at Quebec and Montreal "La Friponne"—the rogue or rip-off. With the spectre of famine haunting the colony, prices having risen 800 per cent in four years, and paper "money" everywhere, the elite revelled in gambling and balls. The commander of the French troops in North America, Louis-Joseph de Montcalm, saw venality everywhere:

Everybody appears to be in a hurry to make his fortune before the Colony is lost, which even, many, perhaps, may desire as an impenetrable veil over their conduct. The craving after wealth has an influence on the war, ... Instead of reducing the expenditures of Canada people wish to profit by everything; why abandon positions which serve as a pretext to make private fortunes? Transport is distributed to favorites. The agreement with the contractor is as unknown to me as it is to the public. 'Tis reported that those who have crowded into trade, participate in it. Has the King need of purchasing goods for the Indians? Instead of buying them directly, a favorite is notified who purchases at any price whatever; then M. Bigot has them removed to the King's stores, allowing a profit of one hundred and even one hundred and fifty per cent, to those whom it is desired to favor. Is artillery to be transported, gun-carriages, carts, implements to be made? M. Mercier, commandant of the artillery, is the contractor under other people's names. Every thing is done badly and at a high price. This officer, who came out twenty years ago as a simple soldier, will soon be worth about six or seven hundred thousand livres, perhaps a million....

Montcalm's own defeatism and incompetence contributed to the British victory on the Plains of Abraham on September 13, 1759. When the colony finally capitulated in September 1760, most of those who had done well in New France's last years sailed back to France, taking whatever wealth they could salvage. For Bigot and Cadet the scavenge was well into the millions of livres. But defeat did not veil misconduct. The French government developed an intense interest in finding someone to blame for the fall of Canada. Bigot, Cadet, and fifty associates were flung into the Bastille, and, in the notorious *"Affaire du Canada,"* were convicted of defrauding the crown and plundering the colony. Their penalties included fines, restitution payments, banishment, and the destruction of their reputations. Another penalty paid by everyone with money from New France's last phase was the loss of more than half its value, for France repudiated most of the notes and cards that had been issued in its name.

The supreme irony of the *Affaire du Canada* was that most of the profiteers and criminals had contributed more to the preservation of the colony than their accusers. Montcalm's opinion notwithstanding, Bigot and Cadet were both brilliant administrators, two of the smartest, most efficient men ever to hold high office in New France. Their private schemes succeeded so well largely because they were so effective in carrying out their public duty to supply the colony. Gradis et fils slipped supply ships into Quebec, for example, more regularly than the French navy got vessels through British blockades. Cadet risked his fortune to get his own ships through in 1758 and 1759 at a time when no one else had the vigour and daring to attempt the feat. He fed the besieged colony to the end, doing well by doing his duty. If the censorious Montcalm had done his job of generalship equally well, the French regime in America might have had a different fate.

The high prices that plagued the colony in its last years were partly due to the Bigot gang's skimmings, but they were mostly caused by inflation. Government spending had soared, war impeded production, and holders of paper shrewdly lost confidence in the French government's promises to redeem it. But everyone needs scapegoats for inflation and defeat. Bigot and company were not unusually villainous by the standards of eighteenth-century France or New France; if anything they were unusually competent products of that century's office-holding system. They did a spectacular job of making the system work. But while they won the battles to keep the civil side of the colony going, the soldiers and the government lost the war.

New France had always been an economically precarious colony, highly dependent on the vagaries of the fur trade, unable to develop other staple products for export. After the boom years of the fur trade, a few Canadian merchants had emerged to trade with the handful of French-based merchants who controlled colonial shipping. The greatest opportunities the colony offered were not to profit from the natural development of a community and its resources, but to get inside the King's purse when it was wide open to finance wars. The risk of exploiting the state and its needs might have been manageable if only the war had been won. When it was lost, the state turned on the risk-takers in its need to find excuses for the loss of Canada.

Notes

1. For several centuries smuggling was the principal activity in what we now call the "underground" or "black" economy, the network of transactions that take place beyond the ken of the state and therefore never show up in statistics. All of the subjective evidence from the French regime in Canadian history—as well as some hard evidence about the movement of French furs to Albany—suggests a very high volume of illicit trade. It may have been so high as to pose a challenge, some historians feel, to the whole idea of a comparatively poor colony with little to export. The difficulty with this view, aside from the problem of evidence, is that it would have to be applied to all other settlements, whose inhabitants were not likely to be less adept smugglers than Canadians. The comparative disadvantage of New France in the Atlantic trade, licit and illicit, would remain.

CHAPTER
4 THE EXPULSION
OF THE
ACADIANS

Although Champlain's decision, in 1608, to establish a settlement at Quebec meant that henceforth French colonizing activity in North America would be centred on the St. Lawrence, a French presence stubbornly persisted in what became known as Acadia. Never very large in terms of population, and frequently handed back and forth between French and British in the ongoing imperial rivalries of the age, Acadia gradually acquired a distinct character of its own. Its location meant both isolation from the main centre of French power at Quebec and considerable contact with the colonies to the south. Although the fur trade was of some importance to Acadia, its economy was much more agriculturally based than that of New France.

Acadia changed hands for the last time during the War of the Spanish Succession. The Treaty of Utrecht, which formally ended that war in 1713, left Acadia in British hands. The British thus were confronted with the problem that would arise in a much greater way later in the century: the position of a French and Catholic colony in an Empire that was English and Protestant. This first experiment ended in 1755 with the forcible deportation of virtually the entire Acadian population, estimated at about 10,000 people.

The readings in this section should be viewed as complementary, differing in emphasis rather than ultimate conclusions. The first, by C. Bruce Fergusson, was written in 1955 on the two hundredth anniversary of the deportation. In this article, Fergusson placed great emphasis on the question of the oath of allegiance. Fergusson's argument that the Acadians refused to choose between the only two options open to them—to remain French nationals and leave Nova Scotia or to become full and unqualified British subjects—implies that the Acadians themselves were ultimately the authors of their own fate.

In the second reading, Desmond Brown argues that, if one is to comprehend the decision to expel the Acadians, it is important to understand the "frame of reference" of the mid-eighteenth-century British governing class, one far removed from our own. He, too, regards the question of the oath of allegiance as fundamental, but he links to it the concept of land tenure, which he views as the other side of the same coin. The refusal by the Acadians to take an unqualified oath of allegiance, according to this argument, nullified both legal and moral right to hold land in a British colony, in the minds of British officials.

In the final reading, Naomi Griffiths examines in greater detail the events of the crucial years immediately preceding the deportation. She emphasizes the strategic significance of the location of Acadia, given the continuing struggle for supremacy in North America between France and Britain. Situated between New France and New England and commanding the entry to the Gulf of St. Lawrence, it could hardly be otherwise. Placed in the context of Britain's military situation in North America and the impending outbreak of hostilities with France, the deportation of a potentially hostile population would seem to Major Charles Lawrence, the Lieutenant-Governor of Nova Scotia, a necessity. The Acadians themselves, viewed from this perspective, become largely helpless pawns in a struggle for imperial supremacy between Britain and France.

Suggestions for Further Reading

Brebner, J.B., *New England's Outpost: Acadia before the Conquest of Canada*. New York: Columbia University Press, 1927.

Daigle, Jean, "Acadia, 1604-1763: An Historical Synthesis," in *The Acadians of the Maritimes: Thematic Studies*, ed. Jean Daigle. Moncton: Centre d'études acadiennes, 1982.

Grant, Helen, "The Deportation of the Acadians," *Nova Scotia Historical Quarterly*, Special Supplement (1975), 101-119.

Griffiths, Naomi, *The Acadian Deportation: Deliberate Perfidy or Cruel Necessity?* Toronto: Copp Clark, 1969.

Reid, John G., "Acadia and the Acadians: In the Shadow of Quebec," *Beaver*, LXVII, no. 5 (October-November 1987), 26-31.

THE EXPULSION OF THE ACADIANS

C. Bruce Fergusson

Some observers have said that Germany's annexation of Alsace-Lorraine was worse than a crime—it was a blunder; others have seemed to say that the expulsion of the Acadians was not a blunder but rather a crime. However that may be, history caught up with the Acadians in 1755, when six thousand or

From *Dalhousie Review*, XXV, no. 2 (1955), 127-135. Reprinted by permission of *Dalhousie Review* and Mrs. Evelyn Fergusson.

more of them were uprooted from their beloved lands in Nova Scotia, placed on board ships and deported to British colonies to the south. Ninety-two years later, moreover, in a blend of fact and fancy, Longfellow caught them up in the unforgettable lines of the poem *Evangeline*. Since that time, it seems, the warp of fact and the woof of imagination have been so interwoven by poetic licence in a memorable mosaic of sentimentality and suffering, that it is difficult to separate fact from fancy and to get at the sober truth of the matter. Yet even the most aloof observer must feel sympathy for any group of people who experience the testing of exile from their accustomed place, no matter whose the responsibility for the exile, and no matter whether that forced expatriation was deserved or undeserved. That being the case, the heart goes out to the Acadians of 1755, without any need for the head to appreciate anything of the circumstances, or for any question to be asked of the why or the wherefore. But the two-hundredth anniversary of that event should provide the occasion for real attempts to understand what actually happened in 1755, and why and how it took place.

Was the expulsion of the Acadians a misfortune or was it a disaster? Were they the undeserved victims of misfortune, or did they reap disaster from their own folly? These are the salient questions which should be borne in mind whenever consideration is given to the fate of the Acadians in the year 1755. Their story, it is clear, is an admirable illustration of the relative strength of the ties that bind, and of the forces that influence, a people, as well as a supreme example of how a dramatic and colourful episode in the history of any people may be readily translated into the misty realm of romance, so that careful attention is needed for an adequate realization and a proper understanding. The story of the Acadians may be regarded as a tale that is told. But its versions differ, some of them are marred or distorted by emotion or bias, by artificial colouring or by unfounded judgments, and new appraisals are sometimes needed.

Centre or core of the Acadian problem was the oath of allegiance. One important factor was the fact that between the final capture of Port Royal by the British in 1710 and the fateful year 1755 most of the Acadians were unwilling to take the unconditional oath of allegiance. They refused to take the unqualified oath, insisted that they should not be required to take up arms in the event of war, and advanced the rather fantastic claim that they should be regarded as "French Neutrals."

Clearly the Acadian demand was an extraordinary one. It was the accepted conception then as now that the obligations incumbent upon those living within the bounds of the authority of a state included the taking of the oath of allegiance to that state. That was the case when New Sweden was obliged to submit to the New Netherlands in 1655, with those Swedes who desired to remain on the Delaware being expected to give an oath of unqualified allegiance to the new authority. That was also the case when the New Netherlands was obliged to submit to the English in 1664, and the Dutch about the Hudson and elsewhere were expected to do the same, if they remained beyond the period of a year. It was likewise the case, so far as France was concerned, when Frontenac received instructions respecting the expedition against New York, in the event of its capture, in 1689; and when the Duke d'Anville received instructions relating to his formidable but ill-fated expedition of 1746. Furthermore, this rule of broad international application was applied not only to the French in Canada after 1763, but also to those of Louisiana after 1803 when that territory became part of the United States, and to the Mexicans of northern Mexico after its cession to the United States in 1847.

Until the war was officially brought to a close by the Treaty of Utrecht in 1713 the situation was rather unsettled, with the articles of capitulation agreed upon at the surrender of Port Royal applying only to those within three miles of the fort and with the other Acadians anxious and uncertain about what the future held in store for them. One of the articles of capitulation provided that the inhabitants within the *banlieue*, an area having a radius of a cannon shot or three miles from the fort, should remain upon their estates, with their corn, cattle and furniture, for two years, if they were not desirous of leaving before the expiration of that time, they taking the oaths of allegiance to Her Britannic Majesty. In accordance with the terms of this article, the inhabitants within the *banlieue*—57 heads of families—did take such oaths by the end of the third week of January 1711, and that, in itself, seemed to portend auspiciously. But the war had not yet ended, French agents were active and the Acadians outside the *banlieue*, not being included in the articles of capitulation, were in a state of uneasiness and uncertainty. These Acadians applied to the British Governor for protection and offered to take the oath of allegiance. But the Governor who told them that by the arbitrament of war they had become prisoners, and who had collected a tribute from them, could give them no terms until Her Majesty's more particular orders were received. As a result of uncertainty over their situation the Acadians outside the *banlieue* became uneasy, tried to keep the Indians hostile to the English and attempted to stir up the Acadians within the *banlieue* who had already taken the oath of allegiance. Further apprehension was also caused by the hostile designs of the Indians and the French from Canada, as well as by the influence of the French missionary priests. That this apprehension was justified is clear from the fact that a party of 65 Englishmen which was sent in two flat boats and a whaleboat in June 1711 for the purpose of encouraging friendly Acadians in supplying wood and timber for the garrison was ambushed by a war party of French and Indians and all but one of them were killed or captured. Soon even those Acadians within the *banlieue* who had taken the oath of allegiance joined their compatriots in blockading the fort at Annapolis Royal, and the English were not only threatened with assault but with being one and all put to the sword.

The Treaty of Utrecht brought the war to an end. By it such of the Acadians as might choose to leave Acadia or Nova Scotia were free to do so within the space of a year,[1] taking with them their personal effects; while a letter of Queen Anne permitted such emigrants to sell their lands and houses. Those who remained in Nova Scotia were guaranteed freedom of worship under certain conditions. These were that they should accept the sovereignty of the British Crown, and that they and their pastors should keep within the limits of British law.

Now two roads lay before the Acadians, and it was a momentous question for themselves and for the local British authorities which one of them they would choose: whether they would remove themselves to French territory within the year stipulated in the Treaty of Utrecht, or remain in Nova Scotia and become British subjects. The one course meant their continuance as French nationals but their abandonment of their lands in Nova Scotia; the other meant the retention of their lands, the taking the oath of allegiance to the British monarch and the relinquishment of their French citizenship. Neither of these alternatives was their choice. Instead they tried for many years to combine what they wished of the two alternatives and eventually found themselves in an untenable position.

The best time to have settled the question of the oath was immediately after the Treaty of Utrecht. Then the Acadians numbered fewer than two thousand and, if the interests of security, as well as international propriety, demanded that they take the oath or leave Nova Scotia and they persisted in refusing to do the one or the other, their deportation then would neither have been as formidable nor regarded with so much disfavour as forty-two years later when they had increased to five or six times that number. The reason why the question was not then settled was that the Acadians themselves were loath to leave their fertile meadowlands in Nova Scotia, whence they drew subsistence by means of cattle raising and farming, for uncleared and unknown or less fertile lands elsewhere, where much hard work would be needed, and the British authorities in Nova Scotia had neither the forces nor the resources to press the question to an issue. Other factors also supported the tendency to let matters drift; including the anxiety of the French authorities to maintain good relations with the British at a time when they were involved in difficulties with Spain.

Time and again the Acadians were given the opportunity to take the oath of allegiance. But the French authorities, who found that the Acadians were in the main reluctant to remove to Cape Breton Island, soon saw and seized advantages in the situation and employed French agents and French missionaries for the purpose of keeping the Acadians faithful to King Louis. This was indeed an anomalous state of affairs: the "year" of the Treaty of Utrecht soon passed; most of the Acadians remained in Nova Scotia; French missionaries, who were French agents as well as Roman Catholic priests, strove to keep the

Acadians attached to both their religion and the French interest, and, on occasion, openly avowed that their object was to keep the Acadians faithful to the French monarch; none of these missionaries was ever molested by the British authorities, except when detected in practices alien to his proper functions and injurious to the government; freedom of worship continued to be accorded to the Acadians, notwithstanding the fact that most of them persisted in refusing to take the oath of allegiance, the condition on which they had acquired that privilege; and the British government, in spite of the concern of the British authorities in Nova Scotia, did nothing effective either to have the French missionaries in that colony give a pledge that they would do nothing contrary to the interests of Great Britain or to have them replaced by other priests to be named by the Pope at the request of the British government.

The chief reasons for this anomalous state of affairs were the feebleness of British authority in Nova Scotia, the neglect and the apathy of the British ministers and the fact that the Acadians leaned so heavily on their French spiritual and temporal advisers. For a while, it is true, the *imperium in imperio* which existed was such that the inner power seemed to wax and strengthen every day while the outer relatively pined and dwindled. But the time was to come when the British ministers would waken from their lethargy, bestir themselves and, warned by the signs of the times, send troops and settlers into the Province at the eleventh hour. Then it was that the Acadians were to find how deplorable their position really was. Perhaps the only thing that could have averted the danger of Acadian hostilities or revolt and have made unnecessary the harsh measures to which such conduct afterwards gave rise was for the British ministry to have sent out a force sufficient both to protect the inhabitants against French terrorism and to leave no doubt that the King of England was master of Nova Scotia in fact as well as in name. But such did not take place until after long delay and until the problem had attained greater proportions. In the meantime, although those Acadians who remained in Nova Scotia had been transferred by France to the British Crown by the Treaty of Utrecht, French officers on occasion denounced them as rebels and threatened them with death if they did not fight at their bidding against Great Britain, and British officers threatened them with expulsion if they did not remain loyal to King George. These were the horns of the dilemma for the Acadians; and while for a time they avoided both they were ultimately confronted with the necessity for a decision they had tried to avoid.

French policy after 1713 reveals that France was unwilling to reconcile herself to the loss of Acadia, although it had with its ancient limits been ceded to Great Britain by the Treaty of Utrecht. Nor was France to neglect Nova Scotia or Acadia, even if for years Great Britain was to do so. On Île Royale the French not only built up a mighty base at Louisbourg, as the watchdog and protector of the Gulf and the approaches to Quebec, and as the base and the guardian for the fishery, but also established there a Governor who was charged with the management of Acadian affairs, and who had zealous and efficient agents among the Acadians in the missionary priests, who were sent into Nova Scotia by the Bishop of Quebec, or in a few cases by their immediate ecclesiastical superiors in Île Royale, and whose services in keeping the Acadians in the French interest were recognized and acknowledged by French political leaders and officials. At first the French authorities endeavoured to induce the Acadians to migrate to Île Royale, where the growing power of the fortress at Louisbourg was a symbol that France was preparing to contest the supremacy of the continent with Great Britain, and sent envoys into Nova Scotia, with the permission of the local British officials, to visit the Acadian settlements and to tell the Acadians what inducements they were prepared to give them to remove. A few of the Acadians did go to Île Royale, and nearly all of them in the emotion of the moment signed declarations of their willingness to migrate to French territory, but it was soon seen that this mood quickly changed and that the Acadians in the main had no inclination to leave their homes. At the same time the British authorities, realizing the value of settlers in Nova Scotia, hopeful of having the Acadians become loyal British subjects, and having no desire to see them migrate to Île Royale where they would greatly add to the numbers and the strength of a potential enemy near at hand, were almost as anxious to keep the Acadians in Nova Scotia as they were forty years later to get them out of it. Soon, moreover, the French authorities realized that the Acadians were of greater benefit to France by remaining in Nova Scotia, whence they could furnish Île Royale with much-needed supplies, where religion and patriotism might be combined or confused in keeping them in the French interest, and where in time of war they might be a source of strength for French invaders aiming at the re-capture of old Acadia or a fifth column which would be a decisive factor in any test of strength. If the Acadians had really wished to emigrate, the British Governor could have done little to stop them for his authority hardly extended beyond gunshot of his fort at Annapolis Royal and all the Acadians except those of Annapolis and its immediate neighbourhood were free to go or stay at will.

While most of the Acadians maintained a careful neutrality in times of trouble, and Mascarene himself declared that their refusal to fight for the French besiegers was one reason for the success of his defence of Annapolis on one occasion, French designs involved the Acadians and some of them were implicated in hostile acts against the British in Nova Scotia. During the 1720s French authorities not only strove to foment trouble between the Indians and the English but they joined the Indians in a raid on Canso. On the outbreak of the War of the Austrian Succession, the French from Île Royale seized Canso before the British on this side of the Atlantic were aware of the outbreak of hostilities. They then attacked Annapolis. In this attack Duvivier, the French commander, expected help from the Acadians who were French in blood, faith and inclination; and the latter, who would not join him openly lest the attack should fail, did what they could without committing themselves and made a hundred and fifty scaling ladders for the besiegers. To this seizure of Canso and this attack on Annapolis a contemporary French writer attributes the dire calamity which soon befell the French. When the capture of Louisbourg in 1745 by New Englanders with the aid of a British naval squadron was followed by French plans to retake it, reconquer old Acadia, burn Boston and lay waste to the other seaboard towns, French officials counted on aid from the Acadians for their designs. The result was the assembling of a vast armada, comprising nearly half the French navy, and carrying three thousand one hundred and fifty veteran troops, under the Duc d'Anville, in 1746. This formidable expedition set out from France, and Ramesay, with a large body of Canadians, was sent to Acadia to cooperate with d'Anville's force. News of this design and the appearance at Chebucto of part of d'Anville's ill-fated fleet caused great excitement among the Acadians, who undoubtedly expected that they would soon again come under the Crown of France. Fifty of them went on board the French ships at Chebucto to pilot them to the attack on Annapolis. To their dismay, however, they found that no such attack would then be made. Early in the next year, when Coulon de Villiers and his men in the depth of the winter led his men from Beaubassin to Grand Pré, where in the dead of night they attacked Colonel Arthur Noble and his force, who were quartered in Acadian houses, and killed many of them in their beds, a number of Acadians acted as guides for Coulon's band and assisted them in other ways. With the restoration of Louisbourg to France, the British Government founded Halifax as a counterpoise to it and commenced their first real attempt at settling Nova Scotia. By the time of the eve of the Seven Years' War it was clear that a showdown would soon be reached with respect to North America. In 1755 Braddock was defeated on the Monongahela and Beauséjour was captured by New England troops. At the siege of Beauséjour about three hundred Acadians aided the French.

The developments of the 1740s, with French attacks on Canso and Annapolis, the d'Anville expedition, the massacre at Grand Pré, and other French designs, as well as the capture of Louisbourg and its restoration and the founding of Halifax, meant a heightened interest and an increased activity in Nova Scotia. New efforts to have the Acadians take the oath of allegiance to the British monarch had no better result than previous ones. British activity at the Isthmus of Chignecto, with a view to protecting the peninsula from French encroachments, were followed by two matters of very special significance. One, in 1750, was the first forcible removal of the Acadians: resolved that the Acadians at Beaubassin should be preserved from the contaminating influence of the British, Le Loutre, who had been unable to prevent the British from reaching that village, went forward with his Indians and set fire to it, in order to force its inhabitants to go to territory claimed by the French near Beauséjour, a short distance away. This was the beginning of the dispersal of the Acadians. Besides these, through great pressure from the French they migrated in such numbers that by 1752 two thousand of them were to be found in Île St. Jean (Prince Edward Island), and about seven hundred in Île Royale (Cape Breton Island). The other, in 1751, was an interesting commentary on the attitude of the French authorities towards the Acadian claim to neutrality which those authorities had encouraged while the Acadians remained under British sovereignty: this was the order of Governor La Jonquière that all Acadian refugees near Beauséjour who did not take the oath of allegiance to the French monarch and enlist in the militia companies would be branded as rebels and chased from the lands which they occupied.

Subsequently, just after the capture of Beauséjour in 1755, while the New England troops, who had achieved that victory, were still in Nova Scotia, and British ships of the line still lay in Halifax harbour, Governor Lawrence of Nova Scotia and his council at Halifax decided that the safety of the colony required that the Acadians should take the oath of allegiance, which they had so often refused to do, or be deported from the Province. They again refused, and they were thereupon deported to British colonies. In the circumstances, and particularly after the attacks on Annapolis Royal in 1744 and 1745 and the deeds done at Grand Pré in 1747, it seems both unfair and inappropriate to attempt to pin the chief responsibility for this decision on either Lawrence of Nova Scotia or Shirley of Massachusetts.

Lack of space prevents an account of the hardships experienced by those Acadians who were expelled or a description of the efforts made by the British authorities to keep families and people from the same community together. Suffice it to say that it might appear that the expulsion was unnecessary, for if the old situation had persisted for but another few years until the French menace on the continent had been eradicated the problem would no longer have existed, or if the Acadians could have taken the oath of allegiance prior to 1755, as those who remained in the Province and those who returned to it afterwards did, those harsh deeds would not have been done. Not many years after 1755, at any rate, probably about 2,000 of the exiled Acadians returned to Nova Scotia, where, along with a like number who escaped the expulsion, they received grants of land, took the oath of allegiance and assumed their full place in the life of the Province. On the two hundredth anniversary of that catastrophe which emerged from the vicissitudes of war and threats of war, all Nova Scotians of every racial origin rejoice with those of Acadian descent in marking the great achievements of the last two centuries.

Notes

1. There have been different views as to the beginning and the end of the "year" of this Treaty, and some have held the untenable one that it was still in effect at the time of the founding of Halifax.

FOUNDATIONS OF BRITISH POLICY IN THE ACADIAN EXPULSION: A DISCUSSION OF LAND TENURE AND THE OATH OF ALLEGIANCE

Desmond Brown

In the seminal work on the Acadian deportation, J.B. Brebner observed that

> if one could see and feel with the *habitants* in 1754 and 1755, one would discover that their temper and circumstance were so different from our own that our terms of description do not adequately portray them.[1]

It is evident, moreover, that he did his best to overcome this difficulty in telling the Acadians' story. Although he did not say so, nor is it too apparent in his writing, Brebner could, nevertheless, have said, with equal truth, that the temper and circumstances of the upper-class Englishman of the time are as far from our ken as those of the Acadians. At first sight, the validity of this assertion may appear open to question because, unlike the Acadians, the Lords of Trade and the colonial governors of the mid-eighteenth century can communicate directly with us through the medium of the fluent and graceful English they used in their letters and papers. But it is precisely this fact which should give us pause; for these men lived in a world whose whole frame of reference was very different from ours; where, for example, powerful monarchs still reigned, where economic thinking was dominated by the mercantile theory, and where a man's faith could bar him from positions of trust. Consequently, because their upbringing and experience were so different, the connotations of their English differ from ours, not to speak of the concepts that were derived from it. Two such legal conceptions, which received much attention in the documents of the period and which were central to British policy in the Acadian expulsion, were the oath of allegiance and qualification for land tenure. In what follows, it will be shown what meaning these concepts had for British officials of the period, in order to provide a clearer perception of the reasoning on which their policy was based.

Although the modern form of the oath of allegiance had only been on the statute books for seventy years[2] at the time of the Acadian expulsion, the concept it then evoked was the outcome of a long development which had its origins in the similar societies evolving in England and Normandy during the century before the Battle of Hastings. Both were engaged in almost continual warfare, both had an agricultural base, and both, therefore, depended on assessments levied on land to provide men and money for their military forces. Under such

From *Dalhousie Review*, LVII, no. 4 (1977–78), 709-725. Reprinted by permission of *Dalhousie Review* and the author.

circumstances, it is not difficult to understand why, on both sides of the Channel, "the law of the land was rapidly becoming little more than the land law."[3] However, while there was a close resemblance between the two systems and each was effective in producing military manpower or its fiscal equivalent, they had developed from different traditions, and this caused them to evolve significantly different qualifications for acquiring and holding land.

In England, Germanic traditions supplanted Roman after the departure of the legions in the fifth century. The invaders from the continent were organized in accordance with the concept of the *comitatus* whereby "a great chief would surround himself with a band of chosen warriors and enter into a close personal bond with them"[4] which was sealed with an oath of fealty to the leader.[5] As the invaders became occupiers, the paramount chiefs assumed regal titles and created a nobility by rewarding the faithful service of their followers with titles of dignity and grants of land. These grants could be large or small and, by the eleventh century, could include one or more "hundreds" or "wapentakes",[6] the Anglo-Saxon administrative divisions on which statutory assessments for men and money for war were levied.

Across the Channel, Duke William followed the European practice of the time which was in the Roman tradition.[8] He also ennobled his followers and made grants of land to them, but the basis of tenure was quite different from the English. The land, or "fief", be it large or small, constituted a single assessable unit[9] and was held at the sovereign's pleasure, which was dependent on the fulfillment of specified services agreed to before the grant was made.[10] This agreement was made binding by the solemn and ceremonial act of homage by which the noble pledged to become the sovereign's man—his vassal—in respect of the land he held of him.[11] If the services required the noble to provide knights for military service, he could, with regal approval, carve out subfiefs from his own lands and enfeoff suitably qualified fighting men who then provided the required services and sealed the bond in an act of homage to the noble. There was, however, a flaw in this system, at least as far as Duke William was concerned, because, if he and his vassal fell out, the vassal had a private army whose men owed allegiance to him alone by virtue of their individual acts of homage to him. Not infrequently, such questions were "solved by the sword".[12]

Briefly then, the important points of difference between the English and the Norman systems of land tenure were that, in the former, the oath of fealty played no part, had no territorial significance, and was expressive rather of a personal bond between king and noble or between noble and retainer. Grants of land were made for past performance, not for services to be rendered. While the lord might be held responsible for insuring that men and money were provided from his lands, the assessments for each were statutory and made on the basis of an administrative unit, the hundred. In contrast, the Norman knight was granted an arbitrarily assessed fief only in respect of services to be rendered and only after he had become the duke's vassal by performing an act of homage.

This was the only tenurial system with which William was familiar and, naturally, he introduced it to England after the Conquest. The first grant of a fief in England with the attendant ceremony of homage of which there is record was made to "Peter, one of the Conqueror's knights, in return for three or four knights"[13] in a charter which is unfortunately undated.[14] But there was no revolutionary change with the introduction of what was, essentially, a feudal system because the process was accomplished gradually over twenty years[15] as the lands of the old Anglo-Saxon nobility were seized by the King after the Battle of Hastings and the rebellions of later years.

But the replacement of the hostile Anglo-Saxons by Normans did not end William's troubles because, as in Normandy, the process of subinfeudation could cause private armies to be raised by his vassals which could be used against him. That he was aware of the danger and took steps to prevent it is demonstrated by the fact that, in 1086, acting in his capacity of paramount lord of all lands in England,[16] he "exacted, not only an oath of fealty, but an act of homage from all the considerable tenants of his kingdom, no matter whose men they were."[17] Thus, it is evident that the King had taken from both old English and Norman practice and had combined the idea of the close personal bond between sovereign and subject in the former to the more legal idea of a contract or bargain expressed in the latter. Moreover, "he insisted that in every expression of homage or fealty to another, there shall be a saving for the faith that is due to him."[18] That his insistence was successful is evident in the writing of the Chief Justiciar of Henry II, Ranulf Glanville. In his discourse on homage, Glanville laid it down that

> he who is to do homage shall become the man of his lord, swearing to bear him faith of the tenement for which he does his homage, and to preserve his earthly honour in all things, saving the faith owed to the lord King and his heirs.[19]

He further specified that, if a man held lands of several lords, "chief homage, accompanied by an oath of allegiance, is to be done to that lord of whom he holds his chief tenement."[20]

These pronouncements were echoed and amplified seventy years later, circa 1250, by one of the first judges of King's Bench, Henry of Bratton, known as Bracton.[21] Men before and after Bracton wrote at length on the subject of homage, but none so eloquently or authoritatively. He began by asking the rhetorical question, "what is homage?"

> Homage is a legal bond by which one is bound and constrained to warrant, defend, and acquit his tenant in his seisin against all persons for a service certain, described and expressed in the gift, and also, conversely, whereby the tenant is bound and constrained in return to keep faith to his lord and perform the service due ... The *nexus* between a lord and his tenant through homage is thus so great and of such quality that the lord owes as much to the tenant as the tenant to the lord, reverence alone excepted.[22]

He goes on to specify who must do homage,[23] who must accept it,[24] when and how often it should be done,[25] and the form of the ceremony, which should be performed "in a public place and openly, in the presence of many in the county or hundred court or the court of the lord."[26] The lord should sit and the tenant kneel in front of him[27] and then he

> ought to place both his hands between the two hands of his lord, by which there is symbolized protection, defense and warranty on the part of the lord and subjection and reverence on that of the tenant, and say these words: 'I become your man with respect to the tenement which I hold of you (or 'which I ought to hold of you') and I will bear you fealty in life and limb and earthly honour (according to some, but according to others, 'in body and goods and earthly honour') and I will bear you fealty against all men (or 'all mortal men,' according to some) saving the faith owed the lord king and his heirs.'[28]

Immediately following, the tenant should stand up, place his hand on the Gospels, and swear the oath of fealty:

> 'Hear this, lord N., that I will bear you fealty in life and limb, in body, goods, and earthly honour, so help me God and these sacred (relics).'[29]

It is apparent that this was a solemn ceremony whose ramifications extended far beyond mere land law.[30] In a real sense, the lord was bound to help his man with aid and counsel in all things, even, in some cases, "if he attacks or molests another,"[31] while the man had to "observe his lord's command in all that is honourable and proper."[32]

But even before Bracton wrote, the almost mystic conception of homage that he evokes had begun to decline and to be replaced by the idea of a higher allegiance to the king. This is nowhere more evident than in the law book known as *Fleta*, published only forty years after Bracton's death (circa 1290). While *Fleta* covers all the ground of earlier works and paraphrases Bracton on homage and fealty, it also includes an oath which, omitting mention of any tenement, "promises a fealty so unconditional that it becomes known as the oath of ligeance or allegiance *(ligeantia)*":[33]

> This hear you, who stand by, that I will bear the king fealty in life and limb and earthly honour, and against him I will not bear arms.[34]

While similar in intent to the modern oath of allegiance, this formulation is more like the oath of fealty sworn to the Anglo-Saxon kings.[35] Moreover, like both of these, it conveys the idea of the oath-taker's personal loyalty to the king but appears to exclude any notion of a bond between the two based on mutual advantages and obligations, such as was explicit in the act of homage. In other words, it has the appearance of being a one-sided covenant in favour of the sovereign whereby those who take the oath receive little or no return for their allegiance. But this was not so. First, the protection of the lord which had enabled his vassal to enjoy peaceful possession of his lands now came to be secured to him in a more definite and impartial manner by the nascent but increasingly powerful courts of the king.[36] Second, by the time *Fleta* appeared in the reign of Edward I, these courts, reflecting the royal will and the sentiment of the time, were becoming increasingly "English" and thus tending to see all men divided into two great classes: liege subjects of the king, and aliens.[37] And it was coming to be the rule that only liege subjects could acquire and hold land in England.[38]

This rule had its origins in the loss of Normandy by King John in 1204 and the succeeding state of hostility between England and France which did not end until 1259 when Henry III renounced his claim to the fief. During that time, claimants to the English estates of the descendants of William I's barons who had adhered to the French king were at first met with the dilatory exception:

> You are within the power of the King of France and resident in France, and it has been provided by the Council of our lord the King that no subject of the King of France is to be answered in England until English men are answered in France;[39]

which, over the years, hardened into the peremptory "you are an alien and your king is at war with our king"[40] and finally became "you are an alien".[41] It is therefore apparent that the concepts of an "alien" and, by extension, a "subject" and the reason why the former could not hold English land arose out of "an exaggerated generalization of [the king's] claim to seize the land of his French enemies. Such an exaggerated generalization of a royal right will not seem strange to those who have studied the growth of the king's prerogatives."[42]

Thus, in the time of Edward II's reign, the law relating to allegiance and land tenure had set in the general form it was to hold for the next five hundred years. The duty of allegiance, a word which encompassed the meanings of the older terms, fealty and homage, was due to the king alone in his capacity as the ruler of all England. Acceptance of the duty was made by taking the formal oath in a court or other appointed place.[43] If the duty were accepted by a subject, certain benefits accrued to him, chief among which was the right to acquire land.

Once the law had assumed this form, legislators and judges concerned themselves with working out details. The first item to engage their attention was the definition of the legal status of children born outside the king's ligeance. Edward III and his army spent much time on the continent in war against the French and, without doubt, fathered many children during their progress. Some, including the King, became concerned that their offspring would be considered aliens and would be barred from inheriting their ancestral lands. Debate on this question was initiated in 1343,[44] but not until 1358 did a statute declare that the king's children, wherever born, and certain other named children "born beyond the Sea out of the Ligeance of England"[45] could inherit. The statute also stated that, in future, all children born "without the Ligeance of the

King" whose parents were by birth of that ligeance would be able to inherit. From these provisions, it is apparent that the king's ligeance is considered to be a geographical area, that the right to inherit real property in that area is central to the status of a subject, and that, by implication, anyone born outside the king's ligeance cannot inherit lands and is thus an alien. Twenty years later, however, the qualifications for inheritability were significantly altered when a statute was enacted which proclaimed that "infants born beyond the Sea, within the Seignories of Calais (Guines and Gascony) and elsewhere within the lands and seignories that pertain to our king beyond the sea, be as able and inheritable of their heritage in England as other infants born within the Realm of England."[46]

By the time the most able legal writer of the fifteenth century, Sir Thomas Littleton, had published his *Treatise on Tenures* (1481), the law had progressed to the point where not only was an alien barred from bringing a real action on the grounds that he could not own or possess real property, but he could not even sue in a personal action. However, while Littleton's words are clear and unequivocal,[47] his famous commentator, Lord Chief Justice Coke, in 1628 interpreted them to mean that only an alien enemy, as opposed to an alien friend, could not sue in a personal action, but he was in total agreement that no alien, friend or enemy, could "maintain either real or mixt actions."[48]

And Coke wrote with authority because it was he who, twenty years before, had written the Report of *Calvin's Case*[49] after hearing this famous action in the Exchequer Court. During the case, all earlier legislation and judicial precedents were cited and reviewed, and precise and ample definition was given to many hitherto hazy and uncertain terms touching allegiance, aliens, subjects, and much more besides. Beginning with Glanville, Coke cited statute and precedent to show that "ligeance is a true and faithful obedience of the subject due to his Sovereign"[50] and defined it as the "mutual bond and obligation between the King and his subjects, whereby subjects are called his liege subjects, because they are bound to maintain and serve him; and he is called their liege lord, because he should maintain and defend them."[51] Coke went on to distinguish four kinds of ligeance recognized by law: natural, local, acquired, and legal. Natural ligeance was the obedience owed to the sovereign by a person born in any of the king's possessions.[52] Such an individual was termed a "natural subject" (*subditus natus*).[53] The bond of ligeance was considered to be indefinite, without limit,[54] irrevocable, and operative from the time of birth whether or not a formal oath of ligeance were taken in court.[55] Moreover, Coke took pains to show that, for over a hundred years, a breach of this bond had been defined and punished as treason.[56] On the other hand, the advantages which accrued to the subject were not inconsiderable, and chief among these were the rights to inherit, purchase, own, and devise real property, and to protect his right to such property in the king's courts.[57] These rights were denied to an alien.[58] However, it was found that such a person owed the sovereign a local allegiance so long as he remained in the king's dominions in return for the king's peace and protection which enabled him to carry on his business or commerce and to protect his interests at law. In these provisions it can thus be seen that there is a direct link with the feudal conception of homage in that there is a *quid pro quo*: protection draws allegiance and allegiance draws protection.[59] Acquired ligeance he defined as the ligeance owed to the monarch by an alien who was granted the status of a natural subject.[60] While grants to individuals were rare and hedged with restrictions,[61] this was, nevertheless, the provision, based on ample precedent,[62] which eventually enabled the British to people a vast empire. For whenever the crown acquired a new possession, whether by conquest, cession, discovery, or inheritance, all its inhabitants, *anti-nati* and *post-nati* alike (infidels excepted), became subjects of the crown in no way inferior to natural subjects.[63] To define legal ligeance, Coke went back to Anglo-Saxon times. He found it to be formal expression of the oath of allegiance by a natural subject in a court of law.[64] The oath itself he traced from a version of the Anglo-Saxon oath of fealty said to have been transmitted to the seventeenth century by the legal writers of medieval times.[65]

In the turbulent years which followed the publication of Coke's writings, the oath of allegiance changed form frequently and the profession of legal ligeance became standard procedure for most subjects, but especially for educated persons and those holding government posts. Finally it became standardized in its modern form in the Abrogation Act of 1689,[66] passed after the accession of William and Mary. This statute repealed all previous legislation and laid down the several oaths that were required to be taken by various classes of subjects. Its provisions reflected the fear of a Stuart revival and a continuing insistence on the suppression of the Catholic religion. It is a long, comprehensive document which reproduces the text of each oath in full, specifies that they are to be taken in the open Court of King's Bench or in the county Quarter Sessions, and details the persons who are to take them. Although this Act was amended in several statutes prior to the Acadian expulsion, with the evident purpose of making the oaths more comprehensive and extending their reach, the oath of allegiance remained unchanged. In none of these statutes is there mention of a conditional oath or of a situation where such an oath may be necessary. Regardless of the motives which prompted the enactment of this statute, it is clear that all Englishmen in positions of trust were familiar with the solemn ceremony attendant on the taking of these oaths. Furthermore, in view of the events of 1745 and the subsequent expulsion of the rebellious Scots clans from their ancestral lands, it is probable that they were fully aware of the punishments and penalties they would incur if they were found to be in violation of their oath.[67]

In 1753, Mr. Justice Blackstone began to lecture on jurisprudence at Oxford and preserved the substance of his texts in his *Commentaries on the Laws of England*. This work was published in 1765, ten years after all-out hostilities began in the North American phase of the Seven Years' War and during which the British deported the Acadian population from Nova Scotia. Thus, we are fortunate to have a definitive statement of the law soon after the expulsion took place. In general, the author took an historical approach to his subject and followed the same reasoning to the same conclusions as had his distinguished predecessors, particularly Sir Edward Coke. Concerning the right of the subject to acquire land and the inability of the alien to do so, the situation was precisely the same as it had been over a century before.[68] But the concept of allegiance had undergone some refinement since Coke's time because, after a discussion of land tenure and the obligations arising therefrom, Blackstone concluded:

> With us in England, it becoming a settled principle of tenure, that *all* lands in the kingdom are holden of the king as their sovereign and lord paramount, no oath but that of fealty could ever be taken to inferior lords, and the oath of allegiance was necessarily confined to the person of the king alone. By an easy analogy the term of allegiance was soon brought to signify all other engagements, which are due from subjects to their prince, as well as those duties which were simply and merely territorial.[69]

He then turned to the legislation of the previous sixty years. During the course of a lengthy treatment in which it was evident that the Abrogation Act had been the subject of much legal thought, he remarked that the Oath of Supremacy which

> very amply supplies the loose and general texture of the oath of allegiance ... must be taken by all persons in any office, trust or employment: and may be tendered by two justices of the peace to any person whom they shall suspect of disaffection. But the Oath of Allegiance may be tendered to all persons above the age of twelve years....[70]

It is evident that the Lords of Trade, and senior officers and colonial officials who carried out the Acadian expulsion would have had a very different conception of the oath of allegiance and its ramifications than we have today. To them, it had real and immediate meaning not only because they themselves had to swear allegiance in a solemn ceremony held in an open law court, but because their qualification to take the oath gave them the right to inherit, acquire, and devise real property anywhere in the British empire. This right was highly important in an age when property was synonymous with wealth and high place. By contrast, an alien could not purchase land for his own use at any price. Moreover, as far as the Western hemisphere was concerned, this common law ruling was reinforced by statute law which expressly forbad the sale or other disposal of lands "upon the Continent of America" to any but the subjects of the crown.[71] From these facts, but perhaps even more from the mental attitude they engendered in crown officials, stemmed much of the problem that the British faced in administering Nova Scotia after the Treaty of Utrecht was signed.

After Acadia was ceded to Queen Anne in 1713, her governor found himself in charge of a relatively[72] large, homogenous French-speaking population already cultivating the most arable land in the province to which they laid claim by reason of title deeds granted by former French administrations.[73] As the years passed and the population grew, more and more of the remaining arable land came under the ploughs of the Acadians,[74] and the colony became, to an extent, prosperous. Under normal circumstances, that is to say normal to that time and place, this would have been a most desirable development because article fourteen of the Treaty of Utrecht made it clear that, if an Acadian remained in the colony after the year of grace allowed for removal to a French colony, he would become a subject of the British crown.[75] As such, he would then assume the rights and privileges of a natural born subject under the doctrine of acquired ligeance because his right to practise his religion, albeit in a circumscribed manner, had been recognized.[76] But this desirable state of affairs never came about because the Acadians would not consent to take the oath of allegiance unless it were qualified with a saving clause to the effect that they would not bear arms against the French; an impossible demand in view of British law and tradition. In essence then, successive governors of Nova Scotia were confronted by a population of indeterminate legal status, neither true subjects nor outright aliens, who were attempting to lay claim to crown land. This situation was a prime factor in causing the British dilemma; for as they saw it, this, and other problems, could be solved only by causing the Acadians to become loyal subjects of the crown or by deporting them.

That British officials on both sides of the Atlantic saw the problems and pondered the solutions there is no doubt. For example, in a letter of September 12, 1720 to King George I, Governor Philipps and his Council requested the dispatch of troops to enable them to subdue the Acadians "or to oblige them to depart and leave this Country."[77] In answer, the Board of Trade directed that the Acadians "ought to be removed as soon as the Forces which we have proposed be sent to you shall arrive in Nova Scotia."[78] This was not a new or original solution for, as Brebner points out, deportation had been a frequent proposal since the British first occupied Acadia in 1658.[79] Likewise, but to a much greater extent, the senior men discussed the oath of allegiance and expedients that would enable it to be administered successfully to the Acadians.

Just as the oath of allegiance receives a considerable share of attention in the letters and papers of British officials of the time, so it does in arguments of most historians who have since written on the Acadian deportation. But a like parallelism is not apparent in the amount of space each group of writers devotes to a discussion of land tenure and its ramifications. On the one hand, British officials gave much attention to land, to the right of Acadians to remain in possession of such, and to their right even to remain in the province. Moreover, their remarks were usually made in the context of their discussion of the oath of allegiance, which is to be expected in view of the close relationship which existed between the two concepts. On the other hand, historians have devoted little attention to the subject of land tenure. None the writer has studied has given a clear explanation of why the right to possess title to land depended on allegiance to the crown.

The first official of record to relate allegiance to land tenure was the first Lieutenant-Governor of Nova Scotia, Thomas Caulfield. In 1715, the year of grace allowed in the Treaty of Utrecht having expired, he was instructed to cause the inhabitants of the colony to take the oath of allegiance.[80] He and his emissaries to the outports were unsuccessful in their mission, as Caulfield made clear in a letter of May 3, 1715 to the Secretary of State:

> ye Inhabitants of this country, being most of them french refuse the oaths, having as I am informed refused to quite this collony intirely and to settell under ye french Govrmt. and I humblie desire to be informed how I shall behave to them.[81]

Succeeding governors were equally nonplussed by the behaviour of the Acadians. In a letter of January 3, 1719, General Richard Philipps told the Board of Trade that the "people ... say they will neither sweare allegiance, nor leave the Country."[82] In September 1720, he observed that

> the Inhabitants seem determined not to sweare allegiance at the same time I observe them goeing on with their tillage and building as if they had no thoughts of leaving their habitations ...[83]

It is not improbable that the Governor's remark was based on observations in a report describing Nova Scotia which had been prepared some months earlier for the Lords of Trade by Major Paul Mascarene who said:

> The Inhabitants of these Settlements are still all French and Indians; the former have been tolerated in the possession of the lands they possessed, under the French Government, and have had still from time to time longer time allowed them either to take the Oaths to the Crown of Great Britain, or to withdraw, which they have always found some pretence or other to delay, and to ask for longer time for consideration.[84]"

Six years later, a new Lieutenant-Governor, Lieutenant-Colonel Lawrence Armstrong, in an attempt to induce a group of Acadian deputies to take the oath, told them that the king, in return for their oath, promised them "the enjoyment of their Estates and the rights and other immunities of his own freeborn subjects of Great Britain."[85] In 1730, after receipt of information from Governor Philipps that he would again attempt to cause the Acadians to take the oath, the Lords of Trade issued an instruction which said in part:

> As to the French Inhabitants who shall take the Oaths, it must be esteemed by them as a mark of His Majesty's goodness that they have not long since been

obliged to quit their settlements in Nova Scotia, according to the terms of the treaty of Utrecht, not having till now taken the Oaths of Allegiance to his Majesty.[86]

Ten years later, Paul Mascarene, now Lieutenant-Governor of Annapolis, when asking for instructions from the Secretary of State on how to deal with land claims from a new generation of Acadians, observed that the Acadian elders

have divided and subdivided amongst their children the lands they were in possession of, and which his Majesty was graciously pleased to allow to them on taking the oaths of allegiance.[87]

With the appointment of Governor Cornwallis in 1749, the substance of official communications stayed the same, but the tone changed. In a declaration to the "French Subjects of His Majesty King George Inhabiting Nova Scotia," Cornwallis laid it down that

His Majesty ... is Graciously pleased to allow the said Inhabitants ... the peaceable possession of such lands as are under their cultivation; Provided that the said Inhabitants do within Three months from the date of his Declaration take the oaths of Allegiance appointed to be taken by the Laws of Great Britain.[88]

Four years later, Cornwallis's deputy, Lieutenant-Governor Charles Lawrence, had occasion to remark how litigious the Acadians were among themselves. In the course of his discussion, he made the following significant observation:

To give them a hearing in our Courts of Law would be attended with insuperable difficulties; their not having taken the oath of allegiance is an absolute bar in our la[w] to their holding any landed possessions....[89]

This remark demonstrated Lawrence's complete knowledge of the connection between allegiance and land tenure, more than a year before the expulsion, as did the answer from the Lords of Trade who, on March 4, 1754 wrote:

We are sorry to find that the French Inhabitants, tho' in other respects quiet, are so much engaged in Litigation and Controversy amongst themselves, and We are the rather concerned for it, because, as you rightly observe, it will be impossible to come to any judicial Determination upon these Disputes without admitting a legal Right in them to the Lands, concerning which the Disputes have arisen, and to which by Law, by the Treaty of Utrecht, and by His Majesty's Instructions, they have in fact no Right but upon condition of taking the Oath of Allegiance absolute and unqualified with any Reservation whatever; such a state of Suspense and Indecision is certainly an Obstacle to the Industry and Quiet of these People, but We cannot see how their Disputes can be decided for the Welfare of the Province without an entire compliance on their parts ...[90]

During the summer of that year, and in accordance with this policy, Lawrence refused to re-admit Acadians to land held by them before their defection to the French "without an absolute compliance on their part."[91]

After the expulsion had begun, Governor Lawrence addressed a circular letter to all governors on the continent stating what he had done and giving his reasons. In part, he explained:

> I offered such of them as had not been openly in arms against us, a continuation of the Possession of their lands, if they would take the oath of Allegiance, unqualified with any Reservation whatsoever; but this they audaciously as well as unanimously refused ... As by this behavior the inhabitants have forfeited all title to their lands and any further favour from the Government, I called together his Majesty's Council ... to consider by what means we could ... rid ourselves of a people who would forever have been an obstruction to the intention of settling this Colony and that it was now from the refusal of the Oath absolutely incumbent on us to remove.[92]

Although Governor Lawrence gave, in the paragraphs just preceding the quoted passage, other and, for him, probably more immediate reasons for the expulsion, he rested his case for what he had done on firm legal ground. And, from what has been demonstrated in this paper, it is unlikely that he did so for purely expedient reasons. He repeated the argument in a subsequent communication to the Secretary of State[93] and, somewhat obliquely, in the first paragraph of a letter to the Board of Trade.[94]

In the foregoing, an attempt has been made to include a comprehensive selection of writers and to choose shorter quotations which demonstrate a clear and intimate relationship between the concepts of allegiance and land tenure.[95] But the interested reader can also discern the close connection between the two concepts from many other passages in the documents. Again, it is suggested that the reason for this is that all the British officials were of the same frame of mind.[96] This is not remarkable for these men were the heirs of an integral and essential component of British tradition which had been conceived at the beginning of British legal and social history. Land tenure then had been directly related to service on the part of the vassal and protection on the part of the lord, which was symbolized in a solemn act of homage. Out of this had grown the concept of a higher fealty, or allegiance, to the king, which, by mid-eighteenth century, had been enlarged to contain all the duties a subject owed to the state. But the feudal principle of *quid pro quo* was retained by granting the subject who owed natural or acquired allegiance certain inalienable rights, chief among which was the right to own land. These facts were part of the reason why British officialdom of the time had a perception of the world so different from the one we have today and of the Acadians in that world. This difference in perception comes through very strongly in the correspondence of the period. And this, in turn, helps to provide a clearer understanding than hitherto has been the case of the reasoning of the men who conceived and carried through the expulsion of the Acadians.

Notes

1. J.B. Brebner, *New England's Outpost* (Hamden, Connecticut: Archon Books, 1965) p. 205.

2. I Wm. & Mary, C.8 (1688(sic)). "I.A.B. do sincerely promise and swear, that I will be faithful and bear true allegiance, to their Majesties King William and Queen Mary." Owen Ruffhead, *Statutes at Large.* London, 1763. III, p. 419.

3. G.O. Sayles, *The Medieval Foundations of England* (2nd ed.; London: Methuen, 1964) p. 207. But see H. G. Richardson and G. O. Sayles, *The Governance of Medieval England from Conquest to Magna Carta* (Edinburgh: University Press, 1963) pp. 22-61 for the fully developed argument.

4. T. F. T. Plucknett, *A Concise History of the Common Law* (4th ed.; London: Butterworth, 1948) p. 480.

5. F.M. Maitland, *Domesday Book and Beyond* (Cambridge: University Press, 1897) pp. 69-70; S.F. Pollock and F.M. Maitland, *The History of English Law before the Time of Edward I* (2nd ed.; Cambridge: University Press, 1898, reissued 1968) I, p. 300.

6. See Pollock and Maitland, I, p. 556ff for a discussion of the hundred and the wappentake.

7. Richardson and Sayles, *Op. Cit.,* p. 42ff.

8. Pollock and Maitland, *Op. Cit.,* I, pp. 66, 77-78.

9. Richardson and Sayles, p. 105.

10. Pollock and Maitland, I, pp. 68-70, 297-8.

11. *Ibid.,* p. 68.

12. *Ibid.*

13. Richardson and Sayles, p. 106.

14. *Ibid.*

15. *Ibid.,* p. 100.

16. Plucknett, *Op. Cit.,* p. 13.

17. Pollock and Maitland, I, p. 299.

18. *Ibid.*

19. G.D.G. Hall, ed. and translator, *The treatise on the laws and customs of the realm of England commonly called Glanville* (London: Nelson, 1965) p. 104.

20. *Ibid.*

21. Pollock and Maitland, I, p. 206.

22. G.E. Woodbine, ed., S.E. Thorne, translator, *Bracton on the Laws and Customs of England* (Cambridge, Mass.: Belknap Press, 1968) II, p. 228.

23. *Ibid.*

24. *Ibid.*

25. *Ibid.,* p. 229.

26. *Ibid.,* P. 332.

27. Pollock and Maitland, I, p. 297.

28. *Bracton, Op. Cit.,* I, p. 332.

29. *Ibid.*

30. It is of interest to learn that, in early Anglo-Norman law, a breach of homage was defined to be the distinctively feudal crime of felony and was punished, in part, by causing the felon's lands to escheat or revert to his lord. "A mere common crime, however wicked and base, mere wilful homicide, or theft is not a felony, there must be some breach of that faith and trust which ought to exist between lord and man." (Pollock and Maitland, I, p. 304.) However, as the king's courts began to develop and to assume jurisdiction over cases concerning real property, homage gradually became a ceremony devoid of any real meaning. Concurrent with this decline and by an unknown process, there came "a deep change in thought and feeling. All the hatred and contempt which are behind the word 'felon' are enlisted against the criminal, murderer, robber, thief, without reference to any breach of the bond of homage and fealty." *(Ibid.)*

31. Pollock and Maitland, I, p. 300.

32. *Ibid.*

33. *Ibid.,* p. 299; Matthew Hale, *The History of the Pleas of the Crown* (London, 1736) I, p. 66.

34. H.G. Richardson and G.O. Sayles, eds. and translators, *Fleta* (London: Seldon Society, 1972) III, p. 40.

35. Pollock and Maitland, I, p. 300.

36. *Fleta, Op. Cit.,* III, p. 110.

37. Pollock and Maitland, I, pp. 459, 463. The earliest use of the word "alien" in legislative writing appears to be in the "Statute of Carlyle" (1306), where alien priors are prohibited from assessing taxes on the property of any English monasteries they control. (*Statutes of the Realm,* I, p. 151.) "Subject" in the sense used in this paper does not appear until 1321 when, in the Bill to exile the Dispensers, the king is said to be "bound by his oath to govern the people and his Liege Subjects." (*Statutes of the Realm,* I, p. 183.)

38. Pollock and Maitland, I, p. 463.

39. *Ibid.,* p. 462.

40. *Ibid.,* p. 463.

41. *Ibid.*

42. *Ibid.*

43. See Sir Francis Bacon's speech to the court in *the Case of Post-Nati* (1608) T.B. Howell, *State Trials* (London, 1816) II, p. 582.

44. 25 Edw. III, Stat. 2 (1350).

45. *Ibid.* See also Bacon's argument in 2 State Trials 585.

46. 42 Edw. III, C. 10.

47. Sir Edward Coke, *The Institute of the Laws of England* (7th ed.; London, 1670) I, p. 128b. Coke translates Littleton as follows: "The third (category) is an alien

which is born out of the allegiance of our Sovereign Lord the King; if such an alien will sue an action real or personal, the tenant or defendant may say, that he was born in such a Country which is out of the Kings allegeance, and ask judgement if he shall be answered."

48. *Ibid.,* I, p. 129b.

49. *Calvin's Case,* the *Case of the Post-Nati,* had curious antecedents. It arose from a desire of James I to unite England and Scotland into one kingdom (2 State Trials 559). To this end, a committee of Scots and English commissioners produced a report which, *inter alia,* recommended that "the common law of both nations should be declared to be, that all born in either nation since his majesty was king of both, were mutually naturalized in both." (2 State Trials 562). The Commons of England would not assent to this, so, in 1608, recourse was had to law to settle the issue. Land was purchased in England on behalf of an infant, Robert Calvin, a post-natus of Scotland (i.e. a person born in Scotland after the accession of James I to the throne of England), of which he was disseised by two native born Englishmen. Suit was brought on Calvin's behalf to recover the lands. The defendants answered with the plea that Calvin was an alien born and so unable to hold land in England or to bring a real action in an English court. After lengthy legal arguments at every judicial level, an Exchequer court composed of the Lord Chancellor and twelve high court judges found for Calvin. In part, their decision rested on demonstrations that whoever is born under one natural ligeance to one sovereign is a natural born subject and, since Calvin was born under one natural ligeance, "*ergo,* he is a natural-born subject*"* (77 English Reports 406) and therefore entitled to acquire and hold land anywhere in the king's dominions.

50. *Calvin's Case,* 77 English Reports 382.

51. *Ibid.,* p. 383.

52. *Ibid.*

53. *Ibid.*

54. *Ibid.,* p. 385.

55. *Ibid.,* p. 382.

56. *Ibid.,* p. 383.

57. *Ibid.,* p. 408.

58. *Ibid.,* p.396.

59. *Ibid.,* p. 382. "*Protectio trahit subjectionem, et subjectio protectionem"* is the phrase Coke coined or quoted.

60. *Ibid.,* p. 384.

61. *Ibid.,* p. 383. Denization, as such a grant was called, required an act of Parliament or letters patent from the king, and the grantees were usually subject to limitations on their right to acquire land or hold office.

62. *Ibid.,* pp. 383, 397, 398.

63. *Ibid.,* p. 398.

64. *Ibid.,* p. 385.

65. *Ibid.*

66. I Wm. & Mary, C.8(1688 (sic)). Ruffhead, *Loc. cit.*

67. A person convicted of treason (as many were after the Rebellion of 1745) died a horrible death by drawing, hanging, and quartering. But this was not the end, at least not for his survivors, because all the property of a traitor, real or moveable, was forfeited to the king. The section of the *Commentaries* in which Blackstone discusses forfeiture is lengthy and informative, and it is obvious that he considers it to be the greater of the two punishments. It is a striking expression of the high regard for real property in Blackstone's time. William Blackstone, *Commentaries on the Laws of England* (12th ed. rev.; London, 1795) IV, pp. 380-385.

68. *Ibid.,* I, p. 371ff.

69. *Ibid.,* I, p. 367.

70. *Ibid.,* I, p. 368.

71. 7 & 8 William III, C. 22 (1696).

72. Colonel Vetch, the commander at Port Royal, estimated that there were approximately 500 families (about 2500 persons) in Acadia in 1713, of whom only two did not wish to remove to French territory. The military garrison was apparently inconsiderable also, and, in 1720, did not number much more than 200 all ranks. T.B. Akins, ed., *Selections from the Public Documents of Nova Scotia* (Halifax: Charles Annand, 1869) pp. 5, 18. Hereafter PDNS.

73. Brebner, *Op. Cit.,* p. 144.

74. Brebner estimates that there were about 10,000 Acadians in Nova Scotia in 1749. *Ibid.,* p. 165.

75. PDNS, p. 14, n.

76. *Ibid.*

77. *Ibid.,* p. 56.

78. *Ibid.,* p. 58.

79. Brebner, p. 122.

80. PDNS, pp. 1-2.

81. *Ibid.,* pp. 7-8.

82. *Ibid.,* pp. 16-17.

83. *Ibid.,* p. 51.

84. *Ibid.,* p. 41.

85. *Ibid.,* p. 67.

86. *Ibid.,* p. 85.

87. *Ibid.,* p. 108.

88. *Ibid.,* p. 165.

89. *Ibid.,* p. 206.

90. *Ibid.,* p. 207.

91. *Ibid.,* p. 214.

92. *Ibid.,* p. 278.

93. *Ibid.,* p. 284.

94. *Ibid.,* p. 281.

95. Only a few of many such passages have been quoted. For example, see *Ibid.,* pp. 21, 65, 91, 121, 171, 187, 251, 262, 279.

96. It is relevant to point out that the British were not unique in this respect. French policy too was much the same and for similar reasons, but the French were not as long-suffering. For example, concerning the Acadians who lived in the area controlled by Fort Beauséjour, the Governor of New France, Marquis de Lajonquière, issued an order dated May 1, 1751 which said in part: "tous accadiens qui (huit jours après la publication d'icelle) n'aurons point prêté serment de fidélité et ne seront point incorporés dans les Compagnies de milices que nous avons créés, seront avérés rebelles aux ordonnances du Roy et comme tels chassés des terres dont ils sont en possession." Quoted from a copy of this letter in J.B. Brebner, "Canadian Policy towards the Acadians in 1751", *Canadian Historical Review,* v. XII, no. 3 (September, 1931), pp. 284-86.

PROLOGUE TO DISASTER, 1749-1755

Naomi Griffiths

In 1749 the Acadians could look with considerable satisfaction on the results of their tactics. War had been fought through their lands and they had survived with few casualties and without irrevocably compromising their position with either the French or the English. Their behaviour had much in common with that employed by the tribes of the North West frontier of India during the nineteenth century: the majority of people within the villages would initiate no revolt and would attempt to comply with the demands of the English, but some of the young men, their numbers always difficult to estimate, would join "their cousins over the border" in raiding the English soldiery. Pathan or Acadian, neither would wholeheartedly help those who came to "free" them, less from attachment to the English than from a profound, and completely understandable, dislike of having their lands made into a battleground. Through Acadian eyes, the period 1710 to 1748 could be seen as one of considerable success: their population had steadily increased, and the political structure of the European empire of which they formed part had not seriously discommoded their development of their settlements according to their own wishes. The future might

From *The Acadians: Creation of a People* (Toronto: McGraw-Hill Ryerson, 1973), 38–51. Reprinted by permission of the author.

appear to be uncertain, but the past success of neutrality as a policy gave them confidence in its value as a tactic for the future. That such was the Acadian position can be seen in their attitude to the new governor who arrived in Nova Scotia in 1749, Edward Cornwallis. It was, however, a position based upon a serious misjudgement: that of concluding that the after-effects of the recent war and of the treaty of Aix-la-Chapelle would be negligible for them. In essence this treaty marks the end of the era in which Nova Scotia and her inhabitants were considered of minor importance by those making the imperial policies of France and England. The intensive consideration which the colony was about to receive would not last, but it would be of sufficient duration to alter profoundly the existence of the Acadians. As far as the English were concerned, this was partly due to the return of Louisbourg to the French and the consequent necessity for the policy-makers of London to pacify the New Englanders. This great fortress had been captured by New England troops and its surrender at the peace table infuriated them. Governor Shirley of Massachusetts, who had taken a considerable part in the negotiations of Aix-la-Chapelle, fighting hard for the retention of the fortress, now renewed his demands for a policy from the Lords of Trade which would make Nova Scotia a proper counter-balance to Louisbourg, and a strong outpost of English force. Partly because of his representations, partly from their own convictions that the problem of Nova Scotia was the most important point to "be determined for settling the same Tranquillity in America as has been so happily established in Europe",[1] the Lords of Trade set about the matter, and gave the colony an attention which it had never before received from the government in London.

Edward Cornwallis, thirty-six years old, twin brother of a future Archbishop of Canterbury, uncle of the Lord Cornwallis who was to surrender at Yorktown, was appointed captain-general and governor of the colony. He was armed with detailed plans to make the Acadians completely trustworthy subjects, to populate the colony with new Protestant immigrants and to replace Annapolis Royal with a new military and administrative centre.[2] He held his first Council meeting on board the "Beaufort" as it swung on the tides in Chedebucto Bay. To that meeting on Friday, 15th July, 1749, came Paul Mascerene, the retiring lieutenant-governor, five of his councillors, and deputies from the Acadian villages. The records of what then transpired show the temper of the new administration. Proceedings opened with Cornwallis reading His Majesty's Commission and Instructions. The new Governor was to issue a proclamation to the Acadians reminding them of their position as subjects of his Britannic Majesty. They were to take regular oaths of allegiance, without any reserve whatsoever. They were to be allowed their priests but provisions were to be made to encourage conversion to Protestantism. Every channel of possible communication between old and new settlers within the province was to be explored, in the hope that the influence of the new Protestant immigrants would encourage the Acadians to display a greater loyalty to the British.

The records go on to say that Mascerene rose at this point and gave the form of the oath that the Acadians had taken in the past:

> Je ... promets and Jure sincerement en Foi de Chrétien que Je serai entièrement fidèle and obeirai vraiment Sa Majesté Le Roi George le Second que je reconnais pour le Souverain Seigneur de l'Acadie ou nouvelle Ecosse. Ainsi Dieu me soit en Aide.[a]

The Council Minutes continue:

> Col. Mascerene informed the Council that the French pretended that when they took this Oath it was upon Condition, that it should be understood that they always be exempted from bearing Arms, therefore it was moved to add to the Oath this clause, & Ce Serment Je prens sans réserve.[b] But the Council was of opinion that no Conditions appear in the Oath they have hitherto taken and subscribed, which Oath is as strong as any Oath of Allegiance can be, it would only be necessary to let the French know that they must take the oath without any Conditional Clauses understood or any reservation whatsoever.[3]

The picture of the Council's agreeing that all that was needed was to inform the Acadians of what they should do, in order to have it done, betrays an English misjudgement of the situation in Nova Scotia as grave as that of the Acadians' misjudgement in trusting in their policy of neutrality.

The Acadians had insisted on neutrality since 1713. Mascerne considered that during the recent hostilities Acadian neutrality had enabled the English to retain Nova Scotia, writing that the "French Inhabitants keep still in their fidelity" and were not "in any ways joyn'd with the Enemy." He did not consider that any more active support of the English could reasonably be expected of them. Cornwallis now informed the Acadians that they would take the "Oath of Allegiance to his Majesty in the same manner as all English Subjects do", thereby asserting implicitly that he expected more from them than had his predecessors. The meeting ended with the Acadians being given a copy of the Declaration which Cornwallis had prepared to be issued to them. This opened with the announcement that a number of British subjects were to be settled in Nova Scotia for the improvement and extension of its trade and fisheries. The Acadians, it continued, had in the past been dealt with most indulgently, having been allowed "the entirely free exercise of their Religion and the quiet and peaceable Possession of their Lands", but that this treatment had not been met with an appropriate loyalty. In future the Acadians could only expect similar leniency "Provided that the said Inhabitants do within Three months from the date of the Declaration take the Oaths of Allegiance."[4] They were asked to

---

[a] I promise and swear on the faith of a Christian that I will be entirely faithful and will truly obey His Majesty King George the Second whom I recognize as the Sovereign Lord of Acadia or New Scotland. So help me God.

[b] and this oath I swear without reservation.

report back from their settlements within two weeks and to ensure that deputies from other villages came to see Cornwallis as soon as possible.

Superficially the English policy appeared to be based upon an overly optimistic estimation of the possibilities of Acadian co-operation. Its real foundation, however, was that Cornwallis had been given much greater resources for the government of Nova Scotia than had his predecessors. He had arrived with instructions for the establishment of a new English stronghold at Halifax, with over twenty-five hundred new colonists, and with soldiers who had, until recently, garrisoned Louisbourg and would now act as veteran troops for the control of Nova Scotia. By 1751, Halifax was a settlement of more than six hundred houses within a palisade, and Protestant immigrants had established themselves sufficiently at Lunenberg for the Acadian monopoly of European settlement within the colony to be broken. However unwilling the Acadians would be to recognise the fact, the English were now committed to making Nova Scotia an effective part of their empire in North America.

At the same time, of equal importance to the Acadians, there was an equally strong desire on the part of the French to make the peninsula once more theirs. It is worth remarking that the peace treaty of 1748 had provided for an international commission to settle exactly the boundaries of the territories ceded in 1713 under the name of "Acadie or Nova Scotia", and that within the conference room the French claimed that only the peninsula itself had been ceded, while the English claimed the territory spread from the banks of the St. Lawrence to the limits of Massachusetts. The governor of Quebec, La Galissonière, commenting to the government of France on the British position, wrote:

> Si nous abandonnions à l'Angleterre ce terrain qui comprend plus de 180 lieue de côtes, c'est-à-dire presque autant qu'il y en a de Bayonne à Dunkerque, il faudrait renoncer à toute communciation par terre du Canada avec l'Acadie et l'Île Royale et à toute moyen de secourir l'un et de reprendre l'autre."[c] [5]

For neither the French nor the English was Aix-la-Chapelle more than a signal for the rebuilding of their respective strengths in North America; and for both, Nova Scotia appeared to be of paramount strategic importance. While the English built Halifax and established new groups of immigrants within the peninsula, the French increased the number of their troops at the mouth of the St. John River and occupied the Chignecto Isthmus. At the same time they used every possible influence to retain the attachment of the Indians to the French cause. This was made easier for them by the return to North America of the Abbé Le Loutre. He had been a missionary to the MicMacs since 1738 and his influence over them was very great. In the summer of 1749 Bigot, the new

---

[c] If we were to abandon to England this territory that possesses more than 180 leagues of coastline, that is to say, almost what there is from Bayonne to Dunkirk, we would have to give up all communication by land from Canada to Acadia and the Île Royale as well as any way to come to the assistance to the first and to win back the second.

intendant of New France, visited Louisbourg where he received news of a possible alliance between the English and the Indians. He reported to his superiors that he and Le Loutre had decided such possibility must be defeated at all costs, and he gave Le Loutre the necessary arms, money and presents to achieve this end. As a result, in September 1749 Cornwallis received a declaration of war from this tribe and their allies the Abenakis.

Thus the early months of the regime of Cornwallis saw the Indians an obvious menace, the French ever watchful for an opportunity to improve their position, and the Acadians temporising once more over the oath. They acted on the assumption that this governor was no different from the rest; they were convinced of the rectitude of their own past conduct and of their right to parlay. The Acadian answer to the demand from Cornwallis for an unqualified oath was that they were willing to take "notre ancien serment avec exemption d'armes à nos et à nos hoirs [sic]"[d] [6] but should this be refused, they would leave their lands. Cornwallis realised clearly what the Acadians needed. He wrote to his superiors in London, "I think 'tis necessary to show them that 'tis in our power to master them or to protect them,"[7] and enclosed detailed plans to this end. He was never able to achieve his aims, however; and while English power was being unostentatiously strengthened in Nova Scotia, French power was wielded not only on the borders but within the colony itself, both the power of the regular army and the power of the Indians acting in the interest of the French. The situation was much more violent than it had been in the years immediately after Utrecht: then the menace of the Indians had been theoretical, now the winter of 1749-50 saw them within the Acadian villages, capturing a company of English engineers at Grand-Pré. After 1713 the French had merely expressed their wish for Acadie; now French forts were built on the edge of Acadian lands, in particular in the neighbourhood of Beauséjour. Also, at the time of Utrecht the French had made representations to the Acadians to persuade them to move to French-held lands; in the spring of 1750 the Indians, led by the Abbé Le Loutre, burnt Beaubassin to the ground in order to persuade its inhabitants to cross on to the mainland. In sum, at the time of the treaty of Utrecht the fate of Nova Scotia was the subject of debate; after the treaty of Aix-la-Chapelle it was a matter of guns. The Acadian reaction towards the debate had been a policy of neutrality; towards the fighting, they made a considerable attempt to follow the same policy.

Acadian accounts of their actions between 1748 and 1755 were written after the deportation. One can compare the versions given by Acadians to authorities in several of the North American colonies, such as Massachusetts, Pennsylvania and Virginia, with those given to authorities in France. Contemporary accounts of Acadian action during these same years come from their administrators, their neighbours, both those of New England and of

---

[d] our previous oath with exemption from bearing arms for ourselves and our descendants.

Louisbourg, and from various French officials. The picture which emerges from these records is that of people becoming more and more enmeshed in a war fought across their lands by other powers. Their own actions betrayed only one consistency: an attempt to avoid reprisals by both sides. Their major difficulty was that English power within the colony was to prove the more durable, but French power was the more obviously threatening during the early years of the 1750s. In a letter describing the situation in Nova Scotia in 1750, for his superiors in London, Cornwallis wrote that the French had gathered together on the borders of the colony a force of twenty-five hundred men, made up of Canadians, Indians and some Acadians. He judged that the Acadians had been brought in by means of force and noted that many on this border were no longer attending to their lands. "They make no scruple to declare this proceeding is entirely against their inclination but that La Corne (the French commander) and Loutre threaten them with a general massacre by savages if they remain in the Province."[8] There is no question that during these years the French were using every means in their power to force the Acadians either to rise against the English, or to move to French territory. Nor is there any doubt about the influence of Le Loutre. A French officer wrote to his superiors in the autumn of 1750 that

> Il est sûr que sans ce missionaire qui a fait croire aux acadiens ce qu'il a voulu et leur a promois beaucoup, ils seroient tres tranquiles et que les Anglois seroient de même à Chibouctou et trés amis des sauvages.[e] [9]

In sum, the development of English strength was slow and the menace of French arms constant during the first year of the administration of Cornwallis. As a result, in the summer of 1750 the Acadians were no more ready than they had ever been to swear an unqualified oath of allegiance to the English. The English were equally unprepared to see the Acadians leave Nova Scotia *en masse* or to admit Acadian neutrality.

The second year of Cornwallis's administration saw a repetition of the situation. English strength within the peninsula imperceptibly increased. Major Lawrence, who would later be the lieutenant-general of Nova Scotia when the deportation took place, prevented further infiltration of French troops into the colony by holding the fort named after him on the isthmus. At the same time, the French were successful in persuading, by blandishments and threats, some two hundred families to leave for Ile St. Jean, the St. John River valley, or the vicinity of Beauséjour itself.[f] These migrants soon found that their new condi-

---

[e] It is certain that, without this missionary who managed to make the Acadians believe what he wanted them to believe and who promised them a great deal, they would remain peaceful and quiet and that the English at Chibouctou would also remain calm and on friendly terms with the Natives.

[f] The number of Acadians involved in such activities during the 1750s is a most contentious matter, estimations depending upon estimations of the total Acadian population. This has been put as high as 18,000 in 1755 by some writers.

tions had very little to recommend them. Many came back to English territory within two years. They found themselves cultivating new land and facing a French administration which expected even more from them than had that of Halifax. In May 1751, for example, the commander at Louisbourg issued an ordnance to the Acadians within his command, stating that they must swear an oath of loyalty and be incorporated into the militia, or be declared rebels to the King of France and expelled from their new lands. This same ordnance spoke of some of the Acadians being guilty of the worst sort of ingratitude, rendering themselves thereby unworthy of participating in the grace of the King of France, because they would not join in the fighting.[10]

There is no denying that by 1751 Cornwallis had made the English presence in Nova Scotia much stronger than it had ever been but, at the same time, there had been strengthening of French forces on the limits of the peninsula. Under the command of Major Lawrence a force of three hundred English soldiers tried and failed to capture Beauséjour that summer. In the light of his wish to show the force of the English, Cornwallis might have been content to have that many troops at his disposal, but their failure could hardly reinforce Acadian belief in the ultimate victory of English arms. At the same time while the new German immigrants were being settled within the colony, on the whole satisfactorily, it was also true that some of them deserted to the French forces, and could hardly be described as an immediate access of strength to the English. As the final winter of his administration began, 1751-52, Cornwallis expressed moderate satisfaction over the state of the colony. He felt that London should accord it even more men and money, and that at least half of its troubles came from the willingness of New York and Rhode Island to trade with Louisbourg. As to the Acadians, he considered that there was every chance of their being made into reasonable citizens, if only they could be removed from the influence of their priests.

The question of the Acadians' religion, and of their supply of priests, had always been a major concern of their English administrators. Eighteenth-century England permitted a much greater amount of religious freedom than did either contemporary France or other societies in North America. While Catholics in eighteenth-century England were barred from the exercise of direct political power, they were to be found at all levels of society and their disabilities very rarely mounted to the level of a persecution. English administrators would thus be accustomed to the legal existence of Catholicism. In France, however, Huguenots suffered from the Revocation of the Edict of Nantes, and the rigidity of New England Protestantism needs no emphasis. What made the Acadians' position of a particular thorny character for the English was that their priests were supplied by France and were linked to the jurisdiction of the Bishop of Quebec. Given the strategic situation of Nova Scotia and the general belief in the unbreakable alliance between religion and politics in French life, it is not surprising that the English looked upon the priests sent to the Acadians as probable spies and *agents provocateurs* for the French cause. This judgement was, of course, justified by men like Le Loutre and quietly contradicted by the existence of other priests, such as Daudin, who spent their energies completely within the permitted bounds of ecclesiastical action.

As far as assigning responsibility for the deportation of 1755 is concerned, the influence of the priests upon the Acadians is only one factor among many. In attempting to discover the limits of this influence, however, a study of the ecclesiastical records shows not only much individuality among the priests themselves but considerable divergence among the hierarchy as to what the main concerns of a priest working with the Acadians should be. The Bishop of Quebec has left several letters, written during the 1740s and 1750s, in which he insisted that the priests must conduct themselves with circumspection and indulge in no political activity which would give the English grounds for their expulsion: the cure of souls was to be their only aim.[11] On the other hand, the Vicar-General of the church in New France, the Abbé de l'Isle Dieu, who resided in France and was largely responsible for the recruitment of the priests for the Acadians, considered that the salvation of their souls could be found only on French territory. He fully backed the efforts of Le Loutre and endeavoured to send priests directly to him, so that their opinions would not be influenced by anyone else.[12] It is not surprising that this subject has been yet one more matter for debate among historians.

At the time of Cornwallis's judgement there were three priests actually working among the Acadian population of Nova Scotia and, of course, Le Loutre, working with the Indians on the border of the colony. Their presence would certainly remind the Acadians of the French, but the Acadians would not necessarily respond to this with an unquestioning loyalty to the fleur-de-lis. Acadian actions before Aix-la-Chapelle, in the judgement not only of Mascerene but also of the French officers sent among them to procure their aid, was a demonstration above all of loyalty to themselves. In the eyes of their contemporaries, however, and in the eyes of many later historians, such a loyalty was inadmissible since it involved a refusal to "take sides" in a question where emotional factors demanded the expression of a preference. On the one hand, it was apparently obvious that French-speaking Catholics would feel the need to support the policies of France. On the other hand it was apparently obvious that a sense of civic responsibility would make the Acadians give a dutiful obedience to the power that had allowed their peaceful development over forty years. But the Acadians were too conscious of the fluctuations of political fortune. Inhabitants of lands which had changed hands fourteen times within a century, with a well-founded knowledge of English power within Nova Scotia and of French power surrounding Nova Scotia, the Acadians gave emotional loyalty to their families, their villages, their lands. Loyalty to either France or England, for the majority of the Acadians, would depend almost exclusively on the ability of these powers to enforce their control of Acadian villages.

The possibilities of a peaceful relationship between Acadian and English, even in the 1750s, can be seen from the short governorship of Peregrine Hopson. Cornwallis left Nova Scotia in the spring of 1752 and by the summer the new governor was in power. He held office for little more than a year. He was on good terms with his counterpart at Louisbourg and from the outset was optimistic about the situation in the colony. In his first report to the Lords of Trade, Hopson reported that the French Inhabitants had no intention of leaving the colony and he had no wish for them to go.[13] By January 1753, Hopson was convinced that peace had come to the borders of his colony and considered that his major problem was the possibility of corruption among the Justices of the Inferior Courts. Even spring did not bring the usual immediate revival of trouble, partly because Le Loutre was in Europe. At the end of the summer of 1753, Hopson summed up the position of the colony for his superiors in London. His verdict was much the same as the judgement of Cornwallis on the situation in 1749: the French were strong on the borders of the colony, the governors of Quebec and Louisbourg openly aided border raids, Nova Scotia needed more aid, and the Acadians were prevented from showing "a firm attachment"[14] to the British by their fear of Indian and French reprisals.

The Acadians had every reason to be of the same opinion as Hopson and to consider that no radical alteration had taken place in their situation during the four years following 1749. After complaining about their attitude in the matter, the English had let the question of an unqualified oath drop. The French were still on the borders of the peninsula and their installations in the immediate region were, if anything, strengthened. The existence of Halifax and the German Protestants at Lunenberg did not seem to have altered the military situation in favour of the English. Nevertheless, to the Acadians, life in French territory was by no means more appealing than life under English rule on the lands of their ancestors. The English demands were no more unreasonable than those made by the French to the Acadians who had moved to their territory. In fact, since the Acadians had a long tradition of co-operating with the English only in those areas in which the Acadians wished to co-operate, life under English government could be preferred to that under the French. In sum, with the arrival of Major Charles Lawrence as the lieutenant-governor of the colony in 1753, the Acadians had no reason to suspect a radical alteration of their lives.

Yet this is precisely what happened, and one of the reasons is the convictions of Lawrence himself. Mascerene, Hopson, and most of their predecessors had governed Nova Scotia with the belief that the Acadians were a fixed part of its population, that ideas of their exile were impractical, and that their attitude towards an unqualified oath of allegiance was an annoyance rather than a source of serious perturbation. Lawrence, however, saw the matter in a very different light. This was partly the result of his experiences. He was above all a military man, born and brought up in a cantonment, a major at the age of thirty-seven. He had first come to Louisbourg in 1747 and since then had been employed mainly on duties concerned with the security of the colony. He had a first-hand knowledge of the strength of the French on the borders of the colony and of the weakness of the English elsewhere. Lawrence summed up his position in a letter written to his superiors some nine months after his appointment. After commenting on the unco-operative attitude of the Acadians, he went on to say:

> While they remain without taking oaths to His Majesty (which they will never do till they are forced) and have incendiary French priests among them, there are no hopes of their amendment. As they possess the best and largest tracts of land in this province, it cannot be settled with any effect while they remain in this situation. And tho' I would be very far from attempting such a step without your Lordships' approbation, yet I cannot help being of the opinion that it would be much better, if they refuse the oaths, that they were away. The only ill consequences that can attend their going would be their taking arms and joining the Indians to distress our settlements, as they are numerous and our troops much divided; tho' I believe that a very large part of the inhabitants would submit to any terms rather than take up arms on either side; but that is only my conjecture and not to be depended on in so critical a circumstance.[15]

In other words, Lawrence could envisage clearly the functioning of Nova Scotia without the presence of the Acadians. He thought of the strategic questions of the colony as being of fundamental importance, and considered all other matters to be subordinate to this factor.

The historical controversy over the events of 1755 has resulted in literally hundreds of books and pamphlets, of which two hundred had been published by the end of the nineteenth century. Part of the interest stems from the sheer complications of the matter; it is that of detection: what exactly happened? to whom? by whom? for what motive? Even more interest, however, has been caused by the apparently obvious ideological explanations of the matter. The deportation of the Acadians has been considered as a prime example of national and religious rivalries, because the labels of Catholicism, Protestantism, French and English can be attached to opposing sections of the groups of people involved. Many of the works which have appeared about the Acadian deportation are informed with a driving demand to assign guilt and innocence in the matter. Yet the reality is much more complex and much more human than such explanations would suggest. What happened in 1755 was the result as much of immediate individual choices and of personal action as it was of past traditions and of the concatenation of official government policies and international pressures.

As the summer of 1754 drew to a close, the external factors which would affect events in Nova Scotia began to take shape. Soon "Washington's first shot beyond the Alleghenies" would completely shatter the hollow pretence of peace in North America. The Governor of Massachusetts, still that Shirley who had fought so hard for the retention of Louisbourg, entered into an assiduous correspondence with Lawrence, whose immediate superior he was, on the security problems of their two colonies. As the winter went on, the two men laid plans to clear the French from the north shore of the Bay of Fundy and from the isthmus of Chignecto. At the same time, with the end of 1754, England and France condemned each other for reopening hostilities, and each set about readying an army for America. By early 1755, England had ordered her fleet to attack any French vessels sailing for that continent and as a rejoinder, France had fitted out eighteen ships to carry some three thousand men overseas, for the support of her colonies in the New World. Once more open warfare for the control of a continent was begun, and this time its most immediate effect would be the social tragedy of the Acadians.

Notes

1. Qtd. in Gipson, L. H.: *The British Empire before the American Revolution,* (New York) 1942, Vol. V, p. 304.
2. *Report,* P.A.C. 1905, II, App. C. p. 49-52.
3. N.S. 106: Council records; partially printed Akins, *op. cit.* p. 116.
4. N.S. 106: Council meeting records.
5. A.N.: C 11 A 93; partially printed in Lauvrière, E.; *La Tragédie d'un peuple,* Paris, 1922 Vol. I, p. 375.
6. N.S. 209: partially printed in translation, Akins, *op. cit.* p. 175-6.
7. N.S.A.: 34, printed in Akins. *op. cit.* p. 561-64.
8. Qtd. Gipson, L. H., *op. cit.* p. 194.
9. *ibid.* p. 192.
10. This ordnance has been published in full with an introduction by Brebner, J. B., in the *Canadian Historical Review* under the title "Canadian Policy towards the Acadians", Vol. XII, 1931.
11. A.A.Q.: Lettres II, Pontbriand, Nov. 9th, 1746.
12. A.A.Q.: Vicaire Générales, III, 133: Paris, 24th June, 1752.
13. P.A.C. N.S.A.: 49, Oct. 16th, 1752.
14. P.A.C.: N.S.A.: 49, Oct. 1st, 1753.
15. P.A.C.: N.S.A.: 55, Aug. 1st, 1754.

CHAPTER
5 THE FRENCH MILITARY IN NEW FRANCE DURING THE SEVEN YEARS' WAR

The Battle of the Plains of Abraham on 13 September 1759 is one of the few world-class events in Canadian history. Usually included in lists such as the One Hundred Most Important Battles in History, it marked the zenith of the first British Empire. In Britain to this day, General James Wolfe remains a magical name to school children. In Canada there is an ambivalence about the siege, the soldiers, the generals and the outcome. Francis Parkman created icons for Canadians with his two-volume *Montcalm and Wolfe* (1884), the story of a battle between valiant heroes on both sides. The tragic Shakespearean ending provided the necessary grief and the glimmer of a better world. Regardless of any reality, that image of brave French and British soldiers fighting for survival and supremacy suited Canadian needs for over half a century.

Since the Second World War, the picture of the battle and the participants has been renovated. Guy Frégault's *La Guerre de la conquête* (1955) was a major reappraisal from a Canadian perspective. The Marquis de Montcalm and the Europeans emerged as inferior, if not incompetent, soldiers, while the *canadiens*, as epitomized by Pierre de Rigaud, Marquis de Vaudreuil, were pictured as inspired worthies obstructed by Montcalm, François Bigot and other Europeans. Wolfe, a bully and a terrorist who won by default, was vilified. C.P. Stacey took a less ideological position in his military analysis, *Quebec, 1759: The Siege and the Battle* (1959). His study of generalship, however, found Montcalm and Wolfe both wanting. A competent strategist, Montcalm made disastrous tactical errors, while Wolfe, a dismal strategist, saved himself from disgrace by successful tactics on the field of battle. W.J. Eccles rejected even that praise for Wolfe. He delighted in telling his students that anybody except the British could have taken Quebec in half the time. Like Frégault, he depicted the *canadiens* as soldiers *par excellence*. In "The French Forces in North America during the Seven Years' War," the first selection, Eccles provided an overview of French military activity over much of the life of the colony.

Neither old soldiers nor wars are ever laid to rest, however, and it was not long before the battle was joined. Peter E. Russell in 1978 rescued the British regulars in a study of warfare in both Europe and America during the 1740s and 1750s (See *Suggestions for Further Reading*). Recently, Martin L. Nicolai examined the French military in both its European and North American theatres, and arrived at similar conclusions in "A Different Kind of Courage: The French Military and the Canadian Irregular Soldier During the Seven Years' War." He rejected the criticisms of the European military as unwarranted, and offered a less sanguine but perhaps more realistic view of the *canadien* soldier.

Suggestions for Further Reading

Frégault, Guy, *Canada: The War of the Conquest*. Toronto: Oxford University Press, 1969.

Russell, Peter E., "Redcoats in the Wilderness: British Officers and Irregular Warfare in Europe and America, 1740-1760," *William and Mary Quarterly*, XXXV, no. 4 (October 1978), 629-652.

Stacey, C.P., *Quebec, 1759: The Siege and the Battle*. Toronto: Macmillan of Canada, 1959.

———, "The British Forces in North America during the Seven Years' War," *Dictionary of Canadian Biography*, Volume III. Toronto: University of Toronto Press, 1974, xxiv-xxx.

Stanley, George F.G., *New France: the Last Phase, 1744-1760*. Toronto: McClelland & Stewart, 1968.

Steele, I.K., *Guerillas and Grenadiers: The Struggle for Canada, 1689-1760*. Toronto: Ryerson, 1969.

THE FRENCH FORCES IN NORTH AMERICA DURING THE SEVEN YEARS' WAR

W.J. Eccles

From 1713 to 1744 France and England were at peace, the span of one generation. During those years French overseas trade steadily increased. Trade with the French colonies rose from 25,000,000 *livres* a year in 1710 to 140,000,000 by 1741. In the latter year the total of French overseas trade was valued at 300,000,000 *livres,* that is £12,500,000 sterling. Much of this trade was with the Spanish empire, one half to seven-ninths of the goods shipped from Cadiz being French in origin. France now supplied all continental Europe with sugar and coffee, and in addition French fishermen were garnering the lion's share of the fisheries on the Grand Banks and in the Gulf of St Lawrence. But while French trade had expanded during the 1730s, that of England had remained stationary. Moreover, a sizable proportion of England's overseas commerce consisted of contraband trade with the Spanish colonies. Thus, when Spain began taking effective measures to curb this illicit traffic the English commercial community became alarmed; half of the world's maritime commerce might still be under the British flag but were its trade to continue to stagnate while French industry and commerce kept on expanding, then England, its population less than half that of France, might well go the same way as the Netherlands, and eventually be reduced to the status of a fourth-rate power. It was to forfend this possibility that England went to war with Spain in 1739, and with France in 1744.

The British government did not pursue that war, the War of the Austrian Succession, known to the English colonies as King George's War, effectively. It chose to engage France on the continent where the poorly officered British army proved no match for the Maréchal de Saxe, the foremost soldier of his age. In North America a combined Anglo-American and British naval force captured Louisbourg in 1745 [*see* William PEPPERRELL and Peter WARREN], but it was not until 1747 that the Royal Navy gained the upper hand and succeeded in severing temporarily France's communications with her colonies. By 1748 the belligerents were exhausted and in October of that year the treaty of Aix-la-Chapelle was signed, which merely restored the *status quo ante bellum.* France recuperated rapidly and her overseas trade quickly recovered. The English commercial community now became convinced that a better conducted spoiling war was essential to prevent the French overtaking them in the struggle for supremacy. The French, on the other hand, had no desire for a maritime war—they had too much to lose; nevertheless, they still had to prepare for it.

Although the West Indies were the great prize—by 1740 the exports of the French islands were valued at 100,000,000 *livres* a year and their imports, mainly slaves, at 75,000,000—the north Atlantic fisheries were also extremely valuable, particularly since they were regarded as vital by both Britain and France for the training of seamen needed to man their fleets. In 1754, 444 ships from France fished in these waters, employing some 14,000 sailors. In addition the resident maritime population of Île Royale (Cape Breton Island), Îles de la Madeleine, and Gaspé provided a large number of mariners. It was estimated that the loss of these fisheries would cost France 15,000 experienced seamen, nearly a third of her total supply. Canada, on the other hand, produced little except furs, in good years some wheat for export to Louisbourg, and a few ships built at Quebec by the crown at great expense [*see* Pierre LUPIEN, *dit* Baron, and Louis-Pierre POULIN de Courval Cressé]. This colony was, in fact, an economic liability much of the time. Politically and militarily, however, Canada was regarded as valuable to curb the expansion of the English colonies, hence of England's commercial strength, and to protect Louisiana for whose resources great hopes were entertained. Moreover, it was calculated that in time of war the Canadians, with the aid of a few reinforcements from France, would be able to tie down a much larger British army and a sizable part of the Royal Navy, thus preventing their deployment elsewhere. The success enjoyed by the Canadians against the Anglo-Americans in the previous wars gave every reason for confidence in this policy.

The fortress of Louisbourg was therefore strengthened to serve as a naval base for a fleet to protect the fisheries, guard the entrance to the St. Lawrence, and prey on British shipping. When an influential group of Anglo-American land speculators began to implement their scheme to seize the Ohio valley, thereby threatening the French hold on the west, a Canadian force was dispatched, on orders of the minister of Marine, to drive the Americans out [*see* Paul MARIN de La Malgue]. Forts were then built in the region. In 1754 came the first clash of arms near Fort Duquesne (Pittsburgh, Pa.). Although war between England and France was not declared until 1756, this skirmish in the wilderness marked the beginning of the Seven Years' War [*see* Joseph COULON de Villiers de Jumonville].

Unfortunately for France the government, its personnel, and methods, were to prove inadequate to meet the challenge offered by Great Britain and her new-found ally, Prussia. Louis XV could rarely bring himself to make decisions and when he attended council meetings he concerned himself with trivia. Moreover, until 1761 when the Duc de Choiseul was given charge of the ministries of War, Marine, and Foreign Affairs, the ministers, all of them mediocrities or worse, did not remain long in office. During the course of the war there were four ministers of Foreign Affairs, four controllers-general of Finance, four ministers of War, and five ministers of Marine. Their ministries were grossly understaffed and overworked, which resulted in interminable delays and too often in non-decisions. To cap it all, the entire decision-making process was beset by intrigue of Byzantine proportions, the king being to the fore in this activity.

Nor were the instruments of government policy, the armed forces, in better condition. Under Louis XIV, and later under Napoleon, the French army was the best in Europe. Under Louis XV it sank to a low level of efficiency. After the demise of the Maréchal de Saxe its commanders were incompetent. Defence predominated over offence in their thinking. Here too intrigue was rife. Every general in the field knew that many about him, and at the court, were scheming to have him removed. At the regimental level also officers were not distinguished by competence, the military capacity of most of the colonels being virtually nil. Commissions were purchased; money and family connections, not merit, governed advancement.

As is always the case, military tactics were dominated by the principal weapon employed, in this instance the smooth-bore, flint-lock, muzzle-loading musket, mounted with a bayonet, making it both a fire and a shock weapon. Even well-trained soldiers could fire no more than two or three rounds a minute; loading and firing required some 12 movements executed to command and drum beat. At close range, under 80 paces, a musket volley could be murderous, but at that distance there was barely time to reload before the enemy's charge, if it were not checked, reached the line. In battle two basic formations were employed, the line and the column. The line, three ranks deep, depended on the fire power of the musket followed by a bayonet charge against the shattered foe. Attack by column depended on the shock effect of an attack on a narrow front to pierce and shatter the enemy's line. Deployment in line demanded the most rigorous discipline to make the men stand fast and deliver measured volleys against the charging foe. Attack by column also required discipline to have the men press on into the hail of fire. The swifter their advance, the fewer volleys they had to endure. The British army relied on the line; the French at this time still had a predilection for the column, believing that the charge with the *arme blanche* was better suited to their poorly trained troops with their impetuous temperament.

To manoeuvre the troops on the battlefield, and have them attack either in line or in column, required that they receive at least 18 months of basic training on the drill ground until they became virtually automatons. After that, five years' experience was deemed necessary to produce a good, dependable soldier. Iron discipline was the essence of it all, instilled by fear and by *esprit de corps*. The men had to be rendered more afraid of their own officers than of the enemy, and to be willing to stand and die rather than turn and run. Everything depended on the ability of the officers to manoeuvre their troops, and on the discipline and training of the men once battle was joined. Compared to other European armies the French army was deficient on both counts. Its officers lacked spirit and professional training, its men were badly instructed, poorly drilled, and wretchedly disciplined; its equipment, with the exception of the Charleville musket, was inferior. The supply system and the cannon were both antiquated, essentially the same as in the time of Louis XIV. All attempts at reform had been blocked by reactionary elements or vested interests.

The French navy was in a better state than the army. Its ships were superior to those of the Royal Navy. They could outsail and outgun the British ships. A French ship of 52 guns was a match for a British 72. The reverse was true of the officers of the two navies. The British officers were better trained and more aggressive. Although the Royal Navy was in poor shape at the onset of the war it had twice as many ships as the French and its reserve of seamen was much greater. To make matters worse for the French, before war was declared the Royal Navy seized 800 French merchant ships and 3,000 seamen. This was a crippling blow. Moreover, during the course of the war epidemics in the French ports took a heavy toll. At Brest alone, in 1757-58, 2,171 sailors died in a four-month period. Many others fled the ports to avoid the contagion. The navy was reduced to impressing landsmen who had never been afloat to work their ships. Yet despite the superiority of the Royal Navy supply ships reached Quebec every year until 1760 [*see* Jacques KANON], after the city had been taken by Wolfe's army.

When hostilities began the French had three distinct military forces at their disposal in North America: the colonial regular troops (*troupes de la Marine*), the militia, and the Indian allies. The colonial regulars were infantry units raised for guard duty in the naval ports of France and for service in the colonies. They were the creation of Louis XIV's great minister Jean-Baptiste Colbert and were under the control of the ministry of Marine, not of the ministry of War, hence were known as the *troupes franches de la Marine*. To obviate the abuses rampant in the regimental organization of the army Colbert had incorporated these marines in independent companies rather than in regiments. Commissions were not purchased but were obtained on merit and, of course, influence. A good reference was essential. Each company consisted of a captain, a lieutenant, a brevet ensign, a second ensign, two cadets, two sergeants, three corporals, two drummers and 41 soldiers. By 1758, 20 companies of these marines were stationed at Louisbourg and 21 in Louisiana. In Canada there were 30 companies in 1756. In that year their strength was increased to 65 non-commissioned ranks per company, and the following year their number was raised to 40 companies with a nominal strength of 2,760 officers and men.

During the half-century following the establishment of the colonial regulars, the officer corps became Canadian although the other ranks were nearly all recruited in France. By the 1740s commissions were reserved for the sons of serving officers, who were invariably seigneurs. Unlike the regiments of the French army the colonial regulars gave no direct entry into the commissioned ranks, except for such privileged persons as the son of a governor general [*see* JOSEPH-HYACINTHE and Louis-Philippe de RIGAUD de Vaudreuil]. With that notable exception, every would-be officer had to serve in the ranks for several years as a cadet. Despite this arduous training, so eager were the Canadians for commissions that in 1728 the age for entry as cadets was lowered to 15, and the waiting list became ever longer. Promotion could not be accelerated by purchase, only by a display of exceptional valour in action, and even then, *only* when a vacancy occurred through death or retirement. This condition served to inculcate a very aggressive spirit in the corps.

When the Seven Years' War began most of the officers of the colonial regulars had had years of military experience at the western posts, in the Fox and Chickasaw campaigns, and in savage raids on the frontier settlements of the English colonies [*see* Louis COULON de Villiers, Jacques LEGARDEUR de Saint-Pierre, François-Marie LE MARCHAND de Lignery, Nicolas-Joseph NOYELLES de Fleurimont]. In addition to their training in the drill manoeuvres demanded in European style warfare these troops had had to master the art of guerilla fighting both against and alongside the Indian nations. They could travel long distances, winter or summer, living off the land if need be, strike swiftly, then disappear before the enemy could muster a force to counter attack. Against them the American provincial troops and militia were no match. Great mobility, deadly marksmanship, skilful use of surprise and forest cover, high morale and, like the Royal Navy, a tradition of victory, gave the colonial regulars their superiority. Just how effective they could be was demonstrated when, in 1755, 250 Canadians with some 600 Indian allies destroyed Edward Braddock's army of 1,500 [*see* Jean-Daniel Dumas].

Supporting, and frequently serving alongside, the colonial regulars were the militia units. In 1669 Louis XIV had ordered the establishment of militia companies for colonial defence. Each company comprised all the able-bodied men between 15 and 60 in a parish and was commanded by a captain of militia (who also had important civil functions), with a lieutenant, one or two ensigns, and sergeants. They all served without pay. During the wars against the English colonies and hostile Indian nations the militia was called out for war parties, to repel invading forces, for corvées to supply the frontier fortresses, or for the building of military roads.

When properly utilized this Canadian militia was a formidable fighting force, but its men were of little use in European style warfare. Faced with regular army units in the open, firing massed volleys, they took cover or fled. They would not stand and be shot at while waiting for an order to fire back. There were other limits to the use that could be made of these habitant soldiers; many of them had to be released for work on the land in the spring and in late summer for the harvest; others had to serve in the canoe brigades to the western posts. A muster roll of 1750 lists 165 companies varying in number from 31 to 176, comprising 724 officers, 498 sergeants, 11,687 men; in all, 12,909. This total may well be too low, by as much as 25 per cent; it gives for one company a total strength of 55 whereas a separate muster roll of that particular company lists 76 names, half of whom are noted as fit to go on detachment. An important factor with these militiamen was their high morale. When they were ordered to Quebec in 1759 to help defend the city against Wolfe's army, Montcalm and his staff were astounded by the number that appeared, boys of 12, old men of 85, all demanding muskets and the right to serve. The contrast with the militia of the English colonies could not be more marked.

In addition to the colonial regulars and the militia the French had the aid of a horde of Indian allies, Micmacs, Abenakis, Ottawas, Algonkins, Delawares, Shawnees, to mention a few. The British, significantly, had virtually none. The operative word here is "allies," for these nations would take orders from no one—indeed their own chiefs had no authority over the warriors. They did not regard themselves as an auxiliary force of the French, but as allies in a joint effort against a common foe. Another inducement was the liberal supplies of food, clothing, arms, and munitions provided by the French, as well as the bounties paid for scalps and prisoners. Although they proved to be highly effective in guerilla warfare, the Indians could never be relied on. They were subject to whims that appeared strange to Europeans. After being well supplied a war party would set out but, en route, suffer a change of heart and quietly disperse. Yet mixed war parties of Canadians and Indians did wreak havoc on the Anglo-American settlements and tied down enemy forces vastly superior in numbers. The enemy's supply lines were constantly threatened, his advanced bases frequently destroyed. The mere knowledge that a French force had Indians with it was sometimes enough to cause a large Anglo-American force to flee or surrender. As scouts and intelligence agents the Indians were particularly useful. Although their verbatim reports were, on occasion, imaginary tales of things not seen, they could take prisoners far behind the enemy's lines who revealed much when questioned by the French. By such means the French were usually better informed than were the British of the opponent's dispositions and intentions.

When, in 1754, the British government decided to launch an all out assault on New France without the formality of a declaration of war, it detached two battalions of regular troops for service in America. France had to counter this threat by reinforcing its units at Louisbourg and in Canada. A serious military and administrative problem immediately emerged. The colonies were in the charge of the ministry of Marine but its colonial regular troops could not be expanded rapidly enough to meet the emergency. Recourse had to be had to the regiments of the French regular troops (*troupes de terre*, so called because most of them took their titles from the provinces of France where they were raised) under the ministry of War, and the mutual hostility of these two ministries was extreme. Moreover, the governor general of New France, always an officer in the Marine, was commander-in-chief of all the French forces in North America whether stationed at Louisbourg, in Canada, or Louisiana. The council of ministers, however, agreed that divided responsibility would be fatal, and that unity of command, at such a remove from the centre of authority, was essential. It was therefore concluded that the reinforcement of six army battalions from the regiments of La Reine, Artois, Bourgogne, Languedoc, Guyenne, and Béarn, 3,600 officers and men all told, would be placed under the orders of the ministry of Marine, which would be responsible for their pay and maintenance.

Two of the battalions, Artois and Bourgogne, went to Louisbourg. The other four went to Canada. In 1756 a battalion each from the La Sarre and Royal Roussillon regiments were shipped to Quebec, and in 1757 two more battalions from the Régiment de Berry were sent to Canada. Each battalion had an officer corps made up of a lieutenant-colonel in command, an adjutant (*aide-major*), and a surgeon major; a captain, a lieutenant, and a sub-lieutenant (*sous-lieutenant*) of grenadiers; 12 fusilier captains, 12 lieutenants, and two ensigns. The other ranks consisted of the grenadier company comprising two sergeants, two corporals, two lance-corporals, one drummer, 38 grenadiers; 24 fusilier sergeants, 24 corporals, 24 lance-corporals, 12 drummers, and 396 fusiliers; a total strength of 557. The grenadier company in each battalion was an élite group of shock troops, men chosen for their superior physique, martial appearance, and training. One of their functions was to stand directly behind the line in battle to prevent, with their bayonets, the fusiliers from turning tail—as occurred at Carillon in 1758 when some of the de Berry regiment made to bolt. If a section of the line reeled under an assault, the grenadiers stepped into the breach.

Separate from both the French regular troops and the colonial regulars were the engineers, represented by two French officers, Nicolas Sarrebource de Pontleroy and Jean-Nicolas Desandrouins, and a company of artillery. At this time the artillery was the weakest branch in the French army. The unit in Canada, commanded by François Le Mercier, comprised eight officers, three of them Canadians, four sergeants, ten cadets, and 86 gunners. The engineers were mainly concerned with fortifications. Pontleroy agreed with Montcalm that all the fortifications in the colony, including Quebec, were worthless and could not resist an assault let alone bombardment. On some points, however, Pontleroy's testimony is palpably false, for example his statement that there was no dry moat beneath the walls of Quebec. After Quebec fell to the British the French officers, including Desandrouins, deemed its defences virtually impregnable. As for the frontier fortresses, in their criticisms the French officers ignored the fact that they had been built to fend off the feeble Anglo-American forces and hostile Indians, not a British army which, although its engineers were poor, had in the Royal Regiment of Artillery one of the finest artillery corps in the world.

At Louisbourg the four battalions from the regiments of Artois, Bourgogne, Cambis, and Volontaires Etrangers, along with 1,000 colonial regulars and 120 gunners, all came under the orders of the commandant, Augustin de Boschenry de Drucour. For the battalions serving in Canada, however, a general staff had to be appointed. Baron Jean-Armand de Dieskau accepted the appointment as commanding officer with the rank of major-general (*maréchal de camp*)—making him one of 170 holding that rank in the French army. He was given a staff consisting of a second in command, an adjutant (*major*), an aide-de-camp, a war commissary (*commissaire des guerres*) in charge of supplies, and two partisan officers for detached duties.

Great care was taken in the drafting of Dieskau's instructions to prevent any conflict or misunderstanding between him and the newly appointed Canadian-born governor general, Pierre de Rigaud, Marquis de Vaudreuil. They carefully spelled out that the governor general was in full command of all the military forces. Dieskau was to take his orders from Vaudreuil, and whether he liked them or not he had no alternative but to obey them to the letter. The governor general was required to leave the details of the command of the army battalions to Dieskau but the latter had to keep the commander-in-chief informed of their strength, deployment, and everything else needed to enable him to make the most effective use of them in any operations he chose to undertake. When, in 1756, the Marquis de Montcalm replaced Dieskau he received the same instructions and the same restricted authority. He and his officers were also subordinate to the governments at Montreal and Trois-Rivières, which consisted of a local governor, a king's lieutenant (*lieutenant du roy*), a town major, and an adjutant (*aide-major*). The army battalions were there for one main purpose, to defend the colony, and they had to take their orders from the colonial authorities.

The council of ministers also decreed, not only that the French regular troops would, contrary to custom, be paid during the Atlantic voyage but that they would be paid over double the normal rate while serving in America. It was anticipated that the colonial regulars would protest, since the increase was not accorded them, but it was pointed out that they were defending their homeland. Their officers, and some of the men who had married in the colony, could enjoy the pleasures of their own homes and attend to their personal and business affairs when not campaigning. The French officers, on the other hand, had to face the prospect of years of exile from their families and friends in a colony where life was harder, and more expensive, than in France. Unfortunately, there was friction between the army and marine officers at the outset, and the pay differential aggravated the problem. More specifically it caused trouble when replacements for both corps were sent from France. The men all wanted to be incorporated into the higher paid French battalions.

Many of the French officers found campaigning in the North American wilderness not at all to their liking. The tedium of garrison duty at the remote frontier forts sapped their morale. Some of them were physically incapacitated and nearly driven out of their minds by the clouds of mosquitoes and stinging flies. Receiving news from home only once a year, and being unable to cope at such a remove with trouble that might arise, was hard to bear. Some of them were repelled by the seeming barbarism of the Indians and wanted nothing to do with them. The guerilla tactics of the Canadians, both regulars and militia, were remote from their concepts of how war should be waged. Even by European standards the French army was seriously deficient in reconnaissance and light infantry units trained for skirmishing and scouting duties. When army companies were detached to serve with the Canadians on their frontier raids their officers were disconcerted to discover that no mobile field hospitals or baggage trains went with them. Were they to be wounded they would have to make their way back to a French base as best they could before receiving medical attention. Their food supplies and equipment they had to carry on their backs like common soldiers. When rivers were encountered they had to wade or swim across. Resentful Canadians who were ordered to carry them across on their backs had an unfortunate habit of tripping in mid-stream. Some of the French officers declared that this was not warfare at all, and they refused to have any part in it. For them military operations required a secure, comfortable base, with servants, camp followers, clean linen, well-prepared food, and wine, close by the chosen field of battle or fortified place, where all the paraphernalia of siege warfare could be brought into play.

The Canadians formed a low opinion of the French officers, and the latter thought that the Canadians had far too high an opinion of themselves. The Canadians thought the French troops displayed too great a reluctance to seek out the enemy, preferring to remain on the defensive and let the enemy come to them. The defeatist attitude of Montcalm and several of his officers did nothing to ease the situation. While the French troops were employed in garrison duty, taking part in a campaign each summer, then remaining in their dispersed quarters all winter, many of the Canadians were fighting on the enemy's frontiers all year round. Vaudreuil felt constrained to complain to the minister of Marine that the French officers were too loath to abandon their comforts for active campaigning. He also complained that some of these officers, including Montcalm, abused the Canadians shamefully, and that unless a stop were put to it there could be serious trouble. He stated bluntly that the moment hostilities ended he wanted the French troops shipped back to France. One cause of this problem, attested to in considerable detail by an official of the Marine recently arrived from France, may well have been that the French army in Europe, since the days of Louis XIV, had fought its wars on foreign soil and was accustomed to live largely off the land, treating the hostile population of the occupied territory with scant regard.

In this controversy one thing stands out clearly: the calibre of the French officers was much lower than that of the Canadians. Among the senior regimental officers physical and mental competence was not always in evidence. In 1758 Montcalm informed the minister of War that the commandants of the Béarn and Royal Roussillon battalions were *hors de combat* and ought to be retired. In fact, only one lieutenant-colonel, Étienne-Guillaume de Senezergues de La Rodde of the La Sarre regiment was fit for active campaigning. After the battle of Carillon Montcalm had to ship nine officers back to France as quietly as possible. One, a knight of Malta and scion of an illustrious family, had been insane for some time and it had become impossible to conceal his condition; five others were sent back for displaying a want of courage—or as Montcalm put it, "pour avoir manqué à la première qualité nécessaire à un soldat et à un officier"—two for stealing from their fellow officers and one for having displayed considerable talent as a forger. Two other officers were allowed to resign their commissions, for good cause. Montcalm pleaded with the minister to see to it that replacements not be sent merely because their regiments, or their families, wanted to be rid of them. Meanwhile, he was obliged to fill the vacancies by granting the sons of Canadian officers lieutenants' commissions. Vaudreuil, although he sanctioned this solution, pointed out that it had established a bad precedent since these young officers entered the service with a higher rank than the Canadians in the colonial regular troops who had had several years of active campaigning. He added that too many of them could never have hoped to obtain commissions in the Canadian regulars.

Because the population of New France was only a fraction of that of the English colonies, some 75,000 compared to over 1,500,000, it is frequently assumed that the outcome of the war was a foregone conclusion. If numbers alone were what counted then Britain's ally, Prussia, also could not have escaped destruction. Such comparisons can be misleading since the size of the forces that either side could bring to bear was governed by the nature of the terrain, communications, and supply routes. The British had 23,000 regulars in America by 1758, but they were not able to make very effective use of their provincial levies. The largest force they could deploy in a campaign against Canada was 6,300 regulars and 9,000 provincials at Lake Champlain in 1758. That army was routed by Montcalm's 3,500 regulars. Similarly, at Quebec in 1759 Wolfe arrived with 8,500 troops, mostly British regulars. By September his force was reduced to 4,500 effectives. To oppose them the French had over 15,000 men—regulars, militia, and Indians. It was not numerical superiority that conquered Canada but poor generalship on the part of Montcalm that lost Quebec in one battle.

During the course of the war, however, the effectiveness of the British army improved, that of the French declined. On the British side the introduction of short term enlistments and the popularity of the war brought forth higher quality recruits for the regulars. Officers who proved to be too incompetent were weeded out; in some instances they were replaced by highly competent Swiss professional soldiers who, ironically, introduced the Canadian methods and tactics in the wilderness campaigns that the French officers sneered at. On the French side the quality of the reinforcements sent from France was low. They were mostly raw recruits, the sweepings of the streets. Some of them were even cripples who had to be shipped back. To make matters worse they brought disease with them that spread through the ranks and among the civilian population in epidemic proportions. In 1757, 500 troops were hospitalized and more than half of them died. Thus as the number of veteran trained soldiers dwindled through the wastage of war the quality of the regulars declined badly. By 1759 both the French battalions and the colonial regulars were not of the calibre they had been three years earlier. Among the French regulars discipline was not maintained; there were mutinies; morale sank to a low ebb. Thieving, looting, and other crimes became rampant. The war commissary was kept busy sending men before the council of war. He complained, "We spend our life having the rogues punished." The effectiveness of the French battalions was further reduced by Montcalm's decision to bring them up to strength by drafting Canadian militiamen into their ranks. It required more than the grey-white uniform of the French army to make regular soldiers out of them, capable of fighting in line. They did not receive the harsh, intensive, parade-ground training that that type of warfare demanded. The lack was to prove fatal on the Plains of Abraham.

Another frequently stated reason for the conquest of New France is inadequate supplies. The question requires more critical scrutiny than it has received to date. Far too much tainted subjective evidence has been accepted at face value. Owing to crop failures and the greatly increased number of mouths to feed, estimated to be 17 per cent, the colony could not produce enough food to supply its needs. It was dependent on supplies shipped from France, but the supply ships reached Quebec every year up to 1759. In 1757 Montcalm reported that a three years' supply of clothing for the troops had arrived and there was nothing to worry about on that score. Moreover, sizable quantities of food and other military supplies were captured by the French; enough to maintain the army for months were captured at Oswego (Chouaguen) and Fort William Henry (Lake George, N.Y.). There is no viable evidence that military operations were curtailed by a shortage of supplies. Poor distribution and the habitants' distrust of inflated paper money obliged the urban population to tighten its belt and eat unpalatable food at times, such as horse meat, but no one starved.

Account also has to be taken of the fact that the British had supply problems. The chicanery of their colonial supply contractors and the provincial assemblies was notorious. At Quebec in 1759 over a quarter of Wolfe's army was on the non-effective list, suffering from the dietary diseases, dysentery and scurvy. Moreover, owing to the military ineptitude of the Anglo-Americans, the British had to import in far larger numbers than the French the most essential military commodity of all, fighting men. Had no regular troops been imported by either side, the Canadians would certainly not have been conquered.

In 1758 Vaudreuil had contrasted the attitude of the colonial regular troops towards the war with that of the French regulars. For the Canadians, he wrote, the colony was their homeland; it was there that they had their families, lands, resources, and aspirations for the future. The French troops on the other hand, being expatriates, wanted only to return home with their honour intact, without having suffered a defeat, caring little what wounds the enemy inflicted on the colony, not even about its total loss.

The events of 1759 and 1760 made all too plain that there was more than a little truth in these charges. After the *débâcle* on the Plains of Abraham the French officers refused to give battle again, despite the fact that they outnumbered the British three to one and still held Quebec. The following year their failure to recapture the city they had abandoned and to block the British drive up Lake Champlain, the arrival of three British armies at the portals of the colony, the failure of reinforcements to arrive from France, all meant that further resistance was completely hopeless. James Murray, advancing up the river from Quebec, ravaged and burned the homes of the Canadians who had not laid down their arms. At one point his men got out of hand and some Canadian women were violated. Yet Lévis and his staff still demanded that the British be resisted for the honour of the army, which meant their personal honour and future careers. When many of the Canadians deserted to protect their homes and families the French officers wanted them apprehended and shot. French troops were sent to seize at gun point the last remaining cattle of the habitants, who resisted vigorously since this was all that was left them to feed their families during the coming winter. Even when the British stood at the gates of Montreal in overwhelming strength, and although the sacking of the town might ensue, Lévis demanded that the capitulation terms be rejected because Jeffery Amherst had churlishly refused to grant the French the honours of war. Vaudreuil would not heed him and capitulated to spare the colony further devastation. The king subsequently declared, in a savagely worded letter from the minister of Marine, that Vaudreuil should not have accepted the terms; that he should have heeded Lévis and continued to resist, come what may, for the honour of French arms. The missive made plain that the loss of the colony and the plight of the Canadians were of no consequence compared to the army's having surrendered without receiving the right to march out of Montreal bearing its arms, flags unfurled, and drums beating.

After the surrender arrangements had to be made for the transport of the regular troops, the civil officials, and the Canadians who chose to quit the colony rather than remain under the British, some 4,000 in all. Of the 2,200 French regular troops who remained on strength, 500 to 600 opted to stay in the colony; upwards of 800 had previously deserted to that end. Among them were 150 British deserters who had enlisted in the French forces. Vaudreuil and Lévis allowed these deserters to make themselves scarce before the capitulation, but most of them were subsequently rounded up by the British. Some French soldiers were persuaded to enlist in the British army, but one of their officers remarked that now they had discovered they were to be transported to serve elsewhere few would be tempted to follow their example.

The officer corps of the colonial regular troops, with the exception of those too severely wounded to make the voyage, crossed to France where they were retired from the service on half pay. With the conclusion of peace in 1763 21 officers returned to Canada to settle their affairs, then went back again to France hoping to receive appointments on the active list. Others quietly gave up and returned to Canada to eke out a living on their seigneurial lands. Those who held the cross of the order of Saint-Louis were in a difficult position as the oath of the order prevented them becoming subjects of His Britannic Majesty without the consent of the king of France. Several of those who chose to remain in France eventually received active appointments in the service, in Gorée, the West Indies, or Guiana. Louis-Thomas Jacau de Fiedmont, for example, the brave gunner captain who, at Jean-Baptiste-Nicolas-Roch de Ramezay's council of war that opted to surrender Quebec, declared that they should hold out until the ammunition was exhausted, eventually became governor of Guiana. Another, Gaspard-Joseph Chaussegros de Léry, returned to Canada and became a member of the Legislative Council of Quebec but sent his young sons to France. One of them, François-Joseph, gained entry into the reformed and prestigious corps of engineers. He ultimately rose to be commander-in-chief of the engineers in Napoleon's Grande Armée. His name is engraved on the Arc de Triomphe along with those of Napoleon's other great generals. For some of these Canadian officers the career was all important; for others, it was their homeland that mattered. Some, at least, who chose the latter did so because, owing to age or lack of means and influential connections, they saw no future for themselves in the service of their king. Their cause was truly lost.

As for the soldiers of the colonial regular troops who returned to France, when an attempt was made to have them enlist in French regiments not one of them would do so. Their almost unanimous response was that they knew the route to Halifax and they could easily find their way back to Canada from there. The Maréchal de Senneterre commented: "All those who have returned from Quebec and Montreal appear to have a great love for that country."

A DIFFERENT KIND OF COURAGE: THE FRENCH MILITARY AND THE CANADIAN IRREGULAR SOLDIER DURING THE SEVEN YEARS' WAR

Martin L. Nicolai

In recent decades two historians of Canada during the Seven Years' War, Guy Frégault and William J. Eccles, have attacked their predecessors' adulation of Louis-Joseph, Marquis de Montcalm, by portraying him as a poor strategist, a mediocre tactician, and a defeatist. However true this might be, they also portray the French officer corps, including their commander, as contemptuous of Canadians and irregular warfare.[1] During the course of the Canadian cam-

From *Canadian Historical Review*, LXX, no. 1 (March 1989), 53-75. Copyright 1989 by University of Toronto Press. Reprinted by permission of University of Toronto Press.

paign, Montcalm and his officers did demonstrate a general lack of respect for the petty raiding of *la petite guerre* and an ambiguous attitude towards the Canadian soldier. This, however, was less a rejection of irregular warfare than an expression of their belief that a more structured and sophisticated use of irregular tactics was necessary when the enemy was no longer simply a colonial militia but a large, well-organized army complete with highly trained regiments of heavy and light infantry. As Ian Steele makes clear, the Seven Years' War in North America marks the end of the days of small-scale raiding and the advent of professional armies on the continent. The war, he states, was won by conventional, European-style battles and sieges, not by skirmishes in the woods.[2]

At first complacent in their use of Canadian irregulars, relying on local practice and their knowledge of the use of light troops in Europe during the War of the Austrian Succession, the French eventually attempted to bring Canadian soldiers onto the conventional battlefield not simply as sharpshooters roaming on the flanks but as actual light infantry operating on the central line of battle in close co-operation with the heavy infantry of the French *troupes de terre*. There is every sign that the Frenchmen finished the campaign convinced by the success of Canadian light troops that units of properly led and disciplined light infantry were a valuable part of a European army.

The War of the Austrian Succession (1740-8) was the training ground of most of the French officers who came to Canada with the Baron von Dieskau and the Marquis de Montcalm, and it was during this war that irregular troops were first employed on a large scale by modern armies. In 1740-1 the young Austrian empress Maria Theresa mobilized her Croatian and Hungarian military borders on the Ottoman frontier and moved them for the first time to the central European front in an attempt to eject Frederick the Great's troops from Silesia. They performed invaluable service in every campaign, and in 1744 Field Marshal Traun successfully forced the Prussians out of Bohemia by threatening Frederick's supply lines and harassing his foraging parties. Over 40,000 Serbo-Croatian "Grenzer" would serve in the Habsburg armies during the War of the Austrian Succession and about 88,000 during the Seven Years' War.[3] These fierce soldiers were usually dispatched on independent operations against enemy outposts and communications, but sometimes they played a small part on the battlefield as sharpshooters posted on the flanks. Faced by these irregulars, the French, Prussians, and British responded by recruiting some light troops of their own. In the Seven Years' War all of the major European armies raised units of irregulars and light infantry and cavalry, and their use gradually became more sophisticated.[4]

The French army began very early to adapt to this new aspect of warfare. Although the use of skirmishers had disappeared in France at the end of the seventeenth century because of the widespread obsession with the firepower of the line, interest in these troops slowly revived during the following decades. There were experiments with skirmishers in military exercises as early as 1727, but only necessity during the 1740s forced the French to raise light troops in any numbers. During the winter of 1744, the Maréchal de Saxe, who had extensive previous experience with light troops in eastern Europe and had written the first modern treatise to deal with the subject, raised a number of *compagnies franches* or free companies for the French army, and would have formed more if the minister of war had approved. He eventually commanded five regiments of light troops, usually combining infantry and cavalry in these units, and by 1748 there were 5000 of them in the French army. At Fontenoy in 1745 Saxe used his irregulars on the battlefield itself, sending a screen of skirmishers against the British centre while he deployed his army. He also stationed Monsieur de Grassin's new 1200-strong Régiment des Arquebusiers in the Bois de Berry on his left flank, where their deadly independent fire or *feu de chasseur* made a British attempt to secure their flank exceedingly difficult. Saxe also used skirmishers at Laufeld in 1747. The tactics of this general, who was one of the greatest commanders of the eighteenth century, were studied with great care by other French officers. Although the French did not make extensive use of skirmishers during the War of the Austrian Succession itself, their presence was customary during the peacetime military exercises of 1748 to 1755 and no French military writer of this period neglected to discuss them.[5]

Montcalm and François-Gaston, Chevalier de Lévis, both served in Bohemia and Piedmont during the War of the Austrian Succession, and had more than enough experience with irregulars on both campaigns.[6] During the operations around Prague in late 1742 and during the subsequent retreat to Germany, Hungarian hussars and other light cavalry constantly harassed French foraging parties and other units, greatly hampering the ability of the Maréchal de Belle-Isle to supply his troops, obtain information about the main Austrian army, or easily manoeuvre his forces.[7] In Piedmont, Charles Emmanuel III organized his Piedmontese mountaineers or *barbets* in militia units, and these men fought beside the king's regular troops in the endless mountain battles of this campaign, also overrunning the French communications outposts in the mountain valleys, taking few prisoners in the process. Throughout most of 1745 and 1746 Montcalm protected sections of the French communications in the Ligurian Alps against repeated attacks by the *barbets*, and in one daring night operation the French colonel led his troops, some of whom were mountain fusiliers, over "impracticable paths" to surprise and capture 150 *barbets* in a village. To counter the Piedmontese militia, the Franco-Spanish recruited two battalions of Catalonian mountaineers from the Pyrenees called *Miquelets*—many of whom were former bandits—and equipped them with carbines.[8]

The exposure of many members of the officer corps to irregular warfare in Europe made them appreciate the effectiveness of this type of military activity. Irregulars could severely hamper reconaissance, slow an army's advance, and harry an enemy's communications so severely that large numbers of fighting men had to be withdrawn from the main body simply to guard the army's baggage and lines of supply and communication. There was, as a result, a general recognition among military men by the end of the 1740s that irregular troops, fortunately or unfortunately, had a role to play in wartime, if only to defend one's own force against enemy irregulars.

What impressions did French officers have of Canadian soldiers during the first few years of the Seven Years' War? One prominent characteristic of the Canadian *habitants*, noted by all of the officers, was their willingness to perform military service, an attitude which was in striking contrast to that of the average French peasant. The long wars against the Iroquois in the seventeenth century, which forced all Canadian males to take up arms and learn Indian methods of irregular warfare, engendered a military ethos among Canadians which was fostered by intermittent campaigns against the English in company with Canada's Indian allies.[9] The reputation of Canadians as a "race of soldiers" was confirmed by the French officers, whose constant refrain in their writings was to contrast the Canadians' skill and courage with their indiscipline.[10] Colonel François-Charles de Bourlamaque, for instance, believed that Canada possessed far more "naturally courageous men" than any other country, and although Canadian militiamen were not accustomed to obedience, when they found firmness and justice in their officers they were quite "docile."[11] They possessed a different "kind of courage," wrote Louis-Antoine de Bougainville, for like the Indians, Canadians exposed themselves little, organized ambushes, and fought in the woods behind a screen of trees, defeating in this way an entire British army under General Braddock.[12] Despite his criticisms of Canadian indiscipline, Bougainville was careful to qualify his remarks: "God knows we do not wish to disparage the value of the Canadians ... In the woods, behind trees, no troops are comparable to the natives of this country."[13] Some of the least charitable comments on Canadians came from the Baron von Dieskau's second-in-command, Pierre-André de Gohin, Chevalier de Montreuil, who, blaming the irregulars for his commander's humiliating defeat at Lake George in 1755, declared sarcastically that the "braggart" Canadians were well adapted for skirmishing, being "very brave behind a tree and very timid when not covered."[14]

Despite a tendency among many officers to make generalizations about Canadian soldiers, most realized that not all Canadian males were experienced irregulars. Stereotypes may have been reinforced, however, by the presence of several hundred *coureurs de bois* and other experienced woodsmen among the militia companies and transport troops, especially before 1785. Captain Jean-Guillaume-Charles de Plantavit de La Pause de Margon, Chevalier de La Pause, found that there was no proper system of drafting soldiers in the parishes, with the result that the same men were chosen each year to fill the parish militia quota. These, according to La Pause, were the poorest *habitants*, presumably men with little land and a greater inclination towards hunting, long-term work as *coureurs de bois*, or related activities which provided the military skills useful for irregular warfare.[15] Bougainville differentiated between the men of the districts of Montreal and Trois-Rivières, who were considered more warlike and accustomed to voyages in the west, and those of the Quebec area, who tended towards proficiency in fishing and other nautical pursuits.[16] Similarly, Lieutenant Jean-Baptiste d'Aleyrac and Montcalm's junior aide-de-camp, Captain Pierre Marcel, made fun of the milita of the cities of Montreal and Quebec, "composed of all kinds of workers, wholesale merchants, who never go to war."[17] Despite these views, however, the officers felt that their generalizations about Canadians were justified.

Constant contact with Indian allies in wartime and the success of their tactics resulted in Canadians adopting not only Indian methods of fighting but also their attitudes towards war, such as the idea that victory involved inflicting losses on the enemy without incurring any and that the campaigning season was over when a victory, however insubstantial, had been achieved and honour gratified. In addition, native ritual boasting of prowess in war may have encouraged some Canadian soldiers to advertise their military talents in a flagrant manner. French officers noticed these characteristics, and generally realized that they were cultural borrowings from the Indians, but they were too ethnocentric and accustomed to professional military conduct to sympathize very much with this type of behaviour.

The Canadian penchant for boasting was of minor concern. Boasts "after the Canadian fashion, that one of their number could drive ten Englishmen" only boosted morale, and this behaviour was considered no more than a minor annoyance.[18] The Canadian and Indian custom of returning home *en masse* every time a "coup" was made, however, was subjected to considerably more criticism. La Pause recounted how the comical race of Canadians departed after the Battle of Carillon, rushing off in their boats within hours, moving "day and night, forgetting, losing and often leaving people behind if they did not embark fast enough." After visiting their families, he noted, they would return at an exceedingly leisurely pace to resume the campaign.[19] At other times, as when muskets had to be fired in an attempt to stem the exodus of Canadian officers and men after the fall of Fort William Henry—a factor which may have influenced Montcalm's decision to discontinue the offensive—the French were even less amused.[20] This behaviour at Oswego and on other occasions decidedly undermined the French officers' respect for Canadian soldiers. Even though they recognized the special nature of the Canadian "race," they expected them, as Frenchmen, to be more amenable to discipline than the Indians.

During the early years of the war the French officer corps simply accepted the traditional role of their Canadian militia and Indian allies. The recent battle on the banks of the Monongahela proved that the Canadians already had considerable potential, and there did not seem to be any immediate need to do more than instil Canadians with obedience and a basic orderliness. Captain Pierre Pouchot regarded Braddock's defeat on the Monongahela as an "impressive lesson" for regular troops who could not fire steadily and were unacquainted with the style of fighting of their opponents, although he did not believe that properly organized and trained regular soldiers should be defeated by irregulars.[21] Training Canadians as heavy infantry was pointless because they already performed satisfactorily as scouts, raiders, and sharpshooters, duties which admirably suited the "natural spirit" of the local people.[22] French officers, accustomed to the mosaic of provinces which made up their country, each with its own distinct culture and identity, saw Canadians as a very peculiar set of fellow Frenchmen. It was easiest to adapt to their particular nature and use their skills rather than try to make them more like other Frenchmen and amenable to European-style heavy infantry training. As Pouchot's companion-in-arms Captain Nicolas Sarrebource de Pontleroy of the Royal Corps of Engineers pointed out, Canadians were brave, but without discipline they could not be expected to fight in open fields against regular troops; they were not even equipped for such an eventuality.[23] The war was not yet desperate enough to require a complete rethinking of the role of irregular troops.

Baron Johann Hermann von Dieskau, who was one of Saxe's aides-de-camp and had experience with light troops in eastern Europe, undoubtedly derived much of his confidence in irregulars from his former commander.[24] However, he learned the limitations of irregular infantry during his campaign against William Johnson in 1755. Leaving behind most of his French troops, he forged ahead with a mixed force of regulars, Canadian militia, and Indians to mount a surprise attack on Fort Edward. He properly posted flank guards of Canadians and Indians to prevent his small column from being ambushed, but was obliged to give up his plans to attack Fort Edward when the Iroquois refused their assistance. He was soundly beaten in an assault on Johnson's entrenchments at the foot of Lake George. Dieskau had not foreseen that Johnson's force would be both entrenched and alerted, for under these conditions he required more regular troops and a few cannon. His Canadians and Indians were simply unable to participate in a conventional assault. While irregulars were occasionally capable of capturing forts and other fortifications if they had the advantage of surprise, they could do little if the garrison was prepared for their attack.[25]

The Marquis de Montcalm, who arrived in New France in 1756 to take command of the French forces, was by a combination of experience, necessity, and advice persuaded to employ the regulars and irregulars in the separate roles to which they were most accustomed. The Chevalier de Montreuil, who condemned the "blind confidence" of Dieskau in his Canadian advisers, made certain to instruct Montcalm to rely upon his regulars and to employ his Canadians and Indians only in harassing the enemy.[26] Montcalm viewed raiding expeditions, especially those directed against military targets, as useful in harassing enemy troops and lowering their morale. He also believed that successful raids maintained the offensive spirit in his troops and encouraged the Canadian civilian population, although he abhorred the atrocities committed by his aboriginal allies just as he had hated the tortures inflicted on prisoners by the Slavic Pandours and Italian *barbets*.[27]

Irregulars were perceived to have a particular role: they tied down large numbers of enemy militia on the frontiers and lines of communication, carried out reconaissance, ambushed detachments of enemy troops, and provided some firepower during sieges and other engagements. Both Captain Jean-Nicolas Desandroüins and Lévis wrote approvingly concerning the contributions of the militia during the sieges of Oswego in 1756 and Fort William Henry the following year. Desandroüins found that the Canadians and Indians showed great enthusiasm at Oswego, and while they wasted a great deal of ammunition firing all day, they did succeed in lowering the garrison's morale. It obviously did not occur to him, however, that they might have captured the fort by themselves, or that the irregulars were anything more than auxiliaries.[28]

The year 1758 was a turning point in the war and in French tactics. For this campaign the British massed an army of 6000 regulars and 9000 provincials at Fort William Henry and advanced on Fort Carillon. Among these regulars were several new specially trained light infantry regiments and Robert Rogers' Corps of Rangers.[29] Few Canadians arrived in time for the Battle of Carillon, and the shortage of irregulars obliged the French to station two companies of *volontaires* in front of the abattis while it was under construction—*volontaires* being the contemporary French term for light infantry. These regular soldiers, probably the pickets from each of the battalions, skirmished all day with the enemy's abundant light troops, and successfully held them at bay while the abattis was hastily completed. Just as the battle opened, the French *volontaires* withdrew to the protection of the abattis or to the army's left flank.[30] A group of 300 Canadians who were present were ordered to leave the protection of the abattis and open independent fire on the flank of one of the attacking British columns, but refused to do so. A few had to have shots fired over their heads to prevent their fleeing the field, although in the latter case Bougainville admitted that "It is true that these were not Canadians of the good sort."[31] Canadians were not accustomed to fighting on the open battlefield and, having only *habitant* militia officers and occasionally a Canadian colonial regular officer of the *troupes de la Marine* to lead them, could not easily be coerced into exposing themselves to enemy fire. Even worse than the refusal of the Canadians at Carillon to follow orders was the rout of Canadian troops during a forest encounter in August 1758 with Roger's Rangers.[32]

Montcalm resolved at the end of this campaign that a higher level of discipline and co-operation was needed from his Canadian soldiers. His aide-de-camp and close friend Bougainville concluded, correctly, that "Now war is established here on a European basis of campaign plans, armies, artillery, sieges, battles.

It is not a matter of making *coup*, but of conquering or being conquered. What a revolution! What a change!"[33] Indeed, the arrival of large regular armies in America had changed the nature of war on the continent. Montcalm believed that a concentration of his forces was necessary to confront the English along the major invasion routes, and he advocated a release of as many of the troops in the garrisons in the west as possible without undermining the Indian war effort. He saw that the Indians tied down large numbers of enemy militia on the frontiers, but doubted that a major French presence in the west had much effect in diverting British regular troops—the chief danger to New France, in his opinion—away from the central front.[34] The British were better able to respond to attacks by irregulars, and raids against military targets in the Lake George area were becoming more and more costly. Irregulars now found it more difficult to defeat regulars without the support of French or French colonial heavy infantry, and these troops had to be conserved for the principal engagements. Montcalm felt that large-scale raids no longer paid off in terms of the manpower, supplies, and effort invested, and he hoped that the Indians and small numbers of Canadians could maintain sufficient pressure on the English to keep them more or less on the defensive. By the fall of 1758 Montcalm knew that no ambush or raid was going to stem the advance of massive English armies against Montreal or Quebec; what he needed were large numbers of regular soldiers and disciplined light infantry who could be depended on to fight in a series of conventional battles.[35]

Montcalm believed that masses of poorly equipped and undisciplined Canadian militiamen who consumed his extremely limited food supplies were of minimal assistance to his army; rather, he needed regulars to reinforce his depleted battalions, which even at full strength were outnumbered approximately four to one by the British.[36] He therefore obtained Vaudreuil's consent to select 4000 of the best militiamen and divide them into three groups. The first group was to be incorporated into the regular battalions of the line, the second into the *troupes de la Marine,* and the third was to be organized separately in the customary militia brigades. A total of approximately 3000 Canadians were intended for the incorporations.[37]

This reorganization was intended to serve several purposes. First, each company of the *troupes de terre* and *troupes de la Marine* would be augmented by fifteen men, and would therefore add good shots, canoeists, and workers to the existing body of regulars, improving the ability of these troops to fight, travel, and build fortifications. Montcalm hoped to have the French and Canadian soldiers teach each other what they knew, making the regulars better woodsmen and the Canadians more dependable infantrymen. The Canadians, who customarily fell sick in large numbers on campaign because they lacked clothing, proper shelter, and enforced camp sanitation, would now live with the regulars in tents and receive uniforms, food, and other supplies. In addition, there had always been a serious lack of officers among the militia—sometimes only one for every 200 men—which resulted in a lack of supervision, discipline, and leadership in battle. Incorporated troops would receive abundant attention from the numerous officers and sergeants of the French line troops and *troupes de la Marine,* thereby, it was hoped, improving discipline and reducing desertion. Montcalm and his fellow officers claimed to have no worries that Canadians would be mistreated in their new companies, for "They live very well with our soldiers whom they love," and their complaints would be addressed by the general himself.[38] The militia and the French-recruited *troupes de la Marine* already camped together, so it was not expected that there would be any serious difficulty in uniting Canadians and the *troupes de terre.*[39]

The 1000 remaining militiamen would be organized in their customary "brigades" of approximately 150 men, each theoretically comprising five companies of thirty men. Three soldiers of the *troupes de la Marine* were usually attached to each company as sergeants, and they gave the Canadians a modicum of discipline and military training.[40] According to Montcalm's plans for 1759, his picked militiamen would be placed under the best militia officers, subjected by special ordinance to the same rules of discipline as the regulars, and since there were fewer militiamen on continuous service, they could be better fed, clothed, armed, and even possibly paid for their longer period on campaign. As a further incentive, Montcalm proposed that distinguished Canadian soldiers receive marks of honour, including gratuities, and that small pensions be granted to those crippled by their wounds. The rest of the militia would remain at home prepared at a moment's notice to assemble and join the troops in the field.[41] All of these ideas centred around an attempt to organize and obtain the most efficient performance possible from irregular troops, either as raiders or as sharpshooters on the edges of the battlefield.

The decision to organize this special militia force to act independently of or in concert with regular troops had the full support of Montcalm's regular officers. Parscau du Plessis and Pouchot both noted the potential of Canadians to form "light companies," and in 1757 La Pause had the idea of establishing four companies of *partisans* composed of French and Canadian troops and guided by Indians; at any one time one or two of these companies could be in the field harassing the enemy. Bourlamaque made a similar proposal that a troop of 150 volunteer chasseurs adept at *la petite guerre* be maintained in the colony in peacetime, usefully employing the *coureurs de bois* whom he believed usually resided in unproductive debauchery among the Indians.[42]

Montcalm's intention to create a new army for the campaign of 1759, however, was only partially fulfilled. The *levée en masse* of the Canadian militia and the need to arm, feed, and supply thousands of these soldiers resulted in an abandonment of the plan to organize a set of elite militia brigades. The only special Canadian units to be formed were a small cavalry detachment led by French officers and the *réserve de Repentigny,* which was attached to

Bougainville's command to patrol the riverbank upstream from Quebec during the siege. Neither unit took part in the Battle of the Plains of Abraham.[43] The planned militia incorporations, however, did take place in the late spring, just before the arrival off Quebec of the first ships of a fleet bearing a large British and American colonial army under Major-General James Wolfe. The number of Canadians actually incorporated is unknown, but it is doubtful whether more than 500 or 600 men joined the 3000 or more regulars at Quebec.[44] Montcalm had only three months to train his Canadian regulars, simply an insufficient amount of time to produce the kind of soldier he wanted. Judging by the behaviour of the incorporated Canadians on the Plains of Abraham, it seems that very little effort had been made to drill them at all, and the abysmal performance of the regulars suggests that drill was not a high priority in the French army in Canada. After the battle, one of Montcalm's aides wrote in Montcalm's journal that "The French soldier no longer knew any discipline, and instead of molding the Canadian, he assumed all of his faults."[45]

The French officers were extremely pleased by the behaviour of the Canadian militia in the Battle of Montmorency on 31 July, for the militiamen were chiefly responsible for repelling a landing by 500 British grenadiers and Royal Americans. Lining the top of the slope overlooking the river, the militia opened a vigorous fire on the climbing troops, inflicting heavy casualties and forcing them to retreat to their boats. The French regulars, held in reserve immediately behind the Canadians, did not have to be committed to the action.[46] According to Captain Pierre Cassagniau de St Félix of the Régiment de Berry, the French generals lacked "any great dependence on the prowess of the Canadians" until this action, "for they intermixed them with their regulars, and gave the latter public orders to shoot any of them that should betray the least timidity: however, they behaved with so much steadiness throughout the whole cannonading, and, upon the approach of [the enemy] troops up the precipice, fired with such great regularity, that they merited the highest applause and confidence from their Superiors."[47] This experience may have encouraged the officers to believe that the incorporated Canadians and militia would show more steadiness in any upcoming engagements.

On the morning of 13 September 1759, as Wolfe's army assembled on the Plains of Abraham and the French brought up their main force, platoons from the districts of Quebec, Montreal, and Trois-Rivières were detached from their militia brigades and sent forward with the pickets of the Régiment de Guyenne to harass the British troops from behind rocks and bushes all along the front of their line. After pushing back some British advance posts, these soldiers kept up a galling fire on the British regulars. Canadian militia and some Indians scattered in the woods on the two edges of the battlefield also kept up a steady fire from the cover of trees and underbrush.[48] Then, at about ten in the morning, Montcalm ordered the advance. In the centre, the battalions of Béarn and Guyenne formed a single deep column. On their right and left, at some distance, two other bodies of regulars formed shallower columns with a much wider frontage than the central formation. In the columns the incorporated Canadians were sandwiched in the second rank, no doubt to keep them in order. There were almost certainly more of them in the ranks further back in the columns.[49] Montcalm was clearly following the military ordinance of 1755, which recommended that attacks be made by a series of two-battalion columns.[50]

The officers lost control of their men almost immediately. The enthusiastic soldiers surged forward at an excessively fast pace, and as they marched over the rough terrain without pausing to dress ranks, they quickly lost cohesion.[51] As they approached the British line they began to collide with the advanced platoons of Canadian militia, which because of the rapidity of the advance had no time to retire in the intervals between the columns, two of which had very wide frontages. This caused further havoc in the French formations.[52] The columns began to move obliquely towards the British flanks, and at a distance of about 130 metres, extreme musket range, the French troops came to a sudden halt and fired several ineffectual volleys. The incorporated Canadians dropped to the ground to reload, as was their custom in an exposed position, and as the French officers urged the troops to advance, many if not all of the Canadians suddenly deserted their units and retired to the right where the platoons of skirmishers were joining the Canadians and Indians who lined the woods on the British flank.[53] This unorthodox behaviour—which left the regular officers somewhat nonplused—demonstrates just how little instruction the Canadian troops had received or accepted.

Pouchot commended the resistance of the militiamen on the right flank, but he also explained that the main attack "confused the [incorporated] Canadians who were little accustomed to find themselves out of cover." This was, however, the kindest assessment of the incorporated Canadians to be made by the French officers whose records are extant. Malartic accused them of cowardice, and others blamed them for setting the French regulars in disarray and abandoning their proper place in the line. The Canadians were shielded from further criticism by the fact that almost immediately after the Canadians left the ranks, the French regulars, who advanced in places to within approximately forty metres of the enemy line, broke under the impact of devastating British volleys and fled madly to the walls of Quebec and across the St Charles River.[54]

At the conclusion of the Battle of the Plains of Abraham, as the French regulars abandoned the battlefield in complete disorder, the Canadians went far in redeeming themselves for their somewhat weak performance during the main encounter, this time in their traditional role as irregular soldiers. A quarter of Fraser's Highlanders were shot down as they attempted in vain to drive the Canadian rearguard from the woods, and they were obliged to retreat and regroup. A further attack by 500 British regulars from three regiments finally drove the Canadians back to the St Charles.[55] The Chevalier de Johnstone, who observed this half-hour-long rearguard action, had nothing but lavish praise for their performance.[56] Pouchot and several other officers mentioned this resistance with approval, although they deplored the indiscipline among the Canadians in the columns.[57]

The French officers had underestimated the extent to which Canadians were attached to the tactics which they had practised for over four generations. Like the Indians, Canadians firmly believed that they should fight in their traditional manner, even if they recognized that conventional heavy infantry tactics might be appropriate for Europeans. Pre-industrial societies are extremely resistant to change because survival is so closely linked to practices—passed on by an oral tradition—which have been proven effective by generations of experience. Also, unlike the American colonists to the south, Canadians had no tradition of training in conventional tactics to make them open to such ideas. As usual, Canadians did their best in their traditional role fighting as skirmishers, and this would be taken into account when the tactical role of Canadians was reassessed for the next campaign, that of 1760.

The Chevalier de Lévis was not present at the Battle of the Plains of Abraham, but the news of the Canadian rearguard action confirmed his already high opinion of the effectiveness of Canadian militiamen when they fought under conditions for which they were trained. Ever since his arrival in Canada he had shown great interest in the use of irregular troops, and this goes far to explain why he was so popular with Vaudreuil and the Canadian officers. As early as 1756, Lévis had outlined the role he expected his light troops to play. In a directive he specified, first, that the *"troupes de la Marine* and those of the colony will fight in their manner on the flanks of the *troupes de terre.*"[58] This role of light troops in guarding the flanks was relatively orthodox in the French army, and was practised from Fontenoy to the middle of the Seven Years' War in both Europe and Canada. Second, Lévis attempted to work out a system whereby regulars and irregulars could support each other in battle and compensate for their respective weaknesses. Of particular significance is the fact that he designated some regular troops to serve as light infantry: "M. de Montreuil will also detach all the good shots of his regiment, who will fight *à la canadienne*, and will keep together only a part of his detachment to receive those who fight *à la canadienne*, so that, in case they were obliged to withdraw, they could do so with security behind the detachment, which, being in order, would face the enemy and give the troops who had fought as skirmishers [*à la légère*] time to rally and recommence the fight.[59] Light infantry depended on line troops for protection on the open battlefield because they lacked the density to deliver the concentrated firepower of a large body of men. In the days when one musket meant one bullet, a few men could do little harm to an advancing infantry unit unless they continually retreated to a new position and renewed their fire.

Meanwhile, parallel tactical developments were taking place in Germany, where light troops were employed by the French army at Sundershausen and Lutternberg in 1758 and at Bergen, Lippstadt, and Minden the following year. Until 1759 grenadiers, pickets, and entire line battalions detached as *volontaires* were used as light infantry, but during the winter of 1758-9 several regiments decided of their own accord to form detachments of fifty men to serve as light infantry, and these soldiers proved so useful at Bergen, in the retreat from Minden, and in other engagements that at the end of the 1759 campaigning season a number of officers successfully urged the Maréchal de Broglie to institute light infantry companies throughout his army. This allowed a battalion to be a self-contained unit which could depend on itself and not on special light infantry battalions elsewhere in the army when it met the enemy during or between major battles. Despite opposition from the Duc de Choiseul, battalion light infantry companies were confirmed by Broglie's French army drill instructions of 1764 and 1769 and officially instituted in 1776, just in time for the Comte de Rochambeau's campaign in America.[60]

It seems unlikely that Lévis knew of Broglie's reforms of the autumn of 1759, since the British blockade of the St Lawrence began in May and communications with France via Acadia were tenuous in the extreme. This makes it especially interesting that he should organize battalion light infantry companies at exactly the same time as Broglie. Both generals, however, were carrying the primarily post-1748 practice of detaching battalion grenadiers and pickets as skirmishers to its logical conclusion.

During the winter of 1759-60 Lévis decided to continue the incorporation of Canadian troops into the regular battalions, but on a significantly different basis than that envisioned by his later commander. Lévis's instructions for the organization of his army in 1760 specified that three companies of militia would be attached to each regular battalion, and to command these companies he designated "a captain who would be the best for this assignment and to manage the *habitants* with gentleness, and three lieutenants to command the said companies."[61] It is especially important to note that these Canadian troops were to be attached to the battalion in independent companies and not merely assimilated into the ranks of the regulars. Their role on the battlefield was explained in detail: "When it is necessary to march in column, they will march by companies or by half-company at the head of the brigade, and when it is necessary to place themselves in order of battle to fight, they will go forward forming a first line, leaving from one division to the next an equal distance to occupy the entire front of the line."[62] In other words, the light infantry would spread out to form a skirmishing line in front of the regular troops. "Once they are thus formed, they will march forward and seek to make use of the most advantageous situations to approach as closely as possible and fire on the enemy, and follow him closely if he withdraws."[63] Lévis further explained that if the skirmishers were pushed back, they would rally and form line in the intervals between the two-company divisions and then march forward with the whole army, firing volleys and then charging with the bayonet.[64]

We see here the final development of the light infantryman, no longer an irregular sharpshooter roaming on the edges of the battlefield but a regular soldier trained to prepare the way for the decisive attack. This not only required a high degree of training and flexibility, but also called for an intelligent, motivated soldier quite different from the automatons advocated by most of the leading generals of the day.[65] Each regular battalion was equipped with light infantry and could employ them offensively or defensively whenever the need arose.

In the spring of 1760 the Chevalier de Lévis incorporated 2264 Canadian militiamen into his eight battalions of *troupes de terre* and two battalions of *troupes de la Marine*.[66] A full 38 per cent of the rank and file of the average battalion was Canadian, with 226 Canadians and 361 regulars in this "average" unit combining to raise its strength to 587 men. There were, however, significant variations from unit to unit, especially in terms of the proportion of Canadians to Frenchmen. In the case of the Régiment de Languedoc, the incorporated Canadians slightly outnumbered the regulars.[67] At the Battle of the Plains of Abraham, the incorporated Canadians had constituted only about 10 per cent of the regulars present. Lévis's militiamen, who wore their traditional costumes and were accompanied by their Canadian *habitant* militia officers and French regular NCOS under the command of French regular officers, were organized in units separate from the French troops in the battalions and, of course, were not officially enlisted in the regular army. While it was usual for three strong companies to be attached to each battalion, in a number of cases more were involved; this is probably due to the fact that Canadian militia companies varied widely in size, and Lévis was reluctant to amalgamate companies from different localities.[68]

The French met the British at Sainte-Foy, on the edge of the Plains of Abraham, and a fierce, desperate battle ensued which left four times as many men dead and wounded as the more celebrated engagement of the previous September.[69] The Canadian militia companies, stationed in front and in the intervals between their battalions, kept up a relentless, accurate fire on the British regulars who, despite repeated attacks, failed to make any impression on their French opponents. The effectiveness of the Canadian troops greatly impressed Malartic: "The Canadians of the four brigades of the right, those who were in the intervals or in front of the brigades, fired a long time and most opportunely. They did a lot of harm to the English."[70] A reserve battalion composed of the townsmen of Montreal and Trois-Rivières under Repentigny of the colonial regulars advanced to fill a gap in the line accidentally created by the withdrawal of a battalion of the Régiment de La Reine, and fighting in a semblance of close order kept a battalion of Germans of the Royal American Regiment and other British regulars at bay.[71] The Canadians showed great steadiness and bravery in this battle, and took part in the set-piece attacks which drove in the British flanks and forced General Murray to order a hasty retreat with the loss of all of his guns.[72] Lévis singled out Dominique Nicolas de Laas de Gustede, a captain in the Régiment de La Reine and commander of the 223 Canadians of his battalion, for distinguished conduct. Although Laas never received orders to advance, when he saw Royal Rousillon and Guyenne marching against Fraser's brigade on the British left flank, he led his Canadian soldiers forward to join in the successful attack.[73] Canadian militiamen had already cleared this flank of Murray's light troops by nearly annihilating the force of American and Highland Rangers sent into the woods to operate against the French right.[74] The fact that nearly one-fifth of the French casualties at Sainte-Foy were Canadians suggests just how heavily engaged they were.[75]

Companies of Canadian skirmishers under French officers had formed a long line in front of their battalions, covering both the French heavy infantry and the gaps between the battalions and remaining in position despite British artillery and musket fire at close range. Joined to their respective battalions by French regular officers, they were able to offer valuable assistance to the heavy infantry and were supported by their fire. A Canadian militia battalion under a Canadian colonial regular officer had actually replaced a battalion of regulars in the line of battle, and other Canadian light troops covered the flanks and defeated trained enemy light infantry. Canadian troops had therefore performed in several roles: as skirmishers in front of the heavy infantry preparing and taking part in the decisive attack, as skirmishers acting offensively and defensively on the flanks, and as heavy infantry in the line of battle.

French officers, including Lévis, Malartic, and artillery lieutenant Joseph Fournerie de Vezon, were unanimous in praising the steadiness, effectiveness, and dash of the Canadian soldiers, and there is little doubt that the officers considered the military reforms of 1760 a great success.[76]

On both sides of the Atlantic, French military men faced the problem of how to increase the efficiency of irregular soldiers while retaining their special attributes of initiative and independence and their unique fighting skills. On each continent they met the problem in a similar way by giving their irregulars more discipline and better leadership, while at the same time cultivating their special *esprit de corps*. Conventional discipline and irregular tactics were combined to produce a new soldier with the ability to deal with a variety of opponents and battlefield situations. They also increased the co-operation between conventional and light troops until the latter, instead of being employed in a completely auxiliary role as scouts and raiders, became an effective tool on the classic, eighteenth-century battlefield.

The French officers who served in Canada during the Seven Years' War were obliged to fight under conditions which were very different from those which they had known in Europe, but their past experience and awareness of important trends in military tactics helped to prepare them for this new campaign. The growing ability of the enemy to deal with irregulars on their line of march and the likelihood of major encounters between the British and French armies meant that Canadians had to expand their skills by learning to fight on the conventional battlefield against enemy light and heavy infantry. Montcalm displayed a lack of judgment in filling the ranks of his regulars with undrilled Canadians, and was not sufficiently imaginative or ambitious enough to develop a closer co-operation between his regulars and irregulars. This job was left to Lévis to accomplish by placing militia units under regular officers and carefully linking these new light infantry units to his regular battalions so as to ensure close mutual support between these two corps—a change which paralleled reforms taking place simultaneously in the French army in Germany. The result was a decisive victory at Sainte-Foy, and this accomplishment justified the faith French officers had in the potential of Canadian militiamen to become what even they might have considered professional soldiers.

Notes

1. For historians who favour Montcalm see Francis Parkman, *France and England in North America,* part 7: *Montcalm and Wolfe,* 2 vols. (Boston 1884); Henri-Raymond Casgrain, *Guerre du Canada, 1756-1760: Montcalm et Lévis,* 2 vols. (Quebec 1891); and Lionel-Adolphe Groulx, *Histoire du Canada depuis la découverte,* 2 vols. (Montreal 1950). For highly critical perceptions of the French general see Guy Frégault, *La Guerre de la conquête* (Montreal 1955); William J. Eccles, "The French Forces in North America during the Seven Years' War," *Dictionary of Canadian Biography* (DCB), III, xv-xxiii; W.J. Eccles, "Montcalm, Louis-Joseph de, Marquis de Montcalm," DCB, III: 458-69; and W.J. Eccles, "Rigaud de Vaudreuil de Cavagnial, Pierre de, Marquis de Vaudreuil," DCB, IV: 662-74. Charles P. Stacey, *Quebec, 1759: The Siege and the Battle* (Toronto 1959), and George G.F.G. Stanley, *New France: The Last Phase, 1744-1760* (Toronto 1968), maintain a more neutral attitude.

2. Ian K. Steele, *Guerrillas and Grenadiers: The Struggle for Canada, 1689-1760* (Toronto 1969). I use the term "irregular" to denote light troops without extensive formal military training. "Light infantry" I define as formally trained light troops, who were often regulars rather than militia or auxiliaries.

3. With the addition of the Hungarian hussars, these light troops formed a very substantial proportion of the Habsburg forces. John F.C. Fuller, *British Light Infantry in the Eighteenth Century* (London 1925), 46-9; Gunther E. Rothenberg, *The*

Military Border in Croatia, 1740-1881 (Chicago 1966), 18-20; John Childs, *Armies and Warfare in Europe, 1648-1789* (New York 1982), 116-17; and Hew Strachan, *European Armies and the Conduct of War* (London 1983), 30

4. For further discussion of Austrian, Prussian, and British light troops in the European theatre during the Seven Years' War see Fuller, *British Light Infantry,* 59-75; Strachan, *European Armies,* 30-5; Childs, *Armies and Warfare in Europe,* 118-20; Rothenberg, *Military Border in Croatia,* 40-52; and Christopher Duffy, *Frederick the Great: A Military Life* (London 1985), 314, 319-20.

5. Maurice de Saxe, *Reveries on the Art of War,* trans. Thomas R. Phillips (Harrisburg, Penn. 1944), 1-11. The *Reveries* were written in 1732 and circulated in manuscript long before they were published in 1757. Saxe deals extensively with irregular infantry and cavalry on pages 40-1, 48, and 50. See also Jean Colin, *L'Infanterie au XVIIIe siècle: La Tactique* (Paris 1907), 47-51, 71; Robert S. Quimby, *The Background of Napoleonic Warfare: The Theory of Military Tactics in Eighteenth-Century France* (New York 1957), 84-5; Jon M. White, *Marshal of France: The Life and Times of Maurice, Comte de Saxe* (London 1962), 129, 147, 157-8; Fuller, *British Light Infantry,* 49-54; Strachan, *European Armies,* 31; and Childs, *Armies and Warfare in Europe,* 118.

6. Thomas Chapais, *Le Marquis de Montcalm (1721-1759)* (Quebec 1911), 16-22, and Lévis, *Journal, Collection des manuscrits du maréchal de Lévis* (*Lévis* MSS), I, 24. Montcalm was aide-de-camp to the Marquis de La Fare in Bohemia, and was colonel of an infantry regiment in Piedmont. Lévis served as a captain in Bohemia and as an adjutant (*aide-major*) with the army in Piedmont; in 1748 he was promoted colonel. Both men displayed extraordinary bravery, and Montcalm suffered wounds on a regular basis.

7. Rohan Butler, *Choiseul,* I: *Father and Son* (Oxford 1980), 304-5, 343, 363

8. Spenser Wilkinson, *The Defence of Piedmont 1742-1748: A Prelude to the Study of Napoleon* (Oxford 1927), 163-4, 208, 309-17; Butler, *Choiseul,* I, 500-52; White, *Marshal of France,* 222; Fuller, *British Light Infantry,* 54; and Strachan, *European Armies,* 31

9. See William J. Eccles, "The Social, Economic, and Political Significance of the Military Establishment in New France," *Canadian Historical Review 52* (1971): 1-22, for an examination of the impact of war and the military establishment on Canada's inhabitants.

10. Georges-Marie Butel-Dumont, *Histoire et commerce des colonies angloises dans l'Amérique septentrionale, où l'on trouve l'état actuel de leur population, & des détails curieux sur la constitution de leur gouvernement, principalement sur celui de la Nouvelle-Angleterre, de la Pensilvanie, de la Caroline & de la Géorgie* (Paris 1755), 40

11. François-Charles de Bourlamaque, "Memoire sur le Canada," *Lévis* MSS, V, 102. See also James Johnstone, "The Campaign of Canada, 1760," *Collection de manuscrits contenant lettres, mémoires, et autres documents historiques relatifs à la Nouvelle-France, recueillis aux archives de la Province de Québec ou copies à*

l'étranger (MRNF), IV, 254, 262; Pierre Pouchot, *Memoir Upon the Late War in North America between the French and English, 1755-60,* 2 vols., ed. and trans. Franklin B. Hough (Roxbury, Mass. 1866), II, 45; Louis-Guillaume de Parscau du Plessis, "Journal de la campagne de *la Sauvage* frégate du Roy, armée au port de Brest, au mois de mars 1756 (écrit pour ma dame)," *Rapport de l'archiviste du Province de Québec* (RAPQ) (1928-9), 221; and Peter Kalm, *Travels into North America,* trans. John R. Foster (Barre, Mass. 1972), 492, for further comments on the warlike spirit of Canadians.

12. Louis-Antoine de Bougainville, "Mémoire sur l'etat de la Nouvelle-France," RAPQ (1923-4), 58

13. Bougainville to Mme Hérault, 20 Feb. 1758, Louis-Antoine de Bougainville. *Adventure in the Wilderness: The American Journals of Louis Antoine de Bougainville, 1756-1760,* ed. and trans. Edward P. Hamilton (Norman, OK 1964), 333

14. Montreuil to d'Argenson, Montreal, 12 June 1756, *Documents Relative to the Colonial History of the State of New York* (NYCD), ed. E.B. O'Callaghan (Albany 1859), x, 4 9. See also anonymous, "Situation du Canada en hommes, moyens, positions," RAPQ (1923-4), 9, a memoir probably by Bougainville, and the account by La Pause, who uses almost the same words as this anonymous officer in describing the inability of Canadians to "defend themselves with countenance." Jean-Guillaume-Charles; Plantavit de La Pause, chevalier de La Pause, "Mémoire et observations sur mon voyage en Canada," RAPQ (1931-2), 66

15. La Pause, "Mémoire et observations sur mon voyage en Canada," 10

16. Bougainville, "Mémoire sur l'état de la Nouvelle-France," 58

17. Jean-Baptiste d'Aleyrac, *Aventures militaires au IXVIIIe siècle d'après les mémoires de Jean-Baptiste d'Aleyrac,* ed. Charles Coste (Paris 1935), 131; Pierre Marcel, "Journal abrégé de la campagnes de 1759 en Canada par M. M[arcel] ayde de camp de M. le Mis. de Montcalm," in Arthur C. Doughty and G. W. Parmelee, *The Siege of Quebec and the Battle of the Plains of Abraham* (Quebec 1901), V, 299

18. Pouchot, *Memoir,* I, 35, 37, and II, 45

19. La Pause, "Mémoire et observations sur mon voyage en Canada," 66

20. Bougainville, *Journals,* 174; Stanley, *New France,* 162; Steele, *Guerillas and Grevadiers,* 108; La Pause, "Journal de l'entrée de la campagne 1760," RAPQ (1932-3), 384; and Lévis, *Journal,* 1, 12

21. Pouchot, *Memoir,* I, 41-3

22. This common philosophy of the time was best illustrated by Montesquieu, who in *De l'esprit des lois* explained the idea that people in a particular environment develop a special character which the laws had to be made to fit rather than making people fit the laws.

23. Nicolas Sarrebource de Pontleroy, "Mémoire et observations sur le project d'attaquer les postes ennemis en avant de Québec, et sur celui de surprendre la place ou de l'enlever de vive force," 18 Jan. 1760, *Lévis* MSS, IV, 199

24. J.R. Turnbull, "Dieskau, Jean-Armand (Johan Herman?), Baron de Dieskau," DCB, III, 185-6. Dieskau's first name is sometimes erroneously given as Ludwig August.

25. Steele, *Guerillas and Grenadiers,* 91; Stanley, *New France,* 102-3; and Guy Frégault, *Canada: The War of the Conquest,* trans. Margaret M. Cameron (Toronto 1969), 103-6. This latter book is a translation of *La Guerre de la conquête* (Montreal 1955).

26. Chevalier de Montreuil, "Detail de la marche de Monsieur de Dieskau par Monsieur de Montreuil," MRNF, IV, 1-4; Montreuil to d'Adabie, St Frédéric, 10 Oct. 1755, MRNF, IV, 9; Montreuil to d'Argenson, Montreal, 2 Nov. 1755, MRNF, IV, 13; and Montreuil to d'Argenson, Montreal, 12 June 1756, NYCD, X, 419. Montcalm, La Pause, and Pouchot shared similar ideas regarding the cause of Dieskau's defeat. See Montcalm to d'Argenson, 28 Aug. 1756, National Archives of Canada (NA), MG 4, A1, vol. 34 7, no 208; La Pause, "Mémoire et observations sur mon voyage en Canada," 20; and Pierre Pouchot, *Memoir,* I, 46-7.

27. Montcalm to Moras, Quebec, 19 Feb. 1758, NYCD, X, 686-7. See also Bougainville, *Journals,* 42.

28. Charles Nicolas Gabriel, *Le Maréchal de camp Desandroüins, 1729-1792: Guerre du Canada, 1756-1760, Guerre de l'indépendence américaine, 1780-1782* (Verdun 1887), 50-64, and W. J. Eccles, "Lévis," DCB, IV, 477-82

29. The French officers had a consistently high opinion of British regulars and a consistently low opinion of American provincials. They referred to the provincials only in order to point out their numbers and incompetence. They did, however, have respect for the Royal American Regiment and Rogers' Rangers—both regular units—even though they enjoyed recounting the numerous abortive or disastrous operations mounted by the Rangers. For the development of light infantry tactics in the British army in North America during the Seven Years' War see Peter Russel, "Redcoats in the Wilderness: British Officers and Irregular Warfare in Europe and America, 1740 to 1760," *William and Mary Quarterly* 3rd ser. 35 (1978): 629-52; Fuller, *British Light Infantry,* 76-110; Hugh C.B. Rogers, *The British Army in the Eighteenth Century* (London 1977), 73; Strachan, *European Armies,* 28; and for a long-term view, Peter Paret, "Colonial Experience and European Military Reform at the End of the Eighteenth Century," *Bulletin of the Institute of Historical Research* 37 (1964): 47-59.

30. Bougainville, *Journals,* 230. In the French army, pickets were not selected on a rotational basis; instead, they formed permanent units which were often detached for special duties.

31. Bougainville, *Journals,* 238. See also Gabriel, *Desandrouins,* 182, and Doreil to Belle-Isle, Quebec, 28 and 31 July 1758, RAPQ (1944-5), 138 and 150-2. In these last two letters, war commissary André Doreil passed on to the minister of war confidential information which he had obtained from Montcalm.

32. For French reactions to this incident see Gabriel, *Desandrouins,* 203-6; Bougainville, *Journals,* 261-2, and Montcalm to Moras, Montreal, 11 July 1757, MRNF, IV, 105-6. In 1756 1900 Canadian militiamen served in the ranks, but another 1100 were needed for transport work and for building fortifications. By 1758 1500 Canadians

were employed on the western supply routes alone. George F.G. Stanley, *Canada's Soldiers: The Military History of an Unmilitary People,* rev. ed. (Toronto 1960), 23

33. Bougainville, *Journals,* 252. Henderson believes that Bougainville may have copied passages from Montcalm's journal into his own, rather than the contrary, since duplicated passages often have a later date in Bougainville's journal. In my opinion, however, Bougainville authored parts of the general's official journal, then copied his handiwork into his own a few hours or days later. The style of the common passages seems more characteristice of Bougainville than of Montcalm. I have therefore ascribed the quoted passage to Bougainville and not to Montcalm, who also records it: Montcalm, *Journal, Lévis* MSS, VII, 419. Susan W. Henderson. "The French Regular Officer Corps in Canada, 1755-1760: A Group Portrait" (PHD thesis, University of Maine, Orono, 1975), 115-16

34. Stanley, *New France,* 220-1; Steele, *Guerillas and Grenadiers,* 109; Henderson, "The French Regular Officer Corps in Canada," 102; Montcalm to Vaudreuil, Carillon, 26 July 1758, NYCD, X, 760-1; Montcalm to Cremille, Montreal, 12 April 1759, MRNF, IV, 224-5; and Montcalm to Le Normand, Montreal, 12 April 1759, NYCD, X, 966

35. Montcalm, "Réflexions générales sur les mesures à prendre pour la défense de cette colonie," 10 Sept. 1758. *Lévis* MSS, IV, 45-6, and Stanley, *New France,* 220-1. Eccles claims, incorrectly, that Montcalm believed that "the guerrilla warfare on the English colony's frontiers had to cease." Eccles, "Montcalm," 463

36. Bougainville, *Journals,* 199

37. Montcalm, "Réflexions générales sur les mesures à prendre pour la défense de cette colonie," 45-8.

38. Ibid.; anonymous, "Milices du Canada: inconvenients dans la constitution de ces milices qui empêchent leur utilité; moyens d'en tirer partie, la campagne prochaine," Jan. 1759, RAPQ (1923-4), 29-31; and anonymous, "The Siege of Quebec in 1759," *The Siege of Quebec in 1759: Three Eye-Witness Accounts,* ed. Jean-Claude Hébert (Quebec 1974), 52. Canadian officers of the *troupes de la Marine* were especially plentiful, for at the beginning of the war sixty of them commanded 900 soldiers. Stanley, *Canada's Soldiers,* 27

39. D'Aleyrac, *Adventures militaires,* 33, 58

40. Montcalm, "Réflexions générales sur les mesures à prendre pour la défense de cette colonie," 45-8, and d'Aleyrac, *Aventures militaires,* 58

41. Montcalm, "Réflexions générales sur les mesures à prendre pour la défense de cette colonie." 45-8, and anonymous, "Milices du Canada," 29-31

42. Parscau du Plessis, "Journal de la campagne de *la Sauvage,*" RAPQ (1928-9), 221. Pouchot, *Memoir,* I, 37; La Pause, "Mémoire sur la campagne à faire en Canada l'année 1757," RAPQ (1932-3), 338; and François-Charles de Bourlamaque, "Memoir on Canada," NYCD, X, 1149

43. Stacey, *Quebec, 1759,* 117

44. See Lévis, *Journal,* I, 209, and H.-R. Casgrain, *Montcalm et Levis,* II, 97, for an indication of the numbers incorporated; Casgrain suggests several hundred. See Doughty and Parmelee, *Siege of Quebec,* III, 154, and John Knox, *An Historical Journal of the Campaigns in North America For the Years 1757, 1758, 1759, and 1760,* ed. Arthur G. Doughty (Toronto 1914), II, 105-6, for estimates of the size of the French army on the Plains of Abraham.

45. Montcalm, *Journal,* VII, 613

46. For the Battle of Montmorency see Casgrain, *Montcalm et Lévis,* II, 133-4; Lévis, *Journal,* I, 187-8; anonymous, "Memoirs of the Siege of Quebec, from the Journal of a French Officer on Board the Chezine Frigate," Doughty and Parmelee, *Siege of Quebec,* IV, 249-50; Gordon Donaldson, *Battle for a Continent: Quebec 1759* (Toronto 1973), 138-40; Stanley, *New France,* 226-7, and Chapais, *Montcalm,* 610-11.

47. Pierre Cassagniau de St Félix, cited in Knox, *Historical Journal,* II, 6

48. Armand Joannès (Hermann Johannes), "Mémoire sur la campagne de 1759 depuis le mois de mai jusqu'en septembre," Doughty and Parmelee, *Siege of Quebec,* IV, 226, and Marcel, "Journal abrégé de la campagne de 1759 en Canada," ibid., V, 296

49. Doughty and Parmelee, *Siege of Quebec,* III, 160; Foligné, "Journal de Foligné," ibid., IV, 205; and La Pause, "Mémoire et observations sur mon voyage en Canada," 97. For scholarly accounts of the battle see Stacey, *Quebec, 1759,* 145-8; Donaldson, *Battle for a Continent,* 175-83; William J. Eccles, "The Battle of Quebec: A Reappraisal," *Proceedings of the Third Annual Meeting of the French Colonial Historical Society* (1977), 70-81. Also, Stanley, *New France,* 299-32; Doughty and Parmelee, *Siege of Quebec,* III, 131-72; and Philippe-Baby Casgrain, *Les Batailles des Plaines d'Abraham et de Sainte-Foye* (Quebec 1908), 1-68

50. Quimby, *The Background of Napoleonic Warfare,* 86. The Ordinance of 1755 was influenced by both Folard and Saxe.

51. H.-R. Casgrain, *Montcalm et Lévis,* II, 249; Lévis, *Journal,* I, 209; and Marcel, "Journal abrégé de la campagne de 1759 en Canada," Doughty and Parmelee, *Siege of Quebec,* V, 296

52. Joannès, "Mémoire sur la campagne de 1759," 226, and Marcel, "Journal abrégé de la campagne de 1759 en Canada," 296

53. Joannès, "Mémoire sur la campagne de 1759," 226, and Anne-Joseph-Hippolyte de Maurès de Malartic, Comte de Malartic, *Journal des campagnes au Canada de 1755 à 1760 par le comte de Maurès de Malartic,* ed. Gabriel de Maurès de Malartic and Paul Gaffarel (Paris 1890), 285

54. Pouchot, *Memoir,* I, 217; Malartic, *Journal,* 285; Joannès, "Mémoire sur la campagne de 1759," 226; and Marcel, "Journal abrégé de la campagne de 1759 en Canada," 296

55. Stacey, *Quebec, 1759,* 152; P.-B. Casgrain, *Plaines d'Abraham et Sainte-Foye,* 53-6; Donaldson, *Battle for a Continent,* 187-9; Stanley, *New France,* 232; Chapais, *Montcalm,* 662; and Doughty and Parmelee, *Siege of Quebec,* III, 151, 171-2

56. Doughty and Parmelee, *Siege of Quebec,* III, 164, 172

57. Pouchot, *Memoir,* I, 217

58. Lévis, *Journal,* I, 51

59. Ibid.

60. Colin, *L'Infanterie au* IXVIII*ᵉ siècle,* 75-80, 106-13, 126; Quimby, *The Background of Napoleonic Warfare,* 92, 98-9; Fuller, *British Light Infantry,* 69-70, 118-23; and Eugène Carrias, *La Pensée militaire française* (Paris 1960), 170

61. Lévis, "Instructions concernant l'ordre dans lequel les milices attachées à chaque bataillon seront formées pour camper et servir pendant la campagne," *Journal,* I, 248

62. Ibid., 250. The divisions Lévis mentions here include two companies, each about thirty men strong.

63. Ibid., 250-1

64. Ibid., 251. See also Lévis, "Instruction concernant les dispositions et ordre de bataille qui doivent suivre toutes les troupes," and "Instructions concernant l'ordre dans lequel les milices attachées à chaque bataillon seront formées pour camper et servir pendant la campagne," ibid., 243-54, as well as Lee Kennett, *The French Armies in the Seven Years' War: A Study in Military Organization and Administration* (Durham, NC 1967), 29-30.

65. Strachan, *European Armies,* 23-5

66. Data derived from table in Lévis, *Journal,* I, 257. Lévis lists 6910 troops, including 2264 incorporated militia and militia officers (who were *habitants,* not professionals) 3610 regulars, and 266 regular officers. There was also a battalion of Montreal militia, 180 Canadian cavalry, and 270 Indians.

67. Ibid., 257

68. Ibid., 253, and La Pause, "Mémoire et observations sur mon voyage en Canada," 107

69. For scholarly accounts of the battle see Jean-Claude Lizotte, Jacques Gervais, and Carl Lavoie, "La Bataille de Sainte-Foy," *Mémoire: Magazine d'histoire et patrimoine,* nos 2-3 (1985): 4-21; P.-B. Casgrain, *Plaines d'Abraham et Sainte Foye,* 69-90; George M. Wrong, *The Fall of Canada: A Chapter in the History of the Seven Years' War* (Oxford 1914), 143-54; Stanley, *New France,* 244-8; Parkman, *Montcalm and Wolfe,* II, 348-51; and H.-R. Casgrain, *Montcalm et Lévis,* II, 350-6.

70. Malartic, *Journal,* 319

71. P.-B. Casgrain, *Plaines d'Abraham et Sainte-Foye,* 69, 87

72. H.-R. Casgrain, *Montcalm et Lévis,* II, 351, 355; Malartic, *Journal,* 319 note: and anonymous, "Narrative of the Expedition against Quebec, under the orders of Chevlier de Lévis, *Maréchal des Camps et Armées* of the King," NYCD, X, 1083. This last account is Canadian, and is attached to one of Vaudreuil's letters to Berryer, dated Montreal, 3 May 1760.

73. Lévis, *Journal,* I, 267; H.-R. Casgrain, *Montcalm et Lévis,* II, 355-6; Vaudreuil to Berryer, Montreal, 3 May 1760, NYCD, X, 1076; and Stanley, *New France,* 248

74. Stanley, *New France,* 247-8

75. Casgrain's casualty figures are not completely reliable, but they indicate that about 17 per cent of the French casualties were Canadian, or 150 men. Casgrain, *Montcalm et Lévis,* II, 356

76. Lévis, *Journal,* I, 267; Malartic, *Journal,* 319; and Fournerie de Vezon, "Evénements de la guerre en Canada depuis le 13 7bre 1759 jusqu'au 14 juillet 1760," RAPQ (1938-9), 6-7

CHAPTER

6 THE MEANING OF THE CONQUEST

No subject has generated more controversy, particularly among French-Canadian historians, than the impact of the Conquest on *la société canadienne*. In the modern, post-1945 era, that controversy centred on two conflicting interpretative approaches. One was the neo-nationalist Montreal school, heir to the Abbé Lionel Groulx tradition, composed of men such as Maurice Séguin, Guy Frégault, Michel Brunet and Cameron Nish. Proponents of the "decapitation thesis," this school viewed the Conquest as catastrophic, eliminating by 1800 the middle-class elites so vital to the economic and national development of the colony. A classic presentation of this perspective is Michel Brunet's "The British Conquest and the Decline of the French-Canadian Bourgeoisie," originally published in 1958.

Challenging this interpretation was the Laval "liberal" school of historians, consisting of individuals such as Jean Hamelin, Fernand Ouellet and Marcel Trudel. While agreeing that by 1800 Quebec lacked a dynamic bourgeoisie, these historians found the explanation not in the Conquest but in the flawed nature of the society of New France itself. What had never existed, they argued, could not be decapitated. Jean Hamelin's "What Middle Class?" taken from Dale Miquelon's *Society and Conquest*, is an equally classic articulation of the Laval school's point of view.

More recently, this debate has taken a somewhat different turn. Applying modified Marxist analyses to the issue, a younger generation of Québécois political scientists has concluded that the traditional historical interpretations, nationalist and liberal alike, have missed the mark. What was really important about the Conquest, argue men such as Gérald Bernier and Vinh Ta Van, was that it caused a "structural rupture" in the economy of New France. The sudden, rapid and external imposition of capitalism onto an essentially feudal society, they believe, was both cataclysmic and far-reaching in its consequences.

The essence of the Bernier-Ta Van argument is sketched in the excerpts presented here in translation from Claude Couture's "La Conquête de 1760 et le Problème de la Transition au Capitalisme." Couture himself is highly critical of this approach, on the grounds that it is a faulty theory premised on a mis-understanding of both British and Canadian history. Students should carefully weigh this critique against the evidence presented by the other authors.

Suggestions for Further Reading

Bernier, G., "Sur quelques effets de la rupture strucurelle engendrée par la Conquête au Québec: 1760-1854," *Revue d'histoire de l'amérique-française*, 35, no. 1 (juin 1981), 69-95.

Blain, Jean., "Economie et société en Nouvelle-France - L'Historiographie au tournant des années 1960: La réaction à Guy Frégault et à l'école de Montréal - La voie des sociologues," *Revue d'histoire de l'amérique-française*, 30, no. 3 (décembre 1979), 323-362.

Brunet, Michel, *French Canada and the Early Decades of British Rule*. Ottawa: Canadian Historical Association, 1971.

Igartua, J., "A Change in Climate: The Conquest and the Marchands of Montreal," CHA *Historical Papers* (1974), 115-135.

————, "Le comportement démographique des marchands de Montréal vers 1760," *Revue d'histoire de l'amérique-française*, 33, no. 3 (décembre 1979), 427-445.

————, "The Merchants of Montreal at the Conquest: Socio-Economic Profile," *Histoire Sociale / Social History*, VIII, no. 16 (November 1975), 275-293.

Ouellet, F., "Michel Brunet et le problème de la conquête," *Bulletin des Recherches historiques*, 62 (avril-mai-juin 1956), 92-101.

Sanfilippo, Matteo, "Du féodalisme au capitalisme? Essai d'interprétation des analyses marxistes de la Nouvelle-France," *Histoire Sociale / Social History*, XVIII, no. 35 (mai 1985), 85-98.

Séguin, M., "La conquête et la vie économique des Canadiens," *Action nationale*, XXVIII, no. 4 (1946-1947), 308-326.

Ta Van, Vinh, "La Nouvelle France et la Conquête: Passage du Féodalisme au Capitalisme," *Cahiers d'histoire de l'Université de Montréal*, II, no. 2 (printemps 1982), 3-25.

THE BRITISH CONQUEST AND THE DECLINE OF THE FRENCH-CANADIAN BOURGEOISIE

M. Brunet

For Marxist historians, the bourgeoisie is the ruling class that has been ar-ranging man's exploitation of man for its own benefit ever since the feudal world disappeared. This is a simplistic explanation of the complexities of mod-ern societies.

From Dale Miquelon, ed., *The Debate on the Bourgeoisie and Social Change in French Canada, 1700-1850* (Toronto: Copp Clark Publishing, 1977), 143-161. Reprinted by permission of Dale Miquelon.

Another historical school, which we may call idealist, has all but ignored the part played by this middle class in the western world's development in the past four centuries, and most particularly in the nineteenth. The work of these historians leaves us believing that modern nations and states emerged by chance, in spontaneous generation. Underestimating the importance of economics, these students have laid no stress on the close relations between those controlling a country's economy and those wielding its political power. They forget the constant, intentional influence of the bourgeois elite in all areas of social life.

The idealist and Marxist schools elicited an inevitable reaction. Some historians have attempted to produce a synthesis between these divergent views of contemporary history. Rejecting all determinism, economic or otherwise, the historians of the realist school have sought to give as precise a description as possible of how our modern society was assembled. Maintaining a strictly scientific approach, they have drawn on the development of economic science and sociology.

Their conclusion is unanimous. The capitalist bourgeoisie has been the ruling class in the modern West. From the medieval commune to the New York skyscraper, without forgetting Montreal's St. James Street, this dynamic class has dominated the Atlantic world. In the sixteenth and seventeenth centuries it waxed wealthy in trade and industry. It was the bourgeoisie that gave monarchs their jurists and top civil servants. A number of its sons won distinction in the Church, the magistracy, the sciences, arts and letters. It played an active part in all artistic and intellectual movements. In its circle, painters, musicians, poets and writers found patrons as well as a public; without these, they would have been unable to produce their masterworks. Under middle-class influence, political institutions were transformed. This was the class that founded the banks and organized the system of credit. It assumed the leadership of the industrial revolution when it placed science at the disposal of technology, built factories, canals and railways. The universities, libraries, museums and research laboratories received its financial support. To Atlantic societies the bourgeoisie gave leaders and orientation.

We can praise or criticize the role of this ruling class in our Western world. No one has the right to deny or downgrade it. Without this elite, no nineteenth-century society was able to develop naturally....

Michel Bibaud, F.-X. Garneau and J.-B.-A. Ferland, the first French-Canadian historians, noted that to a degree their fellow countrymen, unlike the other nations whose historical development had been unmarked by an irreparable split, did not have an elite of businessmen, statesmen, administrators, intellectuals and scientists; in a word, they lacked a bourgeoisie. Admittedly these historians would have had a great deal of difficulty defining the term "bourgeoisie." The absence of this class in French Canada accounts for the very special meaning long assigned to the word by our sociologists and historians, who have used it to identify doctors, notaries, lawyers, and even farmers. The members of these different professions, participating in the creation of wealth and in the country's economic and political leadership, may belong to the capitalist bourgeoisie, but do not in themselves constitute the bourgeoisie.

These historians and their successors, along with the foreigners who have studied the history of Canada since the English Conquest, are unanimous in emphasizing, for example, the leading part played in *Canadien* society after 1760 by the clergy. The Church role had not been as important in the days of New France, however, especially from the late seventeenth century onwards. The colony then had its secular leaders. Pressing their investigations no farther, historians, sociologists and observers have not told us why the conquered *Canadiens* had to rely almost exclusively on their priests for the leadership necessary to any human society. Leadership that was unfortunately improvised and inevitably incomplete. The Church had been forced into an unnatural expansion of its substitute role. What had happened to the secular leaders of *Canadien* society? ...

... It was not until 1899 that Judge Louis-François-Georges Baby issued a thorough study in which he proved with figures that no massive emigration of the ruling classes had occurred. Since that time it has been echoed with a sigh of relief that the Conquest did not deprive the *Canadiens* of their natural leaders.

A reassuring statement which has unfortunately led us to pass over the wretched post-Conquest fortunes of the *Canadien* bourgeoisie. Were the natural leaders of the *Canadien* people free to function in the fullest sense? Did not the Conquest reduce their numbers? Were they not relegated by it to a second-class role? These are the questions we must consider before claiming that the conquered *Canadiens* preserved the structures of their society....

The Business Bourgeoisie and the New Economic Order

In the *Canadien* elite it seems to have been the businessmen who nourished the greatest illusions. They went as far as to see an actual benefit in the Conquest. To comprehend this somewhat arresting reaction we must recall that the businessmen who stayed in the country were among the most impecunious. They did not belong to the group of big businessmen, monopolists and war profiteers. Most of them formed the second stratum of the *Canadien* capitalist middle class at the end of the French regime, the class of the small entrepreneurs of modest income and ambition. Their limited financial resources and their more or less mediocre personal talents had prevented them from reaching the first rank in the business world. Moreover, not being from the privileged camp, they had received no official protection. They were the noisiest spokesmen for the mass of malcontents. The Bigot administration, and the shocking coups of their more fortunate competitors who were associated with or protected by the intendant, had no severer critics than these men. Let us admit that they were not completely objective. They had long envied the good luck of the Cadets, Péans, and Varins. They rejoiced at their fall, hoping it would benefit them. This selfish hope indicated great naïvety.

Their sighs of relief when the conqueror announced that trade would be free may be imagined. This word "freedom" had a fascinating quality for them. One of them, a Monsieur Hervieux who was a militia captain and a merchant, displayed great enthusiasm. As early as September 25, 1761, when the country's fate had not yet been decided, he told a correspondent in France: "Cease this compassion for us, Monsieur; our fate is less unfortunate than before." He went on to explain that trade no longer depended on the will of a single man, that the farmers were no longer being forced to surrender their produce, and that inflation had stopped. Haldimand hastened to inform Amherst that the colony's middle class seemed to be highly satisfied. The citizens of Montreal—priests, nobles and bourgeois—showed no reticence as early as February of 1763 in recalling the abuses of a French colonial administration which, according to them, had reduced "the traders of the country" to the role of "silent onlookers of a trade that should be their own." From this petition, signed by fifty-two members of the "Trading Body," we may assume that its signatories had not shared in the lavish contracts of the Seven Years' War. The bourgeois of Quebec, in their docile acceptance of the "decrees of the Supreme Being" that made them "subjects of our new monarch," were confident that the latter would pour his grace and bounty on them. Had they not "experienced, as conquered subjects, in the most marked manner, the mildness, justice and moderation of his government"?

A memorandum from the new subjects, dated May 1, 1765, accused the French government of having held back the colony's development by refusing to use "tolerance [freedom]." The petitioners envied the "neighbouring colonies" that had been the beneficiaries of a policy inspired by "love of the general good." It was their hope that "this love will be showered on this province." Three traders from Quebec and Montreal, though disappointed in their initial hopes, were confident that England would aid the colony, and that it would prosper along with the mother country. Great Britain would become a new "Spain," and London "the centre of the trade and wealth of the universe." Their mouths were watering: "Our newly English hearts already experience the purest pleasure at the very thought of this great design.... We are bold to believe that we will be treated as beloved children. We choose to assure ourselves of this in advance."

The illusion persisted. Becoming members of a rich and powerful empire, the *Canadien* businessmen who stayed in the country believed they were bound to make alluring profits. With Bigot and his cronies gone, they imagined that the country's trade would thenceforth belong to them, and that the new colonial government, with their counsel, would keep a paternal eye on the furthering of their interests. They refused to realize that the Conquest had put them in an even more painfully inferior position than they had suffered in the last years of French rule. Great disappointments were in store for them.

The colony was not long in prospering, but the biggest profits did not go to the *Canadiens*. As early as the capitulation of Montreal, Amherst had invited the merchants of England and the American colonies to settle in the conquest. About a hundred responded to the appeal from 1760 to 1770. The newcomers did not intend to be last in line. After a struggle of more than seventy years New France had finally been taken. The rich commercial empire of the St. Lawrence Valley, the Great Lakes and the Mississippi would henceforth belong to the conquerors. They had not made their conquest to let the *Canadiens* exploit it....

A series of misfortunes befell them (the *Canadien* traders). The French government's bankruptcy partly ruined the businessmen of Canada. The bills of exchange on the public treasury and paper notes represented virtually all their liquid assets. They would recover only a small percentage. It is not known exactly how much they lost in that unhappy adventure....

Ill fortune continued to dog the merchants of Canada. A number of them had placed large orders in France during the war. These goods had not arrived. At the time trade resumed its normal course after the capitulation of Montreal, their warehouses were empty. They made desperate attempts to get the British authorities' permission to take delivery of the goods they had ordered before the end of hostilities in America. These commitments had frozen the little credit they had. With nothing to sell, they could not resume the business that war had interrupted. A truly alarming situation....

The colonial traders were generally unable to pay cash for the goods they did import. Their European suppliers had to extend generous terms. Moreover no trading activity of any significance can be imagined without the use of credit. By the Conquest, the former markets where they obtained credit as well as the merchandise they needed were closed to the *Canadien* businessmen. It took them some small time to realize what was happening, since for a while they kept trying to reopen trade relations with France. They were in a totally confused state. Weeks after the signing of the Treaty of Paris, François Baby was again attempting to place an order in France. His former supplier wrote him at some length to make him understand how hard it was to continue their business contact:

> I have received your favour of the 7th of this month [Baby was then in Europe]. I foresee numerous difficulties as to your proposed dispatch of a ship of 100 to 120 tons for Quebec. It is not feasible to find French ships to charter for that country since French ships would be impounded with their cargoes. I think you are not unaware that entry to Canada is prohibited for all the goods of French factories, as well as wines, brandy and other beverages. And if these are brought in at present it is by smuggling, unless they leave directly from England with their duties paid.

One by one, the French exporters took leave of their *Canadien* correspondents, who asked them to recommend them to London traders and transfer to London the meagre credits remaining to them in France. The Montreal merchant

Etienne Augé parted regretfully with one of his suppliers, and told him he would like "to be in a position to continue the French business." A letter from François Baby to Simon Jauge sums up the difficulties that had to be faced by every *Canadien* trader:

> I repeat the request I made to you last year, to have the goodness to send me news of you. You must realize that it is an absolute necessity for me to know the state of my accounts with you. I have reason to expect you to extend to me the benefit of the privileges of a British subject. For heaven's sake, Monsieur, send me through Messrs Guinaud and Hankey of London a general and detailed accounting of the funds I left with you as well as those I authorized you to withdraw from M. Havy [a La Rochelle merchant]. My family, involved with all this business, has been pressing me for two years to give them an accounting, and I am not in a position to do so, and in consequence am obliged to face many difficult moments.

Advised and recommended by their French correspondents, the *Canadien* merchants approached London businessmen: Joseph and Henry Guinaud, Daniel and Antoine Vialars, Ponthieu and Co., Isidore and Thomas Lynch, Robert Hankey. A number of them were Frenchmen who had settled in England. They appeared well disposed to their new customers. It did not take them long to discover, however, that these were nothing but very small fry in business, without contacts or credit, and with no influence in their own country. And the London merchants with whom the *Canadiens* corresponded were not among the most important in the City. These modest businessmen—those of London and those of the colony—were not substantial enough to compete with their English rivals. For example, Henry Guinaud, the London merchant to whom three *Canadien* dealers unfolded their ambitious future plans in 1765, declared bankruptcy four years later.

The *Canadien* bourgeois abandoned their earlier optimism. Some Montreal businessmen upbraided Daniel Vialars for taking too high a commission. The accused retorted that these Montrealers were moved by "rancour," and gave them to understand that he set very little store by continued relations with them. Etienne Augé appeared more or less discontented with his London suppliers. It must be noted that they had had the unfortunate idea of asking him for a payment. He thought he would do better to choose Daniel and Antoine Vialars as correspondents. Relations between the new partners rapidly soured. Augé went knocking at another door. Pierre Guy too approached Thomas Lynch. François Baby learned that one of his former Bordeaux contacts could not advance him the funds he needed to pay one of his creditors. Another refused to honour a bill of exchange drawn on him. The Quebec merchant deplored the general situation: "Business is moving very slowly in the country. Money is scarcer there than ever, and bad faith is everywhere." He complained of having received trade goods his customers did not want. He had a surplus in his warehouse and was afraid of not being able to unload it. He begged his suppliers to follow his instructions. M. de La Naudière was dissatisfied with "the Sieur Vialars" who had not filled the order sent to him: "I am waiting to deal with him as he deserves on my arrival in London." Saint-Georges Dupré, a Montreal trader, made no secret of his disappointment on receiving the account for the sale of his furs in London: "I have received your letter, my good friend, with the accounting of the balance of my furs, which you may have found, as I did, sold extremely badly, with a set of charges that swallow a good third of the miserable sale." François Baby came to believe that a certain Mr. Robinson, a fur broker on the London market, favoured a few privileged vendors to the detriment of the others. His London correspondent tried to prove to him that his accusation was unfounded. When a businessman does not succeed while his competitors are prospering, he easily believes himself the victim of a conspiracy.

The *Canadien* merchants saw their profits fall. Several became unable to meet their obligations. A Montreal merchant given the job of recovering the money owing to François Baby did not have an easy time of it. Certain traders became embittered towards their more favoured English rivals. The Montreal dealer Adhémar reported to François Baby: "They tell me that Duperron and St. Martin do nothing but curse the Londoners [English merchants] and are always at loggerheads with the notorious trader at their post." Hervieux, Pierre Guy, François Baby and Saint-Georges Dupré were deep in lamentation. In their view, economic conditions had never been so bad. Saint-Georges Dupré was in a black mood: "If God abandoned me I would soon put an end to this most unhappy life."

Was the colony going through a depression? Quite the reverse. From 1765 to 1771, the trade of Canada experienced years of plenty. The end of Pontiac's war lent new impetus to the fur trade. The American colonies' agitation against the Stamp Act and the Townshend duties benefited the traders of Canada, especially those of Montreal. The American patriots' boycott of English goods had the result of increasing British exports to Canada. Montreal replaced Albany as the storage and distribution centre for English products sold in the north of the continent. From Montreal, this merchandise took the trail of the trading posts and even headed for the American colonies. The boycott called by the "Sons of Liberty" was not always effective. Most Americans had not given up the products of England. Farm prices held at an excellent level. As early as 1771, Quebec exports of food began to rise. Even the price of furs was going up; Saint-Georges Dupré, who would contemplate suicide in October of 1771, had informed his cousin of this that same summer.

The *Canadien* businessmen had shown themselves incapable of holding their own against their English competitors. The Conquest had forced them to compete with unequal weapons. This fact dominates the whole of the economic history of French Canada after the Conquest. While La Naudière, François Baby, Pierre Guy, Etienne Augé, Saint-Georges Dupré and their colleagues fought desperately to obtain credit and merchandise, the newcomers had no difficulty tapping the English market. The importers and exporters from England and the American colonies were quite naturally more inclined to do business with their fellow countrymen than with impecunious foreigners, yesterday's enemies and the vanquished of today. In business, only the rich can borrow. The *Canadiens* had to locate new suppliers. These were not always reliable in filling orders placed with them. Often they simply could not do so. The *Canadien* merchants were forced to change their business patterns, to learn new methods, familiarize themselves with English products. The time of groping and uncertainty lasted a number of years.

The financial losses they had suffered had in addition made them extremely timid. When a businessman's capital is limited, the slightest risk makes him afraid. Little by little, the *Canadien* merchants chose to buy from their English competitors in Montreal and Quebec. A number of their own customers had been going to the English stores for a long time. The traders decided it was wiser to sell their furs on the local market. The profits might have been more modest, but they seemed less risky. A great number looked for safe, gilt-edged investments. They dared not expose their meagre economies to losses in profitable but chancy speculation. Moreover they knew that the most lucrative speculation was not for them. Saint-Georges Dupré would be happy to invest his money at five or even at four per cent. He advised Baby to do the same. The *Canadien* businessmen had had to give up the great export-import trade, the only significant road to wealth in that period. They left the large profits to others, and sought refuge in an honest mediocrity.

Obliged to abandon external commerce to the English merchants, the *Canadiens* also lost control of the fur trade. The two formed a whole. The fur trade was still the great wealth of the colony. It would be so until the end of the eighteenth century and into the first years of the nineteenth, when great Anglo-Canadian fortunes would be built in the timber business. On their arrival, the conquerors showed their interest in the fur trade. For a long time they had been bent on seizing the monopoly from New France. At last they could fulfil their ambitions, satisfy their desires! They were not found wanting. As early as 1762, Malcolm Fraser obtained the monopoly for the Murray Bay posts. In the same year, the officer commanding at Michilimackinac gave Alexander Henry the exclusive fur-trading privilege west of Lake Superior. Also in 1762, Dunn was granted the King's posts of the Saguenay, and Grant acquired the tract that had been Vaudreuil's.

The sequel is really not hard to understand. The fur trade called for large money commitments. The canoes sent to the interior had to be fitted out, the men paddling them paid. Almost totally cut off from credit, the *Canadien* dealers were gradually ousted from the trade. They had to accept the limited role of small traders, providing they were allowed even this by a not over-brutal competition. As for the *Canadien* boatmen and voyageurs whose frugality, obedience and working spirit were so admired by the English explorers and businessmen, their brawn belonged to those with the cash to pay. In 1767, the first year in which the trade was totally open, 121 canoes left Michilimackinac between July 7 and September 12. They carried goods to the value of £39,000 Sterling. Of 80 traders, 70 were *Canadien;* yet the list of businessmen who gave their guarantees of the good conduct of traders and hired men contained only 23 French names in a total of 40....

The careers of La Naudière, Saint-Georges Dupré and François Baby deserve a close look. These *Canadien* dealers and traders managed to maintain a higher standard of living than the farming folk by becoming civil servants of the conqueror. In his letter of July 24, 1773, La Naudière told his cousin that his father had given him the seigneurie of Ste. Anne de la Pérade as part of his inheritance. He was proposing to develop it. There was beginning to be talk of a return to the land. Agriculture offered itself as a refuge for *Canadiens* cut out of their country's trade. Numerous former dealers and merchants became farmers out of necessity; not by vocation. Those searching their family trees have often noted this phenomenon: in the eighteenth century several members of their family were in trade; in the nineteenth, the vast majority were on the farm. Do not suppose that they had freely chosen that existence. It had been imposed on them by the Conquest.

During the Revolution in the neighbouring colonies, the young La Naudière competed in loyalism. His business affairs continued in jeopardy. He attempted to obtain compensation from the British government by invoking losses supposedly suffered during the American invasion. He asked to be appointed a councillor. Not to be discouraged, he laid siege to his official protectors. Carleton's return brought him luck: he became a surveyor and a member of the Council. These two sinecures yielded £600. Saint-Georges Dupré, whose qualities as a businessman La Naudière had already praised, passed a succession of lean years after the Conquest. Until the day when he was made commissioner of militia and put in charge of organizing the forced labour for military transport. His obedience and loyalty to the conquerors had reaped dividends. He had made a good investment. François Baby, a member of the two Councils, surveyor and adjutant-general, was also to bask in Carleton's and Haldimand's bounty.

These *Canadien* bourgeois had managed to find their niche. They were part of the very small minority, the favourites of the regime. But all the rest? To imagine their painful condition, we have only to scan the hundreds of petitions and appeals in the archives! Conquered in the economy because their native land had been defeated on the field of battle and then occupied by the victors, cut off from the vital influence of their motherland, most *Canadien* businessmen had sunk into wretchedness or mediocrity. A scant few stayed afloat, veritable islets exposed to the all-powerful influence of their English competitors, who were the unchallengeable masters of the colony's economic life.

The forming of the North-West Company indicates how modest the *Canadien* share of the country's business was. In 1780, two of the 16 company shares belonged to French-speaking entrepreneurs in partnership, Wadin et Cie. Jean-Etienne Wadin was even a Swiss merchant who had settled in Canada after the Conquest. His associate was called Venant St. Germain. In 1783, Nicolas Montour was the only *Canadien* shareholder, with two shares only. Wadin had died in the previous year, and Venant St. Germain was vegetating as an ordinary company agent. The Gregory, McLeod Company that gave hard competition to the North-West Company from 1783 to 1787 had not a single French-speaking shareholder. French names are found only among the minor employees.

The businessmen of English origin did not restrict themselves to the furs and external trade. They invaded every area. Stephen Moore and Hugh Finlay, who was destined to play an important part in the colony's economic and political life, asked the government for grants of land in the Lower Town of Quebec. John Collins, Benjamin Price and Thomas Dunn made a request for land at the water's edge in Quebec, with the purpose of building wharves. Some competitors had the same plan. John Gray and William Grant too needed land in the Lower Town. A company was formed to obtain the leases on the King's Posts. No point in adding that it included no *Canadiens*. A certain John Marteilhe was interested in the St. Maurice Forges, and disclosed his ambitions to the Board of Trade. Murray seems to have preferred Simon Mackenzie. In 1767 Carleton would rent the Forges to a company of nine shareholders for a period of 16 years. Among these shareholders were three with French names.

The grain and flour trades brought rich profits for the colony's exporters from 1771 to 1775. In 1770, Canada had exported 51,822 bushels of wheat. Exports rose to 460,818 bushels in 1774. In 1776, they returned to normal. Scarcity of wheat had forced the British Parliament to lower duties on imports in 1773. The price of the product doubled on the Quebec market. The farm people profited from this unexpected manna. It helped create a feeling of satisfaction in the mass of the population that served the English propagandists admirably well. Events seemed to vindicate those who claimed that the conqueror had brought prosperity. His business sense and concern for the general good were supposed to be its causes! Freed from a mother country and colonial administrators who had exploited it, the colony could finally develop!

This myth arose during the first fifteen years that followed the Conquest. On a pastoral visit, Bishop Briand had noted the happiness of his flock: "Everything here [in Montreal] seems very quiet to me, and since leaving Quebec I do not recall having heard a single expression of discontent with the government. The people and in general everyone strike me as being as satisfied as if they had never known any other." Henry Caldwell assured Lord Shelburne of the same. The bishop would recall these prosperous years when, during the American invasion, he criticized the *Canadiens* and especially the farming people for their lack of loyalty: "No one at the time of the revolt was feeling the misfortunes of the late war; whatever confusion it may at first have produced in our affairs, was not only repaired, but in fact you had much increased your fortunes, and your possessions had grown considerably more lucrative and rich."

The farmers had sold their wheat well. They were all pleased about that. A few woollen socks contained a few extra coins. However, who had skimmed off the biggest profits? The wheat producers? We must doubt that. Would it not rather be the merchants and exporters? These were not *Canadien*. A certain Jacob Jordan, a Montreal businessman who was closely involved in a number of profitable transactions during the American Revolution, made a fortune as a wheat and flour broker. He had had the necessary capital and contacts to take advantage of the windfall. The *Canadien* merchants had been satisfied to follow his successful operations admiringly. Jordan was not the only English merchant to specialize in the export of agricultural products. It must be recalled that external trade had passed into the newcomers' hands. They also controlled the timber and fishing industries....

The *Canadien* Bourgeoisie and the New Political Order

The *Canadien* nobility made up an important part of the colonial bourgeoisie, as we have previously defined this class. Its fate was no more enviable than that of the *Canadien* businessmen. Will we ever be able to assess the humiliation heaped on these representatives and witnesses of a past that had been brutally ended by the Conquest? The majority of the nobles were not rich. The few noble families who possessed fortunes had won them in trade. Their future was the same as for the other *Canadien* merchants. Another career was open to the colonial nobles: the King's service. This ruling class, even among those holding seigneuries, could not exist independently of the political power. Unless they accepted a lower standard of living. For these servants of the Crown, the Conquest appeared as a true catastrophe. They fell less easily into the illusions cherished by the *Canadien* merchants from 1761 to 1765. Haldimand saw clearly: "The nobility of this country, that class of persons who lived here at the King's expense, cannot imagine that France wishes to cede Canada."

The conqueror was not anxious to keep these unemployed blades in the country. Murray and Haldimand ardently wished for the departure of the "Crosses of St. Louis." These leaders, decorated for their bravery and their services by the King of France, recalled a glorious past that the vanquished had to learn to forget. Their exit would simplify the occupation of the conquered colony.

Worried about their landholdings and anxious not to compromise themselves before the colony's fate was definitely decided, most *Canadien* nobles maintained
a prudent silence at the beginning of the Conquest. This is why the clergy,
knowing they would stay in the country at all events, acted as the chief and
almost the sole spokesmen for the conquered population from 1760 to 1763. A
number of nobles went to France. Those who found jobs and pensions settled
there. A few, disappointed at their reception by the French authorities, decided
to return to Canada, where in any case most noblemen had stayed. M. de
Lotbinière had warned one of his *Canadien* correspondents that the French
King's court "would get over seeing all of us in Canada."

The story of Gaspard-Joseph Chaussegros de Lery (1721-1797) is a good illustration of the wretched fate of the *Canadien* nobility in the wake of the
Conquest. A military engineer and a knight of St. Louis, De Lery went to France
in the spring of 1762. He was forgotten in the ante-rooms of Versailles and
Paris. "Fearing to find myself and my family in the most critical situation," he
took steps to return to Canada. This nobleman, with no job and no resources, felt
no conscience at switching his allegiance: "Since the distinguished services I
had rendered the King [of France] in Canada, and those of my ancestors, could
not secure the welfare of my family ... I became a subject of His Britannic
Majesty." These career officers of the eighteenth century sincerely believed
they could continue to serve the *Canadien* nation under the orders of a foreign
monarch.

Our distinguished beggar knocked at the door of England's embassy in
Paris: "A few days later, Mr. Neville replied on behalf of His Excellency the
Duke of Bedford that he had received favourable reports of my character, and
that if I wished to be an English subject, as the first *Canadien* gentleman who
would return to the colony, I could be assured that I would also be the first recipient of His Majesty's favour. From that time I regarded myself as an English
subject."

Thus, De Lery returned to Canada. There began a long career filled with
carefully veiled humiliations. Murray's reception was apparently more or less
chilly. The governor was suspicious, seeing the French army officers remaining
in the colony as so many spies. He particularly criticized De Lery for having
left two of his children in France. His Britannic Majesty's new subject waited for
Murray's departure to appeal for justice. Carleton appeared more sympathetic,
and got his protégé a pension. In 1775, on the governor's suggestion, the imperial
authorities appointed him a member of the Council. Henry Caldwell accused him
of winning Carleton's favours by "his slavish adulation." To allay the British government's suspicions, he tried to bring his two sons back from Paris where they
were living. However, his French friends and relations persuaded him not to
oblige François-Joseph, the elder, to leave the mother country and a predicted
brilliant military career. In fact, he became a baron of the Empire, commander-

in-chief of engineers in the Napoleonic army, and a viscount under the Restoration. His name is engraved on the Arc de Triomphe.

Louis-René, the younger son, reached Quebec in 1770. His father sent him to study in the Quebec Seminary. In 1774, he vainly sought a lieutenancy in the English artillery for his heir. Eight years later, the young man was still looking for a job. Haldimand told his persistent father that he would give his son a place as soon as he could. In the meantime, he advised him to learn English. The young De Lery, ambitious and full of good will, did study the language of the conqueror. His father again tried with Haldimand, who promised nothing. Hearing that a place had become vacant and been given to another aspirant, De Lery could not hide his dissatisfaction. He asked the governor to let his son go to France where he could enter military service. Haldimand defended himself with the assertion that before he could interest himself in young De Lery's fate, he had to think of the candidates who had served the King of England faithfully in other colonies and came to Canada for the reward for their loyal services. Louis-René went into French exile and served in the royal bodyguard. When the Revolution began he was in Germany with the army of the Princes. Returning to the country in 1794, he would wait until 1798 before being admitted to the English army as captain of the second battalion of the Royal Canadian Volunteers. His patience had been rewarded! As for the father, he died before being able to find his son a job in Canada.

There was not much future in the conquered colony for ambitious young *Canadiens*. If a member of the Council and a favourite of the regime could not find places for his children, what could the other fathers do? Let us recall that Gaspard-Joseph Chaussegros de Lery had seven children to look after. Most of them had to go into exile to carve themselves a future....

The Conquest had sentenced the *Canadiens* of the nobility and those who had held important positions in the administration to be the thurifers of a regime that would use them for its own purposes. Carleton had foreseen that these hungry nobles would be useful: "Moreover if it pleases His Majesty to grant his petition [the Chevalier de Lery's], it would prove to the gentlemen of Canada that they will not forever be excluded from the service of their present sovereign. I have tried to uproot this opinion, for I am entirely persuaded that it is advantageous for British interests on this continent to employ the Canadians." Lord Shelburne approved the clever policy suggested by the governor: "Your observations ... quite show the appropriateness and the necessity of having these brave and faithful people take a reasonable part in the institutions that are to be the basis of the government of Quebec."

For example, Carleton proposed [in 1767] creating a *Canadien* regiment to employ young noblemen wanting to take up a military career. A number of them were then trying to reach France and serve in the army. The conqueror had made it known that he did not need their services. Seven years later there was still talk of this project. A number of people believed it would soon come to pass. During the American Revolutionary War, a few *Canadien* noblemen received commissions as militia officers. However, the regiment Carleton had suggested in 1767 was not raised. The *Canadien* nobles wanted to be in the regular army rather than serve in the militia. The plan for raising a *Canadien* regiment was still current in 1787. Finally, in 1796, the Royal Canadien Regiment saw the light of day!

During a third of a century, the *Canadien* nobility had had the time to lose its military traditions. It was not hard to claim that it was impossible to find young *Canadiens* worthy of the Royal Canadian Regiment. Louis-René de Lery's appointment as captain of the Royal Canadian in 1798 even drew protest from Chief Justice Osgoode. This *Canadien* officer, who had waited more than twenty years for his commission in the English army, certainly did not lack experience. However, Judge Osgoode was critical of his service in Louis XVI's army and that of the Princes. A few other young *Canadiens* had the privilege of serving in the Royal Canadian Volunteers. Already, during the American Revolution, the son of Joseph Fleury D'Eschambault had obtained the favour of being the first *Canadien* to enter the English army. We know that these officers did not Canadianize the army of the colony.

Canadien participation in public affairs was limited, in Lord Shelburne's expression, to "a reasonable part." Moreover Carleton had been precise about the line of action to be taken. It was a question of not systematically excluding the *Canadiens* "from places of trust to which incomes are attached." Their national pride would thus be handled. It would be enough to grant three or four conspicuous *Canadiens* the honour of calling themselves councillors. There their functions would stop. In addition, the governor suggested the "conferring of three or four unimportant places in the civil administration." With these minimal dispensations, "we would at least manage to divide the *Canadiens*." The recommendations Carleton made in 1768 were to serve as a guide to all the governors. Parsimoniously, calculatedly, they dispensed their favour to the new subjects of His Majesty....

A few figures on the distribution of civil service jobs will illustrate the extremely modest *Canadien* presence in the political life of their country. In 1779, the customs and postal service had 13 civil servants of whom one was *Canadien*. In 1781, a list of 22 senior government employees includes only one *Canadien* name, that of surveyor Picotté de Bellestre. Of a total of 38 justices of the peace, we find only 16 *Canadiens*. In the Council there were but six *Canadiens* in a membership of 22. From 1764 to 1791, 48 individuals served as councillors, 33 English-speaking and 15 French-speaking. The average tenure of English councillors was ten years; for the *Canadiens* it was seven years. The list of civil officers in the province for the year 1784 runs to some 136 names. *Canadiens* occupied only 36 posts, or 26.4 per cent of the total, including the humblest ones.

In 1788, *Canadiens* took 22.7 per cent of the salaries and pensions paid by the government. It was impossible for the *Canadiens* to build up an administrative tradition. Moreover we must not forget that those securing the hotly-disputed jobs had merited them far more by their servility than by their competence. Excluded from the top echelons of business, the former *Canadien* ruling class had been excluded from political life as well....

Canadien Opinion

The unjust division of public employment made a stronger impression than the slow liquidation of the capitalist middle class. As early as 1764, *Canadiens* were demanding access to administrative posts. A 1770 petition, one of many calling for the reopening of the Jesuit College, proclaimed the desire to train *Canadien* children "to fill honourable posts in the country, some in the military forces of land and sea, others in the judiciary, in order to make themselves useful to the King, their country and the whole state, for we dare presume of the goodness of our most equitable sovereign that there will never be distinctions among his subjects other than those founded on merit." They were rising in indignation against the habit of distinguishing between "old" and "new" subjects. Evidently the vanquished of 1760 still nourished many illusions. It was before the Quebec Act.

After 1774, their first enthusiasm gone, the *Canadiens* saw that the situation was virtually unchanged. The extremely skilful politics of Carleton—that governor had literally charmed the spokesmen of *Canadien* opinion—forestalled any display of dissatisfaction. Moreover the *Canadien* leaders were feeling more or less sheepish. They had to excuse themselves for the want of loyalty among the mass of the people during the American invasion. France's entry into the war made the English authorities still more suspicious of the *Canadiens*. Their leaders did not dare compromise themselves, and impatiently awaited the issue of outside events to make their pronouncements. For his part, the suspicious Haldimand—it must be admitted that he was not entirely wrong in showing prudence—was carefully intent on the maintenance of order. He would not have tolerated the slightest gesture tending to criticism of the policy followed by the government. Once the war was over, the *Canadiens* had to accept the idea that they would remain under English domination. However they tried to rectify the injustices of which they felt they were the victims, and to improve their lot.

The citizens of Montreal grew angry in the summer of 1783. The governor had refused two French priests who had recently arrived in the town his permission to stay in the colony. Vainly had the Montrealers asked this favour, underlining the serious shortage of priests....

It was decided to send a delegation to London.... An address to the King was drawn up with a petition. The petition tried to prove the necessity of bringing some priests from France. The address claimed, on behalf of the *Canadiens*, "the precious participation in the favours, rights, privileges and prerogatives enjoyed in all the other parts of the globe by all Your Majesty's faithful subjects." This was the notorious Adhémar mission that drew criticism from a touchy Haldimand. He could not stop the departure of the delegates, but he had warned the minister against them. Their efforts had meagre results....

Replying in 1789 to those who criticized the *Canadiens* for lack of interest in their children's education, Bishop Hubert let it be clearly understood that this unfortunate indifference—alas, too real!—arose from the conqueror's policies: "One might add, as a cause for discouragement [in education], the preference given in public employment and responsibility to the old subjects and even to foreigners in this province over the *Canadiens*." The British administrators and the English who had settled in the colony would have been well advised indeed had they the decency not to over-emphasize the ignorance of the *Canadiens*. The latter had not been responsible for the closing of the Jesuit College. The Conquest had meant the end of the King of France's endowments for teaching communities and clergy. The *Canadiens* were too poor themselves to pay the costs of a better system of education. Moreover most *Canadien* parents saw less and less need to educate their children, since the careers of trade, industry, the army and navy and public administration were almost completely closed to them. No one studies to become unemployed. As for the mass of the farming folk—since agriculture had become the chief if not the sole outlet for the *Canadien* population, they could easily do without schools, and did not need colleges and universities. The Bishop of Quebec's reply could have been much more violent.

Indeed, there were some protests. Yet their timidity indicates an advanced condition of servility among the spokesmen of the conquered population....

The first meetings of the Quebec Parliament, elected in 1792, betray the full seriousness of the distress thirty years of foreign occupation had caused in *Canadien* society. The English bourgeoisie had called for the convocation of this first House of Assembly. Aware of their strength they counted, not without a certain naïvety, on making it their own. Parliamentary institutions, we must not forget, had been created by the capitalist entrepreneurial class.

A number of *Canadiens*, especially in business circles, had supported the demands of the British traders in Montreal and Quebec. Naturally, they trailed the more powerful people. However, there were *Canadiens* who had begun to realize that the establishment of representative institutions would not be against the interests of their fellow countrymen; they were the majority of the electorate. They had demanded a House of Assembly intending to serve the community. Their want of electoral experience, however, allowed the English, representing less than a tenth of the population, to elect a third of the House. The election convinced the English members that they could easily manage their *Canadien* colleagues, most of whom, they thought, did not understand how the British institutions worked. The election of the Speaker and the choice of the official language for debates and legislation serve as reminders that they might have overestimated their strength and skill.

But what weakness, hesitation, and confusion were seen among the defenders of the rights of the majority! These unfortunate leaders of a people without independent sources of social leadership were utterly shaken by the events that passed them by. The main speakers maintaining the rights of the French language did so excusing themselves. Rocheblave, Taschereau and Lotbinière all admitted that the day was not far off when only the conqueror's language would be official. They implored their English colleagues not to show cruelty by hastening this inevitable decline. They begged a reprieve for a tongue that was condemned to vanish. Philippe de Rocheblave was frank:

> Let us avoid anticipating in time and leaving to chance an event that unavailing effort could at the least defer, and which at the same time a liberal and public education will bring about without effort. If since the change of domination in this province it had kept the college it had under the former regime, and whose promptest reopening is required for the interest and the glory of the metropolitan country, what is proposed to us today [recognition of English as the sole official language] would be practicable already, and the circumstances would not oblige us to reject it as a danger.

The school as an anglicizing agency was the solution proposed by the leaders! The English language was already being taught to the young *Canadiens* of Montreal and Quebec. The choice of a good English teacher was a matter of concern for the leaders of the Collège de Montréal. On March 1, 1792, Bishop Hubert told the Montreal vicar-general, M. Brassier, with some satisfaction: "I have just established a free English school for the *Canadien* children. It will cost me 1800 livres for the year, not to mention the books I supply. It has 30 pupils and would have sixty or more if I had a second English master and enough to pay him." Setting up this English class meant a big financial sacrifice for the Bishop of Quebec, whose income was very modest. He had had to do it to stop the young *Canadiens* from attending a Protestant school.

Louis-René de Lery had learned English to get a post in the army. François Baby had advised his nephew, asking for a job, to study the English language. The young man attacked the work courageously, but confessed to his uncle that he was not making much progress since he did not have "the occasion to see the English." This confession from the young Baby explains why the complete assimilation of the *Canadiens* did not occur: even in the towns of Quebec and Montreal, they had very little contact with the English population. Moreover the latter were still not numerous enough in the colony. There was no total assimilation because there was no nucleus of assimilation. A few *Canadien* families with the means to do so sent their sons to study in England and the United States. Charles-Michel de Salaberry used English to correspond with his father. What are we to conclude of this general infatuation with the English language? When the majority learns the tongue of the minority it is because the latter is the ruling class.

WHAT MIDDLE CLASS?

J. Hamelin

A great deal is being said about the pre-Conquest French-Canadian bourgeoisie. Its origins are supposed to go back to the founding in 1645 of the Settlers Company (Compagnie des Habitants); the Conquest signalled its downfall. A part of this middle class then emigrated to France, while the rest, cut off from their economic roots in the fishery and the fur posts in the redrawing of the boundaries of New France, succumbed to strangulation. The destruction of the French-Canadian bourgeoisie in 1760 thus becomes the great historical fact dominating and governing the economic development of French Canada until Confederation.

The argument has its attractions, but how exactly does it match the reality? One may well ask, since the hypothesis was issued without benefit of thorough research. The case is then not closed; it remains open to discussion. All the more open, in fact, since perusal of the intendancy correspondence and our knowledge of the failure to develop the colony's natural resources, invite a challenge.

The essential fact on this subject that emerges from the intendants' correspondence is the poverty of merchants and traders as a group throughout the period of French rule.

The comments of the intendants and civil servants always ran in this vein. 1699: "The traders are not rich, and few are even comfortable." 1726: "Fortunes here are such that it takes little to upset them." 1732: "It would be desirable to have rich merchants in this country, were there even a few, for they would be in a position to trade and extend the posts, which now the modesty of their fortunes prevents their even attempting." 1748: "The smallness of private fortunes is the reason for these riches [of the mines] being buried."

The poll-tax roll of 1754 has been used to presume the existence of an "extremely wealthy" commercial class in the towns of Quebec and Montreal. Yet does not this assertion flow from a misinterpretation of the document in question? In fact the roll goes as follows:

---

* From Dale Miquelon, ed., *The Debate on the Bourgeoisie and Social Change in French Canada, 1700-1850* (Toronto: Copp Clark Publishing, 1977), 105-114. Reprinted by permission of Dale Miquelon and Les Presses de l'Université Laval.

TOWN OF MONTREAL

Four categories for the 600 heads of families: 60 *of the most* affluent merchants, £60; 100 less affluent merchants, £30; etc.

Would not this "of the most affluent" that is read in the sense of "extremely rich" actually mean "among ... "? For how are we to imagine that an extremely rich businessman would be taxed at only 60 pounds, when a so-called comfortable farmer was asked 40 pounds by the treasury, and when the Quebec priest whose parish income was estimated at 3000 pounds had to pay 200, and the governor himself 1200?

It is very possible that among these Canadian traders there were a few monied individuals such as the Sieur de Tonnancourt, or the Sieur Martel described by Franquet as being "a very rich man." But what proportion of the commercial class as a whole was represented by these big businessmen? What role did they play? If the answers are to be found in the notarial archives, the intendants' letters yield material that lets us identify some characteristics of the commercial class in various periods.

A first document, the list of the chief shareholders in the Colony Company and the Company of the North supplied in 1708 by Raudot, gives us a highly revealing picture of what is termed the Canadian bourgeoisie at the beginning of the eighteenth century. In this report, Raudot indicates the amount of each shareholder's interest in the companies, and adds a brief comment on his financial position.

If we accept Raudot's picture, the Canadian businessmen of 1708 were going through a time that could not have been more difficult. Of 74 worthies then living, only 24 "have some possessions," 15 "seem to have," 13 were encumbered by debt, and 18 were poor. If the intendant had been able to search their accounts, the numbers of poor and debtor merchants would undoubtedly have been higher. This fact is attested by the list of the deceased notables: 3 had left some possessions, 6 died poor, and 10 had had to present the account of their debts to St. Peter. Yet this roster contains some of the great names of the first period of colonization, such as that of the Sieur Aubert de La Chesnaye, the biggest businessman of the seventeenth century, who died owing 408,000 livres, and the Sieur Gobin, one of the most active members of the Company of the North, who also died a debtor. Note that the Montreal merchants, including the Sieurs De La Découverte, De La Framboise, De La Gorgondière, Pascaud, Perthuis and others, seem to be in a better position than those of Quebec. Could it be that the illegal trade with New England, bringing them shining gold louis, made it possible for them to survive more easily, or is this only a delusion that would be quickly dispelled with the liquidation of the bankrupt Colony Company?

This depression in which the business community of 1708 was floundering tells us a great deal. After 60 years of colonizing effort, New France had not yet seen the emergence of a vigorous, embryonic middle class. Would this not represent a defect, a significant weakness in the colony's socio-economic framework?

In these circumstances it would be surprising to see an upper middle class grow and spread in the country 40 years later. For a bourgeoisie does not sprout like a mushroom; it builds cells, accumulates strength, spreads and unfolds with succeeding years in a climate filled with commercial or industrial tradition, in an environment enriched by the descent of capital from father to son, the accumulation of capital through the development of viable enterprises.

Would it have been possible to make up for lost time in the brief span of peace bracketed by the Treaty of Utrecht and the War of the Austrian Succession? Though we do not have access to an analysis like that of 1708 for the years leading up to the Seven Years' War, we can attack the problem in another way. Every year, the intendant remitted a detailed accounting of the bills of exchange drawn during that year. Through these bills, then, we can get a general idea of what each businessman was doing, establish a certain hierarchy among them, and classify them according to whether they were French, Canadian, or Frenchmen settled in Canada. With this breakdown, we can make a few observations that will shed some strong light on the problem before us.

DISTRIBUTION OF BILLS OF EXCHANGE
(Limited to bills of individuals adding up to a minimum 3,000 livres)

	Livres	*Percentage*
French and itinerants	962,274	47
Canadian and French who had settled prior to 1730	544,962	27
French who had settled after 1730	285,030	14

Although only approximate, this distribution of bills of exchange for the year 1746 gives us food for thought. For the 47 per cent that flowed directly into the coffers of the merchants of the mother country, or their agents, or foreigners shows that the higher reaches of business were eluding the traders living in the colony. If we are still in doubt, let the detailed breakdown of "imports and exports from the port of Quebec in 1739" convince us. It shows that the Canadians, including outsiders and recently settled merchants, controlled barely 25 per cent of the total tonnage of the colony's trade with the mother country, the Windward Islands and Ile Royale.

If the bulk of business was eluding the Canadian bourgeoisie, then, what economic base remained for them? Neither the fisheries nor mining exploitation nor shipbuilding had so developed that these industries could have served as an economic base for an upper bourgeoisie. Quite the reverse; what these industries awaited for their own development was specifically the emergence of a dynamic, rich, trading bourgeoisie in the colony. What certain writers are terming the "upper middle class" seems to boil down to a few individuals like the Charests, the Désauniers, the Hervieux, the Guillemins and the Voyers, who had managed to carve some success for themselves in the internal market, particularly as military suppliers.

Another factor not to be overlooked is the considerable role played by recently settled French. If Canada had experienced a flow of immigration from 1700 to 1745 that compared with that of the Talon era, this would be natural. But the proportion is surprising when we consider the scant effectives the mother country shipped over in this period. Would the ease with which the newcomers found places not amount to an admission of the powerlessness of the Canadian business community? Of 70 traders or merchants registered as such in the 1744 census of the town of Quebec, there are apparently about seven foreign merchants, 20 French merchants who had become resident in the period after 1728, 13 French who had been settled since before 1728, and 29 Canadians. Does this smooth French invasion of the internal market not presage the invasion of the English merchants in 1760?

The war that began in 1745 and Bigot's arrival, we are told, meant the rise of a new oligarchy. Forty millionaires appeared in the period 1745-60. Agreed. Let us note, however, that these accumulations of capital were not very solidly based. When the war ended, the manna would cease falling from the sky. Thus, these 40 millionaires were not produced by decade on decade of organization, were not the proof of economic structures laboured over by generations; they were the sprouts of Mars. They were the accidental products of activities that did not merge with the normal economic life of the colony.

The War of the Conquest gave us millionaires! Is this true? The fact that these millions were not represented by shining gold crowns but by scraps of paper is barely noted. It is fairly important to do so. When we have catalogued annually the approximately 130 million livres circulating in the colony in its final decade, and then added that "these sums, immense for the time, spread through the public and gave rise to large fortunes," we have not finished. We must specify that these millions, most of them, were simply bills of exchange, payment of which was brought forward from quarter to quarter by the treasurer of the navy.

These millionaires' chroniclers make the implicit assumption that the King would have paid up to the last penny once the war was over. Has it occurred to no one that even in victory we might have seen a Bigot arraignment? Mere supposition, of course. Yet we are on more solid ground in asserting that the King would not have redeemed this paper at its face value. The colony's history stands as our proof. After the War of the Spanish Succession, there was about 2 million circulating in cards and paper. In 1713, nonetheless, the King would agree to honour these cards at only half their face value. In 1747, with war in progress, the merchants turned in paper to a value of 2.6 million livres. The navy treasurer did not cash it; he deferred payment. Came the Seven Years'

War and this 1745-48 paper was still not redeemed. Yet it is believed that the King would have honoured the whole 100 million of 1760? The holders of this paper had their own doubts. A number of them only returned to France to realize as many gold crowns on it as they could. Had they been holding coin there would not have been the same homeward rush. They would undoubtedly have had no problem trading with the English; for though the latter understood little French, they responded to the music of hard cash.

From 1745 on, then, the war scattered manna on the land, but it was the manna of parting. Its value was so relative that we would be mistaken in giving the name of millionaire to the people who hoarded it. It would be an even more serious mistake to represent these monopolists as a social class based on solid economic foundations.

Nothing in our investigation, then, entitles us to speak of a French-Canadian bourgeoisie before 1760, and still less of an upper bourgeoisie, unless we are reducing the meaning of the word. The reasons for this economic and social weakness are undoubtedly complex. Any attempt to reduce them to a few simple factors would mean distorting the reality. The difficulties that bedevilled the French treasury in various periods, fires such as that in Montreal in 1724 which tumbled 30 or so businessmen, losses suffered in the wars, are all factors to be counted, but they are episodic factors. It seems to me that there are also some permanent factors which we must try to identify.

At the very root we find the absence of substantial immigrants. Here, believe me, is one of the principal causes. While English immigration flooding New England included bourgeois and merchants who brought in capital along with their commercial experience, French immigration was generally restricted to people in poorer circumstances. A 1699 report is clear on this point: "There is still not the money to meet the costs that all new enterprises need at the outset. This is because few persons in comfortable circumstances have come from Europe." Most people had to "carry on their trade at the expense of others." From the economic standpoint it is to be regretted that the mother country did not channel the Protestant exodus that followed the revocation of the Edict of Nantes in the direction of its North American colony, where these people could have turned their trading experience and knowledge of techniques to advantage, multiplying their capital.

On the other hand, did not the very patterns of trade in the colony impede the development of a bourgeoisie? Was the emigration of some of these businessmen in 1760, represented as a novel occurrence, not in fact a repetition of a periodic phenomenon or the expression of a continuously occurring phenomenon that became more marked under the influence of exceptional circumstances in 1760? The feuding of outsiders and residents attests to the fact that merchants came from the mother country to seek their fortunes and take them home. The problem had existed since the colony began. A 1696 memorandum refers to the outsiders "who have done well in their business and withdrawn." To check this disorder, a Superior Council decree prior to 1686 forbade the outsider to trade from June 15 to August 15, in months when the Indians came to trade in the colony.

But who were the outsiders (marchands forains)? They were people from the mother country who came to do business in the colony for a few years. They were either agents of a French company with one or more posts in the colony or else independent businessmen who came to try their chances, with the possibility of going home with their fortunes made. The first type of outsider was obviously the most dangerous in terms of competition, for he had a marked advantage over the resident traders. These outsiders representing or affiliated with large metropolitan concerns controlled the wholesale and retail trade: wholesale, since they supplied the resident merchants, and retail, since they sold their goods at virtually the same prices to the public as to the merchant. The latter, taking into account his profit of 33 per cent, could then not compete with the outsider in the domestic market. Thus, a large proportion of trading exchanges occurred directly between the population and the men from the mother country. In 1733, Hocquart wrote that "the outsiders have effectively taken in all trade to an even greater extent than in preceding years; their greed even carried them as far as to accept parts of one another's cargoes.... Their storehouses [those of the resident merchants] stand deserted, and they can do no advantageous business with these same outsiders as the latter do all the retail trade." Thus, this commercial pattern favoured the enrichment of the French to the detriment of the resident business community.

Regarding the independent outsiders, it would be interesting to be able to reach an approximate figure for the numbers who came, sorting out those who left and those who stayed. It would be immensely important to know exactly to what extent those who returned home had in fact built up their fortunes. The Sieur Pascaud, one of the big traders at the end of the seventeenth century, possessed a quarter of all the beaver shipped through La Rochelle, and went to settle there as a trader and banker. Was his a unique case? At the bottoms of petitions from traders and in the colony censuses we have encountered names of businessmen that we cannot identify using Tanguay. Could these be nicknames, or badly written, or could they be the names of outsiders who made only a brief appearance in the colony? The private archives may yet have surprises in store for us.

No less revealing would be a thorough investigation of the mentality of this trading class. Might not the headlong pursuit of profit and their immediate interests have caused them to neglect the securing of their permanent interests? In failing to understand that the general good of the colony coincided with their interests, did the businessmen not bring on their own losses? Here are some examples.

Direct exchange between the metropolitan French and the local population seems to have taken on a considerable importance after the Treaty of Utrecht. Why did the authorities not restrain this trade, harmful as it was to the resident businessmen? Part of the reason lies in past experience, in which the resident traders were seen to abuse their monopoly, either to buy the outsiders' goods at prices so low that they returned no more to supply the colony, or else to sell their products at usurious prices on the domestic market, forcing the Superior Council to regulate prices as it did for drink in 1684. A more flexible policy in the exercise of their monopoly would undoubtedly have earned them the protection of the authorities against the outsiders. The profits they would have made in the retail trade would have allowed them gradually to build up enough capital to make their purchases directly in France and thus slip the hold of the La Rochelle merchants.

The Colony Company affair of 1700 may be the most typical example of their blind greed. It was obvious at the time, given the closing of some outlets and the stock of unsold beaver lying in the warehouses of La Rochelle, that if the sales of beaver to the European markets were to be maintained, there would have to be a temporary reduction in the selling price, a limit set on the hunt, and quality inspection of the fur. The plan from Guigues, the metropolitan *fermier*, which provided for a long-term policy, was rejected by a conspiracy of the chief people involved, who would not sacrifice their immediate interests. They dragged the colony into an adventure that took it to the edge of collapse and brought about their own bankruptcy. In the documents, one can glimpse the cliquish wrangling, senseless plotting, cooked books, purchases and sales that were fictitious or usurious. As the King gave Vaudreuil and Beauharnois to understand, the basis of the company itself was imaginary:

> One of the company's greatest misfortunes arises from the high interests it is forced to pay and which are ruinous to it; and the source of this disorder is failure of payment of the funds representing each individual's interest in this business. *The funding of this company is really a figment of the imagination.* No one has put in a penny, and the individuals in it have but signed the agreement of association in the hope of sharing the profits at the end. After this, it is not astonishing that the loans and interest the company has to pay are ruining it.

Were these merchants of the years 1670-80 working in their own interests when they used their power in a time when coin was scarce to oblige the holders of their promissory notes to accept goods that were useless or damaged or overpriced? Or when they asked a usurious rate of the intendant when he needed funds to cover the soldiers' pay? When they might have become bankers to the colony, their selfish policy repelled the population and forced De Meulles to think up the playing-card money.

The megalomania accompanying their greed is another characteristic of these merchants' mentality. It was unleashed in the management of the St.

Maurice Forges, in the administration of the Colony Company, and in the renting of a Quebec house they pompously called "The Exchange," requesting a royal subsidy for its maintenance when, as Riverin claimed, any of their rooms would have been adequate for these meetings of six or eight merchants. With regard to this, we come back to Raudot's expression, "It pleases them." In reading of travellers' astonishment at the dress and luxurious repasts of these merchants we gain the impression that they had something in common with those tobacco and cotton planters in the neighbouring colonies who, over their heads in debt in the English mother country, still kept lavishing their incomes on a ruinous style of life.

No doubt these are the considerations that summoned the disenchanted lines from Hocquart:

> [There is no doubt that the colony] ... might become one of the richest countries in the world if there was as concerted an attempt to take advantage of its natural offerings and find the ways of developing it as there is to amass wealth while ruining it; there is no sight so common as a merchant who makes his fortune in Canada, but none so rare as one who is determined to build it up. The ever-dominant self-interest is stifling the general good of the colony; covetousness is in every act; all views are selfish. If an individual founds an enterprise, he presents it as being in the King's service, and with fine appearances conceals the motive that inspires him; beneath this mask, they often elude the clear-sightedness of those who might oppose their insatiable greed.... It can thus be said that Canada would flourish if its inhabitants ... displayed less eagerness to drain it than the King has generosity in supporting it.

The absence of a bourgeoisie that was rich, strong, and concerned with the common good, was expressed in the colony's development by a deficiency in economic growth. The Canadian merchants were incapable of filling the role that falls to any bourgeois group. Here is the great tragedy of the economic history of New France. Always swamped by the jobs to be done, the commercial class was unable to organize to exploit the colony's natural resources. Here are some passages that eloquently show their incapacity for the work that lay before them:

> (1679) There are so few people in this country in a position to have the iron mines worked, even though these are discovered and abundant in ore, that without aid from people in France there is no reason to hope anyone here will tackle them.
>
> (1682) It is very hard to succeed in this [trade with the islands], since there is no one here substantial enough to undertake it; it would yield abundantly, and give great relief to the people.
>
> (1706) The merchants are so sunk in debt and so poor that in the vessels coming to this country they have but a very small interest, and in others, none.... The merchant in this country cannot carry this trade on by himself.
>
> (1708) This enterprise [shipbuilding] would cost His Majesty too much, and there is no one in this country who could undertake it.

(1709) I encourage all the merchants to increase it [trade], and they lack only the strength to do so.

(1714) The traders of this country will always be poor so long as they take more from France than they return.

(1729) The inhabitants are so far from opulent that they cannot raise large enterprises [these are the inhabitants of the colony in general].

(1735) The greatest obstacle to this colony's trade arises from the poor circumstances of the traders, most of whom carry on their trade, financially dependent on others. The first setback makes it impossible for them to satisfy the French merchants who advance them money, and the charges or interest that they must pay afterwards is ruinous to them.

(1741) Since in fact most of the traders of Canada have not sufficient funds to gather large stocks of grain....

These comments on Canadian businessmen are open to question. They will have to be checked and verified in the private and notarial archives. Yet could it not be assumed here and now that the emigration of a number of traders in 1760 and the ruin of those who stayed in the colony—always given that there was ruin—is but one aspect of a problem that goes much deeper? In fact, supposing a bourgeoisie dominant in trade and owning viable industries to have been established in the colony, what would have happened? They would not have emigrated. Did the farmer who had his piece of land emigrate? Most of the emigrants were agents or associates of French concerns, outsiders on their way through, civil servants involved in their business affairs, and Canadians whose activities were ancillary to those of the French businessmen and the military.

The absence in 1800 of a vigorous French-Canadian bourgeoisie, then, emerges not as the result of the Conquest but as the culmination of the French regime. For the tragedy of French colonization in Canada was its failure to produce a French-Canadian bourgeoisie commanding the rational exploitation of the country's natural resources. The metropolitan trade, the great fisheries, the monopoly on the sale of beaver, were in the hands of the French; the shipbuilding yards and the St. Maurice ironworks were in those of the King.

THE CONQUEST OF 1760 AND THE PROBLEM OF THE TRANSITION TO CAPITALISM[1]

Claude Couture

After analyzing the historical writings on New France from 1900 to 1960, in articles that appeared in 1972 and 1974[2], the historian Jean Blain wrote: "The lively reaction that contains promises for the future comes from sociologists, political scientists and other representatives from the social sciences...."[3]

From *Revue d'histoire de l'Amérique française*, 39, no. 3, (hiver 1986) 369-389. Reprinted by permission of *Revue d'histoire*.

As far as political scientists are concerned, some authors have indeed taken on the duty to provide this "reaction," especially in the early 1980s. Thus, Gérald Bernier proposed a new interpretation of the conquest of 1760 to the readers of the *Revue d'histoire de l'Amérique française* and of the *Revue canadienne de science politique* in 1981. He proposed the idea of a "structural break" in the socio-economy of the former New France, caused by the arrival of a "more capitalistic" parent state.[4] In the spring of the following year, Ta Van, who had taken part in Gérald Bernier's early work on the subject, published an article on basically the same idea in the *Cahiers d'histoire* of the University of Montreal.[5] Then, in September 1982, Gérald Bernier, now writing with Daniel Salée, shocked the readers of the RHAF by proposing a revised view of the British bourgeoisie that settled in the Saint Lawrence valley after the conquest.[6]

In this article, Gérald Bernier and Daniel Salée intended to show that the British bourgeoisie in Canada between 1763 and 1846 was apparently capitalist but basically feudal, because it laboured at the level of reproducing the "trade sphere" (mercantile capitalism), rather than at the level of the "production sphere" (industrial capitalism). A year earlier, however, and as we shall see in greater detail, Gérald Bernier had written that, based on the intervention of a parent state that was "closer" to the industrial stage of capitalism, the institutions inherited from the French regime were taken over by a philosophy of capital accumulation that would cause the transition from feudalism to capitalism to accelerate. Now, since the British merchants who arrived after 1763 and purchased seigneuries were responsible for implanting this capitalist dynamic, exported to the former New France from the new parent state, it was deduced that these merchant-lords were basically capitalists, although feudal in appearance.

This "apparent" contradiction between the two articles is even more surprising since these arguments, which seemed so convincing at first, were meant to be more all-encompassing, more rigorous and better expressed theoretically than those found in other historical writings, whether written by nationalists or, on the contrary, linked to the ideas of Donald Creighton. Although little concerned at being one of Gérald Bernier's main targets, even Fernand Ouellet showed interest in this material when, in a recent report on historical writings, he wrote: "Gérald Bernier and Daniel Salée are on the way to finalizing another Marxist version that pays more attention to the national question of transformations in Quebec society during the century that followed the conquest."[7] But a closer look might show that these contributions contain defects even more serious than those described by Jean Blain concerning historical writing that is overly based on a "national history concept." Since Gérald Bernier and Ta Van mainly support the idea of a "structural break" brought about by the conquest and the appearance of a "more capitalist" parent state, our review will deal especially with this point.

To be more precise, we shall see that the authors sin from an ignorance, heavy with consequences, concerning the complexity of the industrial revolution in England. We shall also see that much writing in economic history long ago invalidated Marx's conclusions on the "disappearance of the yeomanry" in England after 1750, and the formation of a labour force that was "naked and free," phenomena that no one considers essential for the transition to industrial capitalism. Further, we shall see as a result that it is fanciful to try to find "universal" phenomena resulting from "laws of history" that control the passage from feudalism to capitalism in Lower Canada at the end of the eighteenth and during the first third of the nineteenth centuries, when these particular phenomena did not even occur in the "model" country, in this case, England. Finally, we shall see that apparently the economic disorder of 1820 to 1850 in England has been presumed to have occurred in the 1760s. As a result, the whole thing could easily be based on an anachronism.

First of all, however, what exactly does Gérald Bernier mean by the "structural break" brought about by the conquest?

The Structural Break Brought About by the Conquest, According to Gérald Bernier

"Liberal" historians and Marxist sociologists considered by Gérald Bernier to be "continuists" have written that the conquest brought no fundamental change to the socio-economy of the regions.[8] Gérald Bernier intends to show, on the contrary, that the events of 1759-1763 brought about a "structural break".[9]

This structural break would occur from the "brutal" imposition of structures reflecting "the most advanced capitalism of the period"[10] into a society dominated by feudal production methods. In general, these structural changes would have meant "inverting the dominant matrix of the process of linking the ways of production met with in New France"[11]. In other words, feudalism predominated in the linkage of the two modes of production in New France. After 1760, the capitalist mode of production (CMP) predominated, following the change in parent state and not based on the results of an internal development.

In effect, everything relies on the fact that France in the middle of the eighteenth century was feudal and less capitalist in its transition phase than was Great Britain.[12] Gérald Bernier attributes the British lead mainly to the phenomenon of land concentration in England, shown by the "enclosures" and the creation of a "naked and free" labour force resulting from the expropriation of the lower peasantry.[13] Thus, England exported its structural elements to the new colony after the conquest.[14]

> Then the transition phase from feudalism to capitalism began for the Canadian area and even followed the process of English capitalism, including expropriation and proletarisation of the peasantry and turning over the linkages in

production methods with the installation of the CMP and the dominant matrix.... During the two-thirds of a century following the conquest, the reinforcement of the feudal character of the seigneurial system is only apparent. Its meaning does not reflect feudal over-exploitation, but rather capitalist over-exploitation in order to bring together a base for the accumulation of capital and a naked and free labour force, more or less, in the long term.[15]

The effects of the new capitalist dynamic and the tendencies of increased accumulation would have occurred immediately. On the other hand, the formation of a labour force that was "naked and free" would have been gradual in the period 1760-1850. At the heart of this process, the role of the English merchants was obviously essential. Bernier states that these merchants would have quickly adapted the seigneuries that they purchased after the conquest to market needs, because "they were more used to the laws of capitalism."[16] The activities of these merchant-lords would be linked, however, to the mercantile phase (i.e., the circulation process) of capitalist production methods. These merchant-lords made a conscious effort to maintain the status quo, that is to say, the predominance of the circulation process (mercantile phase) over the production process (industrial phase). As a result, they would have contributed to the development of the industrial phase of capitalist production methods despite themselves, through accumulating capital and stimulating the formation of a free labour force.

The role of the new parent state was also contradictory. In effect, if this parent state were able to stimulate the capitalist dynamic in the early days after the conquest, it later enforced a series of limits for the colony that extended the mercantile phase. As far as the bourgeoisie of the parent state were concerned, "the colony exists first of all to the extent that it can fulfil its own needs, in this case, supply basic materials and products and find markets for its manufactured products."[17] As a result, the colonial aspect "tempered" the process of expulsion of the peasantry by the bourgeoisie, by holding industrialization back. This allowed for "the putting in place of mechanisms leading to the expulsion of the peasantry even before the capacity to absorb the surplus was developed."[18] French-Canadian emigration to the United States thus occurred and the first generation of proletarians from Quebec developed across the border. Only after 1846-1851, when England adopted free trade, did all the required conditions for the development of industrial capitalism occur in Canada.

According to Gérald Bernier, this new capitalist dynamic, increased accumulation, and the establishment of an available labour force resulting from the expropriation of the peasantry are the essential elements for the structural break brought about by the conquest and the overthrow of the "dominance model" in favour of capitalist production. These events are the obvious outcome of the "laws of history" that control the change from feudalism to capitalism or, when the change occurs, from the mercantile to the industrial stage.[19] This is also why the institutions inherited from the French regime remained "feudal"

only in appearance, since their basic function after the conquest was to prepare for the emergence of industrial stage capitalism caused by the activities of
an unaware British merchant bourgeoisie who, according to Gérald Bernier,
were acting in complete ignorance of the "laws of history."

The Industrial Revolution, England and the Transition to Capitalism

A — The "Disappearance" of the English "Yeomanry"

The claims of these authors are based essentially on the hypothesis that eighteenth-century England was "the first country to bring together the conditions
that encouraged the appearance of industrial-phase capitalism."[26] The most
important element, according to Gérald Bernier and Ta Van, was that "England
in 1760 made a concerted effort to expropriate the peasantry, the essential factor in developing a proletariat."[27]

This thesis is classic. It was defined by Karl Marx and then taken up by
many writers, especially by Paul Mantoux, and even appears in a recent work
by Michel Beaud.[28] In the English countryside, especially in the south, the
noble large landowners brought about the disappearance of the openfield system. Although a centuries-old activity, the enclosure of common land accelerated
throughout the eighteenth century. From 1730 to 1820, enclosure was even
ratified by more than 5000 "Acts of Enclosure."[29] As a result, 75 000 acres of
communal land were enclosed between 1727 and 1760, 478 000 between 1760
and 1792, and 1 000 000 between 1792 and 1815.[30] Some contemporaries were
extremely impressed by the economic and social outcomes of this movement,
especially in some counties. Based on their opinions, Marx saw that the concentration of lands and the disappearance of common lands would allow the
formation of rural over-population ready to flee to the newly forming manufacturing centres, where they would form an untrained labour force; in other
words, a proletariat. As a result, the squatters and cottagers who simply occupied the common lands in the past would disappear from the countryside and
flee to the cities. The same thing would occur with the small and medium-sized
independent landowners or yeomen, who would also have to abandon the English
countryside. By referring especially to a letter from 1795 from a gentleman of
Suffolk in the south-east of England to Sir T. C. Banbury, "a lawyer who was fa-
natical about the system of large farms," Marx was even able to write, concerning
this group, "Towards 1750, the yeomanry had disappeared."[31] But is this certain?

More than thirty years of research into English regional history lead fairly
clearly to the conclusion that, far from disappearing in 1750, yeomen became
gradually more numerous during the second half of the eighteenth century and
that the rural population in England increased until the middle of the nineteenth century.[35] How was that possible?

One must first take economic events in the eighteenth century into consideration. The years 1720 to 1760 saw a drop in agricultural prices, especially for wheat; profits fell for both large and small English producers, who were thus likely to continue the wave of farming innovations that had begun in the seventeenth century.[36] In contrast, from 1760 to 1815, agricultural prices rose because of the rapid growth of domestic markets, resulting from the unprecedented population increase in England, as well as other causes. While the population of England and Wales remained relatively stable between 1720 and 1760, it grew from about six million in 1760 to twelve million in 1811.[37] At first, the doubling of the population in a half-century was attributed to the drop in excess mortality, brought about regularly by epidemics and food crises. A better-nourished population, improved climate conditions and increased cleanliness, and a "natural immunization" that developed among the populace, after being devastated for several generations by plague and smallpox, would have broken the deadly cycle of the occurrence of excess mortality. Somewhat later, however, as a result of an expanding economy that brought about new job opportunities, the age of marriage dropped and thus the birth rate rose, beginning in 1780.

The agricultural and demographic revolutions are thus closely linked. The growth of the job market, which was a crucial factor in the drop in the marriage age, resulted in further agricultural developments that could not have occurred without the growth in the domestic market and the rise in agricultural prices after 1760.[38] English landowners rushed into intensive agriculture in order to profit from the increase in prices, especially for wheat. This resulted in more rapid crop rotation, the use of fodder crops, less land left fallow and increased sowing on common land.[39] The expansion of enclosure does not appear to indicate the definitive triumph of the aristocracy over the small peasantry, but rather the triumph of agricultural individualism — for both large and small landowners. According to Phyllis Deane, this is why there was an increase in the number of small farming landowners between 1780 and 1815 in England, as attested by all the studies in regional history.

> (...) regional research for period after 1780 suggests that enclosure by Acts of Parliament produced an increase in all grades of occupying owners. Under the Enclosure Acts, many common-right cottagers received compensation for their rights, which permitted them for the first time to buy small plots of land.[40]

When the situation changed after 1815, small landowners were unable to survive the drop in prices and disappeared gradually from the countryside.[41] But even so, rural flight did not occur before the second third of the nineteenth century, a situation that Marx was able to examine so clearly.[42]

There is no reason to think, however, that there was increased migration towards the cities from 1750 to 1800 among those who were pushed out by the enclosures, that is, cottagers who owned only their homes, squatters who were illegally occupying common lands, and tenants at will who had only a verbal agreement for occupying common lands. The massive shift to new farming technologies after 1760 and the process of enclosure as such brought about a gap between the number of jobs and the available work force in the English countryside. Even the spectacular population growth was insufficient, and there resulted a problem of relative scarcity of labourers throughout the second half of the eighteenth century, and even up to 1815. "The new agriculture was labour-intensive"[43] and extra "hands" were required for a wide variety of tasks: "creating and maintaining fences, hedges and ditches; tending more livestock; farming fallow land and new crops more intensively; fencing in forested areas, heaths and marshes." Finally, "agricultural development encourages small trades and cottage industries."[44] In the countryside, all these activities maintained a large population that did not cease to grow until the middle of the nineteenth century.[45]

To sum up, if enclosure converted a large number of former communal-land users into farm employees, it did not have any direct bearing on the development of an industrial labour force. In the first "modern" factories, the cotton-spinning mills at the end of the eighteenth and the beginning of the nineteenth centuries, workers were usually found on the spot among the surplus population and among the first Irish immigrants who were arriving.[46] The real transfer of labour to the cities began only with "the economic difficulties resulting from the drop in prices after 1815, becoming increasingly greater with the Poor Law of 1834…, the abolition of the Corn Laws in 1846"[47] and the ending of enclosure. Thus, many factors other than enclosure influenced this movement in the middle of the nineteenth century.

As we have seen, Gérald Bernier and Ta Van's work indicates the following. The conquest of 1760 brought about a "structural break" in the economy of the former New France because the new parent state was "more capitalist." In addition, if this parent state was more capitalist, this resulted from the "hurried settling of the peasant question" through the expropriation of the lower peasantry. This seizure is a basic element of the transition to the industrial phase of capitalism. The "structural break" occurred when England exported this "structural element" to the Saint Lawrence valley via the merchant-lords who, although unaware of doing so, put into effect the process of "weakening" feudalism in favour of capitalism by creating the conditions that would lead to the mass expropriation of French-Canadian peasants. This thesis raises the following basic question: how could the new British parent state, from 1760 on, "export" a socio-economic phenomenon that had not even arisen in the eighteenth century, let alone in the nineteenth? Further, should one be surprised to discover no serious trace of such a movement in Lower Canada late in the eighteenth and during the first half of the nineteenth centuries?

B — The Industrial Revolution in England

Gérald Bernier has written that it is possible to see "the beginnings of the industrial revolution in England at about the same time as the conquest occurred" and that "any colonial enterprise tends to adopt some of the structures found in the parent state."[48] As we have seen, the break would occur immediately after 1760, since the effect of the British parent state would be to develop and organize production based on capitalist methods, and the British merchant-lords would create the conditions, at least in part, for setting up the industrial phase. As for Ta Van, he insists upon the advanced steps taken by England because of the revolutions of 1642-1660 and 1688 that would establish as a ruling class "a financial (and merchant) capitalist group" responsible for "the economic future of England."[49]

What, however, was the true state of English industry in the middle of the eighteenth century? What was the state of the industrial revolution in that country at that period? In short, what could England "export" from 1760 to 1800 that would prove the idea of an immediate structural break? For more than half a century, there have been opposing arguments among economic historians concerning the industrial revolution in England. As a result, it would be impossible to resolve such a complex question in this article. Nevertheless, it is possible to pin down some essential points.

After the first half of the eighteenth century, which was not as brilliant as the first half of the previous century, it was necessary to wait for the period 1760 to 1820 for the combination of several factors that would make the industrial revolution possible. The combined effects of a growing population, the subsequent increase in the domestic market, the widening of the colonial market, the growth in the number of jobs resulting from new agricultural developments, and the application of new techniques in the developing manufacturing sector — all of which resulted from increased demand — brought about the emerging conditions for a basic economic transformation. At the same time, from 1760 to 1820, there was no fundamental change in the annual growth level for national income and capital formation, compared to the period 1700 to 1760.[55] As a result, it is important to distinguish the first phase of the industrial revolution, from 1760 to 1820, and the second phase, from 1820 to 1850, which was much more spectacular and saw higher and continuous rates of growth.

During the first phase, the cotton industry was the leading sector. Why this industry, rather than another? According to Peter Mathias,[56] at the beginning of the industrial revolution, an industry was required that was linked to a growing market, whose mechanization in one sector could occur without excessive expense, that could bring about the mechanization of other manufacturing steps and that, finally, could completely transform the production process. Encouraged by a large number of customers, especially in the colonies, who wanted light-weight fabrics, the cotton industry was the first to react to these conditions. Fernand Braudel wrote that "the cotton revolution is different from previous revolutions in one important way: it was a success. It did not fail when a period of economic stagnation occurred; it launched a long period of growth that became 'continuous'."[57] During the first stage of the industrial revolution, from 1760 to 1820, only the spinning operation was mechanized in the cotton industry. The great turning point occurred from 1820 to 1850, when irreversible changes developed that would pitch England into a highly industrialized world. During this thirty-year period, weaving became completely mechanized in the cotton industry. As far as the wool industry is concerned, after a long decline, it made up for its losses between 1820 and 1850. During this period, the number of mechanical looms grew from 3,000 to 33,000, thus bringing about the dramatic ruin of cottage workers, who were still quite powerful in the early years of the nineteenth century. Overall, in the second third of the nineteenth century, the increased systematic use of improvements to the steam engine, the development of mining and metallurgy and the spectacular arrival of railroads turned England into the "workshop of the world."[58]

Although absorbing the profits of more than one-third of world trade, England in the middle of the nineteenth century had not yet completely developed large industries. Thus in 1851, out of 1,000 wool fabric mills, 500 had fewer than 10 workers and 82 more than 100.[59] In that same year, out of the leading metal-working companies, two-thirds had fewer that 10 workers, 34 more than 100 and 14 more than 350; out of 1,800 factories producing cotton goods, only 113 had more than 350 workers.[60] In 1850, despite the accelerated transfer of labour from the countryside to the cities, "agricultural workers still make up the major labouring group in the country" and the number of salaried workers in large industry was estimated to be less than two million out of a population of twenty-one million.[61]

We can thus see that the early signs of the industrial revolution in England between 1760 and 1820, essential as they were, did not turn the country completely on its head. Under such conditions, how then could England export a new capitalist dynamic that would bring about a "break" in economic structures between 1760 and 1820, when the country itself did not reach the crucial phase that pushed it into the industrial age until after 1820 and up to 1850? Obviously, compared to its rival across the Channel, England did possess a certain economic edge at the end of the eighteenth century, even if it is difficult to define how important this was for the two countries.[62] In indicating, however, that England was boiling over with industrial growth between 1760 and 1780, when such growth occurred almost a half-century later, is to state an anachronism that contributes little to the understanding of the conquest. As with the peasant question, there is no proof that the events of 1760 brought about major change in the economic structure of the former New France. Several authors, however, who are otherwise rarely found to agree, such as Paquet and Wallot and Ouellet and Hamelin,[63] have claimed that mercantilism remained the economic base of the colony, isolated in the Saint Lawrence Valley after the conquest, with the fur trade as the principal basis for accumulating trading capital, until the beginning of the nineteenth century. How else could it be? There is nothing in the articles by Gérald Bernier and Ta Van to convince us otherwise.

In addition, it is odd how people can go on and on about the economic relations between England and the "Old Province of Quebec" at the turn of the eighteenth-nineteenth centuries without once mentioning the existence of the thirteen American colonies. If there were one event, however, that was likely to bring about radical change in the economy after the conquest, it was certainly the American War of Independence.

In the struggle that arose quite quickly after their arrival in Canada, between the "Montrealers" and the Bostonians, the first group strove to make the (Saint Lawrence) river the commercial heartland of North America at the expense of the Atlantic seaboard. The Todds, Frobishers, Henrys, Peter Pond, the Patersons, Grants, McTavishes, McGills and so on dreamt about just such a commercial empire.[75] The American Revolution should have produced a unique chance for keeping trading rivals from New England away. This did not occur. On the contrary; at the signing of the Treaty of Versailles (1783), the English negotiators agreed to a border that gave the Americans all the drainage basin to the south of the Great Lakes, an area that they had never seized militarily. In return, England received freedom of trade between the two countries that was greatly to her benefit. The geographic integrity of the fur trade based in Montreal was thus shattered. The Jay Treaty of 1794 confirmed the border agreement of 1783, thus smashing the hopes of the Montreal merchants. In this way Great Britain caused a great deal of damage to the economic interests of Canada, based on ideas that were certainly imperialist but not those described by Gérald Bernier and Ta Van.[76]

By guaranteeing trade links with the United States, British diplomats protected the most important foreign market for their country. In 1772, the United States absorbed 37% of the products manufactured and exported by England; in 1797, this had grown to 57%.[77] With 3 734 000 inhabitants in 1790, America was the principal customer for the English and the country remained so for quite some time, while also supplying necessary raw materials such as cotton. Thus, it is easy to understand why the claims of the "Montrealers" were not heard, neither in 1783, in 1794, nor in 1815. Similarly, a half-century later, when the Peel government adopted free trade, beginning in 1846, despite the strong opposition of part of the aristocracy, a true structural break occurred. Since problems in the colony carried little weight in relation to the greater economic interests of Great Britain, the descendants of the first generation of English-speaking Montreal merchants also found little success. What followed is well known: the annexation manifesto of 1849, reciprocity with the Americans in 1854, the American refusal to renew the reciprocity treaty and Confederation.

Conclusion

When referring to historical philosophers at the beginning of the twentieth century, René Rémond had this comment to make:

> Evil tongues would suggest that historical philosophers are quite free to construct their syntheses and to propose simple, synthetic interpretations concerning historical evolution, while being unencumbered by a knowledge of history when they are carrying out their speculations. They prefer wide horizons, shocking syntheses and startling summaries.[78]

Since they are suspicious about these "startling summaries," perhaps historians tend to go too far in the other direction. As Werner Sombart claimed, "If there is no theory, there is no history." We have seen, however, how revelations about the "laws of history" that reveal themselves in imaginary phenomena and anachronisms can throw us into darkness.

The problem of the transition from feudalism to capitalism, which is discussed in the articles that we have just studied, appears as a heavy-handed comparison that leaves little room for an understanding of complex economic, social and political dynamics. Whatever is not part of "feudalism" becomes an integral part of "true" capitalism, in other words, "large industry." Similarly, whatever is not part of industrial capitalism is "feudal," which these authors apparently interpret as a "great darkness," both politically and socially. In addition, according to this theory, the move from one method of production to another could be explained by the fact that, at some moment, the thrust of productive forces is so strong that it leads to an explosion of the social links of production and especially to the appearance of a new dominant class in better agreement with the new method of production. Between 1780 and 1850 in England, however, even though fundamental economic changes occurred, the aristocracy remained powerful until the end of the nineteenth century. How is it possible to take this England at the end of the nineteenth century into account theoretically? Is England between 1780 and 1850 truly "feudal" because it is still dominated by a class that draws its wealth from exploiting work on the land and because, despite the economic changes of the period, large industry is not yet the general norm? In addition, concerning that great bourgeois Montrealer John Richardson, one of the founders of the Bank of Montreal in 1817 and one of the promoters of the Lachine Canal in 1824, are his activities to be considered "feudal" because they don't arise from capitalism and large industry? Indeed, what has been described so strongly as a "transitory phase" could include various details that would escape notice by a theoretical approach based on a simplistic succession of methods of production.

It is necessary to notice as well the lack of precision right at the centre of the argument. Here we learn that the history of Canada from 1760 to 1850 involved a "double transition process": from feudalism to capitalism; and in this latter phase, from a "mercantile phase" to an "industrial phase." A bit later on, however, it is stated that mercantile capitalism always arises from feudalism and that "true" capitalism appears with large industry. Since it takes such a short period of time for "true" capitalism to appear, given that everything that comes before is defined as "feudal," what does the idea of "transition" truly mean?

In his detailed critique of Marx's theories on the agricultural revolution in England, Kins Collins writes: "Proof of the falsity of the theory is not based on Marx's having used false statements to construct it, but rather solely on the fact that after the theory was constructed, false statements were derived from it."[79] Clearly that is the greatest danger in contributions from some political writers.

In closing, if the conquest did not bring about an immediate break in economic structures, it still remains the event in which the national question is rooted. As a result, a theoretical model must be constructed in order to integrate such specificness with the interaction of various dimensions of a society. To sum up, if it is necessary to base questions on the whole, it is also necessary to avoid explanations overly based on a single factor, to be suspicious of the mechanical application of a teleologic vision of history and to take into account the works of historians.

Notes

1. Several people patiently read the earlier versions of this article. I especially wish to thank professors Pierre Tousignant, Louis Michel, Pierre Trépanier and Jacques Rouillard of the Department of History at the University of Montreal, Jean-Pierre Wallot, now a federal archivist, Yves Bourdon, a doctoral student in history at the University of Montreal, Alain Noël, a doctoral student in political science at the Graduate School of International Studies in Denver, and Dominique Jean, a doctoral student in history, at present studying at the University of Boston.

2. Jean Blain, "Economy and Society in New France: Historiographical Advances in the First Half of the Twentieth Century," *Revue d'histoire de l'Amérique française*, 26,1 (juin 1972): 3-33, and, "Economy and Society in New France: The Historiography of the Years 50-60," *RHAF*, 28,2 (septembre 1974): 163-176.

3. Jean Blain, *op. cit.*, (septembre 1974): 185-86.

4. Gérald Bernier, "Concerning Some Effects of the Structural Break Brought About by the Conquest in Quebec: 1760-1854," *RHAF*, 35,1 (juin 1981): 69-95; "Quebec Class Structure in the Nineteenth Century and the Problem of Linking Production Methods," *Revue canadienne de science politique*, 14,3 (septembre 1981): 487-518 (especially p. 494).

5. Ta Van, "New France and the Conquest: Moving from Feudalism to Capitalism," *Cahiers d'histoire*, 2,2 (printemps 1982): 3-25.

6. Gérald Bernier and Daniel Salée, "Financial Appropriation and the Merchant Bourgeoisie: Elements for an Analysis of the Trading Economy in Lower Canada Before 1846," *RHAF*, 36,2 (septembre 1982): 163-64.

7. Fernand Ouellet, "The Dominant Classes in Quebec, 1760-1840: An Historiographic Balance-Sheet," *RHAF*, 38,2 (automne 1984): 242

8. Gérald Bernier, "Concerning Some Effects of the Structural Break Brought About by the Conquest in Quebec: 1760-1854," *op. cit.*, 69, n. 1. The authors in question are Fernand Ouellet and Jean Hamelin on one side and Gilles Bourque, Anne Légaré and Nicole Frenette on the other.

9. *Ibid.*

10. *Ibid.*, 70.

11. *Ibid.*

12. *Ibid.*, 71, n. 4.

13. *Ibid.*

14. *Ibid.*

15. *Ibid.*, 76-77.

16. *Ibid.*, 82.

17. *Ibid.*, 89.

18. *Ibid.*, 94.

19. *Ibid.*, 89. Bernier has written: "In short, the direction taken by agriculture and forced by the merchant bourgeoisie bears the germs that would bring down this class, in that it brings about the development of capitalism in the industrial phase in the long or short term. Such was certainly not the wish of the merchant bourgeoisie... but such precisely was the result when the various conditions are studied in the light of the *laws of history* concerning the *stages* controlling the passage from feudalism to capitalism and, more precisely, inside the MPC itself, the passage from the mercantile phase to the industrial phase."

26. Gérald Bernier, "The Structural Break...," *op. cit.*,71, n. 4.

27. Gérald Bernier, "Quebec Class Structure..., *op. cit.*, 494, n. 4.

28. Paul Mantoux, *La révolution industrielle au 18e siècle*. Paris: Génin, 1959 (first edition 1928, corrected version of a thesis presented in 1906). Michel Beaud, *Histoire du capitalisme: 1500-1980*. Paris: Seuil, 1981, 37-43.

29. J.-P. Rioux, *La révolution industrielle*. Paris: Seuil, 1971, 31

30. Phyllis Deane, *The First Industrial Revolution*. Cambridge: Cambridge University Press,1965, 42; second edition, 1978.

31. Karl, Marx, *Le capital, Livre 1*. Paris: Flammarion, 1969 534 and 689, n. 11 of ch. 27.

35. Several authors have criticized these studies. E. P. Thompson wrote in *The Making of the English Working Class*, (Harmondsworth, Penguin Books, 1968), 238-39 "...the social violence of enclosure consisted precisely in the drastic, total imposition upon the village of capitalist property-definitions. ... Enclosure...was of profound social consequence, because it illuminates, both backwards and forwards, the destruction of the traditional elements in English peasant society." Barrington Moore in *Les origines sociales de la dictature et de la démocratie* (Paris: Maspero, 1969),

29, expressed the same point of view: "Historians of a century ago thought that enclosure in the eighteenth century had been the principal move by the all-powerful landed aristocracy to rid itself of an independent peasantry. Later, this opinion was slowly and patiently broken. Perhaps only a few Marxists would still defend it today. It errs in detail and, at times, in its overview. It had been realized, however, what has been forgotten today: the enclosures were a fatal blow to the structure of English peasant society as found in the traditional village." Admittedly, the traditional village and the people's culture based on the open field were destroyed by enclosure and traditional peasant society was rocked by "capitalist" methods. This, however, is not the important question in this discussion. Marx and several others after him have clearly written that the yeomanry had completely disappeared around 1750 and that the dispossessed peasantry had fled to the developing manufacturing towns of the second half of the eighteenth century. This did not occur, and to continue saying that it did is storytelling and ignorance. For a detailed and sharp review of Marx's errors concerning the agricultural revolution in England, see Kins Collins, "Marx on the English Agricultural Revolution.: Theory and Evidence," *History and Theory*, 6,3 (1967): 351-81.

36. Louis Bergeron, "La 'révolution agricole' en Angleterre," in Pierre Léon, ed., *Histoire économique et sociale du monde: 1730-1840*, Paris: Armand Colin, 1978, vol. 3: 228.

37. W.A. Cole and Phyllis Deane, *British Economic Growth: 1688-1959*, Cambridge: Cambridge University Press, 1962, 6-8.

38. E.A. Wrigley and R.S. Schofield, *The Population History of England: 1541-1871*. London: Edward Arnold, 1981, 421-35. The occurrence of the lowering of the age of marriage at the end of the eighteenth century has been the basis for the debate between those supporting the "optimistic" view of the industrial revolution and the "pessimists." In fact, it is certain that the lowering of the age of marriage starting in the years 1775 to 1780 is linked to the greater chances for work caused by the agricultural revolution. But the greater chances for work were not reflected by a sufficient rise in income to compensate for the increase in the cost of living that was typical of this period. At present, it is generally agreed that there was a drop in real income from 1760 to 1820, as well as a drop in living conditions for the English masses, who found it especially difficult to bear the weight of the various wars from 1793 to 1815. Even so, one must not confuse this impoverishment with the disappearance of the yeomanry, which did not occur between 1760 and 1815, nor with the rural exodus, which could not arise at the moment when the agricultural revolution was keeping a large number of labourers in the countryside. For an update on this question, see Peter H. Lindert and Jeffrey Williamson, "English Workers' Living Standards during the Industrial Revolution," *The Economic History Review*, 36,2 (February 1983): 1-25.

39. Louis Bergeron, "La 'révolution agricole' en Angleterre," *op. cit.*, 227.

40. Phyllis Deane, *The First Industrial Revolution*. 44.

41. François Bédarida, *L'Angleterre triomphante: 1833-1914*. Paris: Hatier, 1974, 27.

42. Karl Marx, *op. cit.*, ch. 25, 468-79, 492-525.

43. François Crouzet, "Agriculture et révolution industrielle. Quelques réflexions," *Cahiers d'histoire*, Lyon, 12 (1967): 72.

44. Louis Bergeron, "La 'révolution agricole' en Angleterre," *op. cit.*, 230.

45. Lawrence White, "Enclosures and Population Movements in England," *Explorations in Entrepreneurial History*, 6 (1968-69): 176-86

46. François Crouzet, "Agriculture et révolution industrielle...," *op. cit.*, 73. E.P. Thompson, *op. cit.*, 470-72.

47. Louis Bergeron, "La 'révolution agricole' en Angleterre," *op. cit.*, 232.

48. Gérald Bernier, "Quebec Class Structure..., *op. cit.*, 71, n. 4.

49. Ta Van, *op. cit.*, 19.

55. Jeffrey G. Williamson, "Why Was British Growth so Slow During the Industrial Revolution?" *The Journal of Economic History*, 44,3 (September 1984): 687, 689 and Charles Feinstein, "Capital Formation in Great Britain," in Peter Mathias and Michael Postan, eds., *The Cambridge Economic History of Europe*, vol. 7: *The Industrial Economics Capital, Labour and Enterprise*. (Cambridge: Cambridge University Press, 1978), 28-96. The annual rate of per capita increase in "national revenue" would have been 0.33% between 1770 and 1815, as opposed to 0.86% between 1815 and 1841 and 1.5% after 1850. As far as the part of national revenue devoted to domestic investment, this grew from 9% in the 1760s to 14% in the 1850s. Based on the works of Phyllis Deane and W. Cole, it was still quite recently thought that the rate of increase had been quite higher beginning in the 1780s. These works, however, have now proved to be in error. For a detailed criticism of Deane and Cole, see F.R. Crafts, "British Economic Growth: Review of the Evidence," *The Economic History Review*, 36,3 (May 1983):177-99.

56. Peter Mathias, *The First Industrial Nation. An Economic History of Britain: 1700-1914*. London: Methuen, 1969, 129-33.

57. Fernand Braudel, *Civilisation matérielle, économie et capitalisme. Le temps du monde*. Paris: Armand Colin, 1979, 494.

58. François Caron, "La Grande-Bretagne vers 1815-1850," in Pierre Léon, ed., *op. cit.*, 3: 385-452.

59. Roland Marx, *La révolution industrielle en Grande-Bretagne*. Paris: Armand Colin, 1970, 231.

60. *Ibid*.

61. François Bédarida, *op. cit.*, 27.

62. Pierre Léon, "L'élan industriel et commercial," in Fernand Braudel and Ernest Labrousse, eds., *Histoire économique et sociale de la France*. Paris: Presses universitaires de France, 1970, 2: 499-524; François Crouzet, "Angleterre et France au 18e siècle. Essai d'analyse comparée de deux croissances économiques", *op. cit.* According to the figures presented in these articles, industrial and trade growth in France between 1720 and 1780 was slightly higher than in England. Among other things, the aggressiveness of French traders during this period, especially in Europe, where they swamped their English competitors in almost all market

areas, and the success of the French sugar industry in the West Indies, as well as of the silk industry, helped France to gain headway. Despite this burst of activity, however, according to François Clouzet, France did not make up for the weakness that occurred in the seventeenth century. One must also recall that seventeenth-century France had a much larger population (twenty to twenty-six million between 1720 and 1780) than England (five to eight million for the same years), and possessed more regional differences. In addition, it is interesting to note that at the beginning, the industrial revolution in England was regional. Finally, it is possible that the Revolution of 1789 and the wars that followed 1792 slowed the economic leap of eighteenth-century France, although the question is still open; see Hubert Bronin, "La Révolution française a-t-elle bloqué la croissance économique?", *L'histoire*, 77 (avril 1985): 98-100.

63. Gilles Paquet and Jean-Pierre Wallot, "Sur quelques discontinuités dans l'expérience socio-économique du Québec: une hypothèse," *RHAF*, 35,4 (mars 1982):500-1. Fernand Ouellet, in his *Histoire économique et sociale du Québec 1760-1850*, (Montréal: Fides, 1971), 1: 13: "The annexation of Canada by the British Empire, however, was not a revolution that could modify its role deeply or in a short length of time as part of the imperial economy. In both England and France, the mercantile system was still quite alive."

75. Donald Creighton, *The Empire of the St. Lawrence*. Toronto: Macmillan, 1956.

76. Gérald Bernier and Ta Van show that the more capitalist Great Britain accelerated the arrival of the "commercial phase" and slowed the emergence of the "industrial phase." Clearly, however, the diplomatic and economic interests of Great Britain led her to slow the "commercial phase" that the Montreal merchants were hoping would take place.

77. P.J. Cain and A.G. Hopkins, "The Political Economy of British Expansion Overseas, 1750-1914," *Economic History Review*, 33,4 (1282 November 1980): 463-90

78. René Rémond, quoted in Maurice Lagueux, *Cours de philosophie de l'histoire*, Université de Montréal, 1967, mimeographed text, 6.

79. Kins Collins, *op. cit.*, 368.

CHAPTER
7 THE LOYALIST EXPERIENCE

The American Revolution was among the most important wars in Canadian history. While the Seven Years' War gave unquestioned supremacy to the British in North America, Canada was marginalized in the aftermath. The American Revolution, on the other hand, rescued Canada from that vast Anglo-American empire and created not just one new nation but two. It also defined the nature of what became known as British North America. The Catholic, French Canada of the *ancien régime* became a bilingual, bicultural, multidenominational colony with the arrival of thousands of United Empire Loyalists, the losers in that American War of Independence. The Loyalists spread across the old French empire, from the eastern tip of Cape Breton Island to western outposts like Detroit. They became the dominant population in the newly created colonies of Upper Canada, New Brunswick and Prince Edward Island. Even in Lower Canada, they occupied whole regions and challenged French dominance.

Since they were the first to reject the American Dream, the Loyalists fascinate historians in the United States, who have analysed those untypical ancestors in an attempt to understand who they were and why they pursued their un-American activities. This has also attracted Canadians, since the Loyalist mentality was transported north during and after the Revolution. Wallace Brown, author of the first article, has written widely on what he calls *The King's Friends: The Composition and Motives of the American Loyalist Claimants* (1965). In "'Victorious in Defeat': The American Loyalists in Canada," he offers the traditional, sympathetic overview of the Canadian experience. Others have been less kind, and there is a significant body of "Loyalist Myth" literature that describes in both positive and negative terms the convolutions of the Loyalist image in Canada over time. The ups and downs are usually tied to attitudes about monarchy, empire, imperialism, anti-Americanism, and the increasing obscurity of the Loyalists with the passage of time.

In most of this Loyalist literature the role of women, both during and after the Revolution, has rarely been considered. With the rethinking of Canada's past from several perspectives over the past quarter-century, Loyalist women have finally been rediscovered. Janice Potter examines several in "Patriarchy and Paternalism: The Case of Eastern Ontario Loyalist Women." Their courageous activities in the Revolutionary War went unrecognized later in British North America, because of "a well-defined power structure in which there were clearly prescribed social roles." This is the position of modern feminist historians, who expose the concept of natural order implicit in the oppressive patriarchal systems.

Suggestions for Further Reading

Bell, David, "The Loyalist Tradition in Canada," *Journal of Canadian Studies*, V, no. 2 (May 1970), 22-33.

Brown, Wallace and Hereward Senior, *Victorious in Defeat: The Loyalists in Canada*. Toronto: Methuen, 1984.

Condon, Ann Gorman, *The Envy of the American States: The Loyalist Dream for New Brunswick*. Fredericton: New Ireland Press, 1984.

Errington, Jane, "Loyalists in Upper Canada: A British American Community," in *"None was ever better ..." The Loyalist Settlements of Ontario*, ed. S.F. Wise, D. Carter-Edwards and J. Witham. Stormont, Dundas and Glengarry Historical Society, 1984.

MacKinnon, Neil, *The Unfriendly Soil: The Loyalist Experience in Nova Scotia, 1783-1791*. Kingston and Montreal: McGill-Queen's University Press, 1986.

MacNutt, W.S., "The Loyalists: A Sympathetic View," *Acadiensis*, VI, no. 1 (Autumn 1976), 3-20.

McCalla, Douglas, "The 'Loyalist' Economy of Upper Canada, 1784-1806," *Histoire sociale/Social History*, XVI, no. 32 (November 1983), 279-304.

Mills, David, *The Idea of Loyalty in Upper Canada, 1784-1850*. Kingston and Montreal: McGill-Queen's University Press, 1988.

Moore, Christopher, *The Loyalists: Revolution, Exile, Settlement*. Toronto: Macmillan of Canada, 1984.

Rawlyk, George, "The Federalist-Loyalist Alliance in New Brunswick, 1784-1815," *Humanities Association Review*, XXVII, no. 1 (Spring 1976), 142-160.

Upton, L.S.F. (ed.), *The United Empire Loyalists: Men and Myths*. Toronto: Copp Clark, 1967.

Wise, S.F., "The Place of the Loyalists in Ontario and Canadian History," *"None was ever better ..." The Loyalist Settlements of Ontario*, ed. S.F. Wise, D. Carter-Edwards and J. Witham. Stormont, Dundas and Glengarry Historical Society, 1984.

VICTORIOUS IN DEFEAT: THE AMERICAN LOYALISTS IN CANADA

Wallace Brown

"They [the Loyalists] would rather go to Japan than go among the Americans where they could never live in peace." Col. John Butler, a New York Loyalist who emigrated to Canada.

As the War for Independence drew to a close, thousands of American Loyalists were looking for new homes.[1] The most attractive location because of proximity, availability of land and continuing royal rule, was what was left of British North America, constituting in 1783 three colonies: Nova Scotia, which included the future New Brunswick; the Island of St. John, renamed Prince Edward Island in 1799; and the ancient province of Quebec, which since 1774 stretched west to include the Great Lakes region. The term Canada, except as a synonym for Quebec, is an anachronism before 1867 (the date of Confederation); but it will be used in this essay to designate the entire area. The Maritimes refers to Nova Scotia, New Brunswick and Prince Edward Island.

Most Loyalists arrived in Nova Scotia by ship, at government expense, from New York City, the last great British stronghold in the "lost thirteen" colonies. The invasion began in October, 1782, with the descent of 300 Americans on the Annapolis Valley. Thousands more soon followed into the peninsula where the greatest concentration, perhaps 10,000, was at Port Roseway, renamed Shelburne, after the man who was the patron of Governor John Parr, but by no means a hero to the Loyalists on account of the generous peace terms he had negotiated with the rebels. A Spring and a Fall fleet in 1783 brought a host of refugees to the St. John valley, some of whom founded the city of Saint John at the river's mouth and Fredericton, seventy miles upstream. Other settlements were made at Passamaquoddy Bay (notably St. Andrews), Sackville, Bay Chaleur and the Miramichi River. Other Loyalists were lured to the Island of St. John, mainly the Malpeque-Bedeque isthmus, where Summerside, the island's second largest town, was founded.

The results of the influx into the Maritimes were dramatic. A new province, New Brunswick, was split off from Nova Scotia, the 15,000 Loyalists swamping the pre-Loyalist population of about 4,000 New Englanders and Acadians. Nova Scotia was further partitioned—temporarily, in this case—when hitherto little-developed Cape Breton Island, acquired from France in 1763, became a separate

From *History Today*, 27, no. 2 (1977), 92-100. Reprinted by permission of *History Today*.

colony as a result of the arrival of 400 Loyalists who more than doubled the existing population. The Americans could not take over the rump of Nova Scotia; but, numbering at least 15,000, they slightly out-weighed the old inhabitants. On the Island of St. John the up to 1,000 immigrants, almost equalling the existing population, were a force to be reckoned with.

Arrival in Quebec was much more sporadic than in the Maritimes as the Loyalists, often pushing hand-carts, trickled in by various water-assisted routes, including the St. Lawrence and Hudson-Mohawk rivers, and Lakes Oneida and Champlain. Some sailed across Lake Ontario, frequently to the Bay of Quinté; others followed the southern shore to the Niagara peninsula; others pushed on to the Thames River and the northern shore of Lake Erie; a few even ascended the Mississippi and settled at Detroit. Again the results were the founding of new towns including New Johnstown (now Cornwall) and Cataraqui (now Kingston), and partition when the western area became Upper Canada (the future Ontario) in 1791. In Upper Canada, as in New Brunswick, the Loyalists, numbering perhaps 7,000, took over a wilderness area from a small pre-Loyalist population of only a few hundred; but in the original colony of Quebec 70,000 French Canadians were not directly threatened by the 1,000 Loyalist immigrants, half of whom settled in the outlying Gaspé peninsula, and half in the old inhabited area, mainly at Sorel and Machiche. Later, the Eastern Townships received some Loyalists.

Government was ill-prepared for the arrival of the Tories, though Governor Frederick Haldimand in Quebec proved much more capable and sympathetic than Governor Parr in Nova Scotia. Halifax and Saint John were severely over-crowded. In the former, churches and warehouses served as temporary quarters, and in both tent-cities sprang up. Congestion, but not always hardship, was relieved when many refugees moved to take up government land grants. Contemporary accounts are few; but some evidence about life in early Fredericton survives. All too soon the Loyalists faced the hard Canadian winter in tents covered with boughs or in half-finished log cabins. Some unfortunates froze to death; others only escaped by organizing shifts through the night to keep the fires going. The want of bedding might be supplied by heated boards. Even in 1787 the Reverend Jacob Bailey, a talented Loyalist from Massachusetts, reported from Annapolis County, Nova Scotia, that: "Many families are confined to a single apartment built with sods, where men, women, children, pigs, fleas, bugs, mosquitoes and other domestic insects mingle in society."

In western Quebec there was also much hardship. In July, 1784 it was stated that "the settlers at Cataraqui are in great disorder, not having yet got upon their land, many of them unprovided with a Blanket to cover Them, scarce any Turnip seed and neither Axes nor Hoes for Half of Them." Brighter reports soon followed; but 1789 was known as the "hungry year" when "dreadful circumstances" were noted: "one spoonful of meal per day, for one person" was the ration; wild leaves, such as beech, were eaten; famished domestic animals were bled Masai-style; one family "leaped for joy at one robin being caught, out of which a whole pot of broth was made."

The Canadian land was quite capable of supplying a living at a simple farming level, but first came the back-breaking work of clearing the forest. Even Beverly Robinson Jr., scion of one of the richest New York families, recounted in 1784 that: "He is now settling a new farm in Nova Scotia by beginning to cut down the first tree and erect a loghouse for the shelter of his wife and two small children, and to accomplish that is obliged to labour with *his own* hands" (my italics). We see here the influence of the frontier at work in a Turnerian way.

Under the strain of the new environment, grown men wept like children and some cracked up completely. Filer Diblee and his family came from a prosperous middle class background in Connecticut. Their Loyalism resulted in an Odyssey of flight, imprisonment and persecution which ended with their arrival at the Kingston peninsula, New Brunswick, where they survived the winter of 1783-84 in a log cabin. But Diblee's "fortitude gave way" at the prospect of imprisonment for debt; he "grew Melancholy, which soon deprived him of his Reason"; and one day in March, 1784, "he took a Razor from the Closet, threw himself on the bed, drew the Curtains, and cut his own throat." Though she lost her house twice by fire, his widow struggled on in what she called "this frozen Climate and barren Wilderness."

Groups as well as individuals were unfortunate. The Loyalist boom-town, Shelburne, had a magnificent harbour, but otherwise was so badly located that it rapidly declined to a hamlet. Port Mouton, Nova Scotia, was settled by over 2,000 refugees, mainly disbanded soldiers, in 1783 and quickly the town of Guysborough was built, and a road hacked through the woods to Liverpool. But in 1784 the town was destroyed by fire, a fate that struck several Loyalist settlements. Most of the inhabitants left and founded the present Guysborough on Chedabucto Bay, Nova Scotia, while some others founded St. Stephen in New Brunswick. Typically, most Loyalist set-backs were temporary. Most Shelburners found new homes. Even the Diblee family endured.

The arrival of the Loyalists in Canada marks the beginning of a great epic tale insufficiently appreciated by historians or the public. It ranks with the history of the Jesuit missionaries and the *coureurs de bois*, but has never found its Parkman.

Although plagued with difficulties, the Loyalists had many advantages. The environment was not completely hostile. Trees that had to be removed also supplied fuel and material for houses, tools and furniture; winters that inflicted frost-bite also provided a free "deep-freeze" for the abundant game and fish; governments that were cursed for incompetence and ingratitude granted tax exemptions, issued provisions, medicines, clothes, tools, seeds, boards, and, most important of all, surveyed and granted, free of charge, land—the basis of survival for most people in those days. For a fortunate minority government largesse went further. Ex-officers received half pay for life; some Loyalists got pensions and lump-sum grants in compensation for losses sustained by the Revolution; all of this injected much needed capital into Canada and ultimately benefited all the inhabitants. A very small minority got government offices, especially in the new provinces of New Brunswick and Upper Canada, but there were never enough to satisfy the vociferous Loyalists' demands. The scorned pre-Loyalist inhabitants were helpful as suppliers and informants. For example, in New Brunswick the Acadians sold cleared land and provisions to the Loyalists, while the Indians introduced them to fiddlehead greens (the edible shoots of a wild fern that are still a local delicacy). Though some observers noted the "vice of every kind, incident of the camp," that prevailed among the many Loyalists who settled as groups of disbanded regiments, particularly at Niagara, on the St. John River and the upper St. Lawrence, others stressed the advantages that military discipline and cohesiveness gave.

It has nurtured the self-esteem of some Canadians, especially New Brunswickers, to consider the Loyalists as mainly colonial aristocrats and Harvard graduates, in the same way it has flattered Virginians to consider themselves the progeny of Cavaliers. In fact, the vast majority of Loyalists were modest farmers (plus some artisans) who were well-suited to pioneering. But the Loyalist myth of gentility has a grain of truth; there *was* a significant minority of the "better sort," again especially in New Brunswick. Sergeant-Major William Cobbett, on duty in New Brunswick in the 1790s, was amazed to find "thousands of captains ..., without soldiers, and of squires without stockings or shoes," some of whom were happy to serve him a glass of grog. There were few fee-paying clients for doctors or lawyers. Not surprisingly a number of gentleman Loyalists left Canada. For example, no less than six members of New Brunswick's first assembly, which met in 1785, had returned to the United States before the session was completed!

Nevertheless the contribution of the élite Loyalists to Canada, especially to government, politics, the law, religion and culture, must be acknowledged and can be suggested by listing a few names. Edmund Fanning (North Carolina) and Sir John Wentworth (New Hampshire) became the lieutenant-governors of the Island of St. John and Nova Scotia respectively; John Saunders (Virginia) and William Smith (New York) became chief-justices of New Brunswick and Quebec; Philip Marchington and Richard Cartwright (both from New York) were leading merchants in Nova Scotia and Upper Canada respectively; Sir John Johnson and Gabriel Ludlow (both from New York) became prominent office-holders in Quebec and New Brunswick; the Reverend Jonathan Odell (a poet of distinction from New Jersey) became the long serving provincial secretary of New Brunswick; and so it went even to succeeding generations—Simon Fraser, the great explorer, was the son of a Loyalist; Sir Leonard Tilley, a father of Confederation, was a grandson.

Most Loyalists were subsistence farmers; but there were other areas of economic endeavour. Canada was slated by the British government to replace the former thirteen colonies as the purveyor of fish, timber and other supplies to the British West Indies. Indeed, some so-called Loyalists only migrated when they learned that the Navigation Acts would be applied against the United States. The West Indian market encouraged Canadian agriculture, fishing and lumbering; but supply never equalled demand, and the British frequently had to open the West Indian trade to the United States. Even much of the early Nova Scotia and New Brunswick timber exports were American, frequently illegally obtained. The French Revolutionary and Napoleonic wars stimulated the Maritime mast trade; but much of it was not in Loyalist hands, and people tended to be diverted from agriculture, which partly explains why the Maritimes were chronically short of food.

The Loyalists dreamed of making the new provinces "a showcase for the continent," "the envy" of the United States; but sometimes the dream fell short. The Maritimes were poor by American standards. In 1790 William Pitt, influenced by laissez-faire principles and the United States policy of selling public lands, ended free land grants in British North America. Lord Dorchester, the Governor of Quebec, ignored the order; little land worth having remained in Nova Scotia; but the ban, which lasted seventeen years in New Brunswick, stunted development. On the Island of St. John most Loyalists could not get clear title to their land because of a complicated matter of absentee ownership. Some refugees bought new land; many simply squatted; others moved away. The issue, which was not resolved until 1875, cast a pall over the island, but stimulated reform politics during the first half of the nineteenth century. Upper Canada suffered from isolation and the barrier of the rapids of the St. Lawrence; but the rich soil presaged a prosperous future in what became the wealthiest part of Canada.

There is a chorus of contemporary testimony that most Loyalists, apart from a few who had "contracted ... rum and idle habits ... during the war," made good settlers. For example, Patrick Campbell visiting Upper Canada in the early 1790s, was impressed with the "immense industry" of the Loyalists, who, he claimed, had cleared more land in eight years than the French had in one hundred; James MacGregor visiting Prince Edward Island in the early nineteenth century found the Loyalists "industrious and independent," very well-suited to coping with "a country in a state of nature." In 1802 Edward Winslow, a descendant of the Pilgrim Father of the same name, looked back at the history of his fellow New Brunswick Loyalists with modest satisfaction. "Immense labour" had transformed a wilderness into a prosperous farming community. "Enquire among 'em. Are you oppressed with taxes? No. Does anybody interrupt you in matters of conscience? No. Do the laws afford you sufficient protection. Why yes." After a few years the Loyalists were strung out along a line of permanent, mainly agricultural, settlements from Cape Breton to Detroit,[2] and they had created two new provinces and several important towns. This is their prime contribution to Canada. They are the English founding fathers, analogous to the Virginians and Puritans of the early seventeenth century.

There remain two questions to be answered: what kind of society did the Loyalists create; and what was their legacy to Canada? The Loyalists were essentially good Americans, rarely docile Tories. As early as May, 1783, the royal surveyor, Benjamin Marston, a Loyalist himself, was complaining about the "curs'd Republican Town meeting Spirit" that made his life in Shelburne a trial. Bishop Charles Inglis was appalled by the democratic implications of "free pews" (i.e. not assigned according to rank) at Trinity Church, Kingston, New Brunswick. The Maritimes were (and are) susceptible to United States frontier-style revivalism; and from the start the hopes of the élite for a strong, established, Anglican Church were disappointed, despite the appointment in 1787 of Inglis as Bishop of Nova Scotia with jurisdiction over New Brunswick and Quebec, and the setting aside of "clergy reserves" of land in the Maritimes and Upper Canada. Too many Loyalists were Erastian. Élite hopes for an hereditary aristocracy were frustrated, and it was even difficult to live in gentlemanly style. Thus, the very wealthy John Saunders sat on his great estate, the Barony, near Fredericton, unable to attract tenants—men naturally preferred to work their own land.

The single characteristic common to the Loyalists was quarrelsomeness. The old inhabitants could not be expected to relish the intrusion, even if the refugees had been exceptionally reticent. Generally the Loyalists disliked the old inhabitants of Canada whom they considered had been too friendly to the American Revolution. "Languid wretches," said Edward Winslow in New Brunswick; "exulting in their beloved Ignorance," said Jacob Bailey in Nova Scotia; "idle" and "indolent," said Benjamin Marston in the Island of St. John; "the Darkest Corner of the Dominion," said William Smith in Quebec.

But the most bitter quarrels were between Loyalists, usually between the élite and the rest. The tone was set even before the evacuation of New York when a group known as the Fifty-Five, on account of their high social standing, petitioned for special large land grants of 5,000 acres each in Nova Scotia. A howl of protest resulted and the scheme was thwarted. The first New Brunswick election in November 1785 led to rioting in St. John which crystallized two parties: the minority, aristocratic Upper Covers, versus the majority, plebeian Lower Covers. In 1787 Lord Dorchester had to send a committee to investigate Loyalist unrest in the future Upper Canada. The committee reported "a very dangerous Jealousy and want of Confidence ... between the Majority of the settlers and their late officers." In New Brunswick the political dispute culminated in "the Glenie affair," in which James Glenie, a Scottish timber merchant, not a Loyalist, led the opposition to Governor Thomas Carleton and the official clique in Fredericton which in 1792 lost its majority in the assembly. The affair finally turned on whether the council had the constitutional right to interfere with the initiate money bills. From 1795 to 1798 an impasse meant no revenue was collected at all until a compromise allowed both houses to initiate.

In Nova Scotia the situation was complicated by a powerful segment of "old comers," and no real Loyalist party developed. But the Loyalists were in the thick of politics and led a thrust against the council. A Halifax by-election of 1788 was marked by rioting and murder; and, a year later, the Loyalists were charged with rebellion. Order was restored in 1791 when Governor Parr, who had long complained about the Americans—they "almost wish to take over the government"—died and was replaced by a Loyalist, Sir John Wentworth.

W. S. MacNutt, the best historian of the Maritimes, comments on the early political history of Nova Scotia and New Brunswick that it was firmly in the tradition of the former American colonies, that "replicas of the constitutional struggles ... of New York and Massachusetts were ... the common lot of the two provinces."

Now to consider the Loyalist legacy. It must be stressed that only in New Brunswick did the Loyalists remain a majority for very long, and even there they were engulfed by other immigrants after the War of 1812. They and their descendants retained political power almost until Confederation; but from the early years the economy was dominated by Scots. Direct Loyalist influence was much more ephemeral elsewhere in Canada. In Upper Canada by 1812 only one fifth of the population of 100,000 were Loyalists or their children, although most of the remainder were American-born; these were the so-called "late Loyalists," American frontiersmen who were simply attracted by Governor John G. Simcoe's offer of free land in an area where the land was very good. Many Canadians with no Loyalist background, however, have acquired Loyalist attitudes. For example, John Strachan arrived in Upper Canada from Scotland in 1799 with pro-American convictions, but by 1809 was convinced that "true liberty" did not exist in the United States; later in the nineteenth century in New Brunswick, Protestant Irish immigrants became "Loyalized," a process aided by intermarriage.

The Loyalists helped establish Canada's tradition of a "cultural mosaic," which is held to contrast with America's alleged, homogenizing melting pot. From the start most Loyalists preferred to leave the French alone, and their own settlements were frequently fragmented; for example, in the Upper Canadian Townships Roman Catholic Scots and Presbyterian Scots kept apart. The Loyalist influx also brought many loyal Iroquois, who settled along the Grand River, and a number of black Loyalists who founded settlements in the Maritimes that persist to this day.

The Loyalists and the British government set the political structure of English Canada which was only in embryo in Nova Scotia before 1783. The aim was to avoid the "mistakes" that had caused revolution to the south. New Brunswick may serve as a model that was generally copied. The lower houses were believed to have become too powerful; so the powers of the appointed council and the Governor, who was made financially independent, were strengthened. The élite were encouraged by appointment to the council and government office, and as JPs in the counties—the New England township was scrupulously avoided. The colonial government of New Brunswick was made less dependent on the home-country; more internal self-government was allowed than had been the case in America. Conservative social institutions, like the Church of England, were supported; and with sad memories of Revolutionary agitation in the American cities still vivid, the capital was moved from Saint John to the inland village of Fredericton. (Many Loyalists had a Jeffersonian dislike of commerce and cities.) But the tone in New Brunswick was far from entirely conservative; the British never attempted to tax the North American colonies directly; thus the essential early goal of the Revolution was secured. In the words of W. S. MacNutt, "democracy ran riot in the Loyalist citadel"; the suffrage was for all men, and the city government of Saint John, with its annual elections, was one of the most democratic bodies of its kind in North America. The Revolution not only made Americans free, but also Canadians, who found that "subjects" could be just as happy as "citizens."

French-Canadians owe much to the Loyalists. The Constitutional Act of 1791, partly because of Loyalist agitation, began representative government in Quebec and introduced freehold land tenure. At the same time, the French way of life, including legal and religious systems, was maintained. The Loyalist numbers doomed the French to become a minority; but the Loyalist strength enabled Canada to withstand the onslaught of American imperialism. It is doubtful if French culture could have survived within the American union.

The Loyalist tradition is often decried in Canada because it has been held responsible for the development of aristocratic governing cliques, known as the Family Compacts. In fact, the Family Compacts were not a Loyalist phenomenon. True, in Upper Canada about half of the leading members of the compact were second-generation Loyalists, men like Sir John Beverley Robinson; but Loyalists' descendants were an important component of the opposition, and the rebellion of 1837 similarly found them on both sides. In New Brunswick the Loyalists were also on both sides of the compact question. Lemuel Allen Wilmot, a grandson of a Poughkeepsie Loyalist, led the struggle, successful in 1836, for New Brunswick to gain control of Crown lands, an important landmark on the road to full self-government. During the same period Joseph Howe, whose father was a loyal Massachusetts newspaper editor, played a similar role in leading the forces of Nova Scotia democracy. Nevertheless, the aristocratic British proclivity of some Loyalists and their descendants has frequently gone against the Canadian grain. The tone was set in 1789 when the Quebec Council resolved to have the Loyalists and their posterity discriminated, from future settlers, "giving them a Marke of Honor," the right to put UE (Unity of Empire) after their names, hence the expression United Empire Loyalists.

New Brunswick is *par excellence* the Loyalist province; and a brief account of some influences there may be appropriate. On the positive side, there is a cultural tradition. In 1784 the Loyalists laid the foundations of the University of New Brunswick at Fredericton, where the residence of the poet, Jonathan Odell, began a literary tradition that leads directly to Bliss Carman and others. On the negative side, we find an over-dependence on government, a scramble for office and patronage, a morbid absorption in politics that sapped more wholesome initiative, particularly economic. Writing in this vein in 1904, John Davidson, a Scottish professor, now perhaps understandably forgotten, at the University of New Brunswick, found the Loyalist tradition baleful. He quoted a local: "in this country men think five dollars of government money is worth ten dollars from anybody else," and added that New Brunswick was the only country he knew where professional and business men had to do their legitimate work at night because politics took up the day.

Discussion of the efforts of the Loyalists often centres on explanations of why Canada is so different from the United States. Such items as law, Parliamentary government and the monarchy are obvious; but Canada's relatively peaceful western expansion, and a general lack of lynching, are also listed. It is even argued that several Canadian provinces have elected mild socialist governments during the last few decades because of the Loyalists. More of a class structure was maintained in Canada, and Canadians, far from starting with a distrust of government authority, positively embrace it.

The Loyalists offered a valid critique of the Revolutionary ideals and moral absolutism. The Nova Scotian writer, Thomas C. Haliburton, the grandson of a Loyalist and a popular satirist, had Sam Slick say simply "there is no tyranny on airth equal to the tyranny of a majority." Similar sentiments were expressed by the Reverend Mather Byles, who, watching the hysteria surrounding the funeral of a victim of the Boston "massacre" in 1771, opined: "They call me a brainless Tory; but tell me ... which is better to be ruled by one tyrant three thousand miles away, or by three thousand tyrants one mile away?"

The Loyalists have profoundly influenced Canadian nationalism. They began an abiding love-hate attitude toward the Great Republic. During the War of 1812, by opting out, the Maritimes demonstrated the love; but there was a bitter struggle in Upper Canada. The Loyalists took pride in victory of sort; but more important were the myths and symbols established: the Loyalist militia had beaten the Yankees; Laura Secord had led her cow through the American lines. Fear of the United States has remained, and Unity of Empire has frequently been invoked as a shield, as in the 1880s which witnessed one of several Loyalist revivals.

It is true that there is a certain Canadian dourness resulting from three losing traditions: French, Scottish and Loyalist. But a Canadian poet's description of the latter is also apt:

> Not drooping like poor fugitives they came
> In exodus to our Canadian wilds
> But full of heart and hope, with heads erect
> And fearless eyes victorious in defeat.

Notes

1. For a general account see my article "Escape from the Republic: The Dispersal of the American Loyalists," *History Today,* February, 1972.

2. Detroit, although legally in the United States by the peace treaty of 1783, was not evacuated until after the signing of Jay's Treaty in 1794, when the Loyalists moved across the border into Canada.

PATRIARCHY AND PATERNALISM: THE CASE OF THE EASTERN ONTARIO LOYALIST WOMEN

Janice Potter

Although the American Revolution did not alter the legal or political rights of women, it changed their lives dramatically in other ways.[1] With the men away fighting, women were forced to shoulder the burden of running the farm, the estate, or the business, and as a result there was less rigidity in the sexual division of labour, women gained confidence in their abilities, and men had more respect for women and their contributions to society. Those experiences were reinforced by public recognition of women's contribution to the Revolution and by the ideology of the Revolution. For example, boycotts of British cloth meant that wearing homespun became a sign of patriotism and that spinning, one of the most time-consuming and clearly feminine domestic chores, was raised in status. Moreover, there was an antipatriarchal aspect of the Revolution that fostered less authoritarian and more reciprocal relationships between men and women. Republican ideology, with its emphasis on voluntary consent, also allowed more scope for women. There was "greater mutuality and reciprocity" in marriages and in some cases "more egalitarian marital relationships."[2] The belief in the need to raise a moral and upright citizenry also enhanced the status of motherhood and made it easier for women to obtain an education, since it was they who would be raising the children. The result was more confident, self-reliant women, some of whom decided not to marry, and a society that valued more highly the domestic sphere generally and women specifically.

But what was the situation of Loyalist women, whose actions did not receive the same recognition and for whom there was no equivalent to republican ideology? The existing material on Loyalist women includes books about individuals, papers about specific groups, such as Loyalist women who filed claims for compensation, and an interesting thesis discussing Loyalist women in gen-

From *Ontario History,* LXXXI, no. 1 (March 1989), 3-24. Reprinted by permission of the author, the Ontario Historical Society and *Ontario History.*

eral terms.[3] This paper, however, considers in a preliminary way the effect of the Revolution on one specific group of Loyalist women—those who lived on the frontiers of New York, New England, and Pennsylvania and eventually settled in the townships created along the St. Lawrence River and Lake Ontario between Longueuil and the Bay of Quinte in what is now eastern Ontario.

Despite the diversity of their ethnic origins, the eastern Ontario Loyalist women shared a common background characterized by paternalism and patriarchy, and their experiences during the Revolution were similar. Virtually all went through several stages in the course of becoming refugees: they were harassed or persecuted, they were forced to flee to British bases for protection, they lived under British military rule in what might be called refugee camps, and with aid from the British they were eventually resettled.

Information about these women can be found in the few personal letters and diaries that have survived, in the claims Loyalists made for compensation from the British government, and in the records of the Patriot committees that interrogated Loyalists and of the British authorities who had to supervise and provision them. And, from records such as military registers, provisioning lists, returns of Loyalists, and land grants, it is possible to compile a reasonably precise statistical profile of the eastern Ontario Loyalists.

The 1786 census reveals that the 1,800 families, or 4,661 individuals, living along the St. Lawrence River and the eastern end of Lake Ontario were an ethnically diverse group that included many recent immigrants. Of the eastern Ontario Loyalists whose birthplace is known, about 45 per cent were foreign and about 45 per cent American-born.[4] Many of the American-born belonged to ethnic groups that had retained their native language, group cohesiveness, and other aspects of their culture. The largest of the ethnic minorities were the Germans, who accounted for about 30 per cent of the total and of whom one-quarter were immigrants and the rest Americans of German ancestry. About 5 per cent were Dutch, mostly more traditional members of the Dutch Reformed Church who had kept their culture and language.[5] Another group of American-born Loyalists who had retained their distinctive culture were the Mohawk Indians, who had played an important military role in the Revolution.

The largest of the immigrant groups, constituting 24 per cent of the total, were the Scots. Many were Highlanders and Jacobites who had emigrated because of poverty and the enclosure of their lands. In the colonies they retained their Gaelic language, Catholic religion, and other aspects of their culture.[6]

Whether American- or foreign-born, the vast majority of eastern Ontario Loyalists had lived on the frontiers of colonial society and were farmers. Over 70 per cent came from the northern New York counties of Tryon, Charlotte, and Albany. About 2 per cent came from each of New Jersey, Connecticut, and Pennsylvania, and many of the Pennsylvanians were from the frontier settlements along the Susquehanna River.[7] They had all been part of the mass movement to the frontiers after the Seven Years' War.

A common theme in the social relationships of many eastern Ontario Loyalists was paternalism. Paternalism has been variously defined as interference with people's liberty for their own good and as the determination by one person what is in the best interests of another. A paternalistic relationship need not be harsh, however, and can even be co-operative in that it is a close and affectionate relationship in which the dependent party feels the need for guidance and is willing to exchange some independence or security.[8] But in such a relationship there is a hierarchy or at least inequality—there are superiors and subordinates, leaders and followers—and the dominant party feels an obligation to protect the interests of the subordinate in return for loyalty and deference.

Eighteenth-century paternalism was exemplified in the relationship between some New York landlords and their tenants. In spite of the rush to the frontiers for land, not all colonial Americans managed to acquire land of their own. In the case of the eastern Ontario Loyalists, only 20 per cent had held their land in freehold, and some had shared land or squatted on disputed land, but the vast majority had been tenants on the northern New York manorial estates owned by families like the Johnsons; indeed, at least 20 per cent of the Loyalist claimants who settled in what is now eastern Ontario had been tenants of the Johnsons.

The Johnsons ran their 20,000-acre estate like quasi-feudal lords. They helped their tenants financially, burned the debtor bonds of over-extended tenants, and helped artisans like Richard Mandevell, a "Breeches Maker" who later settled in eastern Ontario, establish themselves in the local village. They also built roads, schools, and mills; introduced sheep and new crops; and at Johnstown, the county seat, established a county fair and built the local jail, courthouse, and Anglican church.[9] In return for looking after the interests of their tenants, the Johnsons expected loyalty and deference—letters to them from tenants and others, for example, often began, "May it Please your Lordship." When the Revolution came, the Johnson's tenants formed an armed guard to protect their landlord, and when he fled to Canada, they followed.[10]

There were also other paternalistic relationships between eastern Ontario Loyalists and various authorities. Many of the colonists, of German Palatinate or French Huguenot ancestry were Protestants who had fled to England in search of religious freedom and who revered George III as a defender of Protestantism. The Highlanders were accustomed to an authoritarian society, and their family and clan structure was patriarchal. And the Mohawk, although they considered themselves an independent people, spoke of the king as a father and looked to the British government to protect them from the rapaciousness of the powerful New York landlords who spent much of the eighteenth century defrauding the Indians of their land. As they fled the frontiers of the colonies for Canada, the Loyalists who later settled in eastern Ontario did so in groups and as families. This can be seen by comparing them to the immigrants who had come to the colonies in the mid-eighteenth century. As the table below illustrates, 74.3 per cent of the immigrants were male and 25.7 per cent female, whereas 70.6 per cent of the adult eastern Ontario Loyalists were male and 29.4 per cent female.

	Percentage of Males	Percentage of Females
Immigrants	74.3	25.7
Eastern Ontario Loyalists	70.6	29.4

Even these statistics underestimate the female Loyalists in that boys as young as ten belonged to the Loyalist regiments and could be listed as adult male settlers rather than as children, whereas girls of the same age were considered children. Moreover, whereas the number of children per adult female in early-eighteenth-century New York had been only 1.88, among eastern Ontario Loyalists there were about 2.4 children per adult woman.[11]

The social and family structure in which these Loyalists and other colonial Americans lived was also patriarchal if we take patriarchy to mean "the manifestation and institutionalization of male dominance over women and children in the family and the extension of male dominance over women in society in general. ... [It] implies that men hold power in all the important institutions of society and that women are deprived of access to such power."[12] Colonial American society was patriarchal in several senses. Women could not participate in the political process, they could not get a higher education, and men controlled the most basic commodity in the society—land. Not only was the title to the family's property in the man's name, but a widow who remarried lost ownership of her property to her new husband. A married woman's identity was subsumed in that of her husband's. "A married couple," in the words of one historian, "became like a legal fiction: like a corporation, the pair was a single person with a single will"—the husband's. Even within the household it was common for the man to make all of the major decisions about finances and even about raising the children, and in any marital separation the man retained custody of the children.[13]

Patriarchal relationships, like paternalistic ones, did not mean that there could not be affection between husband and wife. To cite one example, a 1776 letter from Alexander McDonald, a captain in the Royal Highland Emigrants stationed in Halifax, to his wife in the colonies began, "My dear Susannah" and ended tenderly, "I have no time to write more. ... Kiss the children for me and believe the one forever to be yours." Yet the patriarchal nature of the relationship was revealed in the instructions he gave her about all aspects of her life: "Keep the Child always clean and well dress'd and you must appear in yr best Colours yourself." Of a fellow soldier, he wrote, "Keep the old gentleman always at a distance from you and never let him again appear in the House."[14]

The subordination of women in the colonial American family was revealed in the diary of Dothe Stone, sister of the eastern Ontario Loyalist, Joel Stone. As Dothe's list of births illustrates, marriage and childbirth were central to women's lives. The average woman was married in her early twenties to a man from one to five years older; she could expect to be pregnant within twelve months, and her childbearing years became a cycle of pregnancy, birth, and lactation.[15]

The birth and care of children, combined with women's other tasks, meant that their life centred on the home. The family farm was the basic economic and social unit on the frontier, and although some women did have to help with clearing and farming the land, women's jobs were more often milking the cows, taking care of the chickens, planting and tending the garden, and harvesting the orchard. As well, they cared for the house, salted beef and pork, preserved fruit and stored vegetables, made cider and cheese, and dried apples. A major chore was making clothing: Dothe writes of spending days with her sisters at spinning wheels. Whereas her husband might get away from home by going fishing or hunting or by travelling to town for supplies or to do business, the woman, especially if she had small children (which was almost always), was tied to the home.[16]

Colonial women found security in what was familiar to them—their homes, their families, and their circle of community friends and relatives. Dothe wrote fondly of her favourite room, her "once loved chamber," and her diary is full of excitement when describing social events, such as weddings, or gatherings at which a fiddler led the party in singing and dancing. Dothe also relied heavily on female companionship. Tasks like spinning were done in the company of other women; women helped each other in childbirth and child rearing, and most of them lived in the same house as, or close to, other female relatives. Some of Dothe Stone's sweetest memories were of times spent with her sisters: "Sunday afternoon Sister Hannah and I have been walking to the far part of Davis' South lots, being very tyred, I lyed down under a pretty bush, I tied my long pocket handkerchief about my head, and took a stone for a pillow and never did I rest more sweetly, while Sister Hannah set by me making some excellent verses about the gracefullness of my appearance."[17] Home, family, and female companionship were what mattered most to colonial women.

Patriarchy was also evident in the Stone family. Whether unmarried and living in her father's or brother's house, or married and in her husband's, Dothe Stone's life was run by men. Her brother, whom she lived with for nine years, "supported and directed" her and made all the decisions, including the one to move, without consulting her. The image of the father as patriarch was captured by Dothe when she described "my Dad an old gentleman ... in the other room with a large family of likely children gathering round and looking to him for support."[18]

Relationships within the colonial family were patriarchal, and even women themselves spoke of their own inferiority and dependence. Widows, like the strong-minded Patriot, Mary Fish, for example, described themselves as "a poor weak and helpless creature, [who] could do nothing but lie at the foot of mercy and look for direction." "What," she asked rhetorically, "Could a feble [sic] woman do."[19] Statements like these do not necessarily mean that women inwardly accepted the notion of their helplessness and inferiority. What they do mean, however, is that the social norms were such that women felt the need to express their feminine dependence and weakness.

But the notions of female helplessness and dependence were brought into question by the Revolution, which posed new challenges for Patriot *and* Loyalist women and forced many to adopt new roles. To Loyalist women, attached to their homes and local surroundings, accustomed to the security of friends, relatives and neighbours, and used to relying on men to direct their lives and make important decisions for them, the Revolution was a shattering experience. Patriot women, it is true, were left to manage the family and farm or business in their husbands' absence; but at least most remained in their homes and communities. Many Loyalist women, however, lost everything they valued most. Their families were scattered and the men who had directed their lives, gone. Many were also wrenched from all that was familiar—their homes, their relatives, and their communities. What all Loyalist women shared was their experiences as refugees, which were far more challenging than those of most Patriot women.

The pattern was set in May 1776, when Sir John Johnson fled from his northern New York estate with 170 tenants to escape arrest by the Patriots and to seek refuge in Canada, leaving behind his wife, Lady Mary Watts Johnson, who was pregnant and already the mother of two children under two. Mary, or Polly, who was from a prosperous New York city merchant and banking family, had married Sir John in 1773 at the age of nineteen and moved north to live in Tryon County. When her husband fled, Polly could not accompany him because of her condition, the hastiness of his departure, and the extraordinary rigours of the trip. Disappointed at the escape of Sir John, the Patriots forced her to turn over the keys to "every place"; her husband's private papers were seized, his "books distributed about the country," and their home, Johnson Hall, plundered and "made a Barrack." Lady Johnson was held hostage in Albany, although she was in touch regularly with her husband through "Indian and white men ... sent through the Woods." After some twenty months in captivity, Lady Johnson escaped, travelling through enemy territory in the cold winter. Although she finally reached the British base in New York City, her youngest child died as a result of its traumatic experiences.[20]

Within months of Lady Johnson's escape the war that was to rage on the frontier for more than four years began, and the hostages in this vicious conflict were the women and the children. As the Patriots attempted to assert their control over the region by forcing suspected Loyalists to take oaths of allegiance or join the militia, many able-bodied Loyalist men were either arrested or followed Sir John Johnson's lead by escaping to British lines, reluctantly leaving their families behind. Once in Canada, most had to join the various Loyalist regiments that collaborated with the Indians to launch retaliatory raids on the American frontier. For the British, the raids had a military purpose: to harass the enemy and destroy food supplies for Patriot forces. For many Loyalist soldiers, the raids were an opportunity to seek revenge on their foes in the colonies, find new recruits, make contact with their families, and occasionally bring the families back to Canada. For the families, the raids complicated their already troubled lives by intensifying Patriot hatred of the Loyalists and compromising them even further, since the families often harboured or helped the raiding parties. As the raiding parties retreated to the safety of Canada, they left their families behind.[21]

With the men in their lives gone, Loyalist women were forced to assume new responsibilities, and some even actively engaged in the war effort. For example, three women were implicated in a plot to kidnap the mayor of Albany, and one, an Indian woman, confessed to having lured the mayor to the woods by reporting that she had found a dead body there.[22] Another woman was arrested and jailed along with twenty men for "having assisted in the destruction of Currey Town."[23] Women were arrested and some imprisoned for taking part in robberies, which were especially common at the manor of Rensselaerwyck in the late 1770s.[24] Loyalist women also provided intelligence and passed messages between the British in New York City and Canada.[25]

Two eastern Ontario Loyalist women who were unusually active in the war effort were associated with the Mohawk Indians. This is not surprising in light of the status of women in the matrilineal Mohawk society, where children belonged to the mother's rather than the father's clan and women chose and deposed the chiefs. The local economy of the predominantly agrarian Mohawk was controlled by the women, who were responsible for planting, harvesting, and distributing the crops. Mohawk matrons were also influential in war councils and in determining the fate of captives.[26]

One very influential Mohawk woman was Molly Brant, or Konwatsi'tsianienni. A member of a high-ranking Mohawk family, sister of the famous Mohawk chief, Joseph Brant, and a matron who had a great influence in the matrilineal Iroquois society, Molly Brant "was a person of great prestige in her nation and throughout the Confederacy." Her power and influence were heightened after 1759, when she became the wife in all but name of Sir William Johnson, superintendent of Indian affairs, with whom she had eight children. Equally at home in the Indian village, in the war council, as the charming and gracious hostess at Johnson Hall, or in running Johnson's huge estate during his frequent absences, Molly Brant was a remarkable woman.[27]

She helped many Loyalists escape to Canada, provided intelligence to the British, and played a decisive part in fostering the ties of loyalty, self-interest, and history that underpinned the Mohawk support for the British during the Revolution. After her home was plundered by the Patriots and she was forced to flee with her family to the safety of the Iroquois villages, Brant came to Canada in 1778 and moved from one British base to another, cementing the Mohawks' loyalty to the British. Daniel Claus, Indian agent and son-in-law of the late Sir William Johnson, said of Molly Brant, "One word from her is more taken notice of by the five nations than a thousand from any white man without Exception." The commanding officer at Carleton Island attributed the good behaviour of the Indians there to Brant's influence: "The Chiefs were careful to keep their people sober and satisfy'd, but their uncommon good behaviour is in a great Measure to be ascribed to Miss Molly Brant's influence over them, which is far superior to that of all their Chiefs put together, and she has in the course of this Winter done every thing in Her power to maintain them strongly in the King's interest." Brant's stature was recognized by the British government, which awarded her one of the largest pensions ever given to any Indian and built her a house at present-day Kingston, where she spent her last years.[28]

Another woman influential among the Mohawk was Sarah Kast McGinnis, an American-born Palatinate German, who as a child in northern New York lived with the Mohawks, was adopted by them, and learned their language. In the 1740s Sarah married an Irishman, Timothy McGinnis, who became involved with Sir William Johnson in the fur trade and as a captain in the Indian Department. After her husband was killed in the Seven Years' War, the widow McGinnis carried on his trading business.[29]

When the Revolution broke out, both sides courted Sarah because of her close association with the Iroquois, the Patriots offering her twelve shillings York currency a day and a guard of fifteen men. But Sarah and her family sided with the British and worked to cement the Iroquois' loyalty, actions that caused them to be persecuted by the Patriots. In 1777, as news spread of Burgoyne's expedition from Canada through northern New York, the Patriots considered it necessary to neutralize Loyalists like Sarah and her family. In Sarah's case, this involved arresting her son-in-law and then confiscating all her property. Sarah, her daughters, and grandchildren watched helplessly as their belongings were sold at public auction; they were then arrested and "so harshly used" that one granddaughter died. When the Patriots mistakenly concluded that the British had the upper hand in the region, Sarah and her family were released. Before they could be recaptured, they "escaped at night with only what they could carry on their backs" and left for Canada with British troops, although Sarah had to leave behind a son "who was out of his senses and bound in chains ... and who some time afterward was burnt alive."[30]

After arriving in Canada, Sarah agreed to a British request to return to northern New York, winter with the Iroquois, and try to counter the harmful effects of Burgoyne's defeat. On her arrival at "the most central village of the Six nations," the Indians "flocked to her from the remotest villages and thanked her for coming ... to direct and advise them in that critical time." Soon after her arrival, the Patriots sent messages to the Iroquois, "with a most exaggerated account of General Burgoyne's disaster" and "belts," inviting them to join the Patriots along with "threats" in case the Indians refused. In response to the Patriot overtures, the Indians "consulted with" Sarah and sought her "opinion and advice": "Then after that with an Authority and privilege allowed to women of Consequence only among Indians, [she] seized upon and cancelled the [Patriot] Belts, telling them such bad news came from an evil Spirit and must endanger their peace and union as long as it was in their sight and therefore must be buried underground."[31] When Sarah spent this long and difficult winter in the Indian villages, she was sixty-four years old.

Although Sarah Kast McGinnis's relationship with the Indians and her active participation in the Revolution were extraordinary, her other experiences were typical of those of other Loyalist women. As able-bodied Loyalist men on the frontiers either were arrested or fled, leaving their families behind, the sins of the fathers and husbands were visited on the wives and children. Patriot committees and mobs assumed, unless there was evidence to the contrary, that families were accomplices in the guilt of one member. If one member of a family fled or was arrested, the rest were vulnerable either to official interrogation by committees or to unofficial harassment by mobs or Patriot neighbours.

The case of the Cartwright family was not unusual. The father, Richard, Sr., a prosperous innkeeper landowner, and deputy postmaster of Albany, had shown his support for the Patriots in 1775 when he gave money to the Patriot expedition against Ticonderoga. But his daughter, Elizabeth, who was married to a British soldier and lived in Niagara, was in touch with his son, Richard, Jr., and when the local committee of correspondence discovered this in February 1777, it forced Richard, Jr., to give security for his future good behaviour. By October 1777 he could no longer give this guarantee, and with his young niece, Hannah, he left on a difficult journey through the northern New York wilderness to Canada. The parents, tainted by the Loyalism of their children, were mistreated, their property was confiscated, and within a year of their son's departure they were taken under guard to the border.[32]

The Cartwrights' experiences were shared by many Loyalist women who had to live with the consequences of their husbands' actions. With the men in their lives gone, the women not only had to assume responsibility for running the farm and taking care of their families, but also had to deal with Patriot harassment or persecution and in many cases they were forced to leave their homes to seek refuge behind the British lines. When Garnet Dingman, who was a squatter on land on the Susquehanna River, joined the British in 1781, he left his cattle, utensils, and furniture to his wife and friends; however, shortly after his departure, the "rebels," in the words of an observer, "stript [his wife] of every thing." Another Susquehanna River squatter was Jane Glasford, whose "husband was to [sic] old to serve, but he sent his Sons to serve" with Joseph Brant, whose troops took some of their stock and grain. Jane described what happened to her and her husband because of their son's military service: "The Rebels came in '79 & plundered them, & stript them of everything. She was almost starvd in her own house. They were all obliged to come away. ... Their house was burnt as soon as they left it." A similar fate was meted out to Mary Waldec, wife of a tenant in Tryon country who fled to Canada with Sir John Johnson in 1776. In 1777 the "rebels ... took most" of her "things ... and sold them at Vendue," and later Mary fled to Canada.[33] The wife of Philip Empy, who had refused to sign a Patriot oath and whose sons had joined the British, was jailed along with her children and then "beat," "abused" by four men, and left on the road. Friends rescued her, but she died soon after.[34]

The severity of the treatment meted out to Loyalist women depended on their husbands' connections and reputation among the dominant faction in the community. The case of two Vermont Loyalist women illustrates this point. Sarah Bottum was the wife of Justus Sherwood, a Vermont landowner, speculator, and entrepreneur in the timber business. Originally from Connecticut, Justus had received his land in Vermont from the New Hampshire government, and he supported Ethan Allen and his brothers, the dominant faction in the disputed territory. When Justus fell afoul of the local Patriots for refusing to take an oath of allegiance and allegedly corresponding with the British, he was threatened with execution and imprisoned, although he escaped and fled to Canada. The Patriots ransacked the Sherwoods' cabin and destroyed some of their belongings, but Sarah could look to her parents for help, and she was allowed to remain in Vermont until she decided to seek permission from the Patriots to join her husband in Canada.[35]

The treatment of another Vermont Loyalist, Mary Munro, was much harsher because her husband belonged to an unpopular faction in Vermont. John Munro, originally from Scotland, had been granted large tracts of land by New York, and this put him at odds with the dominant faction in Vermont, whose land grants came from New Hampshire. Munro became even more unpopular when he was appointed justice of the peace and given the unenviable task of imposing law and order on Ethan Allen and the Green Mountain Boys, who harassed New Yorkers in Vermont. When the Revolution came and Munro supported the British, the Council of Safety drove him from his home and seized all his property, except "a few personal articles left for the support of his wife." Unlike Sarah Sherwood, who had the support of her family, Mary Munro was treated very harshly by her neighbours and shunned by her own family. She wrote to her husband of her plight:

I am in a poor state of health and very much distresst. I must leave my house in a very short time and God knows where I shall get a place to put my head in, for my own relations are my greatest enemies. ... They have distrest me beyond expression. I have scarcely a mouthful of bread for myself or children. ... Is there no possibility of your sending for us? If there is no method fallen upon we shall all perish, for you can have no idea of our sufferings here ... my heart is so full it is ready to break.

Luckily, Mary Munro and her eight children did make their way to Canada within a few months of this letter.[36]

Flight may have represented an end to persecution for many Loyalist women; yet, it was also difficult for them to leave their homes and cut their ties with their families, friends, and communities. Simon Schwartz, the son of tenants of the Johnson family, who described his father's flight to Canada with Sir John in 1776 and the harassment of other family members, stressed that his mother had left only when she had to; she "would not come in [to Canada] before the House & builds [sic] were burnt." Women like Mrs. Schwartz usually had no choice but to leave. If they left voluntarily, it was usually because their property had been confiscated or their homes destroyed and there were no relatives or neighbours to protect them.

Some Loyalist women simply fled, but many others sought permission to leave from Patriot committees. Either permission was granted and the women escorted to the frontiers, or they were exchanged for Patriot prisoners being held in Canada. Mary Cruger Meyers had been alone with seven children under thirteen since the summer of 1777, when her husband, John Walden Meyers, left to join Burgoyne. In October 1778 she and another Loyalist woman requested permission to go to New York.[37] After being dispossessed of their property, the wives of Loyalists in Tryon County petitioned the local Patriot committee to be either taken care of or allowed to join their husbands. Their latter request was eventually granted.[38] When women left, they could only take children under twelve with them; boys twelve and over were considered capable of bearing arms and had to be left behind.[39] Those going to British lines also had to pay all the costs of being escorted there and take fourteen days' provisions with them.[40]

By the late 1770s, however, many Loyalist women were forced to leave. Some were sent to Canada because they were destitute and "subsisted at public Expense." A more common reason for removing the women was that they had assisted the enemy. When their husbands, relatives, or friends returned to the frontiers from Canada to gather intelligence, to recruit, or to raid, the women provided food, shelter, and other forms of assistance, which only further incriminated them in the eyes of the Patriots. Rachel Ferguson and her daughters, for example, were brought before the local Patriot committee in 1779 "for harbouring and entertaining a Number of Tories who came down from Canada with an inte[n]tion of Murdering the Defenceless Inhabitants on the Western Frontiers."[41] For their efforts the Ferguson women were jailed and later forced to leave.

By July 1780 it was official policy in New York to "remove families of persons who [had] joined the Enemy." The families were given twenty days to prepare for their departure, their goods and chattels were to be sold to pay the costs, and any who ignored the edict were to "be liable to be proceeded against as Enemies of this and the United States."[42] Some women asked for and received a reprieve; but this required that "sundry well affected inhabitants" had to testify that the woman had "behaved herself in a becoming manner."[43] In other words, it was up to the woman to prove innocence by having well-known Patriots testify on her behalf. In the absence of such testimony, the woman was assumed to share the guilt of her husband.

Exile was the last stage in a process that profoundly altered the role and responsibilities of many Loyalist women. Like their Patriot counterparts, Loyalist women assumed the responsibility for running the household and farm in the absence of their husbands. But Loyalist women also had to endure harassment, persecution, and often poverty because of the actions of their husbands. Most difficult of all, perhaps, was the necessity of abandoning their homes, relatives, and communities.

In facing these adversities, women were often forced to assert themselves and assume what were generally considered to be male responsibilities. The more public and assertive role of women was illustrated by Polly Watts Johnson, who had the audacity, after being captured by the Patriots, to write directly to General George Washington to complain of being treated "with severity."[44] When an exchange had to be arranged for the prominent New York Loyalist Alexander White, it was his wife who undertook the negotiations with the British. Isabel Parker, who had "aided and succoured his Majesty's Scouts on secret service by procuring them provisions and intelligence and encouraging Sundry persons to join his Majesty's service at her great expense, peril and risk," interceded with the governor of Quebec on behalf of her son, who had been in the British secret service and had been arrested by the Patriots. Mrs. Jeremiah French, whose husband had joined the British and had all his property confiscated and his "cattle driven away and sold," was brought to the attention of the Vermont governor and council because she was "very turbulent and troublesome and refused to obey orders." Known for her "bitter tongue," Mrs. French proved so troublesome that the Patriots dispatched her to the British lines.[45]

Women were also forced to take more responsibility for looking after themselves and families. A group of New York Loyalist women who had established themselves near Saratoga petitioned the Patriots in 1780 for permission to go to Canada; in 1781 they were still on the frontier and regarded as a serious enough threat that they were ordered to move to the interior. The sixteen-year-old daughter of John McDonell, a Scots Loyalist from Tryon county, "was obliged to hire herself to an old Dutch woman to spin in order to prevent starving." And there was the case of Elizabeth Bowman, who, after her house on the

Susquehanna River had been sacked by the Patriots and her husband and eldest son carried off, was left to care for eight children. The Indians helped them through the winter, and in the spring she moved to the Mohawk River and joined other Loyalist women to grow corn and potatoes. When the British rescued them in the fall and took them to Canada, there were five women, thirty-one children, and one pair of shoes.[46]

Exile marked the end of one stage of Loyalist women's refugee experience and the beginning of another. The women had left the American colonies as disaffected citizens considered a threat to the security of the new nation. In British territory they were burdens, mouths to be fed and bodies to be clothed and housed. When they reached Canada, they were usually destitute and the British unprepared for their arrival. In 1777 an officer in Niagara described the refugees flocking to that base: "They are almost naked and have been so long hiding in the woods, and almost famished that it is distressing to behold them. ... I am informed that 50 are on their way, but so weak they can scarcely crawl. I wish your excellency's direction on how to dispose of them."[47] From Crown Point, a base at the other end of the outer perimeter of British defences, came similar accounts of the arrival of Loyalists who "had fled from persecution," especially in the winter when the lakes and rivers could be crossed by sleigh. Often British officials were uncertain what to do with the refugees, and families arriving in Niagara were often sent on to Montreal.[48]

When the women arrived at the bases, they were in need of food, clothing, and shelter. Most had been stripped of their property and many of their possessions before their flight. The journey itself across the wilderness of northern New York was gruelling. Reaching Canada involved either crossing one of the many lakes in an open boat or perhaps a sleigh in winter, or travelling along rugged trails since "there [was] no road by land to go with a carriage." Sir John Johnson and his tenants who fled from northern New York in 1776 travelled for nineteen days, during which they almost starved, going nine days without provisions, except "wild onions, Roots and the leaves of beech trees." When they reached Canada, their shoes were worn through and their clothes ragged.[49]

Sarah Bottum Sherwood's greatest ordeal during the Revolution was her trip to Canada, which began with a wagon ride over trails to the shores of Lake Champlain. Next was a boat trip across the lake and a thirty-mile trek through the bush to the closest British outpost. When Sarah undertook the trek, it was November; she had with her a slave, a child of three, and a baby; and she was seven months pregnant. But she succeeded and was re-united with her husband.[50]

When Loyalists arrived at British bases, penniless and exhausted by the rigours of their journey, they were at the mercy of paternalistic and patriarchal British military regimes. Even Sarah McGinnis, the tough sixty-four-year-old who had wintered with the Iroquois in 1777, was "in dire need" in Montreal the following year. Her daughter was "so scantily lodged" that her mother could not stay with her. She was also refused firewood by the officer in charge, who said that only the governor could make such a decision. Sarah and her family were left "without any money or income except what they could earn by the needle."[51] Thus, Loyalists had to look to the British government to provide shelter, clothing, and rations and at the end of the war to chart their future.

The British government took care of its charges but expected deference and service in return. The British regimes were military ones that dealt quickly and harshly with dissenters. In return for their keep, men had to fight in the Loyalist regiments and women had to do washing and other domestic chores for the army. Questioning of the regime was neither common nor tolerated. When a group of Loyalists in Quebec petitioned the governor for more aid, for example, they were informed that if the governor's plans for them were not acceptable, they could go to Nova Scotia.[52]

Patriarchy and paternalism were also apparent in the last phase of the Loyalists' experience—their resettlement in what is now eastern Ontario. Under the direction of British officials, the Loyalists were transported into the interior and provided with food, clothing, agricultural equipment, and seeds. They were settled on land surveyed by British officials, and British army officers were there to preserve order and ensure that the governor's instructions were obeyed. Although the new communities were on the frontier, from the beginning there was a structure and hierarchy. In a society where land ownership was central to status, the size of one's land grant varied according to one's military rank, the British government compensated Loyalists for their losses on the basis of the value of their former assets in the American colonies, and Loyalist officers received half pay after their regiments were disbanded.[53]

Thus, when Loyalist women reached British lines, they were re-integrated into a paternalistic and patriarchal power structure. Within this paternalistic order there was a hierarchy. There were those who needed to be cared for and those responsible for administering the care, those in leadership roles and those who were clearly subordinates. Deference to authority was built into the military regimes, and deference was accorded to those dispensing benevolent care and expected of those receiving it. Even more so than the civil regimes in the American colonies, the military regimes in Quebec and New York City had no place for women and even shunned them as extra mouths to be fed and families to be housed. Women could only fit into such paternalistic and patriarchal power structures as subordinates needing care and protection.

This subordination was reflected in the Loyalist women's petitions for rations, subsistence, or compensation for losses. The very act of petitioning those in authority for aid cast all Loyalists in the role of supplicant; "the formulation of a petition," in the words of Linda Kerber, "begins in the acknowledgement of subordination."[54] Moreover, many Loyalist petitions were stylized litanies of loyalty, service, and sacrifice. But there was a difference in the substance of women's petitions: women based their claim to British assistance on their feminine frailty and on the service of their husbands. In fact, some did not even petition on their own behalf but had men request aid for them. When Catherine Peck, wife of one of Sir John's tenants who had fled to Canada in 1776, arrived in New York City "in hope of getting a Passage to Canada" and found herself and her child "destitute of any Sort of Support," it was an official from Indian Affairs who appealed to British officials to assist her.[55] Even Molly Brant, who had been so active in maintaining the loyalty of the Mohawk, had to seek male help when it came to approaching the British for support. She sought advice from her brother in 1779, and in 1780 two members of the Johnson clan and another associate discussed helping Molly and her daughters to get a pension from the British.[56] Of the twenty-six eastern Ontario Loyalist women who sought compensation from the British for their losses, four had men file their claims.[57]

Whether Loyalist women petitioned themselves or had others do it for them, what was stressed was their weakness, helplessness, and dependence. Citing a "numerous, small and helpless family" as his main burden, one Loyalist appealed to the governor of Quebec for subsistence, while another asked for aid for his "chargeable family." The Loyalist Jean McConell summed up perfectly the notion of female incapacity when she described herself as "feeble" and added that she also had "a family of daughters."[58] Feeble and helpless were the adjectives used most often by Loyalist women to describe themselves.[59]

These professions of feebleness were very much at odds with Loyalist women's recent experiences. The case of Phoebe Grant, or Grout, illustrates this point nicely. When her husband and son joined Burgoyne in 1777, the "rebels" seized his property and "effects" and turned her "and three helpless Female children Out of Doors destitute." She then had to "fly" to Quebec "for protection." Within days of her arrival in Quebec, her husband drowned and she was "obliged to provide for herself and her three children without an allowance from government which ceased on the death of her husband." After her husband's death she did "everything in her power to support herself," even though she was "in a country far from a single Friend and a stranger to the language." When Phoebe finally had to throw "herself and poor family at your Excellency's feet praying" for subsistence, she could not revel in her accomplishments and seek praise for even surviving such ordeals; all she could do was tell her story as a tale of suffering and depict herself, in her own words, as "a Feeble Woman."[60]

Why did Loyalist women describe themselves as feeble or helpless when their recent experiences suggested just the opposite? One reason was a practical reality. What the British needed from the Loyalists were able-bodied males to raid the frontiers, spy on the Patriots, bring in new recruits, supply British troops, or build fortifications. What they did not need or want was women and children, who, it was assumed, could perform none of these services and would be a burden to the British because they had to be fed, clothed, and housed. Thus, the only way for women to appeal to the British was to cite their husband's valued services, rather than their own undervalued ones, and to invoke the paternalism of the military regimes by stressing their vulnerability and need for protection.

Another reason, however, was that when they reached British lines, Loyalist women confronted a well-defined power structure in which there were clearly prescribed social roles. In the colonies during the Revolution, traditional relationships were disrupted and lines of authority far from clear. Women could and did do things they might have never dreamed of doing in peacetime, and their actions were of necessity considered socially acceptable, if only because the boundaries of socially acceptable behaviour are more flexible in wartime. However, at British bases lines of authority were not only clear, but were better defined than they had been in the colonies. Though there had been elements of paternalism and patriarchy in the pre-Revolutionary experiences of many Ontario Loyalists, the British regimes were much more patriarchal and paternal. And women could fit into such a power structure only as frail subordinates.

But the fact that women used the language of enfeeblement does not mean that they themselves accepted their own weakness. They were supplicants who had to petition for assistance and "the rhetoric of humility is a necessary part of the petition as a genre, whether or not humility is felt in fact."[61] Women had no choice but to stress their dependence and helplessness; whether they actually believed it is another matter.

Yet, whether or not women accepted their own weakness is beside the point. The language they used expressed accurately their position in the power structure. Whether or not they were weak and dependent, they were assumed to be so for all public purposes and were outwardly treated as such. On the other hand, the consistent use of certain words cannot be divorced from one's attitudes about oneself: if women were forced by circumstances to reiterate their helplessness again and again, how long was it before they came either to accept that helplessness was basic to their femininity or to allow their actions to be limited by their supposed weakness? The fact that the eastern Ontario Loyalist women were never allowed to speak of their achievements with pride meant that they never received in any measure the recognition accorded to Patriot women.

It is ironic that many eastern Ontario Loyalist women, though they overcame greater obstacles and met more devastating challenges during the Revolution than their Patriot counterparts, received less recognition. As well as having to take charge of their families and farms in the absence of their husbands, Loyalist women were dispossessed of their property, thrown out of their houses, and even jailed by the Patriots. They had to leave what was most dear to them—their homes, their relatives, and their friends—and travel through the wilderness to the British lines.

Yet these remarkable and heroic accomplishments were never recognized. When they reached British lines, they had to fit once again into a patriarchal power structure in which their inferiority and dependence were assumed. Needing British support, they had to stress their dependence and weakness to appeal to the paternalism of the British regime. Only their suffering and their husband's service counted with the British. Whereas republicanism at least potentially offered more scope to women, paternalism assumed inequality and deference. There were the weak and the strong, the leaders and the followers. Within such a framework, women could only be the weak followers.

Not only were the accomplishments of eastern Ontario Loyalist women not recognized by the British; they were also ignored by later generations. After the Revolution, myths grew up about the Loyalists' undying devotion to the British Empire or their upper class backgrounds, and tales were told of the men's heroism. Virtually ignored, however, were the heroic feats of the Loyalist women. Whereas the contributions of Patriot women, such as their spinning of homespun cloth, became part of the American folklore, the memories of the travails and victories of the eastern Ontario Loyalist women died with them.

These women were also ignored by Canadian historians, who, by focusing on the Revolutionary war on the frontier as it was run by the British and fought by the Loyalist regiments, have overlooked the essential fact that the war was a civil war in which women and children were of necessity participants. The experiences of the eastern Ontario Loyalist women and their part in the civil war that raged on the frontiers are an important part of Canadian history. Recognition of their accomplishments is long overdue.

Notes

1. Mary Beth Norton, *Liberty's Daughters: The Revolutionary Experience of American Women, 1760-1800* (Boston: Little, Brown, 1980); Linda Kerber, *Women of the Republic: Intellect and Ideology in Revolutionary America* (Chapel Hill, N.C.: Univ. of North Carolina Press, 1980). For another view, see Joan Hoff Wilson, "The Illusion of Change: Women and the American Revolution," In Alfred F. Young, ed., *The American Revolution: Explorations in the History of American Radicalism* (DeKalb: Northern Illinois Univ. Press, 1976), pp. 383-446.

2. Jay Fliegelman, *Prodigals and Pilgrims: The American Revolution against Patriarchal Authority, 1750-1800* (Cambridge: Cambridge Univ. Press, 1982); Norton, *Liberty's Daughters,* pp. 235, 229; Jacqueline S. Reinier, "Rearing the Republican Child: Attitudes and Practices in Post-Revolutionary Philadelphia," *William and Mary Quarterly,* 3rd ser., 39 (1982), 150-63.

3. See, for example, Mary Beacock Fryer, "Sarah Sherwood: Wife and Mother, an 'Invisible Loyalist'," in *Eleven Exiles: Accounts of Loyalists of the American Revolution,* Phyllis R. Blakely and John N. Grant, eds. (Toronto: Dundurn, 1982), pp. 245-64; Mary Beth Norton, "Eighteenth-Century American Women in Peace and

War: The Case of the Loyalists," *William and Mary Quarterly,* 3rd ser., 33 (1976), 386-409; Katherine M.J. McKenna, " 'Treading the Hard Road': Some Loyalist Women and the American Revolution" (M.A. thesis, Queen's Univ., 1979).

4. M.S. Waltman, "From Soldier to Settler: Patterns of Loyalist Settlement in 'Upper Canada,' 1783-1785" (M.A. thesis, Queen's Univ., 1981), p. 58.

5. Waltman, "From Soldier to Settler," p. 60; Walter Allen Knittle, *Early Eighteenth Century Palatine Emigration: A British Government Redemptioner Project to Manufacture Naval Stores* (Baltimore: Dorrance, 1937): Eula C. Lapp, *To Their Heirs Forever* (Picton: Picton Publishing Co., 1970); Alice P. Kenney, *Stubborn for Liberty: The Dutch in New York* (Syracuse: Syracuse Univ. Press, 1975); "The Albany Dutch: Loyalists and Patriots," *New York History,* 42 (1961).

6. Waltman, "From Soldier to Settler," p. 62; I.C.C. Graham, *Colonists from Scotland: Emigration to North America, 1707-1783* (Ithaca: Cornell Univ. Press, 1956); Hazel C. Mathews, *The Mark of Honour* (Toronto: Univ. of Toronto Press, 1965).

7. Waltman, "From Soldier to Settler." pp. 39-42.

8. Gerald Dworkin, "Paternalism," in Rolf Sartorious, ed., *Paternalism* (Minneapolis: Univ. of Minnesota Press. 1983), pp. 19-34; Donald Van De Veer, *Paternalistic Intervention: The Moral Bounds of Benevolence* (Princeton: Princeton Univ. Press, 1986), pp. 16-23; John Kleinig, *Paternalism* (Totow, N.J.: Rowman and Allaneld, 1984). pp. 4-5; Jack D. Douglas, "Cooperative Paternalism versus Conflictual Paternalism," in Sartorius, *Paternalism,* pp. 171-200; David Roberts. *Paternalism in Early Victorian England* (New Brunswick, N.J.: Rutgers Univ. Press, 1979), pp. 4-6.

9. Abbott Collection, Ms. 420, Letter and Reference for Richard Mandevell, Sir William Johnson, June 11, 1771. quoted in Robert William Venables, "Tryon County, 1775-1783: A Frontier in Revolution" (Ph.D. thesis, Vanderbilt Univ., 1967), pp. 72, 64; Edward Countryman, *A People in Revolution: The American Revolution and Political Society* (Baltimore: Johns Hopkins Univ. Press, 1981), pp. 21, 33.

10. Countryman, *A People in Revolution,* p. 33.

11. Bernard Bailyn, *Voyagers to the West: A Passage in the Peopling of America on the Eve of the Revolution* (New York: Knopf, 1986), pp. 192-234; National Archives of Canada [hereafter NAC], *Haldimand Papers,* [hereafter HP], MG 21, B 168, p. 100, "Return of Loyalists, October, 1784"; Robert V. Wells, *The Population of the British Colonies in America before 1776* (Princeton: Princeton Univ. Press, 1975), p. 315.

12. Gerda Lerner, *The Creation of Patriarchy* (New York: Oxford Univ. Press, 1986), p. 239.

13. Kerber, *Women of the Republic,* p. 120; Joan R. Gundersen and Gwen Victor Gampel, "Married Women's Legal Status in Eighteenth-Century New York and Virginia," *William and Mary Quarterly,* 3rd ser., 39 (1982), 114-34.

14. NAC, Fraser Papers, MG 23, B 33, Alexander McDonald to his wife, in "Letters Extracted from the Letter Book of Capt. Alexander McDonald of the Royal Highland Emigrants written from Halifax, Windsor and Cornwallis between 1775 and 1779."

15. Archives of Ontario [hereafter AO], Joel Stone Papers, Dothe Stone Diary, 1777-1792 [hereafter Stone Diary]; Joy Day Buel and Richard Buel, Jr., *The Way of Duty: A Woman and her Family in Revolutionary America* (New York: Norton, 1984); Robert V. Wells, "Quaker Marriage Patterns in a Colonial Perspective," in Nancy F. Cott and Elizabeth Peck, eds., *A Heritage of Her Own: Toward a New Social History of American Women* (New York: Simon and Shuster, 1979), pp. 81-106; Norton, *Liberty's Daughters,* pp. 71-72; Laurel Thatcher Ulrich, *Good Wives: Image and Reality in the Lives of Women in Northern New England, 1650-1750* (New York: Knopf, 1982).

16. See, for example, Stone Diary; Norton, *Liberty's Daughters,* pp. 3-14.

17. Stone Diary, Oct. 22, 1783, p. 5; May 30, 1784, p. 11.

18. Stone Diary, Oct. 22, 1783, p. 5; Dec. 3, 1783, p. 8.

19. New Canaan Historical Society, Noyes Family Papers, pp. 39-47, Mary to Joseph and Rachel Fish, Aug. 6, 1769, May 30, 1772, privately owned, quoted in Buel, *The Way of Duty,* pp. 62-63, p. 67.

20. NAC, Claus Papers, C-1478, vol. 1, Sir John Johnson to Daniel Claus, Jan. 20, 1777.

21. Jack M. Sosin, *The Revolutionary Frontier, 1763-1783* (New York: Holt, Rinehart and Winston, 1967).

22. Victor Hugo Palsits, ed., *Minutes of the Commissioners for Detecting and Defeating Conspiracies in the State of New York: Albany County Sessions, 1778-1781,* 3 vols. (New York: J.B. Lyon, 1909), Aug. 13, 1781, vol. 2, 762-63.

23. *Ibid.,* July 25, 1781, vol. 2, 751-52.

24. *Ibid.,* Sept. 4, 1778, vol. 1, 224; May 20, 1778, vol. 1, 122; June 17, 1778, vol. 1, 146; Aug. 3, 1779, vol. 1, 398; Oct. 3, 1778, vol. 1, 252.

25. *Ibid.,* Nov. 8, 1780, vol. 2, 563; Jan. 29, 1781, vol. 2, 624; June 9, 1781, vol. 2, 733.

26. Barbara Graymont, *The Iroquois in the American Revolution* (Syracuse: Syracuse Univ. Press, 1972), pp. 17, 21-23.

27. Graymont, *The Iroquois in the American Revolution,* p. 47; *Dictionary of Canadian Biography,* vol. 4, 416-19; H. Pearson Gundy, "Molly Brant, Loyalist," *Ontario Historical Society Papers and Records,* 45 (1953), 97-108.

28. NAC, HP, vol. 21, p. 774, Daniel Claus to Governor Haldimand, Aug. 30, 1779; NAC, HP, vol. 21, p. 787, Captain Frazer to Haldimand, Mar. 21, 1780.

29. NAC, HP, vol. 21, p. 774, Daniel Claus to Governor Haldimand, Nov. 5, 1778.

30. NAC, HP, vol. 27, p. 302, Petition of Sarah McGinn, Audit Office 14.

31. *Ibid.*

32. Janice Potter and George Rawlyk, "Richard Cartwright, Jr.," *Dictionary of Canadian Biography,* vol. 5, 167-72.

33. *Report of the Public Archives of Ontario* [hereafter *PAO Report*], (Toronto: 1904), Claim of Garnet Dingman, p. 1038; claim of John Glasford, p. 1112; claim of Martin Waldec, p. 1121.

34. Petition by Philip Empy, Mar. 1, 1780, HP, vol. 21, p. 874.

35. *PAO Report,* Claim of Justus Sherwood; Ian Cleghorn Pemberton, "Justus Sherwood, Vermont Loyalist, 1747-1798," (Ph.D. thesis. Univ. of Western Ontario, 1973); Mary Beacock Fryer, *Buckskin Pimpernel: The Exploits of Justus Sherwood, Loyalist Spy* (Toronto: Dundurn, 1981), "Sarah Sherwood: ...," " *Eleven Exiles,* pp. 245-64; Queen's University Archives, H.M. Jackson, *Justus Sherwood: Soldier, Loyalist and Negotiator* (Kingston: n.p., 1958).

36. AO, John Munro Papers, Undated document; NAC, HP series B, vol. 214, p. 35.

37. Palsits, *Minutes of the Commissioners,* Oct. 1, 1778, vol. 1, 248.

38. "Petition of sundry women wives of tories for relief," n.d. Tryon County Committee of Safety Papers, in Kerber, *Women of the Republic,* p. 50.

39. Palsits, *Minutes of the Commissioners,* Aug. 1, 1778, vol. 1, 190.

40. *Ibid.,* Introduction, vol. 1, 57.

41. *Ibid., Minutes of the Commissioners,* Sept. 21, 1778, vol. 1, 237-38; Sept. 8, 1779, vol. 1, 441.

42. *Ibid.,* vol. 3, 795.

43. See, for example, the case of Elizabeth Hogel, in Palsits, *Minutes of the Commissioners,* vol 2, 540.

44. Mrs. Johnson to General Washington, June 16, 1776, Peter Force, *American Archives,* 9 vols. (Washington, D.C., 1837-53), 4th series, vol. 6, 930.

45. Palsits, *Minutes of the Commissioners,* Aug. 15, 1778, vol. 1, 206; NAC, HP, vol. 21, p. 875, Petition of Isabel Parker, AO, French Papers, Loveland Munson, "The Early History of Manchester."

46. Palsits, *Minutes of the Commissioners.* Oct. 29, 1780, vol. 3, 558; Apr. 30, 1781. vol. 3, 696; NAC, HP, vol. 73, p. 54, John McDonell to Mathews, Mar. 20, 1780; "A Letter from Mrs. Elizabeth Bowman Spohn," in J.J. Talman, *Loyalist Narratives from Upper Canada* (Toronto: Champlain Society, 1946). 315-22.

47. NAC, Colonial Office 42 [hereafter CO 42], vol. 36, B 33, pp. 2-3, R.B. Lernoult to Haldimand, Apr. 28, 1777.

48. CO 42, Q13, vol. 36, B 33, Sir Guy Carleton to Lord G. Germaine, May 27, 1777; NAC, Claus Papers, vol. 25, C 1485, Taylor and Diffin to Daniel Claus, Nov. 11, 1778, Claus Papers.

49. Claus Papers, C 1478, vol. 1, Johnson to Claus, Jan. 20, 1777.

50. Fryer, "Sarah Sherwood: ...," *Eleven Exiles,* pp. 245-64.

51. NAC, HP, vol. 21, p. 774, Claus to Haldimand, Nov. 19, 1778.

52. NAC, HP, vol. B 211, pp. 133-34, Memorial: Michael Grass and Loyalists from New York, Sorel, Jan., 1784. NAC, HP, vol. B 63, pp. 109-10, Mathews to Stephen DeLancey. Mar. 2, 1784.

53. H.V. Temperley, "Frontierism, Capital and the American Loyalists in Canada," *Journal of American Studies,* 13 (1979), 5-27.

54. Kerber, *Women of the Republic,* p. 85.

55. NAC, British Headquarters Papers, vol. 16, microfilm, reel M-348, [Name illegible] to Lt. Col. Roger Morris, Apr. 22, 1779.

56. NAC, Claus Papers, C 1478, Mary Brant to Joseph Brant, Oct. 5, 1779; C 1485, Captain Frazer to Daniel Claus, June 26, 1780.

57. Lydia Van Alstine, Flora Livingston, widow Obenholt, Margaret Hare.

58. NAC, HP, vol. 21, p. 875, Petition to Haldimand, Jan. 3, 1783; HP, vol. 21, p. 874, Petition of George Christie, Dec. 16, 1778; HP, vol. 21, p. 874, Petition of Jean McDonell, Nov. 30, 1782.

59. Mary Beth Norton, "Eighteenth-Century American Women in Peace and War: The Case of the Loyalists," *William and Mary Quarterly,* 3rd ser., 33 (1976), 386-409.

60. NAC, HP, A 776, Phoebe Grout, Petition.

61. Kerber, *Women of the Republic,* p. 85.

CHAPTER
8 THE WAR OF 1812

In the long history of human warfare, the War of 1812 is
a very minor event. Even viewed in the context of Canada's participation in
the wars of the twentieth century, this earlier war appears insignificant.
Certainly, from a military point of view, the War of 1812 is of limited interest.
Yet contemporary observers, as well as later commentators, regarded it as a
pivotal event in North American history, effectively confirming the results of the
American Revolutionary War.

In the first reading in this chapter, an American historian, Reginald
Horsman, re-examines the motives and objectives of the United States in pros-
ecuting the war. While not abandoning his earlier position that desire for the
acquisition of British North America did not actually cause the War of 1812, in
this article Horsman concludes that the Democratic-Republicans, who controlled the American government, regarded such acquisition as "a major
collateral benefit" of the war. Tracing the desire for acquisition of British North
America back to the beginning of the American Revolution, Horsman argues that
this was a consistent objective of American policy, which was based on the
premise that the security of the United States required the expulsion of British
sovereignty from all of North America. The War of 1812, he suggests, can be interpreted as part of this vision of American "manifest destiny" to control the
entire continent.

There is thus some irony that historians of Canada should argue that the
major result of the War of 1812 was to confirm the continued existence of British
North America. In the second reading in this chapter, Arthur Bowler suggests
that the war was "one of the most significant events in the formation of a
Canadian nationality." Resentment against American invasion, particularly
in Upper Canada, sparked a nationalism based on Britishness and anti-
Americanism. The Loyalists, who had been swamped by later American
immigrants, reasserted themselves, and a Loyalist mythology gained strength.
Equally important, the War of 1812 reinforced the conservative elements in
British North American society by discrediting the American values of republicanism and democracy. A war which the United States hoped would result
in the acquisition of British North America thus had the opposite effect of assuring the continued survival of these colonies to the north.

Suggestions for Further Reading

Bowler, Arthur, "Propaganda in Upper Canada in the War of 1812," *American Review of Canadian Studies*, XVII, no. 1 (Spring 1988), 11-32.

Errington, Jane, "Friends and Foes: The Kingston Elite and the the War of 1812: A Case Study in Ambivalence," *Journal of Canadian Studies*, XX, no. 1 (Spring 1985), 58-79.

————, *The Lion, the Eagle, and Upper Canada: A Developing Colonial Ideology*. Kingston and Montreal: McGill-Queen's University Press, 1987.

Mills, David, *The Idea of Loyalty in Upper Canada, 1784-1850*. Kingston and Montreal: McGill-Queen's University Press, 1988.

Sheppard, George, "'Deeds Speak': Militiamen, Medals, and the Invented Traditions of 1812," *Ontario History*, LXXXIII, no. 3 (September 1990), 207-232.

Stanley, G.F.G., *The War of 1812: Land Operations*. Toronto: Macmillan of Canada in collaboration with the National Museum of Man, 1983.

Wise, S.F. "Colonial Attitudes from the Era of the War of 1812 to the Rebellion of 1837," in S. Wise and R.C. Brown, *Canada Views the United States*. Toronto: Macmillan of Canada, 1967.

Zaslow, Morris, ed., *The Defended Border: Upper Canada and the War of 1812*. Toronto: Macmillan of Canada, 1964.

ON TO CANADA: MANIFEST DESTINY AND UNITED STATES STRATEGY IN THE WAR OF 1812

Reginald Horsman

When, in July 1812, General William Hull crossed the Detroit River and invaded Canada, he issued a grandiloquent proclamation in which he told the Canadians that he was offering them "the invaluable blessings of Civil, Political, & Religious Liberty." After promising them protection in their *"persons, property, and rights,"* he went on to tell them that they were to be "emancipated from Tyranny and oppression and restored to the dignified station of freemen." To Hull the choice was clear. "The United States offer you *Peace, Liberty,* and *Security,*" he proclaimed, "your choice lies between these, & *War, Slavery,* and *destruction.*"[1] In the next month Hull had to eat his words as he surrendered his northwestern army, but he had set the tone for the American invasion. When in November of the same year General Alexander Smyth prepared to invade Canada on the Niagara front, he was also ready with bombastic proclamations, culminating in the exhortation: "Be strong! Be brave! And let the ruffian power of the British King cease on this continent."[2]

From *Michigan Historical Review*, XIII, no. 2 (Fall 1987), 1-24. Reprinted by permission of *Michigan Historical Review*.

In September 1814, far away in Ghent, the British peace commissioners cited proclamations by Hull and Smyth as evidence that the Americans, in spite of their assertion that they were fighting a defensive war to protect their neutral rights, had in reality intended to conquer and annex Canada. This was denied by the American peace commissioners who stated that the statements by Hull and Smyth were neither authorized nor approved by the American government.[3]

That there should be some confusion regarding the intentions of the American government in the War of 1812 is not surprising. These intentions were argued about at the time—both before and during the War of 1812—and they have been argued about since. Among American historians the intentions of the American government along the Canadian border have usually been considered in the context of the causes of the War of 1812, rather than in the context of long-term American interests in the British North American Provinces and general American ambitions on the North American continent. During the past century American historians have delighted in arguing about the causes of the War of 1812, and the role of Canada in the coming of the war has been particularly controversial. I intend to argue that the form this argument about the causes of the war has taken has brought confusion to the subject of American intentions in regard to Canada. To understand the causes of the War of 1812 it is necessary to focus in detail on the events from 1803 to 1812; but, to understand American attitudes toward Canada in that war it is necessary to understand American fears about the British in Canada that had existed since the Revolution, American dreams of a continent free of British influence and dominated by the United States, and the course of American arguments regarding Canada during the War of 1812.

The historiographical argument about the causes of the War of 1812 is a familiar one. In the nineteenth century it was generally assumed that the United States declared war on England to defend American neutral rights and the national honor. Canada was simply the arena in which the war was fought.[4] For the past sixty years that simplicity has disappeared. In 1925 Julius Pratt argued in his book *The Expansionists of 1812* that a decisive factor in the declaration of war was the western demand that the British should be expelled from Canada to prevent their instigating Indian hostilities on the American frontier. He also maintained that southern support for the war came from a belief that the acquisition of Canada to the North was to be balanced by the acquisition of the Floridas to the South.[5]

Although Pratt's arguments were challenged in the fifteen years after his book was published, it was not until the 1960s that maritime problems and national honor again became dominant in the discussions of the coming of the war. Both Bradford Perkins in his *Prologue to War* and myself in *The Causes of the War of 1812* argued that the causes of the war were to be found on the sea not on the land, and I argued that the invasion of Canada was a method of waging the war not a reason for starting it. The arguments have continued since that time, but discussions of Canada have continued to revolve around the question of how Canada fitted into the specific question of the causes of the war. In one of the latest books on the subject, J.C.A. Stagg argues that President James Madison pressed for war and the invasion of Canada because the growing importance of exports from Canada to Great Britain combined with Republican disunity threatened American policies of commercial restriction. By conquering Canada the United States would better be able to force Great Britain to acknowledge American neutral rights.[6]

When discussing American intentions in regard to Canada, rather than simply the causes of the War of 1812, a problem with all these arguments, including mine, is that later historians have too often allowed Julius Pratt to set the framework of the discussion. Since the publication of Pratt's work in 1925, historians discussing the causes of the war have been anxious to point out that the war was caused by a whole series of maritime acts that were bitterly resented by nationalistic Americans, not by a western desire to conquer Canada to prevent British support for the Indians. But, while it is correct to argue that the United States did not cynically declare war in 1812 to invade and conquer Canada, this does not mean that there was not a strong desire to annex Canada in the United States. Many hoped that a war declared largely for other reasons was likely to have the major collateral benefit of ending the British occupation of Canada.[7]

In disagreeing with those interpretations that have simply stressed expansionism and minimized maritime causation, historians have ignored deep-seated American fears for national security, dreams of a continent completely controlled by the republican United States, and the evidence that many Americans believed that the War of 1812 would be the occasion for the United States to achieve the long-desired annexation of Canada. The United States would not have declared war in 1812 without the British maritime aggressions of almost twenty years, but many believed that a possible benefit of the war would be the annexation of all or substantial parts of the British North American colonies.

From the very beginning of the revolutionary era, the Americans had an acute sense of the importance of Canada for their future security. Nearly a century of conflict with the French and their Indian allies had demonstrated the vulnerability of the American colonies to attack from Canada, and there was also a developing realization of the importance of the St. Lawrence and the Great Lakes system to the trade of northern New England and the whole region south of the Great Lakes.

In October 1774, even before the outbreak of hostilities in the American colonies, Congress had invited the Canadians to join the Americans in resisting

British abuses. "Your province," it told them, "is the only link wanting to compleat the bright and strong chain of union."[8] Further efforts to enlist Canadian support having failed, the Americans in 1775, before declaring their independence from Great Britain, launched an attack on Canada. Montreal was taken, and the invasion only failed before the walls of Quebec.[9] No better indication could have been given of the dangers the revolutionaries perceived from Canada remaining in the hands of the British.

With independence declared, there was no doubt in the minds of American leaders of the necessity of expelling the British from Canada. As early as September 1776, when Benjamin Franklin drafted a set of possible peace terms, he included a provision for the British cession of the Canadian provinces, East and West Florida, Bermuda, and the Bahamas. "It is absolutely necessary for us to have them," he wrote, "for our own security."[10] In this same summer of 1776 the Continental Congress was engaged in discussing a model treaty to provide guidelines for shaping a hoped-for French alliance. One of its provisions was that, in return for American trade, the French should agree to American claims to all the British possessions on the North American continent and nearby British islands. When the French alliance was signed in February 1778, article 5 stated that should the United States see fit to attack the British mainland colonies or the Bermudas "those countries or islands, in case of success, shall be confederated with, or dependent upon, the said United States."[11]

There were high hopes in America in 1778 that the French alliance would enable the United States to conquer Canada. In May 1778 George Washington corrected a rumor that Canada had joined the union, but added: "It is a measure much to be wished, and I believe would not be displeasing to the body of that people." He went on to say that he believed Canada was of major importance to the American Union: "If that country is not with us, it will, from its proximity to the eastern States, its intercourse and connexion with the numerous tribes of western Indians, its communion with them by water and other local advantages, be at least a troublesome if not a dangerous neighbor to us; and ought, at all events, to be in the same interests and politics, of the other States."[12]

Independence without Canada was perceived as creating a major security problem for the United States. In July 1778 George Mason of Virginia argued that though it was natural to wish for peace, war was in the present interest of the United States. It was necessary because the union was "yet incomplete, & will be so, until the inhabitants of all the territory from Cape Breton to the Mississippi are included in it." Canada and Florida were essential, he argued, to stop the British inciting the Indians, and St. Augustine and Halifax were essential for the safety of America's coasts and American trade.[13] John Adams agreed with Mason. At this time in his career Adams was so convinced of the danger presented by British possessions in North America that he was advocating a permanent alliance with France. The basic problem, he believed was contiguity, for "neighboring nations are never friends in reality." Only France could provide the necessary counterweight to the British, for "as long as Great Britain shall have Canada, Nova Scotia, and the Floridas, or any of them, so long will Great Britain be the enemy of the United States, let her disguise it as much as she will."[14] When in October 1778 Congress appointed Franklin minister to France, they provided him with fresh instructions. Congress wanted France to cooperate in a plan for the capture of Halifax and Quebec. This, it was argued, would give the United States two new states—Quebec and Nova Scotia.[15]

American hopes of annexing Canada during the revolution were dashed. France supported the United States for her own purposes, and had no desire to enhance the power of the new republic. The French never supplied the assistance necessary for the United States to be able to take Canada. Congress realized that in the immediate future it was more important to obtain the eastern half of the Mississippi Valley than Canada; and, when possible peace terms were drawn up in 1779, it was argued that a boundary on the Mississippi was essential. Although Canada was desirable, and of great importance, peace would not depend on its cession.[16] In the preliminary peace talks in April 1782, Franklin suggested that the British should cede Canada, but in the eventual peace treaty the American commissioners had to accept the reality that the United States did not yet have the power to force the British out of Canada.[17]

Canada, however, remained of vital importance in American thinking. When the Articles of Confederation went into effect in March 1781 they contained a provision that Canada could enter the union whenever it wanted to, but that other new states would require the agreement of nine of the thirteen states.[18] The desire to remove the British presence to the north remained strong in the years after 1783, but before 1789 American weakness meant that the British in Canada were a much bigger threat to the United States than the Americans were to Canada. In the 1780s and early 1790s, the British in Canada retained the Northwest posts, controlled navigation on the lakes, and encouraged the Indians within American territory to resist the frontier advance. The Americans also suspected them of attempting to split the republic by plotting in Vermont and Kentucky.[19]

In the years after 1789, as the American government grew in strength, it again became possible to envisage the expulsion of the British from North America. In the eyes of the leaders of the United States it was not simply a matter of the British in Canada harassing American frontiers by backing the Indians, it was a belief that the British were pursuing a specific course of blocking America's ultimate triumph and destiny on the North American continent. Washington wrote in 1792 that he did not believe the Indians would ever be in "a quiescent state so long as they may be under an influence which is hostile to the rising greatness of these States."[20]

A remarkable feature of the young United States was the degree to which there was confidence in the future continental destiny of the American people. Since the mid-eighteenth century it had been common for both European and American observers to forecast the future greatness of the American states and the transference of power from the old to the new world. Even in the weak, disunited years of the 1780s these hopes of future destiny had persisted. Thomas Jefferson had written in 1786 that "Our confederacy must be viewed as the nest from which all America, North and South is to be peopled," and in the same year a minor government official in what was to be the state of Tennessee asked: "Is not the continent of America one day to become one consolidated government of United States?"[21] In 1789, as the new American constitution went into effect, geographer Jedediah Morse wrote that "we cannot but anticipate the period, as not far distant, when the AMERICAN EMPIRE will comprehend millions of souls, west of the Mississippi. Judging upon probable grounds, the Mississippi was never designed as the western boundary of the American empire. The God of nature never intended that some of the best part of his earth should be inhabited by the subjects of a monarch, 4000 miles from them."[22]

The outbreak of war between England and France in 1793 led to twenty years of crisis in the Atlantic, and it also renewed the American fears of the British that had made the Americans so determined to conquer Canada during the American Revolution. In the 1790s the Federalists made every effort to avoid war with England, but after 1803, as the crisis at sea intensified, the Democratic-Republicans began to consider the possibility of reacting with force to British policies.

In 1807 the *Chesapeake* affair brought demands for war within the United States, and Canadian fears of American invasion. These fears were real, for had war been declared in 1807 the United States intended to attack Canada. The primary reason for this was, of course, that Canada was the only accessible British possession, and British sea power combined with Democratic-Republican reluctance to enhance the power of the navy, appeared to preclude an effective maritime response. Yet, the general strategy of an attack on Canada was also supported because it promised the possibility of ending a British threat to American security that had been feared since 1774, and because it would help to further the aim of a continental republic.

In July 1807 President Thomas Jefferson told a visitor that "if the English do not give us the satisfaction we demand, we will take Canada, which wants to enter the Union." A Tennessee politician wrote to Jefferson in the fall supporting an attack on British possessions, and stating that "it will be a sublime spectacle to spread liberty and civilization in that vast country, Canada." When in 1808 John Howe was sent by the Governor in Chief of Canada to report on the situation in the United States, he reported back from Washington that no man in either party seemed to think that there would be any difficulty in taking Canada, Nova Scotia, and New Brunswick.[23] Many in the United States were willing to take advantage of what they considered a just war to end the threat from the north and to further the aim of a continent freed from European control and dedicated to republicanism.

Jefferson and the Democratic-Republicans, fully aware of the military weakness of the United States, chose economic coercion rather than war in 1807, but the crisis continued. Great Britain would not change her maritime policies to accommodate the desires of the neutral United States, and by her intransigence increased the Democratic-Republican feeling that Great Britain was an inveterate enemy of the United States. Moreover, in the aftermath of the *Chesapeake* affair the British in Canada responded to the maritime crisis, as they had in 1793-1794, by trying to make sure that the Indians on the frontiers of the American Old Northwest would fight for the British should the Americans invade.[24] This, in turn, intensified the American feeling that the British in Canada were a constant threat to American security and bad neighbors. The United States would no more have risked a war with Great Britain simply to end British support for the Indians than they would have declared war simply to annex Canada, but, given the impasse regarding British maritime policies, the possibility of an invasion of Canada that would respond to British maritime aggressions since 1793 while offering the possibility of achieving other long-desired American goals became increasingly attractive.

William A. Burwell of Virginia stated the position very well in Congress early in 1809 when complaining of the renewed British activity among the Indians. He said that he "would not risk the peace of the country to free us from evils of that kind, yet if we were forced into war, by more irresistible causes, I should certainly consider this collateral advantage gained by it important." He went on to say that the "expulsion of the British from Canada has always been deemed an object of the first importance to the peace of the United States, and their security against the inroads of an enemy."[25]

From 1810 the American Congress and President James Madison gradually and painfully reached the conclusion that war was the only solution to the difficulties with Great Britain. It was painful and difficult because it was known that American military forces were weak, that a war would ruin American trade, and because the opposition Federalist party bitterly opposed the conflict. An important factor in convincing a majority that a war with Great Britain was even possible was the argument of the War Hawks that England was vulnerable in Canada. Oddly, although the desire for Canada did not cause the War of 1812, it is difficult to imagine the United States declaring war if Great Britain had not possessed that region. There would have been nowhere to attack. The only other possibility was to fight the type of naval war that had been fought by the Federalists against France in the late 1790s, and that was out of the question given the attitude of the Democratic-Republican majority toward the use of naval power. As it was, Canada could be attacked, and a successful attack opened up the possibility of permanent possession and the ending of a long-perceived British threat to American security.

When in February 1810 the young Henry Clay first made a fiery speech in favor of war, he said that the United States had just causes for war against both England and France, but that the injuries from England had been greater. There was a solution, said Clay: "The conquest of Canada is in your power." Clay said "conquest" not "invasion," and pointed out that such a conquest would eliminate British support for the Indians and give the United States control of the entire fur trade.[26] In the 11th Congress Clay's appeal fell on deaf ears, but when the 12th Congress met in November 1811 Clay and his War Hawk friends, with the cooperation of President James Madison, were able slowly to move the nation toward war. There was never any doubt that the Democratic-Republicans intended to fight this war by invading Canada. They even voted down a proposal to increase the strength of the tiny American navy.[27]

In the debates of the 12th Congress from November 1811 to June 1812, those who advocated war justified it on the grounds of a long history of British maritime aggressions, which had hindered American trade, harmed American seamen, and besmirched American national honor. They also made it quite clear that they believed Great Britain could only be injured by the invasion of Canada. It was stressed that such an invasion was a retaliation against British policies, but throughout the debates there is ambiguity about whether the War Hawks and their allies are discussing invasion or conquest. Often it is simply argued that Britain will be forced to change her maritime policies because of American success in Canada, but at other times it seems conquest not simply invasion is envisioned. Echoing the speech that Burwell of Virginia had made in 1809, advocates of war often appeared to feel that the conquest and retention of Canada was a "collateral advantage" to be gained from being forced into just war.

Several of the War Hawks were quite overt in their intention to conquer and retain Canada, both as retaliation for the long history of British maritime aggression and to fulfill long-expressed American desires. Felix Grundy of Tennessee said that he was "willing to receive the Canadians as adopted brethren; it will have beneficial political effects." It would preserve the equilibrium of the government by balancing off the peopling of Louisiana. He said that he was "anxious not only to add the Floridas to the South, but the Canadas to the North of this empire."[28] This particularly infuriated maverick Virginian John Randolph who said he could see the American capitol on the move. It would alight at Darien, "which, when the gentleman's dreams are realized, will be a most eligible seat of Government for the new Republic (or Empire) of the two Americas!"[29]

Richard M. Johnson of Kentucky was not affected by Randolph's sarcasm. On the following day he said he wished to force Great Britain to cease to violate America's neutral rights and treat her Americans as an independent people, but he went on to say "I shall never die contented until I see her expulsion from North America, and her territories incorporated with the United States." He accepted fully the idea of a divine plan for the United States on the North American continent. "The waters of the St. Lawrence and the Mississippi interlock in a number of places, and the great Disposer of Human Events intended those two rivers should belong to the same people."[30] Randolph lashed back, arguing that the War Hawks were driven by "agrarian cupidity." He was wrong. In wanting to invade Canada the War Hawks were driven not by a desire for land, but by a desire to retaliate against British maritime policies and by a desire for security and for a continent controlled by a republican United States.[31]

War Hawk John A. Harper of New Hampshire was particularly keen that if war was to come with England then this war should end the British possession of Canada. Like Richard Johnson, Harper was able to see a divine plan in the future of the United States on the American continent: "The northern provinces of Britain are to us great and valuable objects. Once secured to this Republic, and the St. Lawrence and the Lakes become the Baltic, and more than the Baltic to America; north of them a population of four millions may easily be supported; and this great outlet of the northern world, should be at our command, for our convenience and future security. To me, sir, it appears that the Author of Nature has marked our limits in the south, by the Gulf of Mexico; and on the north, by the regions of eternal frost."[32] As a representative from New Hampshire, Harper was more aware than the southerners of the importance of the lakes and the St. Lawrence to the trade of the northern states.

Shortly before the war began, Harper revealed the extent to which he was committed not simply to the invasion of Canada but also to its conquest and retention. He told the governor of his state that he had worked hard and used all his influence to have the idea accepted that Canada should be incorporated into the Union. "I have no idea of having a war for several years to conquer the British Provinces," he wrote "and then surrender them by negociation and unless we can have a pledge that once conquered, they shall be retained, I will never give my vote to send an army there."[33] Harper was more overt than most War Hawks in the extent to which he was willing to press for a commitment that if Canada was conquered it should be kept. Federalist Senator James A. Bayard reported that westerners and southerners were disturbed by this insistence that Canada, when conquered, should be divided into states and incorporated into the union.[34]

Most who pressed for or supported war simply took the line of argument that the only way to fight a war that had been caused by a long history of British aggressions and insults against the United States was by invading Canada, and then in their speeches talked of the advantages that would be gained by conquering Canada even independent of the causes of the war. When in March 1812 Andrew Jackson issued division orders, he summarized why the United States was going to fight. He said it was to reestablish the national character, to protect American seamen from impressment, to defend the American right to a free trade, and open a market for American agricultural products, "in fine, to seek some indemnity for past injuries, some security against future aggressions, by the conquest of all the British dominions upon the continent of north america."[35] It is hard to believe that Jackson was contemplating handing these dominions back to the British.

In June 1812, as the United States went to war, American Secretary of State James Monroe well-expressed the ambiguity of the American position in two of his statements. Less than a week before the war began he told Virginian John Taylor that Canada was to be invaded "not as an object of the war but as a means to bring it to a satisfactory conclusion." Two weeks later in writing to Jonathan Russell, the United States chargé d'affaires in London, he told him to point out to the British the danger for them of allowing the war to persist for any length of time. If American troops entered Canada, this might mean commitments to the Canadian inhabitants, and in the United States the effect of success on the public mind would make it "difficult to relinquish Territory which had been conquered."[36]

In retirement at Monticello, Thomas Jefferson, as often before, well-summarized majority American opinion. Writing to Thaddeus Kosciusko about the war which had just begun, he commented that Great Britain would control the sea but "we shall be equally predominant at land, and shall strip her of all her possessions on this continent." He went on to say that British intrigues to destroy the American government, and among the Indians, "prove that the cession of Canada, their fulcrum for these Machiavelian levers, must be a sine qua non at a treaty of peace." In August Jefferson told another of his correspondents that "the acquisition of Canada, this year, as far as the neighborhood of Quebec, will be a mere matter of marching, and will give us experience for the attack of Halifax the next, and the final expulsion of England from the American continent."[37]

The conquest of Canada was not a question of marching. Canadian inhabitants did not welcome the Americans as liberators, and in 1812 the invasion of Canada was an abysmal failure. For nearly forty years Americans had talked and written of the desirability of the acquisition of Canada, and there had never been the slightest question that the invasion of Canada would be the main way of fighting the War of 1812, yet the preparations for such an invasion had been grossly inadequate. Many Democratic-Republicans wanted the expansion of the republic, and the expulsion of European powers from North America, but they did not want either to pay for or to risk having a military establishment. They wanted to be welcomed as republican liberators bringing liberty from European tyranny.

The failures of the 1812 campaigns did not end American dreams of conquering and retaining Canada. Indeed, one result of the disasters was to make American politicians shun ambiguity and point out that if the nation could unite itself and successfully invade Canada, it might well be able to retain it. James Monroe's reaction to General William Hull's surrender of Detroit was to state that this "most disgraceful event" might have good results. "It will rouse the nation," he wrote. "We must efface the stain before we make peace, and that may give us Canada." In writing to Henry Clay about the same event, he was even clearer in his conclusions. The American people, he argued falsely, had been drawn together by military defeats and naval victories. If Great Britain did not offer peace with honor, he was convinced that the war would become a national one, and would "terminate in the expulsion of her force and power from the continent."[38]

Later in the year, in drafting a plan for the military requirements of the United States, Monroe reached the conclusion that "if a strong army is led to the field early in the Spring the British power on this Continent must sink before it, and when once broken down it will never rise again. The reconquest of Canada will become, in the opinion of all enlightened men, and of the whole British nation, a chimerical attempt. It will therefore be abandoned." When Albert Gallatin was sent as a peace commissioner to Europe in May 1813, Monroe asserted that if his mission failed, and Great Britain prolonged the war, it would simply lead to greater American efforts and "the complete expulsion of the British from the Continent."[39]

In Congress too the failures of 1812 brought the desire for Canada far more into the open. In the winter of 1812-13 Congress debated the necessity of increased military forces. The most important bill for the invasion of Canada—a bill to raise an additional 20,000 troops for one year—was discussed and passed in January 1813 after lengthy debate. What is striking about the debate, compared to those before the war began, is that now there was much less ambiguity about the purposes of the invasion of Canada. Both Democratic-Republicans and their Federalist opponents now seemed to assume that if Canada was conquered it was unlikely to be given up.

Surprisingly, Henry Clay was somewhat more cautious than some of his expansionist supporters. His argument in supporting the increased military force was that he wished to "negotiate the terms of a peace at Quebec or Halifax."[40] This was more along the lines of pre-war arguments that the invasion of Canada would force the British to make concessions regarding neutral rights at sea, but other Democratic-Republicans were now ready to throw caution to the winds in regard to the advantages to be gained from an annexation of Canada. Thomas Robertson of Louisiana dismissed any doubts his southern constituents might have about an extension of northern power in an impassioned speech in favor of the bill. He said that the British possessions in America invited a conquest:

> The power of Britain must be extinguished in America. She must no longer be permitted to corrupt the principles and disturb the peace and tranquility of our citizens. Our frontier inhabitants must not be kept in dread and danger from her Indian allies. And never shall we be secure among ourselves, and exempt from the mischievous intrigues of Europeans, until European power is expelled across the Atlantic.

He argued that no citizen would have consented to an unprovoked attack on Canada just to get possession of it, but that now the United States had the opportunity to drive Great Britain from the continent she should take advantage of the situation. Robertson also used the common argument that contiguity bred trouble, and that when Great Britain was no longer a neighbor a great number of difficulties would be removed.[41]

Although the gaining of security by the expulsion of Great Britain from the continent continued to be the most important argument for the retention of Canada, there was again some discussion of the importance of the whole St. Lawrence-Great Lakes system to American trade. Silas Stow of New York pointed out that the St. Lawrence was the outlet for many United States exports, and that these could be taxed. He also expressed a fear that Canada could draw off United States settlers. Willis Alston of North Carolina also pointed out the benefits of enhancing internal American trade by uniting eastern and western waters.[42] All of this discussion clearly had little to do with invasion as a means of coercing Great Britain but much to do with the desirability of conquering and annexing Canada.

One of the best summaries of the expansionist view in this debate was that given by experienced politician Nathaniel Macon of North Carolina. He differed with those who said that the United States was incapable of conquering Canada, and insisted that not only could it be conquered but that it was "worth conquering, if it was only to get clear of a meddling and bad neighbor, who is always willing to make a strife in our family." The St. Lawrence was needed by the United States, he argued, and whether it was obtained in the present war or not, it would be obtained on some future occasion. "It is absolutely necessary, in my opinion," he said, "to the peace and happiness of the nation, as much so as the mouth of the Mississippi was. These two great rivers seem to have been intended by Providence for an inland navigation from North to South." Not only Canada but also Florida were needed, and their occupation would rid the United States of bad neighbors. Both would be obtained, he said, before many years were up.[43]

The Federalists, who were already completely disgusted at a war which they had opposed, which was ruining American trade, and which had proved ineffective on the Canadian frontier, were now additionally shocked at the overtness with which the Democratic-Republican majority talked of the annexation of Canada. The Federalists spoke at length in opposition to the invasion of Canada and were bitterly opposed to its annexation. In discussing the invasion itself the Federalists drew a distinction between Great Britain and the Canadians themselves, arguing that it was wrong to attack unoffending Canadians to retaliate against British offenses at sea. Josiah Quincy of Massachusetts said: "I consider the invasion of Canada as a means of carrying on this war, as cruel, wanton, senseless, and wicked." Laban Wheaton of Massachusetts objected to the killing of "the harmless Canadians."[44]

The Federalists also delighted in pointing out that the Canadians had not welcomed the American troops as liberators. Elijah Brigham of Massachusetts asked why the United States was bothering the Canadians, who were obviously not panting for American liberties as had vainly been argued at the last session of Congress. Lyman Law of Connecticut said the pretence had been that the United States would not conquer Canada; it would merely be taken from welcoming inhabitants, and then exchanged for maritime rights. This, he said, had been proved false.[45]

The main objection of the Federalists, however, was to the effect the annexation of Canada would have on the United States, for the Federalists now strongly expressed fears for the republic and American liberty. Much of the theoretical writing on republics in the eighteenth century had been concerned with the problem of whether republics had to be small to survive. Montesquieu had argued that a republic that did not have a small territory could not long exist. All authorities agreed that republics were fragile, liable to be destroyed by internal dissent or by external enemies. This problem had much concerned the Revolutionary generation, particularly in the dangerous decade of the 1780s, and the historical difficulties experienced by republics formed a large part of the discussions surrounding the Constitutional Convention in 1787 and the debates on the ratification of the new document. James Madison had maintained that the United States had solved the problem of size by adopting representative rather than direct democracy, but the fear remained. From the time of the Louisiana Purchase a group within the Federalist party launched a bitter attack on the idea of an ever-expanding republic. To the traditional fears of size necessitating a more despotic government, was added a specific Federalist fear that every new state enhanced the power of the Democratic-Republican party.[46]

In the military debates of early 1813 the Federalists strongly took up the cry that the annexation of Canada would bring a major threat to American constitutional government. Josiah Quincy argued that such an annexation would have a dire effect on American liberties and the Constitution. It would create a veteran army and a military leader to subvert American liberties. Elijah Brigham of Massachusetts used a similar argument, maintaining that the conquest of Canada would be "fatal to the civil liberties of the country, and change the character of our Government." Henry Ridgeley of Delaware said that the strength of the United States was already too much scattered, and would be weakened still further by a greater expansion of territory and population. Hermanus Bleecker of New York argued that Canada should not be accepted even if Great

Britain would willingly give it to the United States, for the United States was already too extensive.[47]

Some of the Federalists were shocked at the shift from public statements arguing that Canada was merely to be a hostage for British good behavior to public assertions of the desirability or the necessity of annexing Canada. Daniel Sheffey, one of the few remaining southern Federalists, was puzzled to hear of conquests in the North and South as essential to American "security and happiness," and he questioned the real objects of this bill to increase the military forces. Congress, he said, had sometimes been told that Canada was merely to be conquered to be exchanged for American maritime rights, at others that it was to be retained to prevent future collisions and Indian attacks. Sheffey said he had come to the conclusion from the conduct of American military commanders that this was "a war for the conquest of Canada."[48]

In responding to the Federalists, the Democratic-Republicans took issue with the distinction that the opposition was drawing between the government of Great Britain and the inhabitants of Canada. Joseph Desha of Kentucky wanted to know why there was all this sympathy for "the poor Canadians." The sympathy should be saved for the victims of the Indians. Nathaniel Macon was also puzzled at hearing of the "unoffending Canadians."[49] In general, the Democratic-Republicans talked of Canada as simply part of the power of Great Britain while the opposition Federalists drew a distinction between the British government and the Canadian inhabitants.

For the most part, however, the Democratic-Republicans let the Federalists talk, and spent little time answering their specific arguments. They were no longer concerned with drawing careful distinctions between the invasion of Canada as a means of changing British maritime policies and the invasion of Canada as the way to conquest and the removal of a permanent British threat. They simply merged the objectives. Matthew Clay of Virginia, an old Jefferson supporter, expressed this plainly when he discussed Great Britain early in January 1813.

> We have the Canadas as much under our command as she has the ocean; and the way to conquer her on the ocean is to drive her from the land. I am not for stopping at Quebec or anywhere else; but I would take the whole continent from them, and ask them no favors. Her fleets cannot then rendezvous at Halifax as now.... It is as easy to conquer them on the land, as their whole Navy could conquer ours on the ocean.... We must take the continent from them. I wish never to see a peace till we do. God has given us the power and the means; we are to blame if we do not use them. If we get the continent, she must allow us the freedom of the sea.[50]

Matthew Clay's speech was a triumph of rhetoric over reason. It melded earlier Democratic-Republican arguments that Canada was to be a pawn to be exchanged for maritime rights with later arguments that Canada was to be conquered and kept. It never addressed the question of how the conquest of

Canada would force the British to allow the Americans freedom of the seas, and it never addressed the question of how if Canada were kept it could be used in an exchange of such doubtful results. But Clay's statement well-revealed the ambiguities with which the Democratic-Republicans began the war. They were fighting because of British infringements of American maritime rights, but they were hoping to use the war to solve the lingering problem of the British possession of Canada.

The additional troops voted for in January 1813 solved nothing. Although the United States gained some consolation for earlier defeats by victories on Lake Erie and at the battle of the Thames, the conquest of Canada came no nearer. When James Monroe gave instructions to peace commissioners in June 1813 he had to assume that Great Britain would insist on the restoration of Canada at the end of the war. He did, however, state that the peace commissioners should suggest to the British commissioners the advantages of avoiding future controversies by ceding the upper parts of Canada or even the whole of Canada to the United States.[51]

Moreover, the victory of the Thames restored in the West the hope that perhaps Canada or at least western Canada could be kept. This feeling was so strong that Henry Clay found it necessary to deny "a very unpopular opinion" that had been attributed to him that the conquered region should be given up as a price of peace. Clay's explanation was that in the summer of 1813, when the United States had none of Canada, and the British had Michigan Territory, he had stated that he would be willing for the present to forego the conquest of Canada if the United States could make a peace securing the points in controversy. Clay pointed out that when the war began "Canada was not the end but the means." But he also stated that "it has ever been my opinion that if Canada is conquered it ought never to be surrendered if it possibly can be retained."[52]

With the impending collapse of Napoleon in the winter of 1813-1814, it was becoming obvious that any opportunity of conquering Canada was fast disappearing, but even at this juncture the advantages and disadvantages of such an acquisition were again debated in the American Congress. The Federalist opposition once more launched a major attack on the idea that additional troops were to be used for the invasion and conquest of Canada; this "crusade against Canada" as Morris Miller of New York called it. Miller attacked the proclamations issued by Generals Hull and Smyth in 1812, saying that Hull's proclamation "avows principles and intentions which might well become a robber and a bandit." Daniel Webster said that the United States had failed in dividing the people of the Canadian provinces from their government; they were still hostile to the American cause.[53]

The Federalists again made it clear that they did not want either a larger federal republic or military control of a conquered territory, and in this way foreshadowed arguments to be used by the New England Whigs in the period of the Mexican War. William Gaston of North Carolina asked what the South would think of half a dozen new northern states made out of Canada, and incorporating people who did not want to enter the Union. Artemus Ward of Massachusetts said that if the Canadians were to be admitted to all the privileges of freemen "we shall then have a motley mixture of citizens, ignorant of their rights and of their duties, added to a population already too heterogenous." But if Canada was kept as a conquered province, then the United States would have to maintain an armed force there, led by a Caesar or Bonaparte who could overturn the American government.[54]

Even in this bleak period of the war some of the Democratic-Republicans still talked as though the conquest of Canada was within the power of the United States. John C. Calhoun, in a rather ineffective speech, stressed the peace and security that could be secured by the acquisition of Canada. Nathaniel Macon pointed out that the United States had wanted Canada in the Revolution, that George Washington had wanted Canada, that it was envisioned admitting it to the American Union, and that even now the acquisition of Canada and Florida "would add much to the probability of a peace being lasting."[55]

The clearest statement of how Canada had figured both in the coming of the war and in its prosecution was by Charles Ingersoll of Pennsylvania, who argued that his constituents were certainly interested in the acquisition of Canada. "As a separate cause of war, independent of all others, I will not undertake to say what the popular sentiment may be with regard to the invasion and conquest of Canada; but, as an instrument for waging it effectually, and as a desirable acquisition in the course of its prosecution, most certainly we do look upon those British provinces in our neighborhood as all-important in the account." The United States should persist in its attempts to take Canada, said Ingersoll, "otherwise we may postpone the conquest to the next generation." He also, in answer to those Federalists who claimed that in their areas the invasion of Canada was unpopular, gave his estimate of general public opinion on this question. "With a large majority of the country, the conquest, I am confident, is not unpopular, but looked upon as even a strong independent inducement to the war." A fellow representative from Pennsylvania, Thomas Wilson, agreed with him, saying that Canada had never been a motive to commence the war or a primary objective, but that it was "an incidental but indispensable object."[56]

This debate in early 1814 was even more futile than that of the previous year, for the main problem of the United States in 1814 was not the conquest of Canada but how to prevent being dismembered by a British invasion. Yet, these debates of the war period were revealing of the motivations of the Democratic-Republican party in voting for war. The Democratic-Republicans had reached the decision to support war against England because of a long history of British interference with American trade and American seamen, an interference which infuriated these young republicans who viewed Great Britain as hostile to the rising greatness of their nation. They intended to invade Canada to retaliate against Great Britain and to hurt Great Britain, but they were happy to invade Canada because it had long been perceived as a threat to American security and hated as a surviving example of British power on a continent now dedicated to a new republicanism. The United States did not declare war because it wanted to obtain Canada, but the acquisition of Canada was viewed as a major collateral benefit of the conflict.

Notes

1. William Hull proclamation, 13 July 1812, *Michigan Pioneer and Historical Collections*, 40 vols. (Lansing: 1877-1929), 15: 106-107. There was no "Canada" in 1812. There were four separate British colonies on the mainland: Upper Canada, Lower Canada, New Brunswick, and Nova Scotia. When the Americans wrote and talked of Canada, their immediate objectives were Upper and Lower Canada, but they also wrote and talked of eliminating British power on the North American continent.

2. Alexander Smyth proclamation, 27 November 1812, *American State Papers, Military Affairs* (Washington: 1832), 1:501. See also Henry Adams, *History of the United States during the Administrations of Jefferson and Madison,* 9 vols. (New York: Charles Scribner, 1889-1891), 6: 354-56.

3. The British to the American Commissioners, 19 September 1814; the American to the British Commissioners, 13 October 1814; James F. Hopkins and Mary W. M. Hargreaves, eds., *The Papers of Henry Clay* (Lexington: University of Kentucky Press, 1959-), 1: 978, 983.

4. For early writing on the causes of the war, see Warren H. Goodman, "The Origins of the War of 1812: A Survey of Changing Interpretations," *Mississippi Valley Historical Review* 28 (September 1941-42): 171-86.

5. See Julius W. Pratt, *Expansionists of 1812* (New York: The Macmillan Company, 1925), 12-13.

6. Bradford Perkins, *Prologue to War: England and the United States, 1805-1812* (Berkeley: University of California Press, 1961); Reginald Horsman, *The Causes of the War of 1812* (Philadelphia: University of Pennsylvania Press, 1962); J.C.A. Stagg, *Mr. Madison's War: Politics, Diplomacy, and Warfare in the Early American Republic, 1783-1830* (Princeton: Princeton University Press, 1983). For a discussion of other historians and the causes of the war, see Reginald Horsman, "Western War Aims, 1811-1812," *Indiana Magazine of History* 53 (March 1957): 1-18, and Clifford L. Egan, "The Origins of the War of 1812: Three Decades of Historical Writing," *Military Affairs* 38 (April 1974): 72-75.

7. Writing primarily from the perspective of Canada and the military operations along the United States-Canadian frontier, George F. G. Stanley argues that "the incorporation of Canada into the American union was among the aims of the men who dominated Congress in 1812," *The War of 1812: Land Operations* (Ottawa: Macmillian of Canada, 1983), 29.

8. "A Letter to the Inhabitants of the Province of Quebec," 26 October 1774, in James H. Hutson, ed., *A Decent Respect to the Opinions of Mankind: Congressional State Papers, 1774-1776* (Washington: U.S. Government Printing Office, 1975), 67.

9. Ibid., 84-87; also Richard Van Alstyne, *The Rising American Empire* (1960; reprint Chicago: Quadrangle Books, 1965), 37-38.

10. Quoted in Gerald Stourzh, *Benjamin Franklin and American Foreign Policy,* 2d ed. (Chicago: University of Chicago Press, 1969), 200.

11. Worthington C. Ford, et. al., eds., *Journals of the Continental Congress,* 34 vols. (Washington: U.S. Government Printing Office, 1904-1937), 5:770; 11:450.

12. Washington to Landon Carter, 30 May 1778, *The Writings of George Washington,* 37 vols. (Washington, D.C.: U.S. Government Printing Office, 1931-1940), 11:492-93.

13. George Mason to Richard Henry Lee, 21 July 1788, quoted in Van Alstyne, *Rising American Empire,* 54-55.

14. John Adams to Samuel Adams, 28 July 1778, Francis Wharton, ed., *The Revolutionary Diplomatic Correspondence of the United States,* 6 vols. (Washington: U.S. Government Printing Office, 1889), 2:667-68.

15. *Journals of the Continental Congress,* 12:1046.

16. Ibid., 14: 959-60, 14 August 1779.

17. Richard B. Morris, *The Peacemakers: The Great Powers and American Independence* (New York: Harper & Row, 1965), 262-63 and passim.

18. *Journals of the Continental Congress,* 19:221.

19. See John Jay to Thomas Jefferson, 14 December 1786, William R. Manning, ed., *Diplomatic Correspondence of the United States: Canadian Relations, 1784-1860,* 4 vols. (Washington, D.C.: Carnegie Endowment for International Peace, 1940-45), 1:32. See also J. Leitch Wright, Jr., *Britain and the American Frontier, 1783-1815* (Athens, Ga.: University of Georgia Press, 1975).

20. Washington to Gouverneur Morris, 20 October 1792, Manning, ed., *Diplomatic Correspondence: Canadian Relations,* 1:53-54.

21. Jefferson to Archibald Stuart, 25 January 1786, Julian P. Boyd, ed., *The Papers of Thomas Jefferson* (Princeton: University of Princeton Press, 1950-), 9:218; Judge David Campbell to Governor Richard Caswell, 30 November 1786, in James G. M. Ramsey, *The Annals of Tennessee to the End of the Eighteenth Century* (1853; reprint Knoxville: Steam Power Press of Walker and James, 1926), 350.

22. Jedediah Morse, *The American Geography; or, A View of the Present Situation of the United States of America* (1789; reprint New York: Arno, 1970), 469.

23. Jefferson's comment to Turreau is quoted in Henry Adams, *History of the United States,* 4:36. For the Tennessee quote, see Arthur Campbell to Jefferson, 10 October 1807, Thomas Jefferson Papers, Library of Congress. Also, John Howe to Sir George Prevost, 27 November 1808, in "Secret Reports of John Howe, 1808," *American Historical Review* 17 (January 1912): 342-343.

24. See Reginald Horsman, "British Indian Policy in the Northwest, 1807-1812," *Mississippi Valley Historical Review* 45 (1958-59): 51-66.

25. *Annals of Congress,* 10th Cong., 2d sess., 1 February 1809, p. 1283.

26. Ibid., 11th Cong., 1st sess., 22 February 1810, pp. 579-80.

27. See Horsman, *Causes of the War of 1812,* 241.

28. *Annals of Cong.,* 12th Cong., 1st sess., 9 December 1811, pp. 426-27.

29. Ibid., 10 December 1811, p. 446.

30. Ibid., 11 December 1811, pp. 457-58.

31. Ibid., 16 December 1811, p. 533.

32. Ibid., 4 January 1812, p. 657.

33. Harper to William Plumer, 13 May 1812, quoted in Pratt, *Expansionists of 1812,* 148-49.

34. See the discussion in ibid., 147-48.

35. Andrew Jackson, Division Order, 12 March 1812, in John Spencer Bassett, ed., *The Correspondence of Andrew Jackson,* 6 vols. (Washington: Carnegie Institute of Washington, 1926-33), 1:221-22.

36. Monroe to John Taylor, 13 June 1812, Monroe to Jonathan Russell, 26 June 1812, Stanislaus M. Hamilton, ed., *The Writings of James Monroe,* 7 vols. (New York: G.P. Putnam's Sons, 1898-1903), 5:207, 212-13.

37. Jefferson to Kosciusko, 28 June 1812, Jefferson to Col. Duane, 4 August 1812, Andrew A. Lipscomb and Albert E. Bergh, eds., *The Writings of Thomas Jefferson,* 20 vols. (Washington: Thomas Jefferson Memorial Association, 1905), 13:168-72, 180-82.

38. Monroe to Jefferson, 31 August 1812, and Monroe to Henry Clay 17 September 1812, Hamilton, ed., *Writings of Monroe,* 5:220-23.

39. "Explanatory Observations," enclosed in Monroe to George W. Campbell, 23 December 1812, and Monroe to Gallatin, 6 May 1813, ibid., 5:235, 258.

40. *Annals of Congress,* 12th Cong., 2d sess., 8 January 1813, p. 676.

41. Ibid., 11 January 1813, p. 709.

42. Ibid., 14 January 1813, (Stow), p. 809; 14 January 1813, (Alston), p. 822.

43. Ibid., 12 January 1813, pp. 758, 768.

44. Ibid., 5 January 1813, (Quincy) p. 545; 8 January 1813, (Wheaton), p. 656.

45. Ibid., 4 January 1813, (Brigham), pp. 513-14; 5 January 1813, (Law) pp. 537-38.

46. See Gordon S. Wood, *The Creation of the American Republic, 1776-1787* (Chapel Hill: University of North Carolina Press, 1969), 499-505.

47. *Annals of Congress,* 12th Cong., 2d sess., 5 January 1813, (Quincy), pp. 546-49; 4 January 1813, (Brigham), p. 513; 4 January 1813, (Ridgely) p. 518; 7 January 1813, (Bleeker), p. 628.

48. Ibid., 11 January 1813, pp. 689-90.

49. Ibid., 14 January 1813, (Desha), p. 826; 12 January 1813, (Macon), p. 768.

50. Ibid., 2 January 1813, p. 498.

51. Monroe to the United States Commissioners, 23 June 1813, Manning, ed., *Diplomatic Correspondence: Canadian Relations,* 1:214-15.

52. Clay to Thomas Bodley, 18 December 1813, Hopkins and Hargreaves, eds., *Papers of Clay,* 1:841-42.

53. *Annals of Congress,* 13th Cong., 2d sess., 14 January 1814, (Miller), pp. 975-76; 14 January 1814, (Webster) p. 947.

54. Ibid., 18 February 1814, (Gaston), p. 1569; 5 March 1814 (Ward), p. 1819.

55. Ibid., 15 January 1814, (Calhoun) p. 996; 3 March 1814, (Macon), pp. 1778-80.

56. Ibid., 14 January 1814, (Ingersoll), pp. 952, 954; 17 January 1814, (Wilson), p. 1040.

INTRODUCTION

Arthur Bowler

It is generally agreed among Canadian historians that the War of 1812 was one of the most significant events in the formation of a Canadian nationality. Indeed, if, as has often been proposed, the main component of Canadian nationalism is anti-Americanism, then the War of 1812 is even more important for it was this war which originated the Canadian belief that the United States coveted Canada, and turned the anti-Americanism of the original Loyalist settlers into a popular feeling. Paradoxically, Canada—or more correctly the North American Colonies of Britain which would in time become Canada—played very little part in the events which led up to the war. The causes lay in Anglo-American relations, and to these all but a few Canadians were little more than interested spectators.

The origins of the war are perhaps best seen in the context of the message delivered by President James Madison to the Congress of the United States on June 1, 1812, asking for authority to declare war on Great Britain.[1] The message examined Anglo-American relations since 1803 in roughly chronological order and found British policy seriously at fault on five main points. The first point was the impressment of American seamen. Like the next three it originated in the war which, with only a short interval of peace at the beginning of the new century, had gone on between Britain and France since 1793. In the dis-

From Arthur Bowler, *The War of 1812* (Toronto: Holt Rinehart and Winston of Canada, 1973), 1-21. Reprinted by permission of the author.

ruption of trade patterns which accompanied that war, American merchants benefited enormously. British sea power drove French merchant shipping from the oceans and American traders, operating with impunity under cover of their neutral flag, took their place.[2] To the American shipping boom which followed, high pay and relatively good conditions of service drew a steady stream of British seamen. Provided with easily available naturalization papers, or spurious certificates of citizenship, these British seamen were a significant element in America's growing prosperity. They were also a serious loss to the British navy which was short of trained seamen throughout the war. To counteract this drain on her most precious resource, Britain adopted the doctrine of inalienable sovereignty which held that the duty a man owed to the nation of his birth could never be abrogated. Backing this doctrine with guns, British warships regularly stopped American merchant vessels on the high seas and impressed British seamen found on them. But galling as was the practice of impressment to American national pride, it would probably not have created serious problems had it involved only British seamen. However, British captains, justifiably suspicious of the certificates of citizenship and naturalization presented by crew members of stopped American vessels, usually relied on language and accent to distinguish British seamen from their American brethren. Since the English spoken in Britain and America at this time could often be virtually the same, mistakes could, and were frequently made. And as everyone knew, these were not all inadvertent. The mortality rate at sea was high, particularly on the lower decks, and although warned by their government not to impress Americans, British captains were not infrequently prepared to risk a reprimand for a "mistake" rather than the possible loss of their ship because it was undermanned. The only available figures on impressment are not entirely reliable but it does seem clear that from 1803 to 1807, and again from 1809 to 1812, as many as a thousand Americans a year were impressed illegally into the British navy.[3] There they often served for years before representation to the British government by friends or relatives could secure their release. The impressment issue reached a crisis in 1807. In March that year a number of seamen deserted a British warship lying in Chesapeake Bay and four of them subsequently enlisted on board the American frigate U.S.S. *Chesapeake* at Norfolk. Appeals for the return of the men brought no response from the Americans and when the matter was reported to Vice-Admiral George Berkley, commander-in-chief at Halifax, he ordered that should any of his warships meet the *Chesapeake* at sea they were to search her for the deserters. On June 22, the American ship put to sea and while still within sight of land was overhauled by H.M.S. *Leopard*. When the American captain refused to permit a search, the *Leopard* opened fire, killing three Americans and wounding eighteen. Totally unprepared for battle, the *Chesapeake* struck her colours and surrendered the four alleged deserters.[4]

The United States reacted to the *Chesapeake* affair with intense bitterness and anger. Protests came from all parts of the country, denouncing the British action as an outrageous violation of American sovereignty and demanding retaliation. Only the total lack of preparations for war in the United States, and President Jefferson's strong commitment to peace saved the situation. Indeed, Jefferson hoped that the incident might be capitalized on to force a diplomatic settlement of the whole problem of impressment. He hoped in vain. Although the British government repudiated the attack on an American warship and eventually paid an indemnity for the damage done, it announced at the same time an even stronger policy on the repatriation of British seamen. The United States soon gave up attempts to bring an end to impressment, but the issue remained an open cancer on the relations between the two countries, feeding on continued impressment and further clashes of warships, such as that between the U.S.S. *President* and H.M.S. *Little Belt*.

The second, third, and fourth points made by Madison are best considered together. The first denounced the violation by British warships of the rights and peace of the American coasts. "They hover over and harass our entering and departing commerce. To the most insulting pretensions they have added the most lawless proceedings in our very harbours, and have wantonly spilt American blood within the sanctuary of our territorial jurisdiction." The next point condemned the "paper" blockades proclaimed by Britain, blockades of ports and stretches of the European coast proclaimed on paper but not backed up on the spot by ships. Madison particularly noted that Britain herself had declared that for a blockade to be legal the "particular ports must be actually invested and previous warning given to vessels bound to them not to enter." The fourth point was an extension of this. "Not content with these occasional expedients for laying waste our neutral trade," Madison went on, "the cabinet of Britain resorted at length to the sweeping system of blockades, under the name of Orders in Council, which has been molded and managed as might best suit its political views, its commercial jealousies, or the avidity of British cruisers." Under the authority of paper blockades and Orders in Council "our commerce has been plundered in every sea, the great staples of our country have been cut off from their legitimate interest."

The issue which bound these points together was the rights of neutral traders in time of war. When the British navy drove French commerce from the seas, France responded by repealing her navigation laws and allowing neutral ships—primarily American—to take over the trade between France and her colonies. The American entry into French trade was in fact in violation of an international law known as the "Rule of 1756" which held that a neutral nation could not engage in wartime in a trade which was barred to it in time of peace. To avoid the Rule of 1756, the Americans adopted the idea of the "broken voyage" which held that goods which were brought into an American port in transit between France and her colonies became American and thus neutral. In the first phase of the war with France, between 1793 and 1801, Britain had not strongly objected to the American carrying trade. But when war resumed in 1803 a different attitude prevailed. Napoleon was determined on the complete subjugation of Britain, and Britain in turn was convinced that the defeat of France must take precedence over all other considerations. It was no longer a question of whether Britain would continue to ignore the American carrying trade but for how long. The answer came in May 1805 in the decision of the British Court of Appeals in the case of the American ship *Essex*, seized by a British cruiser for being in violation of the Rule of 1756. Although the *Essex* had touched base at an American port, the court ruled that the mere importation of goods into a neutral nation was not enough to neutralize the goods of a belligerent unless those goods were actually unloaded and a *bona fide* import duty paid on them.

That Britain decided suddenly to enforce the Rule of 1756 was a shock itself to the United States. The manner in which the decision was put into force added insult to injury. The new policy was put into effect without any notification to the United States, official or unofficial. In the summer and fall of 1805, numerous ships were seized in the Caribbean, off the American coast, and in the English Channel and the North Sea, and condemned in Admiralty courts.

But it was not just against the *Essex* decision and its implementation that Madison's War Message was directed. More important, and more current, was British interference in the direct trade between the United States and France which Madison referred to as the "legitimate interest" of American commerce. This problem began in 1806 when Britain and France began to apply economic sanctions against each other.

In October 1805 Nelson's triumph over the French and Spanish fleets at Trafalgar ended Napoleon's plans for the invasion of Britain. Thereafter his only weapon against Britain was his ever-increasing control of Europe. Convinced that Britain was a "nation of shopkeepers" whose power lay in wealth derived from industry and trade, he determined to attack the basis of that power by destroying British trade with Europe. Thus on November 21, 1806, after defeating the Prussians at Jena, Napoleon issued from Berlin decrees which placed Britain in a state of blockade, prohibited all trade in English goods, and closed European ports to ships coming from British ports. Britain responded to the Berlin Decrees with the Orders in Council complained of by Madison in his message. The Orders, issued in November 1807, were long and complicated but their effect was to bar from Europe all neutral trade except that which came through Britain. Napoleon responded to the Orders with further decrees, this time issued from Milan. They stated that every ship which came from a British port, paid a British duty, or allowed itself to be searched by a British ship, became a lawful prize, liable to seizure at sea or in any French-controlled port.

French Decrees and British Orders put the United States in an impossible situation. American ships which obeyed the Decrees were liable to seizure by British cruisers, and by French port officials or French cruisers if they obeyed the Orders. The American government declared that both the British and the French actions were violations of the rights of neutrals under international law, but the trouble with international law is that in the end it is what the countries with the power to enforce it say it is. Thus the United States had no choice but either to go to war with Britain and France or to attempt economic sanctions of its own. Under the cautious and pacific Jefferson, America chose the latter course: in December 1807, moved by the hard British line on impressment as well as by the Decrees and Orders, Congress passed the Embargo Act which forbade any ship of the United States to sail from a U.S. port for any foreign port.

The Embargo could not succeed. Both France and Britain were in some measure dependent on trade with America and thus vulnerable to this form of pressure, but neither was quite so vulnerable as the United States itself. In 1809, economic distress in America plus the obvious immovability of both of the belligerent powers brought the repeal of the Embargo Act. In its place, Congress passed the Nonintercourse Act which allowed American ships back on the seas but banned trade with France and Britain. In May 1810, even those restrictions were removed, but the Act which accomplished this, Macon's Bill No. 2, provided that should one of the belligerents remove its edicts against neutral trade, the United States would revive Nonintercourse against the other.

With the failure of the Embargo and Nonintercourse it seemed that America had no further weapons to bring to bear in the attempt to free neutral trade. Certainly the Tory government of Britain felt that way. It had no desire to see the already poor relations with the U.S. deteriorate further, but at the same time was not inclined to reduce restrictions on neutral trade. But by 1810 something was happening inside America: the desire for peace which produced the Embargo and Nonintercourse was gradually giving way to a war spirit directed more and more specifically against Britain. The confiscation of millions of dollars worth of American property which resulted from Napoleon's various Decrees angered Americans, but nevertheless their attitude towards France was ambiguous. Few saw Napoleon in any sort of heroic light but, on the other hand, France had been America's ally in her time of greatest need. Attitudes towards Britain were more clear cut. The Royal Navy was a far greater and more obvious menace to American commerce than French customs officials; and it was the Royal Navy which hovered off the American coast searching for illegal traders and impressing American seamen. Further, the British actions tended to reinforce the view of Britain as a tyrant inherited from the Revolution, and many Americans could believe that the British actions were a part of an attempt to reverse the decision of the Revolutionary War. This belief received substantial reinforcement when, in March 1812, Madison laid before Congress copies of the instructions and letters of John Henry, who had been employed in 1808 and 1809 by Governor Sir James Craig of Lower Canada to obtain information about the eastern areas of the United States. The letters seemed to show that Great Britain had intrigued with leading anti-government figures in the States and was conspiring to bring about the dismemberment of the Union.[5]

But although moving towards war, America was still very much divided in 1810 as to the stance that should be taken. As long as both France and Britain maintained their restrictions on neutral trade, the government could not logically pursue war against one and not against the other; and no one could see any future in taking on the world's greatest sea power and the world's greatest land power at the same time. The next move was clearly up to the French. As Jefferson noted in a letter to Madison in 1809, "should Bonaparte have the wisdom to correct his injustice towards us, I consider war with England inevitable."[6]

It took Napoleon only three months to grasp the essentials of the American dilemma: in August 1810 the American Minister in Paris was informed by the Duc de Cadore, the French Foreign Secretary, that the Berlin and Milan Decrees would be revoked as of November 1 on the understanding that if Britain did not revoke the Orders in Council the United States would act to cause her rights to be respected. Britain had announced a willingness to revoke the Orders when France repealed her Decrees but in the event failed to do so. The British government explained its reluctance to act by pointing out that there was no clear evidence that the French Decrees were no longer in force. And, indeed, well into 1811 American ships were still being seized in France. But this logic did not apply later in 1811 or in 1812 and it seemed clear, as Madison pointed out in his War Message, that there was another reason for the failure of the British government to act on its promise. Strange as it may seem to us in this era of total war, neither France nor Britain cared to do without many of the products each traditionally imported from each other. Thus despite Orders and Decrees a large and lucrative trade continued between the belligerents under special licenses. "It has become, indeed, sufficiently certain," wrote Madison, "that the commerce of the United States is to be sacrificed, not as interfering with the belligerent rights of Great Britain; not as supplying the wants of her enemies, which she herself supplies; but as interfering with the monopoly which she herself covets for her own commerce and navigation." There was some truth in the accusation. British shipping interests were major backers of the Tory party and had been behind the Orders in Council. Opposition to the Orders from manufacturing interests, anxious to regain the American market, grew steadily in 1811 and 1812 but as long as Spencer Perceval, the actual author of the policy and Prime Minister since August 1810, remained in power there was no chance of their being rescinded. When Perceval was assassinated by a madman in May 1812, however, his successor, Lord Liverpool, immediately withdrew the Orders.

Had the Orders in Council been revoked in 1811 it is possible that war could have been averted. As it was, however the American elections of 1811 brought to Congress the fiery westerners known as the War Hawks. They brought with them a determination to make a stand against Britain, a determination based on national pride, on economic distress in the Ohio and Mississippi valley regions which was blamed on British trade restrictions, and on a new set of grievances over supposed British agitations among the Western Indians.

The grievances concerning the West came to form the fifth and final point in Madison's message to Congress. "In reviewing the conduct of Great Britain towards the United States," he wrote,

> our attention is necessarily drawn to the warfare just renewed by the savages on one of our extensive frontiers—a warfare which is known to spare neither age nor sex and to be distinguished by features particularly shocking to humanity. It is difficult to account for the activity and combinations which have for some time been developing themselves among tribes in constant intercourse with British traders and garrisons without connecting their hostility with that influence....

The Western problem was, in fact, an old one, as old as the Treaty of Paris which ended the American Revolution. By the provisions of that treaty the border between the United States and British North America was drawn through the Great Lakes and thus the forts at Oswego, Niagara, Detroit and Michilimackinac, although held by Britain at the end of the war, were given to the United States.

Since the forts were also major bases for the Montreal fur trade it was provided that their surrender should be delayed until the traders could wind up their business. Ten years later, however, Britain still occupied these bases on American territory and their permanent retention was urged by the Montreal fur interests and by Lieutenant Governor John Simcoe of Upper Canada who hoped to see the establishment of Indian buffer states south of the Great Lakes. At the same time there was growing Indian unrest on the frontier which the Americans, not surprisingly, tended to blame on the British. Only in 1796, following an American victory over the Indians at Fallen Timbers and the negotiation of Jay's Treaty, were the posts finally given up. Nevertheless, the right of the Montrealers to trade on American territory remained and new posts on British territory soon arose at St. Joseph's Island near Michilimackinac, and at Amherstburg on the Detroit River.

As a result of Jay's Treaty, problems between Americans and Britons on the frontier diminished for a number of years. But the situation could not long remain stable. The chief cause of Indian unrest was the relentless advance of the American frontier and although a boundary between Indian and White territory was set following Fallen Timbers it was only a matter of time before it was violated by American pioneers, and the Indians again were forced to the defence of their lands.

By 1807 frontier tensions were again increasing and once more Britain became involved in them, this time as a result of the *Chesapeake—Leopard* affair. As pointed out earlier, that incident brought demands for war from all parts of the United States. And those who called for war pointed most often to the Canadas as the place where Britain was most vulnerable to retaliation. In this situation Britain began seriously to court the friendship of the Western Indians through her Indian agents at Amherstburg and St. Joseph's. The intention was not to provoke war but rather to ensure that the Indians would be on Britain's side in the event of an American attack on Canada. The task was not a difficult one. Even before the instructions went out to the Indian agents, the Shawnee chief Tecumseh and his brother the Prophet had begun their campaign to organize the tribes of the midwest to resistance to further American advances, and were happy to find allies anywhere. Indeed, by 1810 the problem was no longer one of winning Indian trust and support. The Indians were ready for war and the agents' task was to keep them in check while still retaining their friendship. Although the British aims were clearly defensive—so much so that in 1811 the Indians were warned that if they went to war with the Americans no help from Britain could be expected—it is not surprising that the Americans in the West did not see the situation in the same way. The close association of Montreal traders and Indians, the regular conferences between Indian chiefs and officials at Amherstburg and St. Joseph's, and the lavish distribution of gifts convinced them that the British were behind the growing war spirit among the Indians. They saw the refusal of Tecumseh to recognize a new land cession on the Wabash River as proof of the British involvement. Determined to force the Indians off the Wabash, Governor William Henry Harrison of the Indiana Territory gathered an army of several thousand militia in the late fall of 1811 and marched against the Prophet's village at the mouth of Tippecanoe creek. The battle which followed was inconclusive: Harrison's army was badly mauled in an ambush but the Indians were forced to abandon their village. But the clash did bring the issue to a head; war blazed along the whole Indian frontier. The Westerners carried their grievance against Britain to the Congress which met in Washington in November 1811; to resolve it they demanded the expulsion of Britain from Canada.

Madison's War Message had the desired effect. By majorities of nineteen to thirteen in the Senate and of seventy-nine to forty-nine in the House of Representatives, Congress voted to instruct the President to declare war on Great Britain. He did so on June 18, 1812.

As seen by the majority of Americans, war with Britain was the only just and honourable course of action for the United States in 1812; it was the logical response to an intolerable situation. As presented in the newspapers of British

North America, however, the events leading up to the war and the war itself looked very different. There, not only the adequacy of the American grievances, but their very validity was rejected. In considerable measure the interpretations of events which were presented to British Americans came from outside the colonies. In part they originated in Britain where, until the last year or so before the war there was general support for the position put forward in James Stephen's famous pamphlet *War in Disguise; or The Frauds of the Neutral Flags* (London, 1805) that "the neutral powers can subsist without this newly acquired commerce; but Great Britain cannot long exist as a nation, if bereft of her ancient means of offensive maritime war." From Britain also came an unwavering conviction that the war against Napoleonic France was a war against tyranny, a war to preserve liberty in the world. It followed from this conviction that all those who fought against Britain were against liberty.

In some measure also the views put forward in British American newspapers originated in the United States. As the vote for war in Congress indicated, that country was far from united. From the time of the Embargo in 1807 the Federalist party, which drew its support primarily from New England, opposed the policies of the successive Republican administrations of Jefferson and Madison. Much of this opposition originated in the close emotional ties between New England and Britain, and in a common conservatism which recoiled in horror from the excesses of the French Revolution: Napoleon represented tyranny, atheism, and wickedness the New England clergy constantly reminded the people. But, more important, it was New England which suffered most directly under the various American restrictions on trade. The economy of that area was built on maritime commerce and the Embargo and even Nonintercourse had a devastating effect on it. New England was, of course, also the area most affected by the Orders in Council and impressment but clearly adequate profits were possible despite them. When war became a real prospect the opposition of New England was increased by apprehension of the destruction which would be wrought on American commerce by the enormously powerful Royal Navy. With the outbreak of war not only did New England refuse to provide state militia forces for use in the national service but, under the protection of licences issued by Governor Sir John Sherbrooke of Nova Scotia, a huge trade was continued between New England and Nova Scotia and New Brunswick which supplied many of the needs of the British army in Spain and in the Canadas. Not until 1814, when Britain no longer needed supplies for her army in Europe and began to clamp down on the New England trade and even occupied the Maine coast between the St. Croix and Penobscot rivers, did New England cease to follow a basically pro-British point of view. Even then she tended to turn inward rather than to the rest of the Union for defence and the Hartford Convention, to which Massachusetts, Connecticut, and Rhode Island sent official representatives in late 1814, might well have resulted in a decision to seek a separate peace with Britain but for the fortuitous end of the war in December. Expressed in the many newspapers of New England, the Federalist disapproval and suspicion of the policies of the American government easily found their way to British North America where they helped to shape another view of events.

However, while the editors of the newspapers of British America drew on views of American Federalists and British Tories they really did not have to look beyond the colonies for opinions on the nature of the conflict between the United States and Britain. In every province there existed an elite composed primarily of Loyalists of the American Revolution, elites which controlled governments and, directly or indirectly, most newspapers. To these people loyalty to Britain and animosity towards the country which had exiled them were matters of faith. For them there was no question of the justice of Britain's war with France and no question of the injustice of America's policy towards Britain. But their analysis of the situation went much deeper than that. In the view of educated Britons, a view based on classical political science, democratic republics inevitably collapsed into mob rule and tyranny. Such had been the case in Greece, Rome, Carthage, and latterly, Revolutionary France:

> ... there appears to be one material incident to all Republics, which is, the want of that permanence or duration so essential to the progressive improvement and perfecting of any human institution, for it is a well known historical fact, that Republics are most perfect at their commencement, and invariably fall off and degenerate, until, by internal discord, corruption and anarchy (before any great lapse of time) they end in the most intolerable Despotism, or become an easy prey to some neighbouring Power.[7]

The people of these societies sought liberty too passionately, and in the social and political orders they constructed there was no secure place for men of ability and substance, no strong executive force in government. As a result, these states fell into the hands of the mob and its demagogue leaders; rule of law and individual liberty were destroyed. It took very little evidence to convince the Loyalist dominated elites that the American Republic was well advanced in the process of decay. For some the mere fact of American hostility to Britain was enough. Were the Americans truly interested in peace, liberty, and justice, as they professed to be, wrote the Reverend John Strachan, they would "excuse any little failure on the part of Britain."[8] The idea that Americans might view both France and Britain as tyrannies, the one exerting its power upon the sea, the other upon the land, was inconceivable to them. Those who chose to look further through the screen of their prejudices easily found more evidence of American decay, particularly in the division within the United States between Federalists and Republicans. They identified the Federalists as the "better part" of American society—the people of ability and substance—who, because they could not descend to demagogic appeals to the mob, were condemned to perpetual opposition. The Republicans, on the other hand were the party of the "mob." They were led by "Southern epicures," "avowed patrons of slavery and dealers in human blood,"[9] who maintained themselves in power by their willingness to appeal to the base instincts of the worst parts of society. Such leaders were the natural allies of the tyrant Napoleon. To satisfy their ally they had harassed Britain and finally declared war on her; to satisfy the lust for rape and plunder in their constituents they waged war against the innocent people of the Canadas.

There was one further factor which informed the thinking of the British American elites, particularly in the Canadas, and influenced the content of their newspapers. As early as the *Chesapeake—Leopard* affair, the idea was expressed in public circles in the United States that the best, and indeed the only way, for America to retaliate against British insults on the seas was through Britain's American colonies. And as the belief grew that Britain was attempting to stir up trouble in the west, that strategy found more and more adherents. By 1811 so many members of Congress had become vocal advocates of the conquest of Canada that the erratic John Randolph, fearing for the defence of the South, turned to denounce them all: "Agrarian cupidity, not maritime right, urges the war. Ever since the report of the Committee on Foreign Relations came into the House, we have heard but one word—like the whippoor-will, but one eternal monotonous tone—Canada! Canada! Canada!"[10] In some areas of British America these threats could be taken lightly. John Howe, dispatched on a spying expedition to the United States in 1808, by Governor Sherbrooke of Nova Scotia, reported that "it is amusing to hear them talk here of the extreme facility with which they can possess themselves of the British Provinces. No man of either Party seems to imagine there would be any difficulty in effecting the object."[11] Safe in the knowledge that the population of the Maritime provinces was largely Loyalist and that the area was protected from land attack by the wilderness of Maine and from sea attack by the Royal Navy, Howe could afford to be amused. But there was no such confidence in the Canadas. These provinces were both exposed to land attack on a long frontier with the United States and there were only 6000 British regular troops available for their defence in 1812. Clearly they could only be defended against American attack if the regulars were supported strongly by the civilian populations. And there were compelling reasons to doubt not only the willingness of most of the inhabitants to aid in repelling American invaders, but even their loyalty.

In Lower Canada the problem of loyalty was as much a function of the province's racial division as anything else. The English ruling class tended to identify the French Canadians with the French of Revolutionary and Napoleonic France, and to see in every trace of opposition to the oligarchic administration of the province the hand of French and American agitators, and the beginnings of revolution. This fear had some basis in the 1790s. The turbulent Citizen Genêt, who represented France in the United States in 1793 and 1794, was not uninterested in French Canada and one of his tracts *The Free French to their Brothers in Canada* was widely distributed there. There was some response to Genêt's agitation among French Canadians, and considerable apprehension among their English rulers. These apprehensions were increased when, in 1796, Ira Allen of Vermont, with whom Genêt was closely associated, was captured in the English Channel on board a French ship laden with 20,000 muskets to arm the French Canadians for a revolution. By the end of the century, however, the agitations had died down. Perhaps this was due to the execution of the full penalty for treason—hanging, drawing and quartering—on David McLane at Quebec in 1797. More likely the return of peace to Lower Canada was due to the intervention of the hierarchy of the Catholic Church on the side of conservative stability and the introduction of some fifty Royalist emigré priests from France.

By the early years of the nineteenth century, then, there was little sympathy for either France or the United States in Lower Canada. However, few of the English speaking elite in the province could ever bring themselves to believe that anyone who spoke French was not in secret sympathy with France. Like so many English Canadians since then, they equated a refusal to become English in language, manners and religion with a desire for reunion with France. This suspicion reached a climax under the administration of Governor Sir James Craig (1806-1811). Craig was an old soldier with entrenched conservative ideas and a long-standing hatred of France. Under the skilful guidance of local advisors such as Herman Ryland, his secretary, he quickly came to believe that the opposition of the predominantly French Canadian assembly to the policies of his administration was little short of treason. Craig's support of the vicious attacks of the Quebec *Mercury* on the French Canadians and his own attempt to suppress opposition by closing down the province's only French language newspaper, *Le Canadien*, and imprisoning its editors earned his administration the name of "the reign of terror."

Craig was finally recalled to England in 1811 by a government not unsympathetic to his aim of forcing the Anglicization of French Canada but more worried that his policies would drive the French Canadians to support the Americans in the war which seemed imminent. His successor, General Sir George Prevost, was instructed to pursue a policy of conciliation. Prevost was remarkably competent at his task and within a year had restored such good relations with the French Canadians that the assembly quickly voted all the emergency measures he asked for when war broke out. But even he worried about the strength of their loyalty and was sure that the Americans were attempting to undermine it. Well after the war began he conveyed to the Colonial Office his conviction that "there are persons dangerously disaffected towards His Majesty's Government amongst the Canadians as agents of France and America, for in my opinion the Government of the latter country ... is endeavouring to corrupt the minds of the Canadians by means calculated to alienate them from His Majesty's Government."[12]

In Upper Canada the situation was even more critical. There, two-thirds of the ninety-odd thousand inhabitants were of recent American origin. The first settlers were Loyalists, but to hasten the development of the province Lt.

Governor John Simcoe threw open the gates to all Americans in 1792. As a result American land seekers, part of the great westward migration, flooded the province. Clearly these later arrivals could not be depended on to aid in the defence of the province, or even to refrain from assisting an invading American army. Indeed, so small was the population of Upper Canada, so weak the regular force available for its defence, and so exposed its position that most of the population, Loyalist and otherwise, were convinced that resistance in the event of an American attack was pointless. General Isaac Brock, who took over as administrator and military commander of Upper Canada in 1811, was well aware of the rampant "disaffection" in the province and undertook to combat it by a propaganda campaign mounted in the official government newspaper, the *York Gazette*. That paper was normally devoid of editorial opinion and political comment, but in February 1812, following a letter from one of Brock's aides to General Prevost stating that it was intended to "let fly a drive official at [the Americans] in the next *York Gazette*," it burst out with patriotic and anti-American material. It continued to print material in that line until publication ceased in late 1812 due to a lack of paper.[13] But despite the propaganda campaign Brock's worst fears were realized. When war came he called a special session of the legislature in order to obtain passage of legislation he felt necessary for handling the war emergency. The legislature was dismissed after only a week when the assembly turned down a new Militia Act and refused to authorize a partial suspension of Habeas Corpus and "a partial exercise of Martial Law concurrently with the ordinary course of Justice." Further, on August 3, the day he dismissed the legislature, Brock had to report to the Executive Council of the province that,

> ... the enemy had invaded and taken post in the Western District—was multiplying daily his preparations to Invade in others; that the Militia in a perfect state of insubordination had withdrawn from the Ranks in actual service; had refused to March when legally commanded to reinforce a Detachment of the Regular Force for the relief of Amherstburgh, had insulted their Officers, and some, not immediately embodied, had manifested in many instances, a Treasonable spirit of neutrality or disaffection.... That in the Western and London Districts several Persons had negotiated with the Enemy's Commander, hailing his arrival and pledging support.[14]

These weaknesses in the political and social structures of the Canadas were long known in the United States, and when war came, American strategy was to exploit them.

The war which began on June 18, 1812, and continued for two and a half years was a singularly inconclusive struggle. At sea British and American privateers harried each other's trade and American frigates scored some notable successes over their lighter-built and lighter-armed British counterparts. But in no way could the United States hope to achieve redress for its grievances on the sea: British naval dominance was too overwhelming. Shortly after the beginning of hostilities, the Royal Navy established a blockade of the American coast from New York southward. By the end of the war the blockade extended along the whole coast and effectively neutralized the American navy. Along with the blockade went amphibious raids, the most effective of which resulted in the capture and burning of Washington on August 24, 1814. But, then, the United States never sought victory at sea: at best it was hoped that the Royal Navy could be kept at bay and that the destruction wrought by American privateers would result in some pressure for peace by British merchant and shipping interests.

It was on the land that the United States sought victory. The British North American colonies were weak and poorly defended and Britain's commitment to a land war in Europe, it was hoped, would keep them that way.[15] Whether those colonies were to be invaded "not as an object of the war but as a means to bring it to a satisfactory conclusion," as Monroe and some Easterners maintained, or whether they were to be incorporated in the Union was a matter of some dispute. No one in the war party contested, however, that the British colonies were to be the major object of America's war effort.[16] Given that object, there was good reason for selecting the Canadas, and particularly Upper Canada rather than the maritime colonies as the primary objective. First, the maritime colonies were protected by Britain's most potent weapon, the Royal Navy, but equally important was the virtual neutrality of New England. Without the aid in men and supplies of New England there was no hope of mounting a campaign against the maritime colonies. Indeed, as it turned out, a virtual truce existed along the frontier from Lake Champlain to the ocean throughout the whole war, and the supplies which flowed in from New England were a major factor in maintaining British forces in North America. But there were no such objections to the Canadas. They were not only remote from British power but also accessible to the states and territories of the North and West which were strongly in favour of the war. Further, the political and social weaknesses of the Canadas, discussed earlier, were well known in the United States. Jefferson believed that the capture of Canada was "a mere matter of marching," and Henry Clay was sure that the Senate would not deem him presumptuous "when I state that I verily believe that the militia of Kentucky are alone competent to place Montreal and Upper Canada at your feet."[17] The proclamation issued by General William Hull when he moved from Detroit into Upper Canada in July 1812, printed in this collection, indicated that not only did he expect support from the recent American settlers in Upper Canada but also from British subjects who would be happy to take the opportunity to escape from British tyranny.

For two years, until the middle of 1814 when the defeat of Napoleon allowed Britain to reinforce her small garrison in the Canadas, the United States held the initiative in the land war. It was not used well. The Canadas at this time were particularly vulnerable to attack. Together their populations totalled less than half a million (compared with the seven millions of the United States) and they were scattered from the mouth of the St. Lawrence to Amherstburg. Unable to sustain a defending army themselves, they depended on the lifeline of the Great Lakes—St. Lawrence transportation route to connect them to the resources of Great Britain. The easiest way to capture the Canadas was to cut the lifeline. President Madison understood the essentials of the Canadian situation perfectly and favoured an immediate strike against Montreal to sever Upper Canada from Lower Canada. But there were problems. When the war began the army authorized by Congress was still in the early stages of recruitment and organization. If any early blow was to be struck, and that seemed advisable, it would have to be with militia forces. However the organization of a militia army was made difficult in the east by the virtual neutrality of New England. Only in the western states of Ohio and Kentucky was there a large militia eager and willing to strike a blow against Britain. Thus a plan suggested by Major General Henry Dearborn was adopted which called for immediate attacks against Upper Canada from Detroit and Niagara and an attack against Montreal as soon as one could be organized. The plan was perhaps the best alternative to an all out attack on Montreal since it would at least mobilize the enthusiasm which accompanied the declaration of war; but enthusiasm alone does not make an army. The problems of collecting, moving, and supplying troops in the West were enormous and were compounded on this occasion by the selection of Generals William Hull and Solomon Van Rensselaer to command, respectively, the thrusts from Detroit and Niagara: the former was aged and incompetent, the latter merely incompetent. Nevertheless, the plan might well have succeeded. When Hull moved his army into Canada on July 12, the militia force which had been collected to oppose him melted away. Most of the men simply returned home, but several hundred joined Hull's force. It seemed that the conquest of Upper Canada would indeed be a mere matter of marching.

The day was saved for the Canadas by the audacity and military competence of Major General Isaac Brock. Although he expected the main American attack to come on the Niagara and had to leave most of his force there, Brock knew he could not ignore Hull's invasion. To oppose him he collected four hundred regulars and another thousand Indians and militia. Brock's force was only one third the size of the American army but he used it well and played so skillfully on the fears of the aged American General that Hull, without putting up a serious battle, surrendered Detroit and his entire force on August 15. Two months later, on October 13, Van Rensselaer finally mounted his attack across the Niagara and easily established a force on the heights at Queenston. On this occasion the fighting was heavy and Brock was killed in an early assault on the American position. However, the defences of the frontier were so well organized that a strong counterattack was mounted before the disorganized Americans could properly secure their foothold. The day ended with the complete destruction of the American force.

The fate of Upper Canada was decided at the battles at Detroit and Queenston. The disaffection and desertion among the Upper Canadian militia which followed Hull's invasion indicate how quickly and easily the province might have collapsed had Brock followed a cautious, defensive strategy. And, indeed, Brock was completely aware of this. Writing to his brothers in England after Detroit he said of his actions: "Some say that nothing could be more desperate than the offensive measure I took; but I answer that the state of the province admitted of nothing but desperate remedies." As it was, Brock's victories put heart into a people previously convinced that defeat was inevitable, and the chance of an easy American victory slipped away. In the early months of the war only a few Loyalists stood steadily by the British regulars; most Upper Canadians attempted to remain neutral. It was not that they particularly disliked British government, nor were they unaware of the penalties provided by law for those who failed to do their militia duty. Rather, they were sure that they would soon be under American rule and feared the reprisals of a victorious American army. The victories at Detroit and Queenston destroyed the idea of an inevitable and easy American victory and led the cautious Upper Canadians to abandon neutrality and commit themselves to the defence of the province. Although the later years of the war tested them severely, most remained loyal to that commitment.

The Americans fared better in 1813. On Lake Erie the squadron assembled by Commodore Oliver Hazard Perry destroyed the small British fleet under Captain Robert Barclay. With his lifeline cut, General Henry Proctor had to abandon Detroit. Retreating slowly up the Thames River he was caught and defeated in battle near Moraviantown. Proctor escaped with part of his force, but among the dead that day was Tecumseh. That same year another American army routed the British out of the Niagara frontier, and an amphibious force captured York and burned its public buildings. By the end of 1813, however, the American drive had petered out and the British forces began to rally. When the American army which had occupied the Niagara peninsula burned Newark (Niagara-on-the-Lake) and withdrew to the United States it was followed by a British force which in turn devastated the settlements on the American side of the Niagara River. To the east, General Dearborn finally mounted a half-hearted, two-pronged attack on Montreal which was repulsed at Châteauguay and Crysler's Farm.

The army fielded by the United States in 1814 was immensely superior to its predecessors. Well trained and well led, it was indeed a "regular" army, but it met veteran British forces from the European campaigns and battles at Chippawa, Lundy's Lane, and Fort Erie produced only stalemate. However the British attempts to carry the land war to the United States that year were also a failure. The British strategy was not to conquer the United States but to force the American commissioners at the peace talks already underway at Ghent to make major land concessions and to agree to open the Mississippi to British trade and to limitations on American westward expansion. The first British attack, mounted from Montreal by General Prevost, had Plattsburg on Lake Champlain as its immediate objective. When the small navy which accompanied his army was destroyed by an American fleet, Prevost, to the disgust of the Montreal merchant community, aborted the campaign. Prevost's withdrawal from Plattsburg decided the peace talks at Ghent. Neither Britain nor the United States could claim a military advantage and neither wished to put forward the effort necessary to gain one. Britain, after twenty years of war was weary, and the issues of impressment and neutral rights which had led the Americans to war ceased to be important after the collapse of France in 1814. Thus the treaty which was signed on December 24, 1814, provided only for the cessation of hostilities and a return to the *status quo ante bellum*. Looking back, probably the most important decision made at Ghent was the provision in the treaty to refer to commissioners for future settlement, questions of fishing and navigation rights, boundary location, and naval armaments on the Great Lakes. It would be a long time before Canadians and Americans could look upon each other as friends but these commissions were the basis for maintaining a peace—shaky as it often was—on which in time friendship could be built.

But the lack of solid provisions in the treaty does not mean that the war was without results. True, in Britain it was soon all but forgotten, becoming little more than a distasteful side show of the epic war with Revolutionary and Napoleonic France. In the United States, a recent study indicates that the war served as a necessary catharsis. Since at least the beginning of the French Revolution, the left and right in the United States—the Republicans and the Federalists—had been growing further and further apart until it seemed that the Republic must split.

Their positions were symbolized by support for either France or Britain in the European contest. The war of 1812, bringing with it the real possibility of a breakup of the union, drew moderates of both sides together in a determination that the great experiment must not end, and laid the basis for the "era of good feelings" which followed. The success of the reconciliation is indicated by the speed with which the internal divisions were forgotten and the war passionately, if unreasonably, proclaimed as the "Second War of Independence," the victorious effort to fend off British attempts to reestablish colonial dominance.[18]

The war affected the various parts of British North America in different ways. For the Maritime Provinces it was a period of prosperity based on illegal trade with New England and successful privateering. Little touched by the destruction of war those provinces could, as one Canadian historian has put it, "probably have managed to put up with it if the war had lasted five years longer."[19] For Lower Canada too, the advantages of the war just about outweighed the disadvantages. Trade increased, the replacement of Craig by

Prevost eased racial tensions, and the performance of Colonel Charles de Salaberry's Canadian Voltigeurs at Châteauguay put an end, at least for a time, to questions of French Canadian loyalty.

It was Upper Canada which was most affected by the War of 1812. Not only was that province the scene of the majority of the fighting, and thus of most of the destruction of the war, but its very character was changed by its involvement. Until 1812 Upper Canada was little more than a string of scattered settlements along the upper St. Lawrence River and the lower Great Lakes. Although there was a core of Loyalists in the province, the growing majority of the population were American pioneers who came in search of cheap, empty land. Upper Canada was a part of the American frontier and might well have become a part of the American republic in time. The War of 1812 changed that. Those who favoured the American cause were driven out and those who remained developed a sense of community based on a common commitment to protect families, homes, and crops from the American invaders. The anti-Americanism of the Loyalist elite was legitimized, and the commitment to Britain, whose soldiers carried and continued to carry the burden of the defence of the province, was increased and intensified. The War of 1812 shaped the character of the Upper Canadian community and through that, the character of Ontario and all of Canada.

Notes

1. The Message was printed in a number of British American papers. The *Kingston Gazette* printed it in the issues of July 14 and 21, 1812.

2. As an example of the growth in American trade, American exports to Europe of sugar and coffee, which in 1792 were 1,122,000 and 2,136,742 pounds respectively, rose to 74,000,000 and 48,000,000 pounds respectively by 1804. Alfred T. Mahan, *The Influence of Sea Power upon the French Revolution and Empire, 1793-1812*, 2 vols., (Boston: Little, Brown & Co., 1892), vol. II, p. 267.

3. James F. Zimmerman, *Impressment of American Seamen* (New York: Columbia University Press, 1925), pp. 260-3.

4. Of the four seamen one, Ratford by name, was a Briton and was hanged for desertion. The other three claimed to be Americans who had previously been impressed into the British service. One of them died in prison and two were later returned to the United States.

5. For an examination of American fears concerning British intentions see Dennis A. Taylor, *The American Picture of British North America on the Eve of the War of 1812*, unpublished M.A. Thesis, Queen's University, (Kingston, Ont.) 1966, pp. 78-97.

6. Jefferson to Madison, August 17, 1809. Quoted in Reginald Horsman, *The Causes of the War of 1812* (Philadelphia: University of Pennsylvania Press, 1962), p. 178.

7. Mr. Justice William Campbell's charge to the Grand Jury, *Upper Canada Gazette*, April 1, 1822. Quoted in S. F. Wise and R. C. Brown, *Canada Views the United States* (Seattle: University of Washington Press, 1967), pp. 19-20.

8. John Strachan, *A Sermon Preached at York before the Legislative Council and House of Assembly, August 2, 1812* (York, Upper Canada, 1812).

9. See letters signed "Camilus", in the *Kingston Gazette*, December 12, 1812, and "A Canadian", in the *York Gazette*, February 4, 1812.

10. Quoted in Julius W. Pratt, *The Expansionists of 1812* (New York: Peter Smith, 1925), p. 143.

11. *Ibid.,* p. 34.

12. Public Archives of Canada. Colonial Office 42/146, Prevost to Lord Liverpool, March 3, 1813.

13. For an examination of this propaganda, see R. A. Bowler, *Propaganda in Upper Canada: An Examination of the Propaganda Directed at the People of Upper Canada During the War of 1812*, unpublished M.A. Thesis, Queen's University, (Kingston, Ont.), 1964.

14. Public Archives of Canada. Record Group 1, Upper Canada Executive Council Minute Book. See also E. A. Cruikshank "A Study of Disaffection in Upper Canada in 1812-15" in M. Zaslow (ed.) *The Defended Border: Upper Canada and the War of 1812*, (Toronto: Macmillan, 1964), pp. 221-240.

15. George Dangerfield, *The Era of Good Feelings* (New York: Harcourt Brace, 1952), p. 49.

16. Pratt, pp. 49-51.

17. *Ibid.*, p. 40.

18. Anthony W. Rasporich, *Quasi-Alliance with France in 1812: An Ideological Study, 1789-1812*, unpublished M.A. Thesis, Queen's University, (Kingston, Ont.), 1964.

19. C. P. Stacey, "The War of 1812 in Canadian History," in Zaslow, *op. cit.,* p. 331.

CHAPTER

9 THE FUR TRADE AND THE NORTHWEST

The fur trade and Canadian history are indivisible. One might even speak of the tyranny of the fur trade as every trading post, canoe route, and fur battle was pursued by the antiquarians to the point of saturation. At the academic level, Harold Innis established an international reputation with his *The Fur Trade in Canada: An Introduction to Canadian Economic History* (1930), and he provided both an economic and a geographic explanation for Canada's existence. The fur trade was also the glue for A.S. Morton's *History of the Canadian West to 1870-71* (1939), a sympathetic examination of the Hudson's Bay Company as a western institution and eventual Canadian benefactor. To Morton, the Company was an enlightened paternalist with the best interests of its employees, its clients and native suppliers at heart. The fur trade certainly drew the Europeans into the west, and it is the interaction between the natives and the whites that dominates W.L. Morton's "The North West Company: Pedlars Extraordinary," reproduced here. Written in 1966, the article offers what Morton calls a "rather quaint" analysis of the labour market of the "happily primitive" natives. He then turns to the North West Company, the "greatest of all" Canadian fur trading companies and "the first successful combination of European capital and business enterprise with Indian skills."

In recent years, the studies of the fur trade, the native peoples and the companies have assumed a different character. Susan Giannettino, an anthropologist, examines "The Middleman Role in the Fur Trade: Its Influence on Interethnic Relations in the Saskatchewan-Missouri Plains." In a sense, Giannettino extends the middleman concept of the Hunt Thesis (See Chapter 1) to the prairies, though her concern is with the interior of the native society and the interaction among native groups. An even more significant departure in the study of the fur trade is obvious in Glen Makahonuk's "Wage-Labour in the Northwest Fur

Trade Economy, 1760-1849." The relationship between the employees and the companies is placed squarely within the emerging capitalistic-labour system, and the notions of the benign parental companies are challenged at many levels. He points to the exploitive-adversarial encounters as a "clear expression of the disharmony and class tensions in the fur trade economy."

Suggestions for Further Reading

Brown, Jennifer S.H., *Strangers in Blood: Fur Trade Families in Indian Country*. Vancouver: University of British Columbia Press, 1980.

Carlos, A., "The Birth and Death of Predatory Competition in the North American Fur Trade: 1810-1821," *Explorations in Economic History*, 19, no. 2 (1982) 156-183.

Coates, K., "Furs along the Yukon: Hudson's Bay Company - Native Trade in the Yukon River Basin, 1830-1893," *B C Studies*, no. 55 (Autumn 1982), 50-78.

Friesen, Gerald, *The Canadian Prairies: A History*. Toronto: Oxford University Press, 1984.

Judd, Carol M. and Arthur J. Ray, *Old Trails and New Directions: Papers of the Third North American Fur Trade Conference*. Toronto: University of Toronto Press, 1980.

Judd, Carol M. "Native labour and social stratification in the Hudson's Bay Company's Northern department (1770-1870)," *Canadian Review of Sociology and Anthropology*, 17, no. 4 (November 1980), 305-314.

Moodie, D. Wayne, "The Trading Post Settlement of the Canadian Northwest, 1774-1821," *Journal of Historical Geography*, 13, no. 2 (October 1987), 360-374.

Ray, Arthur, *Indians in the Fur Trade*. Toronto: University of Toronto Press, 1974.

Rich, E.E., *The Fur Trade and the North West to 1857*. Toronto: McClelland & Stewart, 1967.

THE NORTH WEST COMPANY: PEDLARS EXTRAORDINARY

W.L. Morton

That the North American fur trade was essentially a commercial marriage of primitive ways and needs to the more advanced techniques and demands of European and Chinese markets is one of those truths so evident and general that they could scarcely be proved if there were need. Similarly, the North West Company before 1821 was an extraordinarily successful union of the primitive culture of the forest Indian tribes with the sophisticated civilization of Western

Originally published in the Winter 1966 issue of *Minnesota History,* copyright 1967 by the Minnesota Historical Society.

Europe. This paper tries to point the way toward a study of the company's effective merger of commerce and culture; it attempts to be a critical essay rather than a piece of research.[1]

Let us begin by noting that the North American Indian with whom the fur trade was conducted was an inland forest dweller. Unlike the Eskimo and The European, he neither lived by nor used the sea. Trade between him and the transoceanic European, accordingly, turned upon either the Indian going to the shore or the European going inland.

The earliest barter was of course entirely coastal, even when separated from fishing voyages and pursued as a distinct undertaking. The scattered references we possess to the fur trade of the sixteenth century all allude to trade on the coast, whether casual or at a seaside rendezvous. The first historically known rendezvous was Tadoussac on the Gulf of St. Lawrence; Quebec, Trois Rivières, and Montreal were each in turn meant to be the same, but the trade was carried steadily inland by the happy accident of the great sea entry of the St. Lawrence River. A similar entry was Hudson Bay, and a far more successful example of the coastal trade was that pursued by the Hudson's Bay Company from 1669 to 1774, until the competition of the trade from Canada forced the English company also to begin trading inland.

The obvious commercial advantage to Europeans of the coastal trade was that it placed on the Indians the cost of transporting furs to the seaside and goods inland. More significant to the theme of this paper is that for the Europeans it avoided the necessity of mastering the techniques and manners of Indian travel and life. Coastal trade provided a meeting place for commercial barter with a minimum of cultural exchange, whereas the inland trade could be carried on only by Indian means. The Europeans had to become "Indianized," and cultural exchange was greatly increased. The French traders led in this process, and the North West Company, as the heir of the Frenchmen, became the principal representative of European commerce and culture in the inland fur trade.

Before the rise and character of the company are discussed, it is necessary to examine the part played by one of the two partners in the fur trade—the primitive or Indian. The Indians of the northern forest zone were a seminomadic people who lived by food gathering: hunting, fishing, and picking fruits in season. Tribes like the Montagnais and the Cree, who depended purely on hunting and fishing, were more strictly speaking nomadic. Many tribes, however—notably the Iroquoian—had acquired the culture of Indian corn; some were harvesters of wild rice; and some tapped the hard maple for sugar.[2] The need to return to or remain by the cornfields, the rice lakes, and the sugar bushes explains why they are termed seminomadic, and even this is perhaps not to be applied to tribes like the Hurons or the Onondaga, whose lands were rich in corn. But these people had a "shifting" agriculture, and almost no Indian tribe was fully and finally committed to one spot—"settled" in the European sense of the word.

Even with supplements like corn, wild rice, and maple sugar, most Indians relied in the main on hunting and fishing for their food. Both meant considerable movement, dispersal in the winter to the hunting grounds, and congregation at the fishing runs and the fields and berry patches in summer.[3] On the hunt the Indian relied almost wholly on deer hide and beaver robes for his clothing. Thus his culture possessed two necessities of the fur trade: the means to live on the country as it was, and furs themselves.

Commerce with the whites might improve the means of hunting and of fishing. Such items as the gun, the iron hatchet, and the steel trap increased the Indian's efficiency, but his own culture had long provided the essential tools, such as the bow and arrow, the stone ax, and the deadfall—plus a forest craft not easily learned, let alone improved upon. To live in the forest it was imperative to be able to move, both as a lone hunter and in bands. This the Indian could do with a skill which the European was to surpass only by the aid of the mechanical inventions of the nineteenth century. The Indian possessed the canoe in its most exquisite form—the birchbark. This product of the northern forest and the remarkable craft of canoe building was in fact to be the prime mover of the Canadian fur trade. It was used from the first by the Indian to bring furs to the coastal rendezvous, and by the European to penetrate inland. Fragile it was, but it possessed the inestimable advantage that it could be repaired on the spot, given a readily available supply of birch bark, spruce root, and spruce gum.

The canoe gave to the Indian a summer range of hundreds—even thousands—of miles. No such travel was possible in winter, but the Indian culture did provide means for the movement of men and goods necessary to hunting and following trap lines. Snowshoes and moccasins made walking possible over the deep, soft snow of the northern woods, and the toboggan enabled the hunter to transport his game and furs. These two means of movement were as indispensable to the fur trapping of the winter as the canoe was to the fur trade of the summer.

Thus there were in the primitive economy all but two of the elements needed to sustain the fur trade. These two—market demand and capital to finance a year's operation of fur collection, transport, and sale—Europeans were to supply, along with the management that was to bring all together in a functioning system. But it was not only tools and techniques that the Indian culture supplied to the trade. Most important of all was manpower.[4] The aboriginal Indian was the first hunter and trapper, the first canoeman and snowshoer, and the white trapper and voyageur were his pupils. In the lands that became the United States the latter largely supplanted him as trappers and boatmen, but in the Canadian forests the local Indian has remained the principal fur-taker down to the present. The fur trader relied not only on local hunters; he sometimes persuaded whole bands to move with him or used Indians like the eastern Iroquois, who found regular employment in following the trade.[5]

The work of the Indian hunter and trapper was augmented by that of the Indian woman, preparer of food, carrier of burdens, curer of furs, and sewer of shirts, leggings, and moccasins. These tasks, of course, were exclusively the squaw's work, such being the rigid division of labor between the sexes in the Indian culture. It was therefore practically impossible to live off the country and carry on the fur trade without the assistance of Indian women. It is not necessary to mention their additional role as mothers of new manpower, but it is perhaps fitting to recall the remarkable economy with which they performed all these necessary functions. As the Chipewyan chief, Matonabbee, pointed out in man-to-man fashion to Samuel Hearne, "Women were made for labour; one of them can carry, or haul, as much as two men can do.... the very licking of their fingers in scarce times, is sufficient for their subsistence.... [and they] keep us warm at night."[6]

Even this does not quite exhaust the services of the Indian woman to the fur trade. As in all commerce, there was a considerable element of diplomacy, which was necessary to soothe tribal rivalries and prevent tribal wars, and as in all diplomacy, women had a part to play. From the day of Pocahontas on, there are indications that women sometimes eased diplomatic relations between Indian and European. Certainly, as astute traders noted from time to time, marriage to a chief's daughter might well be good for business, and the kin-ship marriage conferred greatly eased the difficulty of persuading Indians to remain loyal to those who financed their hunt.

Children born of such unions came to be a significant and useful group in the fur trade. Not European, not Indian, although closer as children of the wilderness to the Indian way of life, the métis, or mixed-bloods, came to make up a large part of the work force and were a striking example of the Indianization of the European in the fur trade. They were in their own persons—not always happily—the very realization of that union of the primitive and the sophisticated that was the fur trade as practiced by the North West Company.

In the Canadian fur trade, therefore, the only good Indian was not a dead one; he was, on the contrary, a live one who would follow his trap line. From this need for the Indian as a fur-gatherer arose the traders' interest in Indian population and the attempts to estimate it, as in the census of the Northwest recorded by Alexander Henry the Younger.[7] The Indian band had its own hunting grounds, a territory on the wildlife of which it could live by hunting, aided with such other food as could be grown or gathered. Hunting grounds were vague areas, changed by war or epidemic disease, or by deliberate migration, such as that of the Chippewa from north of Lake Huron westward to the Lake of the Woods and the Red River country. In exploring for new fur country it was therefore necessary to know not only the wildlife, food resources, and waterways; equally important were the number, disposition, and needs of the people. It was never enough that there should be beavers and martens; there must also be Indians from whom to buy food and purchase furs.

Solemnly to discuss the historic Indian in the language of a modern labor gazette is, of course, rather quaint. The Indian was a happily primitive person. He had not been made a laborer, a hand, or a businessman of punctual habits and tense drive by centuries of disciplined civilization. He suffered many miseries, but unemployment and gastric ulcers were not among them. He did only what was necessary to keep himself alive. It was exceedingly difficult to add to his wants, except by replacing a known article by a superior one of a like kind: a bow by a gun, a birch-bark vessel by a brass one, or a moose hide by a woolen blanket. Only liquor—and for the Plains Indian, the horse—created a want hitherto unknown and a means of inducing him to trap beyond the need to obtain the essentials of his simple life. Liquor, however, could not be used merely as a commodity, because drunken Indians were likely to become murderous and reduce their scant numbers at an alarming rate. Accordingly, the skilled trader used it as a treat, a loss leader, an inducement given freely to win the Indian to work.

To what degree the Indian ever understood or adopted European commercial and economic concepts of exchange is open to question. He was of course quite as intelligent a being as the European trader and had a very keen sense of how the primary producer benefited from the rivalry of competing buyers and of how he suffered from monopoly. But this arose from practical observation, not from economic reasoning. His culture gave exchange another meaning than the commercial one. His nomad's sense of hospitality to the stranger, his tribal sense of obligation to kindred, led him to give freely what others needed and to expect to receive freely in return. To him trade was reciprocity in giving, not mutual benefit in exchange.[8]

The Indian and even the métis lacked the commercial sense. He did not precisely understand credit or price changes, and he felt little obligation to pay debts. He did, however, acknowledge the obligation to give to those who had given to him, a sense that had to be kept alive by constant care lest the image of the trader who had given credit should fade in the presence of a rival who would offer new presents for the furs that should have gone to settle the accounts of his competitor.

Similarly, the Indian quite lacked any sense of the need to work for the morrow or to grow in riches. He met each day's needs if he could; if not, he starved, enduring privation with singular equanimity. Except for some individuals, he was as unsatisfactory a workman as he was a producer. How unsatisfactory he could be to a well-brought-up young Scot or Yankee can be seen on page after page in the journals of the younger Alexander Henry or of Daniel Harmon.[9] In this the Indian was the product of his total environment. His being so only increases the significance of the skills, endurance, and courage of the fur trader who had to be everything from doctor to policeman, while filling his canoes as well. The greatest accomplishment of such men was the North West Company, a mighty business organization that existed by the capacity of its wintering partners to induce the Indian to trap regularly.

It was this ability of the North West Company to use the manpower and the skills of primitive culture that made it at its height the greatest of all Canadian—perhaps of all—fur trading companies. Its ultimate failure was as a business concern, not as a fur-gathering organization. Probably the most significant commentary on its efficiency is the fact that between 1774 and the union of 1821 the Hudson's Bay Company adopted all of its field techniques except the use of the canoe.

The success of the North West Company stemmed in large part from adopting and developing the modes and personnel of the French fur trade as it existed before and in the years just after 1760. Personifying French skill in the trade were the voyageurs, or canoemen. Under the system of "engagement" young men from the Quebec parishes (usually bound for three-year terms) were employed and trained as voyageurs, then returned to the land and later re-engaged, or left as "freemen" in the Northwest. Some of the latter were employed at the wilderness posts in such capacities as smiths, carpenters, canoe builders, or ax men. Others were used as traders *en derouine*—that is, were sent to drum up business with the Indians and to collect debts in the form of furs. Still others, if literate, might rise from clerks to be "bourgeois." The bourgeois was the trader who had invested his skill, his courage, and (if he had any) his money. He was responsible for the returns from the district to which he had been assigned.[10]

The voyageurs remained both the symbol and mainstay of the Canadian fur trade, but as traders the French generally proved too individualistic, too much devoted to small and limited enterprises, and too poor at business to compete with their Yankee or Scottish rivals.[11] It may well have been this, rather than lack of access to capital, which explains the gradual replacement of the French-Canadian bourgeois by Scottish, English, and American traders after 1760.

The Nor'Westers also adopted the canoe, as developed by the French in the *cânot de maitre* and the *cânot du nord*, and the custom of provisioning the brigades with dried corn and grease to Grand Portage. Also taken over was the use of the fur post in all its variations from a log shack for a winter's occupation to the stockaded fort with its component dwelling houses, stores, and shops. (The Hudson's Bay Company used forts also, but those on the shores of the bay were English structures built by naval carpenters, not wilderness stockades.) Incorporated, too, as the name indicates, was the *regale* or treat—liquor given the Indian in the spirit of nomadic good fellowship to establish cordial relations and encourage the hunter to trap for his friends.

The *regale* was only a symbol of the French genius for accepting the Indian with all his casualness, his moodiness, his sensitivity, his insistence that the door always be open to him, his expectation that if in need he would be given what he required. In these respects the Nor'Westers, especially the Scots, were apt pupils of the French, and often succeeded where the Englishmen and the Orkney

men in the service of the Hudson's Bay Company failed, through private reserve or restraints imposed by the organization. (It is of course to be noted also
that the detachment of the Bay men usually preserved them from involvement
in the passions, feuds, and trickery of Indian life and often was rewarded in
the long run by a reputation for honesty and fair dealing.)

Another North West inheritance from the French were the métis, with all
that their existence implied. The rough judgment that on balance the métis
added to the strength and success of the North West Company is probably de-
fensible. They were an important part of the labor force of the Canadian fur
trade, particularly in their role as buffalo hunters during the company's last
years. By 1816, the year of the affair at Seven Oaks, they probably held the
fate of the Northwest in their hands. One of the first needs of the united company was to conciliate them and to employ them as dependents of the fur trade
and as defenders against the Sioux.[12]

All these inherited and borrowed techniques for dealing with the wilderness
were combined by the shrewd Nor'Westers with a superior business organization. Connections with English business houses gave the Canadians access to
higher quality trade goods and better credit than their French counterparts
had secured. When the entrepôt for much of the American fur trade, formerly
centered at Albany and New York, was shifted to Montreal, the size and vigor
of the business was increased proportionately. The result was a great strengthening of the trade in capital and managerial ability and also an extraordinary
concentration of resources. Thus for nearly three decades the North American
fur trade, both that of the southwest (the American Northwest) and that of the
Canadian Northwest, was centered in Montreal.

The growth of the company from partnership to partnership has been explained in terms of the need to combine and to marshal the resources and bear
the costs of deeper penetration into the Northwest.[13] This was indeed an important reason for "pooling" resources. It seems not, however, to be the whole
explanation of what occurred. There was in the very nature of the fur trade an
inherent need of monopoly because of its seasonal character, its dependence
on the seeming whims of a primitive and uncommercial people, the easy depletion of the numbers of fur-bearing animals by hunting or disease, and the
difficulty of carrying the loss of a year's outfit. There were probably also reasons
of management in the field, involving the control and distribution of goods, the
giving of credit, and the collection of furs.[14] Competition was not the life of the
fur trade, but its death.

However that may be, the very name North West Company points to the subsequent political division of the fur country of central North America after the
Treaty of Versailles in 1783. More and more there was a southwest and a north-
west fur trade from Montreal. After the final implementation of Jay's Treaty in
1795 the southwest trade was increasingly surrendered to Americans. The

North West Company grew in importance to the fur trade of Montreal, and the Canadian trade was pressed back upon the uninhabitable and permanently primitive wilderness of the Canadian Shield and the northern forest.

The gradual forcing of the Canadian fur trade toward the northwest intensified the need for large-scale organization. Supply bases were necessary, and with the beginning of the new century the posts on the Red River, the Assiniboine, and the Saskatchewan, along the line where the northern forest and the plains merged in the long grass and the park belt country, became more and more supply centers and less and less fur posts. The buffalo hunt and the métis buffalo hunter began to emerge as an institution and a type. Their function was to obtain from the plains the dried meat and pemmican that would provision the Saskatchewan and Athabasca brigades in the long reaches from Bas de la Rivière on Lake Winnipeg to the Methy Portage into the Athabasca country.

In these developments lay the beginning of strain on the loose-jointed organization of the company, particularly in the relations between "wintering" and Montreal partners. In them lay the need to shorten the continental haul of furs to Montreal, either by shifting the entrepôt from Montreal to Hudson Bay, or by seeking a western outlet on the Pacific. In them also lay an ever increasing dependence on the labor of the Indians and the métis, a dependence that required the carrying of a rapidly growing number of métis families.

The greater the strain, the greater was the need for monopoly and the need at last to take seriously the competition of the much smaller and less effective but enduring, stable, and slowly learning Hudson's Bay Company. The longer the canoe haul and the larger the labor force, the greater was the necessity of provisions from Red River. The clash between the two remaining fur organizations of the Northwest would seem to have been inevitable even had it not been precipitated by two external factors, namely, the War of 1812 and the Earl of Selkirk's passion for colonization.

Both these factors put pressure on the North West Company at tender and vital points: the main supply area at Detroit-Michilimackinac, from which came corn for the Montreal canoe brigades; and the Red River, from which came pemmican for the canoes bound for the far Northwest. The Astor venture on the Pacific Coast was regarded by Canadians as part of the War of 1812, in that it challenged the formation of a western outlet and supply base at the mouth of the Columbia River.

Because of early British military successes, the alliance with the Indians, and the isolation of the Astorians, the War of 1812 was a means of alleviating the pressures on the Montreal and Columbia routes. There remained the pemmican base at Red River. As the Nor'Westers saw it, the character and the seriousness of Selkirk's part in the new aggressiveness of the Hudson's Bay Company might not by themselves have led to a clash had it not coincided with the War of 1812. Nor'Westers had, after all, dealt successfully with competition before by cultivating the loyalty of their Indian and métis hunters with liquor and blandishments, and by the use of their bullies (*batailleurs*) to harass competitors. Despite their suspicion of Selkirk's purposes from the first, the Nor'Westers behaved with exemplary patience from 1811 to 1813. But by the spring of 1814, under the influence of the war temper, they had come to think strategically and to act drastically. By the spring of 1815 they knew they had lost the territorial gains of the war to the United States in Michigan and perhaps in the Columbia Valley. In the winter of 1814-15, because of the action of Miles Macdonnell, governor of Assiniboia, in first prohibiting and then limiting the export of pemmican from Red River, they became convinced that Selkirk's colony was an immediate and intolerable threat to the supplying of their northwestern posts and brigades. They resolved, therefore, to remove or destroy the colony. Thus the return of peace elsewhere saw the beginning of "war" on the Red River.

The struggle on the Red River in 1815 and 1816, and in the law courts of Canada from 1817 to 1821, reveals little that is new about the North West Company. It fought with all the resources it could command—commercial, primitive, and legal—against a rival who used all these in return and added to them a small army of mercenaries hired after their discharge from service in the late war. In every field the company at least held its own, and beyond doubt deserved to. It could not, however, overcome the inherent weaknesses of its own loose organization, of dependence on a labor force that was constantly growing in size and unruliness, and of the high costs of its extended transportation routes. The aroused Hudson's Bay Company, still a David to the North West Company's Goliath, needed only to keep on fighting to have the giant collapse of his own weight.

The final union of the rivals was at once a victory and a defeat for each. The Hudson's Bay Company was victorious in that its supply route by the bay triumphed over that by the St. Lawrence as did its charter over the partnership of the North West Company. It was defeated in that it won only when it had adopted in large part the techniques and methods of its rivals inland. The North West Company lost its name and legal entity, but not before it had forced on its great competitor the mode of operation and the labor force which it had developed and by which it had flourished. The united company was very much the old North West Company operating out of Hudson Bay.

The North West Company was the first successful combination of European capital and business enterprise with Indian skills. As such, it holds a special place in the history of the North American fur trade and in the history of Canada. Its distinctive character arose from the fact that it came to grips with the unique conditions prevailing in Canada—conditions of climate, distance, and resources, which prevent a large proportion of the country's area from sustaining a pattern of economic and social life like that of Europe or the United States.

The company faced for the first time the fundamental question of how to maintain a western-oriented society in a severely northern, largely uninhabitable land. For much of Canada can be exploited only by extremes: by a primitive culture like that of the Eskimo, skilled in the special techniques of survival and content with merely maintaining life for a tiny population; or by a civilization with a technology so highly developed that it can overcome almost any obstacle of environment if the necessary expenditure is justified on grounds of private profit or state policy.

The effort to deal with this permanent northern frontier makes Canada what it is, and the influence of the effort can be traced all through Canadian history and contemporary society, most obviously in the comparative lack of both people and wealth in a country territorially so vast. The successful solution reached by the North West Company would seem to point toward the two channels through which a sophisticated culture and economy may exploit the North to its own best advantage and with the least detriment to the primitive culture of the people dwelling there. These channels are private monopoly or state development.

Notes

1. The history of the North West Company has now been reconstructed with sufficient completeness both to establish the character of the company as a business organization and to explain its role in the North American fur trade. This has been done despite the lack of documentary evidence for most of its business affairs. The historical task has been carried so far chiefly by two recent and massive works: Paul Chrisler Phillips, *The Fur Trade* (Norman, Oklahoma, 1961); and E. E. Rich, *The History of the Hudson's Bay Company 1670-1870* (London, 1958, 1959).

2. Maple sugar is rarely taken into account by fur trade historians; yet note the frequent references in Elliott Coues, ed., *New Light on the Early History of the Greater Northwest: The Manuscript Journals of Alexander Henry and of David Thompson, 1799-1814*, 1:4, 25, 30, 101, 112, 122, 130, 162, 170, 192, 196, 211, 244, 259, 275, 281; 2:492, 629, 681 (New York, 1897); and in Charles M. Gates, ed., *Five Fur Traders of the Northwest*, 32, 37, 44, 165, 234, 236, 270, 273 (St. Paul, 1965).

3. The necessity for this movement is brought out with painful clarity in Edwin James, ed., *A Narrative of the Captivity and Adventures of John Tanner* (Minneapolis, 1956). On the importance of fruit, see, for example, Henry, in Coues, ed., *New Light on the ... Greater Northwest*, 2:485.

4. This is one of those self-evident facts which, if not made explicit, is sometimes seriously neglected. The importance of Indian manpower was drawn to my attention by Mr. Jan Kupp and will be developed by him in his doctoral dissertation for the department of history, University of Manitoba.

5. See Henry, in Coues, ed., *New Light on the ... Greater Northwest*, 1:44-77; 2:452; Richard Glover, ed., *David Thompson's Narrative, 1784-1812*, 229 (Toronto, 1962).

6. Quoted in J. B. Tyrrell, ed., *Hearne: A Journey from Prince of Wales's Fort in Hudson's Bay to the Northern Ocean*, 102 (Toronto, 1911).

7. See Henry, in Coues, ed., *New Light on the ... Greater Northwest*, 1:282; 2:516, 522, 530.

8. For a discussion of these attitudes, see E. E. Rich, "Trade Habits and Economic Motivation Among the Indians of North America," in *Canadian Journal of Economic and Political Science*, 26:35-53 (February, 1960). Mr. Rich emphasizes the Indian's lack of a "sense of property" rather than a lack of a commercial sense.

9. See W. Kaye Lamb, ed., *Sixteen Years in the Indian Country: The Journal of Daniel Williams Harmon, 1800-1852*, lxxxv (Toronto, 1957).

10. How much of this was actually French practice, and how much developed from French practice it is difficult to state in our want of detailed knowledge of the organization of the French fur trade. There is a revealing though brief description of the resumption of activity by French traders after 1760 in a forthcoming volume by Hilda Neatby of the University of Saskatchewan, to be published under the title "Quebec: The Revolutionary Age," as one of the *Canadian Centenary Series*.

11. See David Thompson's comments on this point in Glover, ed., *Thompson's Narrative*, 41.

12. This aspect of the fur trade is discussed in Margaret Macleod and W. I., Morton, *Cuthbert Grant of Grantown: Warden of the Plains of Red River* (Toronto, 1963).

13. This thesis has been given its classic statement by Harold A. Innis in *The Fur Trade in Canada* (New Haven, Connecticut, 1930).

14. See Matthew Cocking's comment on the need to prevent "Confusion of Goods" among separate traders in one place, in W. Stewart Wallace, ed., *Documents Relating to the North West Company*, 45 (Toronto, 1934); also Alexander Mackenzie, *Voyages from Montreal ... to the Frozen and Pacific Ocean*, 18 (Toronto, 1927).

THE MIDDLEMAN ROLE IN THE FUR TRADE: ITS INFLUENCE ON INTERETHNIC RELATIONS IN THE SASKATCHEWAN-MISSOURI PLAINS

Susan Giannettino

The entrance of European fur traders into the northeast coastal woodlands of North America in the mid-16th century most likely had a profound effect on the intertribal trade networks that crisscrossed the northern interior. In striv-

From *The Western Canadian Journal of Anthropology*, 7, no. 4 (1977), 22-33. Reprinted by permission of the Department of Anthropology, University of Alberta.

ing to acquire trade goods that the Europeans offered in exchange for furs—primarily the guns, knives, axes, brass kettles, blankets, and metal for projectile points—the native peoples became involved in two distinct economic systems. Jablow (1950:12) notes in relation to the Upper Missouri area that, "On the one hand they functioned in a system of intertribal trade, while on the other, they were producers and traders in furs in the European mercantile system." With time, the native peoples became increasingly dependent on the White trade goods for their survival, and hence became more deeply involved in the fur trade.

Those Indians who were in closest contact with the European traders found themselves in a lucrative position as middlemen. The profit-minded Whites had established a coastal toehold on the North American continent and had begun immediately to pursue their acquisition of furs. Eager to amass as many valuable pelts as possible, they traded assorted goods with the proximate natives in exchange for furs. These Indians, in turn, traded their recently acquired White goods for the furs of the more isolated natives of the interior. Richard Slobodin (1960:88) writes that such people were

> ... in circumstances which have been experienced by a number of non-urban peoples in relation to the expanding economy of an urban civilization. They were between the civilized traders and more distant aborigines.

The middlemen served as intermediaries in the indirect trade between the White traders and more distant native groups. In the trade there was little or no direct contact between the two peripheral groups. As the natives realized the superiority of many of the White trade goods, especially guns and ammunition, they increased their efforts to obtain them.

Because of the obvious advantages accruing to those groups holding the middleman position, ethnic groups sought to gain and then retain total control over direct trade with Whites. This enabled them not only to make a profit in the redistribution of goods to groups located farther into the interior, but also to control the types of items made available to those groups. In this manner, they limited arms distribution, while keeping the superior White weaponry for themselves. Hence, the middleman role was extremely desirable, since through a superiority in firearms the middlemen were assured greater success in intergroup conflicts.

Intertribal conflict was an important characteristic of the interrelationships of North American native people. Combat was frequent, being a result of a group's desire or need for horses, women, better hunting grounds, or increased status. Alliances between ethnic groups were transitory and fragile. The European fur trade, thrust into the aboriginal trade complexes, added a new dimension to the "status quo" of conflicts and alliances. The magnitude of the profit and power held by the middlemen prompted the development of a new pattern of conflicts and alliances that soon came to dominate interethnic relations.

In addition to the traditional reasons for conflicts and alliances, conflict began to occur as a direct response to the middleman trade position. Native groups fought to maintain and exploit a middleman position; or in efforts to rise from a subordinate position and assume the middleman role. Native groups united to maintain and protect their middleman position; for protection against the groups holding the middleman role; or to rise from a peripheral position and become the middlemen themselves. The process involved in trading through middlemen, and the associated interrelationships of the participating ethnic groups, I term the 'middleman role complex'.

The conflicts engendered by competition for trade goods were sometimes carried over to the White trade sources. Groups unable to obtain sufficient arms through the middlemen attacked the Whites both in attempts to arm themselves and in retaliation for the Whites having dealt with the middlemen. Conversely, those holding the middleman position, anxious to maintain that role, opposed—on occasion with violence—fur traders' attempts to initiate direct trade relationships with the peripheral peoples.

The native middleman role and its effect on interethnic relations in the North American fur trade has been recognized and described by several anthropologists whose studies focus on various areas of the continent. The Eastern Kutchin apparently acted as middlemen to the Eskimo trade. According to Slobodin (1960:90-91), the Kutchin had no tradition of aggression with any peoples other than the Eskimo, and in fact there might be some truth to their folk tales of friendly relations with the Eskimo prior to Kutchin involvement in the fur trade. The repeated instances of Eskimo-Kutchin hostilities reported by early fur traders and explorers, and the efforts of the Kutchin to prohibit Eskimo expeditions from reaching the fur trading posts were motivated by the desire to retain middleman dominance in the fur trade.

McClellan (1975), in an ethnographic survey of the southern Yukon, describes a series of middleman positions extending inland from the Pacific coast fur trade outlets. The coastal Tlingit dominated native trade with the seafaring American, British, and Russian traders. "However, the tribes closest to them in the interior—the southern Tuchone, Tagish, and the inland Tlingit—were in turn able to dominate Athabascans living farther inland" (McClellan 1975:501). According to McClellan's informants, the only motives for warfare between these groups were "the capture of women, the desire for blood vengeance, or the attempts to control access to goods brought by the whites" (*ibid:*518).

Jablow (1950) found extensive evidence illustrating the existence of the middleman trade pattern and related conflicts on the Missouri River:

> The tribes all along the length of the Missouri invariably attempted to prevent the progress of the White traders further than their own villages. Each tribe wished as far as possible to retain control of the White trade and to prevent the goods, especially guns, from flowing freely into the coffers of other tribes....

So long as they retained the trade advantage and a superiority over other tribes and they could dispose of the goods as they saw fit, they were willing to share the bounty unequally.

... each tribe wanted to prevent guns from falling into the hands of their enemies, and this undoubtedly was the most important interest the Indians had in attempting to control the trade [*ibid:*35-36].

Thus, it is apparent that the native middleman was an integral element in the expansion of the North American fur trade and a major determining factor in native interethnic relations during that period.

The conflicts and alliances in the plains area between the North Saskatchewan and Missouri rivers during the early historic period have generally been thought of as relatively unstructured, and with little perceivable significant pattern or organization. The result in the literature has been a general hodgepodge of interethnic encounters and relationships. To better interpret interethnic relations in this region, I have used the fur trade and the middleman role complex as an analytical focus for viewing the region's interethnic social network.

As the middleman role complex moved across the North Saskatchewan-Missouri plains from northeast to southwest, the major ethnic groups, one after another, became involved—first in a subordinated role as they traded with more easterly middlemen; and then in a dominant role, as the contact zone in which there was direct trade with Whites moved westward and they became the middlemen themselves. Successively, the Assiniboine, Cree, Northern Blackfeet, Blood, Piegan, Atsina, and the Rocky Mountain Plateau groups—the Kutenai, Pend d'Oreille, Nez Perce, and Flathead—were peripheral subordinates and then middlemen. The pattern of alliances which developed assumed a form similar to the process of complementary opposition, or the "massing effect" described by Marshall Sahlins (1961:332): "In any opposition between parties A and B all those more closely related to A than to B will stand with A against B, and vice versa." On the North Saskatchewan-Missouri plains, the "haves"—those with privileged access to guns and ammunition—united in defense of or extension of their shared interests, while the "have nots" joined in efforts to attain the middleman role.

The alliance pattern that occurred as part of the middleman complex is summarized in the schematic diagram in Fig. 1. This diagram necessarily is a very generalized, overall interpretation of interethnic relations. Interrelations were not always precisely along these lines, and dates for changes in alliances overlapped, but the basic pattern can be seen here. The active trade complex consistently moved southwestward, with little trade occurring to the northeast because the fur-bearing animals were usually harvested more rapidly than they could successfully reproduce. Solid lines in the diagram signify direct White trade contact, while broken lines signify trade filtered through the middleman.

FIGURE 1   The Middleman Pattern

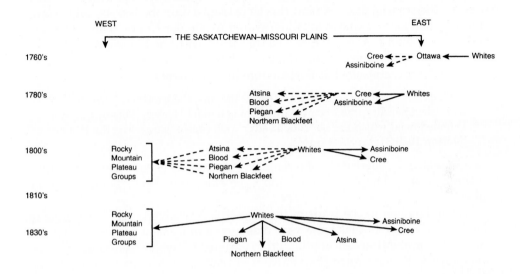

The reports of Hudson's Bay Company emissaries and French Jesuit missionaries (e.g., see Ray 1974) clearly document the early fur trade involvement of the eastern groups of the region, the Assiniboine and Cree. By the late 1700s the Assiniboine and Cree were allies in warfare and trading partners seeking French goods through Ottawa middlemen (Ray 1974:12). As the fur companies expanded operations westward in the 1770s, the Assiniboine and Cree began to trade directly with Whites for guns and ammunition.

In the 1770s and 1780s, Hudson's Bay Company and the French Canadian traders established trading posts all along the North Saskatchewan River. With the construction of these inland trading posts, the Assiniboine and Cree became the peoples with whom the Europeans dealt directly. Though each company and individual trader had a different relationship with the natives, the very existence of each post as an outlet for armaments was of primary importance to the Indians. The Assiniboine and Cree found the traders of the North Saskatchewan posts eager to trade guns for their abundant supplies of pelts. They rapidly built up a profitable trade relationship—the Whites obtaining the furs they desired, and the Indians gaining possession of the coveted guns and ammunition. With the development of this relationship, the middleman complex moved in its entirety into the North Saskatchewan-Missouri plains.

The Blackfeet groups (Northern Blackfeet,-Blood, and Piegan) and the Atsina, who lived to the west of the Cree and Assiniboine, had farther to travel to reach the trading posts, and at this time traded only the less valuable skins of wolves and foxes. Duncan M'Gillivray and Alexander Henry, both employees of the North West Company, recorded that trade with the Blackfeet and Atsina was not worth the time or effort (Morton 1929:31, Coues 1897:541). For example, M'Gillivray, stationed at Fort George in 1794, wrote:

> ... Blackfeet, Gros Ventres [Atsina], Blood Indians, Piedgans, etc., are treated with less liberality, their commodities being chiefly Horses, Wolves, Fat and Pounded meat which are not sought after with such eagerness as the Beaver [Morton 1929:31; brackets mine].

Consequently, there was not a significant direct flow of guns and ammunition to these groups. The Assiniboine and Cree exploited their advantage to the fullest.

As middlemen in the trade of the area, the Assiniboine and Cree came to dominate the North Saskatchewan-Missouri plains social network. They attempted to prohibit access of other ethnic groups to the posts, and filtered the westward and southward distribution of trade goods so as to prevent the Blackfeet groups, the Atsina, and other peoples from acquiring a supply of guns. Most conflicts in the area revolved around the Assiniboine-Cree attempts to maintain the middleman position, and the efforts of other groups to reach the trading posts and acquire weapons through direct trade. The documents of this period (e.g., the journals and correspondence from Edmonton and Chesterfield Houses (Johnson 1967), the journals of Duncan M'Gillivray (Morton 1929), and the journals of Alexander Henry (Coues 1897), and David Thompson (Tyrrell 1915)) give ample testimony to conflicts between the allied Assiniboine and Cree on the one hand, and the three Blackfeet groups, the Atsina, and, to some extent, the western Plateau peoples on the other. Strife was a frequent occurrence and battles often resulted in massacres. For example, John MacDonald of Garth reported at Fort George in 1793 that a war had broken out that summer between the Plains Cree and the Atsina in which several had been killed on both sides (MacDonald in Morton 1929:xlix). In 1801 a party of Blood Indians informed Peter Fidler of Hudson's Bay Company that the "Southern Indians [Cree] from below and the Stone Indians had killed fourteen men and sixty women and children of the Fall Indians [Atsina] thirty-four days ago" (Johnson 1967:293; brackets mine). Still other fur traders, among them Daniel Harmon (1911:55) and Duncan M'Gillivray (Morton 1929:156), reported numerous instances of large scale conflicts between the armed Assiniboine and Cree and their less effectively armed, more westerly enemies. Alexander Henry cites repeated attempts of Assiniboine and Cree to prevent their enemies from obtaining ammunition in the early 1800s (e.g. Coues 1897:540,558), a pattern which is repeated until as late as the 1810s as recorded by John Franklin (1824:133,166) who also noted:

The Stone Indians [Assiniboine] keep in amity with their neighbours the Crees from motives of interest; and the two tribes unite in determined hostility against the nations dwelling to the westward, which are generally called Slave Indians [Blackfeet]—a term of reproach applied by the Crees to those tribes against whom they have waged successful wars [1824:166; brackets mine].

White traders became involved in the native conflicts and alliances from two perspectives. On the one hand, they were perceived by the outlying ethnic groups as enemies since they were suppliers and allies of the dominant Assiniboine and Cree. Duncan M'Gillivray wrote in 1795 that the Atsina, considering the traders to be allies of their enemies the Cree, had decided to attack the fur trading posts. "For this purpose a Strong party endeavoured to plunder Pine Island Fort [Fort de l'Isle] the ensuing Winter, but the attempt was fortunately unsuccessful ..." (Morton 1929:63; brackets mine). The Atsina plundered Manchester House on the Saskatchewan River in 1793, and attacked and burnt to the ground South Branch House in 1794, in both instances attempting to get weapons with which to defend themselves against the raids of the Assiniboine and Cree (Johnson 1967:xvii).

On the other hand, from the perspective of the Assiniboine and Cree, the westward advancing White traders were adversaries, intent on toppling them from the dominant middleman position by opening direct trade relations with the Blackfeet, Atsina, and western Plateau groups. Alexander Henry recorded in the fall of 1808 that a large assembly of Crees had gathered at Battle River, determined to halt his trade expedition to the Blackfeet. They wished "to prevent the Slaves from receiving arms and ammunition." They feared, he continued, that a serious war would result (Coues 1897:495).

The Assiniboine and Cree shared a dominant social position based on privileged direct access to White traders. The more western groups were allied against both the Assiniboine and Cree, and the Whites who supplied the Assiniboine and Cree with the weaponry which enabled them to dominant interethnic relations in the area.

Throughout the 1780s, 1790s, and early 1800s, the peltry trade companies and the free traders expanded their activity even farther into the North Saskatchewan-Missouri plains, along the South Saskatchewan River, and in the early 1830s along the upper Missouri River. The more central location of these posts in the North Saskatchewan-Missouri plains, as well as the change in White demand from beaver pelts to buffalo meat and robes, made it much easier for the Northern Blackfeet, Blood, Piegan, and Atsina to obtain guns and ammunition through direct trade. In 1820 Franklin noted that the Crees were no longer a dominant force on the plains because their enemies were now as well armed as they (1824:107-108).

The Piegan were the first of the Blackfeet groups to establish direct relations with the peltry traders. Alexander MacKenzie wrote, "They are the beaver hunters of their nation" (Lewis 1942:32). Living near the foothills of the Rocky

Mountains, they had both the opportunity and the incentive to develop their trapping skills. Because of preferential treatment by the Whites, the Piegan assumed the middleman role before their neighbors the Atsina, Blood, and Northern Blackfeet. Through direct trade, they rapidly acquired a supply of guns and ammunition. As the dominant group in the area, they sought to exploit and maintain their influence while other peoples allied in attempts to topple them. Prince Maximilian, while at Fort McKenzie in 1832, recorded an example of the hostilities between the once allied Blackfeet groups. The traders, he wrote (Thwaites 1906:127-131), treated the Piegan preferentially, encouraging jealousy among the Blackfeet peoples. On an occasion when a new uniform and gun were presented to a Piegan chief in an attempt to make an example of him for the other groups, the Blood Indians were offended and spoke loudly of their plans for slaughtering the Piegan and the White traders. A few days later when a relative of the Piegan chief was shot by some Bloods, the Piegan attacked the Bloods in retaliation (Thwaites 1906:139-142). At a later date, once the demand for furs had changed to one for bison robes, the Blood, Northern Blackfeet, and Atsina were able to obtain guns and ammunition through trade at the posts, and through raids and interethnic trade. They came to share the middleman position with the Piegan.

And so, the balance of power had shifted. Through the early 1800s, the Blackfeet groups and their allies, the Atsina, occupied the role of middlemen in the complex trade relations of the fur trade. The trade pattern evident in the previous decades during which the Assiniboine and Cree were in a dominant position was repeated with only a few minor alterations. The Northern Blackfeet, Blood, Piegan, and Atsina allied against the more peripheral peoples to the north and west as they exploited their temporary, advantageous position. As early as 1795 Duncan M'Gillivray observed this exploitation. While at Fort George he wrote:

> The most general news among the natives at present is.—that the Coutonées [Kutenai] a tribe from the Southwest are determined to force their way this year to the Fort or perish in the attempt ... The Gens du Large [the Blackfeet and perhaps the Atsina] and all the other nations in this neighborhood wishing to retain an exclusive trade among themselves, have hitherto prevented the Intentions of this Band, of commencing a friendly intercourse with the Fort, in order to exclude them from any share of our commodities, which they are well aware would put their enemies in a condition to defend themselves, from the attacks of those who are already acquainted with the use of arms.—The Coutonées have already made several attempts to visit us, but they have been always obstructed by their enemies and forced to relinquish their design with loss [Morton 1929:56; brackets mine].

In 1798 Peter Fidler observed much the same restrictions.

> They [the Kutenai] was never near any of the Trading Settlements altho they much wish it But the Muddy River [Piegan], Blood, Blackfeet, and Southern

Indians always prevents them, they wishing to monopolize all their skins to themselves, which they do giving the Poor Indians only a mere trifle for ... [Johnson 1967:112; brackets mine].

The western Plateau peoples in turn allied in their struggle to acquire guns, for their own protection and to overcome the imposed subordinate role. Oscar Lewis (1942:21) makes the appropriate observation that, "The differences in the rate of arming the various tribes was crucial in determining the balance of power in this area."

As middlemen of the North Saskatchewan-Missouri plains, the Blackfeet groups exploited their military advantages over their neighbors. The Plateau peoples were often raided by the Blackfeet groups, particularly by the Piegan and the Atsina (Young 1899:190, Ross 1956:213-214, Lewis and Phillips 1923, Ewers 1944, Parker 1840). The Reverend Samuel Parker (1840:232) wrote in the 1830s:

> The Indians west of the great chain of mountains, have no wars among themselves, and appear to be adverse to all wars ... except in self defense.... Their only wars are with the Blackfeet Indians, whose country is along the east border of the Rocky Mountains, and who are constantly roving about in war parties on both sides, in quest of plunder.

Captain Nathaniel J. Wyeth, while conducting a government exploration of the Rocky Mountains in the 1830s, wrote in his journal of a mountain battlefield, "where 200 Flatheads, Conterays, Ponderays and other Inds. were killed by the Blackfeet Inds." (Young 1899:190). Hell's Gate—a narrow canyon on the Clark Fork River leading into present day Missoula, Montana—was in the 1820s the pass or "great war road" by which the Blackfeet entered the mountain valleys to raid the Flathead. Alexander Ross (1956:213) noted that, "the spot has therefore often been the scene of many a bloody contest between these two hostile nations."

As middlemen, once the Blackfeet groups and the Atsina had obtained dominance through possession of the gun, they sought to maintain their position through regulation of the goods allowed to filter through them to the west and south. In their efforts to accomplish this, they, in their turn, came into conflict not only with the peripheral groups trying to procure the guns, but with the Whites who were trying to extend their trade networks into the mountains. The attitude of the Blackfeet groups was one of "unremitting enmity" toward the White traders and trappers, both English and American, who threatened to cross the mountain passes and trade with the Plateau groups (Galbraith 1957:85). David Thompson, while attempting to establish trade relations with the Flathead in 1807 wrote of the Piegans' attempts to prevent his crossing the mountains into Flathead territory. They feared, he said, his "arming the Natives on that side" (Tyrrell 1915:375). The Blackfeet warned the traders that all Whites found by them west of the mountains would be dealt with as their enemies. Alexander Ross and his trapping parties who frequented the Rocky Mountain foothills in the early 1820s were constantly harassed by the Blackfeet groups. In his journals Ross (1956) uses the terms Blackfeet and Piegan interchangeably as an equivalent to the word "enemy."

In 1810 David Thompson reported that the Piegan suffered their first defeat at the hands of the Kutenai and Flathead. The latter were apparently sufficiently well-armed at this point to defeat the heretofore dominant middlemen, although it is doubtful that, at this time, all the Plateau peoples had or could operate guns (Tyrrell 1915:424-425). In any case, this was the beginning of the end of the Blackfeet and Atsina's power dominance. The apprehensions the Piegan, Blood, Northern Blackfeet and Atsina had felt toward the peripheral groups obtaining guns were well founded. The Plateau peoples—the Kutenai, Flathead, Pend d'Orielle, Nez Perce, and others—once the easy prey of the Plains Indians, upon becoming well armed became formidable enemies (Murray 1930:15-16). Through the decade of 1810s the Plateau peoples obtained more guns and ammunition from the ever increasing number of Whites in the area. Aware of their new found and rapidly growing strength, they were no longer intimidated. In a March 1810 incident reported by David Thompson this bravery is illustrated:

> ... while at the Saleesh [Flathead] Camp, an alarm came of the tracks of Peeagans being seen near the Camp, everything was now suspended ... About one hundred Men now mounted their Horses proud of their Guns and iron headed Arrows to battle with the Enemy; they soon returned, having found these Cavalry to be the Kootanaes ... but it gave me, as well as the old Men, great pleasure in seeing the alacrity with which they went to seek the enemy, when before, their whole thoughts and exertions were to get away from, and not to meet, their enemies [Tyrrell 1915:420, brackets mine].

As late as the 1830s the plains groups were trying to retain some vestige of their former position as middlemen to the Plateau groups. Prince Maximilian noted that an expedition sent from Fort McKenzie to the Kutenai in August 1832 was cut off by the Blackfeet when but a few days out of the fort. The Blackfeet's vigilance was still active but not effective (Thwaites 1906:153-154). The Blackfeet and the Atsina lost their dominant position as the gun was acquired by the peripheral groups. The pattern established with the Assiniboine-Cree was repeated: the subordinate peripheral groups eventually managed to acquire guns and ammunition and equalize the discrepancy in power.

The middleman phenomenon was for the most part defunct in the North Saskatchewan-Missouri plains by the mid 1830s, and so too was the patterned series of interethnic relations that had been part of the middleman role complex from 1785 to 1830. Following this period, the base of interethnic conflicts reverted to what they had been before the 1790s, centering around hunting ground disputes, and raids for women and horses (Bradley 1900:207-211, Lewis and Phillips 1923:122, 127-128). No longer were conflicts and alliances centered around an ethnic group's desire to exploit the possession of firearms while restricting distribution to others, for all peoples had relatively equal access to White trade outlets.

References

Bradley, James H.
1900   "Affairs at Fort Benton, from 1831 to 1869; from Lieut. Bradley's Journal," *Contributions to the Historical Society of Montana*. 3:201-287.

Coues, Elliot, ed.
1897   *New Light on the Early History of the Greater Northwest: The Manuscript Journals of Alexander Henry and of David Thompson, 1799-1814*. 3 vols. New York: F.P. Harper.

Ewers, John C.
1944   "The Story of the Blackfeet," *Indian Life and Customs Pamphlet #6*. Washington, D.C.: Education Division of the United States Indian Service.

Franklin, John
1824   *Narrative of a Journey to the Shores of the Polar Sea*. London: J. Murray.

Galbraith, John S.
1957   *The Hudson's Bay Company*. Berkeley: University of California Press.

Harmon, Daniel Williams
1911   *A Journal of Voyages and Travels in the Interior of North America, 1800-1819*. Toronto: Courier Press Ltd.

Jablow, Joseph
1950   "The Cheyenne in Plains Indian Trade Relations, 1795-1840," *Monographs of the American Ethnological Society*, 19, New York: J.J. Augustin.

Johnson, Alice M., ed.
1967   *Saskatchewan Journals and Correspondence*. London: Hudson's Bay Record Society.

Lewis, Oscar
1942   "The Effects of White Contact upon Blackfoot Culture," *Monographs of the American Ethnological Society*, 6, New York: J.J. Augustin.

Lewis, William S. and Paul C. Phillips, eds.
1923   *The Journal of John Work*. Cleveland: Arthur H. Clark Co.

McClellan, Catherine
1975   "My Old People Say—An Ethnographic Survey of Southern Yukon Territory," *National Museums of Canada Publications in Ethnology*, 6, Ottawa.

Morton, Arthur, S., ed.
1929   *The Journal of Duncan M'Gillivray of the North West Company*. Toronto: Macmillan Company of Canada, Ltd.

Murray, Genevieve
1930   "Marias Pass," *Studies in Northwest History*, 12, Missoula: State University of Montana Press.

Parker, Samuel
1840   *Journal of an Exploring Tour Beyond the Rocky Mountains.* Ithaca, N.Y.: Samuel
       Parker.

Phillips, Paul C.
1969   "The Fur Trade in Montana," *in* Michael P. Malone and Richard B. Roeder, eds.,
       The Montana Past, pp. 35-60. Missoula: University of Montana Press.

Ray, Arthur
1974   *Indians in the Fur Trade.* Toronto: University of Toronto.

Rich, E.E.
1959   *The History of the Hudson's Bay Company,* 2 vols. London: Hudson's Bay Record
       Society.

Ross, Alexander
1956   *The Fur Traders of the Far West.* Norman: University of Oklahoma Press.

Sahlins, Marshall D.
1961   "The Segmentary Lineage: An Organization of Predatory Expansion," *American
       Anthropologist.* 63:2.

Slobodin, Richard
1960   "Eastern Kutchin Warfare," *Anthropologica.* 2:76-93.

Thwaites, R.G., ed.
1906   "Maximilian: Prince of Wied, Travels in the Interior of North America, 1832-
       34," *Early Western Travels,* 1748-1846, 23.

Tyrrell, J.B., ed.
1915   "David Thompson's Narrative of his Explorations in Western America: 1784-
       1812," *Publications of the Champlain Society,* 12, Toronto.

Young, F.G., ed.
1899   "The Correspondence and Journals of Captain Nathaniel J. Wyeth, 1831-36",
       Sources of the History of Oregon, 1, Eugene: University of Oregon Press.

WAGE-LABOUR IN THE NORTHWEST FUR TRADE ECONOMY, 1760-1849

Glen Makahonuk

Although the history of the fur trade has experienced something of a renaissance over the past decade with the publication of studies on such topics as
demographic patterns, women and family relationships, and Indian/trader economic relations, there has been relatively little done on the wage-labour
situation. In fact, except for a few articles on the subject there seems to be a general assumption that a capitalist labour relations system is not applicable to the

From *Saskatchewan History,* 41, no. 1 (Winter 1988), 1-18. Reprinted by permission of *Saskatchewan
History.*

Canadian fur trade.[1] In a recent review of H. C. Pentland's *Labour and Capital in Canada 1650-1860,* however, Allan Greer argues that the study is "fundamentally incoherent" in the treatment of the transition to capitalism. He suggests that because Pentland confined himself to a very "narrow range of class relations" he was unable to distinguish between "different modes of production," or address the concept of "free" labourers working for wages during a period of primitive accumulation.[2] In other words, what may appear to be contrary to popular opinion, the Northwest fur trade economy of the period 1760 to 1849 operated within an emerging capitalist labour relations system.

I

The Northwest fur trade economy operated during an early stage in the development of capitalism in North America. The Marxist economic historian Maurice Dobb writes that "the development of Capitalism falls into a number of stages, characterized by different levels of maturity and each of them recognizable by fairly distinctive traits."[3] The distinctive traits of the Canadian economy prior to 1850 were petit bourgeois farmers or habitants, family units of independent commodity producers, land and transportation companies, and commercial enterprises involved in the trade of fish, furs or timber.[4] The fur trade economy was based on what may be termed merchant capitalism.

The two main fur trade companies prior to their merger in 1821 were the Hudson's Bay Company (HBC) and the North West Company (NWC). Although both were in competition with one another, they still held a monopoly of the fur trade in which they could pursue their wealth and profits. The NWC had established a large inland trading empire from its base in the St. Lawrence region, while the HBC had been operating from the shores of Hudson Bay since the late seventeenth century. The HBC had both economic and political objectives: the economic one was "to make a sustained profit or gain through trade" and the political one was to maintain the interests of the crown by carrying out exploration, territorial expansion and law making. As was explained by a contemporary writer and critic:

> ... the Hudson's Bay Company enjoys a right of exclusive trade with the Indian population. This right of exclusive trade is, practically and positively, a right of exclusive property in the labour, life and destines of the Indian race. It is an absolute and unqualified dominion over their bodies and their souls—a dominion irresponsible to any legal authority—a despotism, whose severity no legislative control can mitigate, and no public opinion restrain. It knows but one limit, and obeys but one law,—"Put money in thy purse."[5]

A similar opinion was held of the NWC. From its beginning the NWC was a monopoly which sought "higher profits for the merchants and more ruthless exploitation of the native trappers."[6] Indeed, the NWC proved to be an extremely profitable organization in comparison to the HBC and commanded the lion's share of the fur trade by the end of the eighteenth century. Roderick Mackenzie, a Company partner, estimated that "the value of the adventure in 1787 was £30,000 Halifax currency and that this had trebled in eleven years. The profits from 1784 to 1798 totalled £407,151 Halifax currency."[7] The wealthy partners of the NWC, according to historian Stanley Ryerson, "wielded a power equivalent to that of rulers of the colony" and were to become "the precursors of the modern Canadian capitalist class."[8]

II

The profit motive of the fur trade companies had a direct impact on their labour relations policies. It has been argued that their labour relations policies were based on paternalism, or to use H. C. Pentland's term, "personal labour relations," that is, relations that were characterized by the employer's obligation to provide for the welfare of the labourer in exchange for a loyal and reasonably efficient labour force.[9] Historians like Jennifer Brown and Sylvia Van Kirk have used the model of paternalism and patriarchal society developed by Peter Laslett in *The World We Have Lost* to describe the organization and structure of fur trade company posts. But it is the renowned Canadian working class historian Bryan Palmer who has developed a definition of paternalism to include a class conflict relationship.

> Paternalism defined relations of superordination and subordination in an age of commercial capital and nascent industrialism, paternalism grew out of the necessity to justify exploitation and mediate inherently irreconcilable interests. It rationalized inequality and provided for a hierarchical order ... In its historical manifestations, it included kindness and affection of superiors toward subordinates, as well as cruelty, harshness and gross insensitivity. But paternalism's ultimate significance ... lay in undermining the collectivity of the oppressed by linking them to their "social superiors." This did not necessarily imply an absence of social, even overtly class, conflict ... Paternalism was one part self-conscious creation by the merchants, independent producers, and landed gentry, and one part negotiated acceptance by the various plebeian subjects of the producing classes. But these two parts did not constitute the whole. Paternalism was reinforced by the material constraints of the social formation that had spawned it. For much of paternalism's sustaining power lay in the unique economics, politics and culture of each locality in early Canadian society.[10]

In carrying out their labour relations policies, the companies used a hierarchical and authoritarian management structure. In the case of the HBC, councils were established in the Northwest to regulate the local concerns of the company. A council was composed of chief factors who met each year usually at Red River to audit the accounts of the preceding year, to place orders with London suppliers for the goods required for the ensuing year's trade, to station company servants at various posts, to make recommendations in the filling of vacancies and to discipline or suspend any of the Company's servants.[11] After the chief factors came the chief traders, traders (who actually engaged in trade with the Indians), chief clerks and the clerks and postmasters. The apprentice clerks were at the very bottom of what Jennifer Brown has termed a "white-collar" personnel structure.[12] The system operated in such a way that no upper position could be filled without passing through an apprenticeship of at least several years.[13] It was also possible for clerks to be promoted to the ranks of the factors and traders on the basis of "good conduct and seniority."[14] And at the very bottom of the company, what may be termed the "blue-collar," were the interpreters who were described as "intelligent labourers" knowledgeable in "a smattering of Indian" and the labourers (both Native and European), "who [were] ready to turn [their] hands to anything; to become ... trapper[s], fishermen, or rough carpenter[s], at the shortest notice."[15]

Management's power and authority were based on the requirement that all company employees had to follow a code of established rules and to "yield due obedience to such authority in all cases in which [the Governor, Chief Factor or Chief Trader] may find necessary to exercise it."[16] Any employee who did not follow these rules was subject to discipline, which in some cases reached the point of "tyrannical exploitation." For example, John Feeny, a vagabond boy at Red River, was "tied to a tree and flogged on the posteriors" for refusing "to assist in cooking."[17] In an attempt to eradicate private trade in 1773 Humphrey Marten, the factor at Severn Fort, put one of his workers in irons and gave him eighteen strokes of the cat for trading one skin.[18] The Governor at Churchill Fort, according to Edward Umfreville, was so despised by his employees for his cruel behaviour that Orcadian labourers refused to work for him. In one case Umfreville wrote about the woes of a tailor who had to quit and go back to his Orkney Islands' home because of the cruel treatment he received.

> From thence he wrote to the Company, representing in the most humiliating ... manner, the cruel treatment he had received from the Bay Governor; he informed them that the blows he had received would be the cause of unhappiness to him to the latest period of his life, as he was thereby unable to get a livelihood at his business; upon which account he humbly solicited a small consideration, to compensate in some measure for the injury he had undeservedly sustained in their service. Though it would have been an act of the greatest charity to have listened to the prayer of this poor man's petition, yet, so great is the partiality of the Company to their chief officers in the country, that no attention was paid to the petition; and, indeed, an inferior servant, may apply for redress till he is tired, before any notice will be taken of his complaints, or the slightest reprimand given to the authors of his misery.[19]

The NWC was not that much better; James Sutherland, an HBC servant, reported in 1793 that a number of employees of the NWC complained about the frequent beatings they received from the so-called "mad man," Mr. La

Tour.[20] An apologist of the HBC justified "the exercise of strict discipline" on the grounds that it would prevent not only "anarchy among [the employees]," but also "neighbours" from "sowing discontent and rebellion among [them]."[21]

The economic historian H. A. Innis points out that by the late 1700s the personnel policies of the HBC, especially the discipline, actually discouraged Company employees from working harder or expanding the fur trade in the interior to counter the competition from the North West Company.[22] The NWC had labourers and traders who were quite willing to seek the rich harvest of furs in the interior regions. Many of the HBC employees, on the other hand, were loath to exert themselves because they had nothing to expect from the Company in terms of fringe benefits. In testimony before the Select Committee on the HBC in 1857, Governor George Simpson was asked: "Is there any provision made for your servants in case of sickness or old age?" His reply was "There is no provision made for them."[23] And in the case of Indian labourers who were no longer valuable to the Company because of old age or sickness, they were "driven to the woods, to seek a lingering death by famine, with all the honour and dignity of British liberty."[24] Such policies and treatment created a lack of *ésprit de corps* and thus forced a number of employees like David Thompson and Edward Umfreville to leave the HBC and join the NWC, which seemed to have more flexible personnel policies. These policies provided for upward mobility and profit sharing, which, according to the explorer and trader Alexander Mackenzie, "excited among them a spirit of emulation in the discharge of their various duties, and, in fact, made every agent a principal who perceived his own prosperity to be connected immediately with that of his employers."[25] By the early 1800s, however, the NWC changed its policy on hiring ex-HBC employees, because there was no longer a need to win the affection of Indians who were willing to trade furs. And most important the NWC had more than enough employees to contest the bitter trade rivalry with the HBC. At a company meeting held at Fort William in July 1811, it was decided "that none of the Hudson's Bay Servants should in future be received into any of the Company's Forts except in cases of Starvation—and on *no account* to be engaged to the N.W. Co."[26] In a word, then, both companies had personnel policies to control their respective employees.

III

The recruitment of a suitable labour force to produce furs and make profits was a major personnel problem for both the HBC and the NWC during the period under study. To solve the problem the companies set up a two part labour process at each factory or post.[27] The first part involved the actual production of furs—a topic that has been subject to considerable scholarly debate. Historians such as E. E. Rich, H. A. Innis and Arthur J. Ray have clearly articulated the traditional role of Indians in the fur trade as that of hunters, trappers and middlemen.[28] Both companies vied with each other for the trade of the Indians inhabiting the Western Interior. The HBC, in particular, relied on the Indians to do the hunting and trapping. But as the hunting areas dried up the former Indian hunters turned into middlemen in order to control the trade and transportation routes from the new fur areas to the European posts. Furthermore, in their economic relationship with the fur trade companies the Indians, especially those acting as middlemen, were concerned with getting "good measure" in order "to satisfy their immediate needs, to maintain their political alliances, and to gain access to reliable sources of European arms."[29] The Metis researcher Ron Bourgeault, on the other hand, has a different interpretation to explain how the fur companies used the trading system to conquer economically the Indian people and turn them into a dependent labor force which would produce a profit. The companies did this by

> trading the products of European technology, such as guns, traps, hatchets, knives, in exchange for fur. These tools of work were more developed or advanced than the tools then being used in Indian society. These goods were introduced and traded to the people. Once the people had learned how to use them, they were able to reduce the amount of time and labour needed to provide for themselves (necessary-labour). They now had more time and better tools to produce more surplus (surplus-labour production). In other words, it became much easier and quicker to hunt food, cut wood and skin animals with the new European technology than with the old technology or work tools. What the European wanted from the Indians' labour was the ability to produce a surplus ...[30]

The second part of the labour process needed European workers to operate and maintain both the fur trade posts and the transportation system. These workers were recruited from Lower Canada in the case of the NWC and from Europe in the case of the HBC. The NWC hired *hommes-du-nord* who were described as

> rough and simple men, and though used to doing hard work they preferred doing nothing at all and would not even hunt or fish for themselves unless told to do so by their employers. The work that they did while travelling was amazing. On the river at first light and going until dark, their usual respite from the hard work of paddling was the even harder work of portaging. The portages were many and difficult and everything had to be carried over them. Shouldering two or more ninety-pound bales of goods or fur, the voyageur set off a trot across the portage, and later returned for more.[31]

They looked down on the "goers and comers" from Montreal and referred to them as the *mangeurs-du-lard* (pork-eaters). The so-called pork-eaters were employed for four or five months to transport supplies to Grand Portage and then to bring back the cargoes of furs to Montreal; at this point their seasonal contract was at an end and they were laid off. The NWC usually employed about 1280 workers in a season: 50 clerks, 71 interpreters and under clerks, 35 guides and the remainder canoemen.[32] Most of them were French-Canadians (with some Iroquois) and they formed a labouring class which, according to Sylvia Van Kirk, was ethnically and occupationally separate from the British officer class.[33]

The HBC, on the other hand, had a different labour market. The HBC had established regular recruiting policies as early as the 1680s and had relied on common labourers, tradesmen and urban workers from the London area and on some occasions from Ireland and Scotland. By the early 18th century, however, the HBC changed its policy of hiring Londoners because of the recommendation of Joseph Myatt, Governor of Albany. In 1727 Myatt had written to the London Committee that Londoners were becoming better "acquainted with the ways and debaucheries of the town" rather than the hard work necessary in the fur trade economy.[34] Myatt believed that young Orkneymen, who had a reputation for hard work and sobriety, could replace the unsuitable urban workers from London for a wage of only "£6 per annum."[35] Another 18th century writer, Edward Umfreville, had a good opinion of Orkneymen, for he described them as "a close, prudent, quiet people, strictly faithful to their employers ..."[36] As a consequence the HBC started recruiting its labourers and some of its craftsmen from the Orkneys by the late 1730s.

In his important quantitative study of the recruitment patterns of Orkneymen in the HBC, the historian John Nicks points out that most of the HBC employees prior to 1821 came from the middle and lower ranks of Orkney society. Most of them could be classified as plebeians for "they were young, unmarried sons of small tenant farmers, craftsmen, and cottagers."[37] The tradesmen, on the other hand, could be classified as proletarians, for they were recruited from the urban centres like Kirkwell and Stromness in which a Scottish working class was in the making.[38] Although by the end of the 18th century English labourers were becoming a rarity, most of the skilled tradesmen positions and the so-called "white-collar" positions like writers, clerks and officers still continued to be held by Englishmen.

The Orcadians were useful employees at the HBC posts on the coast lines, but seemed to show little initiative to become voyageurs when the need to expand the trade to the interior developed in the late 18th century. The HBC was quite concerned that its employees might not be able to counter the NWC's push inland. The Orcadians were reluctant to move inland because they received no extra wage for a job that offered more toil, more misery, more hardship and the possibility of starvation.[39] As a consequence the HBC had to rely on Indian voyageurs to do the inland work until the Company could hire skilled Orcadian canoeists and canoebuilders who would be willing to do it. To speed the process along Samuel Hearne made the following proposal to the London Committee:

All persons that may perfect themselves, so far as to be capable of steering a canoe up and down will in my opinion greatly embrace the value of their Services; if such person were to meet with some little gratuity it would not only be the means of inducing them to a longer continuance in the Service but would be a great inducement to other young fellows to make themselves qualify for that Station.[40]

The London Committee accepted the proposal and offered extra wages for skilled Orkney canoemen. It seems their skills developed to the point that they became specialists at being "Bowsmen," "Middlemen" or "Steersmen."

The lack of skilled canoemakers was another labour problem. Because of the competition with the NWC for the Western Interior, the HBC needed a greater number of large canoes which could carry as many men and goods as those of the NWC. Since the Orcadians were not skilled in the art of canoemaking, the HBC had to rely on the Indian labouring class to build canoes.[41] However, Indian labourers, according to both Hearne and Turnor, were not reliable in keeping up the production of canoes. And even those canoes that were built were often unsatisfactory because they were too small in comparison to the *canots de maître* and *canots du nord*. Turnor noted that it took ten HBC men with five canoes to carry as much as five Canadians with one canoe.[42]

Realizing the advantages of the Canadians over the HBC, Matthew Cocking, a company writer and commander at York Fort, proposed that "Vessels in Canoe form made of Fir might be contrived of a small Draught of greater burden than the Indian Canoes, and Yet of such a Weight as to be carried occasionally by those who go in them, and the Company's Servants will probably sooner learn the Management of these as they will be much steadier than Indian Canoes, which are dangerous to unskillful Persons."[43] If his proposal failed, Cocking suggested that it might be necessary to hire Canadians who could build canoes in "the Pedlers manner." The HBC's solution to its problems with the canoe was to have its own employees trained in the art of canoe building and canoe handling. In 1792 both Charles Isham, "a noted half-breed," and Robert Longmoor, who had joined the HBC as a sailor in 1771, became the first employees to "attain any degree of Proficiency in Bowing or Sterring Canoes" and "to perfect [themselves] in the Art of Canoe Building."[44]

A different type of personnel problem developed in the early 1800s when a number of managers filed complaints about the laziness and lack of productivity of their Orkney workers. In fact, Governor Miles Macdonell's opinion of Orcadians had become quite negative:

There cannot ... be much improvement made in the country while the Orkneymen form the majority of labourers; they are lazy, spiritless, and ill-disposed-wedded to old habits, strongly prejudiced against any change, however beneficial ... It is not uncommon for an Orkneyman to consume six pounds or eight pounds of meat in a day, and some have ate as much in a single meal.

This gluttonous appetite, they say, is occasioned by the cold. I entirely discredit the assertion, as I think it rather to be natural to themselves. All the labour I have seen these men do would scarcely pay for the victuals they consume.[45]

As a consequence the HBC decided to recruit workers from Glasgow, Island of Coll, Ireland, Lower Canada and, on some occasions, even the jails of Norway.[46]

In a letter to William Auld, superintendent of Northern Department, Governor Miles Macdonell reported that the Orcadians working for the HBC did not like "the arrival of strangers among them" because "they have enjoyed the exclusive advantages of the Trade for a long time unmixed with any others; which might induce them to suppose that no people ought to be employed but themselves."[47] Macdonell was of the opinion that the HBC would be better off to hire workers from other parts of the United Kingdom and get rid of the Orcadians whom he claimed have become prone to insubordinate behaviour and disobedience:

> ... the Company can get abundance of men from other parts of the United Kingdom and experience can be acquired. With regard to settling a Colony, people from other parts would I think ... serve the purpose better than these from Orkney, particularly such of them as have already been in this Country, whose habits of insubordination, idleness, and inactivity will be very difficult to erad-icate. One or two old hands is enough to poison any party—they tell the others that they ought to have this thing and that other thing,—make the whole dis-contented and keep themselves in the back ground. William Finlay has already occasioned a little difficulty, laying down *Factory Law* (as he explained it) and disobedience ...[48]

It seems that Macdonell's suggestion of controlling the labour supply and eliminating the potential bargaining power of the Orcadians was soon adopted. Indeed, the establishment of Selkirk's colony and the introduction of the HBC's new employment policy started to diminish slightly the number of Orcadians and increase the number of French-Canadians, Scots, Irish, Metis and English, es-pecially in the period between 1812 and 1821.[49]

The HBC's attempt at controlling the labour supply was made much easier after the union with the NWC in 1821. The merger meant that much of the ex-isting manpower and the fur trade posts were both redundant and superfluous. Locations that at one time had both a NWC post and HBC post could now do with only one. It was also obvious to Governor George Simpson that if labour costs or the wage bill was reduced by 25 per cent, then profits could be in-creased.[50] Consequently 250 workers were laid off; the first being the older ones with larger families and "the leading turbulent characters," who had car-ried out various protests and strikes against the companies. Simpson was criticized for being too zealous in dismissing family men and retaining only those who were in debt to the company. It was pointed out to Simpson that the

Company could not operate with "inadequate personnel."[51] Simpson, however, dismissed the warning claiming that he could always get new recruits when needed and explained the HBC's new hiring philosophy:

> The relative qualifications and merits of Canadians and Orkneymen have been duly weighed and the preference is given to the former in so far as regards the duties and services to be performed, but in point of expense which is likewise a very important consideration the opinion is in favor of the Orkneymen. The Canadians, generally speaking are a volatile inconsiderate race of people, but active, capable of undergoing great hardships and easily managed by those who are accustomed to deal with them; the Orkneymen on the contrary are slow and do not possess the same physical strength, and spirits necessary on trying occasions ... If brought young into the Country, however, say from 18 to 22 years of age they may be greatly improved; and upon the whole we consider it good policy to have about an equal proportion of each, which will keep up a spirit of competition and enable us to deal with them on such terms as may be considered necessary and proper. Scotch and Irish in any considerable numbers we have strong objections to being quarrelsome independent and inclined to form leagues and cabals [i.e. a secret organization and overthrow authority] which might be dangerous to the peace of the Country.[52]

The policy was to keep a balance between Orcadians and Canadians, especially those from Lower Canada in the regions of Sorel, Maskinonge and Montreal in the period between 1823 and 1849. Simpson's policy also recognized the value of the Indians and Metis in the Red River colony as an important reserve of labourers in this same period.[53]

IV

The determination of wages in the fur trade economy was based not only on a fixed contract rate or social custom, but also on the buying and selling of labour power. Workers had an understanding of the operation of the labour market and would try to increase their wages when the demand was greater than the supply. For example, John Ballenden reported in June 1799 that the workers at Gordon House wanted to negotiate new wage rates. In his report to the Company, Ballenden stated:

> the chief point I had for visiting the Settlement [Gordon House] was to settle terms with the men respecting their contracts which was the most difficult task I ever undertook—from time to time they have hitherto been only engaged for one year—now their times being all expired at once. They did not hesitate to think and tell me that they would get their own terms or leave the service. So one and all declared for home or extraordinary wages which I was determined not to comply with, finding me not to deviate—several came afterwards and entered into Contracts at what your Honours offered them ...[54]

In the buying and selling of labour power Marx states that the "interests of capital and the interests of wage-labour are diametrically opposed to each other."[55] The workers (sellers of labour power) depend on their wages for their subsistence and are therefore forced to maximize them, while the buyers (employers) treat the wages as a cost and are perpetually trying to minimize them. The 18th century economic philosopher Adam Smith had the same conclusion:

> the common wages of labour, depends every where upon the contract usually made between those two parties, whose interests are by no means the same. The workmen desire to get as much, the masters to give as little as possible. The former are disposed to combine in order to raise, the latter in order to lower the wage of labour.[56]

In *A Sketch of the British Fur Trade,* the Earl of Selkirk pointed out that the NWC was able to maintain a monopoly and earn profits by the wage policy it administered. This policy involved the payment of wages in "Grand Portage currency" or "North-West currency," which meant that a dollar in Montreal was only worth 50 cents in Grand Portage, and that goods transported from Montreal to Grand Portage were sold at double the price.[57] The company also encouraged its employees to drink because the profits on rum reduced wages in proportion. To support his argument, Selkirk referred to a description made by Count Paolo Andreani, who had travelled in the Upper Country in 1791.

> It is ... considered as an essential point of duty in the master of a trading post, to take care that the men ... shall have as little as possible of their wages to receive in cash at the end of the year ... Whenever any of their servants begin to indulge in habits of expense, credit is allowed him with unbound facility, till he is deeply involved in debt to the Company. When this has been accomplished he is in complete bondage; and no alternative is left him but absolute submission to his employers, or a gaol. He must therefore submit to every imposition, which his superiors may think fit to practice upon him.[58]

The worker, as a result of this practice, was always in debt to the company and in "a degree of poverty seldom to be met with in other parts of America ..."[59] While visiting Canada in 1797 Francois Alexandre Frederic la Rochefoucault Liancourt, a French nobleman and philanthropist interested in the abolition of slavery, had come to a similar conclusion about the NWC's wage policy and truck payments:

> As the men employed in this trade are paid in merchandize which the Company sells with an enormous profit, it is obvious at how cheap a rate these people are paid. They purchase of the company every article they want; it keeps with them an open account, and as they all winter in the interior of the country and beyond Lake Winnipeg, they pay as a consequence excessively dear for the blankets and the cloths which they bring with them for their wives. These servants of the Company are in general extravagant, given to drinking ... and these are exactly the people whom the Company wants. The speculation on the excesses of these people is carried so far, that if one of them happened to lead

a regular sober life, he is burdened with the most laborious work, until by continual ill-treatment he is driven to drunkenness and debauchery, which vices cause the rum, blankets and trinkets to be sold to greater advantage. In 1791, nine hundred of these menial servants owed the Company more than the amount of ten or fifteen years pay.[60]

This policy stayed in effect until the merger with the HBC in 1821.

The HBC did not have a so-called special currency but did have what Rich calls "the Canadian System" and describes it as "vicious and extravagant."[61] In essence the system was based on the London Committee's instructions to reduce all wages as much as possible, similar to what was being practised by employers in the British Isles. One way to prevent wage increases was to charge high prices for company goods, while commissioned officers paid only 33 $1/2\%$.[62] This policy seemed effective; for example, the wage bill for the Northern Department in 1825-26 was cut by approximately £5000. Another way of carrying out the "Canadian system" was merely to cut wages and post a new scale, despite protests from the servants. On one occasion in August 1822 James Bird, acting on behalf of the clerks, wrote a letter to Governor Simpson protesting the cut in their wages. Simpson's response was to dismiss their so-called "trifling grievances" because they did not "have a right to expect much relief." Simpson also warned the London Committee that "if you once begin to give way there will be no end to their demands and some of those useless old people will never think of withdrawing from the concern but keep more enterprizing young men in the background."[63]

The "Canadian system," however, did not always work to the advantage of the HBC. Changes in labour market conditions and the bargaining strategies of HBC employees, as Simpson notes in his *Athabasca Journal,* contributed to a movement in (exorbitant) wages.[64] Simpson's reference to exorbitant wages was made in response to the Company being forced to pay higher wages than those in the British Isles in order to attract workers. For instance, prior to 1800 labourers, bowsmen and canoemen from the Orkney Islands received wages from £6 to £12 per annum plus room, board, and a basic set of clothing, which was 2 to 3 times greater than what they would have received as labourers on Orkney farms.[65] Skilled labourers or tradesmen, on the other hand, usually received a wage which ranged from £20 to £40, depending upon the craft and the market demand. For example, Nicholas Spence from Stromness, Orkney Islands was hired in 1793 as a boatbuilder at the rate of £25 per year on a three year contract. On the renewal of his contract in 1796 his wage was increased to £36 per year because of the shortage of skilled boatbuilders.[66] And when Indians and Metis were in great demand as hunters, they could earn as much as £30 per year, which was the equivalent of some skilled labour rates.[67] The wages of clerks ranged between £75 and £100 during the early 19th century.[68] And by the 1840s the Council minutes of the Northern Department were listing wages as follows:

the following Servants be engaged for the Northern Department on 5 years Contracts Viz

From Europe
  2 Blacksmiths @ from £25 to £30 per an.
  2 Coopers (Fishcurers) @ from £25 to £30 per an.
  3 Masons @ from £25 to £30 per an.
  2 Joiners @ from £25 to £30 per an.
  6 Sloopers @ £20.
  <u>30</u> Labourers @ £16.
  45

From Canada 3 years Contracts
50 Voyageurs @ prix du Poste or £17 per an.[69]

In comparison to the wage rates paid in the Orkney Islands, the above listed HBC's wages were at least £5 to £10 greater. In fact, the higher wage rates made it possible for some tradesmen to save enough money in order to return home and set up their own shop or farm.[70] But before these tradesmen could return home they were often required to provide instruction in the HBC's apprenticeship program. Chief Factors and Chief Traders were authorized "to engage strong healthy half-breed lads not under 14 years of age as apprentices to be employed with those tradesmen with the purpose of acquiring of their business on a term not less than seven years ..." The wages were £8 per annum for the first two years, £10 for the next two years, £12 for the following two and £15 for the last year.[71] The apprenticeship system was designed to get skilled work done at a cheap price.

V

The adversarial labour relations system in the Northwest fur trade economy created a significant number of disputes. These disputes were part of what both Marx and Adam Smith would call the continuous struggle between capital and labour. The noted French economic historian Paul Mantoux argued that "the disputes between capital and labour afford the best possible illustration of the economic evolution prior to the coming of the factory system."[72] Many British Marxist historians, in particular E.P. Thompson, have also examined this ongoing relationship and have referred to it as class-struggle.

> That we choose to continue to employ the heuristic category of class (despite this ever-present difficulty) arises not from its perfection as a concept but from the fact that no alternative category is available to analyse a manifest and universal historical process. Thus we cannot (in the English language) talk of "estate-struggle" or "order-struggle," whereas "class-struggle" had been employed, not without difficulty but with signal success, by historians of ancient, feudal and early modern societies ...[73]

Thompson further argues that far too little attention has been placed on the concept of class struggle. As he explains it

> ... people find themselves in a society structured in determined ways (crucially, but not exclusively, in productive relations), they experience exploitation (or the need to maintain power over those whom they exploit), they identify points of antagonistic interest, they commence to struggle around these issues and in the process of struggling they discover themselves as classes, they come to know this discovery as class-consciousness.[74]

In a series of articles on Metis history in *New Breed,* Ron Bourgeault points out that it was in "the late 1700s that class formations within the economy of the fur trade became distinct."[75] The class formations, according to Bourgeault, led to class struggle between the fur trade companies and the Indian and European labouring class. Although the concept of class struggle in the Canadian fur trade company is subject to debate, it still may be used in the context of what E. P. Thompson has described as "fragments of proto-conflict." This proto-conflict marked a transition period in which the fur trade labour disputes were being carried out in both the cultural tradition of plebian struggles and the new class relations created by capitalism. One Canadian working class historian has come to the conclusion that

> These eighteenth-century disputes were but the opening skirmishes in a class war that would grow in both extent and intensity. In the years ahead workers would gather their forces for organized battle against an enemy grown more vicious in defense of their increase of wealth and power ...[76]

The labour disputes focused on two major issues which were also common in European society: one involved the lack of adequate provisions, and the second involved insufficient wages.[77] Between 1767 and 1769 Andrew Graham, an employee of the Hudson Bay Company, observed a number of disturbances caused when the company failed "to keep up a stock of cheese, beef, pork or any other ... commodities ..."[78] Samuel Hearne noted in his Journal of 8 February 1775 that "the very scanty allowance of Provisions" has caused "many grumblings among some of the men ..."[79] In a letter to Joseph Colen, resident at York Factory, dated 10 July 1798 William Tomison, Inland Master, describes the dangerous grumblings that his men had about the lack of adequate provisions in their trip from Gordon House to Trout River. He believed that unless a "larger stock of each article" was served to each worker, it "would create animosities disention among the people."[80] And a year later Tomison was still experiencing difficulties with his men when they discovered that he had tried to cut their provisions and brandy by one-half.

A series of these disputes broke out in the Red River region in the 1812-14 period. In most cases the workers carried out short work stoppage protests; they immediately stopped working when provisions were inadequate or when treatment from their overseer was too harsh. Both on 14 September and 6 November 1812 Miles Macdonell reported in his Journal that his "men refused to work under Mr. O. K." because of "bad advise." It seems that their problem was solved, for they "resumed work" the next day and "appeared satisfied."[81] On 11 December 1812 the workers walked off the job protesting the lack of provisions and demanding that more be given. Macdonell refused to give them any. Two days later their hunger forced them to send "one of their number to apologise ... and promise never to quit work again without orders."[82] The promise was shortlived for on 14 January 1813 another incident broke out in which three labourers refused to obey their overseer. Macdonell found them guilty of insubordinate behaviour and fined them £2 each.[83] Another similar incident occurred on 1 February 1813 when the men did not work because of the lack of provisions.[84] Approximately one year later in April 1814 Fort Daer was the site of a protest lead by James Toomy and Mr. Delorme, who used "inflammatory language" in their demand "for an augmentation [of] their daily rations." They held out a week before capitulating; Toomy and Delorme were dismissed and the others were reprimanded with a warning about their "future behaviour."[85] The warning had little impact because on 8 June 1814 fifteen labourers once again struck for more provisions. Two days later they returned to work after "paying a fine of 5 [shillings] per day while they were off."[86] And as a final example, in the summer of 1836 we find "a state of mutiny," as Thomas Simpson refers to it, breaking out in Red River. In a letter to James Hargrave, Simpson demanded that the "mutineers" never "be employed by the Company again."[87] Such discontent and protests continued throughout the period under study and became most acute when the HBC could not provide enough provisions to keep body and soul together.

It was the wage issue which generated the most discontent and heightened the conflict between the fur trade companies and their workers. Andrew Graham observed that much of the "grumblings and discontents" among the labourers, especially at York Fort, was caused by low wages. The labourers would show their unhappiness by getting drunk and then becoming "so haughty and impudent that they will dispute an officer's orders to do any duty but what they term their own business."[88] And another way to show their discontent was to strike.

A number of strikes broke out between 1760 and 1849. The first major one to involve the HBC was the great seamen's strike of 1768 on the Thames. The seamen had gone on strike because of a reduction in their wages. The HBC seamen had notified the Company that its three ships would be prevented from sailing until it agreed to raise their wages to 40s per month. Because of the critical shipping season, the Company agreed to the demand and the ships were allowed to sail.[89] Although combinations were illegal, workers did attempt to form combinations in order to raise wages by means of a strike if necessary.[90] For example, in July 1777 the Orkney labourers at Cumberland House, under the leadership of James Batt and William Taylor, formed "a kind of Combination" and struck for a wage of £15 per year, which was approximately £9 above the existing rate. Humphrey Marten, the Factor, retaliated by threatening the labourers with a forfeit of all of their wages if they did not return to work.[91] Even though the initial strike was defeated, E. E. Rich points out that the Company later responded to the labourers' wage problems by setting up a system of incentive-payments for those who made inland voyages.

Meanwhile the NWC also had its share of labour disputes. A number of them broke out in 1789 on the issue of insufficient wages. On 10 July 1794 the French-Canadian voyageurs at St. Helen formed a combination and struck against the Company's attempts to reduce wages. The magistrates were called in to punish the leaders by having them pilloried. The voyageurs, however, showed their defiance of the law by freeing their leaders and escaping. A month later on 3 August 1794 the voyageurs at Lac La Pluie formed a combination and went on strike for higher wages. Unfortunately, they lost both the strike and their jobs. And in March 1814 a group of voyageurs carried out a protest by going to Montreal to prosecute the NWC for failing to pay their full wages. They were unsuccessful in their case and were subsequently dismissed.[92]

Another major strike broke out again at Cumberland House on 1 August 1799 when canoemen formed a combination and refused to comply with orders to go to Beaver River until they received "additional wages." James Bird warned them that their strike was a "flagrant breach of contract" and they would be punished for it. The workers disregarded the warning and continued the strike. Tomison then wrote a letter to the Governor requesting that an example be made of these men which would "ensure obedience from all the rest on this establishment for the future: for should these escape with impunity the little subordination that has been (but very lately) ... established will be entirely subverted, and it will consequently be utterly impossible to carry on your Honours' concerns in this part with any degree of vigour."[93] Management, in other words, did not view the strike as a mere economic dispute, but rather as a test of power over the control of work. Indeed James Bird argued that it was a challenge to management authority:

> which of the two is esteemed the more probable method of advancing the interest of our Honourable Employers: whether to carry into execution a plan suggested by an experienced and vigilant officer undertaken by one not less active and enterprising aided by the prompt obedience of his men; or whether it be an implicit submission to the will of the servants and supinely to adopt or relinquish such schemes as they may think proper to approve or reject. Now will all know whether for the future the servant is to comply with the orders of his master to act under the immediate direction and control of his servant.[94]

The strike finally came to an end on 30 August 1799 when Joseph Howse notified the strikers that "they were no longer on duty or considered as the company's servants ..." The strikers responded by abandoning the strike and then deciding to join the NWC.

Another example of a strike that actually became a challenge to management authority occurred at Nelson Encampment in February 1812. Governor Miles Macdonell reported that fourteen men under the leadership of William Finlay formed a combination "against the authority of the officers set over them."[95] It seems that the labourers were supporting Finlay who had "refused to conform ... to regulations ... established for the health of the people" and to orders "to resume work." Macdonell had Finlay brought before a magistrate and charged with a number of misdemeanours. Finlay was found guilty and sentenced to "confinement as a refractory servant" and jailed in a small hut. The combination came to Finlay's rescue by burning the hut to the ground and "triumphantly shouting in the most audacious manner ..." Macdonell was unable to get them to return to work, despite threats of having them tried for mutiny. The strikers carried out a more defiant act when they armed and fortified themselves in a nearby house. In retaliation, wrote Macdonell,

> we ... armed ourselves and went down with some of the Gentlemen to prevent insult being offered to the three officers who had first gone. These we met returning without having got any of the arms, and suffered gross abuse with threats of violence. We proceeded onto the Insurgent's authority to deliver up their arms immediately ... and were further informed of the serious consequences of refusal, that they must be treated as people in open hostility who set all order at defiance; they not withstanding remained inflexible.[96]

The Company finally decided to starve them into submission. By June 1812 the strikers were unable to carry on any longer and surrendered. They were sent to Montreal for trial. They were found guilty and dismissed from service.

These disputes and strikes, then, were a clear expression of the disharmony and class tensions in the fur trade economy. Labourers, servants and voyageurs were quite prepared to challenge the authority and power of the Company in order to achieve their demands.

VI

In conclusion, this paper has attempted to examine the unique capital-wage-labour relationship in the fur trade economy between 1760 and 1849. It has tried to argue that even though this period has been considered by a number of historians as pre-industrial Canada, the fur trade workers, both Indian and European, were starting to operate under a capitalist labour relations system. Many economic and social historians would claim that this labour relations system was paternalistic or patriarchal. But "no thoughtful historian," writes E. P. Thompson, "should characterize a whole system as paternalistic or patriarchal."[97] Evidence has been provided to show that both fur trade companies and their workers had an astute understanding of the operation of the labour market, especially as it applied to the buying and selling of labour power. And it was this particular relationship which resulted in class tensions as expressed by the various disputes and strikes. More research, however, is still needed on labour-capital relations and the actual number of disputes in the fur trade economy in order to get a better understanding of this period in working class history.

Acknowledgement

I would like to thank Professors W. A. Waiser of the History Department of the University of Saskatchewan and Frank Tough of the Native Studies Department for reading earlier drafts of this paper and providing many useful comments.

Notes

1. These examples are: Philip Goldring, "Labour Records of the Hudson's Bay Company, 1821-1870," *Archivaria,* 11 (Winter 1980-81), 53-86; John Nicks, "Orkneymen in the HBC, 1780-1821" and C. M. Judd, "'Mixed Bands of Many Nations:' 1821-70" in *Old Trails and New Directions: Papers of the Third North American Fur Trade Conference,* edited by C. M. Judd and A. J. Ray (Toronto, 1980) and Allan Greer, "Wage Labour and the Transition to Capitalism: A Critique of Pentland," *Labour/Le Travail,* 15 (Spring 1985), 7-22.

2. Allan Greer, "Wage Labour and the Transition to Capitalism ...," 8-10.

3. For a more detailed explanation see Maurice Dobb, *Studies in the Development of Capitalism* (New York, 1973), 17-32.

4. George Heriot, *Travels through the Canadas, containing a description of the picturesque scenery on some of the Rivers and Lakes; with an Account of the Productions, Commerce and Inhabitants of those Provinces* (Rutland, Vermont, 1971) (reprint), 208-233, and H. A. Innis, *The Fur Trade in Canada* (Toronto, 1977), Section II.

5. James E. Fitzgerald, *An Examination of the Charter and Proceedings of the Hudson's Bay Company* (London, 1849), 135-136.

6. Stanley Ryerson, *The Founding of Canada: Beginnings to 1815* (Toronto, 1975), 244.

7. For a more detailed account of the returns on the capital of the company, the value of shares and rate of profit see H. A. Innis, *The Fur Trade in Canada,* 258-259.

8. Stanley Ryerson, *The Founding of Canada,* 250.

9. For a more detailed discussion see chapter 2 in H. C. Pentland, *Labour and Capital in Canada, 1650-1860* (Toronto, 1981).

10. Bryan Palmer, *Working-Class Experience: The Rise and Reconstitution of Canadian Labour, 1800-1980* (Toronto, 1983), 14, 19.

11. Canada. House of Commons. Report from the Select Committee on the Hudson's Bay Company; Together with the Proceedings of the Committee, Minutes of Evidence ... 1857. Evidence of E. Ellice, p. 325.

12. Jennifer S. H. Brown, *Strangers in Blood: Fur Trade Company Families in Indian Country* (Vancouver, 1980), 30.

13. R. M. Martin, *The Hudson's Bay Territories and Vancouver's Island with an Exposition of the Chartered Rights, Conduct and Policy of the Hon. Hudson's Bay Corporation* (London, 1849), 67.

14. B. Willson, *The Great Company, being a history of the Hon. Company of Merchant-Adventurers, trading into Hudson's Bay* (Toronto, 1899), 434.

15. R. M. Ballantyne, *Hudson's Bay; or Every-Day Life in the Wilds of North America, during six years' residence in the Territories of the Honourable Hudson's Bay Company* (Edinburgh, 1848), 32.

16. The Minutes of the Council of the Northern Department of Rupert's Land, 1830 to 1843, being the Transaction and Enactment of the Rulers of the Country during that period ... 3 July 1830, 656.

17. Morton MSS C505/1/2.3 Selkirk's Papers. Miles Macdonell's Journal, April 22, 1813 to Feb. 11, 1815, p. 17.

18. E. E. Rich, *The History of the Hudson's Bay Company. Vol. II: 1763-1870,* 103.

19. Edward Umfreville, *The Present State of Hudson's Bay containing a Full Description of that Settlement, and the Adjacent Country; and Likewise of the Fur Trade with hints for its Improvement* (Toronto, 1954), 58.

20. A. S. Morton, *A History of the Canadian West to 1870-71* (Toronto, 1973), 429.

21. R. M. Martin, *The Hudson's Bay Territories ...,* 73.

22. H. A. Innis, *The Fur Trade in Canada,* 155.

23. Minutes of Evidence Select Committee on the HBC ... 1857, 61.

24. J. Fitzgerald, *An Examination of the Charter and Proceedings of the HBC,* 139.

25. Alexander Mackenzie, *Voyages from Montreal through the continent of North America to the Frozen and Pacific Oceans in 1789 and 1793 ... Vol. I* (Toronto, 1911), xlviii.

26. Minutes of the deliberations and transactions of the North West Company assembled at Fort William at their regular meetings in ... July 1811 in *Documents Relating to the North West Company,* edited by W. S. Wallace (Toronto, 1934), 275.

27. Morton MSS C505/1/2.2 Selkirk Papers. Miles Macdonell's Journal Sept. 6, 1812 to April 22, 1813, p. 270; Morton MSS C510/1/2 Journal of Robert Campbell, 1808-1851, pp. 11-12 discusses the division of labour at the HBC experiment farm at Red River in 1831; and David Thompson, *Travels in Western North America, 1784-1812,* edited by V. Hopwood (Toronto, 1971), 73.

28. See E. E. Rich, *The Fur Trade and the Northwest to 1857,* H. A. Innis, *The Fur Trade in Canada,* and A. J. Ray, *Indians in the Fur Trade* (Toronto, 1974).

29. See Arthur J. Ray and D. Freeman, *'Give Us Good Measure:' An Economic Analysis of Relations Between the Indians and the Hudson's Company Before 1763* (Toronto, 1978), 5, and A. J. Ray, *Indians in the Fur Trade.*

30. Ron Bourgeault, "Metis History," *New Breed, 13,* 4 (April, 1982), 8.

31. W. Sheppe, ed., *First Man West: Alexander Mackenzie's Journal of His Voyage to the Pacific Coast of Canada in 1793* (Montreal, 1962), 18-19.

32. The Earl of Selkirk, *A Sketch of the British Fur Trade in North America; with Observations relative to the North West Company of Montreal* (London, 1816), 33 and George Heriot, *Travels through the Canadas,* 242.

33. Sylvia Van Kirk, "Fur Trade Social History: Some Recent Trends," in *Old Trails and New Directions: Papers of the Third North American Fur Trade Conference,* edited by Carol M. Judd and A. J. Ray (Toronto, 1980), 163.

34. G. F. K. Davies, ed., *Letters from Hudson Bay 1703-40* (London, 1965), 123.

35. *Ibid.,* 116.

36. E. Umfreville, *The Present State of Hudson's Bay* ..., 109.

37. John Nicks, "Orkneymen in the HBC 1780-1821," in *Old Trails and New Directions* ..., 122.

38. For a discussion about the making of the Scottish working class in the period 1770 to 1820 see James D. Young, *The Rousing of the Scottish Working Class* (London, 1979), 41-47.

39. See R. Glover, "The Difficulties of the Hudson's Bay Company's Penetration of the West," *Canadian Historical Review* (hereafter *CHR*), XXIX, 3, (Sept., 1948), 245 and "North Western Explorations," *Report on Canadian Archives 1890,* 51.

40. *Ibid.,* 191-192.

41. Norman Zlotkin and Donald R. Colborne point out in "Internal Canadian Imperialism and the Native People," *Imperialism, Nationalism and Canada: from the Marxist Institute of Toronto,* edited by Craig Heron (Toronto, 1977), 163, that as the Indians were being replaced as middle men in the fur trade, they were being turned into proletarians. Also see Ron Bourgeault, "The Indians, the Metis and the Fur Trade: Class, Sexism and Racism in the Transition from Communism to Capitalism," *Studies in Political Economy: A Socialist Review,* 12, (Fall, 1983), 45-86.

42. Turnor estimated that in 1779 the HBC lost 18,000 Made Beaver on the Saskatchewan alone because of the lack of adequate canoes. *Hearne and Turnor Journals,* 154.

43. Cocking's account of his proceedings June 27, 1776 in *ibid.,* 47.

44. HBCA. A. 11/116, fos. 6d., 13d. Journal of George Sutherland 1796-1797 in *Saskatchewan Journals and Correspondence 1795-1802,* edited by Alice M. Johnson (London, 1967).

45. Cited in B. Willson, *The Great Company,* 381.

46. R. Glover points out that Norwegian convicts were hired to build Norway House; see "The Difficulties of the Hudson's Bay Company's Penetration of the West," *CHR,* 253.

47. National Archives of Canada (NAC). *Report on Canadian Archives 1886* (Ottawa, 1887). Miles Macdonell to William Auld, 25 Dec. 1811, p. cc.

48. *Ibid.,* cci.

49. Also see Minutes of Evidence Select Committee on the Hudson's Bay Co. 1857. Evidence of Sir. G. Simpson, p. 61; and Eric Ross, *Beyond the River and the Bay. Some Observations on the State of the Canadian Northwest in 1811* (Toronto, 1973), 18-19.

50. HBCA. D4/1, 20; D4/85, 3, Simpson's Official Reports, 1822 in C. M. Judd, "'Mixt Bands of Many Nations' ...," 130.

51. John Galbraith, *The Hudson's Bay Company,* 21.

52. HBCA. D4/86, 14f-14 cited in C. M. Judd, "'Mixt Bands of Many Nations' ...," 130-31.

53. A. J. Ray, *Indians In The Fur Trade,* 218-219.

54. Journal of William Tomison 1798-1799 in *Saskatchewan Journals and Correspondence 1795-1802,* 173.

55. K. Marx, *Wage-Labour and Capital* (New York, 1977), 39.

56. Adam Smith, *An Inquiry into the Nature and Causes of the Wealth of Nations* (New York, 1937), 66.

57. W. S. Wallace, ed., *Documents Relating to the North West Company,* 272.

58. Earl of Selkirk, *A Sketch of the British fur trade in North America, with observations relative to the North-West Company of Montreal* (London, 1816), 40-41.

59. *Ibid.,* 37.

60. Francois A. F., duc de La Rochefoucault-Liancourt, *Travels through the United States of North America, the Country of the Iroquois, and Upper Canada ...* translated by H. Newman (London, 1799), 330-331 cited in A. S. Morton, *A History of the Canadian West,* 353.

61. E. E. Rich, *The History of the HBC Vol. II,* 482.

62. Appendix No. 8 George Gladman, Chief Trader, Report from the Select Committee on the Hudson's Bay Company ... 1857, 393.

63. G. Simpson to A. Colvile 16 Aug. 1822 in *Fur Trade and Empire: George Simpson's Journal,* edited by F. Merk (Cambridge, 1931), 186.

64. *Journal of Occurrences in the Athabasca Department by George Simpson, 1820 and 1821, and Report,* edited by E. E. Rich (Toronto, 1938), 2.

65. Numerous examples of labourers hired at between £6 and £10 are contained in *Andrew Graham's Observations on Hudson's Bay 1767-91,* 247; Journal of William Tomison 1795-96 in *Saskatchewan Journals and Correspondence 1795-1802,* 34-35, 42, 167; E. E. Rich, *The History of the HBC, Vol. II,* 268; E. E. Rich, ed., *Cumberland House Journals and Inland Journal 1775-82* (London, 1951), 19.

66. HBCA. A. 30/7, fos. 27, 8/; A. 32/8, fo. 49 Journal of George Sutherland, 71.

67. Morton MSS C505/1/2.2 Selkirk Papers. (16746-16818). Miles Macdonell's Journal Sept. 6, 1812 to April 22, 1813, 255.

68. Minutes of the Council Northern Dept. 29 June 1831, 677-678.

69. Minutes of the Council of the Northern Dept. of Rupert's Land, 1830 to 1843, 790.

70. John Nicks, "Orkneymen in the HBC ...," 119.

71. Minutes of the Council Northern Dept. 3 July 1830, 660-661.

72. P. Mantoux, *The Industrial Revolution in the Eighteenth Century* (London, 1970), 74.

73. E. P. Thompson, "Eighteenth-century English Society: Class Struggle without Class?" *Social History, 3,* 2, (May, 1978), 149.

74. *Ibid.*

75. Ron Bourgeault, "Metis History," *New Breed, 13,* 8, (Sept., 1982), 4. Also see L. Bergeron, *The History of Quebec: A Patriote's Handbook* (Toronto, 1971), 12-38 for an interesting discussion of the chain of exploitation in the fur trade and the pyramid class structures in Canadian society during this period. And John Lambert defines the different classes of society in *Travels through Lower Canada, and the United States of North America in the Years 1806, 1807 and 1808* Vol. I (London, 1810), 277-278.

76. Jack Scott, *Sweat and Struggle: Working Class Struggles in Canada. Vol. I: 1789-1899* (Vancouver, 1974), 18.

77. For an excellent account of the European example see E. P. Thompson, *The Making of the English Working Class* (New York, 1968); John Rule, *The Labouring Classes in Early Industrial England 1750-1850* (London, 1986) and George Rude, *The Crowd in History, 1730-1848* (New York, 1964).

78. G. Williams, ed., *Andrew Graham's Observations on Hudson's Bay 1767-91* (London, 1969), 306.

79. *Journals of Samuel Hearne and Philip Turnor,* 136-137.

80. W. Tomison to J. Colen, 10 July 1798 in *Saskatchewan Journals and Correspondence 1795-1802,* 177.

81. Morton MSS C505/1/2.2 Selkirk Papers. Miles Macdonell's Journal Sept. 14, 1812, p. 253 and Nov. 6, 1812, p. 271.

82. *Ibid.,* Dec. 11-13, 1812, 280.

83. *Ibid.,* Jan. 16, 1813, 287-288.

84. *Ibid.,* Feb. 1, 1813, 291.

85. Morton MSS C505/1/2.3 Selkirk Papers. Pp. 16819-16957. Miles Macdonell's Journal April 22, 1813 to Feb. 11, 1815, pp. 73-75.

86. *Ibid.,* June 8-10, 1914, 86-87.

87. G. P. de T. Glazebrook, ed., *The Hargrave Correspondence 1821-1843* (Toronto, 1938), 241-242.

88. *Andrew Graham's Observations on Hudson's Bay 1767-91,* 306.

89. For an account of the strike see B. Willson, *The Great Company,* 295-297.

90. Adam Smith notes that even though there were laws prohibiting the formation of trade unions, workers still combined to either increase wages or prevent a reduction, *The Wealth of Nations,* 66-67. And Marx and Engels wrote that "the

collisions between individual workmen and individual bourgeois take more and more the character of collisions between two classes. Thereupon the workers begin to form combinations ... in order to keep up the rate of wages ...," *The Manifesto of the Communist Party* (Moscow, 1975), 55.

91. HBCA. A. 11/116, fo. 22, H. Marten to the Governor and Committee, Aug. 25, 1777 in *Cumberland House Journals and Inland Journal 1775-82,* edited by E. E. Rich (London, 1951), 142-143.

92. For an account of these disputes see C. Lipton, *The Trade Union Movement of Canada 1827-1959* (Montreal, 1966), 1; H. A. Innis, *The Fur Trade in Canada,* 241-242; A. S. Morton, *A. History of the Canadian West,* 348-350; and E. Coues, *New Light on the Early History of the Greater Northwest* (New York, 1897), 860-861.

93. Journal of James Bird in *Saskatchewan Journals and Correspondence 1795-1802,* 196-197.

94. *Ibid.,* 199.

95. NAC, *Report on Canadian Archives 1886,* M. Macdonell to William H. Cook, 14 Feb. 1812, ccvi.

96. *Ibid.,* M. Macdonell and William Hillier to William Auld, 15 May 1812, ccxiii.

97. E. P. Thompson, "Eighteenth-century English Society: Class Struggle without Class?", 137.

CHAPTER
10 THE REBELLIONS OF 1837-1838 IN LOWER CANADA

The questions raised by the rebellions of 1837-1838 in Lower Canada are many and varied. Were they isolated British North American events, or part of a larger, trans-Atlantic revolutionary phenomenon? If the former, were they the consequence of long-term, structural problems, or merely responses to immediate, localized difficulties? Were they fundamentally political, economic, social, or nationalist in nature, or some combination of the four? Were they initiated by an elitist few, or did they have a much broader base of support within the Lower Canadian population? What were their short- and long-term results?

The answers given to these questions have been equally varied. The classic and long-influential interpretation was that of Donald Creighton, the acknowledged English-Canadian authority on the nineteenth-century Empire of the St. Lawrence. Creighton believed that the rebellions arose mainly from economic conflict between the French agrarian and the English mercantile interests in Lower Canada. For Stanley Ryerson, one of the first Marxist historians of Canada, the events of 1837-1838 marked the failure of a French-Canadian "national-democratic revolution," a view that has been influential among modern New Left Québécois historians as well. Helen Taft Manning interpreted the matter differently again, as she stressed the political and constitutional framework of the revolt.

Other historians have tended to address these questions more within a social context. One of the most prolific and important is Fernand Ouellet. In "The 1837/38 Rebellions in Lower Canada as a Social Phenomenon," Ouellet argues that there were two reformist streams flowing in early nineteenth-century Lower Canada. One, popularly-based and popularly-led, arose from widespread discontent with the old social and economic order in the colony. The other, a product of the new, professional middle class, sought more to acquire economic, political and social power than to effect radical reform. The two were briefly allied in 1837-1838, but, according to Ouellet, to the ultimate detriment of the popular movement.

The second article reprinted here, "For Whom the Bell Tolls" by Susan Trofimenkoff, takes a broader approach to the rebellions. In her view, the key questions about the events of 1837-1838 can only be answered by reference to the interplay of a variety of factors — economic, social, political and nationalist — and a wide range of individuals and circumstances. Students should assess the extent to which Trofimenkoff is indebted to historians like Ouellet, and the ways in which her approach is unique.

Suggestions for Further Reading

Bergeron, L., *The History of Quebec: A Patriot's Handbook*. Toronto: NC Press, 1971.

Creighton, D.G., "The Economic Background of the Rebellions of Eighteen Thirty-Seven," *Canadian Journal of Economics and Political Science*, III, no. 3 (August 1937), 322-334.

Manning, H.T., *The Revolt of French Canada, 1800-1835*. Toronto: Macmillan of Canada, 1962.

Ouellet, F., *Louis Joseph Papineau: A Divided Soul*. Ottawa: The Canadian Historical Association, 1964.

————, *Lower Canada, 1792-1841*. Toronto: McClelland & Stewart, 1980.

Parker, W.H., "A New Look at Unrest in Lower Canada in the 1830's," *Canadian Historical Review*, XL, no. 3 (September 1959), 209-217.

Ryerson, S., *Unequal Union: Confederation and the Roots of Crises in the Canadas, 1815-1837*. Toronto: Progress Books, 1968.

THE 1837/8 REBELLIONS IN LOWER CANADA AS A SOCIAL PHENOMENON

Fernand Ouellet

For a long time historians focused mainly on the political aspect of the rebellions of 1837-8 in Lower Canada. That is why, despite their pathetic failure, the rebellions were seen to have their ultimate justification in the triumph of great constitutional principles that were considered eminently valuable in them-

Appeared originally as "Les insurrections de 1837-38: un phénomène social" in *Histoire sociale / Social History,* no. 2 (1968). English translation used by permission of Oxford University Press Canada and *Histoire sociale / Social History.*

selves, such as responsible government, or were regarded as essential to the survival of the French-Canadian nationality.[1] Once again the world of values had scored a striking victory over petty economic and class interests. Thus, after warning us that the movement of 1837-8 could not be reduced "to a racial or even a class struggle without diminishing and falsifying history", Canon Groulx came to the emphatic conclusion that it was "an episode in a political struggle for a political end".[2] It is true that, from his point of view, the men of 1837 had committed deplorable errors: they had come to terms with "shallow democratic ideologies"; they had surrendered to anticlericalism to the point of grave disobedience to the Church. There was much to forgive Papineau in particular. But, Canon Groulx asked, had Papineau not embodied "the aspirations of a nationality"[3] at a highly critical moment of our national history? "His glory", he added, "will be recognized by more and more of us as the feeling for political independence gains ground."[4]

This version of history, in which the political background dominates the rest, seems to me far too limited. Certainly politics has its own existence, its own standards and procedures; but it is also a setting for the fermentation and confrontation of economic interests.[5] It is no less crucial for the understanding of the phenomena we call politics to discern the manifold links between politics and society. Can political strategies be readily separated from social strategies? Behind groups and parties we usually find social groups and classes rather than isolated individuals. It could even be argued that a lengthy political crisis is one of the surest signs of fundamental social change, or of a transfer of economic and social power from one group to another, whether it be an ethnic group, a social class, or a combination of both. A resort to arms by certain elements in society would then constitute an admission, explicit or implicit, of the failure of normal political strategies. At the risk of diminishing the story of the rebellions in Lower Canada, and tarnishing some of its lustre, but in the certainty of encountering the real problems of real people, I intend to show these revolutionary events in a social light—the only light that, broadly understood, can give us an inkling of the reality of those troubled times. This perspective raises two sets of questions. To what extent, and why, did ordinary people take an active part in the movement? What role did the "élites" play and what were their relations with the common people, urban and rural? All this obviously raises the central question of what the revolutionary ideology was, and involves a close look at class consciousness.

1. A Popular Movement

In his book on the popular uprisings in France in the seventeenth century, Boris Porchnev throws light on a series of spontaneous mass insurrections, spread by contagion and the establishment of popular leadership. To this description Porchnev adds an observation directly relevant to my purpose:

As long as it kept its exclusively popular character, the movement suffered from bad organization and remained blindly impulsive. When its leadership was entrusted to representatives of another social class, they distorted the movement and its essential aims.... They contributed to its social blindness: by confining the platform of the uprising to a fight against taxation, they prevented it from developing into a revolutionary anti-feudal, anti-absolutist movement.[6]

Reading Canon Groulx might tempt us to draw a comparison between the Lower Canadian movement and its seventeenth-century French counterpart. The former is described by Groulx as "an improvised movement, almost spontaneous in its outbreaks of violence; beyond that, a popular movement, a fairly broad and deep rural phenomenon".[7] Unfortunately, Groulx's reliance on the somewhat inconsistent statements made by Papineau after his defeat seems to have misled him about the social origin of the revolutionary movement. By denying any premeditation on the part of the revolutionary leaders, Papineau absolved them—and especially himself—of all responsibility, and incriminated the government against which popular anger was directed. Fair enough, perhaps; but I remain very skeptical. As Wolfred Nelson said, commenting on certain admissions of Papineau's:

> You have to fight liars, whether with their own weapons or with trickery. Frankness is a fine thing among honest men and in private life; in public, it leaves us too exposed. I am annoyed by Mr Papineau's and Mackenzie's admission that we had decided to rebel. That is to justify our opponents and to deprive us of any right to complain that we were attacked.[8]

In fact, the risings of 1837-8, just like the nationalism from which they sprang, started among the upper classes and spread downwards from them. Here is the first variation from the process outlined by Porchnev.

Since 1830 the idea of revolution had gained ground among a section of the militant Patriotes. Some leaders spoke of it as a possibility; others thought it inevitable. However, there was no systematic effort to create a revolutionary organization. It was after the Russell Resolutions in the spring of 1837, which deprived the Patriotes of all hope of success by peaceful means, that the leaders of the party felt bound to change their strategy and consider revolutionary action. It was the leaders of the Montréal region, recruited from the professional class and the merchants, who took on the task of redirecting the Patriote movement. Even though they were careful to destroy the compromising documents—Papineau admitted this himself—there is a mass of corroborative evidence showing precisely what the main lines of the revolutionary strategy were. It consisted of two stages: the first, the so-called "legal" agitation, was aimed chiefly at forcing the government to modify its position; the second involved (in the event that the first one failed) launching a revolution "after freeze-up".[9] This was a compromise between the moderate and extremist elements of the party, the latter leaning more to immediate action. Besides, how was it possible to intimidate the government without preparing the populace for a possible rebellion? The radical leaders never bothered to make this distinction. From the spring of 1837 they were openly preaching revolt. In June, Léon Charlebois, a Montréal tavern-keeper, declared "that it was necessary to help the revolutionary party that was then in existence".[10] At Chambly the Pacauds, who were shipowners, said they "would be happy if the Patriotes could succeed in their plan for independence from the British government".[11] Papineau himself did not escape the revolutionary atmosphere, which was spreading rapidly. At several meetings he even went so far as to make seditious remarks, though without refraining from ambiguity. Thus, when he warned the farmers that when the plums were ripe it was time to pick them, he was using language that was perfectly clear to them. Several witnesses testified that on the sixth of August, at a meeting at Saint-Constant, Côme Cherrier and Toussaint Peltier, two Montréal lawyers from the more moderate side of the revolutionary camp, were to make speeches "tending to incite the local people to rebel if the English government failed to grant them what they had demanded in the Ninety-two Resolutions".[12] These are just a few examples from a mass of evidence indicating that "legal" opposition was more a front than a practical objective: it was a screen behind which an armed uprising could be organized—because it was illusory to think the government would yield to blackmail. If there is no doubt about the premeditation, it is also clear that the movement was not of popular origin. It germinated within the top leadership of the *parti patriote*.

The revolutionary organization, whose centre was Montréal and whose principal body was the Permanent Central Committee, relied for its support not only on the suburbs but mainly on the country districts. Members of the local élites—those who had lined up with the *parti patriote*—formed the local leadership of the movement. It was they who planned the country meetings where the "big men from the city" appeared, held small parish meetings on Sundays after Mass, and in some cases took up collections. Not only was there large attendance at these meetings, but in some places groups of armed farmers gathered to attack local inhabitants of British origin and "known bureaucrats".[13] The response of the rural populace was immediate, all the more since the rebellion was the climax of over thirty years of political conflict. Throughout the summer of 1837 tension and agitation increased in the country parishes surrounding Montréal. In October Montréal acquired its own revolutionary association aimed at reorganizing the populace. The *Fils de la liberté,* with its military and civil sections (the latter a screen for the former), held meetings at which some leaders gave commentaries on books about the French and American revolutions. Thomas Storrow Brown went so far as to declare that it was time "to arm ourselves, since the country was moving quickly along the road to independence".[14] The *Fils de la liberté,* sometimes numbering as many as a thousand, did not hesitate to hold military exercises. For this purpose they used one of the properties, in a suburb of Montréal, of Denis-Benjamin Viger, a cousin of Papineau. This outbreak of agitation, both rural and urban, came to a head at the Six Counties rally, held at Saint-Charles on 23 October— a massive demonstration that marked a real turning point. As Nelson and Côté put it, the time for speeches was over. Papineau arrived at Saint-Charles with an armed escort of some fifteen men, though he later claimed "to have come to this meeting only because he happened to be passing".[15]

At the Saint-Charles rally the Patriote leaders went beyond mere violent words. They issued a declaration of the rights of man, modelled on the American declaration of 1776, and decided to get rid of all the militia officers, justices of the peace, and small-claims commissioners appointed by the government. All these officials, they declared, must be replaced by men elected by the people. This revolutionary action, openly supported by Papineau, meant the overthrow of all opponents of the movement. The Patriotes were trying to gain control of the militia and the judiciary. It was on this occasion, too, that plans for an open rebellion were again laid out by the leaders. A date was set for the beginning of December. The day after the meeting Dr Kimber, one of the leaders, would say:

> The moment the river is frozen up, we shall go with forty or fifty thousand armed men to seize Montréal; the local people are all well armed, well supplied with ammunition, and firmly resolved, and after Montréal we shall take Québec. I was at Saint-Charles and never in any country has there been seen such a rally, so determined to rid itself of the English government.[16]

Even though Kimber could have been tipsy when he made this revelation, his statement nevertheless contained a basis of truth. A letter from Papineau to Mackenzie in February 1838 confirms this:

> If navigation had been closed down as usual about 20 November, if the election of the magistrates had taken place without violence, and only in December, as had been recommended, so that communication would be cut off between the north and south shores of the St Lawrence, the chances of success would have been better.[17]

On 23 October 1837, the day of the Saint-Charles rally, a Pointe-Claire farmer said "that the damned *chouaguins* [cabbage-heads, or *Canadiens* who had sold out to the English] were going to be whipped now that everybody in the south and the north was armed, that there was no more law ... and you could do what you liked ... Mr Papineau knew that he had to start the revolution at this time, when no help could come from England."[18] It is not surprising that acts of violence increased after the Saint-Charles rally. In most parishes Patriotes held "charivaris", demanding the dismissal of militia officers and other government officials. Verbal violence reached something of a peak. A Henryville merchant, Joseph Gariépy, declared that he "wouldn't rest until all the bureaucrats' heads were cut off".[19] On 4 November 1837 Jacques Surprenant, innkeeper at Blairfindie, shouted at an opponent that he "had a good mind to smash him over the head with a bottle because he, the deponent, was a bureaucrat and all bureaucrats had better get out of the country before their brains were blown out, and the said Surprenant said that he would do his utmost to help chop him into pieces."[20]

At the beginning of November 1837 neither the government, nor members of the clergy who felt a need for strong intervention, could remain passive. Warrants were prepared for the arrest of the principal Patriote leaders. Informed by D.-B. Viger that he was in imminent danger of imprisonment, Papineau had some tense and anxious hours before he finally decided to flee Montréal. A witness to the conversation from the next room, Angélique Labadie, would later report:

> I also heard Mr Papineau say that he would never be satisfied until he was president in this country, and that he would be soon, and that if the government seized this country from him he would snatch it back. Mr Viger then told Mr Papineau that he should keep calm and wait for freeze-up and then he would just have to whistle and all the *habitants* and thousands of Americans would espouse their cause and they would soon be masters of this country.[21]

This first act of the government—the preparation of the warrants—had a magical effect. It prompted the hasty departure of the chief Montréal leaders, who took refuge in the countryside, where they prepared themselves for any emergency. Deprived of its leaders, the urban populace made no move. At Vaudreuil the situation bordered on comedy. The local leaders, fearing imprisonment, begged the people to protect them, on the grounds that they had incited them to revolt from altruistic motives.[22] Camps were formed at Saint-Denis, Saint-Charles, Saint-Mathias, Saint-Eustache, and Saint-Benoît. Intervention by government troops was then unavoidable, and between 17 November and 15 December 1837 military confrontation occurred. In short the government, sensing that matters were coming to a head, forestalled the Patriotes. Apart from this early intervention by government forces, the second rebellion, which took place during the first two weeks of November 1838, was an exact replica of the preceding one. Devised by the élite, especially refugees in the United States, it would spread to the masses through the intervention of the *Société des Frères Chasseurs,* said to have ten thousand members. Once again, lack of leadership on the spot prevented the fourteen hundred *chasseurs* in Montréal from stirring. In Québec City, where the association was supposed to have two thousand adherents, "they are more cautious than in Montréal,"[23] according to an informed witness. On the whole, the two rebellions leave an identical impression: anarchy, disorganization, weak leadership, and paralysis. Are these not the characteristics of purely peasant uprisings, at least as Porchnev understands them? In this regard, he writes:

> These outside elements in the masses certainly left their stamp on the Nu-Pied movement.... There is no doubt that these elements helped the insurgents to or-

ganize, to follow a more or less systematic policy, to become a large armed force—in a word, to overcome the movement's purely impulsive and spontaneous character.[24]

This outline is interesting, but to what extent does it apply to the Lower Canadian movements? Several hypotheses are possible: superficiality of popular support, a marked persistence of the peasant mentality among the élite, or—what is simpler—betrayal by the élite.

Though fomented by the élite, these uprisings nevertheless had a broadly popular character. The rural and urban masses, which provided ninety-five per cent of the actual revolutionaries, made up the movement's striking force. The excuse so often put forward by the *habitants* and many others, that they gave in to the threats of the leaders, must be largely rejected. In my view fear is an extremely far-reaching and subtle phenomenon but it does not by itself account for participation by the lower classes in revolutionary events. Because its range is more general and more varied, the phenomenon of fear is also more complex in its ramifications. On the other hand, different excuses given by the common people merit even less attention: for example, it is easy to assess the origin of one farmer's tale, when arrested on the road early in the morning, that he was on his way to ask his mother (who lived in the home of a top rebel leader) to knit him a tuque; or that of another farmer, arrested after the battle of Saint-Eustache, who said he was about to drive his wife to confession. Where political vows are concerned, it is so often a matter of "swearing with the mouth, not with the heart" that we can delude ourselves about them.

After analysing the files on the rebels of 1837-8, I find it impossible not to perceive a genuine popular phenomenon, widespread and deep-rooted, prompted in large measure by specific, and different, motives than those of the élites who controlled the movement. I reckon that, not counting the sympathizers in Montréal, at least five thousand people were directly involved in the first venture. The following year the number exceeded five thousand, but the incidents took place in a much more limited area. In 1838 the populous parishes north of Montréal made no move. Glancing at the other regions in the province, we find an air of expectation among the people in the Beauce, and in Kamouraska and Charlevoix. Inquiries made at Saint-Joseph de la Beauce in the spring of 1838, after the failure of the first rebellion, revealed that 260 inhabitants were still in favour of the Patriotes. Even if we allow for regional variations that could have a negative effect on popular attitudes, we still find a psychological receptiveness throughout seigneurial Lower Canada. In short, the motives that spurred farmers, craftsmen, and labourers in the Montréal region to revolutionary action operated elsewhere in varying degrees. The myth of the saviour was too widespread for the popular response not to have had firm roots—both at the time and in the past.

This popular movement, moreover, was almost exclusively French-Canadian. It did win over a small minority of Irish, whose motives are readily discernible.

J. Coward, a Montréal merchant, declared: "I am a rebel and I would be one as long as there would be a Scotch rascal in this town."[25] The movement also gained some adherents among farmers of American origin who had settled in the Eastern Townships—a small minority already receptive to democratic ideas. But on the whole the revolutionary phenomenon had its principal support in French-Canadian society. However, it would be a mistake, out of a rigid idea of ethnic character or a concept of "ethnic class", to see it as a revolt of the whole of French-Canadian society. At the popular level, wealth—which is not the privilege of the many—created a very important split. The "bureaucrats" seem to have been drawn mainly from the comfortably-off or wealthy farmers—those who were "fat", as the Patriotes said—while the Patriotes emerged from the most disadvantaged classes. Another observation on the scope of the movement: the distinction between farmer, craftsman, and labourer is not much use in assessing revolutionary fervour. They were attracted equally to the movement, which also appealed as much to the young as it did to older people—meaning that in rural environments economic motivations were the most decisive. Problems like the agricultural crisis and the shortage of land in the seigneuries affected all groups, but especially older people and those with large families. Setting up their children on the land was the central preoccupation for fathers, whether they were farmers, craftsmen, or labourers. The uprisings of 1837-8, then, appear to have been linked to the poverty and insecurity of the working classes, both rural and urban. In the city of Montréal fluctuations in employment were certainly a factor, but let me point out that above all the *parti patriote* brought together those who were most dependent on the land.

Another sign of a movement with a strong popular base is the ability of the rural popular classes to produce their own leadership. Such leaders were innumerable, perhaps too numerous and too unstable for the good of the revolution. I have turned up the names of 721 rural people who in various ways acted as leaders in 1837-8. It must be noted that farmers and craftsmen gained positions of leadership more readily than labourers, who made up at least thirty per cent of the rural population but provided only four per cent of the leaders. Another striking fact to note is that this popular leadership was drawn not from the young but from their elders. Of the 215 leaders whose ages I have ascertained, seventy-six per cent were over thirty and fifty-five per cent were between thirty and fifty. Between the ages of forty and sixty the proportion was forty-six per cent. Only innkeepers—who often came from peasant backgrounds—were older; half of them were between forty and sixty. Finally, fifty-one per cent of the popular leaders had more than five children.

Furthermore, these working-class leaders were far from being nonentities in the movement. A fair number had already held positions in the militia; some had even been members of the Assembly. Louis Dérigé, a Saint-Constant farmer known as Laplante, was described as "dangerous to the British government, since in his capacity as head churchwarden, and by his influence generally, he exerts almost absolute authority over the local people."[26] There was another group, at least as large, who saw a golden opportunity to reach the rank of "great man". The situation lent itself so well to overnight promotions that some of them certainly aspired to be generals. On the whole, however, their promotions stopped at the rank of captain, a level at which they proliferated, showing off with their swords. But there were some exceptions: a few were appointed— or appointed themselves—"Major" or "Colonel", such as Joson Dumouchelle of Beauharnois. The most famous and least authentic was undoubtedly Amury Girod, an immigrant from Switzerland, a well-educated man who called himself with pride "cultivateur de Varennes"; at Sainte-Eustache he had no trouble in securing for himself the coveted title of "General". By dint of their numbers and the noise they made, and in the absence of any vigorous leadership from above, these popular leaders pervaded the movement. Another major point is that, because they were more garrulous than other country people, and probably more aware, we look to them to express the motivations, and perhaps the ideological leanings, of the masses. For we cannot accept the assumption that the masses naturally exuded class consciousness and an ideology of their own. This also needs to be explored.

The sources of rural discontent were various and of long standing. Since the beginning of the nineteenth century resentment among peasants had steadily increased. Economic troubles, especially the chronic crisis in agriculture, over-population—always more pronounced in the seigneurial lands—and increased taxation by landowners were chief causes of unrest.[27] The shortage of land as much as rural debt created deep insecurity and provoked a reaction against all forms of taxation, even the slightest, whether they were tithes, seigneurial dues, or state taxes. In 1837 the situation was aggravated by a general economic crisis. Social conflicts within the élites had helped to discredit the Establishment, especially the old seigneurial families, and even the clergy. Dissension among the clergy, notably the almost public quarrel about the creation of the bishopric of Montréal, had had an effect on the people. Finally, the clergy, because of their ideology and their attitudes to social and political reform, were out of tune with the aspirations and some of the problems of the popular classes. In some ways the clergy were remote from the people.

Under the circumstances it would have been possible to see a growing popular movement against the old social and economic regime—the seigneurial regime and the privileges of the Church. There was in fact a group within the Patriote élite that wanted to aim the blow in that direction. Dr Côté, one of the most active leaders at Napierville, had no hesitation in telling the farmers "that they would be independent and free and pay no more revenues to the seigneurs or tithes to the priests".[28] The Nelson brothers, Girod, and probably Chénier, belonged to this group of radicals, or rather true liberals. It is important to note that wherever this message was preached it found an echo in a section of the populace. Joseph Dumouchelle, a farmer from Sainte-Marie de Beauharnois, who had taken for himself the title of colonel, fought "to abolish tithes and feudal dues".[29] Not only had the farmers—somewhat guiltily—overcome clerical prohibitions and accepted the view that the clergy, through their interests, were tied to the power structure; but a fair number of them seemed inclined to take it out on the priests, whom they sometimes called "black pigs".[30] Jérôme Lompré, farmer, aged forty-four, with nine children, recruiting for the Saint-Eustache encampment, said to another farmer: "Come with us; you're well armed and it's fun; it's like a wedding; we drink, we eat, we play the violin, we dance; we are free, we do what we like. Those who need leather can have it, and make themselves shoes.... It's our right, we don't give a damn for the king, the queen, or the priests."[31] This quotation reveals some of the longings unleashed by hard times and the influence of liberal ideology. Hasty generalizations, however, should be avoided. It is true that the movement of 1837-8 had some of the marks of an "anti-feudal", perhaps a democratic, struggle. All in all the rural people would have emerged with a consciousness of themselves as a class, thanks to the preachings of a small bourgeois élite, and stood up against their lifelong enemies: the monarchy, the seigneurial class, and the clergy. In short, 1837-8 would appear as an abortive attempt to achieve the democratic, bourgeois revolution so dear to the hearts of some Marxist historians. Actually, such anti-feudal and anticlerical tendencies as existed at the time were characteristic only of peasant or middle-class minorities.

In 1837 it was too late to channel popular aggressiveness into a genuinely liberal and democratic ideology. For a long time the dominant influences among the Patriotes had successfully found other outlets for popular discontent. Is this not rather a case of ideological plundering by élites concerned to use the strength of the masses for their own advantage? It would be more accurate to call it manipulation of the people by certain élites. In my opinion, between 1802 and 1838 there was no drawn-out process that could be called an affirmation of class consciousness among the French-Canadian peasants. There was, however, the arrival and the aggravation of a series of vital problems confronting the farmers—who, lacking class consciousness and sufficient political maturity, relied on the élite classes, old or new, for their ideological orientation and their political choices. It was this reliance and their psychological reactions to it that made possible the manipulation of the masses by the élite.

In actual fact the rural masses absorbed an ideology—nationalism—that had been suggested to them by the most influential elements of the *parti patriote,* by people who, though claiming to be democrats, regarded the seigneurial system and the Church as national institutions. Papineau, who would eventually break with the radicals on these issues, was their real leader. They were the ones who sought to uphold traditional economic relationships in opposition to the capitalist class. These élites had taught the common people to recognize their enemies: the government (both colonial and imperial), the capitalist, the emi-grant—in a word, the *Anglais,* who, they said, were responsible for all the ills suffered by the "poor Canadiens". Therefore the government had to be over-thrown and the *Anglais* driven out or killed. "For a long time", declared Marcel Séné, a Saint-Césaire farmer, "our country newspapers urged us to distrust and despise the government. Prominent people in the parish said the same thing, so we believed it."[32] To farmers who were in debt and looking for land to settle their sons on, J.-F. Têtu, a Saint-Hyacinthe notary, said "that before long they were going to be chased off their property by emigrants [i.e., immigrants], who would treat them like slaves and drive them out into barren country, and that poverty would hound them into the grave with no hope of protection from this government, which was set on ruining these farmers."[33] The rural people seem to have been especially sensitive to this land issue, which would be re-solved, the leaders proclaimed, by extending the seigneurial system to the whole province and by confiscating the property of the English and the French-Canadian traitors—those who, as they liked to say, had "betrayed the sacred blood".[34] Meunier, the notary at Saint-Damas, promised for his part that "those who helped the friends of the region would be rewarded with the bureaucrats' property and township lands, where every house must be pulled down or burned."[35] This central problem of land gives the best clue to the infiltration of nationalism into the rural classes. Moreover, it was not a recent phenomenon—it dated from the first decade of the century. Concerning this, William Brewster related a conversation with Christophe Laplanche, a Lacolle farmer: "He told me that the English had no right to be here and that the country belonged to the French Canadians and that there were enough of them to occupy it ... that the country was theirs and that they wanted all the land for themselves."[36] The attacks against, and looting of, English merchants (some of whom were seigneurs) and *chouaguins* need to be seen in this context. The farmers took advantage of these raids to destroy the account-books of these men, who were their principal creditors, for fear they would seize their lands. In November 1836 L. Lavoie, a Saint-Philippe farmer, seems to have accurately interpreted the intentions of many French-Canadian rural people: "If they had succeeded in seizing Laprairie, they wouldn't have left a single English, Irish, or Scotch in-habitant alive—of any age or sex."[37] This verbal violence, which is stressed in a great deal of the testimony, is certainly not without significance. The same is true of certain attacks on Protestants, who were ordered to convert or leave the country: "we only want one religion here."[38] The majority of rural people had no desire to see the establishment of a pluralistic society based on religious toleration, and acted on defensive instincts, notably the idea that the government "wanted to change not only their customs but also their religion".[39] It would be a mistake to think that there was a popular movement of religious disaf-fection. Even though the farmer had doubts about the conduct of the clergy and was reluctant to accept them as political leaders, he remained deeply attached to religion. In this period of anarchy and assorted temptations, his feelings are hard to gauge. But there is no justification for regarding this confusion as the sign of a rift.

Nor does it appear that the rural people were moved by democratic ideology. Once independence had been acquired, they would no doubt have favoured an authoritarian type of republic. However, several depositions indicate that the concept of a "national monarchy", with Papineau on the throne, was closer to their way of thinking. On that score J. Parmentier, a Nicolet shoemaker, declared: "That he would be happy to see the crown on Mr Papineau's head, and that if he didn't behave himself as king, the Patriotes would appoint another one. That it was necessary to become independent like the American government."[40] And this attitude, reflecting an evolution of monarchist sentiment (from monarchy by divine right to national monarchy), was not confined to the farmers. Louis Chaurette, a Sainte-Scholastique innkeeper, clearly expressed the kind of expectation that existed among the people after the defeat of the first uprising: "that Papineau was no longer Papineau but was being called king and that the quarrel was going to be between two kings, that he was coming with America and Germany to fight the English ... that Papineau was coming with fifty thousand men and fifty cannons, several of which had a range of seven leagues."[41] J. Aubin of Sainte-Thérèse conveyed the people's hopes in the same terms: "that we would be much better off under Mr Papineau's government, that he was expected at Montréal any evening now with fifty thousand men, twenty brass cannons, and lots of others, that he was marching at the head of his army."[42]

These uprisings, then, had quite firm roots in the masses. It was not for lack of sufficient motivation among the common people, nor for scarcity of weapons, that they failed.[43] And the clergy's attitude, although it was important, was not a crucial aspect of the successive defeats. The problem lay initially in the quality of the leadership provided by the members of the élite who supervised the insurrectionary movement.

2. The Élites

Who were these revolutionaries that came from the élites? From the beginning of the nineteenth century Lower Canada had undergone an economic and social transformation. The rise of the middle class had challenged the dominance of the old seigneurial families and the clergy. The tensions arising from this situation issued in a struggle for leadership. The old families, no longer representing an important element in the balance of power, were quickly ruled out. All they could do was support the more powerful groups—occasionally wavering between one dominant group and another. At the time of the rebellion their behaviour was very similar to the clergy's. The "nobility" feared the abolition of the seigneurial regime, and saw nothing in the Patriote movement but a liberal and democratic menace. Pierre de Boucherville expressed very well the reactions of this decadent class to the perils of revolution: "The de Boucherville family", he wrote haughtily,

> "has never lacked honour. If a Seigneur de Boucherville et de Verchères joined a rebellion, he would risk losing the heritage that comes to him from his fathers.... If the rebellion had succeeded, he would have lost an income of four or five hundred louis a year."[44]

Aristocratic pride was still there, but dignity was gone.

The clergy, on the other hand, remained in the forefront. Having a strong economic base, able to rely on a powerful institutional network, and retaining in spite of everything considerable moral prestige, they could count on political power as well because of their connections with the State. The fact remains that the changes taking shape in society emphasized the archaic nature of their thinking and their social attitudes, and called for recasting their ideology. The status and power of the clergy were now open to challenge. Despite the efforts of Monseigneur Lartigue to reform clerical ideology and strategy under the inspiration of Ultramontanism and (up to a point) Social Catholicism, the fate of the clergy as a dominant group hung in the balance throughout the pre-rebellion period. By that I mean that the process of clericalizing society initiated by Lartigue could have failed. The explanation for the clergy's antagonistic attitude in 1837-8 lies not only in a system of beliefs and behaviour that can be called traditional, but also in the fact that the priests felt threatened by the rise of the middle classes and their ideological leanings. In this sense the clergy were defending a specific social order that was set out completely in Lartigue's *mandements* of 1837 and 1838—and in the anonymous "Defence" of the first one, which he himself wrote. There were exceptions, of course: a few parish priests sympathized more or less openly with the Patriotes. Father Mercure, for instance, sided with them for moral reasons that had nothing directly to do with the movement. On 21 November 1837 he said from the pulpit: "My children, I am now a Patriote like the rest of you; yesterday or the day before I went and signed up." The effect of this avowal on the congregation was to convince them of the need to resist constituted authority.[45] But only Abbé Chartier was thoroughly committed to the movement—which didn't prevent him from running away at the critical moment.

It must be said that on the whole religious wrath was aimed at the Patriotes. The sermons of the parish priests provoked violent verbal reactions from the most confirmed militants. F.-X. Renaud reported that Édouard Moreau, a Saint-Jérôme farmer, told him at the beginning of November 1837 "that he was on the rebel Council, that he sang a revolutionary song ... and that he said the crudest things about our Sovereign Lady the Queen ... that if he could have found four men like himself he would have pulled Father Poirier, priest of Sainte-Anne, out of the pulpit when he preached a sermon against the revolution at Mass, and that he considered him a cur."[46] The strangest case is that of Father Ricard, a loyalist, who declared from the pulpit "that he had a vision telling us that in 1840"[47] the *Canadiens* would be wading ankle-deep in their enemies' blood.

As for the business class, mainly English-speaking, it drew its social prestige from its economic strength. As the principal agent of economic and social change and institutional reform, the bourgeoisie also laid claim to some control over the political structures. At the political level its leanings were conservative, because its economic future depended on the survival of certain ties between the mother country and the colonies. Like the civil servants, this English-speaking business middle class felt threatened by the assertion of French-Canadian professional classes. It was convinced that it would be ruined in an independent Lower Canada that was tied more closely than ever to subsistence farming, that had no commercial contacts, and was even more attached to the seigneury and the *Coutume de Paris*. The important businessmen were violently opposed to the Patriotes. They preferred Queen Victoria, they said, to Louis-Joseph I.

In actual fact the revolutionary phenomenon was initially an expression of the rise of the French-Canadian middle class and its need for self-assertion. Since the end of the eighteenth century the number of French Canadians active in the liberal professions and small business had been growing extremely quickly in an ever more difficult economic context. Within these groups, overcrowding soon became the rule. Even though a fair number of professionals and small businessmen came from old families fallen on hard times, or were the sons of professionals, the majority had emerged from the lower class.

When all's said and done this rise of the middle class occurred more often than not in a context of poverty, insecurity, and the necessity of really adapting to new kinds of work. These uncertainties were reflected in the numerous contradictions that shaped their aspirations. Very probably they hoped to take the place of the old seigneurial families. If so, Papineau's manor-house at Montebello (the seigneury of *Petite Nation*) would be a good symbol of these vain endeavours. Yet the ambitions of these new social groups were not matched by their economic status or by society's opinion of their professional usefulness. Having a very exalted opinion of their own importance, these newcomers very soon aspired to the leadership of society. A class consciousness emerged that was almost spontaneously accompanied by a national consciousness. The professionals in particular identified themselves closely with what they called the *"nation canadienne"*. It must be said that they were the first to become aware of the economic inferiority of French Canadians, which they attributed to the machinations of English-speaking merchants and the discrimination practised by the colonial government. By controlling the political structures, they counted on acquiring social power, aiming indirectly at seizing economic control. From the start the professionals were no doubt opposed to the clergy, as a rival and as upholders of an ideology that was likely to frustrate their plans; but the clergy remained a secondary opponent in their eyes. The real enemies were the English merchant and his allies: the official and the immigrant. The ideology developed by this class and taken over by a political party, the *parti canadien* or the *parti patriote,* was above all directed against the English merchants who led the bureaucratic party (also called the merchant's party, the English party, or the Tory party) and who were perceived as chiefly responsible for the problems of French-Canadian society. This ideology, closely related to the increasingly hostile attitude of the masses, was destined to rally the farmers, the artisans, and the labourers to the party. This form of nationalism, the first fruit of a reaction of fear against certain economic and social changes then under way, was fundamentally conservative, on both the economic and the social level. It was, in short, opposed to any reform of the institutional apparatus that had guaranteed the survival of the old social structure. On the political level, however, these new élites were largely inspired by liberal and democratic ideologies. Despite certain authentic aspects, this liberalism and this democratic ideal served to a great extent as instruments to justify taking over political power for the sole benefit of professional people—they were actually a springboard to ultra-conservative goals. The contempt these élites displayed for economic realities was equalled only by their exaggeration of the value of political solutions. In the *parti patriote* only a small minority really wanted, as a first priority, to change society under the inspiration of the liberal ideology. A speech made by André Jobin, notary at Sainte-Geneviève, clearly shows the openly reactionary leanings of an influential section of the *parti patriote.* "Gentlemen," he said, "the government wants to seize the seigneuries; you have been burned, robbed, and pillaged; they want to take away the rights of the seigneurs and the priests; it's high time you got moving because they'll come and take away your rights and your lands."[48]

It was, then, from the professions and from small business that the "names", the ideologists, and the principal leaders of the rebellions were recruited. In all, there were 190 professionals in the movement, which is to say the majority of those practising in the Montréal region. Of these, seventy-six were notaries, forty-three lawyers, sixty-seven doctors, and four surveyors. (It is surprising, on the face of it, that so few surveyors were involved. One assumes that they practised their profession mainly outside the seigneurial lands.) There were also a very few teachers, mainly foreigners. This is perhaps surprising in view of the fact that since 1836 there had been serious unemployment among teachers; but this group was dependent on the old social élite. On the other hand, the number of printers (ten) can be considered substantial. It is worth noting that the lawyers were both the most urban and the youngest group: only forty-five per cent of them were over thirty. By far the largest group in rural districts were the notaries, who were also very close to the popular leaders in age: 73 per cent of rebel notaries were over thirty. As for the doctors, 58 per cent of them were over thirty and they were the ones who figured most prominently at the top of the revolutionary hierarchy. Chenier, the Nelson brothers, Côté, and O'Callaghan are the best-known doctors.

Then came the merchants: general storekeepers, urban retailers, and innkeepers. They were very numerous in the movement and were highly motivated. I have collected 388 names, which included a high proportion of the French-Canadian merchants in the Montreal region plus a few Irishmen. They were predominantly rural rather than urban. Among them, two groups emerge. The 130 innkeepers were at the heart of the intelligence network. Though they were no help in enforcing the boycott against imported liquor, they nevertheless played a central role—for the inns were centres of discussion, where most of the various rumours came and went and where the greatest number of indiscretions were committed. None of this prevented the innkeepers from taking part in the military events, most often as leaders. They were also the oldest group: eighty-five per cent of the lessees were over thirty. As for the other merchants, who numbered 258, they were the youngest group after the lawyers. While many innkeepers could neither read nor write, this was almost never the case with the other merchants. We can assume that a fair proportion of them had spent some time at classical colleges. The merchants ranked high in the revolutionary hierarchy and seem to have been particularly fond of the title of colonel.

The strong presence of commercial elements in the rebellions brings us back to the question of economic motivations, which were certainly significant among the professionals. But this group provided a large number of candidates for government positions, since they were not doing well financially. "Dr Ainsley declared that this whole train of events had been started by Mailhiot and a few young idiots to get places."[49] No doubt professional men were looking for economic advancement, but they seem to have been drawn even more by social prestige and political power. In business circles, however, economic motivations were central. The massive involvement in revolutionary activity of small business put it in an awkward position because most successful merchants supported the established order. J.-B. Bernard, a merchant at Beloeil, replied to the urgings of Dr Allard: "You have to understand that my fortunes are dependent on the English government."[50] But small businessmen, besides being too numerous, were the most vulnerable to competition. They wanted to get rid of the British merchants who had become established in country parishes. J.-N. Pacaud, a shipowner, expressed in his own way the frustrations of small French-Canadian business operations: "Pacaud said that the damned English had made him suffer enough, that they hadn't been fair to him."[51] Besides, after 1830 especially, their dependence on the English-speaking business middle class in Montréal had increased at the same time as wheat production was declining. Agricultural surpluses had dwindled after 1800 and trade with the country parishes had increasingly been based on replenishing their supplies. The supremacy the British had acquired in the field of imports—whether of farm produce from Upper Canada or the United States, or of goods from Great Britain or the West Indies—helped them to control local trade. Small French-Canadian merchants in the countryside, or even in the towns, seem to have wanted to shake off the yoke. In this context their nationalism is easier to understand. F.-X. Prieur, a Sainte-Martine merchant, shouted to the farmers under his command: "Fear nothing, my friends, we're going to slaughter the English."[52] Here again we see that this kind of nationalism initially affected the most vulnerable elements. Those who were more secure were to be found in the bureaucratic party.

For the farmers, for rural and urban craftsmen, labourers, most professionals, and some tradesmen, poverty during 1837-8 was certainly a strong factor in creating a climate for revolution. That is why the people of Sainte-Scholastique warned J. Leroux "that he could very well be bled dry and soon be as poor as they were."[53] Was this the case for everyone? I have noticed, more or less in the background, but even within the movement, the presence of a group whose economic status was far from inferior. For instance, hovering around the Banque Canadienne at Saint-Hyacinthe were comfortable farmers, professionals, and merchants whose caginess and anxiety were obvious. It was rumoured everywhere that this institution had been set up to finance a revolution. The same purpose was attributed to the Banque du Peuple, which, it was said, had been founded in 1835 to serve French Canadians who had ostensibly been mistreated by the English banks. Abbé Chartier, who was in on the secrets of the rebellion to some extent, wrote: "As for money, was not the Banque du Peuple, which had been in existence barely a year, universally understood to have been established for the purpose of the revolution, and in order to help it? Is it not this motive, which the shareholders skilfully made known, that underlay the rapid success which came to this most patriotic establishment?" Abbé Chartier went on to say that on the day when payments were due the "cowardly directors" would face a "terrible reckoning". D.-B. Viger told Papineau, before he left Montréal, "that their little venture would never succeed until they had toppled the government".[54] So many trails led to the Banque du Peuple, and those in charge of it, that there had to be something suspicious about it. Édouard Fabre, one of its directors, arrived mysteriously at Saint-Denis before the battle and went away again immediately after having conferred with Papineau—which may have had no connection with the latter's flight and the final decision taken by the bank to refuse to finance the insurrection. But who knows? Some of the evidence makes me suspect that there was a small minority who had an interest in reaping profits from the revolutionary operation. Joseph Bourdon and Joseph Bertrand declared in their deposition that when victory came, the Patriotes "would confiscate the different banks (except the Banque du Peuple) as well as the wholesale houses, to relieve the poor. That they would make John Molson pay eighty thousand pounds and make other people pay enormous sums too.... That Master Benjamin Hart, along with all the other Jews, must be strangled and their property confiscated."[55] They also expected to nationalize the Lachine Canal and the Laprairie railway. As for the Banque du Peuple, it would become the government's bank. When we examine all the family ties, personal relationships, and business connections within the top leadership of the *parti patriote* and the revolutionary movement, speculation about a "family compact"—denounced both then and later—makes more sense. Regarding this, more light needs to be shed on the role of the Vigers—D.-B. and his cousin Louis-Michel, founder and president of the Banque du Peuple. Here we touch on a world that was self-contained, closer to personal ambitions and family interests. It was also a world whose secrets were better kept.

These élites, who formed the top ranks in the uprisings, were most to blame for the collapse of the attempt to make Lower Canada independent because their function was not just to stir up the masses—it was also to provide planning, organization, and strong leadership at the crucial moment. In fact the uprisings, in 1838 as well as in 1837, presented instead a spectacle of anarchy, misdirected impulsiveness, and a sort of incapacity for effective action. The movement was dominated by fear and, except on a few occasions, had no means of overcoming it. The huge gatherings of country people, incapable of really moving of their own accord, were the result of herd instinct rather than of any genuine strategy. Some leaders, like Plamondon, a Saint-Hyacinthe merchant, declared "that the *habitants* ought to take a look at their own cowardice, that all the confusion in the ranks in the countryside was due to their lack of courage".[56] The farmers, on the other hand, blamed the leaders. For instance two of them related that "Maître Ambroise Brunelle was a dangerous agitator ... that he ran away after stirring up the common people".[57] It seems that when it came time for action, the behaviour of the popular elements reflected the weakness of the leadership at all levels, because where leadership was strong, anarchy was overcome. Wolfred Nelson, for example, was responsible for the victory at Saint-Denis. At Saint-Eustache, in spite of Girod's sudden disappearance,[58] Colonel Chénier put up a strong resistance to the government troops. Those are exceptions, but how significant they are!

Most of the problems originated with the supreme leader. Papineau, who personified the movement—which was a sort of will to national regeneration, as it was called at the time—reveled in ambiguity and showed that he was incapable of action, hesitant, and exceedingly weak. Right from the start every serious attempt at organization was obstructed. Some local elements tried to make up for the deficiency,[59] but nobody managed to ensure any unity of action. Papineau's covert flight before the battle of Saint-Denis—which deceived no one except, perhaps, himself—caused astonishment: Lespérance declared that the locals "were very surprised not to see him at the head of the battle."[60] On the eve of the battle of Saint-Charles, Papineau made a speech to the local rebels urging them to be brave.[61] Then he took refuge at Saint-Hyacinthe and fled from there to the United States, where he went around under an assumed name. Meanwhile he had no doubt forgotten that he was supposed to be the negotiator in the event of a defeat. Be that as it may, his strange behaviour was a decisive factor in the failure of the rebellion.

More serious is the fact that Papineau's was not an isolated case. Even though events usually unfolded simply, without a big production, Papineau's defection had its repercussions. Michel Godet, a Saint-Hyacinthe farmer, explained his leaving Saint-Charles "alleging as his reason that none of the big people who got them to march showed up at the camp at all."[62] Robert Nelson and Dr Côté, who in 1837 had accused Papineau of cowardice, cut no better figure the following year.[63] In the case of T.S. Brown, lack of courage was combined with incompetence. This small merchant became famous during a street fight with members of the Doric Club. When he arrived at Saint-Charles he was appointed general by Papineau and throughout the waiting period he flitted about in a state of utter enthusiasm, certain of victory. He even refused the reinforcements Wolfred Nelson promised him and advised the thousand Patriotes gathered at Saint-Mathias to content themselves with cutting off the retreat of the troops after their defeat. Later, Brown was unable to defend himself against the charge that he had fled at the outset of the battle.[64]

There is no need to spin out the list of such defections. It would be depressingly long. Let it be enough to give one last quotation on the poverty of leadership that included too many grandstanders and too few men of action. François Darche, a Saint-Hilaire labourer, related his experience on the day of battle:

> that before the fighting began the said Captain [of the Canadian Republic] Jean Marie Tétro, called Ducharme, inspected his company and their weapons, saying to them, "My children, be brave and pay attention: don't miss those damned villains, aim well and straight, aim at the heart, the stomach, and the head, have no mercy and give no quarter," ... and that nobody saw him after that; that he supposes he ran away.[65]

The élites seem to have thought that all they had to do was egg on the people to revolt and independence would be achieved without serious risk to themselves. Going by the length of the American Revolution, some of the leaders continued to claim—even after the failure of the second uprising—that if the French Canadians would only persevere, success was bound to crown their efforts. They expected a final success to emerge from repeated abortive attempts, believing that England would ultimately, of its own accord, abandon the colony to its fate. In 1837 and 1838 the revolutionary leadership was so weak that even if there had been no serious opposition, the movement could not have succeeded. It is impossible not to detect in all this a more or less pronounced degree of bad faith, either in motives or in methods. The implausible lies told by the leaders about American aid, and its extent, illustrate this aspect. After the failure of the Québec plot—which was supposed to find expression in a rural uprising from Charlevoix to Kamouraska and a raid on the Citadel—a man called Hutton testified:

> They [the Patriotes] were determined to turn it to their advantage as all the troops would undoubtedly be informed of their danger, the habitants shall treat them with the utmost kindness on their way up and then raise a report that the English want to prejudice a strange soldary [sic] against a good and under-signing [innocent] people.[66]

Should we not also mention the treason or defection of a certain group of revolutionary leaders, specifically those who had the most interest in seizing political power and eliminating the British from commercial competition? Did a moment come when this group was afraid it saw a genuinely popular anti-feudal movement developing? The hypothesis is worth bearing in mind and investigating. It is certain that the moderates were outnumbered, especially after August 1837, by the radicals. It is significant that Abbé Chartier was later directed to curb the anticlerical and anti-feudal frenzy of the refugees in the United States.

The rebel movement, then, sprang from the élites and spread rapidly through the masses, where it had widespread support. It was the logical outcome of the nationalist crisis that had taken shape after 1800 and had continued to take root. But this movement contained the seeds of its own defeat. Instead of undertaking the task of social reconstruction and economic renewal, the liberal professions—generally speaking, and often unconsciously—stood firmly against all radical change, bending their efforts towards the preservation of the old institutional structures, raised to the rank of national values. Incapable of basing their actions on the long-term needs of society, these élites could not manage to get beyond their own group interests and ambitions. At bottom their ambition was to succeed the old seigneurial families. Montebello symbolizes this kind of attitude. It is true that a minority of genuine liberals succeeded to a certain extent in awakening a fraction of the populace to class consciousness and anti-feudal, anticlerical ideology. But the professionals on the whole worked to direct popular discontent against a particular ethnic group—the *Anglais;* one that in their eyes stood for an effort to establish a social order dominated by the commercial and industrial bourgeoisie. By doing so the professional men prevented the development of class consciousness among the populace and assured the survival of the old social order, while at the same time securing their own future. This likely explains the defection of an influential portion of the revolutionary leadership.

The deep-seated attitudes of an influential portion of the professional class, which had aspired to run society all by itself, also accounts for the continued growth of clerical power after 1840. A society that up to the end of the eighteenth century had been headed jointly by the old seigneurial families and the clergy was now succeeded by one dominated by the clergy and the profession- als—with the balance tipped increasingly in favour of the clergy, who were at the top of the social hierarchy. Manipulation of the masses had worked against its authors.

Ages of the Leaders
(Provisional figures)

	% Business	% Professional	% Rural	% Merchants	% Innkeepers	% Notaries	% Lawyers	% Doctors
Under 30	40	40	24	46	15	27	55	42
Over 30	60	60	76	54	85	73	45	58
30-50	44	50	55	39	62	57	37	50
40-60	36	24	46	32	50	25	22	26

Notes

1. My analysis is based mainly on a wealth of archival materials, preserved in "Les Événements 1837-38" in the Archives of the Province of Quebec, and in the Public Archives of Canada. These documents make possible an understanding of the so- cial aspects of the movement.

2. Lionel Groulx, *Histoire du Canada français depuis la découverte,* vol. III, p. 235.

3. Groulx, "L.-J. Papineau", in *Notre maître le passé,* première série, p. 195.

4. Ibid., 210 ff.

5. In my *Economic and Social History of Quebec, 1760-1850,* I believe I have demon- strated this interdependence of economics and politics.

6. Boris Porchnev, *Les Soulèvements populaires en France de 1623 à 1648,* pp. 325, 327. Even if one rejects Porchnev's concept of class, his study remains extremely significant.

7. Groulx, *Histoire du Canada français,* vol. III, p. 235.

8. Quoted in my "Papineau dans la révolution de 1837-38", *CHAR,* 1958, p. 13. This essay analyses the ambiguous behaviour of the revolutionary leader.

9. This phrase ("la prise des glaces") recurs frequently in the documents, in refer- ence to the plans of the rebels.

10. Deposition of A. Brisebois, Pointe-Claire. It goes on: "by supplying and contribut- ing with other men of goodwill to supply all the money necessary to buy powder, balls, guns, and other things necessary to put the said rebel party in a position to set forth at the first opportunity to fight against the British government".

11. Deposition of J. Trudel. See also those of P. Martin and N. Berthiaume. On 18 June 1837, A. Archambault, notary's clerk of Varennes, declared "that he was working to overthrow the government of this province to establish it as a republic and unite it to the United States or make it an independent government, whichever would be judged the more advantageous, and to have free trade with the United States and to stop trade with England". Deposition of P. Nichols of Varennes.

12. Deposition of H. Guérin of Laprairie. Towards the end of the summer, at Saint-Eustache, Saint-Benoît, and Sainte-Scholastique, Chénier, Girouard, and Scott spoke of arming themselves and setting up a provisional government. See the depositions of A. Denis and E. Sabourin.

13. Duncan McColl of Saint-Benoît related that after June 1837 the French Canadians had broken off contacts with the inhabitants of English origin. He and his brothers, one a blacksmith and the other a shopkeeper, had lost all their customers. After 3 July, the patriots had even decided to drive the British out of the parish. There are many such examples.

14. Deposition of Weidenbacker. On 1 November 1837, R. Bélair of Montreal was said to have been present at a rally: "that the principal object of such meeting ... was to attack and destroy the city of Montreal." Deposition of A. Leggo.

15. Ouellet, "Papineau dans la révolution de 1837-8", p. 20.

16. Ibid., p. 20.

17. Ibid., p. 15.

18. Deposition of H. Macdonald.

19. Deposition of L. Holmes. In 1838 there continued to be many such declarations. H. Lefèbvre stated his intention to "murder all Bureaucrats as they called the English population and destroy their properties". Deposition of T. Legrand, known as Dufresne.

20. "Les Événements 1837-38", p. 513.

21. Deposition of A. Labadie.

22. Deposition of W. Kell.

23. Deposition of Fratelin.

24. Porchnev, p. 327.

25. Deposition of J. Fisher.

26. Deposition of M. Bruneau.

27. On economic and social conditions before the rebellions, see my *Economic and Social History of Quebec, 1760-1850.*

28. Deposition of J. Lécuyer.

29. Deposition of M. Tremblay.

30. Félix Lussier, a farmer at Varennes and son of the seigneur, said to the habitants: "If you ask the parish priests' advice, they will certainly tell you that our wish to overthrow the government is contrary to religious principles." L. Dumouchelle of Saint-Jérôme said that "the Bishop of Montreal was paid a thousand louis a year

by the government, that for that reason the bishop was on the government's side; that previously he had been a patriot.... He asked the habitants if they wanted to shine the shoes of the English: that, if not, they must defend themselves." Deposition of C.T. de Montigny.

31. Depositions of J. Léveillée and Eustache Cheval.

32. It is to be noted that Marcel Séné could neither read nor write. Propaganda was carried on in open-air public meetings or in the parish halls, "where they read us *La Minerve, The Vindicator,* and *Le Populaire.* Dr Bouthillier and Father Crevier, the parish priest, read us these papers. Father Crevier told us that we ought to be Patriotes, but moderate Patriotes, that we should love our rights but also our country. He often disagreed with Dr Bouthillier." Deposition of J. Normandin. This was a typical situation.

33. Deposition of Frs Robichaud.

34. See the documents on the murder of Chartrand. Deposition of G. Pinsonnault.

35. Deposition of T. Gagnon. G. Lescardeau, a farmer of La Présentation, was ordered to go "to destroy all the bureaucrats and divide up their property, not less than five hundred arpents of land to each man who would help them in the capture".

36. Deposition of W. Brewster of Lacolle.

37. "Les Événements 1837-38".

38. Deposition of M. Marchesseault.

39. Deposition of J. Robillard.

40. Deposition of J. Parmentier in November 1837.

41. Depositions of J. Martin and L. Piché.

42. Deposition of A. Sanche. Gélineau, Bertrand, and Beaudin of Sainte-Martine are alleged to have said that "Mr Papineau was a great man, a man inspired by God, and that the troubles were going to begin again sooner than anyone expected and that Mr Papineau was coming with an army." Deposition of J.-B. Bourgogne At Saint-Eustache, François Nadon said at the same moment: "It's not over, Papineau is going to come and avenge all that; Canadians have been slaves too long. Damned gang of English, robbers with the whole law in their hands, you can't get at them." Deposition of Elmire Richard.

43. By my calculation, the Patriotes in 1837 had at least 1,600 guns at their disposal; in 1838, more than 1,800.

44. Deposition of P. de Boucherville. Some seigneurs, as well as some parish priests, seem to have been ambivalent. It should not be forgotten that they were afraid of the Patriotes; opportunism sometimes prevailed.

45. Deposition of A. Michon. It would be a mistake to exaggerate the effect of such a stand. J. Beauregard told of having gone to confess to Mercure: " 'You're not at Saint-Charles. You must go to Saint-Charles, everybody's there and you must go there too.' Seeing no obligation to comply with this advice, he decided to slip away to Granby." This testimony, like many others, shows that the manipulation of the

peasants by the parish priests or the members of the professions was possible only when they took account of the inclinations and interests of the lower classes. Pure manipulation was difficult.

46. Deposition of F.-X. Renaud, a Saint-Jérôme farmer.

47. Depositions of E. Jones and Father Richard.

48. Deposition of Pierre Étier.

49. Deposition of P. Colette of Saint-Jean.

50. Deposition of J.-B. Bernard.

51. Deposition of J. Trudel.

52. Deposition of N. Boyer.

53. Deposition of J. Leroux.

54. Deposition of A. Labadie.

55. Depositions of J. Bourdon, J. Bertrand, and Glackmeyer. Ovide Gariépy, shop-keeper at Laprairie, for his part "strongly advised deponent and all Canadians to retain all the bills of the Banque du Peuple they possibly could as it was a great deal better than any other bank." Deposition of I. Lavoie.

56. Deposition of J. Varie.

57. Depositions of Lacoste and Morin.

58. A. Fournier reported the flight of Girod, who had ordered him to go and meet the troops on the ice: "We went back to the village where I saw Girod in his sleigh with another runaway; when he saw me he fired at me and the bullet hit a fence near me." Richard Hubert in his deposition admitted that he had run away. For his part, Isaie Foisy, a blacksmith, testified that he had shoed a horse for Hubert and repaired a sleigh for Girod just before the battle.

59. See my article "Papineau dans la révolution de 1837-38", *CHAR,* 1958, pp. 13-14.

60. Deposition of T. Lespérance.

61. Deposition of O. Lussier.

62. Deposition of Michel Godet.

63. See the deposition of Louis Lussier and J.-B. Plante.

64. Another example of outstanding incompetence was the capture of 150 patriots by the Indians of Sault-Saint-Louis. This had a touch of comedy.

65. Deposition of Frs Darche *dit* L'Artifice.

66. Deposition of Hutton.

FOR WHOM THE BELL TOLLS

S. Trofimenkoff

Within the span of a single decade Quebec experienced the liberalism and the imperialism of its tie to Britain and the political hopelessness of a nationalist cause. From the Canada Committee's supporting of many of the colonists' grievances in 1828 to the Durham Report of 1839 advocating the union of Upper and Lower Canada, the political groupings in Quebec played out the penultimate act of a lengthy drama, starring a popularly elected assembly and a group of privileged office holders. The liberalism of the times and the similarity of the Lower Canadian play to that being staged in Upper Canada, the Atlantic colonies of Nova Scotia and New Brunswick, and even in Britain and parts of continental Europe allowed the final act, resulting in responsible government, to be presented relatively peacefully in the 1840s. But like all plays, this one masked another reality. The social and economic dislocations, evident since earlier in the century, continued to take their toll. Indeed they were aggravated by local and international economic conditions peculiar to the decade. Together they gave the play an unexpected twist as during the decade members of the liberal professions donned military garb and staged a brief rebellion to emphasize their plea for social leadership. The incongruence defeated them as much as the presence of imperial troops.

By the late 1820s, the British government recognized the fact that the governor and assembly in Lower Canada were thoroughly fed up with one another. Monetary and political obstinacy on both sides had brought the administration of the colony virtually to a standstill. With similar problems emerging from Upper Canada and changes in Britain's own electoral system in the offing, the British parliamentary Canada Committee was charged with hearing colonial grievances. From Lower Canada the grievances, taken to London in petitions and by personal envoys from the assembly, were explicit: Lord Dalhousie who had served as governor since 1819 was impossible; the legislative council as presently constituted was an insult; the thwarting of the assembly's will concerning finances was intolerable.

In its report in 1828 the Canada Committee endorsed many of the complaints. Although the only concrete result was the recall of Dalhousie that year, the Committee made other recommendations which served to remind moderates that a constitutional path to reform was still possible. For example, the committee regretted the presence of so many place holders in the legislative council and suggested that somehow that body should be rendered more independent, more representative of the interests of the colony. The committee also recommended that the assembly, soon to be enlarged from the original fifty seats of

---

From *The Dream of Nation* (Toronto: Gage, 1983), 67-80. Reprinted by permission of Gage Educational Publishing Company.

1792 to eighty-four, was the most appropriate body for controlling public revenue; it should supervise the raising and spending of all monies. At the same time the committee urged that the colony retain the divergent customs of both French and English. French Canadians should continue to enjoy their religion and their laws; they might even extend the seigneurial system, if they so wished, into new territories, although not those of the Eastern Townships. The English, however, had as much right to their freehold system of land tenure. Indeed, the transfer of seigneurial holding to freehold tenure should be facilitated. True to its liberalism, the Canada Committee was convinced that good will, tolerance, and impartiality could make a fundamentally sound constitution work.

Unfortunately those qualities were in increasingly short supply in Lower Canada in the early 1830s. By naming a few more French Canadians to the legislative council, governors did succeed in having most of the bills of 1830 and 1831 become law. But the assembly was increasingly suspicious and eyed with hostility any of its own members who accepted places in the council. It turned down a conciliatory offer from London to control most of the colony's finances and even the Jesuit Estate funds in order to continue voting the civil list annually rather than for the life of the sovereign as the offer suggested. The speaker of the assembly, Louis-Joseph Papineau, was much too wary to fall into the trap proposed by Lord Aylmer, governor from 1831 to 1835, that he be named to the executive council. Aylmer, Papineau had already concluded, was another of the robbers of the country. In turn the governor began thinking that only a union of Upper and Lower Canada could contain Papineau and his ultra-liberal followers in the *parti patriote*.

Aylmer was not the only one worried about ultra-liberalism. The clergy and indeed many moderates looked askance at a radical bill which the assembly passed in 1832. The *loi des fabriques* proposed secular control over the educational and monetary activities of parish vestries by means of popularly elected church wardens with legally defined powers. Given the *parti patriote*'s political skill, it could count on electing its own—the local notary, doctor, surveyor, or general store merchant—and thereby successfully challenge the *curé* for power and prestige in the parish. The clergy spotted the threat and used its influence with the legislative council to have the bill rejected. In fact, some assembly members disliked the bill as well. A minority group of more moderate members, among them Papineau's long-time colleague from Quebec City, John Neilson, objected to the radical stand of the majority whom they considered too democratic and too anticlerical. Neilson, first elected to the assembly in 1818, had taken colonial petitions to London in 1823 and 1828 and, as a member of the *parti canadien*, had always supported Papineau. After 1832 the two went their separate ways.

So too, in large measure, did French and English after the election that same year. In one of the Montreal ridings, the election became so contested by rival gangs bent on breaking each others' heads that the troops were summoned to maintain order. In the melee, three French Canadians were killed. As the church bells tolled the defeat of reform, a government enquiry exonerated the soldiers and an assembly enquiry registered its scepticism. Armed hostility was now a distinct possibility.

Orchestrating that possibility, although always afraid to look it in the face, was Louis-Joseph Papineau. A second generation representative of the new middle class, Papineau was forty-six years old in 1832 and had already spent half his life in the assembly. His early education in the classics of liberalism led him away from a paternally designed career in the clergy. He never practised law for which he had the rudimentary, quasi-apprenticeship training typical of the time; rather his literary talents, oratorical skills, and a penchant for taking the opposite point of view led him into politics. Among his first electors in 1809 was his mother, exercising the female suffrage that was tolerated in the colony until 1834. He became speaker of the assembly in 1815, a position then entailing the power and the prestige of the leader of the majority. Fighting off all subsequent competitors for the speakership, Papineau gladly accepted the annual salary of £1000 that was attached to it in 1817. He left the management of his seigneury *Petite Nation* to his younger brother and ignored the increasing indebtedness of his *habitants*. Instead he waxed nostalgic about life on the land, pocketed his seigneurial dues, picked up profits from the timber trade on the Ottawa, lived in the grand manner in Montreal, and complained of poverty.

Papineau may have been looking for a new career in the early 1830s. At some point he began imagining himself as the president of a French Canadian republic. He had the skill, the following, and the experience; his career was a combination of ambition and altruism. He delighted in the adulation of his supporters in the assembly and even more so in that of the crowds on the hustings. Like other nineteenth century liberals, he genuinely believed in popular control of the mechanisms of government, but the people to exercise that control were men like himself, members of the new and responsible middle class. To ensure control, however, required the addition of some particularly French Canadian elements to the liberal creed. Toward this end Papineau glorified the seigneurial system and even tempered his own scepticism to give national due to the clergy. He claimed to be an unwilling patriot, drawn into political and later military skirmishes against his will. But he knew of the financial dealings of his friend the Montreal bookseller Edouard Fabre who collected and administered funds for patriotic purposes; as of 1834 there appear to have been distinct plans for organizing and financing a resort to arms. But when the armed rebellion materialized in late 1837, Papineau proved to be a poor rebel. His political ambitions disintegrated as he took flight into exile just after the first outbreak of violence.

That rebellion might well not have occurred had Papineau's magic not marked an entire generation. He was the first of Quebec's nationalist leaders with all the charisma such leaders have subsequently displayed. He had immense personal charm and spoke with great passion. He made *la nationalité* and *les canadiens français*, innovations of the 1820s, into tangible entities under attack from greedy merchants, superior officials, and biassed governors. Much of his popular appeal was a result of his thumbing his nose at the English and tweaking the ears of the clergy. But at the same time he was able to blend *habitant* mockery of people in high places with *habitant* fear of change into a defence of French Canadian language, religion, and laws. Just what that defence might entail Papineau rarely specified, but the crowds that he touched were willing to follow him anywhere. In a time of economic distress, institutional transformation, and political tug of war, Papineau's magic was a heady mix of democratic logic, popular uneasiness, liberal rhetoric, *habitant* indocility, and nationalist dream.

In contrast, the *parti patriote* was much more prosaic. It was never as united as Papineau wished in spite of the fact that most of its members came from the same overcrowded middle class. Assembly members quarrelled among themselves for positions of prestige in the party; they represented different regional, economic, and ideological interests. Often their only point of agreement was hostility to the governor and his councils. Accentuating the disunity were the great number of newspapers claiming to carry the *patriote* message. *La Minerve* was the most consistent, *The Vindicator* added a virulent Irish tone, *Le Canadien* provided a more moderating voice from Quebec City, *Le Libéral* was more doctrinally liberal while *L'Echo du pays* introduced a rural Catholic note. The program of the party always appeared hazy, if not deliberately negative, to people at the time and historians ever since. It opposed public expenditures from both a liberal and nationalist perspective: the government ought not to be favouring a certain class especially since the institutions desired by that class might mean eventual assimilation. And yet on occasion *parti patriote* members could be found dreaming of canals on the Richelieu to favour north-south trade, local manufactures to diminish dependency on British imports, free trade with the United States rather than preferential treatment from Great Britain, even the accumulation of local capital through a *Banque du peuple*. But there never was much precision in defining, let alone agreement over what the party stood for.

It was much easier to unite the party with a few sure slogans. Assembly control of finances worked well in the 1820s but gradually broke down as neither assembly nor governor ever conceded enough to satisfy the other. English hostility to the French was vastly more malleable. It could be combined with a reform demand by pointing out that a predominantly English legislative council consistently blocked the wishes of a predominantly French assembly. One sure way of changing things was to render the council elective and by 1832 this had become the rallying cry of the party, convinced that its electoral success in town and country would carry over from assembly to council. Or it might even abolish the council altogether as the *parti patriote* ally in the British House of Commons, John Roebuck, suggested in 1835. But by then another simple slogan was attracting certain members of the party: independence.

If the slogans rallied, they also repelled. Some adherents of the *parti patriote* began to hesitate early in the 1830s in the face of the secularizing tendencies of the proposed *loi des fabriques*. Others doubted the wisdom of radical constitutional change such as having complete elective institutions. Still others, particularly those from the Quebec City region where British preferential tariffs kept the wood trade closely tied to empire, would have nothing to do with independence. Some too simply did not share Papineau's conviction, expressed to his wife in 1835, that England's aim was to denationalize French Canadians by attacking their religion, laws, customs, and language. The slogans could be as disruptive as they were unifying.

In terms of actual behaviour, the much despised English party was not very different. Indeed, *patriote* hostility lent more cohesion to that loose group than did any internal mechanism. Admittedly its economic program had been clear and consistent since the late eighteenth century: it wanted the assistance of government in designing a commercial empire linking the continental interior to imperial markets via the St. Lawrence. And some of its members avowedly considered French Canadian institutions a hindrance to that plan. But others actually enjoyed and profited from those institutions. The few who had favoured positions of political power clung to them with as much tenacity as the *patriotes* coveted them. They too used constitutional and nationalistic arguments to bolster their case: to tamper with the legislative council was to flirt with dreaded American republicanism. Still others were quite prepared to do just that: if Britain gave in to *patriote* demands, the English in the colony would threaten independence themselves. Some even sanctioned violence as young men formed rifle corps and flaunted their military prowess in the streets of Montreal. From Quebec City, however, came voices of moderation: adherents of the English party there simply did not believe the Montreal *Herald* when it argued that the foreign—meaning French—character of Lower Canada sullied the national honour of England.

In spite of the differences of opinion within the two political groups in Lower Canada, it was actually the economic despair of great masses of ordinary people that caused the two parties' competing dreams of nation to come to blows. As long as many *habitants* could remember they had known agricultural hardship: crop failures in 1805, 1812, 1816, 1818, 1828, 1833, and 1836 competed with depression between 1819 and 1821, 1825 and 1828, 1833 and 1834, and again in 1837 to make their lives miserable. There was no escape because there was insufficient arable land for an increasing population. The attendant poverty of too many people on too little land increased as both seigneur and priest demanded higher payments for the economic and religious services they provided.

The *habitants* grumbled but reserved their anger for the English immigrants pouring through the countryside in search of land and jobs. That the British government was saving immense tracts of land in the Eastern Townships for these newcomers by means of the British American Land Company, formed in 1832, only aggravated the situation. While desperate French Canadian farmers began squatting on Township lands, the assembly petitioned the King in opposition to the Company and the legislative council prepared resolutions in its favour. By 1837 bad harvests throughout the Atlantic world diminished crops and raised prices to such an extent that farm families in Lower Canada could not even feed themselves let alone procure seed grain for the following year. When British and American banks faced imminent collapse in 1837 and suspended payments, the credit shocks were felt throughout the Lower Canadian economy. It was easy enough to combine radical politics and economic disaster and seek the cause elsewhere, among the English.

Patriote leaders knew full well that agricultural problems had little to do with the English. As assembly members, they had often deplored the state of agriculture and had created committees of enquiry. Those committees tended to attribute the agricultural difficulties to bad farming techniques, an accusation that has been repeated in history books ever since. Precisely what the Lower Canadian farmers should have been doing was rarely specified. Certainly notions of crop rotation, summer fallow, effective fertilization, and drainage were known if not always practised techniques, but they all presuppose decent land to begin with, commercialized agriculture, and an easily accessible market. None of those conditions prevailed in Lower Canada in the 1830s. Like others throughout eastern North America, French Canadian farmers tended to reap what the soil would offer for as long and as easily as they could. Then they would break new land, either cutting into their own woodlot or emigrating to new territory. When both of these "techniques" became impossible, as was increasingly the case by the late 1820s, they switched products from wheat to vegetable and roots crops better able to ensure the family's subsistence. Little ethnic variation alleviated the scene. The productivity of English farmers in Lower Canada was scarcely greater than that of the *habitants*. Upper Canada produced better wheat because the land was newer. Agriculture in Quebec was only to come into its own much later in the nineteenth century when a growing urban demand permitted farmers to use mediocre land for its only paying purpose—as pasturage for dairy cattle.

As the economic situation worsened in the 1830s, however, so too did the political scene. In 1834 a committee of radical *parti patriote* members of the assembly drafted ninety-two resolutions as the basis of their electoral program. They accused the governor, Lord Aylmer, of acting contrary to the interests of both Britain and the colony. They damned the legislative council for its servile lackeying to the governor, for its blocking of assembly bills, and for its undemocratic nature. They condemned the administration of justice in the colony that tolerated confusing cases carried on in two languages, sometimes more than two legal traditions, and at great expense. They drew on French and American precedents, as well as their own previous demands, for both the tone and the content of the resolutions and they repeated their already public preference for elective institutions throughout the entire system of government.

If the Ninety-two Resolutions were designed to distinguish the radical from the more moderate members of the *parti patriote,* uneasy with each other since 1832, they succeeded. Some of the moderates may even have agreed with the governor's dismissal of the resolutions as "sham grievances." In any case, twenty-four of them voted against the resolutions when they were debated in the assembly. Seventeen of the twenty-four then decided not to risk the following election campaign and simply disappeared from politics. For them, the charge of republicanism and disloyalty—so easily made by the English party—sat heavily. For the radicals, however, the tremendous popular support they were able to arouse in the countryside for sending the resolutions to London was sufficient sanction for their stand. One of the few priests to take the radical course, *abbé* Etienne Chartier, claimed that the revolutionary intent of the resolutions was quite clear: either England would have to concede or the colony would have to take up arms. Was this in the back of people's minds as they voted in the last election before the Rebellion? Papineau's re-election in Montreal in the late autumn of 1834 was one long street fight. Elsewhere in the province the radical *patriotes* swept out the moderates. Even the respected John Neilson was defeated in Quebec City. The increasingly uneasy governor reported to London on the "character of nationality" displayed in the elections; he had not seen such a display before.

Aylmer's description undoubtedly coloured the approach of his successor. The British government dispatched Lord Gosford to govern the colonies as gently as possible and to enquire into the seemingly perpetual state of political unrest. While attempting to understand the grievances behind the Ninety-two Resolutions and to formulate an appropriate British response, Gosford tried to solve what he saw as a basically ethnic problem with good will. He even behaved so generously towards Papineau and his radical colleagues that many of the English in Lower Canada began to complain. They need not have worried. Gosford had secret instructions in his baggage: affable he could well be, but adamant too, in the maintenance of certain constitutional principles. There was to be no question of an elective legislative council, let alone assembly control of crown lands; nor was there to be any further concession in the financial tug of war between governor and assembly. Somehow Gosford's secret instructions became known in Upper Canada and a fellow radical there, William Lyon Mackenzie, busy copying much of the spirit and even some of the letter of the Ninety-two Resolutions into his own Seventh Report on Grievances of 1835, informed Papineau.

While Gosford blithely prepared his report for the British government, the Lower Canadian assembly balked. After seeing half of its bills disappear into the legislative council, never to be seen or recognized subsequently, while the same council spent months on paltry bills of its own, one of which was intended to suppress charivaris, the assembly decided that further co-operation was impossible. Once again finances provided the lever. As of 1836, the assembly decided to vote government funds for six months only. Gambling that the governor and his councils would not dare dip into provincial funds without the proper constitutional sanction, the assembly expected to gain for itself complete control of all monies raised in the colony. When the governor and council still had not given up after the first six months, the assembly effectively went on strike by adjourning itself. In that instance it gambled that voters would not object too violently to there being no funds for public works or even for schools.

Meanwhile Gosford penned his report. As expected, he could not agree to an elective legislative council although he did think some of the French *patriote* leaders should be appointed to it. Nor would he tolerate any notion of local control over the governor: the tie to Britain had to be maintained with the governor continuing to be responsible solely to London. The Crown too had to maintain some financial independence even if this meant having the civil list voted for a mere seven years rather than for the life of the sovereign; in exchange the assembly could control all other provincial revenues. It could even make laws concerning the crown lands although it could not interfere with the executive's prerogative to manage those lands. The whole, containing nothing that *patriotes* had not seen and rejected years before, was respectfully submitted to His Majesty's government at the beginning of March 1837.

By then the British government had had enough. Within four days of the receipt of Gosford's recommendations, Lord John Russell, government leader in the British House of Commons, had drafted ten short resolutions. Another three days and parliament had given its approval to them. In answer to *patriote* demands and to Gosford's attempt at conciliation, Russell's resolutions said "NO". There would be no responsible executive council, a demand the *patriotes* had only lately borrowed from Upper Canadian radicals. There would be no elective legislative council. There had to be a civil list voted for a reasonable length of time by the assembly. The British American Land Company was there to stay. If the governor could not obtain his required funds by a vote of the assembly, he now had London's authority simply to take them. What was more, if matters did not right themselves in the colonies, the British government would impose a union of Upper and Lower Canada upon them.

Ten years earlier the Russell resolutions might have seemed relatively mild. In 1837 they were inflammatory. French Canadians in the assembly no longer had any confidence in the governor and simply rejected Gosford's last minute dickering in the summer of 1837 as he offered a suspension of the resolutions in return for a vote of funds. Gosford's response was to dissolve what would be the last Lower Canadian assembly. While the members headed for their ridings to suggest that the die was cast, the English population counted the number of British soldiers in the colony and smiled upon the young men of the Doric Club, a paramilitary organization in Montreal. Among the people in general, the agricultural crisis, immigration, cholera, and political propaganda had all made their mark. Well might Sir Robert Peel, Tory leader of the opposition in the British House of Commons, suggest that an army accompany the Russell resolutions to Canada.

Trouble was certainly brewing throughout the summer and fall of 1837. The *patriotes'* Permanent Central Committee, a centre for political discussion in Montreal since 1834, very easily orchestrated a series of mass meetings in most of the populated districts of Lower Canada. There the passions of both *patriotes* and the people were aroused. Papineau preferred to believe that the meetings were merely exercises in popular pressure, preliminaries to a vast constitutional convention planned for December. But the language used suggested otherwise. At St. Ours, on the Richelieu north of St. Denis, *patriotes* informed unhappy farmers that Britain was an aggressor to be checked by economic boycotts and illegal trade with the United States. At St. Marc, south and across the river, farmers were warned to prepare for a fight. In Montreal, Papineau reminded the crowds that the English had used violence in the past to secure their rights. Some of the young men took him seriously enough to form a military group rivalling the English Doric Club. This group, the *Fils de la liberté*, paraded around Papineau's house indicating to all who cared to see that they had revolution in mind with Papineau at the head of it. North of the city, crowds of up to four thousand gathered to hear Papineau justify the American revolt against England; reading their own fears into the *patriote* speeches, many of the listeners dispersed to harass their English neighbours. Back in the Richelieu region, at St. Charles, Papineau phrased resolutions in the stirring language of the French and American Revolutions; French liberty caps were prominently on display and the *habitants* cheered the suggestion that they melt their spoons to make bullets.

The convention planned for December was to be the last attempt at peaceful change. If it did not succeed, Lower Canada might well have to follow the American example and gain independence by armed rebellion. But perhaps it was not intended to succeed. By December the river would be frozen, facilitating all sorts of movements more expeditious than the penning of resolutions or the framing of constitutions. Moreover since the radical *patriotes* were now quarrelling among themselves, perhaps an armed uprising rather than a convention would prove more useful in uniting them. On the one side were people like Etienne Parent in Quebec City, now using the *Le Canadien* to denounce the foolishness of revolution. On the other side were much more radical spirits hoping that revolution would rid them of seigneurs and clergy. In the middle was Papineau, dithering. And watching them all was Lord Gosford, as governor charged with keeping the peace.

Whether or not the convention would have united the *patriotes* or led to any peaceful resolution of the developing conflict was a question left far behind with the outbreak of violence in early November 1837. On November 6, the *Fils de la liberté* and the Doric Club took to the streets of Montreal battling at the offices of the *Vindicator* and at Papineau's residence. Gosford summoned British troops from the other colonies. He also prepared arrest warrants for Papineau and the other *patriote* leaders but did not issue them until they, hearing of the warrants, departed precipitously from Montreal. Assuming that Papineau, last spotted heading east toward St. Hyacinthe, was on his way to rouse the rebellion, Gosford ordered him arrested.

Whether prepared for an armed uprising or not, the *patriotes* were now obliged to show their strength on the spur of the moment. Under Wolfred Nelson's direction, the *habitants* and townsfolk of St. Denis actually defeated a force of British soldiers on November 23. In their glee they may even have believed that Papineau's presence had been required elsewhere, that his leaving St. Denis was not in fact flight. Unfortunately their newly dubbed general, Thomas Storrow Brown, followed Papineau's example in the midst of a battle two days later at St. Charles, further south on the Richelieu. The defeat there took the spirit out of the rebels gathering at St. Mathias and the British troops emphasized the point by attacking and destroying St. Denis on December 1. Those rebels who had fled across the American border rallied momentarily on December 6 only to be pushed back again by English volunteers. A week later British soldiers put a quick halt to the rebellion by destroying the village of St. Eustache, north of Montreal. There some five thousand *patriotes* had been gathering since mid-November, but the actual armed fighting force was a mere five or six hundred. Once again the *patriote* leaders vanished after the initial skirmish, leaving their poorly armed and undisciplined comrades to confront two thousand government troops. By December 14, the three week Rebellion of 1837 was at an end.

Among the rebels who made a hasty escape to the United States was a radical group plotting not only revenge but social revolution. Shunting Papineau aside they planned to make use of a secret society, the *Frères chasseurs*, with members purportedly throughout Lower Canada, to rekindle the Rebellion by staging uprisings all along the Richelieu and simultaneous attacks upon Montreal, Sorel, and Quebec City. Once victorious, the radical rebels would create an independent and democratic republic complete with universal suffrage, the separation of church and state, and the abolition of the seigneurial regime and of French civil law. But after the crushing defeat of late 1837 there was little popular enthusiasm for rebellion, let alone revolution; indeed only by calling upon Papineau's name could the radicals raise the least spark of interest. Neither in February nor in November 1838 did the tiny forces of invasion make the slightest dent on Lower Canadian defences. As an uprising, the Lower Canadian rebellion, like its counterpart in Upper Canada, had been a fiasco.

Numbers had much to do with the failure. In a population of close to 450 000 French Canadians in Lower Canada, the Rebellion engaged only some five or six thousand in 1837 and perhaps a few more the following year. Even allowing for family members—there appear to have been a number of women directly involved in the uprisings—one still has only a fraction of the population implicated in the Rebellion. So small indeed were the numbers that historians can count them. Fernand Ouellet has located on hundred and eighty-six professionals (seventy-six notaries, sixty-seven physicians, and forty-three lawyers), three hundred and eighty-eight small merchants, seven or eight hundred tradesmen and labourers in Montreal, and a few thousand farmers, tradesmen and labourers from the districts north and south of Montreal. For a socio-economic analysis of rebels the numbers are fascinating and Ouellet is able to confirm his view of the conservative nature of the Rebellion by investigating the interests of the professional group in particular. But the numbers are also minuscule. They included neither all groups in society nor all members of any particular group. And they were heavily concentrated in the Montreal region. Timber workers in the Ottawa Valley, for example, carried on their Irish-French disputes sublimely unaware of the troubles in either Lower or Upper Canada. Geography, economics, and ideology restrained the size of the Rebellion.

Leadership had also been a problem. As a group the clergy frowned upon the increasingly rebellious temper of the late 1830s. Monseigneur Lartigue, the bishop of Montreal, made his position clear in 1837 and 1838: good citizens do not rebel against constituted authority and those who do are quite properly denied the sacraments. A number of local parish priests, however, were caught between their doctrinally correct bishop and their economically bewildered and politically aroused parishioners. Two of them actually took up arms with the *patriotes*. More serious was the obvious lack of military skill or even bravery on the part of the middle class fomenters of rebellion. Only Dr. Wolfred Nelson appears to have had any notion of military strategy. The others relied upon words and grand gestures—the stuff of politics—to transform themselves into revolutionary leaders. When that failed, they fled. The *habitants* therefore had two choices: they could stand and watch the skirmishes, waiting to see which way the dice would fall, or they could fight and take the required leadership into their own hands. Most of them did the former, but those who took an active part produced too many leaders for the number of followers. In the face of clerical disapproval, middle class incompetence, and *habitant* hesitation on the one hand and impatience on the other, the Rebellion disintegrated.

No matter how small, localized, badly organized, and badly led, the Rebellion nonetheless left in its wake a number of broken dreams. Those most personally affected were the twelve hanged culprits, the fifty-eight exiles deported to Australia, and the unknown number of rebels who chose flight to the United States. Of a more public nature, the dream of the middle class came to an abrupt halt. Once that class stepped outside the purely political realm, it was out of its depth. If it really did envisage independence, and that appears to have been only a last-minute addition to an incoherent program, it would have to plan for it politically, not militarily. The much more inarticulate *habitant* dream also disintegrated. Land for themselves and for their children was no more abundant or fertile after the Rebellion than before. The English, the immigrants, the seigneur, and the clergy were still there, unmoved and possibly more powerful because of the defeat of the Rebellion. Barely discernible but also definitely shattered by the Rebellion was the hazy notion of the Richelieu River as a major grain and trade route between Lower Canada and the United States. Emigration paths out of the area in the 1840s clearly marked the despair. Perhaps there had been too many dreams for one small rebellion. The land that tossed up the troubles simply could not accommodate them.

Although the British had suppressed the rebellions in both Lower and Upper Canada by military force, they nonetheless sought a political solution to the troubles in the colonies. The British government therefore dispatched a liberal aristocrat, Lord Durham, to investigate the Canadian situation. Engaged in trade and radical politics, Durham was a modern businessman with racist views. Even before he set foot in Quebec, Lord Durham had a solution to Canadian ills: a federation of all the British North American colonies. He came as supreme governor, overriding both the martial law that had been imposed in December 1837 and the special council that was to govern in the absence of a constitution. He arrived in late May 1838 and departed a scant five months later, spending just enough time to make a few enquiries, confirm a few prejudices, and draft a report.

Durham's sympathies, experiences, and whirlwind tour of the Canadas led him to pen a most curious prescription, both liberal and imperialist, for Canadian problems. In Upper Canada his political predilections led him to associate with the reformers. Their idea of an executive responsible to the assembly took his fancy; it was, he thought, precisely the pattern already traced by British reformers in the 1830s. Reconciling such a plan with the maintenance of the governor's responsibility to London was not easy, as Durham was to discover upon the publication of his report. But he was convinced that responsible government would rectify the common problem of all the colonies. This problem, in Durham's own words, was "some defect in the form of government ... the combining of apparently popular institutions with an utter absence of all efficient control of the people over their rulers."

There was, however, something peculiar about Lower Canada. Here Durham's commercial interests led him to associate with the merchant class of Quebec and Montreal. He therefore found it hard to believe that they could be the villains in a similar play, pitting liberal and democratic French Canadians in the assembly against conservative and reactionary English place holders in the councils. That political skirmish surely masked the true problem of "two nations warring in the bosom of a single state." Astute enough to recognize that "it is not anywhere a virtue of the English race to look with complacency on any manners, customs or laws which appear strange to them," Durham nonetheless marked the French Canadians with the more grievous faults. They were uneducated, unprogressive, lacking in history or literature, clinging to ancient prejudices, ancient customs, and ancient laws. They were doomed to hopeless inferiority, to becoming "labourers in the employ of English capitalists." They could not possibly survive as a distinct national entity in the face of English immigration and English progress. Britain had in fact erred ever since the Conquest in encouraging the illusion of a French future in North America.

According to Durham, the kindest solution that the imperial government could now offer French Canadians was assimilation. Not brutal or dramatic— Durham was after all a liberal, he had already expressed sympathy for European peoples struggling to maintain their nationality—but assimilation nonetheless. Union of Upper and Lower Canada was to be the means with the united province having an executive responsible to the popularly elected assembly. A stroke of genius, Durham thought, to solve the political and national problems of the colonies with a simple administrative reorganization. With that, the business oriented aristocrat, the liberal imperialist from the coalfields of Durham County in northern England began spinning his own dream: once French Canadians were attached by political and economic ties to Upper Canada, they would see the superiority and the advantages of the English way of doing things. Prompted too by immigration which would soon make them a minority, French Canadians would choose their own assimilation.

Alas, poor Durham. His dream of assimilation was as unrealizable as the *patriote* dream of independence.

CHAPTER
11 THE MARITIME ERA OF SAIL

Where are the ships I used to know,
That came to port on the Fundy tide
Half a century ago,
In beauty and stately pride?

In they would come in past the beacon light,
With the sun on gleaming sail and spar,
Folding their wings like birds in flight
From countries strange and far.

Bliss Carman, "The Ships of Saint John"
Later Poems (1921)

The yearning for the lost days of the sailing ships in Atlantic Canada remained constant for much of the twentieth century. Succeeding generations repeated the tales of the prosperous Golden Age of Wood, Wind and Water, when local ships flew to all ports of the world. In Saint John, for example, the speed records of the *Marco Polo* are remembered, while in Nova Scotia the *Bluenose* has had several reincarnations. That there was mingling of myth and reality was to be expected, for the eastern provinces of Canada, facing economic dislocation for much of the era since Confederation, have found solace in the good old days while blaming their decline on Confederation.

In the 1920s, when Carman published his poem and Maritime discontent was growing, Frederick William Wallace glorified the past with two books that went unchallenged for fifty years, *Wooden Ships and Iron Men* (1924) and *In the Wake of the Wind Ships* (1927). Over the past two decades much of the mythology has been stripped away from that era, though the significance of shipping has not been challenged. The Maritime History Group, centred at Memorial

University in Newfoundland, has studied the industry intensively and provided a new synthesis. Eric W. Sager and Lewis R. Fischer, two members of the group, offer an analysis in "Atlantic Canada and the Age of Sail Revisited" (1982).

While the primary concern of the Maritime History Group has been to examine the subject from an industry point of view, more or less from the top down, several of their colleagues and others have followed the seamen and dock workers. Judith Fingard presents anything but a Golden Age in several studies of the sailors which culminated in her book, *Jack in Port: Sailortowns of Eastern Canada* (1982). Fingard's article on "The Decline of the Sailor as a Ship Labourer in the 19th Century Timber Ports" offers the essence of her interpretation. In her hands, the lives of those who worked the ships throw into relief the notion of the good old days.

Suggestions for Further Reading

Armour, Charles A. and Thomas Lackey, *Sailing Ships of the Maritimes*. Toronto: McGraw-Hill Ryerson, 1975.

Fingard, Judith, *Jack in Port: Sailortowns of Eastern Canada*. Toronto: University of Toronto Press, 1982.

————, *The Dark Side of Life in Victorian Halifax*. Porters Lake, N.S.: Pottersfield Press, 1989.

————, "The Winter's Tale: The Seasonal Coutours of Pre-Industrial Poverty in British North America, 1815-1860," CHA *Historical Papers* (1974), 65-94.

Spicer, Stanley T., *Masters of Sail: The Era of Square-Rigged Vessels in the Maritime Provinces*. Bedford: Petheric, 1968.

Sagar, Eric W. and Lewis R. Fischer, *Shipping and Shipbuilding in Atlantic Canada, 1820-1914*. Ottawa: Canadian Historical Association, 1986.

Sagar, Eric, *Seafaring Labour: The Merchant Marine of Atlantic Canada, 1820-1914*. Kingston and Montreal: McGill-Queen's University Press, 1989.

Sagar, Eric and Gerald E. Panting, *The Shipping Industry in Atlantic Canada, 1820-1914*. Kingston and Montreal: McGill-Queen's University Press, 1990.

ATLANTIC CANADA AND THE AGE OF SAIL REVISITED

Eric Sager and Lewis Fischer

The wooden ships which once sailed from the builders' yards of Atlantic Canada have little place in the collective mythology of a nation which has long since forsaken its role as a maritime power. As we developed our western frontier and determined to serve as the hinterland of a continental economy, our growth centres shifted from our eastern shores and the Canadian Confederation lost touch with the trade and culture of its thalassic peoples. Today the great ocean fleets of the nineteenth century are present only in the mythology and folklore of provinces eager to revive what few sources of dignity and pride remain from their past. In the 1920s Frederick William Wallace sought to awaken Maritimers' memories of their "past glories," and it is no accident that he wrote in a decade when the eastern economy entered a steep decline and Maritimers raged at the failure of Confederation.[1] Only in recent years have Wallace's valuable chronicles been superseded by the works of other popular historians and by a few serious attempts to assess the economic importance of the Canadian ship-building and shipping industries.[2] Many of the older myths surrounding the age of sail have disappeared in the process and a reassessment of that age is long overdue. The new realities which are emerging come from an empirical base and a methodology which Wallace would not have recognized; but he would have acknowledged that the "era of maritime effort and industry" remains a worthy source of pride, and a salutary reminder to an insular nation of the wider vision and the entrepreneurial acumen of our eastern Canadian forbears.

The traditional views of the history of shipping in the Maritimes, although never combined within a single interpretation, might be summarized as fol-lows. We have been told that shipbuilding and shipping were both directly linked to the timber trade: timber was the major cargo for colonial-built vessels, and timber, together with the British demand for shipping tonnage, determined the pattern of colonial shipbuilding. "Launched, rigged, and loaded with the ubiquitous and ever-ready cargo of timber, the ship would be sent to Great Britain consigned to brokers who made a specialty of selling such vessels."[3] Colonial timber and British demand sustained the industry until some Canadian shipowners, encouraged by mid-century gold rushes and the Crimean War, en-tered into ship operation themselves. But this was still mainly a shipbuilding industry, since "net earnings by entrepreneurs came largely from taking the price risk involved in the marketing of wooden ships."[4] The collapse of British demand for wooden-hulled sailing vessels in the 1860s caused a crisis in the industry and left Maritimers with no option but to keep their vessels on registry in Canada and to run them for what profit they could. Thus there followed the "palmy days" of Canadian shipowning, when the vessels of the Maritimes sailed to all four corners of the world for cargoes of cotton, guano, and tea.[5]

Concerning the vessels themselves, we have been told that the colonial-built vessel was a floating coffin of execrable quality, and that wooden sailing vessels of this period were not susceptible of significant improvements in pro-ductivity.[6] There was in any case no great incentive to improve sailing times or labour productivity, since these "floating warehouses" were often valuable as much for their stowage as for their transportation functions. Despite the clumsiness of his vessel, however, the Bluenose skipper was "the terror of duffers and slackers" and the "reputation of the Bluenose mate is such that sailormen shudder at the mention of the name."[7] But inevitably the industry in which these "iron men" served was destroyed by a new technology. According to Harold Innis, "the competition of iron and steel destroyed a magnificent achievement, an integration of capital and labour, of lumbering, fishing and agriculture, on which rested a progressive community life."[8] From this assumption about the splendid "integration" of shipbuilding with local lumber and trade, Innis concluded that the decline of shipbuilding was the most serious single difficulty faced by the economy of the Maritimes in the half-century before 1930.

Such are the myths about eastern Canadian shipping. Almost everything in this chronicle must now be either qualified or rejected. Only one part of this account has ever been seriously questioned. In 1966 Peter McClelland sought to refute Innis's argument that shipbuilding had been the "linchpin" of the New Brunswick economy.[9] This was not a difficult task, but in the process McClelland left many questions unanswered and he might have created a few myths of his own had his work been more widely read. For McClelland argued that both shipbuilding and shipowning were "of negligible significance" in stimulating economic growth; that shipowning offered "a dubious earnings record after 1865"; and that shipowning meant "gambling" with an obsolete technology, a drain of entrepreneurial talent from manufacturing, and hence a "constraint" on the growth of local industries.[10] In different ways both Innis and McClelland over-estimated the importance of the industries which they studied: for shipbuilding was never so critical in its contribution to the economy as Innis thought; and shipowning was never the wasteful gamble which McClelland thought it to be.

In revising these traditional portraits of the shipping industry we have begun by examining the patterns of vessel registration in the major ports of registry in Atlantic Canada.[11] It is clear that the pattern of investment in both shipbuilding and shipping is a complex phenomenon which cannot be explained merely by reference to the timber trade and to British demand for shipping. This was not a monolithic industry but two industries—shipbuilding and shipowning—and the incentive to invest in either industry varied from one port to another within the region. By far the largest fleet of vessels was registered in Saint John, New Brunswick. Here the timber trade does appear to have had a considerable influence upon both shipbuilding and ship operation in the early decades of the nineteenth century. A series of correlations between New Brunswick timber exports, tonnage clearing New Brunswick ports, and investment in new tonnage in Saint John suggests that the relationship may have been very close: correlating annual changes in these series yields correlation coefficients of between +.61 and +.69 for the period from 1820 to 1850. Since we know that a large proportion of vessels in this fleet were owned initially by

timber merchants or shippers of timber and sawn lumber, it seems likely that
returns from the shipping of timber were the most important single incentive
toward investment in shipping.[12]

While timber provided the major stimulus to the growth of shipping in
Saint John, this was not true of shipowning throughout the region. Large as it
was, the fleet of Saint John accounted for less than a third of all shipping registered in the Atlantic region in the nineteenth century. And a significant
proportion of new shipping in the region was coastal shipping, built for use in
the fisheries, in coastal trading, or in runs to the West Indies. This was true even
in the centres of ocean-going shipping. In the four largest ocean-going fleets—
those registered in Saint John, Charlottetown, Yarmouth, and Halifax—vessels
designed primarily for coastal trading accounted for 30 per cent of all new tonnage between 1820 and 1860 (included among these vessels are schooners,
which averaged fifty-six tons in these ports, and brigantines, which averaged 150
tons).[13] If all ports of registry were included coastal and fishing vessels likely
would account for over 40 per cent of the entire industry in the nineteenth century. The sixth largest fleet in the region, that of St. John's, Newfoundland,
consisted almost entirely of coastal vessels; here the pattern of investment was
determined by the demand for vessels as a factor of production in the cod and
seal fisheries and by the need to supply outport communities and the Labrador
summer fishery. In the fourth largest fleet, that of Halifax, vessels under 150
tons accounted for 45 per cent of all investments in the nineteenth century,
and in the first half of the century there was a close correlation between investment in shipping and patterns of West Indian trading. The timber trade was
a major stimulus to the shipping industry in the Bay of Fundy and on the Saint
John and Miramichi Rivers in the early decades of the century. In eastern Nova
Scotia and ports of the Gulf of St. Lawrence, timber was less important than the
growing demand from coastal and West Indian trades and the fisheries; in
Newfoundland the timber trade was of no significance at all.[14]

Impressed by the importance of shipbuilding for Quebec and New Brunswick,
Richard Rice and others have proposed an even more direct link between shipbuilding and the timber trade. For many places in these provinces shipbuilding
was a forward linkage from the timber industry, inspired not only by the need
to carry timber but by the opportunity to sell the finished product in the British
market. From this quite acceptable assumption stemmed others which, however
true for some shipbuilding centres, were less valid for the Maritimes as a whole:
it was assumed that the pattern of investment in shipbuilding was determined
primarily by British demand and that the shipowning industry in eastern
Canada was confined mainly to the 1860s and 1870s.[15] Of the importance of
British North America as a supplier of vessels for Britain there can be no doubt.
But those who argue the primacy of British demand for Maritime Canadian
shipbuilding run the risk of under-estimating the substantial local demand for

coastal and fishing vessels, vessels which were least likely to be transferred to Britain. Even in the major shipbuilding centres the importance of British demand has been exaggerated. Of all tonnage built in Saint John and its immediate outports between 1820 and 1850, only half was transferred ultimately to Britain, and much of this transferred tonnage had first been retained for use by Saint John's shipowners.[16] The fleet of vessels retained on registry in Saint John grew particularly rapidly in the 1830s (an annual rate of 12.5 per cent), and in the three decades after 1826 our estimates of the fleet actually on registry in Saint John show that this fleet grew almost as rapidly as did gross physical investment (4.4 per cent compared with 4.7 per cent per annum). This suggests that the sale of vessels to Britain did not limit the sustained long-term growth of the local shipowning industry.

The second largest fleet in the Atlantic region was registered in Charlottetown, the only port of registry on Prince Edward Island. Of all tonnage registered in PEI between 1787 and 1914 (and this includes almost all vessels built on the island), 69.3 per cent was transferred to ports elsewhere. Of these transfers 72 per cent of the tonnage went to Britain. But in the peak decades of vessel construction in PEI, from 1840 to 1889, only 57 per cent of all transferred tonnage went to Britain. British North America (and particularly Newfoundland) was always an important market for vessels built in PEI, as well as for vessels built around Miramichi and Pictou. And there was a substantial shipowning industry in PEI itself. After the 1840s island shipowners retained their vessels on registry for longer periods of time: the mean registry life of all vessels rose from 2.2 to nine years between the 1840s and 1880s, and the mean life of transferred vessels rose from 1.9 years to four years over the same period. Our estimate of the size of the fleet on registry suggests an impressive long-term growth rate of 3.9 per cent per annum between 1826 and 1875.[17] Clearly PEI was more than a shipbuilding factory for Great Britain. Thus even in the major shipbuilding centres of New Brunswick and PEI there was substantial capital accumulation in shipping. For the industry outside New Brunswick and PEI, and for the entire region after the 1840s, it is no longer possible to argue that "few of these (Canadian) vessels were operated under Canadian register" or that "net earnings by entrepreneurs came largely from taking the price risk involved in the marketing of wooden ships."[18]

The great boom in Canadian shipowning in the 1860s and 1870s was not a novel "gamble" forced upon shipbuilders and owners by the decline in British demand for wooden sailing ships. The scenario in which "the would-be short-term owner became a full-time shipowner by default" does not explain what happened in the 1860s and 1870s. The boom in Canadian shipping in these decades was merely the accelerated growth of an industry already well established in the North Atlantic. Table I suggests that there was a sustained high growth in the fleets of the major ports from the 1830s to the 1870s. The industry grew more

TABLE I Annual growth rates of gross physical investment and of tonnage on registry in major ports

Port	Years to peak (per cent)	Tonnage on registry* (per cent)	Gross investment
Saint John	1826-77	+4.0	+2.1
Charlottetown	1826-75	+3.9	+2.9
Yarmouth	1843-79	+6.9	+4.4
Halifax**	1826-74	+2.3	+3.0
Windsor	1853-91	+5.8	+2.0
St. John's	1826-74	+2.1	+1.2
Pictou	1846-84	+1.9	+3.5
Miramichi	1833-64	+3.3	+4.1
Total*** (8 ports)	1828-78	+4.3	+2.8
UK (all ships)	1828-78	+2.5	+3.6

* All growth rates are calculated from regression equations of the form $\log Y = a + bt$. In our estimates of tonnage on registry, the date when the vessel actually went out of service was used, rather than the official date of registry closure. Where the date of actual disposal is unknown, the vessel was given an estimated service life based on the mean service life of vessels with known dates of disposal. The result is a much more accurate estimate of capital stock than that given in official figures.

** Halifax growth rates are calculated for vessels with at least one owner resident in Halifax County, in order to reduce the impact of fluctuations caused by the opening of new ports of registry in Nova Scotia, particularly Yarmouth (1840), Pictou (1840), and Windsor (1849).

*** All vessels registered in Halifax are included here, since this was the major port of registry in Nova Scotia before the opening of Yarmouth, Pictou, and Windsor.

SOURCE: BT5 107/108 vessel registries; B.R. Mitchell and Phyllis Deane, *Abstract of British Historical Statistics* (Cambridge 1962), Transport 1 and 2, 218-22

quickly than did the fleet of the United Kingdom in every decade before the 1880s. The pattern of investment in all ports (except St. John's, Newfoundland) was very closely correlated with the pattern of investment in shipping in Britain. This coincidence in trends results only in part from shipbuilders' responsiveness to British demand; of greater importance is the fact that British and Canadian shipowners were responding to the same demand for ocean shipping during a period of sustained growth in the volume of international trade.[19] No single model of growth will apply to the shipbuilding and shipping industries of Atlantic Canada. But it is clear that there was a gradual extension of trading activities from an early dependence on timber or coastal trades to a wider involvement in many North Atlantic trades by the 1850s, and from there to varying degrees of involvement in certain world trades.[20]

Virtually nothing has been known until very recently about the voyages of Canadian vessels. On the one hand Innis's argument about the "integration" of the industry with the local economy assumes that vessels on Canadian registry must have operated from Canadian ports. On the other hand Wallace leaves us with the impression that Canadian vessels never saw their home ports after launching but traded in every part of the world.[21] Our analysis of the "Agreements and Accounts of Crew" (see figure 1) for our major fleets allows some greater precision about the deployment of ocean-going vessels, at least after 1863.[22] It is likely that a substantial proportion of voyages earlier in the century began from ports in Canada; by the 1860s this was no longer true. But it is no more true that Canadian vessels were operating extensively in all world trades. As Figure 1 indicates, Canadian ocean-going vessels operated mainly in the North Atlantic after 1863. In spite of this concentration on North Atlantic trades, they operated infrequently from Canadian ports. The United Kingdom, United States, and Europe accounted for 63 per cent of all entrances into port by Saint John vessels, 76 per cent of all entrances by Yarmouth vessels, and 70 per cent of all entrances by Halifax vessels. Vessels in the Saint John fleet traded more often outside the North Atlantic throughout the period, but in all ports there was a significant shift out of the North Atlantic after the 1870s. Nevertheless, it is clear that the growth and decline of total entrances were determined very largely by North Atlantic trades, and particularly by trades between the United States and Britain or northern Europe. The Yarmouth fleet, for instance, was particularly narrowly based. David Alexander has estimated each region's contribution to the net growth of world entrances by Yarmouth vessels: these estimates suggest that 98 per cent of the growth of total entrances before 1879 was accounted for by ports in the USA, UK, and Europe.[23] In the 1880s the same regions contributed almost as much to the rapid decline in world entrances. Maritimers' vessels did not operate extensively in Canadian export trades; nor did they penetrate all world trades. Canadian shipowners had seized the opportunities afforded by a narrow range of staple exports from the United States. It is no surprise to find a high correlation between investment in ocean shipping in our major ports and freight rates for such American exports as grain, tobacco, petroleum, and cotton. We have constructed an index of freight rates for the major American bulk cargoes for the three decades after 1855. The high correlation between this index and investment in ocean shipping in our major ports tends to confirm that returns from such freights were of crucial importance for the growth and decline of Canadian shipping before and after the late 1870s.[24]

In retrospect the decision to deploy wooden sailing vessels in trades soon to be overwhelmed by iron and steam may seem a short-sighted gamble. But shipowners were businessmen, not economists or social engineers. They were not planning the economic future of the Maritimes within Confederation; they were

FIGURE 1   **Voyage Distribution of Vessels on Registry in Saint John, Yarmouth, Halifax, and Windsor**

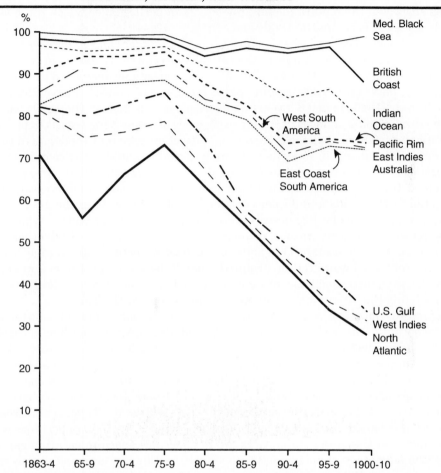

SOURCE: Crew Lists and Agreements for vessels registered in Saint John, Yarmouth, Halifax, and Windsor.

making profits in a business which they understood thoroughly and in which most had worked for two decades. They continued to make profits, and they adjusted the supply of vessels to meet a dwindling demand. They did this not by disposing of vessels recently purchased, but by drastically reducing all new investment in response to the declining freight rates of the late 1870s and 1880s. At the same time they guaranteed the returns from vessel operation by wresting improvements in performance and productivity from the vessels which they retained. Although some historians have noted the improved reputation and rating of Canadian-built vessels by the middle decades of the century, none has suspected the remarkable improvements in performance which these vessels achieved between the 1860s and 1880s.[25]

We know, first of all, that eastern Canadian builders and owners were able to effect a remarkable change in the rate of depreciation of vessels in the nineteenth century. In the Halifax fleet vessel life expectancy increased by over 50 per cent between the 1840s and 1870s, for instance (vessels above 250 tons built in the 1840s lasted 6.3 years on average; vessels built in the 1870s lasted 9.6 years). Similar changes in the life expectancy of ocean-going vessels happened in all ports. These changes occurred in spite of an apparent tendency to take greater risks at sea: in some fleets there was a substantial increase in the proportion of vessels involved in marine disasters after the 1850s (in Halifax marine disasters accounted for 12 per cent of registry closures for vessels registered in the 1850s and 34 per cent for vessels registered in the 1870s; the comparable figures for PEI vessels are 13 per cent and 25 per cent).[26] Whatever the reason for registry closure, mean life expectancy increased. If all other factors remained constant (and in spite of short-term fluctuations average vessel prices remained quite flat or declined slightly between the 1850s and early 1870s), then increased longevity had increased by 50 per cent the likelihood of amortizing the investment in an ocean-going vessel by the 1870s.

Improvements in vessel productivity must at the same time have increased total output in the fleet and even compensated for much of the decline in freight rates in the 1880s. In all fleets, first of all, there was a substantial increase in mean tonnage from one decade to the next, as owners sought to reap the advantages of greater carrying capacity. The average Saint John vessel operating in the growth period from 1863 to 1877 was 801 tons; there was a 36 per cent increase (to 1093 tons) in the period from 1878 to 1890, and a 37 per cent increase in the next period, from 1891 to 1912 (to 1497 tons).[27] Of equal importance was the fact that Canadian shipowners did not sacrifice speed to carrying capacity: the advantage of operating these vessels as "cheap warehouses" does not seem to apply. Data on passage times leads inescapably to the conclusions, not only that passage times were shortening, but also that actual sailing speeds were increasing over time. On westward passages from Liverpool to nine major ports, and on four eastward passages, passage times improved on eleven of thirteen routes between the 1863-77 period and the 1878-90 period (improvements ranged from 1.3 per cent on the Liverpool-New Orleans route to 26.1 per cent on the Liverpool-Philadelphia run; the mean percentage change was 5.3 per cent).[28] A similar analysis was undertaken for passages by Halifax vessels from eastern American ports (between New York and Baltimore) to ports in the UK or northern European ports (between Amsterdam and Havre). These passages were chosen to allow a sufficient number of cases and to reduce the possibility that shorter distance might account for reduced passage times.

Sailing eastwards, over six days were saved between the 1860s and 1880s, representing a 15 per cent improvement; in the other direction eleven days were saved, which means that sailing times improved by 20 per cent. At the same time significant improvements were recorded in turn-around times between the end of one voyage and the beginning of the next, and in port times during a voyage. In the Saint John fleet there was a 7 per cent decrease in all turn-around times between the periods 1863-77 and 1878-90, with the biggest decreases recorded by the largest classes of vessel and by European and American ports. Port of call times declined by 10 per cent between the same two periods. Taking into account the changes in sailing times and port times, the typical voyage from an eastern American port to the UK and back, with stops on both sides of the Atlantic, took fourteen fewer days between the periods 1863-77 and 1878-90. This represented a potential gain in gross output of over 10 per cent between the two periods. These changes apply to sailing vessels only, since steamers were excluded. After 1890 all port times increased, and they increased most rapidly in British and American ports. These improvements suggest that great efforts were made to maintain the profitability of vessels by forcing masters to make more voyages within the same period of time.

Improvements in vessel productivity were accompanied by improvements in labour productivity. Labour productivity can be measured either by the ratio of labour to capital (the man-ton ratio), or in terms of output per unit of labour employed. In the fleets of Halifax and Yarmouth the man-ton ratio fell by over 2 per cent a year between 1863 and 1899; in the large Saint John fleet there was a comparable saving in labour to 1890, and then a much steeper decline, at an annual rate of 5 per cent between 1891 and 1912. A major reason for this improvement was that capital inputs increased faster than did labour inputs, even in this "traditional" industry. As vessel size increased there was not a proportionate increase in labour requirements, because in these fleets the number of masts and sails to be handled did not increase as hull size expanded. But increases in vessel size are not the only reason for declining man-ton ratios. It has been possible by various methods to hold tonnage constant and to observe changes in labour requirements owing to factors other than changes in tonnage. A significant proportion (probably about a third) of the decline in man-ton ratios was due to factors other than increasing vessel size. For instance, between the 1860s and the 1880s masters of 1000-ton vessels reduced their crews by 20 per cent, and shipowners benefitted from a substantial saving in their wage bill.[29]

It is difficult to determine what caused these improvements in the performance of vessels and crew. There appears to have been no major change in the structure of vessels, apart from their increasing size, although students of naval architecture might well pursue the question further. So far no satisfactory explanation for increasing vessel life has emerged, although the desire of shipowners to extend the revenue-earning life of their assets was likely to be an important factor, particularly when freight rates were declining. The improved Lloyds rating of Canadian vessels after mid-century, and the prices received for Canadian vessels in Britain, suggests that improvements in construction had occurred.[30] Some technological innovations did help to save labour and improve performance: these included the use of double rather than single topsails, wire rigging, patented reefing gear, canvas windmill pumps, and donkey engines.[31] Masters and officers were also more experienced in handling larger crews as time passed and as vessel size increased, and as G.S. Graham noted long ago masters were becoming more familiar with prevailing winds and currents in this period.[32] It is likely that when freight rates declined after the mid-1870s shipowners pressured masters to cut costs and improve performance. If the correspondence published in the *Novascotiaman* is representative, shipowners scrupulously trimmed expenditures wherever they could. N.B. Lewis and B.F. Gullison repeat the credo of parsimony on almost every page: "Hold things up as cheaply as possible and make all you can of it."[33] It is also possible, as Robin Craig has suggested, that improvements in performance reflect the "different time horizon" of owners of short-lived softwood vessels: "Canadian shipowners did not sacrifice speed to carrying capacity because they were operating softwood vessels in which the capital had to be written down fairly rapidly."[34] Certainly Lewis preferred not to leave his vessel waiting for an uncertain advance in freights: "Were glad to get her fixed even at this low rate. Never found any money in waiting. Any advances is lost in time and expence with the best of softwood ships."[35]

There may also be some substance to the old image of the brutal Bluenose masters, "those crude bully-boys that bang their way around the world with belaying pins and pistols, taking pot-shots at people on the royal yards when they feel a little disturbed or unhappy."[36] Certainly Canadian shipowners preferred to hire local masters: in the fleets of Yarmouth, Windsor, and Halifax, Maritimers were a majority among masters and officers (in the Yarmouth fleet 81 per cent of voyages were undertaken by Nova Scotian masters); and in the fleets of Halifax and Yarmouth the Nova Scotian master achieved more rapid savings in labour than did other masters (with other factors held constant), particularly when he was working for a Nova Scotian managing owner.[37] Captain B.F. Gullison of the *N.B. Lewis,* writing from New Orleans to his managing-owner in Yarmouth, suggests how far a master was prepared to go in order to secure a good first officer, preferably one "from home": "I telegraphed you on Saturday asking you to send me mate. I received yours today. 'Can't find mate, will have to do best you can.' I am very sorry as I am in want of one very much, the fact is I cannot get along with the one I have and there is none here at present that I would take and no likelihood of being any very soon. I know the cost is considerable from home here but sometimes the dearest article is the least expensive in the end ..."[38]

There is also some evidence of preference for local sailors, and in large port cities masters were able to exercise some discretion in selecting their crews. The seafaring labour pool as a whole may have been a polyglot mixture (we shall soon be able to answer this question for British shipping in the late nineteenth century); but the labour force on Canadian ocean-going vessels was not, as Wallace believed, truly international or "composed of all nationalities."[39] A majority were English-speaking, coming particularly from Canada, the United States, and Britain. The proportion of Canadian sailors decreased over time, presumably because alternative opportunities for employment on land became more attractive in the last decades of the century. The proportion of European (particularly Scandinavian) sailors increased, until by the 1890s British and western European sailors were the overwhelming majority of the crew. There existed, however, a noticeable preference for local sailors: it is necessary to take into account the relative size of the national populations from which crew might be drawn. On a per capita basis Nova Scotians and New Brunswickers were conspicuously over-represented in our fleets, even if masters and officers are excluded (in the Yarmouth fleet Nova Scotians had by far the highest participation rate on a per capita basis, at sixty-two per ten thousand population; the rate for New Brunswickers was thirty-three per ten thousand followed by Scandinavians at a mere nine per ten thousand).[40] Wherever possible masters exercised discretion in selecting their crew; furthermore there is no reason to believe that sailors were drawn from a depressed and relatively ill-educated lumpen-proletariat.[41] These factors, and the greater experience of crews (their average age increased over time), help to explain improvements in labour productivity between the 1860s and 1890s. Labour costs were a major component in the costs of vessel operation, and savings in labour helped to sustain profit levels for the owners of sailing vessels in these decades. Since wages in the industry increased only slightly in the 1860s and thereafter fell slightly, and since other costs (capital cost of hulls, insurance, port charges, victualling) remained constant or declined slightly in these decades, the chances of amortizing the investment in a wooden sailing vessel remained favourable even as freight rates declined in the 1880s.

The continued investment in wooden sailing vessels in the 1860s and 1870s was not an unpropitious gamble but a finely judged attempt to seize expanding opportunities, and then to maintain rates of return as the demand for sailing ship services fell. The hypothesis that investment in wooden shipping was an unfortunate diversion of resources and a constraint on the growth of other industries can be accepted only if one could prove that better investment opportunities existed in the Canadian context in the 1860s and 1870s, and that these better opportunities were rejected in favour of investment in shipping. No such proof exists. It is not yet possible to compare rates of return in shipping with rates of return on landward investments. But we have been able to estimate the growth of output in shipping, and so to compare output in shipping with output in landward enterprises. These output growth rates allow a rough comparison between the expansion of market opportunities in landward and seaward sectors. The estimates of output in shipping also help to confirm that labour productivity improved in terms of output per unit of labour employed.

In estimating the growth of output in shipping we begin by measuring the annual rate of growth of physical output in terms of the relationship:

$$\overline{GO} = \overline{EN} + \overline{SV}$$

where $\overline{GO}$ is the rate of growth of gross output, $\overline{EN}$ is the rate of growth of the total number of entrances into port by all vessels operating in the fleet, and $\overline{SV}$ is the rate of growth of average vessel size. This relationship measures the growth in output in terms of both total entrances into port and cargo capacity entering port; this growth will be determined by available freights, sailing and turnaround times, time lost in repairs, total fleet size, and so on. This method of measuring output is feasible only because our sample of Crew Lists is so large.[42] The equations are then revised to take into account the inevitable increase in the ratio of ballast to cargo on North Atlantic routes. We think it reasonable to assume that vessels entering British or European ports carried cargo and that outward sailings to regions other than North America were mainly with cargo. But we know that an increasing number of sailings to North America were with ballast. We assume, very conservatively, that only 75 per cent of North American entries in 1863 were fully laden, and that this proportion fell at a constant rate to only 10 per cent in 1890. The trend in total entrances is then deflated to produce $\overline{REV}$, which estimates the growth in cargo-carrying entrances. The equation allows only an estimate of physical output, however. Estimates of revenue are introduced by adjusting for trends in freight rates. For Saint John and Yarmouth the Isserlis index was used; for Halifax our own index of sailing-ship freight rates for American bulk cargoes was used (the two indices follow very similar patterns, in fact). These freight rate indices have been deflated to take into account price changes in the Atlantic economy; since Canadian owners would be likely to assess their investments in terms of prices in the Canadian economy, a Canadian import price index has been used. Real gross output in each fleet is estimated by

$$\overline{GO} = \overline{REV} + \overline{SV} + \overline{FRW}$$

where $\overline{FRW}$ is the rate of growth of the weighted freight rate index.[43]

The results (Table II) suggest that a very high growth in output occurred in all three ports well into the 1870s. Market opportunities allowed an expansion of output substantially higher than output growth in other sectors of the econ-

TABLE II   **Estimated gross output in shipping, 1869-90**

	Gross output	
	$\overline{GO} = \overline{REV} + \overline{SV} + \overline{FRW}$	
Saint John	1869-77 + 6.8%	1878-90 - 0.8%
Yarmouth	1869-79 + 7.4%	1879-90 - 1.6%
Halifax	1866-76 + 5.4%	1877-90 - 4.9%

SOURCE: Crew Lists and Agreements for vessels registered in Saint John, Yarmouth, and Halifax. In each case the two periods are centred on the peak year of investment in each port.

omy. It has been estimated, for instance, that Canadian GNP grew at 2.4 per cent per annum in the 1870s and that gross output in manufacturing grew at 2.9 per cent in the same decade.[44] In Nova Scotia total industrial output in real terms grew at an annual rate of 5.7 per cent in the 1870s; output in shipping grew at a similar rate in Halifax until 1876, and somewhat faster in the Yarmouth fleet until 1879. In New Brunswick industrial growth was much more sluggish in the 1870s (growing at an annual rate of 1.9 per cent), and our estimate of output in the Saint John fleet suggests that market opportunities in shipping were growing three times as fast as were opportunities in landward industries.[45] It is difficult to argue that shipowners were collectively mistaken about potential returns in landward industries, since we know that shipowners were already involved in a range of businesses, including banking, insurance, retailing, mining, and occasionally manufacturing. If the census data on "capital invested" have any meaning, then the value of fixed and working capital in industry grew more quickly than did real output or value added in both Nova Scotia and New Brunswick in the 1870s, which suggests that returns on capital invested may have been disappointing (a unit increase in capital was not matched by a comparable increase in real output or value added).[46] On the other hand, in those counties where local resources or the arrival of a railway expanded market opportunities, and where the growth of output was faster than the growth of capital stock, the exodus from shipping occurred as early as the 1870s (this applies particularly to Halifax, and to Northumberland and Westmorland counties in New Brunswick, which were located on the Intercolonial Railway).[47] In the 1880s shipowning was even less a constraint upon investment in industry, since tonnage in service declined in all ports except Windsor, while industrial investment and output accelerated in both Nova Scotia and New Brunswick. Where other opportunities appeared favourable the movement of capital from shipping was smooth and rapid, and it is difficult to imagine how in these circumstances one industry acted as a constraint upon others.

Although we cannot yet compare profits in shipping with profits in landward enterprises, it is likely that profits as well as total output were increasing rapidly in the 1860s and 1870s. The decline in freight rates in the late 1870s did not prevent an output growth rate of over 7 per cent for the Yarmouth fleet in that decade. In the same period total man-months of labour grew by only 4.1 per cent a year, and total wage costs for the fleet grew by 5.1 per cent, which suggests that output per unit labour cost was growing by more than 2 per cent a year. Even in the 1880s there were significant gains in labour productivity in the Yarmouth fleet, since estimated output fell by only 1.6 per cent a year, whereas total man-months fell by 5.8 per cent a year and the total wage bill fell by 4.6 per cent a year. Since other costs were generally steady or falling rates of return must have increased in the 1870s. In the 1880s rates of return likely remained positive for those vessels retained in service (otherwise the vessels would have been sold or abandoned), but returns were probably lower than in the 1870s, since freight rates (and hence gross earnings) were falling more quickly than were operating costs.

Rates of return may have improved in the 1860s and early 1870s, but it is possible that profits began at a low level and remained relatively poor, as McClelland argued. Freight rates and costs fluctuated steeply in this industry. In favourable circumstances the returns from a particular voyage could be enormous; but the overall earnings record in a fleet could still be poor. McClelland's evidence is based mainly on an analysis of net earnings by Moran family vessels between 1867 and 1878.[48] Earnings per ton and net earnings after depreciation were calculated for an average of eleven vessels a year from 1867 to 1878. If they do nothing else, the results lend further weight to our argument that output and revenues were growing rapidly at least until the mid 1870s. Between 1867 and 1874 gross earnings per ton increased by 4 per cent a year, and the rate of return (net earnings as a percentage of the depreciated value of the fleet) increased by 7 per cent a year.[49] But how large were those earnings? Certainly they were greater than McClelland believed: he under-estimated the rate of return on these vessels because he over-estimated the capital value of the vessels when newly built, and under-estimated the rate at which the average wooden vessel in this period depreciated. If we recalculate the rate of return using an initial capital valuation of seven pounds per ton rather than ten pounds, the mean annual rate of return on these vessels was close to 20 per cent before 1874, and it remained positive, although declining steeply, after 1874.[50] Such a rate of return is remarkably high; but analysis of returns for other ocean-going vessels, where detailed records exist, suggests that net earnings as a proportion of the depreciated value of a vessel were often as high as 20 per cent, and for some vessels the rate could remain above 10 per cent even in the 1880s. The *Magna Charta* of Saint John, for instance, earned gross revenues of $8300 a year between 1868 and 1883; deducting operating costs and depreciation, the annual average return was 15 per cent of the depreciated value of the vessel.[51] The *N.B. Lewis* of Yarmouth earned over $3100 a year, net of operating costs and depreciation, between 1885 and 1892 (a rate of return of about 12 per cent).[52] We have attempted to reconstruct the potential earnings of vessels carrying particular cargoes in the North Atlantic, using a standard formula and available data on freight rates, vessel tonnage, stowage factors, and operating costs (mainly wages, depreciation, insurance, victualling, port charges, and repairs). The results of this exercise (with grain as the standard cargo) tend to confirm that a rate of return of 20 per cent was not unexpected in the early 1870s.[53]

It is risky to assume that entire fleets enjoyed precisely the same rates of return as did particular cases. But it is no longer possible to argue that shipping experienced a "dubious earnings record after 1865." Capital stock in the industry in the Maritimes was growing by almost 4 per cent a year in the 1860s and 1870s; it is difficult to believe that such a sustained growth would have occurred if profits had not been high. If rates of return were high, then shipping must have made a significant contribution to capital accumulation in Saint John, Yarmouth, Windsor, and even Halifax. It is unlikely that all such savings were lost to the community, since we know that shipowners were investing in many local enterprises in this period.[54] If the entire Saint John fleet experienced rates of return approaching 20 per cent, then shipping would have accounted for a net flow of income of over a million dollars a year in the early 1870s, or a fifth of the declared value of New Brunswick exports in each year.

This does not confirm the argument that shipping and shipbuilding were the "linchpin" of the economy; nor does it refute McClelland's argument that these industries were poor contributors to economic development. The shipping industry probably contributed to the accumulation of savings in shipowning centres, and to the extent that shipowners channelled these savings into a variety of landward enterprises (as we know many did), there was an important contribution to industrial growth and diversification. But in other ways these industries were weak contributors to economic development: this was McClelland's argument in 1966, and it remains substantially unquestioned.[55] Since Maritimers' vessels operated largely outside Canadian trades, the linkages between shipping and the local economy were few (except with shipbuilding). In spite of the preference for local sailors, employment opportunities offered to Maritimers were not numerous. Shipbuilding itself employed little more than 2 per cent of New Brunswick's labour force, and its demand for timber and metals was not a significant stimulus to either industry.[56] Although shipping was a capital-intensive service industry, it did not directly stimulate much local capital formation. The skills acquired in shipping and shipbuilding were highly specialized ones, and not readily transferable (except in the case of ship carpenters, who moved into construction). Even the entrepreneurial skills acquired in the shipping business were specialized, and not easily shifted into manufacturing industries serving Canadian markets. The evidence collected by Gerry Panting suggests that shipowners (although not shipbuilders) tended to move their capital and energies into banking, transportation, and other service industries, rather than into manufacturing.[57] The shipping industry was no engine of economic growth; and it is worth noting that the 1870s was a decade of slow industrial growth in most of the region's shipowning centres and a decade of massive out-migration from the major shipping centre, Saint John.[58]

In one respect McClelland's argument about the direct economic benefits of shipping may be qualified. In Newfoundland and Nova Scotia particularly coastal and fishing vessels were themselves a type of backward linkage from another marine industry, the fisheries. Shipping was the linchpin of a marine-based economy, such as that of Newfoundland, since the supplying of outport communities, the extension of the fishery to Labrador and the Grand Banks, and the very existence of the seal fishery depended upon capital inputs in the form of vessels of various types. It is no surprise to find a very high positive correlation between the growth of outport populations and the building of schooners. There is also a positive correlation between the gross value of fisheries output and investment in schooner tonnage.[59] Nevertheless, McClelland's argument about linkages from shipping itself remains intact: even if the owners of ocean-going shipping made respectable profits, they were investing in a service industry having limited linkage effects, particularly of the kind which might have stimulated the development of a more diversified manufacturing industry. Until this argument is refuted, it is not possible to claim that the decline of shipping and shipbuilding was a major cause of the relative economic weakness of the Maritimes in the decades which followed.

At the same time it remains difficult to accept McClelland's more extreme claim that shipping and shipbuilding acted as serious constraints upon the growth of other industries. Capital employed and revenues earned in the industry were highly mobile; when alternative investment opportunities appeared more tempting, shipowners could shift their capital and run down their investment in shipping very quickly. It was all the more easy to do this since a majority of the major shipowners in the region were involved from the beginning of their careers in merchandising, banking, finance, and other landward activities. By the late 1870s and 1880s a declining portion of shipping revenues was being ploughed back into shipping; shipowners were probably contributing capital to the growing industrial and service sectors of the 1870s and 1880s.[60] Shipping was also an essential factor in many of the primary industries which continued to exist in the new industrial age. Coastal shipping was essential not only to the production and marketing of fish, but also to trade within the region and to trade with other parts of British North America and to the United States. As S.A. Saunders pointed out, coastal shipping in the Maritimes was briefly stimulated by railway construction, until branch lines and steamships reduced the demand for small wooden coasters.[61] The argument that traditional economic activities such as shipping and shipbuilding constrained the growth of manufacturing industry and a more diversified economic development has not been proved. It is more likely that the eager pursuit of new industries diverted capital and resources from traditional marine-related activities, and particularly from the fisheries. If these conclusions appear tentative it is because informed discussion of these issues has scarcely begun.

These conclusions have a direct bearing upon the most potent of all myths about the Canadian shipping industry. The decline of the industry has always been explained in terms of technological obsolescence: the Canadian industry was destroyed by the competition of iron and steam. The difficulty of making the transition to a new technology may help to explain the decline of the shipbuilding industry: it would have required an enormous effort and substantial subsidies to compete with British and European builders. But technological obsolescence merely begs the question: why did shipowners in Atlantic Canada not invest in iron and steam vessels? It appears that shipowners did not lack the capital to make such investments. Certainly they did not withdraw from the shipping industry because they were losing money: shipowners in Windsor appear to have been satisfied with returns in the North Atlantic even in the 1880s, and expanded their stock of vessels until 1891. There were still 110,000 tons of shipping on registry in Saint John by the mid-1890s (78 per cent of these were deep-sea vessels of 250 tons or more); it is unlikely that businessmen would retain so large a fleet if they were not making some profits. Since it is not possible to compare rates of return in shipping with rates of return in landward enterprises, we cannot estimate precisely the opportunity costs of capital invested in shipping. There can be little doubt, however, that by the 1880s (and in some ports in the 1870s) various landward enterprises appeared to offer rates of return which, if less spectacular, were at least more stable than returns in shipping. In both Nova Scotia and New Brunswick market opportunities in landward sectors appeared to be expanding very rapidly in the 1880s: in Nova Scotia industrial output grew in real terms by 6.4 per cent a year and value added grew by 7.2 per cent; in New Brunswick industrial output grew by 3.6 per cent a year and value added by 5.4 per cent a year.[62] Growth rates were above the provincial average in the major shipowning counties of Yarmouth, Hants, Pictou, and Saint John (in Halifax they were already above average in the 1870s). By the 1880s there were sound reasons for not reinvesting in wooden sailing vessels: given the continuing decline in freight rates, a rapid amortization of the investment seemed less certain than before. There were even better reasons for not investing in iron steamers: the initial capital cost was high, amortization would require a long-term commitment, and the management of fleets of iron steamers probably required a different corporate structure from the old family firm which had dominated the wooden shipping business. Even if in some cases the returns from shipping remained high, this was an industry subject to great risk; the young Canadian Confederation, and its National Policy, appeared to be offering stable opportunities in a range of landward enterprises. Most shipowners were content to expand their existing assets in landward service industries, and to reap what they could from an expanding industrial economy.

The passing of the eastern Canadian shipping industry was not simply the result of businessmen's calculation of opportunity costs. The decline of this industry occurred in no textbook free market, but in a society where political decisions and national policy shaped the environment in which businessmen made their choices. The economic power of the Canadian state was used in this generation to stimulate western development and central Canadian manufacturing. There would be massive subsidies for railways but few for shipbuilding or ship operation; there would be no Canadian Navigation Acts. This is not to say that public investment in shipping would have been a better allocation of Canadian resources than was our public investment in railways. To prove such a contention would require a complicated (and probably inconclusive) exercise in counter-factual speculation. It is worth reminding ourselves, however, that a political decision was taken to subsidize certain sectors and not others; the choice necessarily involved costs and foregone opportunities. There were opportunities for profitable investment in Canadian carrying trades, both before and during the "wheat boom." The demand for carrying capacity in Canadian ports grew by 4.5 per cent a year in the 1880s and by 3.1 per cent a year in the 1890s; in the early 1900s tonnage clearing all Canadian ports grew by 4.2 per cent a year.[63] Even if we take into account the decline in freight rates there remained an expansion of gross returns from Canadian carrying trades; in the 1910s opportunities mushroomed as freight rates soared.

It is not self-evident that our economic and political interests were best served by the collective failure to sustain a shipping industry to serve Canada's export trades. There were politicians, both local and national, who wanted the National Policy to include a shipping industry and Atlantic seaports as part of a truly national economic structure. But the vision of Canada as a maritime power soon faded, even in the Maritimes.[64] It is impossible to know how far a shipping industry might have contributed to prosperity in the Maritimes in the twentieth century. We are spared that knowledge by the decisions of the late nineteenth century, when Canadians pursued a landward development strategy and left the people of the Maritimes to dream of past glories and foregone opportunities.

Notes

This paper is based on research undertaken by members of the Atlantic Canada Shipping Project at Memorial University of Newfoundland. The paper is therefore the result of a collective effort by many friends and colleagues. We are particularly indebted to David

Alexander, Gerald Panting, Keith Matthews, and Rosemary Ommer. The Atlantic Canada Shipping Project is funded by the Social Sciences and Humanities Research Council of Canada and by Memorial University of Newfoundland.

1. Frederick William Wallace, *Wooden Ships and Iron Men* (London 1924); *In the Wake of the Wind Ships* (Toronto 1927); *Record of Canadian Shipping* (London 1929)

2. See particularly Stanley T. Spicer, *Masters of Sail: The Era of Square-rigged Vessels in the Maritime Provinces* (Toronto 1968); Charles A. Armour and Thomas Lackey, *Sailing Ships of the Maritimes* (Toronto 1975): Richard Rice, "The Wrights of St. John: a Study of Shipbuilding and Shipowning in the Maritimes, 1839-1855," in David S. Macmillan, ed., *Canadian Business History: Selected Studies, 1497-1971* (Toronto 1972); David Alexander and Gerald Panting, "The Mercantile Fleet and its Owners: Yarmouth, Nova Scotia, 1840-1889," *Acadiensis,* VII, 2, 1978, 3-28; Eric W. Sager and Lewis R. Fischer, "Patterns of Investment in the Shipping Industries of Atlantic Canada, 1820-1900," *Acadiensis,* IX, 1, 1979, 19-43. The proceedings of the conferences of the Atlantic Canada Shipping Project are mentioned below. For a review of some recent literature on the subject see David Sutherland, "Wooden Ships and Iron Men Revisited," *Acadiensis,* VIII, 1, 1978, 101-7.

3. Wallace, *Wooden Ships and Iron Men,* 35; see also J.G.B. Hutchins, *The American Maritime Industries and Public Policy, 1789-1914* (New York 1941), 300-1, 412.

4. Peter D. McClelland, "The New Brunswick Economy in the Nineteenth Century" (PH.D. thesis, Harvard University, 1966), 186

5. Wallace, *Wooden Ships and Iron Men,* ix; J.P. Parker, *Sails of the Maritimes* (Halifax 1960),

6. Hutchins, *The American Maritime Industries,* 300-1

7. Wallace, *Wooden Ships and Iron Men,* 165, 174

8. C.R. Fay and Harold Innis, "The Maritime Provinces," *Cambridge History of the British Empire,* VI: *Canada and Newfoundland* (New York 1930), 663

9. McClelland, "The New Brunswick Economy (thesis); "The New Brunswick Economy in the Nineteenth Century," *Journal of Political Economy,* XXV, 4, 1965, 686-90

10. McClelland, "The New Brunswick Economy" (thesis), iii, 168-235

11. Data on major fleets are taken from the Board of Trade [BT] series 107 and 108 vessel registries in the Public Record Office, Kew, supplemented where necessary by data from port copies of registries held by Canadian registrars of shipping or by the Public Archives of Canada. Registries have been analyzed (from 1820 or from date of registry opening) to 1914 for the following ports of registry: Saint John, Miramichi, Halifax, Yarmouth, Windsor, Pictou, Charlottetown, and St. John's.

12. On Saint John shipping see Esther Clark Wright, *Saint John Ships and their Builders* (Wolfville 1975); Lewis R. Fischer, "The Great Mudhole Fleet: the Voyages and Productivity of the Sailing Vessels of Saint John, 1863-1912," in David Alexander and Rosemary Ommer, eds., *Volumes Not Values: Canadian Sailing Ships and World Trades* (St. John's 1979), 117-55.

13. By coastal vessels we mean those rigged as schooners, brigantines, sloops, shallops, and ketches. There was a high correlation between rig and tonnage, and almost all vessels having these types of rigging were under 150 tons.

14. On the Newfoundland fleet see Eric W. Sager, "The Merchants of Water Street and Capital Investment in Newfoundland's Traditional Economy," in Lewis R. Fischer and Eric W. Sager, eds., *The Enterprising Canadians: Entrepreneurs and Economic Development in Eastern Canada, 1820-1914* (St. John's 1979), 75-95.

15. Richard Rice, "Measuring British Dominance of Shipbuilding in the Maritimes, 1787-1890," in Keith Matthews and Gerald Panting, eds., *Ships and Shipbuilding in the North Atlantic Region* (St. John's 1977), 109-55.

16. BT 107/108 vessel registries

17. Ibid. On PEI shipping see R.S. Craig, "British Shipping and British North American Shipbuilding in the Early Nineteenth Century, with special reference to Prince Edward Island; in H.E.S. Fisher, ed., *The Southwest and the Sea* (Exeter 1968); Lewis R. Fischer, "The Port of Prince Edward Island, 1840-1889," in Matthews and Panting, *Ships and Shipbuilding,* 41-70. In the 1840s 41.5 per cent of all vessels transferred from the Pictou registry went to other ports in British North America; see Rosemary E. Ommer, "Anticipating the Trend: the Pictou Ship Register, 1840-1889," *Acadiensis,* X, 1, 1980, 75-6.

18. Hutchins, *The American Maritime Industries,* 301; McClelland, "The New Brunswick Economy" (thesis), 186

19. There was a fairly close correlation between annual changes in new tonnage added to the registry in our ports and annual changes in sailing tonnage built and first registered in the United Kingdom, particularly in the early registration cycles (1820-30, 1830-43, 1843-53) and from 1858 to 1869; this applies not only to PEI but also to the non-transfer-trade ports (Yarmouth and Halifax).

20. A non-computerized analysis of early Crew Agreements in the BT 98 series for vessels registered in Halifax and Saint John confirms that an overwhelming majority of voyages were in the North Atlantic in the 1840s and 1850s; see Lewis R. Fischer and Gerald Panting, "Harbour and Metropolis: the Shipping Industry of Saint John and the Urban Economy, 1820-1914," in Lewis R. Fischer and Eric W. Sager, eds., *Merchant Shipping and Economic Development in Atlantic Canada* (St. John's 1982).

21. Wallace, *Wooden Ships and Iron Men,* 193

22. Most of these "Crew Lists" for vessels registered in the British empire between 1863 and 1939 are contained in the archive of the Maritime History Group, Memorial University of Newfoundland. We have analyzed 4172 voyages for Yarmouth vessels, 8829 voyages for Saint John vessels, 3577 voyages for Windsor vessels, and 1844 voyages for Halifax vessels. The Crew List computer files for these four ports also contain entries for 170,000 seamen. See Lewis R. Fischer and Eric W. Sager, "An Approach to the Quantitative Analysis of British Shipping Records," *Business History,* XXII, 2, 1980, 135-51.

23. David Alexander, "Output and Productivity in the Yarmouth Ocean Fleet, 1863-1901," in Alexander and Ommer, eds., *Volumes Not Values,* 84-5

24. Sager and Fischer, "Patterns of Investment," 41-2. Correlating annual changes in Keith Matthews' sailing-ship freight index and annual changes in newly-registered ocean-going tonnage for four ports yielded r^2 = +.61 for 1869/70-1879/80 and r^2 = +.67 for 1879/80-1885/6. See Keith Matthews, "The Canadian Deep Sea Merchant Marine and the American Export Trade, 1850-1890," in Alexander and Ommer, eds., *Volumes Not Values,* 195-243.

25. It is worth noting that Douglass North found no significant improvement in sailing speeds between 1820 and 1860, and doubted that the fall in real shipping costs in this period was influenced by increased speed. Our data suggest that, for Canadian vessels at least, there may have been some productivity improvements as a result of increased sailing speeds. North, "Sources of Productivity Change in Ocean Shipping, 1600-1850," *Journal of Political Economy,* LXXVI, 5, 1968, 1953-70.

26. BT 107/108 vessel registries. For Yarmouth, however, marine disasters as a proportion of tonnage on registry did not increase significantly. Loss rates were never so high that they might have threatened the financial basis of the industry. Alexander and Panting, "The Mercantile Fleet and its Owners," 15-16

27. There were disadvantages, however, to larger vessels: the range of ports was restricted, and so was the range of cargoes that could be carried profitably. See Robin Craig, "Conference Summary," in Alexander and Ommer, eds., *Volumes Not Values,* 364.

28. The routes selected were Liverpool to New York, Boston, Philadelphia, New Orleans, Saint John, Callao, Quebec City, Havana, and Rio de Janeiro; New York to Liverpool, London, and Havana; and Saint John to Liverpool. Fischer, "The Great Mudhole Fleet," *Volumes Not Values,* 136

29. On man-ton ratios see David Williams, "Crew Size in Trans-Atlantic Trades in the Mid-Nineteenth Century," and Eric W. Sager, "Labour Productivity in the Shipping Fleets of Halifax and Yarmouth, Nova Scotia, 1863-1900," in Rosemary Ommer and Gerald Panting, eds., *Working Men Who Got Wet* (St. John's 1980), 105-53, 155-84.

30. The firm prices for Canadian vessels are reflected in the papers of the shipbrokers Messrs Kellock and Co of Liverpool, contained in the National Maritime Museum, Greenwich; the improved Lloyds' rating is noted by R.S. Craig, "British Shipping and British North American Shipbuilding in the Early Nineteenth Century," in Fisher, ed., *The Southwest and the Sea.*

31. On the purchase of a windmill pump see Clement W. Crowell, *Novascotiaman* (Halifax 1979), 123. We are indebted to Neils Jannasch for pointing out many of these improvements.

32. G.S. Graham, "The Ascendancy of the Sailing Ship, 1850-85," *Economic History Review,* IX, 1, 1956-7, 75-81; R.O. Goss, "Economics and Canadian Atlantic Shipping," in Fischer and Sager, eds., *Merchant Shipping and Economic Development*

33. Crowell, *Novascotiaman,* 153

34. Craig, "Conference Summary," 364

35. Crowell, *Novascotiaman,* 95

36. Craig, "Conference Summary," 364. One of the best descriptions of a pistol-car-rying Bluenose master appears in Samlet au Svein Molaug, *Sjofolk forteller; therdagshistorien fra seilskutiden* (Oslo 1977), 15-16. We are indebted to Captain Lewis Parker for this reference.

37. In the Halifax fleet, for instance, the Nova Scotian master sailed with a smaller crew in every tonnage class under 1500 tons; his man-ton ratio was 5.3 per cent lower than that for non-Nova Scotians, when time and tonnage class are held constant (calculated from the Crew Lists for Halifax vessels).

38. Crowell, *Novascotiaman,* 158

39. The portrait of crews serving on British vessels will come from our current anal-ysis of a 1 per cent sample of the entire Crew List archive for British imperial shipping from 1863 to 1913.

40. These ratios are merely the total appearances from 1870 to 1889 by crew born in each region relative to the average of the total population of that region in two decennial censuses (usually 1871 and 1881). For a more refined analysis see Rosemary E. Ommer, " 'Composed of All Nationalities": The Crews of Windsor Vessels, 1862-1899," in Ommer and Panting, eds., *Working Men Who Got Wet,* 191-227.

41. Literacy rates suggest that sailors usually did not come from an illiterate sub-stratum of the national populations from which they were drawn. In the late 1860s 69 per cent of all crew were literate, and this proportion rose to 85 per cent in the 1890s. See David Alexander, "Literacy Among Canadian and Foreign Seamen, 1863-1899," *Working Men Who Got Wet,* 1-33.

42. The Yarmouth Crew List file probably contains data on two-thirds of all voyages ever undertaken by Yarmouth ocean-going vessels between 1863 and 1900.

43. It is possible that the use of vessel entrances as a basic component in this esti-mate may produce misleading results: as time passed more voyages were on long-distance routes having fewer entrances, even though vessels may have been profitably employed on those routes. A second estimate, replacing REV with RVT, where RVT represents the growth of time spent on potential revenue-earning voy-ages, yielded the following annual growth rates for Saint John: 1863-77: +6.4 per cent; 1878-90: -0.2 per cent. See Fischer and Panting, "Harbour and Metropolis," *Merchant Shipping and Economic Development.*

44. O.J. Firestone, "Development of Canada's Economy, 1850-1900," National Bureau of Economic Research, *Trends in the American Economy in the Nineteenth Century* (Princeton 1960), 222, 234

45. Growth rates for Nova Scotia and New Brunswick are calculated from Canada, *Census,* 1871, 1891, and 1901. In order to approximate growth in landward in-dustries ship construction was excluded from the totals. Values from which growth rates were calculated were constant 1935-9 dollars; census figures were deflated by the Canadian wholesale price index J34 in M.C. Urquhart and K.A.H. Buckley, *Historical Statistics of Canada* (Cambridge 1965), 294.

46. Thus in New Brunswick fixed and working capital grew by 4.6 per cent a year in real terms between 1870 and 1880, whereas gross value of industrial production grew by 1.9 per cent a year and value added by 0.8 per cent a year; the comparable figures for Nova Scotia in the 1870s are 6.5 per cent, 5.7 per cent, and 4.3 per cent, respectively. Canada, *Census,* 1871, 1881

47. In Northumberland industrial output grew by 10 per cent a year in constant dollars in the 1870s; in Westmorland the growth rate was 9.8 per cent a year, and in Halifax City it was 7.7 per cent a year.

48. His calculations are from the Moran-Galloway Account Books, New Brunswick Museum.

49. We use "rate of return" in the same sense as McClelland did: it is net profit after depreciation as a percentage of capital employed. Loan capital and working capital are excluded from capital employed: there is little evidence that major shipowners borrowed extensively to acquire new vessels, and even if they did profits net of debt charges must still have been high; and large amounts of working capital were not required, since most operating costs were paid out of vessel earnings, often by a broker.

50. McClelland relied heavily upon data contained in the Moran-Galloway Account Books for his cost estimates, but this superb source has led to an over-estimate of building costs because by the early 1870s the firm was buying most of its new tonnage from shipyards in Saint John City, where building costs were higher. Our time series on newly-built tonnage has been compiled from a variety of sources, including the Peake Letterbooks (Public Archives of PEI) and the Hilyard, Fisher, and Ward Papers (New Brunswick Museum). For a more complete description of sources see Lewis R. Fischer, *Enterprise in a Maritime Setting: The Shipping Industry of Prince Edward Island, 1787-1914* (forthcoming, St. John's 1982), chap. 5. We have estimated depreciation, very conservatively, at 7 per cent a year.

51. Calculated from Hilyard Papers, New Brunswick Museum. See also the examples in Spicer, *Masters of Sail,* 196-7.

52. Calculated from data contained in Crowell, *Novascotiaman.* We are indebted to Rosemary Ommer for compiling data from this source. Insurance expenditures of $800 a year are included among costs; the vessel (purchased in 1880 for $40,000) was depreciated at a rate of 7 per cent a year.

53. The results appear in Lewis R. Fischer, Eric W. Sager, and Rosemary E. Ommer, "The Shipping Industry and Regional Economic Development in Atlantic Canada, 1871-1891: Saint John as a Case Study," in Fischer and Sager, eds., *Merchant Shipping and Economic Development.*

54. See, for instance, Gerald Panting, "Personnel and Investment in Canadian Shipping, 1820-1889," in Ommer and Panting, *Working Men Who Got Wet,* 335-60; Panting, "Cradle of Enterprise: Yarmouth, Nova Scotia, 1840-1889," in Fischer and Sager, eds., *The Enterprising Canadians,* 253-71. Shipowners had always invested in a variety of landward enterprises; thus twenty-nine of T.W. Acheson's "Great Merchants" were among the largest shipowners in Saint John. Acheson, "The Great Merchant and Economic Development in St. John, 1820-1850," *Acadiensis,* VIII, 2, 1979, 3-27

55. McClelland, "The New Brunswick Economy," (thesis); see also Peter D. McClelland, "Commentary: On Demand and Supply in Shipping and Regional Economic Development," in Fischer and Sager, eds., *Merchant Shipping and Economic Development.*

56. McClelland, "The New Brunswick Economy" (thesis), 181, 275

57. Gerald Panting, "Shipping Investment in the Urban Centres of Nova Scotia," and Fischer and Panting, "Harbour and Metropolis," in Fischer and Sager, eds., *Merchant Shipping and Economic Development*

58. In a recent study of population movement Thornton has discovered significant out-migration from both New Brunswick and Nova Scotia as early as the 1870s; Saint John lost over 20 per cent of its population in the 1870s. Patricia Thornton, "Some Preliminary Comments on the Extent and Consequences of Out-Migration from the Atlantic Region, 1870-1920," in Fischer and Sager, eds., *Merchant Shipping and Economic Development;* see also T.W. Acheson, "The National Policy and the Industrialization of the Maritimes, 1880-1910," *Acadiensis,* I, 2, 1972, 5-7.

59. Eric W. Sager, "The Port of St. John's Newfoundland, 1840-1889: a Preliminary Analysis," in Matthews and Panting, eds., *Ships and Shipbuilding in the North Atlantic Region,* 36. There is a consistently positive correlation between estimated returns to schooner tonnage (in terms of the dollar value of cod exports per ton in service) and new investment in schooner tonnage between 1880 and 1929. Each upward surge in revenues from the fishery and in average prices per quintal of cod was followed by a flurry of new investment in schooner tonnage, and also in such imported inputs as fishing gear, gasoline engines for boats, cordage, seines, and lines. This point is discussed in detail in Eric W. Sager, "Sailing Ships and the Traditional Economy of Newfoundland, 1850-1934" (paper presented to the Annual Meeting of the Canadian Historical Association, Halifax, 1981).

60. The size of investments in landward industries remains to be discovered, but the active participation of shipowners and former shipowners is known from the work of Gerald Panting, T.W. Acheson, and others. It is likely that some portion of ship-ping revenues were lost to the region; see J.D. Frost, "Principles of Interest: the Bank of Nova Scotia and the Industrialization of the Maritimes, 1880-1910" (MA thesis, Queen's University, 1979); Christopher Armstrong, "Making a Market; Selling Securities in Atlantic Canada before World War I," *Canadian Journal of Economics,* XIII, 1980, 438-54.

61. S.A. Saunders, *The Economic History of the Maritime Provinces* (Ottawa 1939), 17-18

62. Calculated from Canada, *Census,* 1881, 1891. See also Acheson, "The National Policy and the Industrialization of the Maritimers, 1880-1910," 4-5.

63. Calculated from Dominion Bureau of Statistics, *The Maritime Provinces Since Confederation* (Ottawa 1927), 88

64. There was, however, federal support for shipbuilding in Nova Scotia during the First World War; L.D. McCann, "The Mercantile-Industrial Transition in the Metal Towns of Pictou Country, 1857-1931," *Acadiensis,* X, 2, 1981, 57.

THE DECLINE OF THE SAILOR AS A SHIP LABOURER IN THE 19TH CENTURY TIMBER PORTS

Judith Fingard

Although ship labourers in Canada have received scant attention from historians as one of the crucial elements in King Timber's work force, they have at least been treated more amply than the seamen who sailed the ships in which the timber travelled to market. Yet an analysis of the role of seamen in the timber trade is overdue, not only because a more accurate picture of the labour side of the industry is required, but also because the nature of the sailors' conditions of work and search for higher wages materially affected the way in which opportunities for longshore labour were initially created in the timber ports. In the first half of the nineteenth century the failure of sailors on timber ships to abide by their written contracts in fact gave rise to the occupation of ship labourer in Quebec and Saint John. After the emergence of these shore-based ship labourers, competition from sailors for handling cargoes was governed by a combination of factors ranging from regulations designed to curb desertion of seamen to the increasing volume of foreign shipping in Canadian ports. Despite the marked militancy and significant achievements of the ship labourers' unions, some cargo handling by sailors was sustained by circumstances relating to the internationalizing of the carrying trade and the collapse of the old staples trades. It is the purpose of this paper to trace the diminishing but persistent role that sailors played in working cargo in Canadian timber ports from the 1820s to the 1880s.

Opportunities for ship labouring as a distinct form of work were initially created by the disobedience of sailors, men whose conditions of employment, like those of the pre-industrial apprentice, were regulated by law and enforced in court. According to the terms of their binding agreements or articles, sailors were supposed to perform all the discharging and loading of cargo if required. This represented a significant obligation in the timber ports where seamen arriving under contract for return voyages to ports outside Canada greatly outnumbered the sailors entitled to discharge in the colonies. In the early years of the century the only labouring functions articled seamen appear not to have fulfilled were the skilled job of timber-swinging and the task of loading the newly-built vessels which normally took on their cargo before crews were hired. Some additional opportunities for local labour were created by the arrival of the ships in batches and the anxiety of masters to complete two round Atlantic crossings in a season. Ideally, however, shipowners and masters preferred to rely on sailor labour because it was cheaper. Other considerations such as the speed

---

Reprinted with the permission of the editor from *Labour/Le Travailleur,* II (1977), 35-53. Copyright by the Committee on Canadian Labour History.

of loading, which depended on skill at loading, were to become influential in the second half of the century and to favour the shore-based labourer. But in the decades before the pressures of competition in shipping and of steam technology were felt, it was the undependable nature of sailor labour that determined the distinctive customs pertaining to ship work in port.

Sailors failed to engage in their ship's port work primarily because they found the temptations to desert in Quebec and Saint John irresistible. Not only did these towns lay within reach of larger urban centres where diverse opportunities for work were plentiful, but alternative employment offered in the actual ports of arrival was also exceedingly attractive. In particular, absconding sailors were eager to take advantage of the markedly higher wages available to seafarers in these leading shipbuilding ports of British America where a chronic shortage of seamen existed to man the new vessels destined for overseas purchasers. The wage rates provide a graphic illustration of the contrast between British and Canadian levels of supply and demand. In Saint John in the 1840s the wages of sailors signed on for the run to Britain averaged about £12. Since the voyage usually took a month, the sailor received between four and six times the wages he had made on the voyage out at the long prevailing British rate of £2 or £3 a month.[1]

Low wages afforded little incentive for seamen engaged in Britain to stand by their existing contracts. To this discouragement we must add the sailors' experience of the outward-bound voyage in some of the most unseaworthy vessels afloat. On arrival in a Canadian port the loyalty of the worn out, underpaid, and frequently underfed sailor to his vessel was certainly not enhanced by the prospect of weeks of arduous toil stowing the ship with timber for the return voyage. It was taxing enough that he had usually to discharge the incoming ballast of sand or a cargo of salt, coal, brick or iron before he was allowed ashore. The job of unloading completed and shore leave granted, the sailor looked for the first opportunity to make good his escape. As an association of shipmasters and owners engaged in the Quebec trade pointed out in 1845, "the greater part of seamen generally desert before the ship has commenced receiving her homeward-bound cargo."[2] The sailor was repelled by the loading of timber as part of his expected duties as positively as he was attracted by the prospect of higher wages on another vessel. The attitude towards timber handling comes out clearly in one of the sailors' work songs or shanties of the nineteenth century.

> Wuz ye ever in Quebec,
> Launchin' timber on the deck,
> Where ye'd break yer bleedin' neck,
> *Chorus:* Ridin' on a donkey?[3]

Moreover, once he began to be replaced as a cargo handler by locally hired labourers, the knowledge that his substitute would be paid two or three times the wages positively drove the sailor from his ship.

In addition the palpable absence of two restraints also inspired sailors to break their engagements. Firstly, the majority of the sailors had no financial incentive to remain with their ships. It was customary to advance one month's wages before the vessel left its original port in Britain. A quick and direct voyage would find them in Quebec or Saint John with no wages due and therefore no wages to lose through desertion. Secondly, though laws against desertion had existed from the earliest times in British America, captains often did not trouble to pursue deserters. The ensuing court cases might delay departure from port and could be expensive. But even if a captain wished to bring his deserters before the court he was seldom able to apprehend them. The sheer extent of a port like Quebec, encompassing ten miles of timber-loading coves, frequently defeated the determined efforts of even the most conscientious or vengeful master to reclaim his crew.

As a result of the sailors' avoidance of port work on their ships the opportunity was created for local labourers in fairly large numbers to pursue casual but often steady summer employment at the various booms, timber coves, and wharves in and around Quebec and Saint John. Until mid century absconding sailors themselves frequently took advantage of these chances for a spell of ship labouring before entering a new shipping engagement. Shipmasters abandoned by their crews fully appreciated that part of the attraction of desertion lay in port work, which provided not only better remuneration but a welcome break in the harsh discipline and awesome perils of a seafaring life. To counteract this tendency a voluntary association of masters visiting Quebec passed an abortive resolution in 1820 calling on all shipmasters stowing their own ships to refrain from hiring erstwhile seamen as ship labourers.[4] The situation had changed little by 1848 when a similar meeting of masters resolved to caution the stevedores—the emergent middlemen in the ship labouring business—not to hire merchant seamen as members of their work gangs.[5]

This prevailing practice whereby sailors augmented the local labour force in Canadian ports during the busiest weeks of the commercial season paralleled the habits of seamen in the United States. Work that sailors loathed as articled seamen they found quite palatable in small doses as hired labourers.[6] From Saint John sailors could, if necessary, easily travel to the smaller but busy timber ports of St. Andrews or St. Stephen for work as ship labourers or cross the border to Maine, returning to the major crewing-port of Saint John only when the sailors' wage rates to Britain were particularly favourable.

Before mid-century significant numbers of articled seamen found that they did not even have to desert their ships in order to seek alternative means of employment. Many sailors exploited widely acknowledged grievances, genuine or concocted, to obtain legal discharges from their engagements. Often the state of his wages was the factor that decided the sailor's choice of desertion or court proceedings. If he had money due to him for the voyage out, he had an interest in securing a discharge, accompanied as it always was by the payment of the balance of wages owed. A whole host of pretexts—deviation in the voyage, insufficient lime juice, maltreatment, improperly witnessed articles and so forth—provided sailors with ample justification under merchant shipping law to summons their captains. Frequently, however, the mere threat of court proceedings accomplished the desired object. Captains tended to accept blackmail by the crew as the lesser evil. This unofficial practice of granting discharges abroad grew to such proportions that the masters of regular trading vessels did not always wait to be threatened with a court case before they acquiesced in what had become by the 1840s a widespread custom.

Those sailors who remained faithful to their articles and resorted neither to desertion nor to discharge continued to load their vessels assisted, when needed, by hired ship labourers comprising runaway or ex-sailors and colonists, usually Irish immigrants.[7] Faithful sailors, however, constituted a dying breed. By the late 1840s the tendency to terminate existing agreements in one way or another at Quebec had become so common that sailors intimidated, bribed, or otherwise persuaded to stay by their ships expressed resentment by spinning out port work in order to delay the return to sea and subject the ship to additional expenses. Their slow rate of loading, the only effective protest seamen could make on the job, made them appear to be poor workers in comparison with ship labourers, a comparison that worked decidedly to the latter's advantage.

During the middle years of the century (roughly 1848-1865) sailors were edged still further out of the business of cargo handling and eliminated completely from the shore-based ship labouring market. They were excluded from the casual ship labouring, which they had hitherto as deserters performed with impunity, by colonial legislation implemented in Quebec in 1848 and Saint John in 1850. The principal innovation introduced by the statutes, the establishment of government shipping offices where deserters on reshipping could be discovered and reported to the appropriate authorities, had rather different long term and short term effects. In the long term these local acts (combined with a number of underlying circumstances unfavourable to sailors' independent action, such as the reform of the vice-admiralty courts, the establishment of water police, and the revamping of the imperial merchant shipping code) subjected deserters to readier detection and severer punishment. This meant that, although sailors continued to abscond at a notoriously high rate, they did not now reveal their presence in port by hiring themselves out as ship labourers. Nor presumably did stevedores willingly include seamen in their work gangs and thereby expose themselves to prosecution for harbouring deserters. In the long term, then, the legislation that removed sailors from the ship labour market failed to force sailors to remain with their vessels. This failure was evident in Quebec within two years of the proclamation of the act by which time the established custom was resumed wherein sailors deserted from their ships and the lion's share of the ship labour was turned over to the stevedores.

But, in contrast, in the short term the new legislation, coming on top of commercial depression, interfered dramatically with the patterns of port work in Quebec and appeared to contemporaries to endanger the economic infrastructure of which ship labouring and merchant sailoring formed a part. Instead of continuing to favour the recently established course of discharging their men on arrival in Quebec and turning the loading of ships over to local stevedores, captains took advantage during 1848 and 1849 of the act's reinforcement of articles to threaten crews with reprisals should they attempt to desert. Quebec residents argued that this rigorous approach simply impelled even more sailors to abscond to the United States. At the same time, however, advocates and opponents of the shipping act claimed that the legislation had seriously disrupted the livelihood of thousands of recent Irish immigrants who had come to depend upon ship labour for their employment. This interruption in the work customarily performed by resident labourers would seem to suggest that an unusually large proportion of the ships were loaded by sailor labour. This development is confirmed by evidence presented to the special legislative committee of 1849 which recommended unsuccessfully the repeal of the new act. Critics of the measure insisted that the sailor labour predominating in the summer of 1848 had proved to be greatly inferior to that usually performed by the shore-based ship labourers. The work of loading by articled sailors had been completed tardily and inexpertly, often to the physical injury of the sailor; this had caused delays for shipowners or charterers and had increased the ships' victualling costs because men remained on board who in previous seasons had left the ships. The effect had been far-ranging: the trade of the Lower Town had been depressed by the failure of ship labourers to earn and spend their accustomed wages and of sailors between engagements to exhaust discharge pay and advances on clothes, food, drink, lodging and amusements.[8]

Shipowners, on the other hand, who endorsed the legislation with enthusiasm, showed little sympathy for the estimated 3000 labourers who had lost their summer employment because the sailors had finally been forced to remain at their posts. Indeed to businessmen in Britain the legislation appeared to be entirely just if it had interfered with the costly rate of desertion and thwarted local arrangements whereby so many sailors had escaped ship work in port. The London *Shipping and Mercantile Gazette* considered it wrong that tradesmen and labourers

> ... in a Christian country have been allowed to habituate themselves to rifling the pockets of others, under the pretext of custom, till they are impressed with a belief that they have a presumptive right to continue the exercise of their callings, and that any effort to protect the party plundered, is an usurpation of power uncalled for and oppressive.[9]

In Saint John the act did not produce quite the same agitation and disruption on the waterfront as had its counterpart in Quebec two years earlier. One major reason why ship labourers would not have felt the same threat to their jobs was the more diversified nature of the shipping trades in Saint John. The act did not extend to the coasting trade in which a considerable proportion of smaller vessels frequenting the port were engaged. Moreover, since both coasting vessels and a number of the transatlantic timber ships enlisted and discharged their crews in Saint John, they were not governed by legislation which was aimed specifically at seamen recruited in Britain who were supposed to remain with their ships during the stopover in a Canadian port.[10]

Once the ineffectiveness of the mid-century legislation had become apparent in Quebec and Saint John, seamen in the timber trade reverted to their accustomed habits. Ship work in port, particularly cargo handling, remained an odious task to be avoided if possible. Desertion offered an escape from this irritating work, but, more important, it enabled men to change ships and secure higher wages. For while the fifties and sixties were not years of uninterrupted prosperity, the expansion in colonial trade and shipbuilding, based on buoyant world markets and the continued supremacy of the wooden ship on many oceanic routes, sustained a high demand for sailors. At the same time the greater care needed to avoid detection as deserters and the determination to counteract the regulation of wages practised in the new shipping master's office encouraged sailors to ally more than ever before with that familiar entrepreneur in the sailor's labour market known as the crimp.

Crimping was not created by the colonial shipping legislation of the mid-century, but it was certainly bolstered by it, acquiring ultimately an unsavoury reputation. Whereas the sailor had earlier needed the crimp to introduce him to a captain requiring crewmen, now the sailor needed the crimp to shelter and hide him. Moreover, the legislation which made the deserting seaman a fugitive also outlawed crimping and drove underground men who had previously seen themselves as legitimate but unofficial shipping masters. Accordingly their tactics became more high-handed. When not enough sailors sought protection and employment, the crimps guaranteed their livelihood by resorting to kidnapping or deception. Nor were those shipmasters who favoured the employment of expert local timber stowers innocent spectators of the new developments. One common, underhand practice to which captains resorted after mid-century to rid themselves of their seamen was the acceptance of bribes from the highly competitive crimps for the right to entice or spirit away their crews. Captains then demanded fees from those same crimps for the right to supply substitute seamen when the loading had been completed.[11]

Some articled seamen, however, resisted the temptations to desert and the importunities of the crimps and stayed with their ships as the recent legislation required. They could still be found in the fifties and sixties in Quebec and Saint John working the cargo alongside the local ship labourers. The evidence that sailors performed the work is scattered but indisputable. In 1850 Henry Mayhew in his survey of the London labouring poor interviewed a seaman in the Quebec trade who described how he and his mates loaded deals on a 400 ton barque. Further corroboration can be found in the annals of the local ship labourers. In 1860 the high cost of local labourers' wages in Quebec, averaging some 15 shillings a day during an exceedingly busy season, prompted captains to greater exertions in trying to retain their crews. Apparently some of them achieved this by offering their men a bonus for loading amounting to 1s.6d. or 2s. a day over and above their regular seamen's wages. Reports of accidents also confirm the participation of seamen in loading. In August 1864 a sailor of the ship *Saiem* was drowned after he had been accidentally pushed off a raft of timber alongside his vessel from which he and his fellow crewmen had been handing deals into the hold. Similarly in Saint John in November 1870 and English sailor drowned while stowing his vessel, the barque *Lady Elma Bruce,* with deals from a scow.[12]

Despite these instances, however, most vessels were loaded wholly or substantially by local labourers under the watchful eyes of the ships' officers. The more usual procedures were set out by Captain William Lord who described how, as an ordinary seaman about mid-century, he had helped officers and ship labourers to stow square timber in his ship after all the other foremast hands had deserted.[13] Although ship labourers now did most of the work, no local regulation yet stipulated the size of the local work gang. The number of labourers working the cargo appears still to have been governed by the number of sailors who deserted ship. In 1854 a vessel of 691 tons lost twelve of its eighteen able seamen at Quebec. To supply their places twelve local labourers were hired for eleven days at a daily wage each of 12s. 6d. replacing seamen whose wages had been £3.10s. per month or not much over two shillings a day plus rations. At the end of the loading period the twelve labourers were replaced by twelve seamen hired in Quebec and paid at the rate of £16 a month, nearly five times the English wages of the deserters.[14] While we can be fairly certain therefore that in the fifties and sixties the sailors' cargo handling became auxiliary to that of the resident ship labourers, the point to stress is that the strengthening of the latter's position, like the creation of their employment in the first half of the century, depended on sailors' patterns of work rather than on the deliberate aspirations of local labourers.

By the prosperous mid sixties, however, the ambitions of local labour had come to exert a decisive, if inconsistent, impact and ship labourers were collectively beginning to dictate the conditions under which they would tolerate some participation in cargo handling by sailors. The Quebec Ship Labourers' Benevolent Society, after its incorporation in 1862, began to pass bye-laws relating to working conditions and wage rates. Similar tactics were adopted by the Saint John Labourers' Benevolent Association which emerged in 1865 as the successor to the short-lived association of 1849. These early unions encountered the problem of increased cargo handling by sailors during strikes, as in Quebec in 1866 when ships' crews were used wherever possible to load the ships. During a bitter strike in Saint John in the spring of 1875, when the Labourers' Association tried to enforce a closed shop, captains attempted to overcome the disruption in the local market by resorting to sailor labour. In May, for example, the captain and crew of the Yarmouth barque *Sabra Moses* ignored the dispute between the society men and the rebels, imported by shippers, by loading the vessel themselves with the captain, as in the old days, acting as stevedore.[15]

The period that marked the emergence of organized ship labour was also characterized by a growing resistance by sailors to their masters' attempts to dictate their terms of employment. Several significant instances occurred in Saint John which reveal the reluctance of sailors to submit to unconditional loading duties and to be exploited as cheaper labour whenever the Labourers' Association struck work. The outlook of the sailors in Saint John should be seen within the context of the much closer affinity which existed between seamen and labourers in that city. The explanation, which set Saint John apart from Quebec, was the existence of a body of native sailors. There is suggestive evidence in the late sixties and early seventies both of cooperation between local sailors and resident labourers and of attempts by Saint John sailors to promote collective action. A newspaper in 1868 reported the case of a seaman on a steamer drowned and accompanied to his grave by the members of the Labourers' Association to which he, a seafarer, was supposed to have belonged. It may be that the occupations of sailor and ship labourer had become interchangeable in Saint John. This would seem a most likely tendency as local ownership and encouragement of the port's shipping increased and as southern routes, often involving winter voyages complementary to the summer ship labouring season, replaced the transatlantic trade. The most striking development, however, was the formation of a sailors' union. The Seamen's Mutual Benevolent Association was already wealthy enough in 1868 to donate $110 to a local charity. By 1873 it had successfully established a monthly wage rate for sailors entering engagements in Saint John.[16]

The achievements of the local sailors in Saint John seem to have infected the crews of visiting vessels. In 1872 eleven seamen of the English ship *Eunice Nicholas* adamantly refused to enter the hold of an adjoining woodboat for the purpose of fetching the deals that the captain wanted them to stow on board ship. Arraigned on a charge of refusal of duty, they alleged that their articles applied to the one vessel only: "they would work on the deck of the wood-boat but not in the hold." Neither the sailors' aim to secure what they conceived to be their rights nor their defence by one of Saint John's well known sailor's lawyers, shielded the men from the magistrate's determination to prevent the obstruction of "the Maritime interests of this port by allowing such combinations among sailors to have sway." He sentenced them to twelve weeks' hard labour in the penitentiary fully expecting them to prefer the alternative of a return to work. He was not disappointed in this expectation.[17]

Nor were sailors always willing to continue to perform the role of strike-breakers in ship labourers' disputes. In February 1877 the demand of the Saint John Labourers' Association for the 1876 wage level of two dollars per day was complied with by all vessels in port except the *Ada Barton,* where the sailors and a few non-union workers took over the loading after the withdrawal of the union men. But four of the barque's crewmen responded to the pleas of the Labourers' Association and struck work. Because of the repressive nature of shipping law which demanded the unquestioning obedience of sailors to their masters, the men were subjected to arrest on complaint of their captain and sentenced to two weeks' imprisonment for refusing to work.[18]

Through the sixties and seventies as masters continued to resort to sailor labour at the very time that organized resident labour was aiming to monopolize loading, the labourers grew increasingly hostile to the employment of sailors on cargo handling. It hampered the developing professionalism of ship labouring. Union spokesmen argued that ship work did not fall within the province of the sailor and that the work of loading timber was too highly specialized for mere sailors to be considered competent partners. Ship labourers held their work to be so skilled that not only timber swingers but stowers, hoisters, and holders must serve a long apprenticeship in order to work timber safely and expeditiously. In Saint John ship labourers earned the distinction of being "in a certain sense, skilled workmen, for the ordinary laboring man would be as much out of his depth stowing deals in the interior of a vessel as an ordinary auctioneer would be in a pulpit."[19] Quebec ship labourers who gave evidence before the Labour Commission in 1888 unanimously insisted that ship labourers had to be born and raised to the work. "I never knew a man to go into the hold of a timber ship unless he was brought up to it", claimed one ship labourer, "and I know at the winch they are skilled labourers, and as far as swinging timber is concerned if a man does not learn to swing timber as a boy, he will not as a man."[20] While local shipping interests deplored the demands made by combinations of working men, they did not deny that the ship work should be done by experienced gangs. Visiting masters who preferred to use their own crews therefore met with little encouragement from local residents.

Since sailors' terms of employment allowed them little room for manoeuvre, the later years of the century saw no change in their behaviour in port. To them cargo handling remained a loathsome activity. The sailor's lackadaisical, if not downright hostile, attitude towards the work could make him a liability in the extremely dangerous task of loading timber, especially as the pressures to load faster increased with competition between maritime countries and the refinements of steam technology. Ship labourers further emphasized that seamen, having no pride or vested interest in ship work, often turned up for work inebriated and could not be trusted to co-ordinate their activities smoothly and safely with those of the stevedore's gang. However unfairly exaggerated the landsman's view of the sailor's behaviour in port may have been, the sailor's penchant for drink could cause near disaster during loading operations.[21]

Quebec ship labourers put forward another grievance against sailor labour as the timber trade of their port increasingly passed to non-British shipping and more particularly to Scandinavian-registered vessels. They found that the inability of foreign sailors to understand orders given by the local stevedores produced new dangers. In one case cited by a Quebec stevedore, a labourer in the hold asked a Norwegian sailor for a rope to which the latter responded by heaving deals down on his head. Labourers claimed that their objection to working with foreign crews was based entirely on a concern for the safety of both labourers and sailors. To give substance to this anxiety a bylaw of the Quebec Ship Labourers' Benevolent Society dating from no later than 1869 stipulated that ship labourers would not work on foreign ships where sailors were also employed in stowing timber. Foreign masters who used their sailors were also denied the future services of union labour.[22] Nevertheless, evidence in Saint John in 1872 indicates that, in addition to difficulties over language, Scandinavian masters were discriminated against because they were foreigners and "not liked".[23]

Whatever the degree of prejudice involved, the principal reason ship labourers of Quebec and Saint John singled out European ships for special treatment can be more persuasively traced to the customary behaviour of their sailors in port. Scandinavian sailors were much less likely to desert since they were seldom given the opportunity to go ashore and thereby escape loading duties and since they feared the severe punishment meted out to deserters who returned to the Baltic states. Sailors on British (including Canadian) and American vessels, on the other hand, were tacitly the ship labourers' friends since they continued to desert in droves at least until the mid 1870s by which time the associated business of crimping had come under stricter control. Thereafter the labourers' attitudes even towards the more familiar sailors turned sour and far less accommodating. In 1874 Canadian legislation for the first time extended the regulations governing the shipping of seamen beyond Anglo-Canadian ships. This change may well have lessened the rate of desertion and produced new competition from sailors particularly for labourers in Saint John where the volume of American shipping was considerable. Moreover, shipowners who chaffed under the labourers' charges for port work became more determined either to use sailor labour or withdraw their business to ports with unorganized labour.[24]

Such changing circumstances made local labourers determined by the mid seventies to exclude from loading all sailors regardless of the flag under which they served. For this purpose labourers in both Quebec and Saint John held a trump card which they could from time to time effectively employ to extend their control over cargo handling. It so happened that in the timber trade, where most of the carrying was done by chartered vessels, local timber merchants steadfastly refused to assume the responsibility for delivering the cargo to the sailing vessels.[25] They thereby avoided considerable risks but by the same token they lost the chance to become influential in the ship labouring market by employing directly the boat crews and stevedoring gangs who delivered the timber and loaded the ships. By the 1870s this lack of control was a crucial consideration since the bateau-men of Quebec and the scowmen of Saint John were either integral members or separately organized allies of the respective ship labourers' unions in those ports. When local labour stood united in its demands, the crew of a vessel was little use to a ship without timber to stow.

The knowledge that they did indeed have the power to bring the port to a standstill encouraged the labourers' unions to begin their campaign for excluding sailors from loading vessels which had earlier been exempted from their rules. Admittedly, sailors had already been confined to specific jobs. By the 1870s sailors in Quebec were allowed to do no more than work the winches and lop the timber. In Saint John local labourers were operating the winches by 1871 though perhaps not exclusively. The first attempt in Quebec to eliminate sailors' loading altogether took the form of a new rule in 1875 which prohibited the employment of sailors on ships loaded by members of the ship labourers' union. Since the ranks of the Quebec labourers were wracked by ethnic dissension during the next few years, the imposition of the ban had little effect. The final exclusion of sailor labour came instead in 1879 when the union officially extended to British as well as foreign ships the proscriptions on the use of sailors as longshoremen. Evidence indicates that the new regulation may not have been completely successful. But it was another irritant to capitalists and British shipowners responded to this and other protectionist union rules by refusing to send out their vessels for the second summer voyage in 1879 and 1880, a move that weakened the position of the labourers while it increased their determination to retain hard-won advantages. Thereafter sailors seldom loaded ships alongside labourers in Quebec. Where seamen handled cargoes, they did so alone. On Scandinavian vessels sailors continued to do the port work whenever they could obtain cargoes. But British vessels, which seldom retained the full complement of crewmen, had to abide by the union rules when the union was strong or had to turn to other ports for cargoes as they increasingly did. In the process of eliminating sailor labour the Quebec labourers further extended the range of their control during the 1880s by taking over the unloading of ships, a task which had largely been performed in that port by sailors in the previous decades. Labourers felt compelled to demand more and more of the diminishing opportunities for work as Quebec fell rapidly into decline as a major shipping port.[26]

Meanwhile, gaining strength from improved commercial conditions after the bleak mid 1870s, the labourers' union in Saint John delivered what it regarded as the final blow to sailors' port labour in the spring of 1877. Alarmed by a revived tendency in that decade for shipowners and masters to resort to sailors' brawn in the loading of vessels, the Saint John labourers threatened to strike on the ground that it was not "the legitimate business of sailors to do such work." One suspects that the sailors readily demonstrated their concurrence, a circumstance that undoubtedly contributed to the immediate compliance with the labourers' demand "that sailors be prevented from working at loading vessels."[27]

The labourers successfully maintained this dominant position for several years. But after a strong union monopoly during the early 1880s, they encountered effective competition by 1886 from both mechanized loading on steamships and sailor labour on sailing vessels as the port of Saint John once more sank into commercial depression. Formal acknowledgement of defeat in the campaign to exclude sailor labour came in 1887, ten years after its elimination had seemed complete. That year the union came to its first negotiated agreement with the shipping interests which removed all the union restrictions on the use of articled sailors and power-driven machinery in the loading and discharging of cargoes. The third such annual agreement in 1889 improved the labourers' position slightly because it limited the number of seamen-labourers to six in a ship and four in a barque. While the reinstitution of seafarers' labour reflects a sign of weakness on the part of a declining resident labour force in a declining port, it may also have reflected a grain of self-interested local patriotism. The use of steam winches, which the labourers could no longer resist, was beneficial only to steamers, donkey engines being too dangerous for use on sailing vessels in the strong currents of Saint John harbour. Ocean-going steamships were not locally owned, whereas the sailing vessels on which the port's existence had so long depended had been since the 1860s largely Maritime-owned vessels. By allowing local ships, which had been forsaking Saint John for the outports, to cut their expenses through a resort to some measure of sailor labour, the labourers may have been trying to preserve the shipping and welfare of the port on which their livelihood depended.[28]

At the end of the age of sail in the 1880s the local labourers of Quebec and Saint John had gone as far as they were able towards eliminating sailor competitors from cargo handling. Economic conditions no longer favoured the labourers and had already in the case of Saint John weakened their position *vis à vis* the sailors. The inability of Quebec labourers to prevent the employment of sailors on foreign vessels was a prevailing reality of increasing significance: by the mid 1880s the number of Scandinavian vessels clearing at Quebec for the sea began to outnumber those of British registry.[29] Indeed the international nature of the carrying trade meant that only positive and coordinated action by seamen sailing under the various national flags could have produced a division of work in Canadian ports that would have satisfied the labourers' aspirations. In contrast to the common resort by individual sailors to desertion, such a collective course might also have served to free the articled sailor from the servant-master relationship in which he had been so long bound, one that required his absolute obedience to the ships' officers "in everything relating to the said Ship and the Stores and Cargo thereof, whether on board, in boats, or on shore."[30] Instead, what little concerted challenge there was to the imprecise wording of the articles occurred in a piecemeal fashion and depended for success on legal interpretations that might vary from day to day. In very few cases did the magistrates adopt an approach so favourable to the sailors' cause as that handed down in Saint John in 1877 when two sailors objected to discharging cargo on the ground that such work had not been spelled out in their agreement. "You may rest assured," the magistrate sympathized, "that you cannot be bound down to anything not specified in the articles."[31] As it transpired, however, the effective elimination of the sailors' cargo handling was more closely related to technological than to human considerations. The steamship, the sailing vessel's rival and successor, had for financial reasons to be discharged and loaded with great speed during a brief stop-over in port that had none of the leisurely features of the sailing vessel's visit. This meant that local labourers were needed to supply the large gangs for loading and that the seamen were preoccupied with making the vessel ready for sea. In these altered circumstances in the age of steam the work of sailors and ship labourers became quite distinct, except in so far as employers were able to manipulate sailors as strike breakers during periods of dockside unrest.[32]

Notes

This paper was presented at the Canadian Historical Association meeting in June 1977. It is an offshoot of a larger study of merchant seamen in port in the nineteenth century. The present brief treatment of sailors' working conditions and the relationship between transient seamen and resident dockside society will be more fully discussed and documented therein.

1. The wage rates at Saint John seem to have been designed in part to compensate native sailors for being stranded in Britain by the one-way voyage. If they shipped by the 'run' to Britain rather than for a round trip by the month, they received between two and three times the monthly rate. *Shipping and Mercantile Gazette* (London), 6 November 1847; *New Brunswick Courier* (Saint John), 8 December 1849. The stopover in London of sailors from Saint John was noted by Henry Mayhew in 1850. He claimed that the lodgers of the crimps' boarding houses in London's dockland were in the main sailors from Saint John. *Morning Chronicle* (London), 2 May 1850.

2. Memorial of Masters and Owners of British Ships Trading to the Port of Quebec, 19 June 1845, printed in 'Return of Government Correspondence with reference to the Act to regulate the Shipping of Seamen in the Port of Quebec', Canada, *Sessional Papers* (W.W.), vol. 8 (1849), App. No. 2.

3. Letter from An Old Mariner: 'Desertion of Seamen', *Quebec Gazette,* 10 June 1839: Stan Hugill, *Shanties and Sailors' Songs* (London 1969), pp. 52, 95-97, 201-2 and *Shanties from the Seven Seas: Ship Board Work-Songs and Songs used as Work-Songs from the Great Days of Sail* (London 1961), pp. 75, 145, 147, 149.

4. Rules and Regulations of the proposed Marine Register Office, Quebec, adopted by Shipowners and Masters in Quebec Trade, 26 July 1820, printed in 'Return of Government Correspondence ...', Canada , *Sessional Papers* (W.W.), vol. 8 (1849), App. No.2.

5. *Quebec Morning Chronicle,* 8 June 1848.

6. David Montgomery, 'The Working Classes of the Pre-Industrial American City, 1780-1830', *Labor History,* IX (1968), 16; Hugill, *Shanties and Sailors' Songs,* pp. 49-50. According to Arthur Lower, the sailor's only occupation in port was drinking. *Great Britain's Woodyard: British America and the Timber Trade, 1763-1867* (Montreal 1973), pp. 193-4.

7. J. I. Cooper's failure to investigate the nature of the work force in the years preceding the formation of the Quebec Ship Labourers' Benevolent Society in 1857 led him to adopt Dr. James Douglas' assertion that the vessels were loaded in the 1830s and 1840s by their sailors assisted by hired immigrants. 'The Quebec Ship Labourers' Benevolent Society', *Canadian Historical Review,* XXX (1949), 337; James Douglas, *Journals and Reminiscences of James Douglas, M.D.* (New York 1910), p. 147.

8. Canada: 10 & 11 Vict., Chap. 25: An Act for regulating the Shipping of Seamen at the Port of Quebec: Report of the Special Committee on an Act for regulating the Shipping of Seamen, with minutes of evidence, Canada, *Sessional Papers* (R.R.R.R.), vol. 8 (1849), App. No. 3; Resolutions of a Meeting of Citizens of Quebec, *Quebec Morning Chronicle,* 19 June 1848; *Quebec Gazette,* 15 September and 25 October 1848.

9. *Shipping and Mercantile Gazette,* 22 November 1848. For a sampling of like-minded colonial opinion see *Montreal Transcript,* 15 May 1849.

10. New Brunswick: 12 Vict., Chap. 50: An Act for regulating the Shipping of Seaman at the Port of Saint John: Observations of J. H. Brown, Registrar-general of Seamen upon points of difference between the Quebec and Saint John legislation, New Brunswick, *Journal of the House of Assembly,* 1850, 225-6. For the Quebec influence on this legislation see Archives Nationale du Québec, Quebec Board of Trade Minute Book, 1842-1852, 14 Nov 1848.

11. John Wilson to President of the Board of Trade, London, 10 November 1867, Public Record Office, C.O. 42/665, ff. 497-514.

12. E. P. Thompson & E. Yeo (eds.), *The Unknown Mayhew: Selections from the Morning Chronicle 1849-1850* (London 1971), p.316; *Quebec Morning Chronicle,* 6 June 1851, 11 October 1854, 31 May 1860; *Quebec Mercury,* 16 August 1864; *Morning News* (Saint John), 4 November 1870.

13. William R, Lord, *Reminiscences of a Sailor* (Edinburgh & Glasgow 1894), pp. 22-23; *Quebec Morning Chronicle,* 5 November 1852. By the 1860s the right of ships'

officers to give orders to hired labourers and workmen on their ships in port was being challenged in Saint John, *Morning Freeman* (Saint John), 22 September 1863.

14. *Shipping and Mercantile Gazette,* 19 November 1856. A good illustration of the disruptive effects of crimping on sailors' port work is provided by the experience of the Belfast vessel, *Queen of the West,* in Quebec in 1860. *Quebec Morning Chronicle,* 12 July 1860.

15. *Quebec Morning Chronicle,* 24 July 1866; *Daily Telegraph* (Saint John), 17 October 1872; *Halifax Morning Chronicle,* 4 May 1875.

16. *Morning Freeman,* 25 August and 26 December 1868; *Daily Telegraph,* 14 January 1873. The monthly rate was set at $25 and probably applied to the coasting and West Indian trades. As explained in note No. 1 the wages for the run to Britain were between two and three times the local monthly rate. The shipping master in Saint John reported wages by the run in 1873 to be $55. Canada, *Sessional Papers,* VII (1874), No. 3, Sixth Annual Report of the Department of Marine and Fisheries, App. No. 19, Report of the Shipping Master, Saint John, p. 142.

17. *Morning News,* 7, 8, 9 November 1872; *Daily Telegraph,* 8 November 1872: Public Record Office, Board of Trade 99/857/48712.

18. *Morning News,* 15, 16, 26 February 1877: *Morning Freeman,* 15 February 1877: *Daily Telegraph,* 15 February 1877.

19. *Daily Sun* (Saint John), 18 April 1888.

20. Royal Commission on the Relations of Capital and Labor in Canada, *Evidence-Quebec,* Part. II, p. 754.

21. RCRCL, *Evidence-Quebec,* Part. II, pp. 1085-6; *Daily Sun,* 19 March 1886.

22. RCRCL, *Evidence-Quebec,* Part. II, pp. 1079, 1085; *Shipping and Mercantile Gazette,* 12 January and 17 November 1877.

23. *Daily Telegraph,* 17 October 1872.

24. Canada: 36 Vict., Chap. 129: An Act respecting the Shipping of Seamen. Henry Fry, a prominent Quebec shipowner, claimed in 1873 that: "When seamen desert, labourers have to be employed in their stead at four times their wages." *Quebec Mercury,* 20 January 1873.

25. See for example *Morning Freeman,* 1 and 4 May 1875; *Maritime Notes and Queries: a Record of Shipping Law and Usage,* vol. II (1875), pp. 89-90, 100-1.

26. *Maritime Notes and Queries,* vol.III (1876), p. 59; *Morning Freeman,* 21 September 1871: Canada, *Sessional Papers,* XIV (1880-1), No. 6, Annual Report of the Department of Marine and Fisheries, Supp. 1, App. No. 39, Report of the Chief of the Quebec River Police, p. 332; *Shipping and Mercantile Gazette,* 12 June, 4 and 25 August, 12 September 1879, 20 July 1880; Lord, *Reminiscences of a Sailor,* p. 21; *Quebec Morning Chronicle,* 3 July 1858; *Quebec Mercury,* 23 May 1872; RCRCL, *Evidence-Quebec,* Part II, pp. 757-8.

  Quebec ship labourers were exceedingly uncompromising. It was reported that one captain who made his crew put a bateau load of deals on board after regular work hours was forced next day by the ship labourers' gang to make his crew replace the deals in the bateau before the day's loading operations could commence. *Daily Sun,* 31 July 1886.

27. *Daily News,* 19 and 20 April 1877; *Daily Telegraph,* 20 April 1877.

28. *Daily Sun,* 24 April 1884, 20 March 1885, 2 December 1886, 23 April and 26 August 1887; RCRCL, *Evidence-New Brunswick,* pp. 64, 238; *Daily Sun,* 5 April 1889. For a discussion of ship labourers in Saint John in the 19th century, see J.R. Rice, 'A History of Organized Labour in Saint John, New Brunswick, 1813-1890' unpublished M.A. thesis, University of New Brunswick, 1968, pp. 20-109 *passim.*

29. RCRCL *Evidence-Quebec,* Part II, p. 842.

Sea-going Shipping at Quebec (in numbers of ships)

Registry	1869-70 In	1869-70 Out	1874-5 In	1874-5 Out	1879-80[*] In	1879-80[*] Out	1884-5[*] In	1884-5[*] Out	1889-90[*] In	1889-90[*] Out
British	820	756	540	686	410	349	270	215	208	140
Scandinavian	271	194	269	303	168	170	214	232	201	191
Total ships	1091	999	854	1041	657	611	541	561	477	403

[*] By 1879-80 Canadian-registered vessels were listed separately from the British in the statistics and are not included here. In 1889-90 Canadian vessels out totalled 51 which means that the British plus Canadian totals equalled the Scandinavian.

SOURCE: Canada, *Sessional Papers,* IV (1871), No. 2; IX (1876), No. 2; XIV (1880-1), No. 2; XIX (1886), No. 1; XXIV (1891), No. 3.

30. This form of wording can be found in the printed agreement or articles signed by sailors on British- and Canadian-registered vessels. See Canada: 36 Vict., Chap. 129: An Act respecting the Shipping of Seamen.

31. *Daily Telegraph,* 24 April 1877. Sailors in Hull, England in 1881 refused to work the cargo during a waterfront strike on the ground that there was no specific mention of such an obligation in their articles. Raymond Brown, *Waterfront Organisation in Hull 1870-1900* (Hull 1972), p. 31. The approach of both the Saint John and Hull sailors was firmly in the tradition of forcing the shipping authorities to be precise in drawing up agreements with crews.

32. For the use of seamen on steamships and sailing vessels in Saint John during labourers' strike in the 1880s see *Daily Sun,* 28 April 1883, 6 August 1884, 15 and 16 July 1886.

CHAPTER
12 RESPONSIBLE GOVERNMENT, THE EMPIRE AND CANADA

Responsible government was the most written about and, in the view of some, most important subject in Canadian history until as recently as the mid-twentieth century. It was "the crowning achievement of the second empire," according to the doyen of Canadian historians, Chester Martin, the "Great Experiment" in British North America that demonstrated how a colony could evolve into a nation yet remain within the British Empire. The centrepiece of this thesis was Lord Durham's *Report* with its suggestion of colonial self-government. The multiracial British Commonwealth, a significant international institution, was a product of the recommendations in Lord Durham's *Report* and their celebrated application in British North America.

In Canada, as well as in Great Britain, the notion of the brilliance of responsible government had served several generations of politicians and historians. In Canada it formed the essential link in the Whig-Liberal interpretation of a past divided into forces of light and forces of darkness. The 1848 success of Robert Baldwin and L.H. Lafontaine against the philistine Tories was but the first in a series that led through George Brown, Edward Blake and Wilfrid Laurier to William Lyon Mackenzie King, the grandson of William Lyon Mackenzie, the Upper Canadian leader of the Rebellion that helped to precipitate Durham's *Report* and responsible government.

In Great Britain Durham's *Report* and the concept of self-government played an essential role in the justification of Empire. This idea is traced in the first selection, "The Influence of the Durham Report," by Ged Martin. He examined far more than the title indicates, for he discussed responsible government in Canada as part of Imperial history and indicated how several myths or traditions were invented, especially the notion that the *Report* was the "Magna Charta for the empire." As Martin stated in his conclusion of this highly critical paper, it is time for "more realistic perspectives," since "the British empire is all but an episode of the past."

That process had been underway in Canada for some time. Chester Martin's *Foundations of Canadian Nationhood* (1955), quoted above, was almost the last study of its type. The relevance of the empire was in sharp decline as he wrote, and Canadians were already reconstructing a past with less emphasis on Britain. Nowhere was this more obvious than in Quebec. Separatist historians denounced all accommodation with the English, including responsible government. Others, such as Jacques Monet, sought to understand rather than condemn the generation of the 1840s that turned its back on rebellion. In "French-Canadian Nationalism and the Challenge of Ultramontanism" Monet provided a convincing analysis of the unlikely alliance of political nationalism and conservative Catholicism in Canada East that would survive for a century. "A funny thing indeed," he concluded, "had happened to French-Canadian nationalism on its way to responsible government."

A more recent examination of responsible government by S.J.R. Noel, the third selection, is almost exclusively political. In "Brokerage and the Politics of Power Sharing" he offered a Canadian "politics of byzantine complexity," in which "almost everything was legitimate grist to a political mill." Noel did not ignore the role of the British nor that of the ultramontane nationalists, but in his analysis the key was brokerage politics, the product of astute politicians in a unique Canadian situation.

Suggestions for Further Reading

Buckner, Phillip A., *The Transition to Responsible Government: British Policy in British North America, 1815-1850*. Westport, Conn.: Greenwood Press, 1985.

Careless, J.M.S. (ed.), *The Pre-Confederation Premiers: Ontario Government Leaders, 1841-1867*. Toronto: University of Toronto Press, 1980.

————, *The Union of the Canadas: The Growth of Canadian Institutions, 1841-1857*. Toronto: McClelland & Stewart, 1972.

MacNutt, W.S., *The Atlantic Provinces: The Emergence of Colonial Society, 1712-1857*. Toronto: McClelland & Stewart, 1965.

Monet, Jacques, *The Last Cannon Shot*. Toronto: University of Toronto Press, 1969.

THE INFLUENCE OF THE DURHAM REPORT
Ged Martin

"It has long been recognised as the greatest state document in British imperial history." Thus in 1945 Sir Reginald Coupland described the Durham Report. Few works can have had such a chequered career as Lord Durham's *Report on the affairs of British North America.* Largely rejected by contemporaries and ignored for half a century, it became the most revered of texts for the Edwardian empire and continued to be regarded as the Magna Charta of the Commonwealth until the 1960s. As late as 1971 Ward could complain of "what ought to be known as the great Durham illusion," and the myth was still strongly enough entrenched in standard works to provoke two strong and independently inspired assaults.[1] Although the old orthodoxy is by no means universally rejected, it is strange that it should have remained unchallenged for so long. The case for the Report's significance was riddled with logical fallacies. For instance, the celebratory generation of imperial historians recognised that the Report made little impact on influential contemporaries, yet never wholly explained how its initial failure could be reconciled with their claims for its formative influence. Second they failed to see how far Durham's two main aims were contradictory. The Report recommended both the anglicisation of the French and the introduction of a form of local self-government in which the French themselves would take part. These historians never explained how a powerful French minority could be persuaded to commit communal suicide, and failed to understand that the Report was intended as a Utilitarian "package" of interdependent points. Durham's hostility to the French was apologetically downgraded by Coupland to "the only first-rate blunder in his *Report,*" when arguably it was an inaccurate diagnosis of the Canada he so briefly visited and it certainly proved to be no prediction for its future. Third, although admitting that the scheme of local autonomy sketched in the Report would have been highly restricted, historians have tended to excuse Durham by their own speculation about his posthumous reactions to imperial change. Sir Charles Lucas in 1912 gave a good example of this technique:

> it is of course a vain thing to ask what a man would have said or done many years after his death, in altered conditions or with fuller knowledge. A broad-minded man moves with the times, and Lord Durham would never have stood still....

although in this case Lucas implicitly forbade Durham's shade to move further into the twentieth century by hurriedly adding that the Report offered "a British prescription for a British community," and not "a recipe for non-British

From Ronald Hyam and Ged Martin (ed.), *Reappraisals in British Imperial History* (Toronto: Macmillan, 1975), 75-87. Reprinted by permission of the author.

communities."[2] The point remained, however, that historians were prepared to measure Durham's contribution to the development of the empire not by the limitations of what he actually wrote, but by how his ideas might have changed had he outlived his generation. No one ever thought of allowing this indulgence to Lord North or Sir Francis Bond Head. Durham actually considered allowing British North America to elect members to parliament at Westminster, which suggests that in 1838 at least he did not contemplate further extensions to colonial autonomy. No doubt this charity was largely inspired by Durham's untimely death—a parallel would be the apologia for John F. Kennedy's Vietnam policy, just as Campbell-Bannerman's death earned him a reputation for "solving" the South African problem. Benevolent as it may be, it is a misleading argument. It is easy to overstress the extent of Durham's radicalism. He was not in general politics the most single-mindedly radical or adaptable of his contemporaries, and he was certainly not the most prescient in colonial affairs. Others wanted Canada to have more freedom than he proposed—men like Howick, Roebuck and H. S. Chapman, whose involvement in the subject was deeper than Durham's own: as late as August 1837 he dismissed Canada as an "unfortunate business" in which he did not intend to be involved. By concentrating on "the great Durham illusion" historians have succeeded in conveying the impression that no serious thought had been given to the Canadian problem until he offered his brilliantly simple device of responsible government. In fact the problem of reconciling colonial autonomy with metropolitan supremacy was a good deal more complicated than the Report's superficial analysis allowed, and contemporaries were unimpressed by it precisely because they knew how much detailed and fruitless consideration the problem had already received. Historians, however, allowed themselves to be dazzled by Durham's confident prose, and took for perspicacity what infuriated contemporaries dismissed as arrogance. The *Morning Herald,* for instance, attacked the Report as a device for

> representing John George Lambton Earl of Durham as the only wise, discreet, virtuous, and truly intelligent statesman that ever cast a glance at Canadian affairs.[3]

The Report had its background in a mission flawed in many respects. One major weakness lay in Durham's poor relations with the ministers he served and with Melbourne the prime minister in particular; in a mission in which mutual confidence was vital, neither side really trusted the other. Opportunities for misunderstanding were increased by Durham's vanity. He certainly laid great stress on his own magnificence, and arguably an imposing front was necessary for the success of his mission. His mistake was to delay his departure for nearly four months while assembling his equipment and retinue. While Canada was in crisis, the high commissioner made apparently leisurely arrangements for his journey, including the dispatch of his racehorses, plate and an orchestra. Durham's vanity was in itself a source of amusement, but coupled with his poor judgement of men and issues it became a fount of disaster. His most obvious blunder was the appointment of Thomas Turton and Edward Gibbon Wakefield, the first a central figure in a sensational divorce case, the second a former inmate of Newgate prison as a result of his abduction of an under-age heiress. Parliamentary attacks on the appointments helped to widen the breach between Durham and Melbourne. Yet damaging as these associates were, Durham's fundamental error of judgement was his reliance on his kinsman Edward Ellice, a great Canadian landowner and an influential figure in politics. Ellice was regarded by French Canadians as "one of their bitterest, most indefatigable, and most powerful enemies." From the outset Durham adopted Ellice's view of the Canadian problem and consulted closely with him. Even before the high commissioner had left Britain, he had adopted the francophobic view which was a fundamental weakness in the mission. In the short term he missed a great opportunity. French Canadians did in fact welcome him as a deliverer, and Durham alone among British statesmen at the time had the stature to rally moderate leaders into the communal partnership which Elgin presided over a decade later. By dashing French hopes, and adding the insult of anglicisation to the injury of repression, Durham made subsequent reconciliation of French and British more difficult. And in the long run no Canadian settlement could be made which involved the mastery of one over the other.[4]

The major weaknesses of the Durham mission—his authoritarian behaviour, his lack of sympathy for French Canada and his poor choice of advisers—were all united in the affair of the Bermuda Ordinance. This dealt with his proposed exile of leading rebels. Overruled on a technicality, Durham responded by an abrupt and spectacular resignation. Resignation in itself seemed bad enough— an abandonment of a difficult post—but the timing was unfortunate, and Durham's behaviour was widely criticised. Durham now intended to adopt a dignified and tenable position by writing a report giving his views on Canada— although from the government's point of view a report in London was a poor second to a settlement in Quebec.

Writing a report on Canada increased Durham's dependence on Edward Ellice, both for his influence in politics and for his interest in Canada, and who noted: "Ld. Durham is going to produce a plan & hopes & intends to redeem himself thereby." Subsequent events suggest that Durham or his staff intended the Report to appeal over the heads of the ministers to the Crown and the people. For most of December a haughty feud continued between Durham and the Whig leaders. There is little sign that ministers intended to give much weight to Durham's opinions. The hostile Melbourne bluntly said: "I do not expect much from Durham's suggestions." Thus at the time the Durham Report was being written, there was no question of guilty ministers eagerly awaiting the pronouncement of a triumphant high commissioner. The government was united in condemning Durham's behaviour, and Durham himself was hoping to re-establish his position in politics.[5]

In January 1839 work on the Report progressed rapidly and, as the Tories had cynically predicted, Durham and the ministers patched up their feud to avoid open conflict when parliament met. Naturally, as the Report was produced hurriedly, it contained mistakes. But its fundamental error was much more one of analysis. In 1836-7 the government, under the prompting of Howick, aided by James Stephen of the Colonial Office, had been moving towards the idea of British North American federation. This was broadly the plan which Durham took to Canada. Not the least unfortunate aspect of his resignation was that it aborted an intercolonial convention about to meet in Quebec to discuss the possibility of a federal union with the Maritimes. But a second French rebellion, late in 1838, seemed to rule out any federal solution. After two revolts in a year, a French Canadian unit in a federation had become unthinkable. Under Ellice's influence, Durham turned instead to a legislative union, in which the French would be outvoted centrally but without the nuisance of their own local legislature. Poor communications made a legislative union with the Maritimes virtually impossible, although Durham hoped they would eventually be incorporated. Circumstances, then, dictated a union of the Canadas alone: a solution which Ellice and the Lower Canada British minority had advocated as far back as 1822. Durham concluded that the French identity would have to disappear altogether. A Canadian Union would have an English-speaking majority, which immigration would reinforce. As a result, the French would be anglicised.

Durham had thus shifted from the idea of a locally autonomous federation based on some accommodation between French and British colonists, to proposing a locally autonomous legislative union, in which immigration was to be used to swamp and absorb the French. As a solution it contained several basic weaknesses. To give the united province any measure of self-government was tantamount to inviting the French, who formed about two-fifths of the population, to acquiesce, if not co-operate, in their own demise. So open an avowal of an anglicising policy could be expected to unite the French in self-defence. Furthermore, in attempting to define the scope of local self-government, Durham reserved to British imperial control not only foreign relations, but the local constitution, tariffs and public lands. The limitation of colonial autonomy had been and remained an almost insoluble problem. Durham had simply drawn up an agenda for disagreements, while giving little indication how imperial supremacy in the disputed areas could be upheld. As Sir George Arthur pointed out, Durham had never had to handle a colonial legislature. At one and the same time he wished to thrust the British imperial government into Canadian affairs, while driving the French into opposition. It pointed to a period of instability for, as Bagot was to complain in 1842, it was one thing to rely on the anglicising effects of immigration in the long term, but quite another to keep the government going in the short term.[6]

The Report was not well received. Praise from liberal journals was hardly enthusiastic, and several promised "due attention to this important document hereafter" and then abandoned the subject. Only the radical *Spectator* and the *Colonial Gazette,* both influenced by Wakefield, loudly defended the Report. It was certainly not "greeted with public acclamation by Englishmen of liberal sympathies," as Burroughs has claimed. The *Morning Chronicle* contented itself with saying "that great good will be effected by the mere circulation of this report." Even the radical *Leeds Mercury* was less enthusiastic than it had expected to be. The field was left virtually clear for the opposition press to denounce the Report for "its mass of verbiage and its scantiness of fact," and to dismiss it as a "fatiguing mass of impertinent trifling and newspaper trash." It was widely noted that one of its major recommendations, the Canadian Union, was "whether good or bad, practicable or impracticable, not a *new* scheme," and one which Durham had adopted, "without giving it any very profound consideration." Many thought the Report superficial, containing nothing which "any man of third-rate abilities who had visited Canada for three or four months might have written just as well." In February 1839 the Durham Report was certainly not recognised as the charter of the colonies.[7]

A recent writer has confused press reception of the Report with its influence on the cabinet. However, there is independent evidence that ministers were little more impressed than journalists. Howick criticised the limitations Durham wished to place on colonial self-government. Russell, although listing the Report in a cabinet memorandum as one of the authorities for union, rejected Durham's portrait of communal hostility and thought his restrictions on self-government unenforceable. Normanby, who succeeded Glenelg as colonial secretary in February 1839, argued that the government should check "whether Durham speaks the opinions of the Representative Men of the English Party in Lower Canada." To Normanby, Durham's own recommendation was not important. What mattered was whether union was supported by the Lower Canadian minority: "If so this would decide the point of attempting to form a Legislative Union." Other ministers cared even less for Durham. When Normanby wished to tell him what policy was to be adopted, the cabinet refused its permission. Ministers had already decided not to consult Durham during their own deliberations. It seems unlikely, then, that the cabinet decided "to adopt in principle Durham's proposal for a legislative union of the Canadas," as Burroughs has restated the myth. Overall, they realised, as Durham had realised, that there was no real alternative to union. Following the rebellions, the French could not be allowed to control Lower Canada. Yet equally a liberal government could not indefinitely deprive a North American colony of a constitution. Union with English-speaking Upper Canada was the only way out. Nor did the principle of union come from Durham. Ellice had drawn up a complicated scheme of his own in December 1838, but as part of his policy of rehabilitating Durham, he did not submit it to the cabinet until February, when "Durham had paved the way by giving his report." When ministers accepted the principle of union, they decided to draw up a bill "mainly founded on Ellice's project." Its provisions were rewritten in detail several times in the next year, but the Report offered little guidance about the mechanics of Union. In its final form the government's scheme differed from Durham's on one important point, by giving Upper Canada equal representation with the lower province. Above all, it is difficult to see what other scheme the cabinet could have adopted. As Russell said, it was "the best principle of a settlement, not because the principle of a union did not in itself contain very great difficulties, but rather from the difficulties attending every other plan." When they did adopt it, they began with Ellice's scheme, not Durham's.[8]

Nor is there much evidence from parliamentary debates on Canada in 1839-40 that the Report had many supporters. It seemed, as Greville noted, "enormously long," and even Stanley, a leading opposition spokesman on colonial affairs, did not have time to *"skin"* it until June 1839. It seems unlikely that ministers or anyone else had "got it almost by heart" as Brougham emphasised, in what was ironically one of the more favourable references to the Report—apart from those of Durham's secretary, Buller. Durham did not prove a good parliamentary authority. In the summer of 1840 Melbourne quoted parts of the Report, arguing that "whatever opinions might be entertained of some parts of it," it was still "a very able and impartial view of the matter." A week later he found it necessary to qualify even that endorsement:

> There were unquestionably many things in that report which he did not praise, and which he did not think were prudent matters to be brought forward, and which he thought it would have been wise to have omitted, and he therefore did not say, that the report was an important authority.

Nevertheless he still thought "it contained much which was of very great value, and which was well deserving of consideration and attention. A month later the sympathetic *Colonial Gazette* complained that the Report was "well-nigh forgotten" in Britain.[9]

It may of course be argued that the impact of the Report either on the British government or British opinion is only a secondary question, and that the important issue is its reception in the colonies. It might also fairly be objected that British policy stemmed less from prescript than from reaction to events in the colonies, and hence Durham's Report could have had a major roundabout effect in shaping the empire. Among French Canadians Durham's impact was traumatic, though hardly in line with his intentions. His advent inspired a burst of optimism in a beaten people: all would be well at last, it was felt, for if the British really wished French Canada ill, how could they have sent their most liberal statesman to start a new chapter in its government? Disillusionment was rapid and brutal, as Durham moved openly into the arms of the francophobe British minority in Lower Canada, and excluded the French from all but minor appointments. The satirical journal, *Le Fantasque,* which had applauded Durham's firmness in July 1838, was by October lamenting that they had regarded him as a god when he was only a man after all. The Report's cold dismissal of French Canadians as a people without history or literature helped to spur on a local renaissance, paradoxically helping to ensure that within a couple of decades French Canadians had a more self-consciously local culture than the still derivative British colonials. Durham's relations with the French were doubly disastrous. They had trusted him almost alone among British statesmen, and he might have been able to draw them into a British American federation based on a new chapter of communal co-operation. Instead he chose to trumpet a policy of assimilation which was threatening enough to reinforce French bitterness, but never in fact consistently enough adopted to destroy French identity. A good opportunity for statesmanship was discarded in favour of an unreal project of social engineering. When M-P. Hamel edited a French edition of the Report in 1948, he made it clear that the suspicions remained.

In Upper Canada the Report was mainly important for its effect on parties. The reformers, previously split into factions, were able to rally behind "responsible government," and Durham flags appeared at their meetings. Egerton Ryerson, the Methodist leader, was able to cover his tracks by insisting that Durham's view of responsible government differed from previous conceptions which he had opposed. Yet the unity which the Report gave the party was one of tactics rather than of intellectual revelation. Leading reformers differed in their responses to Sydenham's blandishments in 1841, and Ryerson himself broke with them in defending Sir Charles Metcalfe in 1844. Nor was this surprising. Responsible government was hardly a novel issue in colonial politics. Indeed, reformers had to make this point in order to defend themselves against the charge that they wished to abandon established constitutional forms in favour of the crochet of a visiting English peer. Nova Scotia's Joseph Howe denied in 1840 that the responsible government cry had been "learned from the Earl of Durham.... I am glad to have such an authority in support of my argument; but it was not learned from him." The Nova Scotian Assembly had been asking

> for a government responsible in local affairs, before his lordship saw this continent.... I am happy to have the concurrence of so celebrated a man; but I think it right to show that we are not mere followers of his report, but had asked for responsible government before that document appeared.

Taking a wider perspective, it may be noted that the Report made less impact in New South Wales, despite extravagant claims by Wakefield. Few newspapers there seemed even to realise the full import of Durham's proposals. The *Sydney Herald* dismissed the Report as "not of very great interest," and the *Australian* thought it lacked "the least pretension to originality, or grandeur of thought." D. Beer concludes that in 1839 at least, the Report "had no significant effect on public opinion in New South Wales," and he indicates that the same was probably true of other Australian colonies. The English language press in South Africa was more enthusiastic. The *Graham's Town Journal* thought it one of the most massy, and the same time one of the most lucid, documents which we have been privileged to read. Every thing like ornament has been discarded; and yet, as a whole, it is extremely beautiful.

It predicted that Durham's mission would be a landmark "in the future history not alone of Canada, but of all the British colonies." The *Commercial Advertiser* in Cape Town went further: "Nor will the mere colonist alone discover his face as in a glass looking into this Report." It would shake the foundations of the peerage and of the established church. Yet when it came to deciding how far Durham's lessons from the two communities in Canada applied to multiracial South Africa, there was less certainty. The *Commercial Advertiser* published thirteen extracts from the Report over two months, but never delivered its promised article on the Report's application to the Cape. The subject faded quietly away.[10]

What influence then did the Durham Report have on the Victorian empire? Conventionally it has been seen not only as the blueprint for colonial self-government, but also as a general picture of colonial affairs which made it, in Craig's phrase, "a document of enduring value and interest." There is a logical problem in arguing for the informative value of the Report. Lucas admitted that it contained "one or two instances of direct mis-statement, and more numerous instances of obvious exaggeration," while Coupland pointed to "some palpably unfair judgements in it and one or two small mistakes of fact." The real informative value of an inaccurate report may be doubted. Furthermore, even where the Report provided a mass of evidence, it understandably arranged it to make a particular point. MacDonagh has commented that the Report's evidence on emigration, although sensational enough to administer "a very healthy jolt" to the government machinery involved, was largely "high-purposed manipulation of evidence to antecedently determined ends," amounting to "an unprincipled indictment." The Report was anything but the "first-rate piece of research" which G. S. Graham asserted as recently as 1970. Nor should the Durham Report be considered in isolation. It had been preceded by two major inquiries into Canadian affairs, the parliamentary committee of 1828 and the Gosford commission of 1836-7, both of which had produced lengthy and less hurried reports. Admittedly, Durham had the burden of administration to cope with, but it is none the less true that the amount of enquiry on which his findings were based fell far short of that given to other major reports. Compare Durham's mission, for instance, with that carried out upon penal settlement by J. T. Bigge as special commissioner in Australia between 1819 and 1821. Durham spent five months in Canada; Bigge spent seventeen in Australia. Durham's impressions of the 400,000 people of Upper Canada were based on a ten-day steamboat tour; Bigge took six days to inspect a few hundred convicts at Port Hunter. Durham did not visit the Atlantic colonies at all, and confessed to "no information whatever, except from sources open to the public at large" about Newfoundland; Bigge spent three months in Van Diemen's Land. Not surprisingly, Durham's account was often superficial. Unfortunately, it was some of his more sensational comments which lingered. The Whig government was embarrassed by his description of "two nations warring in the bosom of a single state." Russell labelled the description as "highly coloured," since if hostility between the two communities was so bitter it hardly made sense to unite the provinces. Similarly, Durham's picture of a striking difference between American prosperity and Canadian stagnation seems to have been occasionally referred to in the 1840s and 1850s.[11]

These peripheral references make all the more striking the absence of extended reference to the Report during discussions of the painful emergence of Canadian self-government in the 1840s. Exactly how Canada achieved a system of parliamentary self-government in 1847-8 remains a matter for debate. One quaint suggestion, recently made, is that "it was the apparent resolution of the French question in 1840 that made British ministers willing to concede greater self-government"—which makes nonsense of the political crises under Bagot and Metcalfe. The concession of virtual tariff autonomy to the colonies in 1846 made possible a wider measure of self-government than Durham had contemplated, and the adoption by the USA of an expansive policy under the presidency of Polk made a Canadian settlement more vital. The British concession of responsible government to the mainland colonies of North America in 1847-8 represented a timely realisation that Canada at least could not be retained in any other way. Durham's idea of local self-government had involved the quasi-presidential rule of an anglicising governor, controlling a wide field of reserved topics, including land policy and tariffs. Canada in the late 1840s evolved a cabinet system explicitly based on Anglo-French partnership, and evading a close definition of local and imperial powers. When the first contentious legislation of the LaFontaine-Baldwin ministry was attacked in the British parliament, Brougham alone quoted Durham, and quoted his view of the "war of races" to criticise the idea of partnership with the French. In fact as early as 1842, when Bagot was forced to admit the French to office, it was clear that Durham's mixture of autonomy and anglicisation had gone astray. In the *Morning Chronicle,* Charles Buller was unwise enough to hail the new ministry as the triumph of Durham's policy. *The Times* took up the subject:

> It is not a little curious, and reflects no great credit on the penetration of the late Lord Durham, to compare the working of the new union of the Canadas, adopted in accordance with his report, with the purposes for which he recommended it.

Subsequent events had not inspired "implicit reliance on the predictions of that well known, and certainly very interesting report." A year later it returned to the theme, blaming Durham for the "strange combination of blunders" by which a union designed to end French influence had given them control of the province.

> He it was ... who contrived to revive and set the seal upon the worst suspicions of the French Canadians by the same act which conferred upon them an unlimited power of avenging themselves—to unite the evils of provoking tyranny with those of the most dangerous concession.

Yet few of the many detailed press discussions of the problem of colonial self-government in the 1840s mentioned Durham's views. Perhaps the reason was revealed by a journalist reviewing one of Sir Francis Head's books in 1846, who said of Durham's Canadian mission, without any trace of hostility: "It has been hinted that mental malady afflicted his Lordship at this period of his political career, and it is but fair to think so."[12]

How then did the Report become an imperial symbol? Its rediscovery came late in the nineteenth century. Historians trained in the Whig tradition found in its clear and vigorous style an equivalent of Magna Charta for the empire. Durham's career, both heroic and tragic, added to the Report's stature as an imperial testament. Moreover, with hindsight it was easy to minimise the theoretical weaknesses of Durham's idea, and credit him with prophecy. Irish and South African problems seemed to give the Report a continuing relevance. In the latter case, those who wished to anglicise the Afrikaners and those who wished to reconcile them could equally appeal to his authority. The South African crisis of the 1890s marked, however, a rediscovery, if not a rescue, of a largely forgotten document: the republication of the Report in 1902 was the first reprinting since 1839. This process is notably evident in the case of John X. Merriman of Cape Colony. Although born in England, Merriman had opposed British intervention in South African affairs from his entry into its politics in the 1870s, and consequently disapproved of the Anglo-Boer War. In 1900 he argued strongly in favour of clemency for Cape rebels who had risen in support of the Afrikaner armies, and he began to read about the Canadian rebellions of the 1830s in order to seek precedents. Admiration for Durham's policy led him to read the Report, finding in the picture of communal hostility "much that applies to this country, but much that is so different." He was struck by the fact that he should have known so little about it.

> Lord D's Report is, of course, the Magna Charta of Colonial Government much talked about but seldom if ever read or looked at, and I say this with a guilty blush as being a very tardy reader myself of this particular document.

In 1902 he observed that Elgin and Durham had established the British Commonwealth. "Yet how few even know their names?"[13]

Within a few years this complaint could no longer be made. A mammoth biography by Reid in 1906 and a magisterial edition of the Report by Lucas in 1912 enshrined Durham firmly in the imperial pantheon. The report thus became the symbol of the empire's success in solving one of its problems, namely relations with the colonies of settlement. In the twentieth century, it had less relevance than ever. For the empire as a whole, the central problem was with non-European peoples, to whom Durham's anglocentric remedies could hardly be applied. In Canada, national status was replaced by cultural partnership as the major issue, and here the Report became a positive embarrassment. Historians' references gradually faded from the passionate to the merely polite, a process which ironically helped to shield the Durham myth from basic challenge. Consequently "what ought to be known as the great Durham illusion" continued to be enshrined in general histories and respected textbooks. Probably the myth was a benevolent one in the twentieth-century empire, stressing some of its more liberal elements and incidentally making its demise less painful. Now that the British empire is all but an episode of the past, we should discard the Durham myth in order to seek more realistic perspectives on the imperial experience.

Notes

1. For editions of the Report, C. P. Lucas (ed.) *Lord Durham's Report on the affairs of British North America* (1912); R. Coupland (ed.) *The Durham Report* (1945), and quotation from cxlvi; G. M. Craig (ed.) *Lord Durham's Report* (1963). For biographies: S. J. Reid *Life and letters of the first Earl of Durham 1792-1840* (1906); C. W. New *Lord Durham* (1929). For criticisms: J. M. Ward in *HS* xiv (1969-71) 592; R. S. Neale "Roebuck's constitution and the Durham proposals" ibid. 580-90; Ged Martin *The Durham Report and British policy* (1972), on which this essay is based. For recent strong affirmations of the importance of the Report: N. Mansergh *The Commonwealth experience* (1969) 30ff; and G. S. Graham *A concise history of the British empire* (1970) 152-4.

2. Coupland (ed.) *Durham Report* clxi; Lucas (ed.) *Lord Durham's Report* I 311, and cf. Craig (ed.) *Lord Durham's Report* vii.

3. C. R. Sanderson (ed.) *The Arthur Papers* (1957-9) I 274; for Head *The Times* 28 Aug 1869; Lord Esher *The girlhood of Queen Victoria* (1912) I 280; New *Lord Durham* 78; *The life and times of Henry Lord Brougham* (1871) III 502 Durham to Brougham 7 Dec 1827; Reid *Life and letters* II 143-4 Durham to Ellice, 27 Aug 1837; *Spectator* 17 Nov 1838, 1084-5; *Morning Herald* 11 Feb 1839.

4. L. C. Sanders (ed.) *Lord Melbourne's Papers* (1889) 428-9 Melbourne to Durham 18 Jul 1838; *The Times* 21 Sep 1863; *Spectator* 17 Nov 1838, 1084-5; National Library of Scotland, Ellice Papers E30, Durham to Ellice, private, [Jan 1838] 43-4; J. Monet *The last cannon shot* (1969) 19-20; PAC, Chapman Papers, O'Callaghan to Falconer, Apr 1838; W. Ormsby "Lord Durham and the assimilation of French Canada" in N. Penlington (ed.) *On Canada: essays in honour of Frank H. Underhill* (1971) 37-53.

5. Buller to Mill (most private) 13 Oct 1838, A. G. Doughty (ed) *Report of the Public Archives for the year 1928* (1929) 74-6; Ellice Papers, Lady Durham to Ellice [1 Dec 1838] 151-2; Russell to Ellice 24 Dec 1838, 24-5; Russell Papers (microfilm B-970), Russell to Melbourne 9, 12 Dec 1838; University of Durham, Grey Papers, Howick Journal 5 Jan 1839; Melbourne to Russell 19 Dec 1838, Sanders (ed.) *Lord Melbourne's Papers* 443-4.

6. Ellice Papers, E30, Durham to Ellice 18 Jan 1839, 79-80; Melbourne to Russell 11, 23 Dec 1838, Sanders (ed.) 441-2, 444; Lucas II 168-73; Arthur to Colborne 6 Apr 1839, Sanderson (ed.) *Arthur Papers* II 110-11; PAC, Derby Papers (microfilm A-30), Bagot to Stanley (private) 10 Jun [Jul] 1842.

7. H. E. Carlisle (ed.) *A selection from the correspondence of Abraham Hayward, Q.C.* (1886) I 68-70; *Leeds Mercury* 8 Dec 1838; *Globe* 8 Feb; *Examiner* 10 Feb, 90-1; *Manchester Guardian* 9 Feb 1839; P. Burroughs (ed.) *The colonial reformers and Canada 1830-1849* (1969) 128; *Morning Chronicle* 9 Feb; *Leeds Mercury* 16 Feb; *Morning Herald* 9, 11 Feb; *Morning Post* 9, 18 Feb 1839.

8. P. Burroughs *CHR* LV (1974) 320-2; Howick to Durham 7 Feb 1839; A. G. Doughty (ed.) *Report of the Public Archives for the year 1923* 338-40; Russell Papers, memo, 28 Mar 1839, Normanby to Russell [misdated 1841]; *3PD* XLVII 3 Jun 1839, 1254-75; Grey Papers, Howick Journal 2, 24 Mar, 13 Apr 1839; P. Burroughs *The Canadian crisis and British colonial policy, 1828-1841* (1972) 107; PRO CO. 880/1, Ellice to Melbourne (private) 24 Feb 1839, enclosing plan of 21 Dec 1838, 10-12; *3PD*, XLIX 11 Jul 1838, 174-5.

9. H. Reeve (ed.) *Greville memoirs—the second part* (1885) I 162; Graham Papers, microfilm 31, Stanley to Graham 6 Jun 1839; *3PD* XLIX 26 Jul, 852, and LV 30 Jun, 7 Jul 1840, 232, 515; *Colonial Gazette* 12 Aug 1840, 529.

10. M-P. Hamel (ed.) *Le Rapport de Durham* (1948) 16, 26, 50-1; Monet *Last cannon shot* 17-20, 24-33; M. Wade *The French Canadians* (1968 ed.) I 284-5; G. W. Brown "The Durham Report and the Upper Canadian scene" *CHR* XX (1939) 136-60; G. M. Craig *Upper Canada: the formative years 1734-1841* (1963) 264-71; D. C. Harvey "Nova Scotia and the Durham mission" *CHR* XX (1939) 176; D. Beer "A note on Lord Durham's Report and the New South Wales press, 1839" *JRAHS* LIV (1968) 205-7; *Graham's Town Journal* 23 May 1839; *South African Commercial Advertiser* 8 May 1839.

11. Craig ix; Lucas I 116; Coupland xlviii; O. MacDonagh *A pattern of government growth 1800-60* (1961) 135, 131; Graham *Concise history of the British empire* 152; J. Ritchie *Punishment and profit: the reports of Commissioner John Bigge* (1970); *Lucas* II 202, 16 and cf. *3PD* XLVII 3 Jun 1839, 254-75. Durham's comments on Canadian economic backwardness were cited by *The Times* 12 Aug 1848, and in a speech by Elgin, *Daily News.*

11. Jan 1855.

12. P. Burroughs *CHR* LV (1974) 320-2; *3PD* LVI 19 Jun 1849, 455-7; *The Times* 29 Oct 1842, 16 Dec 1843, 5 Dec 1846.

13. P. Lewsen (ed.) *Selections from the correspondence of J. X. Merriman* (1960-69) III 196-9. When the Report appeared in 1839, Abraham Hayward, a lawyer and journalist sympathetic to Durham, noted that it was thought to be "well-written, but all well-informed people say that it is superficial and one-sided." This verdict remains closer to a balanced judgement than Graham's recent claim that the Report was "a great, if not the greatest landmark in the history of the British Empire." (Carlisle *Correspondence of Hayward* I 68-70; Graham 153.)

FRENCH-CANADIAN NATIONALISM AND THE CHALLENGE OF ULTRAMONTANISM

Jacques Monet

A funny thing happened to French-Canadian nationalism on its way to re- sponsible government. It became ultramontane.

At the end of the 1830s French Canada was in ferment. Under British dom- ination for some 75 years, the French had succeeded in surviving, but not in developing by themselves a full, normal, national life. They had kept the es- sentials: their ancestral land, their French language, their Catholic Faith, their time-honoured and peculiar jurisprudence, and their long family traditions. But they needed a new life. The seigneurial system could no longer hold the growing population, the economy lagged, the problems of education had reached such an impasse that the schools were closed, and the old civil code no longer ap- plied to modern circumstances. Above all, the upward thrust of the growing professional middle class created a serious social situation of which the rebel- lions of 1837-38 were only one expression. Clearly, if the struggle for national survival were to hold any meaning for the future, French-Canadian nationalists needed new solutions.

They were divided, however. Inspired by the ideology of Louis-Joseph Papineau some considered *la survivance*[a] could be assured only by political iso- lation in a territory over which French-Canadians would be undisputed masters. Militant idealists, they were led by John Neilson and Denis-Benjamin Viger until Papineau returned to politics in 1847. Others, broader minded and more practical, held to a doctrine of which the Quebec editor Etienne Parent was the clearest exponent, and which Louis-Hippolyte LaFontaine translated into politics. They reasoned that it was the flexibility of the British constitutional sys- tem that could best assure not only their acquired rights, but also (by means of self-government) the certain hope of a broadening future for their language, their institutions, and their nationality.

Before achieving responsible government, however, LaFontaine needed to accomplish two things. He had to forge the unity of his people in favour of British parliamentary democracy and, along with this, form a united political party with the Upper Canadians. Neither was easy. In the years immediately following the rebellion French Canada's strongest sympathies belonged to the leaders of the Viger-Neilson group, believers neither in responsible govern- ment nor in Union with Upper Canada. After the election of 1841, for instance, out of some 29 members elected by French-Canadian ridings, LaFontaine could

---

From Canadian Historical Association, *Annual Report* 1966, pp. 41-55. Reprinted by permission of the author and the Canadian Historical Association.

[a] survival

count on only six or seven to be sympathetic to his views. By 1844, he had suc-ceeded in persuading many more—at least he could then count on some two dozen. But not before the end of the decade could he be certain of victory, for until then Papineau, his followers, and especially his legend remained one of the strongest forces in the country. Still, after a decade of fistfights on electoral platforms, scandals, riots, and racial fury; after a brilliant, dynamic, and flex-ible partnership with Robert Baldwin, LaFontaine became in 1848 the first Canadian Prime Minister in the modern sense and, by means of the British Constitution, the first French-Canadian to actually express and direct the as-pirations of his people.

He had also gradually, and all unwittingly perhaps, presided over the mar-riage of ultramontanism with the practical politics and the nationalist ideology of his party. At the beginning of the decade, the hierarchy and priests of the Roman Catholic Church in French Canada hardly conceived that practical party politics could be their concern, nor did they think of adding significantly to the nationalist theme. They worked behind the scenes; and, in 1838, for in-stance, after deciding to oppose the Union, they composed and signed an unpublicized petition which they sent directly to London to be presented to the Queen. But in 1848, during the crisis which consecrated the practice of re-sponsible government, they openly took sides with LaFontaine's party, and allowed their newspapers to give approval to his administration. Likewise, at the time of the rebellions, most of the priests, and especially those among the hierarchy, had officially disassociated themselves from what seemed to be the main preoccupations of the leading French-Canadian nationalists. "Des mauvais sujets ... prétendus libéraux, attachés à détruire dans nos peuples l'amour de la religion,"[b][1] Bishop Jacques Lartigue of Montreal called the *Patriotes,* while Archbishop Signay of Quebec tried to explain to his flock that Colborne's dev-astating march against the rebels had been undertaken "pas à dessein de molester ou maltraiter personne, mais pour protéger les bons et fidèles sujets, pour éclairer ceux des autres qui sont dans l'erreur et qui se sont laissés égarer."[c][2] Within a decade later, however, they openly wrote and talked of the doctrine that the Catholic Faith and French Canada's nationality depended one upon the other. "Tous les rapports qui nous arrivent des divers points du diocèse," the *Mélanges Religieux* reported on July 7 1843, about the Saint-Jean-Baptiste day celebrations, "prouvent combien sont vifs et universels les sentiments de reli-gion et de nationalité de nos concitoyens. Partout ces deux sentiments se sont montrés inséparables dans les coeurs: la pompe et les cérémonies religieuses ont accompagné les démonstrations civiles et patriotiques ... C'est parce que nous

---

[b] "Some evil subjects..., claiming to be liberal and determined to destroy our people's love of religion."

[c] "not with the intent of bothering or molesting anyone but to protect true and loyal subjects, to enlighten those others who are in error and have allowed themselves to wander from the correct path."

sommes catholiques que nous sommes une nation dans ce coin de l'Amérique, que nous attirons les regards de toutes les autres contrées, l'intérêt et la sympathie de tous les peuples ... Qu'on nous dise ce que serait le Canada s'il était peuplé exclusivement d'Anglais et de Protestants?"[d] Of course, much happened between 1838 and 1848 to change the thinking of both nationalists and Catholic clerics.

One very important thing was the advent of Ignace Bourget. A short time after succeeding to the See of Montreal in 1840, this earnest and authoritarian Bishop made it clear how much he intended to renew the face of Catholicism in French Canada. During his first year—incidentally, after successfully reasserting in an interesting conflict with Poulett Thomson the doctrine of Papal supremacy and of episcopal independence of civil authority—he had organized a great mission throughout his diocese, preached by Bishop Forbin-Janson, one of France's foremost orators. Between September 1840 and December 1841, the French Bishop travelled across Lower Canada, visiting some sixty villages and preaching rousing sermons—two of which Lord Sydenham attended in state at Notre-Dame—before crowds sometimes estimated at ten thousand. Bishop Bourget thus initiated close and large-scale religious contacts with France.

Indeed, while Forbin-Janson was still in Canada, the new Bishop of Montreal left on the first of some five voyages to France and Rome, a trip from which he would return carrying with him the reawakened energies of the Catholic revival. While in Europe, he held discussions with a cluster of interesting and influential Catholic ultramontane leaders. At this time, European ultramontanes—whose intellectual roots reached as far back as the quarrels between Philippe LeBel and Boniface VIII, the pope "beyond the mountains"—had outgrown the traditional belief that the Pope held doctrinal and jurisdictional supremacy over the whole Church. Brought up on DeMaistre's *Du Pape,* a book that urged Papal dominion over temporal rulers in all Church matters, and feverish with romanticism's revival of all things medieval, they urged the subservience of civil government to the papacy, of State to Church. They had not understood that there was a difference between the surrender of all men to God's will, and the obedience of civil society to the Pope. They were mistaken—but they were, perhaps because of this, all the more dogmatic, energetic, aflame with zeal: they directed newspapers, notably Louis Veuillot's *L'Univers,* entertained crucial political polemics over education, censorship, and "secret

---

[d] "All the reports that we receive from all over the diocese... prove how alive and widespread are religious and national feelings among our fellow citizens. These two sentiments have shown themselves to be inseparable in hearts everywhere: ceremony and religious rites have always been part of lay and patriotic demonstrations... This occurs because we are Catholics and a nation in this corner of America. As a result, we draw the attention of all other lands, the interest and sympathy of all peoples... We would like to know what Canada would be like if it were populated only with English and Protestants."

organizations"; by the 1840s, they had founded hundreds of pious societies for desirable ends, collected a multiplication of relics from the Roman catacombs, covered Europe with imitation Gothic, and filled their churches and parlours with Roman papier-maché statuary.

In Chartres, the Bishop of Montreal also had a long conversation with Bishop Bourget fell under their spell as soon as he arrived. In Paris he had long conversations with the Abbé Desgenettes, curé of the ultramontane cenacle at Notre-Dame-des-Victoires, and the founder of the Archconfraternity of the Most Holy and Immaculate Heart of Mary; he met Théodore de Ratisbonne, a convert from Judaism and the founder of the Daughters of Sion, Jean-Marie de Lamennais, the founder of the Brothers of the Christian Schools, and the most noted of them all, Louis Veuillot, who attended a sermon of Mgr Bourget's at Notre-Dame-des-Victoires and gave it a rave review in *L'Univers*. At Chartres, he was entertained by the compelling personality of the Abbé, later Cardinal, Louis-Edouard Pie, the future exponent of Papal infallibility at the Vatican Council. In Marseille, he was impressed by Bishop de Mazenod, another staunch defender of the Vatican; and in Rome, he was greeted by Fr. John Roothaan, the General of the Jesuits, with whom he spent eight days in retreat and meditation. Finally, several audiences with the kindly Gregory XVI crowned the series of discussions that made him the most ultramontane churchman of his generation in Canada.[3]

In Chartres, the Bishop of Montreal also had a long conversation with Bishop Clausel de Montals. The latter was a strong Gallican, but nonetheless the acknowledged champion in the fight for Catholic institutions against the State University. He doubtless recited for his Canadien colleague a long list of the dangers and evils of the *école laïque*.[e] For from that day onwards Mgr Bourget would battle tirelessly to keep the Church in control of education in Lower Canada. And all Canadian ultramontanes would follow him in this.

Back in Montreal, Mgr Bourget began injecting into the Canadien mood the full fever of his Roman creed. With a crusader's singleness of purpose, he arranged for the immigration from France of the Oblate and Jesuit Orders, of the Dames du Sacré-Coeur and the Sisters of the Good Shepherd; he founded two Canadian religious congregations of his own, established the Saint Vincent de Paul Society; carried out an extensive canonical visitation of his diocese, and pressed Rome to establish an ecclesiastical Province that extended within a few years to new dioceses in Toronto, Ottawa, British Columbia, and Oregon, "une vaste chaîne de sièges épiscopaux qui doit s'étendre un jour de la mer jusqu'à la mer: a mari usque ad mare."[f][4] He also organized a whole series of Parish revivals and religious ceremonies superbly managed to stir the emotion

---

[e] non-religious schools

[f] "a long chain of episcopal sees that one day must stretch from sea to sea: a mari usque ad mare."

of all classes. At Varennes on July 26, 1842, for example, before a huge crowd of several thousand, surrounded by some sixty priests and in the full pontifical splendour of his office, he presided over the crowning of a holy picture of Saint Anne, according to "le cérémonial usité à Rome pour de semblables solennités."[g] (The end of the day was, perhaps, more Canadien: "Tous ces feux," reported the *Mélanges,* "des salves d'artillerie ou de mousquetterie au milieu du silence d'une nuit profonde, après toutes les cérémonies de la journée, faisaient naître des émotions nouvelles inconnues."[h] [5]) Another time, in November 1843, he presided over a huge demonstration in honour of the transferral to the chapel of the Sisters of Providence of the bones of Saint Januaria, ancient Roman relics which he had negotiated away from the custodian of one of the catacombs. At this service, the golden reliquary was carried by four canons of the cathedral surrounded by eight seminarians bearing incense, and "la foule eut peine à se retirer, tant était grande son émotion."[i] [6] Throughout the 1840s, he ordered many more such occasions. For the blessing of the bells for the new towers of Notre-Dame Church, "on exécuta parfaitement le jeu du *God Save the Queen—Dieu sauve notre reine* auquel la bande du régiment fit écho de toute la force de ses instruments."[j] [7] (Yes, the ultramontanes were also strong royalists. The *Mélanges* often published articles on royalty, one of which began by praising "les principes d'honneur, de devoir, d'ordre, de générosité, de dévouement, qui dérivent de l'idée monarchique."[k] [8]) A not untypical reaction to this type of demonstration was that of the politician Joseph Cauchon who wrote to a colleague about the funeral of Archbishop Signay in October 1850: "Le deuil de l'Eglise était grandiose et solennel à l'extrême. L'installation du nouvel archevêque s'est faite avec une égale solennité. Il y a quelque chose de grand, de sublime dans ce développement des cérémonies soit lugubres soit joyeuses du Catholicisme."[l] [9]

The new Orders naturally aided Mgr Bourget with his ultramontanism—especially the Jesuits who began in 1843 to lay the foundation of Collège Sainte-Marie, an institution that would train so many energetic young na-

---

[g] "the rites used in Rome on similar solemn occasions."

[h] "After all the ceremonies during the day, at ll these artillery salutes and rifle-fire breaking the deep silence of the night stirred up strange new emotions."

[i] "the crowd could hardly hold back so greatly was it stirred."

[j] "we performed *God save the Queen — Dieu sauve notre reine* perfectly accompanied by the regimental band playing its instruments very loudly."

[k] "the principles of honour, of duty, of order, of generosity and of devotion that derive from the idea of the monarchy."

[l] "The mourning of the Church was great and solemn in the extreme. The installation of the new archbishop was carried out with equal solemnity. There is something great and sublime when Catholic ceremonies occur, be they sad or joyful."

tionalist Catholics. The *Mélanges Religieux* also helped. In this bi-weekly newspaper, the priests from the bishopric published over and over again long articles of praise for the papal states, and copious excerpts from the works of leading ultramontanists: speeches by the Spanish conservative Donoso Cortés, Montalembert's famous oration on the Roman question, Mgr de Bonald's pastoral letter "contre les erreurs de son temps,"[m] and long book reviews such as the one condemning Eugène Sue's salacious *Les Mystères de Paris* for trying to "répandre sur la religion et ses pratiques tout l'odieux possible."[n] [10] They also issued vibrant appeals to Canadian youth to join their movement: "Vous voulez être de votre siècle jeunes amis, vous voulez marcher avec lui? ... Avez-vous trouvé mieux où reposer votre âme que dans les oeuvres immortelles des DeBonald, de Maistre, de Chateaubriand, de Montalembert, du Lamartine *catholique,* de Turquety?"[o] [11] They also gave news of Catholicism throughout the world, concentrating especially on the independence of the Papal States and the University Question in France. "Pour parvenir à remplir leur mission," the *Mélanges* noted on March 31, 1846, "les Éditeurs n'ont rien épargné; ils ont fait venir à grands frais les meilleurs journaux d'Europe, *L'Univers, L'Ami de la Religion, Le Journal des Villes et des Campagnes de France,* le *Tablet* de Londres, le *Freeman's Journal* de New York, le *Cross* d'Halifax, le *Catholic Magazine* de Baltimore, le *Catholic Herald* de Philadelphie, le *Propagateur Catholique* de la Nouvelle-Orléans."[p] In a word, the *Mélanges* opened a window on the Catholic world. And through it there blew in the high winds of ultramontanism, which, for the Canadiens, felt so much like their own aggressive and assertive nationalism.

Through it there also came for the clergy a novel regard for the layman. Since the Restoration in Europe, the Catholic Bishops and priests had achieved some success there in reintegrating the Church into educational life and social services. Very often they had done this with the assistance of influential laymen. Through the *Mélanges* publication of articles and speeches by these European ultramontane politicians, the Canadien priests gradually developed a fresh respect for their own lay politicians. They began to think of new ideas

---

[m] "against the errors of the present time,"

[n] "spread as much filth as possible on our religion and practices."

[o] "Young people, do you wish to be part of your century and march with us? ... Have you found a better spot to find comfort for your souls than in the immortal works of DeBonald, Maistre, Chateaubriand, Montalembert, of the Catholic Lamartine or Turquety?"

[p] "In order to carry out their mission ... the Publishers have spared nothing; they have brought in at great expense the best newspapers from Europe: *L'Univers, L'Ami de la Religion, Le Journal des Villes et des Campagnes de France,* the *Tablet* from London, the *Freeman's Journal* from New York, the *Cross* from Halifax, the *Catholic Magazine* from Baltimore, the *Catholic Herald* from Philadelphia, the *Propagateur Catholique* from New Orleans."

on how they could work with them. In fact, with the coming of responsible government the old ways which the priests had grown accustomed to were passing into history forever. The Union had marked the end of the courteous and courtly style which the Bishops and the British governors had so carefully devised over the years to fuse the good of the throne with the good of the altar. Now, effective political power was passing from the hands of Governors-General to those of the Canadien electors. And if the Church was to exercise the influence which the priests felt in conscience it must, then the clergy must begin to deal directly with the politicians and the people.

Besides, they were finding nationalist politicians whom they liked. Indeed, by the middle of the decade, it was becoming obvious how much LaFontaine's followers and the priests seemed made to understand each other. The debate on the Union, during which they had been on opposite sides, was settled. And since then, they had forged new personal friendships. In Quebec, politicians such as René-Édouard Caron, Étienne-Pascal Taché, and especially Joseph-Édouard Cauchon, the editor of the influential *Journal de Québec,* enjoyed frequent hospitality at the Séminaire. Taché and Cauchon were also close correspondents of the Archbishop's secretary, the talented and ubiquitous abbé Charles-Félix Cazeau. In Montreal, LaFontaine's close friend, Augustin-Norbert Morin, also received a cordial welcome at the bishopric, especially from Mgr Bourget's *Grand-Vicaire,* Mgr Hyacinthe Hudon. So did other partisans like Lewis Thomas Drummond and Joseph Coursol. Indeed, as these priests and politicians grew to admire each other, a new esteem was also developing between their leaders, between the new Bishop of Montreal and the man who in 1842 had become French Canada's Attorney-General. Despite initial suspicion on both their parts, Bourget and LaFontaine were by temperament made to understand each other. Both were heroes to duty, strong-willed leaders, unyielding in their principles, and expert at manoeuvring within the letter of the law. Especially they had this in common that each one thought in absolute terms that he was in total possession of the truth. Neither could accept from an adversary anything but complete conversion.

Thus it was that slowly within the womb of LaFontaine's party, despite appearances, the pulse of the clerico-nationalist spirit began, faintly, to beat.

None of these things—Bishop Bourget's trip to Europe and its effects in Montreal, the historical turn in Canadian politics caused by responsible government, the new intimacy between ultramontanes and nationalists—none could weigh enough to bring the priests officially into LaFontaine's party. But they did prepare the way. Then, in 1846, the public discussion over a new Education Bill and over the funds from the Jesuit Estates revealed to the clergy which politicians were its natural allies and which were not. The Education Bill of 1845, proposed by Denis-Benjamin Papineau, the great tribune's brother, who was

Commissioner of Crown Lands in the Viger-Draper administration, did not satisfy the clergy. Although it provided for the Curés being *ex officio* "visitors" to the schools, it did not give them the control they wished. They therefore began a campaign to have the project amended in their favour.

The *Mélanges* took the lead, repeatedly emphasizing the close connection between education and religion. "Nous ne comprenons pas d'éducation sans religion, et conséquemment sans morale," it had written back in November 8, 1842, in words which could easily have been inspired by Bishop Bourget's conversation with Clausel de Montals, "et nous ne voyons pas ce qui pourrait suppléer à son enseignement dans les écoles. Que sera donc l'instruction et l'éducation des enfants sans prières, sans catéchisme, sans instruction religieuse et morale quelconque?"[q] Even as the Bill was being debated, the *Mélanges* kept up the pressure, receiving great assistance from A.-N. Morin, "ce monsieur dont le coeur est droit,"[r] as one curé wrote.[12] From his seat on the Opposition benches, with the aid of his colleagues Taché, Drummond, and Cauchon, Morin proposed amendment after amendment to bring about a system which would happily unite clerical authority on the local level with centralized control by the Superintendent at the Education Department. "M. Papineau, auquel j'ai eu le plaisir d'administrer quelque dure médecine pour lui faire digérer son Bill d'Éducation, ne veut pas que l'éducation soit religieuse," Cauchon reported to the abbé Cazeau. "J'ai dit, moi votre ouaille, qu'une éducation dépouillée de l'instruction religieuse mènerait à de funestes résultats."[s] [13] Finally, in mid-1846, Denis-Benjamin Papineau bowed to the pressure, and accepted the Morin amendments.

If the Bishops accordingly felt happy about the Act in its final form, they owed it in great part to the support of politicians like Morin and his friends. At the same time, they were receiving support from LaFontaine's friends on another critical issue: the Jesuit Estates.

The problem of these lands which had been granted by a succession of French Kings and nobles to serve as an endowment for education, had definitely passed to the British Crown in 1800 at the death of the last Jesuit. Their revenues were used by the Colonial Office for any number of Government sinecures until 1832 when as a gesture of conciliation it agreed that they be

---

[q] "We cannot understand education separate from religion and therefore from morality ... and we don't see what could take the place of religious teaching in schools. What would the education and instruction of children be without prayers, without catechism, without religious and moral instruction at all?"

[r] "this gentleman whose heart is true,"

[s] "Mr. Papineau, to whom I had the pleasure of giving a nasty dose of medicine to help him digest his Education Bill, does not want education to be religious, ... As a member of your flock, I said that education that does not include religious instruction would lead to fatal results."

administered by the Lower Canadian Assembly. Then there began another struggle with the Catholic Bishops who claimed that they and not the Assembly were the true heirs of the Jesuits. By 1846 the controversy had reached the floor of the House, and the Provincial Government, led by Denis-Benjamin Viger, refused the Bishops' claim. As in the debate over Papineau's Education Bill, LaFontaine and his party supported the priests. LaFontaine, Morin (who had been acting as confidential advisor to the clergy on the question), Drummond, and Taché each delivered an impassioned speech against the "spoliation" of French Canada's heritage; Morin himself proposing that the funds be transferred entirely to the Church. Viger defended the Government's action on the grounds of precedent and Parliamentary supremacy. He won the vote. But in appealing to Parliamentary supremacy, he began a disagreeable discussion which continued in the press for over three months. At the end, it was clear how wide a division had taken place among French-Canadian nationalists: a division as explicit as the opposing doctrines of liberalism and ultramontanism.

While traditionally nationalist papers such as *Le Canadien*, and *L'Aurore des Canadas*, defending Viger, assailed the Church's position, *La Minerve, Le Journal de Québec*, and *La Revue Canadienne*, all LaFontaine papers, became like the *Mélanges* defenders of the Faith. In a series of articles probably written by Viger,[14] *L'Aurore* insisted that the Bishops had at most a very tenuous claim to the Jesuit funds which had never, in fact, belonged to them, and which, if the intentions of the donors were to be respected, should be applied to the whole territory of what had been New France. Since they were being spent exclusively in Lower Canada, as the Bishops themselves agreed was correct, then the revenues derived their title from the Imperial decision of 1832 which put them at the disposal of the "volontés réunies des pouvoirs exécutif, législatif, administratif"[t] of the Lower Canadian Assembly, and hence of the Union government which was its heir. When the LaFontaine press generally replied that the taking of the property from the Church in the first place had been a sacrilege, the argument rose to a higher level.[15] Running through precedents that went back to Justinian, La Régale, and the *coutumes*[u] of pre-Revolutionary France, *L'Aurore* retorted that since the Church's possession of property derived from the State's civil law, any change by the government could hardly be a sacrilege. To which, in best scholastic manner, the *Mélanges* retorted that since the Church possessed property by divine and natural right, civil recognition added nothing. And to this *L'Aurore*, in best liberal tradition, asserted that since nature knew only individuals, no corporate body such as the Church could claim existence by natural law.[16]

---

[t] "combined intentions of the executive, legislative and administrative powers"

[u] legal ordinances

And so the controversy proceeded. It was one which could not easily be resolved. For while the *Mélanges* was reasserting the doctrine so dear to the nineteenth-century ultramontane that the Church, by natural and divine right, was autonomous with respect to the State, Viger, brimming with the liberal's faith in the individual, denied any natural right to a corporate body. It was an argument that could not be settled for generations; indeed not until both the liberals and the ultramontanes, in the face of other problems, would come to modify their intransigence.

This was not the first difference of opinion that had brought Viger's party and the *Mélanges* into conflict. Back in 1842 they had measured paragraphs against each other over the interpretation of Bishop Lartigue's famous *Mandement* against rebellion in 1837; and at that time also they had been quarrelling from the viewpoint of opposing ultramontane and liberal doctrines.[17] Yet somehow that discussion had not caused any overt split. The 1846 one did—and soon with the reemergence of Louis-Joseph Papineau into political life, all bridges were broken between his party and the clergy. By 1849, the priests had become one of the great forces on the side of responsible government in Canada.

Having returned from his exile in liberal, anticlerical France, the great rebel found little to encourage him in Canada. He was disgusted by LaFontaine's politics, repelled by the growing power of the priests. Especially he suffered at being forced to witness his people's growing commitment to the British Connection. In the late fall of 1847 he issued what Lord Elgin called "a pretty frank declaration of republicanism,"[18] reviving his dreams of the 1830s for a national republic of French Canada. Around himself he rallied Viger's followers and a group of enthusiastic young separatists who edited the radical newspaper *L'Avenir*. They shared the rebel leader's philosophy: if it only depended on them they would win through the sharpness of their minds what he had not by sharpness of sword.

What struck the ultramontanes about Papineau and *L'Avenir* was of course not so much the attacks against LaFontaine and responsible government. It was their anticlericalism. As things turned out the republicans would hurt their own cause more than they would the Church: on the subject of responsible government, Papineau might conceivably weaken LaFontaine, especially if he concentrated on nationality and the defects of the Union. But by challenging the Church, the *rouges* merely helped to cement the alliance between LaFontaine and the priests.

On March 14, 1849, *L'Avenir* created quite a stir by publishing large extracts from the European liberal press on the Roman revolution which had forced Pius IX into exile and proclaimed Mazzini's republic. The articles were bitter: and the Lower Canadian republicans left little doubt where their own sympathies lay. The *Mélanges* took up the challenge. Through several series of learned front pages, it tried to show "les Messieurs de l'Avenir" how serious were "l'injustice et la faute qu'ils ont commises."[v] [19] But the young editors did not understand. They continued to insult the Pope; and at their Société Saint-Jean-Baptiste banquet that year, they replaced their traditional toast to the Sovereign by a defiant speech on "Rome Régénérée."[w] "Les journaux socialistes et anti-religieux sont sans cesse à vanter les hauts faits de MM.-les rouges à Rome," the *Mélanges* complained,[20] adding sadly that "la manie d'aboyer contre la soutane semble être à la mode."[x] [21]

Indeed it was. On July 21, 1849, *L'Avenir* led another attack which would lock the journalists in another discussion for two months: this time on tithing. "La dîme," it pronounced, "est un abus encore bien plus grand que la tenure seigneuriale."[y] Then later, when it began to campaign for the abolition of seigneurial tenure, the radical paper again attacked the Church for its ownership of seigneurial lands. In fact, it averred, one of the very reasons against the system was the amount of revenue which accrued from it to the Séminaire de Québec and other religious institutions.

On September 14, 1849, the *Mélanges* warned the republican youngsters at *L'Avenir:* "Nos adversaires ne doivent pas se dissimuler que par leur conduite et leurs écrits ils se font plus de tort qu'ils nous en font à nous-mêmes."[z] True enough. For as the priests were being attacked by their own political enemies, LaFontaine's publicists naturally came to the clergy's rescue. Thus, all during 1849, the *Journal de Québec, Le Canadien,* and *La Minerve,* defended the Church as if they themselves had been directly concerned.

While the dispute raged about the Pope's temporal sovereignty, for instance, Cauchon's *Journal* featured a serial on the subject by the French Bishop Dupanloup of Orleans, and another series covering several instalments by "Un Canadien Catholique" assailed *L'Avenir* for "la prétention qu'il entretient de catéchiser le clergé sur ses devoirs."[aa] So also on the issue of tithing: Cauchon spread an article defending the Church over the front page of three issues in October 1849, and underlined the connection between anticlericalism and the republicans: "Ce sont les aimables procédés du passé, la haine entre le peuple et ses chefs religieux pour assurer le triomphe des doctrines pernicieuses et anti-nationales."[bb] [22] When the *rouges* criticized the clergy's role in the schools, Cauchon answered by giving the clergy credit for *la survivance:*

---

[v] "the gentlemen of the future ... the injustice and the errors that they caused."

[w] "renewed Rome."

[x] "The socialist and anti-religious newspapers continually praise the great deeds of the left-wing gentlemen in Rome, ... The craze for barking at cassocks seems to be in style."

[y] "Tithing ... is a much greater abuse than the seigneurial land-hold system."

[z] "Our opponents must admit that their conduct and articles have done them more harm than us."

[aa] "A Catholic Canadian ... the claim of the newspaper to instruct the clergy on its duties."

[bb] "These are the friendly actions of the past, stirring up hate between the people and their religious leaders in order to guarantee the triumph of destructive and anti-national doctrines."

> D'où vient cette haute portée d'intelligence, ce caractère si beau, si noble, si grand de franchise, d'honneur, de grandeur d'âme et de religieuse honnêteté qui distingue nos premiers citoyens et qui contraste si étonnamment avec cette populace de banqueroutiers qui soudoient les incendiaires, les parjures, les voleurs et la lie des villes pour commettre en leur nom, pour eux, et à leur profit des crimes dignes de Vandales? Du clergé national, sorti des rangs du peuple, identifié avec tous ses intérêts, dévoué jusqu'à la mort, initié à tous les progrès des sciences modernes, des arts et du génie, aux tendances des sociétés actuelles.[cc][23]

Finally, when the *rouges* hurled insults, the editor of the *Journal* answered flamboyantly:

> Détrôner le Dieu de nos pères et lui substituer l'infâme idole du sensualisme, voilà leur but; vilipender le prêtre, calomnier son enseignement, couvrir d'un noir venin ses actions les plus louables, voilà leur moyen ... Quel but, quelle fin vous proposez-vous en livrant à l'ignominie le prêtre du Canada, votre concitoyen, votre ami d'enfance, l'ami dévoué de notre commune patrie! Aurez-vous relevé bien haut la gloire de notre pays lorsque vous aurez avili aux yeux de l'étranger ses institutions les plus précieuses, couvert de boue ses hommes les plus éminents dans l'ordre religieux et civil, enseveli sous un noir manteau de calomnies le corps le plus respectable de la société comme un cadavre sous un drap mortuaire?[dd][24]

Le Canadien wrote less lyrically, but like the *Journal,* it too came to the defence of the priests, and struck back at *L'Avenir.* It found that the republicans' articles "représentent trop de passion et par conséquent une notable injustice envers les hommes en qui le pays a confiance."[ee][25] And at the height of the

---

[cc] Where does this great amount of intelligence come from, these beautiful and noble traits of character filled with openness, honour, high-mindedness and religion that contrast so amazingly with the qualities of the bunch of bankrupts who bribe the arsonists, the perjurers, the thieves and the scum of our towns and cities to commit crimes worthy of the Vandals in their name, for them and for their gain? These virtues come from the national clergy issuing forth from the ranks of the people, at one with its interests, devoted for life, aware of all the progress made in modern science, the arts and knowledge as well as of the trends in today's societies.

[dd] Casting down the God of our ancestors and raising up the foul idol of self-indulgence in His place — such is their aim; vilifying the priest, slandering his teaching, covering his most praiseworthy actions with black poison — such are their methods.... What end, what goal do you intend by bringing to shame the priest of Canada, your fellow citizen, your friend since childhood, the devoted friend of our common fatherland! Will you have raised the glory of our country when you have debased its most valuable institutions in the eyes of foreigners, covered with mud the most eminent men in religious and civil life, buried under a black coat of slander the most respectable part of society like a corpse in its shroud?

[ee] "contain too much passion and, as a result, a great amount of injustice towards the men in whom the country has confidence."

temporal power dispute, it noted how the same republicans who praised Mazzini had also supported those who burned down the Canadian Parliament buildings, and signed the manifesto demanding Annexation to the United States.

In return, of course, the priests supported LaFontaine. At the time of Papineau's Manifesto at the end of 1847, during the general election that swept LaFontaine to the final achievement of responsible government, reports from different parts of Lower Canada came in to Montreal that "certains prêtres, même à Montréal, ont prononcé en chaire des discours presqu'exclusivement politiques."[ff] [26] But more important still than such electoral advice was the increasing involvement in party politics of the *Mélanges Religieux* and its junior associate in Quebec, the weekly *Ami de la Religion et de la Patrie*. Edited by Jacques Crémazie, *L'Ami* first appeared in early 1848 under the interesting motto: "Le trône chancelle quand l'honneur, la religion, la bonne foi ne l'environnent pas."[gg] It endorsed LaFontaine's ideas so unequivocally that Cauchon was glad to recommend it to his party leader for patronage:

> Il ne faudra pas oublier quand vous donnez des annonces d'en donner aussi à l'*Ami de la Religion* ... qui montre de bonnes dispositions et fait tout le bien qu'il peut.[hh] [27]

As for the *Mélanges,* since mid-1847 it had practically become a LaFontaine political sheet. In July 1847, the clergy had handed over the editorship to a twenty-one-year-old law student who was articling in the offices of A.-N. Morin: Hector Langevin, whose religious orthodoxy they felt well guaranteed by his two brothers (and frequent correspondents) in Quebec: Jean, a priest professor at the Séminaire, and Edmond who in September 1847 became secretary to the Archbishop's *Grand-Vicaire* Cazeau.

With mentors like Morin, the youthful editor soon threw his paper into the thick of the political fight. In fact he became so involved that at last the priests at the Bishopric felt they had to warn him (they did so several times) to tone down his enthusiasm for LaFontaine. He did not, however. His greatest service was perhaps the publicizing of the clergy's support for LaFontaine at the time of the trouble over Rebellion Losses. At the height of the crisis, on May 5, 1849, he issued the rallying call:

> En présence de cette activité des gens turbulents et ennemis de la Constitution, on se demande ce qu'ont à faire les libéraux [i.e. LaFontaine's supporters] ... Regardons nos Évêques, regardons nos prêtres, regardons notre clergé; il vient

---

[ff] "some priests, even in Montreal, have preached sermons from the pulpit that were almost entirely political."

[gg] "The throne trembles when it is not surrounded by honour, religion and good faith."

[hh] When you place advertisements, you mustn't forget to give some of them to the *Ami de la Religion* ... It shows that it is inclined in your favour and is doing all the good that it can.

de nous montrer l'exemple en présentant lui-même des adresses à Son Excellence Lord Elgin, et en en envoyant d'autres à notre gracieuse souveraine. Après cela hésiterons-nous à agir avec vigueur, promptitude et énergie? Hésiterons-nous à suivre la route que nous trace notre épiscopat, que nous trace notre clergé tout entier?[ii][28]

Half a year later he spelled out his full sentiments in a letter to his brother Edmond:

Si les rouges avaient l'autorité en mains, prêtres, églises, religion, etc., devraient disparaître de la face du Canada. Le moment est critique. Il faut que le ministère continue à être libéral tel qu'à présent, ou bien on est Américain, et puis alors adieu à notre langue et à notre nationalité.[jj][29]

Perhaps it was inevitable that during the closing years of the decade the French-Canadian clergy would come to play an increasingly political role. For with responsible government the Canadiens had, for the first time in their long national life, taken over the direction of their own destiny. And as the Catholic Church had long played an important part in fashioning their thought, it was natural for most of those on the political stage to welcome the support of the priests. Yet, would it have happened as effortlessly if Bishop Bourget had not fallen in with the *Veuillotistes*? If LaFontaine and Morin had not supported clerical schools in 1846? If Hector Langevin had not articled in Morin's office? If *L'Avenir* had not attacked the Papal States? Would it have happened at all if Denis-Benjamin Viger had won the election of 1844? If the Papineau legend had persisted? Be that as it may, the *bleu* alliance of priest and politician (since we can now give it its name) radically transformed LaFontaine's party and French-Canadian nationalism.

Except when the rights of the Church were in question, ultramontanes tended to consider politics as secondary. They concentrated rather on Church-State problems, thus gradually moving away from areas of cooperation with Upper Canada—especially at a time when the "voluntary principle" was converting Baldwin's party as ultramontanism was LaFontaine's. Gradually they came to appeal almost exclusively to ideas and feelings which were proper only

---

[ii] Faced with the actions of these troublemakers and enemies of the Constitution, we can only wonder what the Liberals [i.e., LaFontaine's supporters] have to do. ... Behold our bishops, our priests, our clergy; they have just shown us a good example by presenting addresses to his excellency Lord Elgin and sending others to our gracious sovereign. Will we hesitate to act with vigour, speed and energy after this? Will we hesitate to follow the path that our bishops, that all our clergy have traced out for us?

[jj] If the *rouges* had power in their hands, priests, churches, religion and so on would have to disappear from the face of Canada. The moment is critical. The ministry must remain liberal as it is at present. If it doesn't, we will become Americans and then good-bye to our language and nationality.

to French Canada. When he began in the late 1830s LaFontaine aimed at political and economic reforms in which both Canadas would share. In his famous *Adresse aux Électeurs de Terrebonne*,[kk] he described the problems of French Canada in political and economic terms alone. As the decade moved on, however, under pressure from his opponents and his followers, he found himself becoming more and more involved with ultramontanism and a narrower nationalism. Reluctantly, it seems. Late in 1851, several weeks after his resignation, he recalled to Cauchon, who had bragged about rallying the priests, how he had cautioned him about the faith-and-nationality theme. "Je me rappelle ce que vous m'avez dit," Cauchon admitted, "par rapport à la question nationale. Mais je vous répondais que c'était la seule corde qu'il était possible de faire vibrer avec succès."[ll][30] Later, to another admonition from the former premier, the editor of the *Journal de Québec* admitted that "la question de nationalité était délicate," but protested again that "c'était la corde qui vibrait le mieux. J'espère que vous avez en cela parfaitement compris ma pensée et que vous êtes convaincu que je n'ai pas voulu employer un moyen malhonnête pour atteindre mon but."[mm][31] LaFontaine had wanted to break with Papineau's particularist and republican nationalism. He appealed to a more general, open point of view, founding his hopes on cooperation with Upper Canada and in the British political system. Yet, in the end, he found himself the head of a party which tended to be as particularist as Papineau's (although for different reasons).

His party also turned out to be one which did not understand Parliamentary institutions. The ultramontanes were not rigid republicans like Papineau, but they were rigid Catholics, used to "refuting the errors of our time," with a doctrine which they proudly wanted as "toujours une, toujours sublime, toujours la même."[nn][32] They were accustomed to think in an atmosphere rarified by unchanging principles. Instinctively they reacted in dogmatic terms, pushing ideas to their limits—and students of the absolute make poor parliamentarians. The ultramontanes could not really understand parliamentary practice as LaFontaine and Parent had. They lacked political flair and skill in manoeuvring. They could not adapt to the gropings and costs of conciliation. To them, "rights" were an objective reality which could not be negotiated, only acknowledged. "Toleration" could not mean respect for an opposing opinion; at best it was a necessary evil. Applied to theology, their attitude might have had some validity

---

[kk] Speech to the Voters of Terrebonne

[ll] "I recall what you told me ... concerning the national question. But I told you that it was the only string that could be made to vibrate with success."

[mm] "the nationality question was tricky ... it was the string that vibrated the best. I hope that you have completely understood my opinion in this matter and that you are certain that I did not intend to use dishonest means to attain my goal."

[nn] "always united, always noble, never changing."

(although not for ecumenism!) but transferred to politics and nationalism—as inevitably it was—it could not but extinguish LaFontaine's hopes for a broadening democracy of the British type.

For years the *bleus* and their Upper Canadian colleagues supported the same men, but as the French party gradually concentrated so dogmatically on Faith and Nationality, there could be no true meeting of minds. Outwardly, LaFontaine's and Parent's wider nationalism seemed to have prevailed: responsible government and British Parliamentary institutions were secured. Also, a political party uniting Upper and Lower Canadians continued to govern the country for over a generation. But this was external appearance only: in reality, the party from which LaFontaine resigned in 1851 was assiduously becoming less concerned with the larger perspective than with the particular Church-State problems of French Canada; it was becoming decreasingly parliamentarian, increasingly authoritarian.

A funny thing indeed had happened to French-Canadian nationalism on its way to responsible government.

Notes

1. Archives de l'Archevêché de Montréal, Mgr Lartigue à G.A. Belcourt, 24 avril 1838.

2. Archives de l'Archevêché de Québec, Mgr. Signay à A. Leclerc, 25 novembre 1837.

3. I want to thank Fr. Léon Pouliot, author of *Mgr Bourget et son Temps* (2 vols., Montréal, 1955-56) and of *La Réaction Catholique de Montréal* (Montréal, 1942) for pointing out to me the importance of this trip in the formation of Mgr Bourget's thinking.

4. *Mélanges Religieux* [henceforth *MR*], 13 mai 1842.

5. *MR*, 28 juillet 1842.

6. *MR*, 14 novembre 1843.

7. *MR*, 4 juillet 1843.

8. *MR*, 27 janvier 1843.

9. *Archives de la Province de Québec* [henceforth *APQ*], Papiers Taché A50. Joseph Cauchon à E.-P. Taché, 9 octobre 1850.

10. *MR*, 20 novembre 1849.

11. *MR*, 26 novembre 1842.

12. *APQ*, Fonds de l'Instruction Publique. Lettres reçues. P. Davignon à J.-B. Meilleur, 23 novembre 1843.

13. Archives de l'Archevêché de Québec, DM H-245. Joseph Cauchon à C.F. Cazeau, 24 février 1845.

14. *L'Aurore des Canadas*, 3, 6, 13, 16 juin 1846.

15. *L'Aurore des Canadas*, 13 juin 1845.

16. *MR*, 26 juin 1846, *L'Aurore des Canadas,* 30 juin 1846.

17. Cf. F. Ouellet, "Le Mandement de Mgr Lartigue de 1837 et la Réaction libérale," *Bulletin des Recherches historiques,* 1952 (58), pp. 97-104.

18. Elgin-Grey Papers I, 102. Elgin to Grey, December 24, 1847.

19. *MR,* 30 mars 1849.

20. *MR,* 6 juillet 1849.

21. *MR,* 21 septembre 1849.

22. *Journal de Québec,* 2 octobre 1849.

23. *Journal de Québec,* 2 mars 1850.

24. *Journal de Québec,* 6 décembre 1849.

25. *Le Canadien,* 31 mai 1848.

26. *MR,* 14 décembre 1847.

27. Public Archives of Canada, MG 24, B-14. LaFontaine Papers. Joseph Cauchon à LaFontaine, 24 octobre 1849.

28. *MR,* 5 mai 1849.

29. *APQ,* Collection Chapais, 253. Hector à Edmond Langevin, 25 janvier 1850.

30. LaFontaine Papers. Joseph Cauchon à LaFontaine, 11 novembre 1851.

31. *Ibid.,* décembre 1851.

32. *MR,* 15 décembre 1843.

BROKERAGE AND THE POLITICS OF POWER SHARING

S.J.R. Noel

> *You are, of course, aware how strongly LaFontaine holds to the principle of the two majorities ... I think this quite absurd, and I am inclined to think so do you. Nevertheless I would have no objection to see it tried. I am sure it would strengthen us materially as a party ... [and] it would drive the Tories here mad...*
>
> —Francis Hincks to Robert Baldwin, 23 September 1844

I

The general election of 1847 brought LaFontaine and Baldwin triumphantly back to power, each with clear majority support in his own province.[1] The inauguration of their ministry marked the full and unambiguous acceptance by all concerned, including the British government, of the Baldwinian version of responsible government. In effect, the control of patronage that had been so completely exercised by Draper could no longer be withheld from the reformers. Theirs was seen as a party victory, and it was assumed that they would function in office as a party government; that is, it was assumed that they would have the right to allocate patronage as they saw fit. The new governor general, Lord Elgin,[2] who had replaced Metcalfe in 1846, would do nothing to upset this assumption. Unlike his predecessor, he had no mandate, and no desire, to be a "partisan governor." Instead, he aimed to establish "a moral influence," which, he hoped, would "go far to compensate for the loss of power consequent on the surrender of patronage."[3] The age of "governor generalities" had arrived. In fact, there was no sweeping introduction of an American-style spoils system, as the opponents of party government had feared. LaFontaine and Baldwin simply picked up where Draper had left off; that is to say, they dispensed the usual patronage in the usual way, but there was no wholesale turnover of public officials. Over the next few years, however, the public service was considerably expanded as the reform ministry pressed ahead with policies that expanded the role of government generally, and the newly created posts naturally went mainly to supporters of the winning side.[4]

Yet in the long run it was not the final establishment of responsible government that mainly distinguished the LaFontaine-Baldwin administration, nor even its record of progressive and reformist legislation in such areas as education and municipal government, but rather its entrenchment of a unique system of power-sharing. This was basically the system that the two leaders had successfully introduced in 1842-43, only now their positions were more secure, for not only had the British government decided not to intervene, but the whole course of the Draper administration had served to underline the essential practicality, even the necessity, of their approach. They were thus free to extend their system, refine it, and pragmatically adapt it to fit the political circumstances of the time. To satisfy Baldwin—who insisted that the conventions of Westminster-style responsible government could not be stretched to include a dual premiership—LaFontaine was nominally prime minister.[5] But in reality the ministry was a dual one in which they functioned as co-premiers, with each responsible for filling his allotted share of cabinet posts, the one in effect leading the government in matters pertaining to Lower Canada and the other in effect leading it in matters pertaining to Upper Canada.[6] Within the Assembly, their respective parties retained their separate identities; that is to say, it was a genuine coalition and not a blending or amalgamation of the two.

Given the notoriously unstable nature of Upper Canadian party alignments, however, the question was bound to arise of whether, or to what extent, such a system of government required adherence to the principle of "concurrent" or "double" majorities. In other words, in addition to the ministry's maintaining the confidence of the Assembly as a whole—which was now totally accepted as the basic principle of responsible government—did each *section* of the ministry (the Lower Canadian under LaFontaine, the Upper Canadian under Baldwin) have to maintain majority support *within its own section of the Assembly?* There could be no doubt that the ministry would enjoy a considerable advantage if each of its sections could do so. But there could also be no doubt that it was not a constitutional requirement. The real question, therefore was whether it was an *operative* requirement. And if it was, what were its implications? Did it mean, for example, that "sectional legislation should be the exclusive concern of the representatives from the affected section, and the majority from each section should govern only that section?"[7] Or did it mean only that the ministry should in general maintain the confidence of both sections of the House, but that on a day-to-day basis sectional exclusivity in the passage of legislation was not required? Also, considered more broadly, did it mean that, in future, whichever party won a majority in its own section would automatically be entitled to claim all of the ministerial seats for that section?

Both LaFontaine and Baldwin rejected the extreme sectionalist position, but otherwise their viewpoints diverged widely. LaFontaine supported the double majority principle in theory but recoiled from accepting its practical implications. In particular, as he had shown by his rebuffing of Draper's overtures in 1845, he was not prepared to participate in a coalition with the Upper Canadian conservatives. But it was only with great difficulty that he had been able to restrain some of his colleagues from doing so (for, following his own logic, they could see no reason why they should be deprived of lucrative ministerial positions for the sake of an alliance with the Upper Canadian reformers, who were plainly a minority in their own section.[8]) At the time, however, responsible government had not been conceded; now that it had been, it was unlikely that LaFontaine would be able to prevent such a coalition from being formed should the situation arise again. Baldwin, by contrast, consistently denied the validity of the double majority principle in theory but, as it turned out, was prepared to accept its implications in practice. Hence, when in June 1851 he failed to secure majority support in his own section in a division on a strictly sectional issue—an opposition motion to abolish the Upper Canadian Court of Chancery—he promptly resigned.[9]

On the face of it there could hardly have been a more stunning demonstration of the practical force of the double majority principle: Baldwin still had the confidence of the House as a whole, since the motion had been defeated by a margin of thirty-four to thirty, yet had regarded a defeat in one section as sufficient to compel his resignation from the ministry. But beyond that obvious fact the matter remained shrouded in ambiguity. The other Upper Canadian ministers did not resign with him, nor did he ask them to, and in giving reasons for his resignation he cited almost everything *except* the double majority principle—including the rise of "mere demagogue clamour," which he blamed for the defection of his former supporters.[10] The principle remained, as Stephen Leacock put it, "the will o' the wisp of the rival politicians."[11] But it was a will o' the wisp that would haunt every ministry that followed.

As LaFontaine and Baldwin had shown, however, if a ministry possessed majority support in both sections of the Assembly, it could enjoy the luxury of appearing to comply with the double majority principle without having either to define it or declare undying adherence to it. Not surprisingly, this was Hincks' preferred approach. And since no realistic alternative was ever found, it remained a convenient evasion to the end of the Union era. The trouble arose, as it did for Baldwin, when a ministry lost its majority in one section or the other, for to do so was to advertise weakness, nearly always to invite trouble, and frequently to compel resignation.

Finally, the double majority principle itself was in many respects less important, and less influential in the long run, than the assumptions and understandings on which it rested. This was something the Upper Canadian tories understood perfectly, which explains their persistent inclination to view it purely in instrumental terms. For them it was a means of combating the centralizing tendencies of the Union and of maintaining the essential separateness of Upper Canada. In this attitude, ironically, they were closer to the Lower Canadian French than to any other group.[12] Hence, in spite of the apparent absence of consensus, the Union of the Canadas was not ungovernable. What was required to make it work was above all a tacit acknowledgment by each ministry of the validity of the old provincial boundaries, for once that acknowledgment was made, other political arrangements became more readily negotiable—such as the operation of government on a double majority basis as far as possible; the sharing of executive power on a mutually acceptable basis; and the distribution of patronage within each section by the members of the cabinet drawn from that section.

II

To maintain such a system required continuous attention to the art of brokerage politics, especially in the Upper Canadian section of the coalition. Baldwin's party, for example, was never as cohesive and disciplined as LaFontaine's. Many of its moderate reform members were in fact quasi-independents whose support generally had to be secured issue by issue—perhaps in this respect accurately reflecting the view of their constituents, who likewise tended to show little consistent attachment to reform principles. In consequence, in addition to dealing with their French colleagues, the Upper Canadian ministers had also constantly to deal with their own loose assemblage of supporters—a collection of local patrons, aspiring brokers, disappointed claimants for office, individualists, and political mavericks, among whom there were also potentially disruptive differences of region, religion, and business connections. As Donald Swainson observes: "Backbenchers might be simple tools of powerful regional leaders; often, however, they were men of substance and local power who could and did challenge their party leaders, sometimes successfully."[13]

Moreover, the reformers' appetite for patronage was insatiable. As James Morris (who would later be appointed postmaster-general) wrote to Baldwin: "Now that we have fully assumed the helm of state you will feel no surprise at the numberless missives which reach you asking for all sorts of favors, reasonable and unreasonable."[14] Little wonder, therefore, that Baldwin attached such importance to brokerage skills in the filling of the Upper Canadian ministerial posts. Francis Hincks was of course indispensable, becoming in effect minister of finance (inspector-general), and in short order places were found for two more of the ablest brokers of their time, William Hamilton Merritt (who thus completed his passage across the political spectrum from tory to reform) and the young John Sandfield Macdonald,[15] the leading reform politician of Glengarry and the eastern counties—and the political heir of the old tory grand patron, Alexander Macdonnell, a line of succession that accurately reflected the evolution of the Upper Canadian clientele system as a whole in this period.

In its main features, the form of power-sharing that became entrenched in Union politics was of a type that has since become fairly common in culturally segmented societies and is now generally identified in the literature of political science as "consociational democracy." Its basic premise, as a theory, is that stable, electorally based political systems can function successfully in societies that are not culturally homogeneous as long as the following conditions are met: (1) at the top, power must be shared through some form of coalition, either formally or informally; (2) the political leaders of each cultural segment must be willing (and sufficiently trusted by their respective communities) to make the deals and compromises necessary to maintain the system (a process of brokerage usually labelled "elite accommodation"); (3) proportionality must be observed in the legislature and in the distribution of government benefits, including patronage; and (4) in general the principle of "mutual veto" must take precedence over the principle of rule by simple majority. The first three of these conditions obtained, if not perfectly, at least to a considerable extent in the political system of the United Canadas as it took shape during the LaFontaine-Baldwin era; and while more problematical, the fourth, in the form of the double majority principle, was at least honoured in the breach in that the political cost of contravening it was shown to be high. Though the LaFontaine-Baldwin coalition foundered in 1851, the system itself proved durable. Thereafter every administration more or less was modelled on theirs, and, though over the years deadlocks grew more frequent and effective coalitions harder to achieve, no practical alternative emerged until the idea of forming a federation of all the British North American colonies found currency in the 1860s—but that federation, too, would retain certain strong consociational features.[16]

III

That the Union of the Canadas came to operate in a manner different from that intended by its imperial architects, reinforcing and entrenching cultural particularisms instead of obliterating them, is perhaps not in itself very remarkable; after all, the consequences of constitutional change were as unpredictable then as they are now. But that it operated in a manner so diametrically at odds with that intended, and yet on the whole so peacefully and constructively, is very remarkable indeed and requires further explanation.

Part of the answer undoubtedly lies in the economic context, for the period of the Union also happened to be a period of sustained and at times even exponential economic growth. The working out of a new set of political arrangements and understandings thus took place within a generally favourable economic environment. This was not something for which LaFontaine and Baldwin, or for that matter any administration, could claim responsibility. The immensely productive agriculture of Upper Canada and the forest resources of Lower Canada and the Ottawa Valley needed only the right combination of external factors to produce a booming economy, and with the rising cycle of world trade after 1850, fuelled by British and American industrial growth, new steam technology, and the Crimean War (which removed competing Russian grain and Baltic timber from British markets), that combination had arisen. For example, exports of wheat and flour via the St. Lawrence grew from 3,645,000 bushels in 1849 to 4,547,000 in 1850 and to 6,597,000 in 1853. By 1856 it had reached 9,391,531 bushels. There was a similarly rapid increase in timber exports, both to the United States and Britain.[17] Ironically, in so far as government played a role, it was the public investment policies of the old Family Compact regime in Upper Canada, especially in improvements to the St. Lawrence waterway, that had now come to fruition—largely to the benefit of their reform opponents. But by the time the Hincks-Morin coalition lost power in 1854 it was abundantly clear that the Union of the Canadas, for all its peculiar anomalies, was a goose with a demonstrable capacity for laying golden eggs. Thereafter, for all but the most extreme sectionalists, it was the underlying premise of politics that whatever changes might be contemplated, nothing ought to be done that might risk killing that goose. And since it was also clear that the two Canadas were, and for the foreseeable future would probably remain, effectively separate entities, there was thus a strong incentive for the politicians of each to seek to maintain the Union through the processes of brokerage and accommodation, processes that success had endowed with an undeniable legitimacy.

A second factor that no doubt contributed to the distinctive *modus operandi* of the Union is more problematical but perhaps ultimately no less important: namely, the capacity of each subculture to produce political leaders who possessed a sure grasp of the mechanics of brokerage politics. This was most crucial in the early formative years, for the Union began as a constitutionally complex entity, unnecessarily burdened with hostilities and with an enormous potential for disaster. That it also began with two extremely able and creative political elites suggests that the old pre-1841 provinces of Upper and Lower Canada— of which those elites were the product—possessed more sophisticated political cultures than is generally realized.

Arend Lijphart has remarked on the extraordinary development of consociational devices in the United Canadas in spite of the fact that "not even a trace of prior consociational traditions can be detected." While this is obviously true, in the sense that neither Upper nor Lower Canada displayed the sense of cultural pluralism of the smaller European states that were once part of the Holy Roman Empire, and subsequently evolved consociational political systems, it is misleading to conclude (as Lijphart does) that there must therefore have occurred a "spontaneous development of a series of key consociational devices arising from the necessity of ruling a plural society in the United Province,"[18] *for that development arose out of a significantly different historical experience.* In Upper Canada, as we have seen, brokerage politics evolved out of an indigenous clientele culture and directly reflected the transition of the society as a whole towards more complex, triadic forms of economic and social interaction. So far from being "spontaneous," then, the growth after 1841 of consociational arrangements was but a natural extension of brokerage politics. It was not by accident that a key role was played by Francis Hincks, the broker *par excellence.* And though brokerage norms might have been relatively weaker in French-Canadian political culture (though that has by no means been established—they might only have been less commercially oriented), the shrewd understanding of them on the part of LaFontaine, A.N. Morin, and their successors suggests that they were by no means alien or unfamiliar. Moreover, there clearly existed in that culture, even more strongly than in Upper Canada, another of the important prerequisites for the success of a consociational system: a bond of trust between the elite and the mass of the people such that the elite were free to make the deals and accommodations necessary to ensure the system's survival. It was that bond of trust that allowed LaFontaine, for example, to work so effectively with Baldwin, A.N. Morin with Hincks, and later, George-Etienne Cartier with John A. Macdonald.

None of these embraced consociationalism as a doctrine or practised it as a matter of rigid convention. Instead, in practising it they usually trod (and occasionally crossed) the fine line that separates the pragmatic from the cynical. And even those who attempted at times to enunciate and defend the "double majority" principle, such as John Sandfield Macdonald, would not themselves be absolutely bound by it when circumstances dictated otherwise.[19] The result was a political system that was full of anomalies and inconsistencies. Some ministries, for example, were split down the middle along Upper Canadian-Lower Canadian lines, from top to bottom; others were partially split in a variety of ways; some maintained a semblance of administrative unity; others did not; and some actually were fairly well unified. Within the legislature, governing coalitions invariably formed across segmental lines, but their actual composition, in detail, was always subject to negotiation. Within each section of a ministry, moreover, the allocation of portfolios and the determination of who would be inside the cabinet and who outside it in practice involved a good deal of political horse-trading. Even the location of the capital was settled in a supremely realistic (and roughly consociational) way: Kingston was chosen first, but proved too much of a backwater to make a suitable capital; Montreal was next, but proved too volatile when an English mob rioted and set fire to the legislative chambers. Thereafter, from 1849 to 1865 the capital rotated between Toronto and Quebec City. This curious arrangement worked surprisingly well until, with Confederation in the air, Ottawa became the capital in 1866.

IV

That the Union of the Canadas was an economic success is undeniable, and indeed the visible signs of that success are still very much in evidence in such things as the splendid heritage of Union-era architecture and in the many contemporary institutions, both public and private, that arose originally out of its burgeoning growth. But what is less commonly acknowledged, perhaps because the evidence is less materially visible, is that the Union was also a political success. To view it merely as a prelude to the greater political act of Confederation, or as a "problem" that Confederation solved, is grossly to undervalue its very real and very great achievements, not only legislatively in specific areas of public policy such as education, municipal government, social services, and communications, important though these were, but above all in its evolution of a unique political system that was in some respects in advance of any other in the world at that time.

It is useful to view the Union of the Canadas in comparative perspective. It was not without its defects, but no other form of government anywhere was conspicuously more successful in providing its people with a framework of peace and order, or in maintaining their rights and freedoms as individuals and as communities, or in generally supporting conditions favourable to the growth of economic, social, and religious institutions. It must be remembered that in the mid-nineteenth century the United States, for all its commitment to the idea of liberty, allowed nearly four million of its people to be held in slavery, a contradiction that would shortly tear the republic apart; in Europe for the most part the price of peace was still acceptance of autocratic rule, while in Britain it was deference to an aristocracy (except in Ireland, where submission was required). No student of European politics, especially, can fail to be struck by one startling feature of the political system of the United Canadas: virtually everything was open to negotiation. In contrast to the bi- or multi-ethnic European states and empires, where the forces of popular democracy were either suppressed or kept under tight rein and inter-elite bargaining restricted to a limited range of traditional rights and privileges, in the United Canadas the combination of responsible government and brokerage politics produced a system in which practically all the important areas of public policy (with the exception of external relations, which remained in the hands of the imperial government) were dealt with through the processes of bargaining, deal-making, and compromise; in other words, almost everything was legitimate grist to the political mill.

The result was a politics of byzantine complexity. At its worst it was flagrantly cynical, utterly scurrilous, and more than a little corrupt. But at its best it was innovative, practical, and wonderfully civilized. Such were its intricacies and so finely balanced were its mechanisms that almost invariably among the leading politicians, both French and English, those who were winners and held power had also at some point been losers and sat in opposition, and *vice versa*. And those who were on opposite sides of the House had always to keep in mind that in the next coalition they might well become allies; they were thus naturally disinclined to treat politics as a winner-take-all proposition, a zero-sum game. Moreover, the quality of decision-making does not appear to have suffered unduly: there were fewer stalemates than might reasonably have been expected, and the overall record of governmental accomplishment compares favourably with that of any other era, either before or since.

Notes

1. Paul G. Cornell, *The Alignment of Political Groups in Canada, 1841-1867* (Toronto 1962), 22-5, 100. LaFontaine was returned at the head of a party of thirty-three, including nine English members. Baldwin's supporters numbered twenty-three, to eighteen for the Conservatives. Hincks was later declared the winner of a disputed election in Oxford, increasing the Reform total to twenty-four and reducing the Conservative total to seventeen.

2. *Dictionary of Canadian Biography,* IX, 89-93

3. Quoted in J.M.S. Careless, *The Union of the Canadas* (Toronto 1967), 116

4. J.E. Hodgetts, *Pioneer Public Service: An Administrative History of the United Canadas* (Toronto 1955), 56-7; and J.M.S. Careless, "Robert Baldwin," in J.M.S. Careless, ed., *The Pre-Confederation Premiers: Ontario Government Leaders, 1841-1867* (Toronto 1980), 133-4

5. George E. Wilson, *The Life of Robert Baldwin* (Toronto 1933), 243

6. Careless, "Baldwin," 132; and R.M. and J. Baldwin, *The Baldwins and the Great Experiment* (Toronto 1969), 215-18

7. M.E. Nish, "Double Majority: Concept, Practice and Negotiations, 1840-1848," MA thesis, McGill 1966, 146

8. See R.S. Longley, *Sir Francis Hincks* (Toronto 1943), 144-9.

9. To add insult to injury, the author of the motion was Baldwin's old enemy, William Lyon Mackenzie. See Wilson, *Baldwin,* 284-90.

10. Ibid., 289

11. *Baldwin, LaFontaine, Hincks* (Toronto 1907), 259

12. Nish, "Double Majority," 141-2

13. "Sir Henry Smith and the Politics of the Union," *Ontario History* 66 (1974): 161

14. Quoted ir Longley, *Hincks,* 276

15. *DCB*, X, 462-9

16. See S.J.R. Noel, "Consociational Democracy and Canadian Federalism," *Canadian Journal of Political Science* 4 (1971): 15-18.

17. Careless, *The Union,* 133-4

18. *Democracy in Plural Societies* (New Haven 1977), 128-9

19. The Macdonald-Sicotte ministry remained in office, to the derision of the opposition, after sustaining a defeat in the Upper Canadian section in 1863. See Bruce W. Hodgins, "John Sandfield Macdonald," in Careless, ed., *Pre-Confederation Premiers,* 274-7.

CHAPTER
13 FAMILY LIFE IN MID-NINETEENTH CENTURY BRITISH NORTH AMERICA

Glimpses of the family and children growing up rarely emerge from the pages of Canadian history. Stereotypes do exist, such as the *habitant* flock on the seigneury or the street urchins in the industrial cities. These are rare and atypical, yet the most characteristic of Canadian institutions was the family unit, either nuclear or extended, and the majority of Canadians for much of the past were children and teenagers. The preoccupation of Canadian historians with political developments largely explains their aloofness from numerous topics. With the broadening of content areas in the 1960s, the family and childhood were discovered. The sources, unfortunately, are always difficult, and the concept of family itself has divergent meanings at various times and places. Insights have been borrowed from sociologists, psychologists, educationalists and demographers. Approaches to the subject have been diversified as well, ranging from the traditional impressionistic study to advanced statistical analyses.

In her introduction to *Childhood and Family in Canadian History* in 1982, Joy Parr stressed the changing nature of concepts such as childhood and family, which are formed by historical rather than biological phenomena. She also saw them as social rather than natural associations, being molded by economic and cultural forces. The readings included here confirm her observations. For

Canada during the pre-industrial era of the first half of the nineteenth century, the nature of the family and ideas about children were fluid. Whether it was in the fur trade, on the farm, in urban shops, or in the family mansion, children were essential participants. In this unit, three strands of the study of growing up in Canada are presented. Jack Bumsted and Wendy Owen, the authors of the first selection, examined "The Victorian Family in Canada In Historical Perspective: The Ross Family of Red River and the Jarvis Family of Prince Edward Island." Using anecdotal evidence from the papers of two geographically separated families, the authors stress the "extraordinary parallels" in the family structures and activities of the elite Jarvis and Ross families.

Alison Prentice, in "Education and the Metaphor of the Family: The Upper Canadian Example," begins her study with the "traditional ideal of the family" and follows it into the school system being formulated by Walter Eales and Egerton Ryerson. Their idealization of that family experience, Prentice argues, dominated their notions of how the child should relate to the "larger society" and what the role of the school should be. That theme of responsibility is also found in the third reading, by Patricia T. Rooke and R.L. Schnell, "Childhood and Charity in Nineteenth-Century British North America." No typical family existed for the "poor, uncared-for, destitute children," and this article examines some of the alternatives, such as the Protestant Orphans' Homes. The role of such agencies in their offer of "protection, segregation and dependency" was more complex and encompassing than might be expected.

Suggestions for Further Reading

Brown, Jennifer S.H., *Strangers in Blood: Fur Trade Families in Indian Country*. Vancouver: University of British Columbia Press, 1980.

Davey, I., "The Rhythm of Work and the Rhythm of School," in *Egerton Ryerson and His Times*, ed. N. McDonald and A. Charter. Toronto: Macmillan of Canada, 1978, 221-253.

Gaffield, C., "Canadian Families in Cultural Context: Hypotheses from the Mid-Nineteenth Century," CHA *Historical Papers* (1979), 48-68.

Houston, Susan E. and Alison Prentice, *Schooling and Scholars in Nineteenth-Century Ontario*. Toronto: University of Toronto Press, 1988.

Mattingly, Paul H. and Michael B. Katz (eds.), *Education and Social Change: Themes from Ontario's Past*. New York: New York University Press, 1975.

Mays, Herbert J., "'A Place to Stand': Families, Land and Permanence in Toronto Gore Township, 1820-1890," CHA *Historical Papers* (1980), 185-211.

Medjuck, Sheva., "Family and Household Composition in the Nineteenth Century Case of Moncton, N.B. 1851-1871," *Canadian Journal of Sociology*, IV, no. 3 (Summer 1979), 275-286.

Parr, Joy (ed.), *Childhood and Family in Canadian History*. Toronto: McClelland & Stewart, 1982.

Rooke, Patricia T. and R.L. Schnell (eds.), *Studies in Childhood History: A Canadian Perspective*. Calgary: Detselig, 1982.

THE VICTORIAN FAMILY IN CANADA IN HISTORICAL PERSPECTIVE: THE ROSS FAMILY OF RED RIVER AND THE JARVIS FAMILY OF PRINCE EDWARD ISLAND

J.M. Bumsted and Wendy Owen

While a good deal has been written in recent years about the family in nineteenth-century Britain and the United States, the study of the family as an institution is in its infancy in Canada. How were families organized, what were their preoccupations and ambitions, how did their households function? Unlike Britain and the United States, Canada had precious few self-conscious literary families in the Victorian era, and so one of the most common sources for study of the individual family—private papers assiduously collected by literary scholars—simply has not existed. At the same time, substantial bodies of personal and intimate papers of articulate Canadian families, carrying sufficient detail to enable some sort of reconstruction, do survive. Two such sets of family papers are those of the Jarvis Family of Prince Edward Island and the Ross family of Red River. The Jarvis Papers are in the New Brunswick Museum in Saint John, N.B., and the Ross Papers are in the Public Archives of Manitoba. A careful reading of these geographically widely-scattered documents suggests the danger of approaching them as merely local records.

Some extraordinary parallels exist between the two sets of papers and the two families, although they were separated by nearly 3,500 kilometers in two relatively isolated colonies in British North America. In terms of the study of the nineteenth-century family, what is most striking about the parallels is how well they fit into the larger patterns of recent secondary literature on the Victorian family. The Jarvises and the Rosses were not simply unique colonial families, but very much part of a transatlantic culture. Given the facts that mama Ross was an Indian and the children "half-breeds," the similarities between the Ross and the Jarvis families suggest that we must be careful not to make too much either of colonial location or of racial and cultural differences.

There was a middle-class culture in the nineteenth century which transcended many theoretically exceptionalist factors. One hesitates to limit the culture to the label "Victorian," since it was equally powerful in the United States and much of Europe. Those researching the family in nineteenth-century Canada ought not, we would suggest, assume that their Canadian subjects existed in splendid isolation from general cultural developments in the western world and thus produced localized and unique patterns of behaviour. Colonial societies less often initiated than imitated, and while identifying deviations from larger patterns is crucial, one must begin with the larger patterns.

From *Manitoba History*, no. 13 (1987), 12-18. Reprinted courtesy of *Manitoba History*, published by the Manitoba Historical Society.

Before turning to our analysis, it might be well to introduce the two families briefly. Edward Jarvis was born in Saint John, New Brunswick, in 1789, the son of Munson Jarvis, a leading Connecticut Loyalist. Educated at King's College, Windsor, he was admitted to the New Brunswick bar in 1812 and subsequently to the bar at Inner Temple, London. He served in Malta before his appointment as Chief Justice of Prince Edward Island in 1828. In 1817 Edward married Anna Maria Boyd, the daughter of another influential Saint John family active in mercantile affairs; the Jarvis and Boyd families would intermarry frequently over the succeeding years. The couple had eight children, three of whom died in infancy and one in childhood. Those surviving to adulthood were Mary, Munson, Henry, and Amelia. Their mother—Maria, as she was known— died in 1841, and Jarvis remarried in 1843 to Elizabeth Gray of Charlottetown. This union produced three children, one of whom died in infancy. Elizabeth herself died in childbirth in 1847, and Edward a few years later in 1852. The correspondence to be discussed, mainly between members of a close-knit family writing between the Island and mainland New Brunswick, covers the period from 1828 to 1852.

Alexander Ross was born in Nairnshire, Scotland, in 1783. He emigrated to Canada as a schoolmaster, but became involved in the fur trade, joining John Jacob Astor's Astoria expedition in 1811. Ross subsequently served in the Pacific coast fur trade until his retirement to Red River in 1825. While in Oregon he had married Sarah, the daughter of an Indian chief (an Indian princess, went the family tradition) according to the "custom of the country," and formally remarried her in Red River in 1828. The couple had at least thirteen children, of whom the important ones for our purposes are William, Henrietta, James, and Jemima. In Red River Ross became a prominent government official—sheriff, magistrate and member of the council of Assiniboia—as well as titular head of the Scots Presbyterian community. In his later years he authored three books describing his experiences in the fur trade and chronicling the development of Red River, a trio of works woefully neglected by Canadian literary scholars and students of Canadian historiography. The Ross family correspondence upon which we will concentrate in this study covers a shorter period of time than the Jarvis set, since only during the years 1852-1856, when young Jemmy Ross was studying at Knox College in Toronto, did the family correspond intimately and regularly.

Edward Jarvis and Alexander Ross were contemporaries, and both were important political and social figures in their respective communities. Their residential accommodation reflected their positions. Edward began planning his house in 1833, when he bought a farm on the outskirts of Charlottetown for 500 pounds. As he intended the house to be a family seat for "generations yet to come," his plans called for the use of brick, an uncommon Island building material. Most of the material was imported from England, and the construction was not completed until 1835 at enormous expense—more than "one hundred per cent upon the original estimates and contracts." Furnishing of "Mount Edward" was finished in 1836, and early in 1836 the Jarvises held a housewarming ball for 81 persons. We know considerably less about "Colony Gardens," the Ross residence in the Point Douglas area of what is now Winnipeg, but it was a large and substantial frame house, a landmark in its day. On the other hand, the later (1854) construction efforts of William Ross are discussed in the correspondence. William himself enthuses, "without boasting it is the best, the handsomest and most comfortable house on the banks of the Riviere Rouge," befitting, added his father, a "son who had stepped into the shoes of his father." The William Ross house still survives in Winnipeg, a museum open to the public as the oldest house yet in the city.

As paterfamilias, Edward Jarvis had a limited share in the day-to-day operations of his household. Like many nineteenth-century fathers he was often away—on circuit as the only judge of the Island's supreme court, on the mainland seeing to business matters in the summer months, and in England (for six months during the fatal illness of his first wife). At that, Jarvis was far more housebound than some of his contemporaries; the Earl of Dalhousie, when he returned to Britain from governing in Canada, had been away so long that he was totally unable to recognize his eighteen-year-old son. But absence aided the remoteness which most Victorian fathers liked to maintain, and Jarvis does not appear to have been especially close to his children, especially the boys, who unlike the girls were sent away to school for much of their adolescence and brought home only under financial stringency. At the same time, Jarvis did play a key role in the upbringing of his children. Major decisions were his, and many minor ones were deferred if he were absent. Jarvis did not lose sovereignty over the household, and the family, especially the women, were expected to subordinate themselves to his needs and wishes.

The Ross papers suggest that Alexander Ross was substantially closer to his children than was Edward Jarvis. In part this attitude reflected personality, in part the fact that there was nowhere to travel in remote Red River, in part probably his wife's background. Ross did make an annual hunting expedition to Shoal Lake after the harvest, but characteristically, he turned it into a family affair which became one of the high points of the year. The Ross situation was complicated by the presence of "mama" (both families called the mother "mama"), who at least by the time of the correspondence of the 1850s was no longer running the household, a position assumed by the eldest unmarried daughter. Ill health was obviously a key factor in her stepping down. Nevertheless, Ross's domination of his household was typically Victorian, the family revolving around him as it did around Jarvis. While it was true that "Ross shaped the upbringing of his half-Indian children," as Sylvia Van Kirk has emphasized, it should be noted that most middle and upper class Victorian fathers behaved similarly without the presence of an Indian wife. While Ross may have been less distant from his children than Jarvis, his correspondence with his absent son James demonstrated a stiffness and formality quite different from the tone of Jemmy's letters from his brothers and sisters. And like Jarvis, Ross was far more affectionate with his daughters than with his sons.

Middle-class family life in the Victorian era was characterized by two related developments. The first is generally referred to as the "domesticization" of the household, a clear separation of work-life and home-life and the withdrawal of the various household members into the privacy of the home, which became the central social unit for "the transmission of culture, the maintenance of social stability, and the pursuit of happiness." This process had been completed by the Jarvis family before the opening of the surviving correspondence in 1828, and by the Ross family by the time of the intimate letters of the 1850s and indeed probably years earlier. Closely connected with domesticization was a new attitude toward human emotion usually labelled "sentimentalization." In its Victorian context, this attitude encouraged the effusiveness of personal feelings and sentiments on certain approved topics relating to the home and the family: love, death, marriage, and "making it" in the outside world. Gone was the stoicism and terseness of earlier generations toward the vagaries of family life and relationships, replaced by open avowals of sentiment, often overstated. It should be emphasized that this openness was confined to approved topics and closely circumscribed by fairly clear and generally held ground rules of respectability. It is this new attitude of sentimentality, combined with the standards of respectability, that finds its closest parallels in the Jarvis and Ross papers.

In terms of the traditional milestones in the cycle of life—birth, education, marriage, and death—the Jarvis and Ross correspondence exhibit sentiment most openly and frequently on the subject of death. Indeed, nearly half of the Jarvis letters between 1828 and 1852 contain some reference to death: reporting one, responding to a report, or mourning the death of a loved one. The incidence is little different in the Ross letters. This emphasis is not surprising, since death and its aftermath were matters that often provoked a correspondent to take pen in hand. For the modern taste the sentiments expressed may border on the morbid and maudlin, but they filled a real need for those involved. Those familiar either with Victorian novels or the literature of Victorian piety will not be surprised, for example, to learn of the fascination of both our families with detailed descriptions of death-bed scenes.

We are given two eyewitness accounts of the final sufferings in 1841 of Maria. One, by her son, is of her last hours, and another, by her daughter, describes the terminal weeks. According to young Mary Jarvis, her mother had twice before the fatal day "called us all together to bid us farewell for ever and had recovered." A few years later Elizabeth Gray Jarvis died in childbirth, a particularly important rite of passage and a major family event, usually occurring in the home with the woman surrounded not only by the medical folk but often by friends and family as well. Spiritual preparation was important, since the risks were considerable. One gains some impression of the event and the rituals surrounding it from Munson Jarvis's description of the death of his stepmother:

> From the sudden manner of her death she must have been totally unconscious of his approach, time not even given her to bid her family farewell. Poor woman to be so suddenly summoned to appear before her Maker leaves upon us a melancholy reflection. To be promising fairly and the next moment awake in Eternity is awful. To give an idea of its suddenness, after being delivered and her little infant dandled in the arms of the nurse and kind friends around her bed and the birth announced all which took some little time, the mother called for her child and seemed most affectionately fond of it, kissing it as I was told several times, but no sooner did she resign the now Motherless babe to its nurse (but was not complaining) the Dr. was told by one in attendance that mrs. J's feet felt cold, at once the Dr. said he was so afraid she would die, and so suddenly and apparently so easily after saying she did not feel cold had her spirit taken flight, no assistance could be rendered....

Obviously the doctor had not been able to help.

Within a few months in 1856 the Ross family experienced two deaths, first that of William and then that of his father Alexander. Again, there are detailed descriptions of the last hours. Alexander Ross described William's demise to James in Toronto:

> About half an hour before his last, he called me to his bedside, clasped both my hands in his, then called for his wife and Mr. Black [Presbyterian minister of Kildonan and married to Henrietta Ross] and while he held my hands he offered up a most fervent and impressive prayer to God, asking forgiveness for all his sins, and resigning himself into the arms of his maker. "I know," said he in conclusion, "that my redeemer liveth and I know that I am going to be with him, Lord receive my spirit to everlasting rest, Amen." Then laying his head quietly on the pillow, soon expired without struggle or motion to the right or to the left.

The accounts of the death of Alexander himself were even more explicit. According to John Black:

> About daylight he called all the family around him and we were all there but poor James and gave them his parting blessing—the most affecting sight I ever saw was when he held William's poor little orphans by their little hands altogether and spoke to and blessed them.... Margaret received her dying grandfather's parting kiss and blessing—Willie was at home and poor Lettie was too sick to come in. All the rest of the grandchildren were present. It was like old Jacob blessing his sons and Joseph's sons.

Further details came from Jemima:

It was 23rd before daylight he called us all around his bed one by one and shook hands with us and spoke to every one of us and blessed us and told us to be kind to one another and not feel sorry for him, though he was going away.... He took all their hands and held them in his for a long time that was after breakfast and at last Mr. B said that will do now you are tiring yourself; he still held them, and all the time sitting. He asked S. to say the fifth commandment, she said it, and then they went and sat down and asked for all the C. But they were not all here W. not but the baby so he asked Mr. B. if he could let him have the pleasure of kissing his babe so he kissed the baby too.

The Ross accounts all emphasize the fortitude of the sufferer and the peace with which death was faced—not hidden from view in some distant antiseptic hospital but at home, in the immediate presence of the family circle.

They also emphasize the importance of proper spiritual preparation. As the account of the death of Elizabeth Gray Jarvis suggests, the most disturbing feature here was its suddenness. The Ross correspondence makes similar points frequently. In 1852 William Ross wrote of the death of "young James Fraser" noting "only seven days sick—what a warning for all those who are alive to prepare for death while in health for we know not the day nor the hour when the "Knock" shall be at our door." Both Jarvis and Ross papers are full of the reminders of the constant razor-edge upon which life was balanced.

A willingness to acknowledge the trauma of the death of a loved one was also a central feature of the correspondence. The death of his first wife hit Edward Jarvis very hard, partly—one suspects—because he felt guilty about being in England for his own health while Maria was battling her fatal illness on Prince Edward Island. Daughter Mary certainly thought her father's absence, however unavoidable, contributed to her mother's demise. As Edward wrote to his wife's sister upon his return to Charlottetown late in 1841:

> My own feelings have now become so nervous and sensitive that I seem to participate as much in any anxieties of my friends as if it were my own case. I cannot shake off the dreadful weight and oppression which hangs increasingly upon my spirits and the slightest exciting cause wholly overpowers me.... The utmost indifference to every passing event and occupation possesses me and I cannot overcome it.

Such a sense of depression was hardly surprising under the circumstances. What was different from earlier times was the openness with which Edward confessed his feelings in his correspondence for several years thereafter. Alexander Ross admitted to his son James with regard to William's death, "The event has given a severe shaking to your mother, to myself also; but we thank God that we are able to bear with it as we do. Nevertheless our position is one of pain." Such pain was now openly acknowledged.

If death and mourning were sentimentalized by the Victorians in words, they were also enshrined in new and more extreme ritualization. Mourning and commemoration of the dead took on new forms. Even the physical letter it-self was part of the process. Munson Jarvis opened a letter to his Aunt Caroline with the words, "You must be aware upon seeing the border of this letter that our family has been deprived of one of its members." The first letter home of James Ross upon hearing the news of William's death was edged in black. The Jarvises were not invited to Government House on New Year evening in 1848 because "there has been a death so recently in the family"—in this case of Edward's eldest daughter Mary.

The dead were also commemorated in ways both more ostentatious and more personal. In one letter of 1842 to his sister-in-law, Edward reported or-dering from England a monument to his wife ("of white marble, of the Sarcophagus shape") and added:

> I promised you a small portion of a lock of her hair—but I find there was but a very small lock preserved—and Mary is anxious to have some of it. Your sister and I therefore concluded that it would meet with your approbation that I should send you some for your locket, only in case a little could be spared after the division with Mary. I should feel very desirous to save some for you, if possible.

Burial became a matter of considerable ritualization and a symbol of the re-lationships of the deceased while living. Edward's parents, after an even more protracted correspondence among the family, were disinterred and placed in a family vault in the new burying ground of Saint John. John Black reported after the death of Alexander Ross, "On Monday 27th amid great concourse of people we laid him in the narrow house here at the Frog Plain—not alongside of William so that the graves are in a line—William lying at his father's feet." And although the correspondence does not show it, Edward Jarvis was buried in Elm Avenue Cemetery in Charlottetown next to his first wife, while his sec-ond wife was buried elsewhere in the same cemetery along with her family.

Another important aspect of the household was the raising of children. Expectations and training were quite different for boys and girls. Both sexes were educated at home for most of their early years by both the Rosses and the Jarvises, owing as much to the scarcity of acceptable schools as to the wishes of their parents. Neither family employed governesses or tutors. The Jarvis boys were subsequently sent off Island to school, while it was hoped that a projected academy for young ladies on the Island would serve for the girls. When the academy did not appear, the girls were either taught at home or, after Maria's death, bundled off to relations on the mainland to learn the requisite skills. As for the Ross children, the younger boys all attended Red River Academy or its successor St. John's College, essentially a grammar school in the British tradition established by the Church of England in Red River. For James Ross to go away to university in Toronto was a considerable step for both James and his family, although others of his contemporaries from the College attended Oxford and

Cambridge. Cousin Roderick Ross, Alexander Ross reported in 1854, was off to "Swell the list of Pussyites at degraded Oxford." The arrival of John Black in Red River and his subsequent marriage to Henrietta Ross opened new educational opportunities in the colony, especially for the younger Ross girls. Jemima was sent off to the manse at Kildonan in 1855 to pursue her studies, learning geography, grammar, French and ciphering, and Henrietta Black herself "got very clever" after her marriage.

As for expectations, Edward Jarvis intended his three sons to enter the professions. Munson, the eldest, was trained for the law on the Island. Second son Henry was sent to Edinburgh to medical school, and youngest son William entered the Church. According to Edward, "I am unwilling to oppose a decided inclination in my boys for any particular profession," but it all seemed somehow to work out in fairly orthodox fashion. One suspects that Edward would have preferred the eldest to be the doctor, but Munson was not a favourite:

> Munson is very studious when required to be so and has great application, but he is very idle when there is no immediate call for his exertions, he is not inclined to volunteer hard study, but pays more attention to the young ladies and driving his tandem than to more desirous matters.... Henry is, on the contrary, all life, activity and industry—he greatly resembles in mind as well as countenance his beloved mother. Sir Henry Huntly told me that when he first saw Henry he thought he had never seen a countenance in which were blended so much of benevolence and intelligence.

So Henry was allowed to go to Edinburgh, where he did well professionally but disappointed his father by marrying too quickly an "unhealthy" wife.

As for the Ross boys, the first-born son Alexander died early. William stepped smoothly into his father's shoes, as his father had obviously intended, and James was able to go to Toronto, where he prepared for the ministry, a career approved by the entire family. Upon the death of William, James hesitated, obviously debating whether to continue his studies or come home to assume his family responsibilities. His father wrote him a few weeks before his death that "sacrifice ... is in my opinion a better plan for all the time we expect to live to enjoy this life, than withdraw our children from those pursuits in which their future happiness depends." After Alexander's death, James did return to Red River and assumed leadership of the family.

For the daughters there were clearly different expectations. In one letter William Ross described the Ballenden daughters as, "so far as we Red Riverians can judge perfectly accomplished ladies." He continued to list the requirements:

> They can play elegantly on the Harp, guitar, piano, they sing melodiously and methodically. They can dance and waltz like true English dames, and I guess they can play the coquette too if that be any part of Ornamental Education—to tell the truth they are very nice girls.

While marriage was the ultimate goal, household management was extremely important. After the death of Maria Jarvis, Edward attempted to replace his wife as household manager with his eldest daughter. Mary escaped by marrying herself, after some agonizing over whether "I make up my mind to leave my dear Papa." Only Edward's remarriage prevented Amelia from becoming her successor. In the hiatus between Mary's marriage and his own in 1843, Edward found it difficult to continue Amelia's education, writing "I hardly know how I can get on without her management of my household, for I shall have no one at present besides the two servant girls." After the death of his second wife, Amelia again had the responsibility for her father, but this time she had assistance from a succession of maiden aunts.

Henrietta and Jemima Ross could easily have sympathized with the problems of Mary and Amelia Jarvis. Henrietta was running the household at the time of her marriage to John Black, and Jemima was forced to step into Henrietta's shoes. Her letters to her brother indicated her problems. "I write to tell you," she announced in 1854, "that I have no time to write with Hay and harvest all are busy and I am no less busy baking and cooking for those out of doors." Mama and Isabella had gone berrying, she added. "I wanted to go too, but I had to stop and keep house." A few months later she wrote, "I suppose you have heard that Hen has left me to do for myself, ... I am now Miss Ross Master in the house." Within a few days she commented that she was "tired with house-keeping and all its duties, for there is no end of working."

Brother William dealt perceptively with Jemima's dilemmas in a letter discussing family reactions to the annual excursion to Shoal Lake. "Sister Jem," he wrote:

> only forbodes something portentous in this trip to Shoal Lake, as mama now and then gives a hint as to who is to keep house while out—poor Jem thinks she ought to go out and finds it very hard to be made to keep house before the time, but the question comes back, whose to keep house? Papa says oh I must stay and let Jem go out, but Jem knows well that she would rather stay than her pa stay.

While Jemima was at Mr. Black's pursuing her studies, her mother's health suffered, presumably because mama was forced to take over the running of the household. After a few months she was recalled to Colony Gardens. The family "can't do rightly without her at home," William reported.

As we have been suggesting, while the household functioned around the needs of the males, it was the women who made it work. The Victorian woman's role as wife and mother ought not to obscure her onerous responsibilities as housekeeper. The role immobilized the woman and made it difficult for her to travel from the house. "I must reluctantly stay at home," wrote Maria of a projected visit by her husband to Saint John in 1837, "to take care of the establishment." To see people, especially in remote colonies, women had to expect them for long housevisits, only adding to the burden. Houseguests invited by her father were coming, reported daughter Mary reluctantly in 1843, adding, "I was very sorry for it as it will give me much more to do, ... but I did not like to say so to Papa as he seemed to wish to have them." Maria found herself unable to report on her housewarming ball to her sister, commenting, "I was much too fatigued in mind and body to enjoy it and even the repetition is painful to me for I was obliged to force my spirits.... You will be astonished that I am alive," she concluded, proceeding to catalogue a herculean series of labours which ranged from supervising the slaughter of seven hogs to hanging the draperies in six public rooms. There is no evidence in either the Jarvis or the Ross papers of a direct act of defiance of male wishes by a female. The Ross and Jarvis women were not advanced thinkers; there was nothing in their upbringing to encourage notions of independence.

Both sexes had to beware of the great abyss for Victorians: the fall from respectability. This subject was a matter of considerable concern in both sets of correspondence, usually in terms of the peccadilloes of other people. When H. Wright married an illegitimate daughter of Sir H. Lowe, despite the fact that the girl "lived in his family and is very well educated," her sister's concluding comment to Maria Jarvis was "Silenzio." A young Scotch lady in Red River was "guilty of having made a faux pas," wrote William Ross to his brother, "she was delivered of a boy last week." Edward Jarvis obviously found some satisfaction when his "old antagonist" John Stewart, after burying his wife left for England almost immediately, having "married his servant girl, 18 years of age—he is nearly 80 himself." Jarvis continued:

> The girl made him execute a will in her favor of all his property, which is to a large amount. He has commenced prosecutions against some of his acquaintances who interfered to prevent the marriage and alleged that he was insane.

Jarvis took equal satisfaction in recounting that a certain "young sprig of a parson ... with his true orthodox spectacles upon his nose," had secretly breached the canonical law by marrying his late wife's sister. This form of "incest" remained legally forbidden in Britain, despite frequent attempts to revise the law, until well into the twentieth century. "So you see John Gunn found out by sad experience," noted William Ross with satisfaction equal to that of Edward Jarvis, "that instead of gaining by Slander he had lost by a good deal his former little respectability."

Everyone well understood the implications of breaking the codes. As Edward Jarvis wrote of the Smiths, who were "dreadfully depressed about their unfortunate brother" who had committed some unspecified offence: "well they may be—death would be far preferable to the never-ending disgrace." Fortunately, no Jarvis appears to have blotted the family name during the course of the correspondence.

While both families were conscious of the abyss, it gaped open much more widely for the Ross family, both because "mama was an Indian" and because Red River was commonly perceived as a colony of semi-civilized half-breeds. The point came out quite clearly in responses to James Ross's early success as a student in Toronto. Cousin Roderick hoped to join James at university, calling for "a mighty effort to try to make poor Red River respectable," and John Black described old Alexander's response to son-in-law George Flett at news that James had won a scholarship: "What will they say of the Brules now, Geordie?" William was already "in a fair way of becoming respectable," exulted his father, and James was not far behind, although extremely self-conscious about his origins.

All of the Ross family had to deal with racial hostility, even in Red River. Jemima was upset in 1854 at comments overheard at church about the number of "blacks" in the front pews, for example. But none of the family were more sensitive than James. John Black was forced in 1855 to give James a written lecture in response to the young man's attempts to derive a complex classical etymology for the word "halfbreed." Black observed, "Half breed is a simple natural homemade English term which we could have invented if we had known as little of Greek and Latin as we do of the Japanese." Although James was extremely proud of his father's books and literary success, he protested strenuously to the old man about his treatment of halfbreeds in his writings. After the death of his father, James wrote an extremely revealing and agonizing letter to his family in Red River, in which his concerns about the abyss were clearly revealed:

> Remember, dear sisters, that we at present occupy a certain standing in the community. Owing to papa and to William—and to our connection with our worthy minister Mr. Black—I say owing to these things, we have a certain standing and respectability, and we must keep it.... It seems generally the case that halfbreed families dwindle into insignificance as soon as they lose their head. But why should it be so?

James would spend the remainder of his life attempting to prove that halfbreeds were as good as anyone else.

But if the abyss for James Ross (and perhaps for the remainder of his siblings) was perhaps wider and the descent into it considerably shorter, we ought not to over-emphasize the differences between the Ross and the Jarvis families. The assumptions and concerns of the two families on this and other matters were, in the last analysis, remarkably similar. Both were Victorian, colonial branch. Perhaps the Jarvises were more comfortable with their status than were the Rosses, but there was considerably more common ground than one might anticipate.

EDUCATION AND THE METAPHOR OF THE FAMILY: THE UPPER CANADIAN EXAMPLE

Alison Prentice

The condition of the family was a subject that much preoccupied school promoters in Upper Canada. Like educators in other times and places they blamed the weaknesses of the family for many social ills; at the same time they put forth an idealized portrait of domestic relations as a major hope for social progress. Besides the usual vague complaints and exaggerated hopes, they also had some very specific anxieties about the family, among them two that were clearly associated with the spread of formal schooling and that occurred in many parts of the United States as well as in Canada. The first was the recurring suspicion that some kinds of schools, especially those controlled increasingly by the state, were gradually undermining family authority.[1] The second, which is the subject of this essay, was intimately related to the first and concerned the education of children and adolescents away from home. How could schools and colleges replace the authority, affection, and advice normally provided by families, for these absentees from the domestic fireside?

The need to send some children to school away from home posed an increasingly serious problem. The obvious answer to some educators was that despite their size, schools ought to imitate families. Indeed it is fairly clear that without the ability to see the schools and colleges that they founded as substitute families or households, many of the early school promoters would have thought their own creations dangerous both to the youth attending them and to society at large. It was the metaphor of the family[2] that made possible for such people the transition from the instruction of children at home, or in small household-like settings, to their schooling in institutions outside and often far away from relatives and friends.

Not all Upper Canadian educators thought that schools could successfully replace the family however. Mid-century discussions of the subject reveal the existence in fact of doubt and finally serious disagreement among school promoters whose basic attitudes were otherwise often very similar. What accounts for the differences of opinion and for the depth of feeling sometimes associated with them? The argument that I wish to develop here is that these debates were fundamentally related to changing conceptions of the ideal family.[3] As the ideal of the large patriarchal household, with its many public functions, gave way to that of the relatively small democratic, and private family, educators saw schools and colleges in new ways. Or conversely, as they perceived or promoted

From *History of Education Quarterly* (Fall 1972) as revised by author. Reprinted by permission of the author.

what they believed to be essential changes in education, they were forced also to look at the family in a new light. It is impossible to say which was cause and which effect; changes in the conceptions of the ideal family and ideal education were interrelated and occurred over a long period of time, as different individuals and groups were gradually won over to new attitudes.[4] Both of course were tied to the disappearance of pre-industrial economic ways, to rapid population growth and urbanization; but then these in turn must have depended in part on shifts in ideas about family life and education that predisposed people to seek and accept a new social order.

I

To what extent did the traditional ideal of the family still persist in early Upper Canada and what was this ideal? It is worthwhile noting, first of all, that traditional attitudes and practices could easily have survived in Upper Canada longer than in many parts of the United States or Western Europe. The colony was first settled by conservative fugitives from the American Revolution. It was also tied by legislative union for twenty-seven crucial years in the middle of the century to the conservative and Roman Catholic province of Lower Canada (Quebec). Add to this the isolation from change caused by pioneer conditions, the probable conservatism of immigrants attracted to the colony, and the relative slowness of economic development compared to that of many of the neighbouring states, and it is entirely plausible that in Upper Canada one would find many vestiges of pre-industrial society.

For a definition of the traditional family, one must go to diaries and letters. These suggest that many early nineteenth-century Upper Canadians did not yet define the family as exclusively composed of biologically related people. Peter Laslett has pointed out that in pre-industrial Britain the word "family" was often used where most twentieth-century speakers would use "household," that is, to denote occupants of the same dwelling,[5] and it is not surprising that in British colonies this use should have continued. Certainly households enlarged by the occupancy of people unrelated to the biological family occurred frequently, if only among those who could afford to perpetuate such arrangements. Schoolmasters often lived in the homes of their employers, as did apprentices, friends, and servants of one type or another. Frequently also the living quarters shared, as in one-room log houses, were extremely cramped. But to what extent was the distinction between household and family, as they are generally understood nowadays, still blurred?

Evidence that there was no absolute distinction even as late as 1846 may be found in a discussion of voter qualifications that took place in that year? When asked if boarders were "householders" under the school law, and thus qualified to participate in the election of school trustees, Upper Canada's

Superintendent of Schools, Egerton Ryerson, replied that they were not. "It appears to me that a man is a householder within the meaning of the Act who rents any sort of house; but a boarder in a family forms part of that family, and cannot, I imagine, be a householder, merely because he has the exclusive occupation of a room."[6]

Further clues may be found in the use of the word "friends" during the period as an all-encompassing term to designate parents, guardians, and relatives, as well as dependent members of households. It was the students' friends who came to the annual exhibitions at John Strachan's grammar school in the 1820s.[7] Upper Canada College in the 1830s expected the friends of scholars to let the headmaster know when they planned to withdraw their charges from the school.[8] It was once again the friends of students who would be kept informed of breaches of discipline that occurred at the Upper Canada Academy in 1841.[9] Certainly some children were sponsored at school by people other than their parents, but it is also apparent that there was no absolute or final distinction between friends and family in Upper Canada during the first half of the century.

Many people expected that their way in the world would be made easier by friends and felt the lack when this was not the case. They also admitted that friends would occasionally be a burden. As one young teacher confided to Egerton Ryerson in 1849, there was little hope of getting a school in the city if one had "neither friends nor interest" there.[10] Another petitioner requested Ryerson's assistance in gaining admission to the newly formed provincial Normal School in 1850. Death had taken his friends, he apologised, hence the necessity of appealing to a stranger. Attendance at Normal School was going to be difficult for this teacher because he had to support an aged father and "a friend"; there were many others like him, he said, who "with want staring them in the face as well as their little families," could ill afford to take time out for special training.[11]

For a long time, the blurred line between family and friends, and the political and economic power of a network of certain notorious friends in the province, was a basic Upper Canadian political issue. The "Family Compact," an ill-defined but functioning elite that monopolized or attempted to monopolize property and power in the colony during the first part of the century, became the focus of most political and social criticism. It was this elite in fact that was almost the creation and certainly a major vehicle of one of the province's most famous educators, John Strachan. Lured to Upper Canada from Scotland in 1799 by the promise of a university to be founded, Strachan had stayed to become a popular grammar school master. It was through a prosperous marriage to the young widow of a member of the wealthy McGill family, but above all through his students and friends (the friends who were ultimately stereotyped as the Family Compact), that he gradually climbed to a position of eminence in the colony, reaching the pinnacle of power as the first Anglican Bishop of Toronto.[12]

Only the privileged few could belong to the Family Compact; most were destined merely to wish that they had useful and influential friends. More, perhaps, could claim membership in a traditional household. But nearly everyone who had anything to do with children could share in the normal processes of education, which took place for most people at home, since the family's formal educational role was still extensive. Bishop Jacob Mountain made much of contemporary neglect of duty in this respect in 1822. "How many complaints of rebellious children, how many exclamations of astonishment at the perverseness and ingratitude of dependents," the Bishop complained to his Quebec parishioners, "might justly be charged back upon the heads of the Parent and Master!" The moral was obvious.

> To Servants, then, to Apprentices, to Labourers retained in our employment, to all our dependents, to all who feel our influence, (especially if they are young, and wholly withdrawn from the charge and inspection of their own friends,) but far above to our own children, we owe it as a sacred duty to think of the furtherance of their salvation.[13]

As might be anticipated, spiritual education was not the only obligation of household heads; contracts frequently stipulated that apprentices receive some elementary literary instruction,[14] and parents as well as masters and guardians expected or were expected to teach their charges the three "R's." John Strachan noted with a certain amount of professional alarm in fact that many parents actually considered themselves as knowledgeable as schoolmasters in the art of instruction, claiming that the only reason they sent children to school was the "want of time" to teach them at home.[15] A private school which appeared very early in Upper Canada's history invited parents to send "their" pupils to be taught; clearly teachers were not the only ones to have pupils at the turn of the century.[16] Instruction at home was to most people, and for some time after 1800, still the norm, and probably in many rural areas the most practical solution. Household heads, parents, guardians, and friends all shared the responsibility of teaching the young, along with the occasional schoolmaster.

Coexistent with these traditional views of the ideal family's educational duties were certain ideas about the structure of the family, which was still perceived to be patriarchal. To King's College divinity professor James Beaven in 1846, the family was to be compared to a limited monarchy; one of the greater faults of American republicanism was the related or consequent weakness of parental authority in the United States.[17] A decade before, another writer had rejected "monarchy" in favour of the term "patriarchy" itself, in a comparison of school and family government: "Like a household, a literary institution should have but one head, and that head should have the ability to govern or he is unfit for his office."[18]

The traditional ideal family may thus be characterized as follows. It was enlarged by the inclusion of friends or dependents over and above those members who were biologically related. It had formal educational obligations beyond the early nurture of its own children. Finally, it was governed by a male parental figure. But it could not be said, even in the early part of the century, that this ideal held absolute sway over every mind; and as time wore on, there was evidence that new ideas were being given increasing publicity in Upper Canada. First of all, there was the tendency to see the family more and more as an entity composed strictly of people who were biologically related. Secondly, the whole idea of the Family Compact, of getting ahead through the efforts of well-placed friends and relatives was gradually discredited. In addition, notions about the purposes and structure of the family were visibly changing as the institution came to be seen more and more as a private retreat from the world and one that for large portions of the week was almost entirely governed by women. Finally, new and contradictory educational roles were perceived for the family, which was urged both to protect its children from the viciousness of the larger society and at the same time prepare them to enter it. The function of formal literary instruction and of much moral education as well was increasingly transferred to schools and colleges, to which parents were asked and ultimately compelled to commit their children for longer and longer periods of time.

There was very little, of course, that was novel in what I am calling the new family ideal, as it was eventually adopted by many people in Upper Canada. Philosophers and educators as different in their views as the New England Puritans[19] and Jean Jacques Rousseau[20] had preached or practiced one or another of the tendencies described above. All that can be said is that a subtle shift occurred in Upper Canada, as in other places before and since, as more and more people saw that the traditional ideals of the household-family or of elite networks like the Family Compact could no longer be effectively sustained in what was rapidly becoming a mass society.

Two of the earliest exponents of the new ideal in Upper Canada were men who were concerned also with the expansion of formal educational institutions. One was a little-known promoter of mechanics' institutes called Walter Eales. The other was Egerton Ryerson, Chief Superintendent of Schools in the province from 1844 to 1876 and, from that high eminence, in a good position to popularize his opinions.

The ideal family described by Eales in 1851 already suggests the direction of change. The centre of it was no longer the patriarch, but the highly idealized wife, queen of a realm of peace who kept the house all week in anticipation of her husband's return on the sabbath.

> It is ... cheering for the matronly wife, to be privileged, for one day in seven, to entertain her lord in the peaceful realms wherein she lives and reigns. Exiled to a great extent from his presence in the week, she ardently longs for the day, when her husband shall fill the vacant chair beside the hearth, irradiate the cottage with his smiles, and delight her ear with that voice, whose tones of tenderness whispered away her heart in the romantic days of her early youth.[21]

The mother was the first book read by her children, according to *The Canadian Gem and Family Visitor,* one of the first Canadian periodicals directed to women. Woman was the centre of the domestic circle; she should "diffuse sunshine and warmth through the whole atmosphere of the home."[22] But it was Eales who explained why. Families, in his view, constituted havens from the rest of society. They were the "arks" that sheltered mankind "from the raging tumults and storms of life" and especially from the world of work where the mechanic spent most of his time and where he was surrounded by "comparative strangers." For the returning husband the wife made the home into a much needed oasis of calm; for the children starting out, it was a happy memory—strong fortification against the coming encounter with "the wild waters of a turbulent world."[23]

But perhaps the best promoter of the new outlook was Chief Superintendent of Schools, Egerton Ryerson, who is interesting not only because of his apparent commitment to the new ideal but because his life and writings are themselves illustrations of the change. One of the numerous children of a loyalist landowning family, he had been an adolescent convert to Methodism and, during the late 1820s and 1830s, one of the most vociferous critics of John Strachan and the Family Compact. His campaign against the Compact idea found its major expression in the statist and bureaucratic ideology of the provincial school system, and ultimately Ryerson, as superintendent, became a promoter of the new family ideal. But he had also been a founder of the Methodist Upper Canada Academy and his letters and autobiographical writings frequently suggest that he clung to the patriarchal concept of family government (perhaps the last vestige of the traditional family idea to go in any society). He appears to have maintained in Toronto, in spite of continuing financial difficulties, a traditional household with its usual complement of servants and nonfamily members—the latter often young Europeans who were temporary protégés of his.[24]

Some of Ryerson's official correspondence during the early years of his superintendency also suggests loyalty to the older family ideal, especially the statement (quoted above) that boarders constituted family members for purposes of the 1846 School Act. When queried about the responsibilities of guardians to pay rate-bills for the schooling of dependent children in 1850, he replied that their duties were no different from those of parents in this regard.[25] But by the 1860s and 1870s, materials coming out of the Education Office suggest a growing commitment to the ideal of the small, self-contained biological family, unencumbered by boarders or unrelated dependants on the one hand, or guardians on the other. It is true that much of this propaganda was directed to members of the growing urban middle classes of society, or constituted unfavorable commentary on working-class people whose aspirations and attitudes were insufficiently middle class for Ryerson and his fellow propagandists to suffer gladly. Indeed its class orientation was one of the significant things about the new family ideal. Increasing loyalty to it was clearly a reflection of a gradually changing social order in which the formally schooled, with small families and universalist values, were slated, in theory at least, to become the new establishment. The new ideal was also closer to what most people could afford to achieve, given the economic realities of Canadian or perhaps of any society.

For Ryerson, economic self-sufficiency was a major family goal and common school textbooks that he published in the 1870s made much of this theme. Parents are exhorted to maintain their children, and reminded of the guilt of those who would, through drunkenness or other vices, expose their offspring to hunger or nakedness and "throw them as paupers upon others to support." But they are also advised to refrain from seeking wealth as such; a respectable standard of living, in accordance with the family's "position and circumstances," is held to be enough.[26]

What Ryerson and many of his contemporaries worried about increasingly was the tendency of families to put material goals ahead of the schooling of their children. As the *Journal of Education for Upper Canada* complained in 1854, there were selfish parents who kept their children away from school "on the slightest pretext of pressure of business," and would "starve their intellects in order to enrich their own pockets."[27] A respectable standard of living was not to be bought apparently at the expense of formal education. In fact by 1864, Ryerson was able to state explicitly that the obligation to educate children was more imperative than the duty to clothe and feed them.[28] In addition, the duty to educate was for him as for others increasingly equated with sending children to school. Instruction at home seemed less and less acceptable and local superintendents of common schools were obliged to give specific reasons for poor average attendance, where this existed, in their annual reports to the chief superintendent. A compulsory attendance law was finally passed in 1871.

Ryerson was among those who saw the protection of children from the larger society as an important function of the family. He compared the selection of library books to the care that parents took, or ought to take, in the selection of their children's companions. Any "intelligent and discreet" parent, furthermore, would prefer the high-priced land of an industrious and moral community for raising his family to a "neighbourhood of drunkenness, lawlessness and vice." Although the intention was to show that widespread schooling would increase property values, the underlying assumption was that all right-minded and virtuous people would and should attempt to isolate their families from the evils of society, presumably by moving their homes away from those districts inhabited by its worst elements.[29]

Children had to be protected, but the home did not on that account have to become a prison. The secret, according to Ryerson, was to make the domestic household more attractive than the world outside. "If parents would protect their children from the snares and dangers of seeking social enjoyment abroad, they must make the home the seat of such enjoyments."[30] Somehow the family (always complemented by the school) was to become the focus of children's lives.

It had to be an environment, however, in which there was some room for differences of opinion, especially in spiritual matters. In 1854, Ryerson took a stand against the expulsion of baptized children from the Methodist Church for nonattendance at class meetings. He argued essentially for the right of the unconverted to remain within the church of their parents, thus helping, as C. B. Sissons has pointed out, to push Methodism in the direction of becoming a family church.[31] The implication, as with the tribalism attributed by Edmund Morgan to the New England Puritans,[32] was that the strength of the family was now more important than the purity of the church, and that adolescents needed a measure of freedom within the confines of both. Traumatic departures from the parental home would be avoided by seeking, in theory at least, a slightly more democratic model for the family.

Thus Upper Canada's chief superintendent of schools gradually advocated new functions and a new structure for the family: a nuclear household of parents and children, an inward-looking institution that was to concentrate on the nurture of its own offspring at home and in schools. But the contradictions inherent in this idea—of children separated from society on the one hand but committed to society's schools on the other—led to anxiety, which was expressed particularly clearly in discussions about the pros and cons of boarding halls.

II

To John Strachan and many other supporters of denominational colleges in Upper Canada, boarding schools and colleges were viable substitutes for the Christian family. It was this, perhaps, more than any other fact, that accounted for the depth of their concern when they believed that these institutions were being attacked, and, in Strachan's case, for the urgency with which he set about the work of founding Trinity College. His ambition to establish a university in Upper Canada had been thwarted until 1843, when King's College finally opened its doors; but the secularization of King's by the University Act of 1849 once more left Strachan without an institution of higher learning that he could conscientiously support. His response to these events was Trinity, which was established in 1852 as a Church of England institution and the embodiment of Strachan's views on the relationship between education and the family. "It will constitute a great Christian household," he promised, "the domestic home of all who resort to it for instruction, framing them in the Christian graces, in all sound learning, and sanctifying their knowledge, abilities and attainments to the service of God and the welfare of their fellow men."[33]

It was to be a rule of Trinity that all students should be resident in the college, except those given special permission to live with their parents in or near Toronto.[34] In his 1852 inaugural address, Strachan explained why. He admitted that no system of education could really replace "the domestic fireside," but argued that because so many young men would come from a distance, it was essential to provide that which came nearest it. It would gladden the hearts of parents to know that, though their children were no longer immediately under their eye, everything would be done "to supply the place of paternal counsel and maternal tenderness."[35]

> Now one of our principal objects in this Institution will be to bring back to the hearts and affections of our youth the fresh and innocent impressions of early infancy ... the holy truths ... which a pious and tender mother whispered into their ears, invoking the protection of their God and Saviour before she kissed them and consigned them to their night's repose.... Our desire is to build upon this holy foundation, to form ourselves into a large Household, and to keep as near as may be practicable to the order and economy of a well-regulated family.[36]

Strachan expressed the conviction that there would grow among the young men "an affectionate brotherhood," and that such intimacy could only be provided by residential college life. This and all other advantages would be lost if the students were "scattered about and living here and there in lodgings" in the city.[37]

There were two further reasons for preferring the family boarding hall to lodgings. One was the age of the scholars, who Strachan estimated would be between 18 and 22 and therefore in his view at the most critical period of their lives. The other was the dangerous environment created by the city. In vague but alarmist terms Strachan stressed the dangers awaiting young men cast loose in a large city like Toronto, without friends or counsellors. To leave them to choose their lodgings, hours, and companions, and to govern their own religious lives, was to court, he thought, their almost certain destruction.[38]

Not all college or boarding school authorities went to such lengths to defend or promote the residence of their scholars. There had always been purely practical reasons for most such arrangements. It had long been a common practice for grammar school masters, among others, to take in boarders in order to make their schools available to those who lived too far away to be day pupils. This usage continued at least into the 1860s. In the early days, these small schools probably functioned much like other families enlarged by the inclusion of apprentices or servants. But they were not advertised as such. Most notices simply stated that the master would concern himself with the manners and morals as well as the literary attainments of his charges.[39] Nor were the benefits of family life apparently connected with the boarding hall planned for Upper Canada College in 1831; it was designed, according to the Board of Education minutes at least, to reduce expenses for youth coming from distant places.[40] It was therefore a major change of emphasis when, by the middle of the century, the supporters of denominational colleges everywhere began, like Strachan, to relate the need for boarding halls to the necessity of providing the warmth and restraint associated with the household or family.

Egerton Ryerson was an interesting exception to this trend. Before he became superintendent of schools, he had been one of the major promoters of the Methodist Upper Canada Academy, and from 1842 to 1844 had been principal of its successor, Victoria College. His early vision of the academy had placed it in the small community of Cobourg, at a remove from the "polluted waters of corrupt example," in a district of "moral and intelligent people."[41] Even with these precautions, the rules of the institution were very strict; the students lived in boarding halls and were prevented as much as possible from contact with the townspeople.[42] But Ryerson's experience as principal of the college must have altered his opinions,[43] for by 1847, although he remained a strong supporter of Victoria and of denominational colleges generally, he was steadfastly opposed to the idea of boarding halls. They were specifically rejected for the provincial Normal School that Ryerson founded in Toronto during that year, in spite of the fact that faculty-supervised residences were considered an essential part of Dublin Normal, the institution on which the Upper Canadian training school was modelled,[44] and despite the fact that students were to come to it from all over the province.

Ryerson's counter proposal and the one decided on was to arrange for non-resident pupils to board in the city with local families. The houses were approved and licensed by the Council of Public Instruction, which also saw to it that the headmaster inspected them regularly and that the strict rules governing the extracurricular lives of students were carefully enforced.[45] There was certainly little free choice of lodgings or companions, no freedom in the matters of hours of attendance at public worship, in fact none of the options that Strachan later insisted were the necessary alternatives to properly supervised boarding halls. Certainly many Normal students were well over the 22 years of the oldest Trinity College scholars, and a large number, old and young, had been teachers before coming to the school. But there were also many young women, most students of both sexes were under 22, and the minimum age was only 16.[46] What then accounts for Ryerson's insistence on city lodging arrangements for the Normal School?

In his history of the American boarding school, James McLachlan makes the point that similar family boarding arrangements in early nineteenth-century academy towns reflected a conception of the community as an important extension of the school. It, too, transmitted values and knowledge to the learners. He also argues convincingly that such close integration of school and community presupposed "a relatively stable, homogeneous society."[47] Parents and teachers alike would have had considerable confidence in the townspeople whose households the students shared, because it was expected that similar values were shared as well.

Several explanations for Ryerson's choice seem plausible at this point then. One could argue that he was simply less pessimistic than Strachan about the dangers of the Toronto environment to which the students would be exposed. But this seems quite inconsistent with his early arrangements for the Upper Canada Academy, and with later complaints of the moral ruin that had befallen unsupervised youths in the wicked metropolis.[48] Toronto was smaller and less evil perhaps than some of the big American or European cities; it certainly had its fair share of informers who let the authorities know what Normal School students were up to—especially if their activities had moral or political implications. Reports came into the Education Office naming students who had been seen at the theatre in the company of the opposite sex, or in taverns; students were even turned in for attending a meeting for former rebel William Lyon Mackenzie.[49] But although it may have been a factor, it is doubtful that the predictable or relatively homogeneous nature of the Toronto community was the only or even the major reason for Ryerson's preference for family boarding arrangements for the Normal School.

A more likely explanation is to be found in the character and background of the students who came to the school from out of town. It is probable, to begin with, that they were not as wealthy as the grammar school graduates who would attend Trinity, and most did not expect to stay for more than one year. Many students came for a summer or winter session only and even then at considerable financial sacrifice. It is possible that Ryerson may have considered living in urban families as a way of transmitting new and different values to the predominantly rural youth who came to the city and that he considered the exchange of rustic ways for a degree of urban sophistication part of the preparation of a teacher.

But certainly this was not all, as Ryerson made clear in statements about boarding halls made at a later date. For Ryerson was opposed to such halls not only for the Normal School and for the short-lived Model Grammar School associated with it,[50] but for almost any school or college, regardless of the character of the students or the community in which it was situated. In an 1850 letter to a trustee of the classical grammar school at Kingston he explained why.

> As to connecting a Boarding Hall and Master's Residence with your School Houses, I would advise you to have nothing to do with the one or the other, but reserve all your resources for your School House and School.... In regard to a Boarding Hall in connection with any Academy, Grammar School or College, experience has led to its abandonment, almost universally in the United States, on both economical and moral grounds. The Boarding Hall of Upper Canada College, which has not been used as such for several months, has been nearly the financial ruin of that Institution, and a great injury to the morals of numbers of pupils.... [51]

It is unclear whether Ryerson was right or wrong about the decline of boarding halls in the United States. In some circles educators and parents were increasingly turning to them as they became disillusioned with the urban environment and caught up, like Strachan, with a vision of boarding schools modelled on the Christian family.[52] In others, however, parents and educational reformers promoted the establishment of public high schools in part, quite explicitly, to enable them to both educate and keep at home their adolescent children. But Ryerson was definitely right about Upper Canada College. The boarding halls connected with that school had had a long history of trouble, and in March and once again in June of 1849, the master in charge had begged to be relieved of responsibility for them.[53] Later in 1856, a Mr. J. W. Stephens declined the headmastership because he did not wish to become involved in overseeing the boarding houses,[54] and discipline problems and scandals involving masters as well as students seemed to take up an inordinate amount of the University of Toronto Senate, the governing body of the school.

Ryerson elaborated very little on the moral dangers associated with boarding halls, but one of his basic points is crucial to an understanding of the institutions he created and his conception of the ideal family. This was that such halls weakened rather than strengthened the domestic feelings, exciting, as he put it, "a disrelish for the quiet and retirement of the domestic circle, and a fondness for the extravagance and bustle of public places." The social tastes and feelings learned at school were as important as the intellectual knowledge acquired, and therefore the nearer the living arrangements approached "those at home, or a private family," the better. Students who came from a distance should be boarded privately in the homes of the masters or with other families in Kingston.[55] The essential point was that no boarding hall could really duplicate what Ryerson conceived to be the important characteristics of family life.

The practical financial considerations were also a factor. Buildings cost money both to construct and maintain, as Ryerson was fully aware from his connections both with Victoria College and the Normal School. Trustees and governments rarely found sufficient funds, nor did the chief superintendent wish additional costs to be born by the students, as the weekly cost of living subsidy paid to first year Normal students proves. One might attempt to save money by building dormitories instead of separate bedrooms for the pupils, but then they were dangerous to the morals, especially of young boys, as Ryerson pointed out in the Kingston letter.[56]

It is probably true that many institutions, especially those paid for by the government, simply could not afford boarding halls of the type idealized by Strachan. When schools and colleges reached a certain size, the former convenient arrangement of master and pupils living together was no longer easily financed. It would take the strong convictions of a Strachan and the metaphor of the Christian family to foster financial and moral support for the larger boarding schools and colleges of the mid century. But if cost was one factor, another was one's view of the ideal family. Ryerson disliked boarding halls because they were too "public"; privacy, tranquility, and retirement were for him the dominant virtues of family life, and he opted for rather old-fashioned family boarding arrangements to promote his modern view of proper domestic relations. Strachan's version of the Christian household at Trinity, on the other hand, represented an innovation of sorts, but one clearly designed to perpetuate the traditional or older view of the family: its virtues were community of fellowship, worship, and concern, as well as the advice and assistance provided by patriarchal authority. Although he shared with Ryerson the value of privacy, and once advised a friend not to take in boarders out of respect for the "peaceful tranquility" of his amiable family,[57] this did not affect Strachan's view of the new, larger educational institutions. That students should live the public lives deplored by Ryerson seemed to him entirely natural.

Despite this basic difference of emphasis, both solutions to the problem of nonresident students focused on reproducing the advantages of family life as Strachan and Ryerson perceived them. And several times during his long career, Ryerson implied that his position was not very far at all from Strachan's. In 1847, he expressed the view that boarding schools were even the best answer for some—in this case for Indian children, for whom he recommended agricultural labour schools in which farmer, schoolmaster, and "parent" were one person. But these would probably have been, if developed, small institutions that really could have functioned like traditional pupil-master households. The interesting thing about them was Ryerson's own feeling that his proposal was impractical; he thought it the ideal solution, but doubted in fact that one man could any longer be found who could, or would wish to, perform the three functions of father, farmer, and teacher at once; a possibility that several decades before surely would have struck no one as remote.[58]

But then by mid century day schools were seen by Ryerson and most of his contemporaries as the usual institutional substitutes for family education, possibly because it was thought increasingly important by middle-class parents and educators that children live at home with their natural families. But lest parents should become alarmed about what went on in day schools, here too the family metaphor was used. The authority of the teacher had to be great, as the superintendent of schools wrote to a somewhat beleaguered grammar school master in 1859; he needed considerable power to exercise discipline in his "large family."[59]

A measure of Ryerson's ability to accommodate several viewpoints almost at once, and of the closeness of his views to those of Strachan in some essential ways, is the fact that if there was no alternative, he was able to accept Strachan's version of the family boarding college in its entirety. Thus an 1854 report on King's College, New Brunswick, which was largely his work, recommended the accommodation of students with private families, but qualified the advice with the aside that, if a boarding hall was found to be a necessity, provision should be made therein for "the observance of all the duties of a Christian family."[60]

When students had to live away from home, residential colleges were certainly preferable to institutions that did not concern themselves at all with the moral or religious lives of their pupils.

The long battle between the denominational colleges and the nonsectarian University of Toronto, as King's College was renamed, over provincial funds for higher education, found Ryerson on the side of the denominational colleges for this reason, in spite of the fact that he was for some years a member of the university's governing senate. The university adopted the boarding hall concept for its undergraduate college and claimed to take an interest in the extracurricular lives of its scholars. For Ryerson, however, as for Strachan, proper family guidance and restraint were inseparable from religion, and if he had doubts about the wisdom of boarding halls in general, he was at one with other critics of the university in being virtually certain that the ideal of the Christian family could never be approached in a large nondenominational institution.[61]

The fact that neither the Toronto Normal or Model Grammar Schools, nor probably the grammar school at Kingston, could very well have been under denominational control may have been an important additional reason for Ryerson's preference for boarding students with local families. It would seem entirely possible that he rejected Strachan's version of the "public" boarding hall for the institutions that he was concerned with partly because the public that would attend or control them was far too diverse. Strachan's community was limited by the shared values of a common religion, insofar as the faculty and most of the students at Trinity would be members of the Church of England, and of a common grammar school background. In the Normal School, this was not the case; all the major denominations were represented among the students, and educational backgrounds varied.[62] Strachan was still able to visualize an educational institution that served a recognizable and easily defined community and when it came to Victoria College, Ryerson could do the same. But institutions like the normal and grammar schools of the province were characterized by the diversity and transience of their student bodies, and this was a fact that could not be ignored. It was this fact, indeed, that made the very distinction between public and private education seem increasingly necessary.

This distinction did not take root easily in Canada, however. Ryerson joined with Strachan and the other promoters of denominational colleges in demanding for them a share of provincial educational funds, a share that they ultimately received with university federation in the latter part of the century. And in the meantime, publicly financed religious institutions, in the form of Roman Catholic separate schools, defended their existence successfully in Upper Canada as in other British North American colonies. But they were not without opponents. On their side, supporters of non-sectarian institutions like the University of Toronto seem to have doubted the wisdom of either close denominational supervision or the protective family ideal, at least as applied to college-age students. Was it really a good idea to protect youth from the mixed society that in the end they would have to enter and confront?

> I am by no means sure that a youth, who has soon to go out into the world without any control, is not the better for a preparatory training amongst those of his own age, with such supervision as can always be exercised in College; and that a higher tone of morality may not be cultivated under the influence of the public opinion of a large body, than by mixing only with a limited society.[63]

What can one conclude about the nature of Upper Canadian society or the social attitudes of educators from these discussions? To begin with, no matter what point of view was taken, they clearly expressed a deep anxiety about the relationship of the child, especially the adolescent, to the larger society. The complexity of Egerton Ryerson's approach to the subject may have been extreme, but it was not untypical. Toronto at mid century was perhaps small enough that Normal School students could occasionally be recognized, but it was big enough for Walter Eales to complain that a man's workmates might often be "relative strangers" and for Ryerson and other school and college authorities to insist on extremely restrictive rules governing student life, no matter what the age and previous experience of the scholars. Upper Canada does not seem to have undergone the strong rejection of cities that occurred in the United States and resulted there in the founding of large numbers of boarding schools and colleges in remote rural areas, but it cannot be said that the use of private family boarding arrangement presupposed great confidence in the stability or homogeneity of the community either.

Ryerson's commitment to the new family ideal and to the idea that students should live in the relative seclusion that he associated with private family life seems to have been a response rather to the feeling that both the society and the new educational institutions that he was building were too large and complex to be familial as he understood the term. Unlike Trinity, the Normal School could never be a family; real families and the inward-turning family ideal seemed more appropriate answers to the heterogeneous realities of the emerging mass society, as Ryerson saw it.

And too there was the fact of class. Few Upper Canadians could afford the luxury of maintaining either the traditional household or expensive residential colleges. Perhaps this was why people like Egerton Ryerson continued, without any great feeling of contradicting themselves, to seek state financial aid for the latter. Elites would always be necessary and for them the old ideology of the family as household was not inappropriate. The new ideology of the family on the other hand, like the common school system itself, was designed to serve different people, in particular the urban middle class of an emerging mass society.[64]

Notes

1. The theme of the family and the state and others referred to briefly in this essay are discussed in my thesis, "The School Promoters: Education and Social Class in Mid-Nineteenth Century Upper Canada (Ph.D. diss., University of Toronto, 1974).

2. James McLachlan, *American Boarding Schools: A Historical Study* (New York, 1970). For McLachlan, it was "one of the major controlling metaphors in American social thought and popular culture" in the antebellum period (p. 115).

3. A helpful discussion of ideal as opposed to actual family patterns may be found in Marion J. Levy, Jr., "Aspects of the Analysis of Family Structure," in Ansley J. Coale et al., *Aspects of the Analysis of Family Structure* (Princeton, N.J., 1965).

4. Philippe Ariès, *Centuries of Childhood: A Social History of Family Life* (New York, 1962). The gradual acceptance of new ideas by different social classes is one of Ariès' major themes.

5. Peter Laslett, "Size and Structure of the Household in England Over Three Centuries," *Population Studies 23,* no. 2 (July 1969): 202. See also, *The World We Have Lost* (Cambridge, 1965).

6. Egerton Ryerson to Arch. Fletcher, January 15, 1846, Ontario Archives Education Papers: RG 2, C 1, Letterbook C, p. 17 [the Education Papers of the Ontario Archives are hereafter re-referred to under Code and Series numbers as listed in the archives, RG 2, etc.].

7. John Strachan, *A Letter to the Rev. A. N. Bethune, on the Management of Grammar Schools* (York, Upper Canada, 1829), p. 43.

8. "Minutes of the Board of Education for Upper Canada, 1823-1833," February 23, 1831, RG 2, A, p. 152.

9. *Circular of the Upper Canada Academy* (Cobourg, Upper Canada, 1841), p. 15.

10. Edward Dewar to Egerton Ryerson, November 13, 1849, RG 2, C-6-C.

11. Joseph H. King to Egerton Ryerson, July 12, 1850, RG 2, C-6-C.

12. For details of Strachan's early views and the Family Compact, see my article, "John Strachan and Early Upper Canada, 1799-1814," *Ontario History* 52 (1960):3, and R. E. Saunders, "What Was the Family Compact?" *Ontario History* 49 (1957):4.

13. Rev. G. J. Mountain, *A Sermon on the Education of the Poor, the Duty Of Diffusing the Gospel, and, more particularly, on the Importance of Family Religion* (Quebec, 1822), pp. 16-18.

14. For an example, see C. E. Phillips, *The Development of Education in Canada* (Toronto, 1957), p. 111.

15. Strachan, *On the Management of Grammar Schools,* p. 36.

16. J. C. Hodgins, ed., *Documentary History of Education in Upper Canada* (Toronto, 1894), 1:32.

17. John A. Irving, "The Development of Philosophy in Central Canada from 1850 to 1900," *Canadian Historical Review* 31, no. 3 (1950): 257-59.

18. *Doctor Charles Duncombe's Report upon the Subject of Education* (Toronto, 1836), pp. 30-31.

19. Edmund Morgan, *The Puritan Family* (Boston, 1956).

20. Eva Figes, *Patriarchal Attitudes* (New York, 1970).

21. Walter Eales, *Lecture on the Benefits to be derived from Mechanics' Institutes* (Toronto, 1851), p. 11.

22. *The Canadian Gem and Family Visitor* 2, no. 2 (February 1849): 35-36.

23. Eales, *Mechanics' Institutes,* p. 12.

24. C. B. Sissons, ed., *Egerton Ryerson: His Life and Letters,* 2 vols. (Toronto, 1937-1947), and *My Dearest Sophie: Letters from Egerton Ryerson to His Daughter* (Toronto, 1955).

25. Egerton Ryerson to John Russell, March 23, 1850, RG 2, C 1, Letterbook E, pp. 156-57.

26. *First Lessons in Christian Morals for Canadian Families and Schools* (Toronto, 1871), p. 21; *First Lessons in Agriculture; for Canadian Farmers and their Families* (Toronto, 1871), pp. 171-72; and *Elements of Political Economy; or How individuals and a country become rich* (Toronto, 1877), especially p. 9.

27. *Journal of Education for Upper Canada* 7, no. 9 (September 1854): 148.

28. *Annual Report by the Chief Superintendent of Schools for Upper Canada* (1864), pt. 1, p. 26.

29. *Elements of Political Economy,* p. 140.

30. *First Lessons in Christian Morals,* p. 26.

31. Sissons, ed., *Egerton Ryerson,* 2:268.

32. Morgan, *The Puritan Family,* chapt. 7.

33. Hodgins ed., *Documentary History,* 10:59.

34. Ibid., 9:114.

35. Ibid., 10:64.

36. Ibid.

37. Ibid., pp. 64-65.

38. Ibid.

39. Ibid., 8:302; see also Headmaster of the Cobourg Grammar School to J. G. Hodgins, February-March 1859, and Master of the Barrie Grammar School to Ryerson, May 15, 1865, RG 2, C-6-C.

40. *Minutes of the Board of Education,* RG 2, A, p. 155.

41. Hodgins ed., *Documentary History,* 2:4.

42. *Circular of the Upper Canada Academy,* pp. 16-17.

43. A memorial from the students to Ryerson on his retirement as principal suggests that his residence among them was "anything but agreeable," and at least one letter to him implies that he had complained at some length about the difficul-

ties of his position. Memorial from Students of Victoria College, 1844, and James Spencer to Egerton Ryerson, January 9, 1843, *Ryerson Correspondence,* United Church Archives Toronto.

44. T. C. Young to J. G. Hodgins, June 3, 1847, RG 2, C-6-C; and Hodgins, ed., *Documentary History,* 7:99.

45. *Council of Public Instruction Records,* RG 2, B (3 vols.), contains many references to student discipline and staff inspection of boarding houses.

46. *Toronto Normal School Register of Students, 1847-1873,* RG 2, H.

47. McLachlan, *American Boarding Schools,* p. 47.

48. Hodgins, ed., *Documentary History,* 16:288; and ibid., 17:178.

49. See for example Anonymous to Ryerson, February 21, 1849, and Robert Yathy to Ryerson, March 26, 1849, RG 2, C-6-C.

50. Hodgins, ed., *Documentary History,* 13:65.

51. Ibid., 9:206.

52. McLachlan, *American Boarding Schools;* and M. B. Katz, *The Irony of Early School Reform* (Cambridge, Mass., 1968), pp. 51-52.

53. Hodgins, ed., *Documentary History,* 8:192.

54. Ibid., 12 224 and 267.

55. Ibid., 9:206.

56. Ibid.

57. Strachan to Dr. Brown, December 1, 1818, in *The John Strachan Letterbook: 1812-1834,* ed. G. W. Spragge (Toronto, 1946), p. 184.

58. Ryerson to Varden, May 20, 1847, RG 2, C 1, Letterbook C, p. 380.

59. Ryerson to Muir, September 6, 1859, RG 2, C-6-C.

60. Hodgins, ed., *Documentary History,* 16:5.

61. "The University Question in a Series of Letters," *Documentary History,* ed. J. G. Hodgins, 16:261-300, contains Ryerson's defense of denominational colleges.

62. The diversity of religious backgrounds was apparent from the beginning. Of 108 students who attended during the fairly typical 3d session (1848-1849) there were 6 Roman Catholics, 21 members of the Church of England, 42 Methodists, 20 Presbyterians, 6 Baptists, 2 Congregationalists, and 13 whose denominations were other or not given. *Annual Report of the Chief Superintendent of Schools* (1859), table M.

63. Hodgins, ed., *Documentary History,* 15:194.

64. The relationship of educational innovation to perceptions of social class in the mid-nineteenth century I have explored elsewhere. *See* note 1.

CHILDHOOD AND CHARITY IN NINETEENTH-CENTURY BRITISH NORTH AMERICA

Patricia Rooke and R.L. Schnell

> From six in a bed in those mansions of woe,
> Where nothing but beards, nails and vermin do grow,
> And from picking of oakum cellars below,
> Good Lord, deliver us![1]

In *Children in English-Canadian Society,* Neil Sutherland argued that the transformation of attitudes and institutions that came to characterize modern child welfare had occurred by the 1920s. It will be demonstrated in this paper that Sutherland's focus on the period 1880-1920, with a look at the 1870s as an introduction and the 1920s as a conclusion, placed severe constraints on the possibility of an adequate historical understanding of the development of modern, scientific and professional child welfare in Canada.[2] It will be argued further that child welfare underwent several substantial and influential changes between 1800 and 1900 and that a careful examination of the establishment and transformation of that most Canadian of child-rescue institutions, the nineteenth-century Protestant Orphans' Home, provides a useful means of explicating those changes.

In an earlier article based on trans-Atlantic studies, one of the authors formulated a theoretical framework for analysing the development of the concept of "childhood," which demonstrated that it entailed the criteria of protection, segregation, dependence, and delayed responsibilities. It was further argued that childhood as a concept implied rescue and restraint, that is, child rescue and childhood are synonymous.[3] The four criteria will be used to map the history of child rescue sentiment and institutions by examining their manifestations in provisions for dependent and neglected children and youth in British North America. In order to establish the colonial and imperial context out of which late nineteenth-century Canadian child welfare developed, the Old World background and implementation of poor relief in the New World will be examined.

The paper consists of three parts. The first part is an explication of the dominant themes of pre-Victorian child rescue in Great Britain. Although customarily acknowledging the influence of Victorian evangelicals on social action in the slums of Great Britain, the United States and Canada, scholars less frequently note the institutional development of the late seventeenth and eighteenth centuries that provided the base for Victorian activism.[4] The arguments behind the establishment of these early orphan asylums, schools and houses of

---

From *Histoire sociale / Social History,* XV, no. 29 (May 1982), 157-79. Reprinted by permission of *Histoire sociale / Social History.*

industry, and other charitable institutions and the debate over boarding-out and general policies of relief, intervention, and prevention in trans-Atlantic anglophone communities will introduce the study. The second part describes the mixed forms of relief and rescue available in British North America in the early nineteenth century.

The third and most developed section will demonstrate, that, contrary to Sutherland, the first significant shifts in Canadian sentiment toward dependent child life had occurred well before the 1880s and that the transformation is best understood by examining the establishment and growth of children's homes.

I — British Models of Child Rescue

The eighteenth-century charity school movement was a major extension of ideas concerning character development to the children of a class deemed a potential threat to the civil and religious stability of British society. As children's institutions, the schools were the first substantial "modern" attempt to use formal education to instruct children in a protective environment, and as means of child rescue they were the prototypes of nineteenth-century pedagogical experimentation that culminated in the common schools.[5]

The charity schools with their concern for children were supplemented by older mixed forms of relief such as houses and schools of industry that included adults and children and the worthy and unworthy poor. Aware that indiscriminate association of inmates was "destructive of industry, order, and decency," the acting governors of the Dublin House of Industry in 1798 sought to classify them according to age, qualities, conduct and abilities so that a "class of merit"—based on superior industry, moral conduct and obedience to House rules—would be lodged and fed separately from their less worthy fellows.[6] The belief in the value of employment and the danger of idleness was succinctly put in 1756 by the founders of the Ladies' Charity School (Bristol), who observed that "when youth, idleness, and poverty meet together, they become fatal temptations to many unhappy creatures."[7]

In *An Essay Toward the Encouragement of Charity Schools,* Isaac Watts asserted that it would "be a great and unspeakable advantage to these Schools ... if ... some methods whereby all the children of the poor might be employed in some useful labours one part of the day" could be contrived. Watts recommended that children sufficiently instructed and improved should "be placed out, and fixed either in country-labours, in domestic services, in some inferior post in a shop, or in mechanical trades, that so they may not run loose and wild in the World."[8]

The insistence on useful employment and religious training as fundamental elements in the rescue of children and adults is a major theme in the reports of all the societies. In 1813, the Edinburgh Society for the Suppression of

Beggars argued that its object required that "a great portion of their attention must be devoted to the education of the children of the poor in habits of morality and industry." In one of the earliest discussions of the contamination of children by their parents, the Edinburgh Society cited the expense of residential care and hoped that, given a proper day school, "the injury they will sustain from the society of their parents will not be so great as is apprehended." Although much of the interest in schools and houses of industry was aroused by the presence of sturdy beggars and other undeserving objects of charity, tract writers and philanthropists were equally attracted by the educational cure for pauperism promised by institutionalizing and instructing children. The schooling provided children lodged in houses of industry was in most cases very limited. The 1759 rules of a house of industry in Suffolk required a school "where all children above three years of age shall be kept till they shall be five years old, and then set to spinning and such other proper and beneficial work as they are able to perform."[9] The Ladies' Charity School (Bristol), much affected by the danger of idleness, had said little about learning and much about spinning.

It is not until the nineteenth century that the more subtle possibilities of education were recognized by those seeking to promote a spirit of independence or self-reliance among the poor. Charitable institutions were to be an essential means of impressing on them that "it is upon their own exertions, habits of economy, and prudent foresight alone, that they and their families, must depend for their comforts, as well as their daily bread." That the poor were not unaware of such possibilities for self-help is shown in the complaint of the Bath Society that when "the children can earn something for themselves exclusive of clothing, and contribute towards defraying the expenses [of the school], they are taken away by their parents." Such calculative self-interest, later observed in Canada also, was not the kind of self-reliance that the patrons of the poor had in mind. Many societies such as the St. James School of Industry, limited parental visits to Sundays to diminish family influence over the children, a practice followed in nineteenth-century Canada.[10] The Shrewsbury House of Industry sought to prevent the children of depraved families from "inevitably imbib[ing] the contagion by a *total and complete separation of [children and youth] from the abandoned and depraved* [that would] place them out of the way of temptation, and prevent the fatal contagion of profligate discourse, and vicious examples."[11]

The conditions that had given rise to the eighteenth-century efforts at child-saving continued into the nineteenth century. In 1846, a Manchester committee originally formed to found a ragged school established instead the Manchester Juvenile Refuge and School of Industry. The society aimed "to rescue a large class of destitute and neglected children from the paths of vice, misery, and degradation, and to train them to honesty, industry, and virtue." Rejecting confinement as an inadequate means of reformation, the committee stressed prevention through an education that would "render them better fitted to endure and overcome the necessary hardships and temptations of a poor man's lot." The required education included three elements: first, reading, writing, and arithmetic, which were both useful and an excellent means of keeping the mind engaged; secondly, moral and religious training which were pre-eminently suited to exercise a "purifying, restraining and elevating influence" on children; and finally, industrial training to prepare the boys for a self-supporting occupation.[12] Unlike earlier emphases on habituation as a means of ensuring a decent life in the midst of appalling poverty, the new view saw education as a double rescue from immorality and incompetence. On the other hand, the Aberdeen industrial schools organized in 1841 saw the protection of children from their "debased" families in terms of separating them and binding them in order that they might have the advantages of family life while ensuring that they be made dependent through such surveillance.[13]

In addition to private philanthropic ventures, the poor laws provided a wide variety of indoor and outdoor relief. With the 1834 Poor Law Act Amendment, the process of unionization and rationalization of public charity created the reformed workhouses as the central institution of relief. The new workhouse allowed, at least theoretically, the classification and provision of special facilities for inmates. Education and other services for children offered the possibility of depauperization of future generations; the 1850s, however, witnessed the controversy over the results of institutionalization and the effectiveness of workhouse schooling. Advocates of boarding-out, drawing on Irish and Scottish experience, argued for the superiority of rearing poor law children in families over the stultifying atmosphere of the workhouse.[14]

Thus, with those precedents, sentiments and attitudes toward dependent children clearly established in Great Britain by the eighteenth and early nineteenth centuries, such institutional models and ideas were often transplanted by reformers involved in Canadian efforts at child rescue.

II — British North American Child Rescue

Information about the care of children who were neglected, abandoned or destitute is spotty in early colonial records; however, it seems clear that protection, segregation, dependence, and delayed responsibilities were not generally part of child life. The care of these children was considered part of the general provision for the poor.

The Atlantic colonies of Newfoundland, Nova Scotia, New Brunswick, and Prince Edward Island were typical of the extension of poor law ideas and practices to the New World. In Newfoundland, public relief was distributed on a casual basis by commissioners of public roads, who provided minimal funds during the colony's periodic and endemic seasons of distress. Nova Scotia, the most progressive and prosperous colony, had a flourishing number of private in-stitutions and societies to relieve the misery of its inhabitants as well as a system of poor relief. New Brunswick also closely approximated the earlier British model in both its system of poor relief and religiously connected orphan asylums. Prince Edward Island with its predominantly rural population and parsimonious ruling class resembled a rural English parish.[15]

The Halifax Orphan House, established in 1752, which bound out its older orphans and engaged the younger ones in carding and spinning of wool, the picking of oakum and "other little offices" around the garden and hospital, was an initial, largely unsuccessful, attempt at a public-supported specialized facility in British North America. According to the earliest nineteenth-century records it was in disarray within a short time and the young public charges were pro-vided for in the Poor Asylum along with aged, diseased, infirm, and degenerate adult paupers.

An inquiry into New Brunswick provincial institutions in 1857 expressed dis-may at the young male offenders between ten and under eighteen years incarcerated in the penitentiary for crimes of the "most trivial kind." Since these boys were "without parents or friends to instruct and guide them, and without homes to attract and improve them," the report observed that they were "thrown into circumstances of exposure and temptation, and thus become an easy prey to vice." It recommended a separate facility to be called a "Reformatory School" with a special keeper in charge where the lads would be taught the elementary branches of education for several years instead of the pre-vailing custom of months, so that "real improvement" could be achieved. This would be done under the 1855 and 1857 acts that provided for juvenile offend-ers. Young females were recommended to be placed in a segregated section of the almshouse. Similar concerns were being expressed elsewhere about the neces-sity of segregating and protecting dependent young people.[16]

The 1822 plan of Captain Robert Parker Pelly, the Governor of Assiniboia, for the care of "half breed" children whose parents had died or deserted them was part of the general concern for safety of the trading posts if men with large families were discharged and left in "an uneducated and savage position" to "collect across the country" without "proper superintendence." Using arguments almost identical with Isaac Watts', Pelly concluded that "it will therefore be both prudent and economical to incur some expense in placing these people where they may maintain themselves and be civilized [and] instructed in reli-gion." The expense was only temporary since once the boys had been trained for agriculture and the girls for industry they could be apprenticed. Children were merely part of a larger problem of an unsettled population and were not given any special treatment.[17]

As in the case of the Society for Promoting Education and Industry among the Indians and Destitute Settlers in Canada in 1828, schools of industry were to combine economy and industry along with elementary education and a knowledge of agriculture and the mechanic arts. At Quebec City, for example, "children [were] engaged in some useful branch of labour half of each day, which [the Ladies' branch conceived] ought to be the case in all schools which may be opened for the children of the poor." The plan for a school of industry at Montreal, intended for "the amelioration of the poor and the establishment of honest industry," offered employment for those able to work, instruction in some useful branch of work for the unskilled, relief of the helpless poor in their own dwellings, and instruction in reading to the illiterate.[18]

Although the school of industry was intended primarily to relieve adults, the Society's agent, T. Osgood, on "seeing a number of orphans and poor children out of employment, destitute of bread and the means of instruction," placed them under the care of the superintendent and provided them with bread and clothing in return for their labour. Moreover the agent brought into the institution the blind and the lame who with the help of cheap machinery were employed in sawing and boring holes in stone. The Montreal Society freely mixed the objects of its charity in the school of industry.[19]

Canadian institutional arrangements under the poor laws in the Maritimes and the modified legislation of Ontario, as well as the orphan asylums that sprang up in the second half of the century, were dissimilar in several ways from those of Britain. While using much of the same rhetoric and seemingly transplanting institutional models, the houses of industry and of refuge, even before the segregation of their child inmates, never became the huge, impersonal and architecturally pretentious buildings of the new 1834 British poor laws. These buildings were mainly showpieces while certainly older buildings like Westminster Asylum for Female Orphans, or the London Orphans' Asylum, could not have been designed with the needs of children or of adults in mind. As bleak as life must have been for the Canadian dependent poor compelled to remain in their parish and municipal "almshouses," they retained more the appearance and organizational patterns of earlier models and bear a striking resemblance to the American colonial buildings discussed by David Rothman in *The Discovery of the Asylum*.[20] Therefore, while being parsimoniously governed, the Canadian poorhouses were frequently ordinary, although decrepit and cheerless, "homes" or farmhouses, and did not exude quite the same forbidding aspect of Britain's "pauper palaces" and congregate systems.

The Toronto House of Industry, founded by a private committee in 1836, aimed at "the total abolition of street begging, the putting down of wandering vagrants, and securing an asylum at the least possible expense for the industrious and distressed poor." Supported in part by a parliamentary grant and the City Council, the House in its first year had relieved 857 persons of whom 638 were children and had 46 inmates of whom 26 were children. By 1853, the House of Industry was giving its "most anxious attention ... to making permanent provision for orphans, deserted children, and those whose parents have rendered themselves liable to legal punishment." A system of apprenticeship was devised by which a "large number of children were placed out with respectable persons in the country" whereby they were removed "from the temptations and vices to which they are exposed in a large city." To encourage training of children in habits of industry and sobriety that "will prepare them for usefulness and competency through life," the House of Industry received children whose parents and friends were unable to support them, placed them at school, and cared for and protected their morals and persons, until suitable country homes could be found.[21]

Still, by the 1850s the need to separate and distinguish children from adults was not general. An interesting example of mixed categories occurred in 1856 with the City of Toronto's purchase of a tract of land to be used as an industrial farm "where offenders (particularly juveniles) may be classified and reformed, while punished, but also where many of the infirm and maimed might be made to assist, in some way, to their support."[22]

Kingston provides a powerful example of the shift in the concept of childhood, which included the growing recognition of children as a special class with particular needs such as protection and segregation. The central charitable institution was the House of Industry founded in 1814 and not closed until 1916. The details of this institution, which are well preserved, give all the appearances of the workhouses under the English poor laws.[23] Children, who were abandoned, orphaned, or destitute, were received by the House which acted *in loco parentis* with regard to placing them out or employing them in household chores. Children remained part of the House of Industry until the Orphans' Home and Widows' Friend Society opened its first building in 1857. Citing the degraded habits, predisposition to idleness, and the dubious health and morality of inmates as an undesirable environment for the young, the Society charged that the children were not "cared for, supervised [or] protected from the vice and degradation" of an institution that offered "no humanizing influences."[24]

Between 1830 and 1860 the first institutionalized care for dependent and orphaned children began to emerge in the form of the Protestant Orphans' Homes in Montreal, Kingston, Toronto and Halifax, to be followed soon after in London, Ottawa, Victoria and Winnipeg. None of these ever sheltered the many hundreds of children at a given time as did the British orphan asylums.

Moreover, although unable fully to create the domestic atmosphere and family spirit their directors idealized, the Protestant Orphans' Homes were able to approximate it more closely than their British counterparts. First, most orphan asylums in Canada were modest undertakings with populations ranging from merely a score or so as in Victoria to several hundred at their height in Toronto, Winnipeg and Saint John.

Secondly, the Canadian institutions exercised remarkable control over the selection of their clients by careful admission procedures which articulated the implicit assumptions made by the ladies' committees regarding who were the "worthy" and "unworthy" poor. In fact, since these institutions largely received custodial cases for nominal fees rather than full orphans, they did not admit the most alarming or desperate situations or the chronic poor as was the case in the large British institutions and the North American Roman Catholic ones. The open-door policy of British homes such as Ashley Down in Bristol, the National Children's Homes, and the Barnardo Homes, was shared in Canada by the Roman Catholic orphanages which subsequently were more crowded.

Thirdly, the debates that resounded in Britain over the psychological consequences of institutional life—the lack of spontaneity and initiative on the part of children—did not apply in the same degree to Canada although in the twentieth century such arguments would be used to advocate fostering practices. True, a matron and superintendent might be harassed by too many children, too many tasks, too little money and too small a domestic staff, but there is little sense of the barracks-like discipline and the anonymity of a militaristic atmosphere that later critics suggested were prevalent. Statements in some annual reports that "regular methodical habits" and "cleanliness, order and good management" were enforced, and that "a spirit of docility and subordination testified to good management" must be interpreted cautiously since the minutes of many asylums testify that such management was not as mechanistically induced or as impersonally imposed as the rhetoric suggests. Indeed, some homes seem as much arguments for confusion and nonchalance as for orderliness and inflexibility and as reflections of the various temperaments of the matrons themselves as any institutional plans.[25]

Finally, repressive religious fervour and the excesses sometimes associated with evangelical enthusiasm as a means to disciplining young and suggestive minds are surprisingly missing, given the "Protestant" origins of the homes, in the Canadian records. Interdenominationalism, even if on pragmatic and economic grounds rather than on principle, it seems, had a neutralizing effect on such fervour. In sum, there appears to be a dissonance between the rhetoric (a rhetoric almost identical to British sentiments) expressed at annual meetings and fund-raising functions, and in annual reports, and the actual conduct, the physical arrangements and the clienteles of the Protestant Orphans' Homes.

If these were the differences between the British congregate systems and the Canadian homes, then what were the similarities? Four aspects seem worth noting: (1) the application of the new awareness for the peculiar needs of children that resulted in actual institutional environments which rendered them objectively and psychologically dependent upon those maintaining them while assuring the inmates of maximum protection and segregation; (2) the ultimate segregation of children from undesirable adult influences by controlling the inmates, *in loco parentis,* even to the point of interfering with parental access by binding children out if fees had not been forthcoming; (3) the segregation of various classes of children from each other, that is, the distinction between "dependent" and "delinquent"; and (4) the training of children into menial occupations through indentures and the regimens of the homes.

The following section will examine these aspects by a survey of the rise of the Canadian Protestant Orphans' Homes as a conscious and concrete articulation of the concept of childhood whose origins can be discerned in the debates and practices of the late eighteenth and early nineteenth centuries.

III — The Rise of Protestant Orphans' Homes

In 1854, the Reverend Mr. William Bond preached an edifying sermon before the ladies' committee of the Protestant Asylum for the Aged and Infirm, which included children among its residents. Pointing out that the home was the only institution in Montreal that accepted children who had not lost both parents, the future Anglican bishop warmed to his subject by praising the ministrations of womankind—"her softening, elevating, purifying, gladdening influence; her fond companionship in the seasons of joy, her devoted tenderness in the hours of sickness." His remarks were intended as a salutary reminder that those ladies who had organized themselves into benevolent societies to found houses of refuge and orphan asylums were gentlewomen of means and respectability with virtues peculiar to their sex and entirely suited to such philanthropic endeavours.[26] Largely through the efforts of such women the first segregated institutions for children were organized. Even in those cases where gentlemen's committees founded such institutions or retained official governance, it was through the ladies' committees that actual management and control were directed.[27]

Founded in 1857 to train "poor, uncared-for, destitute children" in "the habits of virtue and regularity," the Kingston Orphan Asylum reported two years later the condition of many of these children was "more desolate than that of children left wholly orphans, as the very circumstances of their having a parent living prevents their adoption into families that would gladly receive an orphan." The ladies of the Women's and Orphans' Friend Society had decided that a separate institution for children was necessary when their attention was drawn to the numbers of them living in the overcrowded house of industry without suitable supervision and being placed out as household drudges without proper circumspection. From the beginning, fee-paying children who required residential accommodation in times of need or emergency were admitted along with whole or part orphans. To control the admission of children who had guardians, the Kingston Asylum in 1862 stipulated that parents had to agree not to remove their children without consent of the Society or to prevent them from taking a situation if a good one occurred.[28]

As with the Kingston institution, the Toronto Protestant Orphan Home and Female Aid Society (founded in 1851) received children from the house of industry, which had been founded to provide "for the industrious and distressed poor." In that year alone, the house listed in its registry 638 children in addition to 37 deserted women, 87 widows, and 95 ill and unemployed. In 1853, the Toronto Protestant Orphans' Home noted that it assisted mothers in service by caring for their children for a minimal fee and provided a custodial service for the poorer members of society as well as for the widowed and orphaned. Fee-paying children were usually returned to their living parent or to relatives rather than being adopted or indentured as happened with the first clients of the Toronto Girls' Home and Public Nursery in 1859. Sarah and Mary Anne Kingwood, aged five and three years, the first entry in the register, were duly adopted because their father was dead and their mother was in a penitentiary. In the case of the Toronto institution, the number of runaways suggests that for fee-paying children the ties of kinship were strong enough to induce them not to remain in the institution.[29]

Managed by males but superintended by women, the Newfoundland Church of England Orphans' and Widows' Aid Society of St. John's was established in 1855 as a thanksgiving for the departure of cholera from the city. John Tunbridge, its first honorary secretary, acknowledged the orphanage's debt to the "deadly pestilence" whose chief victims had been the poor. "It scarcely entered a dwelling of any other class" and its "desolatory presence ... bequeath to us, as it were the widow and the orphan." From the outset, however, the majority of inmates proved to be not full orphans but the children of the fatherless whose mothers were "incapable of providing for them." During its decades, the home received somewhat more unusual objects of charity than elsewhere. Among those of "affecting and interesting circumstances" were children who lost their fathers in the 1855 Sealing Disaster and the survivors of the 1863 shipwreck of the *Anglo-Saxon*. The Methodist Orphanage of St. John's, founded in 1888 but whose first official residence was not purchased until 1901, received mostly the children of the widowed and deserted. The poverty in Newfoundland, particularly in the outposts, was more general, constant and dire than anywhere else in British North America and the dependence of many candidates on the various Protestant and Roman Catholic asylums was frequently the result of tubercular mothers or fathers who had died of this disease which proved an unremitting scourge throughout the colony's history.[30]

Both the Methodist and Anglican homes remained relatively small—the Methodist never having over forty-two girls and the Church of England averaged between seventy and eighty for both sexes at its height. Given the appalling destitution in Newfoundland and the constantly inadequate provisions for relief, such small numbers of children from working-class families are astonishing; however, the rates of child mortality and the frequency of disaster and disease suggests that a calloused colonial administration had such problems repeatedly alleviated by what often amounted to a grim "final solution." Children whose mothers remarried were customarily returned to them, but those whose mothers did not wish to receive them, either through circumstances or through choice, remained in the homes which continued to receive the orphan grant allowed institutions by the commissioners of the poor.[31]

The Halifax Infants' Home is another example of an institution whose function was as useful as it was benevolent. Although infants were received free of charge owing to parental inability to pay for a child's board, many were actually boarded by mothers who visited and nursed their babies, or in cases of weaned children, visited and clothed them, paying for their maintenance and thus using the home as a residential custodial institution. In 1884, the new physician, Dr. Oliver, recommended that it would be preferable for the child if the mother were actually boarded with it and that in order to ensure the character of the home and preserve the privacy of the infants the home ought not to accommodate by the day the children of women who were in daily service.[32]

An interesting small select orphanage, the Wiggins Home for Boys at Saint John, New Brunswick, founded and generously endowed in 1867 for the sons of lost and deceased mariners, also provided similar facilities. The sons of deserted wives and widows were received until their parents were able to provide for them.[33]

The Saint John Protestant Orphan Asylum, founded in 1854, admitted five classes of children which were usually included in the rules of other orphans' homes. In the case of the New Brunswick home, the orphaned were generally in the minority. The majority of inmates consisted of poor and indigent children; children, both or only one of whose parents were dead, insane, inebriate, helpless or confined to penitentiary; children deserted by either or both parents; and destitute children. The orphanage was typical in its exclusion of delinquent youngsters and those with contagious diseases. It admitted children as "nominal boarders or by voluntary surrender" and claimed custody if the terms of the contract were disregarded for over three months after notice had been given to relatives or guardians.[34]

In the founding years of the Protestant Orphans' Homes, these modest schemes were obviously the expressions of a self-indulgent benevolence. Anomalies in admissions sometimes merely reflected the private patronage of members of the ladies' committees as in the case of the deserted Mrs. Stewart who, in April 1860, wanted her three children admitted to the Kingston home. Although her situation was so desperate that she was voluntarily entering the house of industry, the committee decided against the admitting of the children "as both parents were alive." The Stewarts were clearly perceived of as part of the unworthy poor. When Mary Moore's mother, now "remarried and very comfortable," was unwilling to take her home, the ladies' committee acknowledged that the girl was "a favourite with the matron and agreed to keep her at one dollar a month." Such inconsistent policies were common in the first decades of their operations when the institutions are appropriately seen as an extension of the individual women and reflecting their preferences and prejudices. In the face of increasing urban problems, even in relatively small Canadian cities, individual eccentricities diminished and admission became standardized to meet the demands of all types of poverty.[35]

Through its history, the Ottawa Protestant Orphans' Home reflected more faithfully than most institutions the "philanthropic mode." Women such as Lady MacDonald and the wealthy Mrs. Bronson, first and second directresses respectively, seemed impervious to the visible demands of public poverty. Founded in 1865 by the Ladies' Protestant Benevolent Association, the home received widows and women out of place although full and part orphans were seen as "the proper objects for the cure of the institution." In the first months of its mandate eleven ladies were elected to "search for destitute children," which suggests careful selection. Indeed, a year later only twelve orphans were enjoying the ladies' assiduous solicitude. Illegitimate children were not received, as a desperate Mrs. Armstrong of Brockville discovered in 1866 when she was obliged to produce her marriage certificate before her three children were admitted. While the girls assisted in the housework, the ladies' committee was quite cheerfully sending the boys to work in Mr. Bronson's mill during the summer of 1869. One-half of each boy's wages was paid to the home and the other half put aside for the boy's future benefit. The first choice of girls as domestic servants and boys as apprentices was always given to subscribers of the society or to others recommended by the ladies' committee. This policy of first choice was obvious and consistent in all homes examined. The exclusive admission policies of the Ottawa institution did not alter until the late 1890s when it began to receive "transients" from the newly-organized Children's Aid Society. Just as the children of various Sunday schools had not been considered suitable companions on picnics and outings, the original Children's Aid Society cases were judged as being unfit to mix with the Protestant Orphans' Homes children.[36]

The results of epidemics such as ship fever, cholera and typhoid frequently spurred middle-class efforts to found orphanages, refuges and houses of industry in the nineteenth century. The Montreal Protestant Orphans Association, founded in 1822, felt compelled by "an unfortunate, ill-directed immigration from Ireland" to hire a house on William Street for immigrant children. In 1847 during another epidemic, ninety-five children were taken from the ships. Of these, ten died, fifty-four were placed or reclaimed, eight returned to the fever sheds at Point St. Charles, and twenty-three refused to remain in the home. In 1832, the Montreal Ladies' Benevolent Society, organized to counteract the effects of the "most awful visitation of asiatic cholera," founded a refuge for widows and the fatherless.[37]

As early as 1854-56, the Toronto Protestant Orphans' Home publicly appealed to carpenters, joiners, and other members of the working class for aid in adding another floor to its building since the prevailing epidemic caused it to be short of space. The working class responded "nobly, kindly, and cheerfully" with each shop contributing a half-day's free labour to the enterprise. Again in the 1870s, typhoid nearly doubled the number of admissions.[38]

Periodic economic dislocations, by pushing many families into destitution, made the problems of admissions and institutional funding more acute. The depression of the 1890s aggravated poverty and distress and contributed to new problems of indigence and pauperism. The Boys' Home in Toronto placed out many of its children between 1893 and 1896 because relatives could not make support payments and the depression caused a drop in donations for the support of the home. The annual reports lamented "the scarcity of work" and "the hard times" which forced the institution to rescue little ones under the usual required age of five, and that compelled "many unfortunate parents to part with their boys ... until they can take them home again." Preventive help was offered to another class by the Toronto Boys' Home that, beginning in 1861, provided a temporary refuge and lodging for working lads who might otherwise have been convicted of vagabondage. These and many "friendless little orphans" were rescued not only from want and misery but also from being put "among vagabonds, thieves, and burglars—the pests and the curse of the city" in the deplorably squalid city jail. Judging by newspaper accounts five years later the problem of "young thieves and beggars" in Toronto was far from resolved for some of the public was agitating for a law to be passed to round them up and bind them out as the Protestant Orphans' Home and house of industry did, or establish a ragged school to educate them.[39]

Even during good times, the need for day-care facilities that would allow working mothers to leave their children in decent surroundings was apparent in the major cities. Had there been more crèches, day nurseries, and settlement houses, fewer parents would have been compelled to resort to orphanages. The Girls' Home of Toronto had included a public nursery in 1856 but four years later this home began to provide resident services on both a permanent and a daily basis and by 1868 day care was abandoned.[40]

Protestant groups, often working in conjunction with the homes, established lying-in and after-care for unmarried mothers and their infants as well as job placement bureaux with some training for domestic service. The assistance given to this class of needy women was in part a crude attempt to counteract the pernicious effects of "baby farming," which later was the object of the 1914 Ontario Maternity Boarding House Act. The babies of these women were often given over to the orphans' or infants' homes in some cities. The Christian Women's Union of Winnipeg confronted the resentment of inmates of their home by requiring a nine-month stay after confinement. Although there was an insistence on time for "repentance," the stay guaranteed the necessary nursing care for infants before weaning. Without this, the lives of babies were in constant jeopardy unless immediately adopted. Some mothers, not wishing to have their infants adopted, paid a monthly fee of four dollars while they sought employment and a suitable home for themselves and their child. Children remaining in the Winnipeg home past their third birthday became the "property" of the institution.[41]

The Women's Refuge and Children's Home of London, Ontario, required a twelve-month stay during which the mother was to be trained for a "gainful situation, or at least be religiously improved." Four years after its opening in 1876, thirty-two infants under two years were part of its clientele. The London Orphans' Home, which included the aged and friendless when founded in 1874, excluded children under two years. This Protestant Orphans' Home, however, kept mothers and children together on occasion as in 1875 when it maintained Mrs. Noodes and her two little girls for three months while she saved enough money to buy a sewing machine.[42] All the homes were reluctant to receive infants and most stipulated ages of admission over two years because of the dangers to the lives of the very young children, their vulnerability to even the mildest contagion, and inadequate nursing staff.

The reluctance of most homes to receive illegitimate children might be understood as more than punitive moralizing when it is recalled that most of them would be infants. The problems, of course, were where could the unmarried mother go during pregnancy and labour and where could the child be placed once the mother had to seek employment? A deputation from the Christian Women's Union of Winnipeg to the Manitoba legislature in 1890 stated the problem when they pleaded for funds for their essential social service—a female refuge. The refuge was to enable unmarried or recently widowed women "to keep their infants with them until they are old enough to do without a mother's care when they are admitted into the Children's Home or otherwise provided for." The deputation pointed out that infant mortality in institutions was high and the use of wet-nurses unsatisfactory.[43]

In the first year of the Halifax Infants' Home, the managing committee bought "cheap thin cotton" to be made into shrouds. Several months later with scarlet fever in the home, the committee requested from the commissioners of the Poor Asylum the use of their hearse in order to save the expense of cab-hire for funerals. In the three summer months of 1875, thirteen babies died. The home averaged twenty-two boarded children during the time. In 1875, the death rate was thirty-five percent and as late as 1890 it was twenty-six percent.[44]

Some institutions hired women to live in as wet-nurses. At times, a wet-nurse was guaranteed temporary relief for herself and her children. The desperation and poverty that forced women into homes to engage in an occupation, which traditionally had been delegated to the meanest classes and one which was no longer a common practice, need no elaboration. In 1875, the

Halifax Infants' Home required wet-nurses wishing to have their own infants with them to pay three dollars a month for the privilege. Its first wet-nurse was a girl taken from the Poor Asylum.[45]

In addition to the humiliations suffered by these women, regular fee-paying parents customarily had to meet a variety of institutional demands. With wages barely covering their own subsistence, widows, unmarried women, and deserted wives paid nominal fees to keep their children clothed, sheltered and fed in the homes. The fees usually ranged from one to five dollars a month, depending upon the number of children admitted or the actual financial circumstances of parent or guardian. Domestic service often required women to live in, and other occupations took up long hours during which children were unsupervised. The fees were often meagre but the homes found them essential for their survival because of the parsimony and slowness of provincial and municipal grants and unreliable private funding.

An example of the compromising positions in which both parents and the institutions found themselves is provided by Dr. Wishart's demand in 1891 that he be provided with a "perpetual grant of children" from the Toronto Girls' Home for medical demonstrations every Saturday morning. These children, he argued, were "callous both morally and physically and therefore not to be compared with other children." The ladies' committee reluctantly agreed when the good doctor threatened to withdraw his medical services, given gratis to the home and worth $400 per annum. A month later, an irate mother objected to her children being used in this manner and forced the home not to refuse the doctor's demands but to decide instead that only orphans would be used![46]

The Children's Home of Winnipeg, founded in 1885 by the Christian Women's Union, had been "formerly an adjunct of the maternity hospital but its doors were opened to any destitute child." It finally became of so much importance as to require a board of management and a charter of its own. This Protestant home, the first in the west, was officially separated from the Christian Women's Union in 1887 although the women always retained a special interest in its affairs and management. Initially it included fourteen mothers and children but within four years it housed forty-eight children with a few adults. Although many children were reclaimed by parents once they had established themselves, the indenture rates of children were extraordinarily high as were the delays on the part of employers in finally signing adoption or indenture papers. While all Protestant Orphans' Homes had incidents of legal action over the binding out or adoption of children, which were informal and arbitrary processes before the passage of provincial legislation controlling custody and adoption in the 1920s, the Winnipeg home was particularly beset by such problems until the 1912 Manitoba Children's Act gave the custody of deserted children to the superintendent of neglected and dependent children.[47]

Although the homes usually preferred orphans because rights over them were clearly defined, part orphans and destitute children constituted a large proportion of their inmates. All the homes under discussion stipulated that older children, usually those over six or seven years, were not to be given out for "adoption" because this frequently was a cloak to use the children as cheap labour without the safety clauses of indenture which included schooling, minimal conditions of food, clothing, and shelter, as well as some remuneration. Until modern legislation, such "adopted" children could not claim the rights of a family member with regard to inheriting property or money. Many "adopted" children were returned sometimes after several years for trivial reasons such as foster parents going on holiday or for irresponsible ones such as a child requiring medical treatment. The wages under indenture, which were always below prevailing rates for usual apprentices, were divided between the institution and an account at the home which was to be given the child at the expiration of the apprenticeship.

Not all parents willingly signed over their children for either indenture or adoption and many objected strenuously to the automatic abdication of parental authority as a result of merely handing their children over to the homes or by failing to pay maintenance fees. Usually such protests were ignored and few incidents ended in litigation. If poverty resulted in children being placed in institutions, it was unlikely that their parents would have the money for a court case. A widely publicized case, Robinson vs. Pieper, occurred when Mrs. Robinson, after having placed her infant daughter Alice in the Toronto Girls' Home in 1883, sought to have her returned to her when she was apprenticed with Mrs. Pieper of Owen Sound in 1892. The verdict, upheld in 1896, in the Divisional Court, did not recognize parental rights.

> The learned judge can find no reason whatever for holding that the mother is entitled to have this indenture set at naught and the child returned to her. She was clearly a child having the protection of the Home, when she was apprenticed: her mother was, and had been for years an assenting party to her being at the Home, and under its protection and made no application for her return until she ceased to be helpless.[48]

All the Protestant Orphans' Homes insisted that their rights of *in loco parentis* included not only the wardship of children in the homes but also the right to indenture children at an appropriate age. Since all homes had set ages for demission and since many claimed an absolute wardship, many refused to return children to their families when they reached the age of demission. Indeed, in most cases the homes saw family interest in older children as evidence of greed and self-interest. In 1873, the secretary of the Montreal Ladies' Benevolent Society remarked that twenty-two girls had been reclaimed that year. The girls had been spirited away or blatantly taken by relatives and placed for "the scarcity of servants made them valuable acquisitions to some who had entirely neglected them in their helpless infancy." In 1894, the corresponding secretary of the Toronto Girls' Home decried the too common occurrence of girls absconding from their places to join their mothers and expressed profound suspicion of "maternal tendencies" that were so "suddenly revived" after several years of "neglect." Although the annual reports cited assistance to all classes as a major aim, the home viewed with a singular lack of sympathy the reuniting of its inmates with their lower-class families. Parents requesting the return of their children were usually identified as part of a certain unscrupulous class of dependent poor willing to fob off their familial responsibilities onto charity.[49]

There can be no doubt that some parents reclaimed their children at the age of indenture when they had rarely visited or paid the slightest attention to them previously. The literature of rescue societies, boy brigades and asylums, all mention the problem. The English child emigration societies wanted to separate children from disreputable families by sending them to Canada. As a result children rescued from potential exploitation by parents or relatives were often subject to actual exploitation by strangers. The enforcement of school attendance laws, which forced poor families to forego additional income needed to maintain family integrity, led to an increased number of children being admitted to charitable institutions.

Although endeavouring to protect the autonomy of their institutions, Protestant Orphans' Homes directors routinely petitioned provincial and municipal governments for funds. Believing in the advantages of private philanthropy with governmental assistance, the ladies of the homes were committed to ideas that saw private philanthropy as the superior means of securing financial support for public charities. At a public meeting of the Ottawa home in January 1887, the Governor-General praised Canadian philanthropic efforts. He told "a large and fashionable audience" that unlike the poor-rate system that perpetuated Old World pauperism such efforts were spontaneous, private, "and almost entirely unaided by the State."[50]

The approval given by the ladies of the homes to such sentiments was matched by civic leaders and Canadian child savers who advocated a policy of private prosperity and public parsimony. In 1894, the Toronto City Corporation, rejecting amalgamation of various charities and any suggestion of a common budget assisted by rates, opposed the city taking over the "entire management of all the different classes of our dependent poor" because the financial burden would fall "upon the rate-payers and private benevolence would be withdrawn."[51]

Writing in the English *Charity Organization Review* of August 1900, J. J. Kelso, Ontario's first superintendent of neglected and dependent children, supported a central associated charities bureau for Toronto while discouraging any tendency to fall back upon charity as typified by British poor law unions. Observing that "there is, unfortunately however a class who, from inherent laziness will not work or make any effort to improve the condition of themselves or their children," Kelso denounced the ticket system of the Toronto House of Industry which provided outdoor relief. Although such schemes assisted families to stay together, which was a prime goal of the new generation of Canadian child savers, Kelso was unable to resolve the basic contradiction in public responsibility for maintaining family stability when it required public funds.[52]

Although the Protestant Orphans' Homes did not share such delicate feelings about family integrity in their efforts to rescue children from pauperism and immorality, such attitudes did not ensure that conservative English Canadians would support the homes as superior to out-door relief schemes. Mr. Goldwin Smith, addressing the fortieth annual meeting of the Toronto home, heartily condemned the "mischief" done by philanthropists. He protested that their very existence removed parental responsibility and that "in many instances this interference tended to have the parents neglect their children so that they could get rid of them or see them reared with greater possibilities than they could furnish."[53]

Throughout the previous discussion it can be seen that the protection of child life from the contaminations of adult improvidence and vicious example was effectively ensured by segregation in specialized asylums. Moreover, in their treatment of children and parents, the Protestant Orphans' Homes represented a transition from the policy of indiscriminate mixing of sexes and ages common in the houses of industry to the growing twentieth-century Canadian commitment to keeping children within a family if not their own. They also represent a significant transformation in British North American child rescue.

No matter how unclear the original policy on eligible subjects for the institutions, the homes soon restricted their inmates to children and their mothers. In time, most of them became segregated institutions for orphaned, abandoned and destitute children between two and fourteen years of age. By removing children from the companionship of degraded adults and inadequate care, which were two common criticisms levelled at houses of industry and other charitable institutions, and by claiming that they exercised a control *in loco parentis* over their inmates, the Protestant Orphans' Homes sought to regulate contacts between children and their parents and kin, and thus reinforced in an extreme manner the criteria of protection, segregation and dependence. Since, other than in exceptional situations, most homes admitted many more non-orphans than orphans, they were compelled to modify their policy with regard to the surrender of parental rights. For those parents and guardians who were able to pay boarding fees, the right to withdraw children was clearly recognized; economic hardship and illness, however, often made even nominal fees a heavy burden, particularly on single parents. Consequently, such children were frequently reduced to a status identical with those who had been surrendered to the homes.

The final criterion of the concept of childhood—"delayed responsibilities"— is less clear in nineteenth-century child rescue. This criterion is best associated with the creation of a new category of childhood, namely "adolescence," which in turn was extended and even objectified through the legal compulsions of schooling for all children in the twentieth century.[54] Before the vertical extension of compulsory schooling, however, the majority of working-class children and those of the dependent poor in Britain and Canada were excluded from this last entry into the world created by a modern concept of childhood.

Nowhere is this denial of entry clearer than in the institutions under discussion, as their attitudes toward indenture along with specific attitudes towards the children and work within the home itself indicate. The children were to assume responsibilities regarding household tasks in the homes and to earn their keep through indentures and apprenticeship, bearing in mind that such responsibilities were directly related to their future employment and status in society. It was thought that the children were peculiarly suited to menial occupations both by social status and by disposition. In this respect, although they were protected, separated, and made dependent in a manner that was more concrete and rigidly enforced than their working-class peers "outside," the expectations regarding their tasks and duties as children and their future roles in the work force were identical with middle-class expectations of the lower class generally.

Keeping such an assumption in mind, we can appreciate the 1875 Kingston report that advocated the "systematic apportioning of household duties" with even little girls being "admitted into the circle of usefulness" as an essential benefit to the children. In the following year, the British Columbia Protestant Orphans' Home insisted that, as an important part of their education, the children were to be taught how to do dishes, wash clothes, scrub floors, attend young children, and do all domestic work.[55] At the Halifax home for the first two decades from its founding, the children did all domestic chores without outside help.[56] The Winnipeg Children's Home perhaps summarizes all those comments made uniformly by the Protestant Orphans' Homes throughout their history regarding such an urgent matter. The ladies' committee agreed that the public was inclined to over-indulge the children with too many "treats" and that in the long run it would spoil them "for their future life." It was strongly urged that "the children be taught to work, and to understand that they have to look forward to work, and that they be made to do it."[57]

IV — Conclusion

Charity children of the last century were not permitted the luxury of forgetting their antecedents or their prospects and were made to bear the burden of their poverty and dependence. The delaying of responsibilities for lower-class children, thus including them in a universal application of the concept of childhood in Canada, was to be postponed until the first decades of the twentieth century.

In his pioneering study, Neil Sutherland suggests a rapid acceptance of the concept of childhood and its consequences by middle-class Canadians between 1880 and 1920. His discussion of child life in the seventies and eighties fails to account for the sentiment and practices during the previous thirty years. By the 1850s a substantial number of children's homes had appeared in the major centres of British North America. These institutions, soon to be copied in the Canadian West, ensured for their inmates the beginning of a modern childhood, that is, protection, segregation and dependence.

The debate regarding the appropriate care and control of these children prepared the way for the extension of all aspects of childhood to children in the twentieth century. In particular, Sutherland's excellent explication of the "new education" demonstrates the coming victory of the common school that provides all normal children with a "childhood." In the case of dependent and neglected children, the final triumph of the Canadian consensus had to wait for the beginnings of the welfare state in the decades following 1945.

Notes

1. Joseph A. Chisolm, ed., *The Speeches and Public Letters of Joseph Howe,* 2 vols (Halifax: Chronicle Publishing Co., 1909), 1:67.

2. N. Sutherland, *Children in English-Canadian Society* (Toronto: University of Toronto Press, 1976).

3. R. L. Schnell, "Childhood as Ideology," *British Journal of Educational Studies,* 27 (February 1979): 7-28. Also see P. T. Rooke, "The 'Child-Institutionalized' in Canada, Britain, and the United States," *Journal of Educational Thought,* 11 (August 1977):156-71.

4. Kathleen Heasman, *Evangelicals in Action* (London: G. Bles, 1962): Carroll Smith Rosenberg, *Religion and the Rise of the American City* (Ithaca, N.Y.: Cornell University Press, 1971); and Sutherland, *Children in English-Canadian Society.*

5. M. G. Jones, *The Charity School Movement* (London: Frank Cass, 1964).

6. *An Account of the Proceedings of the Acting Governors of the House of Industry* (Dublin, 1798), p. 10.

7. *The State of the Ladies' Charity School Lately set up in Baldwin Street, in the City of Bristol, in Teaching Poor Girls to Read and Spin* (Bristol, 1756), p. 3.

8. Isaac Watts, *An Essay Toward the Encouragement of Charity Schools* (London, 1728), pp. 8-9.

9. *Society for the Suppression of Beggars; for the Relief of Occasional Distress and the Encouragement of Industry Among the Poor Within the City and Environs of Edinburgh* (Edinburgh, 1813), pp. 13-14; Andrew Gairdner, *A Looking Glass for Rich People and People in Prosperity* (Edinburgh, 1798); and *Rules, Orders, and Regulations ... the House of Industry ... in Suffolk* (Ipswich, 1759), p. 9.

10. *Hints Toward the Formation of a Society for Promoting a Spirit of Independence Among the Poor,* 2nd ed. (Bristol, 1812), pp. 16-17; and *Plans for the Sunday Schools and Schools of Industry, established in the city of Bath* (Bath, 1789); and *Rules, Orders and Regulations in the Parish School of Industry in King Street* (London, 1792).

11. I. Wood, *Some Account of the Shrewsbury House of Industry* (Shrewsbury, 1791), pp. 3, 8 and 33.

12. *Manchester Juvenile Refuge and School of Industry* (Manchester, 1846), pp. 2, 4, 5 and 6.

13. Alexander Thomson, *Industrial Schools* (Aberdeen, 1847), pp. 7-8 and 11-16.

14. Ursula R. Q. Henriques, *Before the Welfare State* (London: Longman, 1979); Derek Fraser, *The Evolution of the British Welfare State* (London: Macmillan, 1973); and Maurice Bruce, ed., *The Coming of the Welfare State* (London: B. T. Batsford, 1968). For contemporary discussions of boarding-out versus the congregate system, see Mary Carpenter, "What Shall We Do With Our Pauper Children?," Social Science Association (Dublin) pamphlet (London: Longman, 1861); *Reports on the Boarding-Out of Orphans and Deserted Children and Insane belonging to the City Parish, Glasgow* (Glasgow, 1872); and Henry F. Aveling, *The Boarding Out System* (London, 1890).

15. Useful information is found in three typescript studies held by the Centre for Newfoundland Studies, Memorial University of Newfoundland: Stuart R. Frey, "Introduction to Social Legislation in Newfoundland" (1979); Barbara Smith, "The Historical Development of Child Welfare Legislation in Newfoundland from 1832 to 1949" (1971); and Richard Urquhart, "A Survey of the Policies of the Newfoundland Government Towards Poor Relief, 1860-1869" (1973). NEWFOUNDLAND, *Journal of Assembly* (1848-49), pp. 446-54, Report on the Lunatic Asylum; (1862), pp. 408-11, Rules and Regulations for the Management of the St. John's Poor Asylum; and (1885), pp. 471-72. Report of the Superintendent of Poor Asylum; Public Archives of Nova Scotia, MG 20 214, House of Refuge, Proceedings of Committee (Halifax 1853-57); LEGISLATURE OF NOVA SCOTIA, *Report on Public Charity* (Halifax, 1900); Provincial Archives of New Brunswick, MAL (1853-1963), Saint John Almshouse; NEW BRUNSWICK, *Journal of House of Assembly* (1857), Appendix, pp. DXLIX-DLXI; Provincial Archives of Prince Edward Island, 236/8, Prince Edward Island Poor and Work House Minute Book (1869-1880).

16. Public Archives of Nova Scotia, CO. 217, vol. 18, Report of the State of the Orphan House (circa 1753); NEW BRUNSWICK, *Journal of House of Assembly* (1857), Appendix, pp. DXLIX-DLXI.

17. Provincial Archives of Manitoba, MG2 A5, Pelly Documents, 1816-23.

18. *The Second Annual Report of the Central Auxiliary Society for Promoting Education and Industry Among the Indians and Destitute Settlers in Canada* (Montreal, 1829), pp. 17, 12 and 38.

19. Ibid., p. 40.

20. David Rothman, *The Discovery of the Asylum* (Boston: Little Brown, 1971).

21. Metropolitan Toronto Library (hereafter MTL), MS 385(2), Toronto City Council Papers, 4 May 1837; MS 88(1), Baldwin Papers, 11 July 1837; *Report of the Trustees of the House of Industry* (Toronto, 1853), pp. 5-6.

22. *Report of the Trustees of the House of Industry* (Toronto, 1857), p. 8.

23. Queen's University, Coll. 604, Kingston House of Industry, 1814-1916.

24. Queen's University, Coll. 94, *Kingston Orphans' Home and Widows' Friend Society, Annual Report* (1882).

25. Ibid., *Annual Report* (1859, 1871). Certainly one is never intimidated by such order and industry in the records of the Victoria home founded in 1888. Provincial Archives of British Columbia, British Columbia Protestant Orphans' Home (1888-1942). For a discussion of this aspect of institutionalization, see Patricia T. ROOKE and R. S. Patterson, "The Delicate Duty of Child Saving, Coldwater, Michigan 1871-1896," *Michigan History,* 61 (Fall 1978): 195-219.

26. MTL, BR(S) 361.75 B58, Sermon Preached before Ladies Benevolent Institution in St. George's Church, Montreal, 9 April 1854.

27. Fully discussed by the authors in "Protestant Orphans' Homes as Women's Domain (1850-1930)," presented to the Berkshire Conference on Women's History, Poughkeepsie, N.Y., 18 June 1981.

28. Queen's University, Coll. 94, *Kingston Orphans' Home and Widows' Friend Society, Annual Report* (1859), p. 5; *Constitution* (1862), rule 16.

29. MTL, MS 88(1), Baldwin Papers, 11 July 1837: and Toronto Girls' Home and Public Nursery, Register, 22 June 1859.

30. Anglican Archives, St. John's, Newfoundland, *Church of England Orphans' and Widows' Aid Society, 60th Annual Report* (1914), p. 5, and *First Annual Report* (1855), p. 3. Clayton W. Puddester, "The United Church Orphanage," in *The Book of Newfoundland,* ed.: J. Smallwood (St. John's: Newfoundland Book Publishers, 1937), p. 308.

31. Anglican Archives, St. John's, Newfoundland, *Church of England Orphans' and Widows' Aid Society, Annual Reports* (1855-1929); United Church Archives, St. John's, Newfoundland, Methodist Orphanage, Minutes, Annual Reports, and Correspondence (1855-1952).

32. Public Archives of Nova Scotia, MG 20 177: 13, Halifax Infants' Home, Minute Books (1875-1949).

33. Saint John City Archives, Wiggins Male Orphan Institution, Minute Book (1891-1901), and The Act Incorporating the Governors and Wiggins Male Orphan Institution, 10 June 1867.

34. Saint John City Archives, Max G. Baxter, "New Brunswick Protestant Orphans Home," typescript (1965). The New Brunswick Survey conducted by the Canadian Council on Child Welfare noted as late as 1928 that the home was still claiming the "exclusive and complete control and custody" of such children as if they had been

totally surrendered in the first instance. During the previous year only 20 of the 227 children admitted had lost one or both parents while most admissions were the result of unmarried parenthood and desertions (Public Archives of Canada, MG 28 I 10, vol. 38 (1928-29), file 167).

35. Queen's University, Kingston Protestant Orphans' Home, Minutes, 10 April and 18 November 1860.

36. Public Archives of Canada, MG 28 137, vols 1-3, Ottawa Protestant Orphans' Home, Minutes, 18 January 1865, 28 November 1867, 26 April 1869, 28 August 1871, 24 February 1896 and 30 March 1896.

37. *Montreal Protestant Orphan Asylum, Constitution* (1852); *Philanthropy: Care of our Destitute and Criminal Population* (Montreal, 1857); *Historical Sketch of the Montreal Protestant Asylum from its Foundation ... 16th February 1822 to the Present Day ...* (Montreal, 1860), p. 9; and *Montreal Ladies' Benevolent Society, 76th Annual Report* (Montreal, 1909), pp. 2-3.

38. MTL, L30 PCH(E), Toronto Protestant Orphans' Home, Letters and Papers (1854-56).

39. MTL, *Boys' Home for the Training and Maintenance of Destitute Boys not convicted of Crime, 33rd Annual Report* (1893), p. 6; *36th Annual Report* (1896), p. 6; and *2nd Annual Report* (1861), pp. 5-6; *Daily Globe,* 4 January 1866, "The Arabs of the Street."

40. *Protestant Children's Homes of Toronto Milestones (1851-1951)* (Ottawa: Canadian Council on Social Development, 1951), p. 6.

41. *Christian Women's Union, 21st Annual Report* (Winnipeg, 1903); Provincial Archives of Manitoba, Greenway Papers; also, MG10 B24, Children's Home of Winnipeg, Minutes, Correspondence and Annual Reports (1885-1937); RG5 G2, Box 4, Health and Welfare, Welfare Supervision Board, Files 1916-45.

42. Margaret Johnson, *The First One Hundred Years, 1874-1974* (London: Women's Christian Association, 1974); Caroline L. CONRON, *Merrymount Children's Home—A Century in Retrospect, 1874-1974* (London: Merrymount Children's Homes, 1974); University of Western Ontario, VF640, London Protestant Orphans' Home, Minutes, 23 April and 30 July 1875.

43. Provincial Archives of Manitoba, Greenway Papers, 1890.

44. Public Archives of Nova Scotia, Halifax Infants' Home, Minutes, 7 September 1875 and 5 March 1877; *Halifax Herald,* 3 February 1890.

45. Public Archives of Nova Scotia, Halifax Infants' Home, Minutes, 2 March 1875.

46. MTL, Toronto Girls' Home, Minutes, 3 November and 1 December 1891.

47. Provincial Archives of Manitoba, MG10 B24, Children's Home of Winnipeg.

48. MTL, Toronto Girls' Home, Minutes, 12 November 1895.

49. *Montreal Ladies' Benevolent Society, 40th Annual Report* (Montreal, 1873), p. 6. Those attitudes about parental exploitation of similar children in Britain are found in the records of various child-rescue societies who exported juvenile immigrants

to Canada. This and the psychological problems of child abandonment and family separation are fully discussed by the authors in "The King's Children in English Canada: A Psychohistorical Study of Abandonment, Rejection and Colonial Response," *Journal of Psychohistory,* 8 (Spring 1981): 387-420.

50. Public Archives of Canada, Ottawa Protestant Orphans' Home, "Clippings," vol. 4 (1884-89), 19 January 1897.

51. MTL, L30 PCH(6), Toronto Protestant Orphans' Home, "Miscellaneous (1895-1915)." The authors have discussed the relationship between the professionalization of charity and the shift from child rescue to child welfare, emphasizing Charlotte Whitton's contribution in "Child Welfare in English Canada, 1920-1948," *Social Service Review, 55* (September 1981): 484-506.

52. *Charity Organization Review, 7* (August 1900):89-93.

53. Queen's University, *Kingston Protestant Orphans' Home, Annual Report* (1875).

54. Schnell, "Childhood as Ideology," pp. 17-23.

55. Provincial Archives of British Columbia, *British Columbia Protestant Orphans' Home, Annual Report* (1886), File 7, p. 2.

56. Public Archives of Nova Scotia, *Halifax Protestant Orphans' Home, Annual Reports* (1858-77).

57. Provincial Archives of Manitoba, Children's Home of Winnipeg, Minutes, 2 July 1908.

CHAPTER
14 CONFEDERATION

Confederation solved a variety of political, economic, diplomatic and ethnic difficulties that jeopardized British North America's future in the 1860s. Despite early discontent, the union was not seriously threatened in its first century. Not surprisingly, historians have generally treated Confederation as the inevitable unfolding of a scenario stretching back to the American Revolution. The leading Fathers, such as Sir John A. Macdonald, Sir George-Etienne Cartier, George Brown and Sir Charles Tupper, were ascribed heroic qualities in the numerous studies that preceded the Centennial in 1967. Donald Creighton's *Road to Confederation: The Emergence of Canada, 1863-1867* (1964) was the preeminent narrative depiction of heroes and villains in a drama that ended with a rising sun on shining faces. His study and others surveyed every conceivable aspect of the happy story. English Canada paid scant attention to naysayers in Quebec, such as Abbé Lionel Groulx and Maurice Séguin, whose disciples drew different pictures and were preparing another agenda.

In "The United States and Confederation," a paper delivered at the University of Chicago in 1958, Creighton looked back at the abortive British North American union attempt a century earlier, in 1858. That was his starting point in explaining the success of the movement that culminated in Confederation. The paper enunciated several of the themes that Creighton and others would expand upon in the years leading up to the Centennial. Political deadlock, western expansionism, British inducement and American militarism combined to make the era one of "prophetic significance in Canadian history." Canadians "had to build a nation," which "had to be built in the midst of a great war."

In the years since the Centennial in 1967 the imperfections in the Confederation arrangement have, on occasion, eclipsed the advantages and raised questions about its inevitability. Regional alienation, francophone discontent, uncertain leadership and ill-defined national aspirations have forced historians to reappraise the union movement and those opposed to Confederation in the 1860s. In March of 1990, for example, the *Canadian Historical Review* offered a "CHR Dialogue: The Maritimes and Confederation: A Reassessment."

Several disturbing questions were raised, as they were at a seminar at the Centre of Canadian Studies at the University of Edinburgh, Scotland, in May of 1988. Ged Martin, the Director of that Centre, has written several prodding articles on the Confederation movement of the 1860s. The one offered here rejects the notions of inevitability of historians like Creighton. It was presented as a Canada House Lecture on 8 February, 1989 as "History as Science or Literature: Explaining Canadian Confederation, 1858-1867."

Suggestions for Further Reading

Buckner, Phillip, P.B. Waite and William M. Baker, "CHR Dialogue: The Maritimes and Confederation: A Reassessment," *Canadian Historical Review*, LXXI, no. 1 (March 1990), 1-45.

Creighton, Donald, *The Road to Confederation: The Emergence of Canada, 1863-1867*. Toronto: Macmillan of Canada, 1964.

Martin, Ged (ed.), *The Causes of Canadian Confederation*. Fredericton: Acadiensis Press, 1990.

―――――, "Launching Canadian Confederation: Means to Ends, 1836-64," *Historical Journal*, 27, no. 3 (1984), 575-602.

Morton, W.L., *The Critical Years: The Union of British North America, 1857-1873*. Toronto: McClelland and Stewart, 1964.

Silver, Arthur, *The French-Canadian Idea of Confederation, 1864-1900*. Toronto: University of Toronto Press, 1982.

Smith, Jennifer, "Canadian Confederation and the Influence of American Federalism," *Canadian Journal of Political Science*, XXI, no. 3 (September 1988), 443-463.

Waite, P.B., *The Life and Times of Confederation, 1864-1867: Politics, Newspapers and the Union of British North America*. Toronto: University of Toronto Press, 1962.

Winks, Robin, *Canada and the United States: The Civil War Years*. Montreal, Harvest House, 1960.

THE UNITED STATES AND CANADIAN CONFEDERATION

Donald Creighton

In the next decade both the United States and Canada will face an impressive succession of important centenaries. On April 12, 1961, it will be a hundred years since the Confederate bombardment opened upon Fort Sumter in Charleston harbour. On June 22, 1964, it will be a century since a coalition

From *Canadian Historical Review*, XXXIX, no. 3 (September 1958), 209-222. Copyright 1958 by University of Toronto Press. Reprinted by permission of the Estate of Donald Creighton and University of Toronto Press.

Government of Reformers and Liberal-Conservatives took office in the Province of Canada with the declared intention of establishing a general federal union of the whole of British North America. Between these two events—the Civil War in the United States and the federation of British North America—there exists an interesting relationship which I should like to explore with you tonight. It is an important, but also a complex, imprecise, and ambiguous relationship; and it seems to me that there might be more enlightenment in approaching its analysis circuitously than directly. These two famous dates and the national dramas which they recall and commemorate will therefore, for the moment, be set aside; and we can go back a little in time. There is an earlier episode in Canadian history, which could be most appropriately examined on this occasion, for its centenary will be reached, though certainly not enthusiastically celebrated, during the summer of 1958. It is an episode much less well known than the foundation of the coalition Government and the declaration of the coalition Government's purpose in June of 1864; but, for all that, it has its own real significance. And an examination of it may throw some light upon the curious relationship between the American Civil War and the federal union of British North America, upon the influence of the United States on Canadian Confederation.

In the summer of 1858—it was in August, to be precise—the government of the Province of Canada came to a momentous decision. It was, in itself, an important decision, and it was much more important simply because it was the Province of Canada which had reached it. In 1858, the province was only a little over fifteen years old, for it had been formed in 1841 by the union of the two older and smaller provinces of Upper and Lower Canada; but already, in size, ambition, political consequence, and political influence, it was clearly the "empire province" of British North America. From the Gulf of St. Lawrence, it extended westward along the whole long line of the great river and the Great Lakes. On the south, its limit was the international boundary between British North America and the United States; to the north, its frontier was that highly uncertain, vaguely defined line which bounded Rupert's Land, the chartered territories of the Hudson's Bay Company. The other British provinces—Nova Scotia, New Brunswick, Prince Edward Island, and Newfoundland in the east, and Vancouver Island and British Columbia in the far west—were undeniably dwarfed in importance by the Province of Canada. Canada was more prosperous than any of them. Canada was more populous than all of them put together.

It was all true, as the other colonies somewhat enviously admitted; but it was also true that the "empire province" was a socially turbulent and politically agitated community, and that the division between its French-speaking and English-speaking citizens had created a cultural cleavage far more serious than existed elsewhere in the North American Empire. The other northern provinces regarded Canada with a measure of doubt and distrust. The eyebrows of sober Nova Scotians, in particular, were lifted often in pained disapproval at its erratic course. It was always in the throes of some political crisis or other; its citizens were invariably at each other's throats; and it had the highly reprehensible habit of breaking its word in cheerful disregard of the interests of the rest of British North America. Its whole record, in fact, was simply deplorable. And yet, the unwelcome but inescapable fact was that Canada counted. However violent its actions and however incomprehensible its purposes, they had to be taken seriously. And once again, during the agitated summer of 1858, the Canadian government had given the other provincial administrations considerable food for thought. On August 16, when, after a long and turbulent session, the Governor, Sir Edmund Head, finally prorogued the session of the Canadian legislature, he made a brief formal announcement of the policy which his new Government intended to follow. "I propose in the course of the recess," he told the Houses, "to communicate with Her Majesty's Government, and with the Governments of the sister Colonies, on another matter of very great importance. I am desirous of inviting them to discuss with us the principles on which a bond of a federal character, uniting the Provinces of British North America, may perhaps hereafter be practicable."

What had happened? What had persuaded this most important of British American governments to adopt, as its declared policy, the plan of a British American federal union? Long before this, of course, British governors and high commissioners, colonial statesmen, authors, and public speakers had been talking and writing about federal union; but until Governor Head made his famous announcement on the afternoon of August 16, 1858, the whole question had remained almost entirely academic. Why had George E. Cartier and John A. Macdonald, the leaders of the Canadian Administration, decided to commit themselves to an ambitious policy which no other British American government had ventured to espouse before? Nearly six years later, on June 22, 1864, another Canadian Government, as we have already seen, was to make another open profession of faith in a federal plan and, after an interval, was to succeed in carrying it out. Yet these two general declarations of purpose are very similar; and at first sight, the occasion, if not the cause of both of them seem very much alike. Each appears to have arisen out of the chronic weakness and instability of Canadian politics.

The fact was that the Canadian union of 1841 had been formal, not real. In theory, the province was a unitary state; in fact it was an unacknowledged federal system. Its two sections, Canada East and Canada West, the one largely French and the other overwhelmingly English, were united economically by the St. Lawrence transport system and divided socially by their two contrasting cultural inheritances. They had found it impossible to live apart as the separate provinces of Upper and Lower Canada; they were finding it almost equally difficult to live together as the two divisions of a single government. It was true, of course, that the Union Act had itself helped to make these difficulties almost insuperable. By its terms, Canada East and Canada West had been given equal representation in the provincial legislature, irrespective of population; and this political equality tended to harden the sectional division of the province and to exacerbate its inevitable cultural misunderstandings. The cabinet and several of the important departments of government were organized on a sectional basis. Much of the legislation that was passed had to be sectional in character; and the political parties, although they tried, of course, to win a following in both French- and English-speaking Canada, had an irresistible tendency to become strong in one section of the province and correspondingly weak in the other. They tended also, as a natural consequence, to reach a level of approximate political equality; and thus the public affairs of the province were characterized both by a permanent state of sectional conflict and a persistent condition of political instability.

During the summer of 1858 this chronic political unsettlement reached a sudden, sharp crisis; and it was this crisis which provided the occasion for the Cartier-Macdonald Government's dramatic announcement of its adoption of the federal plan. Earlier in the session, the Assembly had been discussing the constitutional problem which lay at the root of its sectional difficulties. The Assembly was always discussing the constitutional problem. It was always anxiously reviewing a number of contradictory proposals for constitutional reform—including federal schemes—which, it was argued, would remove the province from the inveterate embarrassments of sectionalism; and this painfully familiar exercise was barely over, when there occurred an episode which was, in effect, a preposterous, almost ludicrous, illustration of the political stalemate which everybody was so anxious to end. Its origins were simple and absurdly characteristic of the province's real nature. The political crisis of the summer of 1858 arose out of the endless and agonizing problem of deciding where the capital of this politically united but sectionally divided province was to be.

Ever since the union in 1841, this question had been arousing the most acrimonious dissension. Originally, the seat of government had been fixed at Kingston in Canada West; it had then been transferred to Montreal, in Canada East—a distinctly unfortunate removal, as it turned out, for a few years later, in 1849, the enraged Montreal Conservatives burnt the Parliament Buildings to the ground. For some time after this disgrace, the attempt to find a permanent capital was tacitly abandoned; and the seat of government alternated, at intervals, between Quebec, which was the old capital of Lower Canada, and Toronto, which was the old capital of the upper province. Every few years, the cabinet ministers and a small army of civil servants, together with great masses of official records, government furniture, and personal effects, were laboriously transported, up or down the river valley, in trains and steamships, to their new political headquarters. It is hardly surprising that everybody in politics found these fairly regularly recurring removals an intolerable nuisance; and in 1857 John A. Macdonald had hit upon what was thought to be a most ingenious method of securing permanence. Queen Victoria was invited to name a permanent capital for the united province; and Queen Victoria, duly but privately advised from Canada, decided in favour of a little backwoods town, some distance up the Ottawa River, once called Bytown and now Ottawa.

Ottawa had the advantage of a location on the west bank of the river which formed the boundary between the two sections of the province; but it was definitely in Canada West. Still more obviously, it was neither Quebec nor Montreal; and the French-Canadians in the legislature, even though the great majority of them were members of the Conservative party which had referred the problem to the Queen for final decision, regarded the choice of Ottawa with the darkest disapproval. It was always possible, on a question of such enormous sectional prestige, to persuade some of them, at least momentarily, to forswear their Conservative allegiance; and this was exactly what happened on July 28, 1858. An address to the Queen on the subject of the capital was under consideration. An amendment, declaring flatly that Ottawa ought not to be the permanent seat of government was deliberately moved by the opposition. A small, but sufficient bloc of French-Canadian votes changed sides, and the Government was defeated on this issue.

Macdonald and Cartier decided to resign; and George Brown, the leader of the Liberal Opposition, accepted the Governor's invitation to form a new Government. What followed is of considerable interest in the law and custom of parliamentary institutions in the British Commonwealth. The political crisis of the summer of 1858 anticipates, in some measure, though the circumstances were widely different, the much more famous Canadian constitutional crisis of the summer of 1926 and even finds a faint echo in the speculations and discussions which went on for some time in Canada after the general election of June, 1957. Our concern here, however, is not with constitutional issues as such, but with the political instability which resulted in part from the defective constitution of the Province of Canada. Rapidly it became apparent that Brown and his associate French-Canadian leader, Dorion, were in a much more precarious position in the Assembly than their predecessors, Macdonald and Cartier, had ever been. The French-Canadian opponents of Ottawa as the Canadian capital would quickly, if sheepishly, return to the Conservative fold; and, by the law as it then stood, George Brown, Dorion, and the other new ministers would be obliged, on accepting office under the Crown, to resign their seats in Parliament and to seek re-election. With numbers so seriously reduced in such an evenly divided Assembly, the new Government would not be able to meet the inevitable want-of-confidence motion; and Brown, with failure staring him in the face, requested the Governor to grant him a dissolution of Parliament. The request was declined; and on August 4, after having held office for only two days, the Brown-Dorion Administration, "Her Majesty's most ephemeral government," as the Conservatives derisively called it, was obliged to resign, and Macdonald and Cartier were back in power once more.

The crisis had not lasted a long time; it had begun on July 28, and it ended, with the installation of the old ministers, on August 6. Yet this short period of fewer than ten days had provided an almost grotesque illustration of the political instability and futility which was sectionalism's evil gift to the Province of Canada. The Conservative ministers did not, of course, admit that the episode had taught them a lesson—their own triumphant return to office precluded any such embarrassing avowal; but, at the same time, their subsequent actions proved only too clearly that they had now decided to escape, if possible, from the existing state of affairs. Up to this time, it had been the Liberals or Reformers, not the Conservatives, who had kept suggesting solutions for the sectional problem—who had kept pointing out possible exits from the constitutional impasse in which the province found itself. Now, for the first time, the Conservatives took their stand also upon a new policy. For a colony such as Canada, whose two sections could not afford to be separated and did not want to be too closely united, what could be more suitable than a federal form of government? On August 7, the day after the Ministry was formed, Cartier briefly alluded to the new policy, and on August 16, when he prorogued Parliament, Head formally committed his cabinet to the federal scheme.

II

Undoubtedly the political crisis of the summer of 1858 had precipitated the Canadian Conservatives' adoption of the plan of a general British North American federal union. A way out of the political deadlock of sectionalism had been proved to be peremptorily necessary; and a federal union was surely the solution best calculated to preserve the essential character of the Province of Canada. Yet what kind of a federal union? Why had Macdonald and Cartier declared themselves in favour of a comprehensive scheme which would embrace not only all the Maritime Provinces but also, at some future date, the enormous territories of the British north-west? Why had they not been content with the project of converting Canada into a federation of two provinces? This second, smaller plan, which was actually adopted a year later by the Reform party as its policy, was a much more manageable enterprise. It could have been carried out by Canada herself, at her own convenience, and without the slightest reference to the other colonies. Yet this was not the plan which the Conservative party adopted. Instead it had accepted a vastly more ambitious, vastly more difficult undertaking, which could only be completed with the concurrence of four other colonial governments. Why? The urgent necessity of finding a solution for sectional problems is not a satisfactory explanation, for the sectional problem could have been solved just as effectively, and much more expeditiously, by "applying the federal principle," as contemporaries called it, to the Province of Canada alone. What were the other purposes and intentions which lay behind Macdonald's decision? Why had he and his colleagues conceived the grandiose design of a transcontinental British North American federation?

Now it is quite obvious that Canada, in contrast with the Maritime Provinces, had always held to a tradition of western empire. The Maritime Provinces—New Brunswick, Prince Edward Island, and, above all, Nova Scotia and Newfoundland—had grown up in a world in which the three words "ships, colonies, and commerce" formed the indissoluble principles, the virtual "holy trinity," of empire. The dominion in which, on the whole, they had been so comfortably adjusted, was an oceanic dominion; but the empire which Canada had sought to achieve through the centuries had been essentially continental in character. From the days of the French explorers onward, all the political and commercial leaders of the community of the St. Lawrence valley had tried to make the Great River and its Great Lakes the basis of an enormous inland empire. The peace treaty of 1783, which cut a line, at that time artificial and almost meaningless, through the centre of this vast region, had transferred its south-west sector to the United States; and it was these tragic losses on their left flank which helped to impel the Montreal fur traders, the real westerners of the period, into the territories north-west of Lake Superior. Here, in a region which could still be made good for the British Empire, the great trader-explorers of the North West Company, Alexander MacKenzie, David Thompson, and Simon Fraser, drove the fur trade across the prairies and through the mountains to the ocean. They clinched the claims of Cook and Vancouver; they helped to give British North America its wide open window on the Pacific. But the terrible struggle with the Hudson's Bay Company, of which these western exploring enterprises were only a part, had exhausted the North West Company; and in 1821 it virtually capitulated to its great rival. From then on, the Hudson's Bay Company held the north-west quarter of the continent in trust for the future Kingdom of Canada; and for a generation the provinces on the St. Lawrence almost forgot their traditional western empire.

Then, fairly suddenly and without much warning, Canadian interest in the region beyond Lake Superior began to revive. The date of the revival is highly significant, for it began just about eighteen months before the Conservatives adopted their federal scheme in the summer of 1858; and this near coincidence in time suggests that, in matters other than its sectional and constitutional problems, the Province of Canada was reaching a species of crisis in its development. It had, in fact, come nearly to the limit of its possibilities of expansion in the circumstances of the moment, and this at the very time when the rule of the Hudson's Bay Company in the north-west was becoming increasingly uncertain and precarious. There was no longer an agricultural frontier in Canada West, for the good lands south of the Precambrian Shield had all been occupied. There was no real prospect of acquiring the bulk of the trade of the international North American west, for the St. Lawrence was obviously losing in its struggle with the American Atlantic ports. The expansive energies of Canada were being held back in frustration and defeat; but far to the north-west, beyond Lake Superior, was an immense and empty territory which lay waiting for both agricultural settlement and commercial exploitation. Why should not the Province of Canada acquire these lands for its own and British North America's good? Why should it not take over from a moribund seventeenth-century commercial company whose chartered claims were fraudulent, whose rule was baneful, and whose feeble authority was quite incapable of protecting the north-west from encroachment?

Macdonald and his colleagues looked both eagerly and dubiously upon the domain of the Hudson's Bay Company. They were both fascinated and frightened by the thought of acquiring Rupert's Land and the North-west Territories. Inside Canada itself, the popular impulses towards its annexation were very strong; and their strength was powerfully increased by pressures in the same direction which came from outside through both the United Kingdom and the United States. There was no doubt at all that Great Britain was anxious to make new arrangements which would enable her to cut her commitments and reduce her contingent liabilities in North America. In 1857, two years before the Hudson's Bay Company's trading licence was to expire, the British government sponsored a parliamentary committee to consider the state and prospects of Rupert's Land; and although the committee's report made simply a guarded and general recommendation in favour of Canadian settlements in suitable parts of the Red and Saskatchewan valleys, it was quite plain that the imperial government was eager to have Canada take over the responsibility for the north-west.

Yet even this was not all. To the spur of British encouragement was added the stimulus of American rivalry. Canada was determined, sooner or later, to acquire Rupert's Land; the United Kingdom was anxious to arrange a secure British North American future for Rupert's Land; and finally, for both British and Canadians, the irrepressible fear that the United States might succeed in forestalling them lent an additional urgency to their plans for Canadian expansion. This fear was, of course, simply a new western variant of a much older fear, which went back as far as 1775 when, nearly a year before they declared their independence, the Thirteen Colonies launched an attack on Quebec. The armed occupation of Quebec in 1775-6 and the repeated American invasions of the War of 1812 had bred in the British colonies the unshakeable conviction that the United States was the one real threat to their survival on the North American continent. The events which had occurred in the forty years since the Peace of Ghent had, in the main, confirmed rather than qualified this view. At every moment of trouble in British North America, on every occasion of dispute between the United Kingdom and the United States, the threat of American intervention or American attack returned. Only two years before, in 1856, the

Crimean War had brought a brief renewal of the old danger. The Nova Scotian, Joseph Howe, with some encouragement and assistance from J. F. T. Crampton, the British Minister at Washington, attempted to secure recruits for the Crimea from among the currently unemployed in the republic. This childishly inept and foolhardy venture was discovered in due course; it was described, a little grandiloquently, by the American Administration as "an act of usurpation against the sovereign rights of the United States." Crampton's recall was demanded; the American newspapers fulminated in indignation. And all this occurred, as similar dangers had occurred so often in the past, when the size of the British garrisons in the northern colonies had been sharply reduced and when Great Britain's hands were tied with a war in Europe.

The fear was an old one, frequently renewed. And now it had taken on a new shape and found a fresh expression. The survival of the existing colonies in a continent dominated by the United States was still not entirely certain; but far more uncertain was British North America's acquisition of the north-west and its expansion to the Pacific Ocean. Would the transcontinental dominion, of which people were already dreaming, ever become a triumphant reality? The Convention of 1818 and the Washington Treaty of 1846 had settled the international boundary, at least on paper; but might not the hard, solid facts of human occupation determine it ultimately in a quite different fashion? There were only three tiny British American communities in the whole north-west—at Red River, on Vancouver Island, and on the mainland of British Columbia; and the tide of American frontier settlement, the network of the American communication systems, were creeping steadily closer to them with every year that passed. Minnesota became a state in 1858, Oregon was to follow in 1859. Hudson Bay had ceased to be the sole centre of the Hudson's Bay Company's transport system; and the Red River settlement was becoming an economic outpost of St. Paul, just as the Pacific colonies were becoming economic outposts of San Francisco.

All this was part of the speculations of informed Canadians in the summer of 1858. All this was inevitably present in the minds of Macdonald and his fellow ministers when they decided to adopt the policy of a general British North American federation. The sectional crisis in the Province of Canada had led them to the idea of federal union; but the shape and scope which they gave to their federal plan had been determined with a view to British North America as a whole. They were eager, not only to reconstruct the constitution of a province, but also to lay the foundations of a nation; and they were convinced that this was the only way in which a transcontinental nation in the northern half of North America could be built. Union with the Maritime Provinces was essential to secure the future nation's Atlantic frontage; but union with the Maritime Provinces was almost equally necessary to provide a base broad and strong enough to support the acquisition of the north-west. Alone, the Province of Canada might not have been sufficiently powerful to bear the responsibility;

and even if she had been willing to try, the basic division between her French- and English-speaking citizens would almost certainly have prevented her from making the attempt. Even if only a part of Rupert's Land and the North-west Territories had been added to the united province, the addition would simply have emphasized the already existing preponderance of Canada West. It would probably have forced the adoption of representation by population and led to the abandonment of sectional equality in the provincial legislature. It would, in the eyes of French Canadians, have seriously threatened their distinctive culture; and the union might have broken apart in fear and anger.

British North American federation would prevent all this. British North American federation could transform a provincial crisis into a national triumph. It would provide a framework in which French-Canadian culture would be given the protection of provincial status and in which Rupert's Land and the North-west Territories could be gradually organized as they developed. Only in this fashion, in all probability, could a transcontinental nation be created; and the potential strength of transcontinental nationhood would perhaps alone suffice to ensure the survival of British North America.

III

As one looks back, over the intervening century, at the events of the summer of 1858, one cannot help but be impressed by their prophetic significance in Canadian history. As one regards those three years from 1856 to 1859, one feels almost a sense of astonishment at the closeness of their resemblance to another, much more famous three years which began with the formation of the coalition Government in 1864 and ended with Canadian Confederation in 1867. It is almost as if the period from 1856 to 1859 could be looked upon as a preliminary experiment, a species of dress rehearsal, for successful federal union. Many of the actors have already taken their positions on the stage; some of those with star parts are already clearly discernible. And, as one reads over the letters and memoranda in which the Canadians tried to explain their federal plan to the British Colonial Office during the autumn of 1858, one gets the distinct impression that the dialogue is taking shape and that some of the very best lines have already been written. The situations in the years 1856-9 seem vaguely to anticipate those of 1864-7; and the two plots have an odd family relationship as if, at least, they had been contrived by the same author. The scenery in both cases is identical—a few small, underpopulated, staple-producing provinces, set in the howling wilderness of half a continent, with somewhere in the background, lurking menacingly in the shadow, that sinister villain of all Canadian dramas, the United States.

And yet the dress rehearsal of 1856-9 was not the immediate prelude to a real production. The famous announcement of the summer of 1858 had no direct consequences, while the declared purpose of the summer of 1864 was achieved three years later in Canadian Confederation. How is the success of the one and the failure of the other to be explained? The two episodes lie before us, implying contrasts, inviting comparisons; and one is inevitably tempted to use that method, regarded so fondly by sociologists in general and logical positivists in particular, and, in my opinion at least, so properly distrusted by historians. If we embark on an exercise in the comparative method, we shall probably not discover a general law about movements towards federal union, or even, to narrow the field very sharply indeed, about Canadian movements towards federal union. We may discover that the apparent resemblance between these two examples of the same historical species is a superficial resemblance, observable only from the outside; and that, on closer examination from the inside, the two episodes will turn out to be two separate and quite distinct cases.

One important contrast emerges immediately when one compares the purely parliamentary events of July and August, 1858, with those of June, 1864. The rapidly changing political situation of the summer of 1858 certainly provided a much better illustration of the governmental instability which sectionalism had brought to the Province of Canada. The constitutional crisis of 1858 was far more dramatic than that of 1864. And yet—and this, surely, is the important point—its parliamentary consequences were a good deal less significant. The federal plan of 1858 was adopted by a Conservative Administration; but it was a coalition Government of Conservatives and Reformers, commanding a large majority in the House and formed with the express purpose of attempting constitutional reform, which, in June, 1864, announced that it would seek a federal union of the whole of British North America. There was a good deal of truth in the charge of one of the officials in the Colonial Office that in 1858 the Confederation issue was still in "a crude state of party politics." By 1864 it had been lifted out of the crude state of party politics; and both parties, and all but a small minority of the House, had agreed to end a situation from which everybody had suffered.

The agreement of the Canadian parties was not the only new factor in the situation. The attitude of the United Kingdom had altered in an important and striking fashion in the short period of six years. It was true, of course, that Great Britain's major objectives in the north remained fundamentally much the same. Labouchere and Bulwer-Lytton, the Colonial Secretaries of the late 1850s did not differ materially in purpose from Cardwell and Carnarvon who held office at the time of Canadian Confederation. All of them wished equally to cut British commitments in North America; all of them hoped to persuade the colonies in general, and the Province of Canada in particular, to assume a larger part of the responsibility of government in the new world. Here they were agreed; but Cardwell and Carnarvon realized, as Bulwer-Lytton most emphatically did not, that a British North American federal union would be of immense assistance in achieving these purely imperial objectives. The temperamental Bulwer-Lytton, who, one sometimes suspects, carried the melodrama of his romances into the conduct of the Colonial Office, was at one and the same time hotly insistent that Canada should take over Rupert's Land and the Northwest Territories, and coldly discouraging to the plan of federal union. It was Cardwell and Carnarvon, not Bulwer-Lytton, who understood the essential connection between the west and Confederation. It was Cardwell and Carnarvon who sensibly realized that if Great Britain wished to get rid of some of her burdens in North America, she must help to found a British American state which was strong enough to bear them. From the moment when the new Confederation scheme was first broached in 1864, Cardwell, and later Carnarvon, supported it with conviction and vigour.

British encouragement was much stronger in 1864 than it had been in 1858. And so also, in the eyes of Canadians, was pressure from the United States. The increasing weight of this negative influence, of which British Americans were becoming more and more anxiously conscious during the early 1860s, is attributable largely to the American Civil War. The danger of the encroachment of American settlement and exploitation on the tiny British outposts in the northwest was much as it had been a few years before; it may, indeed, have been developing a little more slowly, as a result, in part, of the republic's concentration on its own desperate domestic struggle. But there was no real reason for assurance here; and there was much cause for disquiet elsewhere. The special peril which threatened Rupert's Land and the new colonies on the Pacific coast might not have increased very noticeably; but the general danger facing British North America as a whole was greater than any of its citizens then living could remember its ever having been before. It is here, perhaps, that we touch upon one of the greatest, if not the greatest of the differences between the situation of 1858 and that of 1864. The Crimean enlistment controversy of 1856 had produced a short, sharp explosion of American annoyance; but the Civil War led to a steady and ominous deterioration of the relations between the United Kingdom and the United States.

British North America was inevitably involved in this mounting antagonism, either directly through the breaches of neutrality which the United States alleged she had committed, or indirectly through the controversies which arose between the United Kingdom and the republic. The *Trent* incident, which led John A. Macdonald to propose a militia force of one hundred thousand men for Canada alone, provoked the first of these angry quarrels; but the *Trent* incident, for all its seriousness, occurred early, when the hands of the North were more than full and when the outcome of the struggle was still far from certain. In June, 1864, when the Canadian coalition Government was formed and when the battle of Gettysburg was nearly a year in the past, the situation had greatly changed. It had changed still more by the autumn of the same year, when a handful of Confederate soldiers launched, from the Province of Canada, their stupid and ineffective raid upon the town of St. Albans in Vermont. By that time the United States was ready and eager for reprisals. It announced the abrogation of the Reciprocity Treaty with British North America; it threatened—and, in the circumstances, no more sinister threat could have been imagined—to suspend the Rush-Bagot agreement limiting naval armaments on the Great Lakes.

It is easy to exaggerate the influence of the American Civil War upon the movement for Canadian Confederation. It is easy, in particular, to overestimate the effects of the St. Albans Raid. The coalition Government of June, 1864, was formed and its purpose declared in direct response to a domestic, not an international, crisis. The Quebec Conference, which laid the bases of the federal constitution, met nine days before the St. Albans Raid occurred and the British government's favourable attitude to Confederation had been decided upon even earlier. The American Civil War did not inspire the Canadian desire for constitutional reform or the British wish for retrenchment; but it did help to give both amplitude and urgency to the Anglo-Canadian plans for achieving their objectives. For both Canadians and British it was not enough to do a little constitutional tinkering and make a few budget cuts. They had to build a nation. And their nation had to be built in the midst of a great war which had convulsed the North American continent and threatened to embroil the English-speaking world.

HISTORY AS SCIENCE OR LITERATURE: EXPLAINING CANADIAN CONFEDERATION, 1857-67

Ged Martin

Long ago, there was a controversy among British historians about the nature of their discipline. J. B. Bury's proclamation, in 1903, that "History is a science, no less and no more" led G. M. Trevelyan to complain a decade later that the new school of history was "to the world of older learning what Western Canada is to England today. Settlers pour into the historical land of promise who, a generation back, would have striven for a livelihood in the older 'schools' and 'triposes'.[1] The analogy, underpinned by a disapproving reference to "raw materialism," suggests that Trevelyan did not think much of Canada, and would have been surprised at the notion that it possessed a history at all.

My intention is to explore the idea of history as a science with particular reference to the attempts by historians to explain the differing fates of the two attempts to establish a union of the British North American provinces, the first in 1858-59, and the second between 1864 and 1867. Canadian Confederation, it might be felt, is hardly a subject which calls out for re-examination, for the

From Canada House Lecture Series Number 41 (1989), 1-33. Reprinted by permission of the author and the Academic Relations Section, Canadian High Commission, London.

textbook accounts present an unusually neat and satisfying consensus of historical explanation.[2] For some time, I have been suspicious of the very neatness of this explanation, feeling that Lady Bracknell's famous dictum about truth must apply—that it is rarely pure and never simple. It can hardly be that distinguished scholars and diligent researchers have failed to grasp the events of Canadian Confederation itself. The problem lies much deeper, in the very nature of the way in which history is written—a literary art form which too often poses as an exercise in scientific explanation.

History has at least a superficial affinity with the physical sciences in that it seeks to arrange events into ordered explanations. The chemist establishes that compound A causes a reaction, the physicist that particle B breaks a nucleus, the historian that statesman C caused a war. Yet, as Arthur Marwick reminds us, "there *is* a difference, and we all know there is a difference. The physical scientist can repeat his experiments; the historian cannot call for a repeat performance of the past.[3] This does not mean that explanation in the physical sciences is necessarily *better* than that laboriously argued by the historian. Persistent experimentation may enable a medical researcher to establish that a particular drug cures a dangerous disease. The Nobel Prize would not be withheld from such a benefactor of humanity merely because our scientist confessed total inability to explain how the drug actually managed the miracle. Yet there would be little professional acclaim for the historian who announced that there was a correlation between the presence of Bismarck and the outbreak of wars of Prussian aggrandisement, but confessed inability to offer any elucidation of this perceived link. Explanation in the pure sciences, then, is not necessarily *superior* to that offered by historians. It is merely *testable*.

In the case of Canadian Confederation, a very superficial equivalent of the experimental method is offered by the fact that the circumstances of 1858-59, unsuccessful, can be compared with those of 1864-67, successful. The most obvious factor present in the second case but not the first was the American Civil War. Yet although the context of the Civil War—perhaps more narrowly, its impending conclusion in a Northern victory—is undoubtedly important, it does not follow that the Civil War is thereby proven to be a crucial causal element. It may simply be that those who failed in 1858-59 had learned from their mistakes. The only way to test the hypothesis that it is the American Civil War which represents the crucial causal difference between 1858 and 1864 would be to put the eighteen sixties back in the bell-jar of time, where events could be endlessly re-run, with minute variations in endless permutations—this time with no Civil War, then with a Southern victory, a stalemate, European intervention, a negotiated peace, and each of the near-infinite possibilities in combination with millions of alternative developments within the British North American provinces themselves. Of course we cannot do this, but merely to sketch the possibility is to grasp its absurdity. People are not particles. The behaviour of one individual on one occasion is no predictor for the behaviour of another in the same or—more realistically—similar circumstances.

Most historians would probably agree that because the past is not testable and human behaviour cannot be reduced to predictable formulae, Trevelyan was right to protest that "there is no way of scientifically deducing causal laws about the action of human beings in the mass."[4] Yet lurking behind many textbook explanations of the coming of Canadian Confederation, there is the assumption that individual events in the eighteen fifties and sixties can be given meaning by an appeal to implicit general laws. Occasionally, these assumptions are spelt out as part of a softening-up process to prepare the reader for the inevitability of the outcome. Thus Chester Martin stated: "Nothing but a compelling necessity can reconcile self-governing provinces to the surrender of cherished rights to the exigencies of a distant national state." The "scientific" context is made yet more evident in the elaboration:

> Like chemical reagents which are inert towards one another under normal conditions of pressure and temperature, the most disintegrated provinces may react in a national emergency with unpredictable responsiveness. That reaction at the time may be due to abnormal pressure and temperature but once it has resulted in organic federation, the product may be a permanent chemical compound capable of withstanding the stresses and strains of normal atmospheric conditions with complete organic stability.[5]

We are being prepared here, of course, for an explanation which stresses the hot blast of the Civil War, but at least we are being prepared openly. More recently, Peter Waite began his account of Confederation in the *Canadian Encyclopedia* with the statement:

> The Confederation movement followed Newton's first law of motion: all bodies continue in a state of rest or of uniform motion unless compelled by some force to change their state.[6]

The attractiveness of a bold statement of this kind to historians is demonstrated by the fact that it has been prominently cited in a recent—and indeed excellent—textbook.[7] The problem, of course, comes back to the question of *testability*. A few societies, such as Tokugawa Japan, may have succeeded for a time in walling themselves off from external influences, but most are subject to continual and random buffeting from outside. If we accept Waite's "scientific" dictum, we can indeed easily apply it to the circumstances of British North America in 1864, for the apparently Newtonian pressures for change are obvious. Unfortunately, what we cannot do is discover, by repeated experimentation, whether some or all of these forces might not in reality have bounced harmlessly off the immovable provincial objects.

Chester Martin and Peter Waite are open in their appeal to scientific laws. Other historians deplore the political shortcomings of the province of Canada before Confederation, implying that it was characterised by internal communal divisions and avoidance of real issues to a degree which simply could not be allowed to continue in the face of an overwhelming external threat. Such an assumption could only be valid if it rested upon a general law of political physics, which would mean that it would be as true of the Lebanon in the 1980s as of the province of Canada in the 1860s. In fact, there is no such law, and the explanation which implies its existence is not logical so much as teleological: it proceeds from the knowledge of hindsight that Confederation is coming just around the corner and brazenly proceeds to conflate *post hoc* with *propter hoc.* The problem, then, as David Hackett Fischer has put it, is not that history is an inexact science but that historians are inexact scientists.[8]

These difficulties are complicated by the fact that history is also a literary art form. My concern is not so much with literary *style,* which is rare enough among historians, as with literary *craftsmanship.* In assembling the construct which we call history from the totality which was the past, we like to think that we get a general idea of what the sources are trying to tell us, before approaching them in more detail with our own hypotheses to test how far the evidence will sustain our theories. The best experimental scientists employ exactly the same approach, and their greatest discoveries stem from just such imaginative leaps. However, the physicist is protected from utter foolishness by the intractability of particles: repeated experimentation will destroy a factually incorrect hypothesis. For the historian, there is a fine distinction between the careful compilation of a case and the outright filtering of evidence in order to impose a pre-conceived crotchet. In a subject which aroused as much long-winded controversy as did Canadian Confederation in the mid-1860s, supporting quotation can be adduced, from somebody, somewhere, to provide the historian's decorative sprig of spurious contemporary endorsement for just about any hypothesis.

In short, we face a problem in the way in which our literary *craftsmanship* builds up a deceptively scientific argument and then triumphantly produces as supporting evidence one or two clinching sentences from a contemporary source. But what of the motives of that source? Peter Stansky has reminded us of an occasion when Gladstone was suddenly threatened by an attack of brevity. As an inexperienced front-bencher charged with the duty of responding to a debate, he turned to his chief, Sir Robert Peel, and asked, "Shall I be short and concise?" "No," replied Peel, "be long and diffuse. It is all important in the House of Commons to state your case in many different ways, so as to produce an effect on men of many ways of thinking."[9] Gladstone managed to resist the temptation to concision for the rest of his career; his colonial contemporaries seem never to have been tested. Some, I am sorry to say, not only advanced arguments in forms designed to appeal to different viewpoints, but were even guilty on occasion of uttering statements which they may not have believed at all. At a banquet in Halifax in August 1864, Joseph Howe seemed to speak warmly of the idea of uniting the British North American provinces—a speech which he was challenged to explain since shortly afterwards he became an out-and-out opponent of Confederation. His indignant explanation of the apparent inconsistency was that he had risen to speak at ten minutes to midnight. "Who ever heard of a public man being bound by a speech delivered on such an occasion as that?"[10] Historians, in their literary personae, may crown their own explanations with the clinching flourish of contemporary evidence. But it may be that the contemporary statement was made by a minister who wished his arguments to chime with the concerns of the Member for Mudville, or that it was advanced by the Member for Mudville in the hope of becoming a minister.

Not surprisingly, most of those who have written about Canadian Confederation have been Canadians, and English-speaking Canadians at that. Understandably, it has stirred their patriotism. Through Confederation, as Careless puts it, "a new Canadian nation was born" and it is not surprising that he should describe it as "one of the most compelling stories in Canadian history."[11] Arthur Lower even regarded Confederation—along with the adoption of the Constitution of the United States—as one of "two political miracles"[12] to have taken place on the North American continent. Provincial politicians are suddenly ennobled to become statesmen, in another continental echo, "Fathers of Confederation." Yet, confusingly, while as *Canadians* the historians have been misty-eyed at the vision so bravely grasped, as inexact scientists they have tended to argue that there was really no alternative. The causes of Confederation are portrayed as being not only overwhelming and above all *interlocking*. "Only a general union, balanced with all the care and precision of a cantilever, was practical in 1864," wrote W. L. Morton in 1963.[13] The apparent contradiction between the inevitability of the solution and the magisterial vision of those who grasped it may owe something to the atmosphere of the 1960s, which saw the publication of both Creighton's *The Road to Confederation* and Morton's *The Critical Year,* when English Canadians finally began to face the need to define a national identity entirely independent of British world power, at a time when a newly assertive French Canadian nationalism in the province of Quebec actually threatened to break the Canadian state apart. Bereft of the empire, it was tempting to laud the wisdom of the Fathers of Confederation as a *national* symbol: in Creighton's biography, John A. Macdonald single-handedly combined Washington's leadership, Jefferson's draftsmanship, Lincoln's melancholic integrity and Grant's fondness for the bottle.[14] Faced with Quebec separatism, it was reassuring to convince oneself that Confederation had been the only possible solution for the northern half of the continent in the 1860s for, by implication, this meant that it was also the inescapable context for the solution of the problems of the 1960s. It is as if the circumstances of 1864 had been fed into a computer which had churned its disks and printed out the single word "Confederation."

The causes cited for the coming of Confederation usually begin with the internal divisions of the province of Canada. Upper and Lower Canada had been ruled by a single legislature and governor since 1841, but in a curiously quasi-federal union. When the British parliament had enacted the Union, English-speaking Upper Canada had the smaller population, but since the Union was intended both to swamp and to anglicise French Canadians, each section of the province was given equal representation in the Assembly. By the late 1840s, internal self-government was established in the province of Canada, but the local ministries had a dual character and were usually led by co-premiers, English and French—LaFontaine-Baldwin; Hincks-Morin, Cartier-Macdonald. That was certainly one development which British legislators had not foreseen in 1840. But another was that the principle of equal representation of the sections, originally intended to bolster Upper against Lower Canada, in fact became a grievance in the upper province. By 1851, Upper Canada's population just exceeded that of Lower Canada; by 1861, the figures were 1.4 million to 1.1 million. Increasingly, Upper Canada demanded "rep. by pop.," the majority voice inside the united province. Such a demand was obviously dangerous to a two-headed system, for it risked a confrontation in which one section's major demand was the very concession which the other could not make. Hence the oft-quoted aphorism of Goldwin Smith that "the real father of Confederation was deadlock."

However, the interlocking explanatory package has other attractive elements. The rapid population rise in Upper Canada—numbers trebled in the twenty years from 1841 to 1861—brought a sensation of impending land shortage, especially as new settlement ran up against the intractable barrier of the Canadian Shield. As early as the mid-1850s, the felt need for more land had led various Upper Canadians to cast covetous eyes on the vast and largely empty westward territories of the Hudson's Bay Company. A timely gold rush in the Fraser valley in 1858, which gave birth to the colony of British Columbia, added to the attraction of expansion. But, so the historians argue, the vast western territories could only be absorbed into a wholly new political structure.

If some eyes in the province of Canada were looking west, others were drawn eastward, to the Atlantic seaboard. The 1850s were a time of railway construction, and by 1859 the province of Canada could boast the longest railway line in the world. In fact, few Canadians were tempted to boast about the Grand Trunk. It was at least mildly corrupt, but its real problem was that it ran parallel to the cheap water route of the St Lawrence and petered out about one hundred miles below Quebec City at Rivière-du-Loup. On several occasions from the late 1840s negotiations had been undertaken to extend the Grand Trunk through to the Atlantic ocean, which would give the province of Canada access to the ice-free ports of Saint John and Halifax. Barely half a million people lived in Nova Scotia and New Brunswick, and as a commercial proposition, the Halifax to Quebec or "Intercolonial" railway had little to commend it. From

1851, the Grand Trunk was linked to the Atlantic through a spur line to Portland in Maine, and the American bonding system made it possible to export goods through US territory without payment of duty. The British government was interested in principle in a railway for defence purposes, but the route they favoured naturally ran far from the United States border—and incidentally away from the centres of population and votes. By 1860, the British railway magnate, Edward Watkin, had come to the conclusion that the Grand Trunk should be extended both to the Atlantic and to the Pacific. Watkin's role in the coming of Confederation is shadowy, but his evidence makes it possible for historians to interlock Canada's westward expansion with the need for a railway to the Atlantic seaboard.[15] The urgency of the latter project seemed underlined by the *Trent* crisis of December 1861, which brought Britain and the United States close to war. British troops reinforcing inland positions had to sledge across New Brunswick. The Civil War thus makes its appearance in the web of causation. The argument then reverts to the deadlocked state of the Canadian Union, which in 1862 is seen to be unable to cope with the challenge of either defence or railway construction. It also brings in another element—trade. In 1854, a Reciprocity Treaty had been negotiated between the United States and the British North American colonies, providing for free trade in natural products. During the Civil War, incautiously expressed sympathy for the Southern Confederacy in the provinces played into the hands of Northern opponents of the Treaty, and in 1865, the USA gave twelve months' notice that Reciprocity would end. Thus to the political, settlement and communications aspects of the Confederation package, historians could also add a commercial incentive: if the provinces could not trade with the United States, they could at least unite and trade with each other.

Other causal elements make their appearance in the package. Some proponents talked largely of a "new nationality" in British North America. Historians as various as the socialist Kenneth McNaught, and the undoubtedly Tory Donald Creighton included this element in their analyses,[16] for here, again, the 1860s seemed to be offering reassurance which the 1960s wished to hear. In fact, we need to adapt George Bernard Shaw and recall that the nineteenth century and the twentieth are two eras separated by a common language. Oratorical invocations of a "new nationality" fell a long way short of hoisting a Maple Leaf flag, as the enthusiasts of Canada First sardonically noted when they attempted to build on the rhetorical platform in the decade after Confederation. "The authors of Confederation once appealed to the spirit of nationality," *The Nation* complained in 1875. "Now some of them tell us that their object was limited and that they set the forest on fire only to boil their own pot."[17] But the main framework of the explanatory package starts with rising population in Upper Canada, its paralysing effect on the Canadian Union, its by-product, the demand for westward expansion, and the way in which this came to be interconnected with railway construction to the east at a time when the American

Civil War precipitated a defence and trade crisis. To adapt Chester Martin's imagery, the ingredients were there. It needed only the hot blast of the Civil War to bake the cake.

Was the province of Canada really, as J. B. Brebner put it, "on a downward spiral"[18] from the mid-1850s, or does that verdict depend on the fact that we happen to know that Confederation was coming just around the corner? Within a single lecture, there is but little time to discuss such episodes as the "double shuffle" of 1858, the defeat of the Militia Bill in 1862, the collapse of the Intercolonial railway talks later that year, or the passage in 1863 of the Upper Canada Separate Schools Act—forced on the resentful Protestant section by Lower Canadian votes.

The double shuffle was a dodge by which Macdonald and his colleagues avoided having to contest by-elections on re-appointment to portfolios which they had just resigned during an incident which a student of modern Belgian or Italian politics might term a hiccup rather than a crisis. The senior civil servant in the British Colonial Office—usually a rich source of contemporary condemnation of political standards in British North America—merely commented on "the general air of lunacy which hangs over the whole proceedings."[19] By contrast, historians have been mightily disapproving of the double shuffle. "People of all political hues began to wonder how workable was a union that depended upon trickery for its continuation" say J. L. Finlay and D. N. Sprague.[20] It is at least possible that nineteenth century colonials were less shockable than twentieth century academics, but in any case, there was nothing illegal about the double shuffle, and even if the law had been broken—as it was, for instance, in the Watergate affair in the United States—that would be to the discredit of the politicians and not of the political system. Canada was to endure murkier political scandals: six years after Confederation, Macdonald was forced to resign in the face of charges that he had given the contract for the transcontinental railway to the man who had funded his election campaign. Imagine the outraged rhetoric with which the historians would condemn the worthless, ramshackle federation which could produce the Pacific Scandal, had the new Dominion broken up in failure after a dozen years! In fact, the admittedly lukewarm element of corruption in the Pacific Scandal is forgiven because villainy may be excused if it is in the interests of Canadian nation-building. Lower was unabashed to admit that the purchase of votes with Canadian money may have played a role in swinging New Brunswickers into line in 1866. "Bribery is a form of consent," he concluded, "and the alternative to consent is force."[21] Confederation, it seems, was not just historically inevitable; it was an offer which could not be refused. In fact, if we abandon the silver trumpets view that Confederation was the beginning of a whole new era, it is possible to perceive that the common element in 1858, 1862 and 1873 was the volatility of members of parliament. Arguably, what Canada needed was not a new political structure but a much firmer system of party government to sustain ministries in difficult times. "Anybody may support me when I am right," Macdonald retorted to a high-minded independent. "What I want is a man that will support me when I am wrong."[22]

The Cartier-Macdonald ministry finally fell over the Militia Bill of 1862. Its replacement, headed by another Macdonald, John Sandfield, is usually regarded as the nadir of the old system. But was the "pawky Highlander"— Morton's dismissive description—really so bad?[23] True, in his two years clinging to office, he consistently sought to evade issues, but so did his more famous and successful namesake—John A. was nick-named "Old Tomorrow"—and so, for a quarter century, did Mackenzie King, an equally unprepossessing physical specimen, of whom it was once said that he did nothing by halves that could be done by quarters.[24] Sandfield Macdonald has been the fall guy of the Confederation story: we are expected to conclude that any political system which could produce a Sandfield had hit rock-bottom and deserved to be swept away in disgrace. One feels that if Sandfield Macdonald had not existed, the historians of Confederation would have been obliged to invent him. Indeed, it is possible that the Sandfield they portray in the textbooks *was* invented. In 1867, when that great statesman of Confederation, John A. Macdonald, was looking for an ally to instal as premier of the new province of Ontario, on whom did his far-sighted and patriotic choice fall? Joseph Pope, who knew John A. Macdonald, recounted that he "came to the conclusion that John Sandfield Macdonald was just the man to undertake the task."[25] Donald Creighton's great chronicle of Sir John A's nation-building achievements does not mention the selection at all.[26]

If we put aside the unfavourable stereotype of Sandfield Macdonald and look afresh at the question of militia reform in Canada in the 1860s, a less dramatic picture emerges. While acknowledging that it was a complex question, historians have not been very sympathetic in explaining the defeat of the Militia Bill of 1862. Disapproval is evident in Creighton's comment that "Canadians had not as yet become very excited over the alleged danger of the great new military machine which the North was building up"[27] and in Lower's verdict that political rivalry "was so bitter as to cause party advantage to be placed before public necessity."[28] Both comments are fair enough, but they do not tell the whole story. First, the Militia Bill of 1862 contained a contingent element of conscription: if a district did not contribute enough volunteers for training, the shortfall would be made good by ballot. The extent of the continental crisis may well have justified this step, but Canada's historians have been more inclined to assess handling of the conscription issue in terms of the susceptibilities of French Canada than the imperatives of military need.[29] Secondly, the proposed militia reform was to cost almost a million dollars, raising expenditure to twelve and a half million dollars at a time when revenue was estimated at just over seven millions.[30] No doubt posterity may riposte that it was up to Canadians to face realities and pay their way—but it may be the rejection of the bill proves not that the province of Canada was incapable of responding to challenge, but that parliamentary systems are not very willing to embrace costly defence projects. In Britain, a warning from no less an authority than the Duke of Wellington that the country was wide open to a French invasion by steamships led Lord John Russell's government in 1848 to propose militia reform on a scale similar to that contemplated by Macdonald and Cartier in 1862. Russell proposed to raise and train, over a three-year-period, a militia of 120,000 men backed by 80,000 reserves—about four times the force contemplated for Canada, from over ten times the population—coupled with extensive expenditure on ships and fortifications. To pay for this, the income tax—which was actually due to lapse—would have to be increased from seven to twelve pence in the pound. As in 1862, the government's parliamentary exposition of its plan was hampered by the illness of its chief spokesman: Russell had influenza, Macdonald's indisposition was self-inflicted. Despite a decade of often-inflamed relations with France, the House of Commons mutinied at the scale of the plan, which ministers ingloriously withdrew. "The chances of invasion seemed preferable to the certain addition of fivepence to the income tax."[31] Russell's government never fully recovered from the setback, but struggled on for another four years, until Palmerston, his ousted rival, took his revenge—his "tit-for-tat" as he elegantly styled it—by defeating the Militia Bill of 1852.[32] In fairness, Palmerston beat the government after arguing that they had not done enough, but there may have been people in Britain who wondered how long a system of government could continue which made defence the childish sport of parties. If so, their anonymous doubts do not make the textbooks, for not even the shock of the Crimean War could compel constitutional change. Instead, Palmerston himself got into the saddle and between 1859 and 1865 gave a very successful imitation of Sandfield Macdonald, bringing stability to government by the simple expedient of refusing to introduce any major reforms at all.

Yet this comparison may actually be unfair to the abused Sandfield. In 1863, he carried an extensive militia reform, to provide the province with a trained force of 35,000. Actually, Sandfield's reform looked more impressive on paper than on the parade ground, where only a minority of the force ever put in an appearance, but politics—perhaps especially in Canada—is about the possible rather than the ideal. Sir Etienne Taché announced his government's intention of tightening up the 1863 act the day before his minority Conservative ministry was overthrown, to be replaced by the coalition which introduced Confederation. Thereafter, the militia dramatically disappears from the history books. A British officer, Colonel MacDougall, took charge of training, increasing the efficient strength in the province of Canada to 25,000. If the new Dominion was intended to show a larger and more responsible attitude to such questions, it produced a very muted response. Cartier's Militia Act of 1868 seems to have been largely a consolidation of existing forces, and was based on the existing militia laws of the province of Canada—passed in 1863 by

Sandfield Macdonald. It aimed at a force of 40,000 men. Of course, the Civil War was over, but the militia was primarily a defence against contingent threats—and there were still Fenians across the border. Cartier's main aim seems to have been to legislate the militia very firmly under the control of the politicians, or—to put it another way—to put patronage before patriotism. When the much-praised Colonel MacDougall argued for the prosecution of men who attempted to leave the militia before the end of their service, Cartier in effect had him fired.[33] The British, who pulled their garrisons out in 1870, continued to allege that Canada did not do enough for its own protection, and in 1874, the impatient nationalists of Canada First included "An improved militia system, under the command of trained Dominion officers" as one of their eleven planks.[34]

In fact, the indictment of the old political system of the province of Canada rests upon a very few episodes, not all of them shiningly improved upon by the succeeding Dominion. It is surely going too far to compare the Canadian Union with the French Third Republic, as Arthur Lower did. "In the twenty-seven years of the Union there were eight parliaments, innumerable ministries ... and some ten persons who could have been designated 'premier'."[35] By my calculation, there were in fact fourteen, but we should bear in mind that most ministries were double-headed, and that at the very least, we should divide Lower's ten by two to get a fair comparison with other parliamentary systems. In the twenty-two years between 1902 and 1924, Britain had eight prime ministers; between 1951 and 1979, there were nine. In any case, what did it matter? Lower's concern appears to reflect an implied scientific law that frequent changes of ministry are in themselves undesirable. Between June 1891 and July 1896, Canada had six prime ministers: the decade which followed was one of exploding prosperity and national growth. The province of Canada prospered mightily under the Union. Lower Canada's population virtually doubled under the Canadian Union; Upper Canada's tripled. The political problems were those stemming from success, not failure.

True, in justifying the astonishing union of former enemies to form the coalition of 1864, which launched the successful Confederation initiative, the premier, Sir Etienne Taché, warned that "the country was bordering on civil strife." But a few weeks earlier, the governor-general had opened parliament, reading a ministerial speech which thanked "a beneficent Providence for the general contentment of the people of this province."[36] The notion of a terrifying crisis, within and without, suited the politicians to justify their actions. It suits the historians to quote those politicians to account for the major change which they carried. "Two elections and four ministries in three years!" exclaims Lower. "Everyone recognized that it was impossible to go on."[37] Did they now? Britain had three general elections in under two years between 1922 and 1924. The outcome was not constitutional revolution, but Stanley Baldwin Ireland had three elections in 1981-82: the decade is ending, as it began, with Charles J. Haughey as Taoiseach. For what it is worth, the bell-jar of comparison does not proclaim the same law as the crystal ball of hindsight. But there is a far more crucial weakness in the argument. How was it that after *allegedly* failing to confront a series of crucial challenges—I stress the word "allegedly"—the Canadian Union was suddenly able to carry through the greatest challenge of all, the creation of a new, potentially transcontinental union? Well might Lower call it a "miracle":[38] the logic of his sweeping condemnation of the old system left him with little option. There were certainly contemporaries who asked, on the one hand, why a coalition could not have been formed to work the existing system, or who wanted to know, on the other, how a system of government which had supposedly quarrelled its way to a standstill would work any better when writ large across half a continent.[39] Lower's conclusion that "the two races could not forever be driven in double harness,"[40] is surely a condemnation not of the old province of Canada but of the Canadian experiment as such. If we seek to explain why Confederation was *necessary,* we may indeed be tempted to dwell on the weaknesses of the old province of Canada. If we seek rather to explain why Confederation was *possible,* we are more likely to appreciate the strengths of the Canadian Union.

If the first difficulty in stressing the quarrelsome failure of the Canadian Union is to explain how it managed to sustain the great success of Confederation, the second is to explain why it was possible to persuade the Maritimes to consider climbing into bed at all. According to the textbooks, they were swept along by the interlocking logic of Confederation itself as a solution to the problems of British North America, hammered home by external pressures from the United States and Britain. But how far did the case for Confederation really interlock, cantilever-fashion, from anyone's point of view? And how far did the external pressures compel Confederation, rather than some other solution—or outright and paralysed inaction?

As already noted, railways form the basic ingredient of the interlocking explanation. Canadian duality meant that the Intercolonial railway, needed both for defence and trade reasons, could not be built without counter-balancing expansion to the West—one of those trade-offs which seem so squalid when encountered in the workaday horse-trading of the old province of Canada.

These arguments do not stand scrutiny, either individually or collectively. There is no more reason to assume that political union was an essential precondition for the construction of the Intercolonial than there is to postulate a need for a Franco-British parliament at Calais in order to complete the Channel Tunnel. The outline scheme of 1862 indicated that a railway could have been built by agreement among the separate provinces. The imperial loan guarantee which was invoked in 1867 was the one offered to the separate provinces in 1862. The British government was careful to foster the idea that without

Confederation, the House of Commons might rebel against endorsing the guarantee—but even after the passage of the British North America Act in March 1867, the Guarantee Bill had a rough ride. In practice, Confederation and the Intercolonial came to be linked, but it is by no means proven that they had to be.

The argument that the ending of Reciprocity made the provinces draw together is equally unconvincing. There were thirty-one million Americans, and a little over half a million people in the Maritimes: from the point of view of the province of Canada, the smaller colonies could hardly even rank as a second-best. Even so, as critics pointed out at the time, the logic of the argument, such as it was, pointed not to political union but rather to intercolonial free trade.[41]

But was there any trade to develop? Lower implies that there was: "Oceanic forces towed the Maritime colonies out to sea; continental forces split them in two."[42] Contemporary trade figures would suggest that continental forces barely chipped the Maritimes. New Brunswick in 1863 sent less than one per cent of its exports to Canada, which was the source of under four per cent of its imports. On the other hand, the province of Canada sent 2.2 per cent of its exports to the four Atlantic colonies in 1863, and took 1.1 per cent of its imports from them. Doubters pointed out at the time that since the Maritimes and the province of Canada produced similar staples—timber, potash, fish—they were unlikely ever to become complementary trading zones.[43] Historians may use the purely literary device of claiming that in the 1860s there was enormous potential for the development of trade between Canada and the Maritimes, but by the same token, there is enormous potential for agriculture in the Sahara desert. Nor was the Intercolonial seen as an obvious route for Upper Canadian exports. William McMaster, a Toronto merchant (and academic benefactor), challenged the claim that the line was "an indispensable necessity in order to secure an independent outlet to the sea-board." Rather than use the existing railways to American ports, Upper Canada merchants preferred to pay warehousing, insurance and interest charges to keep wheat and flour in store through the winter "until the opening of the navigation."[44] It is true that by 1874, Ontario manufacturers had captured a large slice of the Maritime market for agricultural equipment, but this owed nothing to the Intercolonial (which was not completed until 1876): goods were sent by steamer to the local railhead at Pictou, Nova Scotia.[45] In any case, the manufacturing sector of the pre-Confederation Upper Canadian economy was far too small to be cited as an explanation for the province's support for intercolonial union.

Weaknesses in individual parts of the explanation of Confederation are glossed over by linking each argument to the overall interlocking package. Whether or not the Intercolonial railway would be useful, its place in the standard account is copper-fastened by arguing that it was a trade-off for westward expansion. Thus Morton, building up to his "cantilever" image:

A local federation of the Canadas was not enough, for Upper Canada wanted not only freedom from the French majority (sic) in domestic matters; it also wanted, and the Brownite Liberals especially, to annex the north-west and build a Pacific railway. But Lower Canada could scarcely agree to the annexation of the north-west unless this were offset by guarantees of its historic rights in the new union, and by the adherence of the Atlantic provinces to the union to balance the indefinitely growing population of Upper Canada. Neither would Lower Canada and the Atlantic provinces assent to the cost of building a Pacific railway unless they were matched by the building of the Intercolonial.[46]

This statement arouses many questions. If the united province of Canada was not working, why could it not have been reconstructed on federal lines? The Fathers of Confederation themselves saw no necessary objection, for the fall-back position of the Great Coalition of 1864, should the wider union prove unattainable, was a promise to solve "existing difficulties by introducing the federal principle for Canada alone."[47] How urgent was Upper Canada's need to expand westward, and was the campaign focused on the Pacific coast or on the prairies? Was there a straight trade-off between the construction of the Intercolonial and westward expansion, between Upper and Lower Canadian interests? Was Confederation the necessary precondition for annexation of the north-west?

It is possible to overstate the extent to which Upper Canada urgently needed land for expansion. The agitation for the incorporation of the Hudson's Bay Company territories had begun in earnest with the campaign of the *Globe* in 1856, and had a great deal to do with the completion at the end of 1855 of Toronto's Northern Railway to Collingwood, which gave the city easy access to Georgian Bay and consequently an interest in the North-West.[48] While the last blocks of wild land within Upper Canada had been auctioned the previous year, creating what Lower called "a sense of spacial limitation,"[49] it did not mean—as the *Globe* itself acknowledged—that the province had run out of land: there was plenty of room for in-filling of settlement but no new frontiers to open up. As late as 1865, John A. Macdonald told Watkin that the western territories were "of no present value to Canada" for the province had "unoccupied land enough to absorb the immigration for many years."[50] Secondly, there is little to suggest that the kind of westward expansion George Brown hoped for was expected to include a railway to British Columbia—at least not at the outset. In his 1858 lectures, *Nova Britannia,* even the visionary Alexander Morris seemed to locate a Pacific railway up to twenty years in the future.[51] When Edward Watkin embraced the idea in 1860, he accepted that he was perhaps "somewhat visionary for even suggesting it."[52] In one important respect, his vision failed entirely: it was not the Grand Trunk which built the Pacific railway, and from 1872 onwards, the two ventures were to be deadly enemies. The speed with which Cartier was to offer a Pacific railway to the bemused British Columbia delegates in 1870 suggests that the idea was not far below the surface, but Morton is wrong to imply that it formed part of a Confederation package in the 1860s. When George Brown moved a resolution at the Quebec conference providing for the future admission of Newfoundland, the prairies, British Columbia and Vancouver Island, he remarked that the inclusion of the last two was "rather an extreme proposition."[53]

What, then, was being traded off and by whom? Early in 1864, a meeting had taken place between Brown and C. J. Brydges, the manager of the Grand Trunk. Brydges offered Brown the chair of the Canadian Board of the recently reorganised Hudson's Bay Company—a proposition which does not seem to have excited any moral outrage in the textbooks—and went on to convince him "that nothing could be done about the Northwest without the Intercolonial."[54] If he had indeed convinced George Brown that the two projects could be traded, subsequent events suggest that—as with the dual aim of British North American union or a federation of the Canadas—Brown was out-manoeuvred in the coalition. Article 68 of the Quebec Resolutions bound the new general government to "secure, without delay" the completion of the Intercolonial. Article 69 spoke more generally of the importance of improving communications with the North West, and promised that they would "be prosecuted at the earliest possible period that the state of the Finances will permit."[55] Given the state of the finances, complained one critic, this meant that the North West was "hermetically sealed" for all time to come.[56] There was no trade-off.

In any case, who was doing the trading? It was not "Lower Canada" which wanted the Intercolonial, but *some* Lower Canadians—and by no means all of those francophones, for many of them objected strongly to any further favours for the Grand Trunk. There were also French Canadians who supported the Intercolonial but opposed Confederation on wider cultural grounds.[57] In any case, if the Intercolonial was designed to provide a winter trade outlet, it would presumably be of as much—if not more—benefit to Upper Canada. And if Lower Canadians and Maritimers did indeed purchase the Intercolonial by a tacit agreement to back a counterbalancing line to the Pacific, the bargain was a shaky one, for in the two decades which followed they were at best lukewarm and indeed eventually even hostile to the project.

There are also logical difficulties in accepting the claim that French Canadians felt safer in a union in which the Maritimes would join them in counter-balancing the population of Upper Canada. Cartier indeed advanced the argument—but, then, he would, wouldn't he?[58] Surveys of the Lower Canadian debate on the merits of Confederation by Peter Waite and Arthur Silver do not suggest that French Canadians saw Maritimers as the guarantors of their rights.[59] Joseph Cauchon, one of the most articulate supporters of Confederation, accepted that from the point of view of protecting the basic identity and rights of French Canada, "la confédération des deux Canadas eût pu être aussi bonne que la confédération de toutes les Provinces de l'Amérique Britannique du Nord."[60] The conventional wisdom of Canadian history is that French Canadians have always resisted annexation to the United States for fear that they would be swamped. Why, then, should they seek union with any more anglophones than were absolutely necessary? One French Canadian opponent argued that his compatriots would be in a four-to-one minority in the federal parliament: "What could so weak a minority do to obtain justice?"[61] French Canadians accepted Confederation because it offered them their own province, in which the local majority could safeguard its educational system and so protect its religion and culture—although some were uneasy that the central government's power of disallowance made the federal structure a legislative union in disguise. What determined the preference of French Canadians was that in 1864-67, a negotiated scheme for local autonomy within British North American Confederation was actually on offer, whereas autonomy within a federation of the two Canadas was not. Yet this is not to say that a similar solution could not have been negotiated, creating a smaller federation confined to the St Lawrence valley. In this context, we might perhaps recall that in 1867, the very year of Confederation, Austrians and Hungarians decided to substitute hyphenation for unification as a basis for sharing the Danube valley. In the absence of the belljar, we might equate Bismarck's Prussia with the victorious Northern States. Yet no-one, so far as I am aware, seriously argued that the internal stresses of the Austrian Empire could only be solved by federation with Serbia and Moldavia.

Where one argument is weak, appeal is implicitly shifted to some other aspect of the package. A federation of the two Canadas, Morton asserted "could hardly have met the need for expansion."[62] Why not? The British parliamentary enquiry of 1857 had recommended the annexation of the fertile districts of the prairies to the province of Canada, and the gentlemanly legislators of Westminster were not always unstinted in expressions of confidence in the governmental capacity of their colonial counterparts. The internal reconstruction of the province of Canada along federal lines could in fact have made it easier to add the Hudson's Bay territories as an eventual third wheel. Representation for the Red River settlement, which in the 1860s had a francophone majority, coupled with local autonomy for Lower Canada, might have offered just as satisfactory a constitutional settlement as union with the Maritimes. In fact, if Canadians had borrowed from the precedent of territorial government south of the border, the twelve thousand people of the Red River might have been incorporated without affecting the balance of representation at all.[63] The United States constitution permitted territories to send a non-voting delegate to Congress, barring them from seeking statehood—and full voting rights—until they had a population of sixty thousand. Manitoba did not achieve this figure until 1881. Historians rightly inform us that these things *did* not happen, but when they tell us that such things *could* not have happened, they not only pronounce on what they cannot possibly know but distort understanding of what actually occurred.

Some may quibble with an approach which picks holes in this or that part of the postulated causal package. The ingredients may not always be palatable to the fastidious scholar. What matters is the process, the crisis which baked them into the Confederation cake. In a general sense, of course, the historian cannot dismiss the importance of what C. P. Stacey called the "atmosphere of crisis" at the end of the Civil War.[64] It is without doubt the essential *psychological* context for understanding the adoption of Confederation. "The tide of war is rolling towards us," cried a Halifax newspaper. "What do men mean, talking about cents per head of taxation[!]"[65] "Look around you to the valley of Virginia," McGee challenged those who doubted the need for Confederation, "look around you to the mountains of Georgia, and you will find reasons as thick as blackberries."[66] Statements of this kind are a reminder that what we term "arguments" in favour of Confederation were in reality a mixture of inducements appealing to self-interest and threats which fed on fear. Historians delude themselves if they assume that contemporary debate was intended to supply posterity with the pieces of a satisfying intellectual jigsaw.

The beguiling temptation to treat the evidence in this way may be illustrated by Gladstone's memorandum, penned on 12 July 1864 in response to demands for vast expenditure on fortifications in Canada, in which the parsimonious chancellor of the exchequer doubted whether Britain could do much to defend the provinces. "Their long and comparatively thin strip of occupied territory extends for 2,000 miles between the States on one side, and the sterility of pinching winter on the other.... I say, nothing can defend them except the desperate energy of a brave, self-relying population, which fights for hearth and home." Assuming, perhaps optimistically, that the "United States can scarcely have a quarrel with Canada for its own sake," he argued that the more provinces were "detached, as to their defensive not less than their administrative responsibilities, from England," the better cross-border relations would become. Consequently, Gladstone opposed the spending of money on any defence projects, with the possible exception of the naval base at Halifax, and argued instead that "the true aim of all our measures at this important juncture should be to bring the people of our British North American Colonies ... as nearly to a national sentiment and position as their relation to the British Crown will permit." Accordingly "efforts should be made, without delay, to ascertain whether it is practicable to establish a Federation or Political Union of these Colonies."[67]

Read in isolation, Gladstone's memorandum makes Confederation seem a mathematical deduction from the circumstances of the defence crisis arising out of the probable end of the Civil War. In fact, it was almost certainly written in the light of the announcement in *The Times* of the previous day of the formation of a new Canadian ministry dedicated to the achievement of precisely that aim of general federation.[68] Gladstone's far-sightedness may be judged by the fact that in July 1864, he still believed that the Civil War would end with the disruption of the United States. He was a consistent opponent of defence projects in Canada: his own prime minister, Palmerston, even complained to Queen Victoria that the chancellor was "troublesome and wrong-headed" on the subject.[69] The only mathematical deduction which motivated Gladstone was the hope of knocking a large item off his expenditure column: Confederation was not so much an alternative as a diversion.

In fact, examined closely, Gladstone's argument was open to serious challenges. The assumption that political unity would strengthen defence is one which appeals to the modern world where the military alliances require sovereign states to accept an element of interdependence. When applied to self-governing colonies in the mid-nineteenth century, the argument was of little relevance: as the duke of Newcastle had written in 1862, "none of the objections which oppose [Confederation] seem to impede a union for defence."[70] Yet even under a unified command, the provinces would remain weak in the face of the United States: the North had put 2.3 million men into the field—almost equal to the entire population of the province of Canada. Canadian critics could not see how union with the tiny province of New Brunswick—which had one third of the population of neighbouring Maine—could do anything but weaken their already parlous position.[71] As for creating a national community ready to fight to the death for home and hearth, Gladstone's panacea threatened to have exactly the reverse effect. In the Atlantic provinces, critics bitterly objected to the imposition of a government which could order their militia away to distant frontiers—as one Newfoundlander would put it, to leave their bones to bleach "on the desert sands of Canada."[72] British North America would continue to be a narrow corridor between aggressive Yankees and pinching winter. In fact, the rest of the package—massive territorial expansion westward—would actually make Canada's position weaker in relation to its powerful neighbour.

Nor was the Intercolonial Railway an indisputable addition to the defensive capabilities of the provinces. Gladstone certainly did not think so: he had fought bitterly against the Intercolonial guarantee in 1861-62, and his 1864 memorandum opposed any commitment to defend territory not accessible year-round by sea. If the danger of American invasion were so immediate and terrible, the construction of a railway—it was to take nine years to complete—was hardly an appropriate response. In fact, the argument that the Intercolonial would strengthen the provinces at all was open to strong challenge. Even if the New Brunswick section of the line was diverted from the St John valley to the remote Gulf coast of the province, the existing Grand Trunk line still ran very close to the United States—"in some places not more than fifteen or twenty miles from the frontier.... An enemy could destroy miles of it before it would be possible to resist him, and in time of difficulty it would be a mere trap for any troops passing along it, unless we had almost an army to keep it open."[73]

Summarising the argument that Confederation offered a defence against the Americans, a young French Canadian radical called Wilfrid Laurier claimed that it was like being "armed with an egg-shell to stop a bullet ... a wisp of straw in the way of a giant."[74]

It is when we turn to Gladstone's argument that Confederation would be a step in disengagement from Britain—and hence a defensive measure by avoiding American anger—that the fundamental flaw of the interconnecting explanation becomes obvious. Sir Richard MacDonnell, lieutenant-governor of Nova Scotia, was not one of the more towering intellects of the colonial service, but it was not simply obtuseness which made him

> unable to see in what way England would be less vulnerable through Canada or Canada less vulnerable through England when a confederated Parliament meets at Ottawa than now. There is not a foot of territory in all these hundreds of thousands of square miles which would become less English than now, so long as the Queen's representative is head of the Federation; nor is there any obligation in regard to these Provinces which now devolves upon Britain that would be diminished by their being thus huddled into one heterogeneous assemblage.[75]

Palmerston refused to admit that there was even a question to be discussed "whether our North American provinces are to be fought for or abandoned."[76] "You can best tell whether the Government at Washington look to unite our provinces to their own Northern Dominion," wrote Lord Russell to the British minister there. "But if they do, they must look to a fight with us."[77] Sir Frederic Rogers, permanent undersecretary at the Colonial Office, felt that, "nothing can be more provoking than to be obliged (if we are obliged) to fight the United States in the place and manner which are most disadvantageous to ourselves, for a colony which is no good to us and has no real care for us. Yet somehow I would not wish England to refrain from doing so; for England would not be great, courageous, successful England if she did."[78] "Let all foreign States know that in touching the North American provinces they touch England," warned a London newspaper.[79] There is abundant contemporary evidence that the British would have rallied to the defence of the Canadians just as they honoured their treaty obligations to Belgium in 1914 and their imperial responsibility to the Falkland Islanders in 1982. As late as 1879, Salisbury referred to the "solid and palpable fact that if they are attacked England must defend them."[80] This is not to deny that there was speculation that the colonial tie might eventually be broken, but this was more speculation than the prediction which Donald Creighton portrayed in his analysis of British press response to the Quebec Conference. "The present status of the federation, *The Times* observed, 'will be only a state of transition, marking the passage of British America from colonial tutelage to national independence'." *The Times* did indeed use those words, but the opening clause of the quotation actually read: "it may be that such a

Government will be only a state of transition."[81] Having garbed themselves in the laboratory coat of the scientist to assert that British North American union was necessary, the historians then proceed to use literary sleight of hand to blur three very different concepts: Confederation, independence and neutrality.

In short, it does not follow that a union of the British North American provinces was the logical deduction from the circumstances and problems of 1858-64. Asked to chew upon the continental imperatives so evident in the 1860s, the computer of historical destiny would surely have been far more likely to have anticipated the verdict which Goldwin Smith pronounced ten years later: "Canadian nationality being a lost cause, the ultimate union of Canada with the United States appears now to be morally certain."[82] If French and English really could not co-exist in a single province which shared the mighty common interest of the St Lawrence system, by what logic could they build a transcontinental nation? If the overarching threat was the challenge of the United States, with ten times their population, by what logic could the provinces choose that moment to create a new polity, and one still linked to Britain? This was precisely the kind of ill-timed provocation which lay behind the Mexican empire—as British ministers realised when they vetoed the Canadian wish to style the new union a "kingdom." In bloodless logic, the only enduringly safe solution to the continental crisis of 1864-67 would have been to have sought terms of annexation to the United States. But people are not particles: British North Americans did not wish to become United States Americans. The *logical* alternatives to annexation all involved some kind of neutralisation, either by remaining as separate provinces or by establishing a form of union under explicit United States hegemony. New Brunswick in 1865-66 might well have moved along the first path, had Washington showed any interest in supporting the "westward extension" of its railway system into New England. Joseph Howe feared that Confederation would only be workable in terms of the second alternative. "Inevitably it must succumb to the growing power of the republic. A treaty offensive and defensive with the United States, involving ultimate participation in a war with England, would be the hard terms of its recognition as a separate but not independent state.[83] Some might feel that the terms of the Treaty of Washington of 1871 indicate that Canada had the worst of the muddled bargain. Britain and the new Dominion each continued to be vulnerable through their mutual association, and it was Canada which paid most of the price of appeasing American anger.

Historians and scientists share one important common feature in their method of working: both must master the trick of asking the right question. We can now see that it was pointless for scholars to ponder how it was that leeches managed to cure the sick, or to speculate on the reasons why long-distance mariners avoided sailing over the edge of the world, because we realise that their very assumptions were unfounded. Historians may fall more subtly into a similar trap. There is a world of difference between asking "why did the British North American provinces decide to adopt Confederation in the 1860s?" and identifying the real issue: "why was it that it was the idea of *Confederation* which dominated the British North American response to the crises of that decade, rather than other logically deducible solutions?"

The starting point for explaining Canadian Confederation, then, must be the idea itself.[84] It was not the only solution which could be deduced from the circumstances of 1864; indeed, we are not entitled to assume that it was necessarily the obvious one. (The American Civil War, as opponents of Confederation were fond of pointing out, did not provide strong *prima facie* evidence in favour of the adoption of any form of federal system.) Why then did the idea of Confederation come to dominate in this way? The answer is that it had been around for a long time, always seen as a future aim, an ultimate destiny. But, so it may be retorted, that could also be said of its United States counterpart, Manifest Destiny, which was equally confident in seeing Canada's destiny as part of the American republic. There are important differences. Confederation, in a curious way, had been felt to be coming closer. Even in 1858, the Canadian ministry had defined its policy not so much as Confederation as in terms of an investigation of "the principles on which a bond of a federal character ... may perhaps hereafter be practicable."[85] One participant in the 1862 railway negotiations recalled that it was still regarded as "a matter in the distance."[86]

It was in this context that the elements of the interlocking package had become familiar. In an age of railway building, arguments had been advanced that a line from Halifax to Quebec would increase trade and offer advantages for defence. Since the railway could not be built overnight, these arguments really had no validity when applied to an immediate crisis, such as the imminent ending of Reciprocity or the likelihood of American invasion. However, the importance of the "atmosphere of crisis" of 1864 lay not in the emergence of Confederation as a logical response, but in its adoption as the only measure large enough to provide psychological reassurance. "For the first time we are being brought face to face with the reality," said a New Brunswick newspaper.[87] "Everybody admits that Union must take place sometime," said John A. Macdonald. "I say now is the time."[88] Arguments which had a measure of plausibility when applied to the stately flow of British North American development were nonetheless thrown in, because of their very familiarity, to the Niagara of the 1860s. In practical terms, Confederation was a substitute rather than a centrepiece, a tacit recognition that real and immediate answers could not be forthcoming. "Conscious as we are of our inability to protect these colonies by land in case of war, we must naturally rejoice at any event which seems to place them in a position in which they would be better able to protect themselves," commented *The Times* on the Quebec Conference.[89] The key word, of course, was "seems"; and the substantive point the impossibility of providing effective defence. Anticipating Chester Martin, the Irish journalist W. H. Russell was convinced that "the white heat of American strife" provided the moment for "welding" the provinces together, but he warned against assuming that "any confederation ... would yield such an increase of force as would enable the collective or several members of it to resist the force of the Republic of the Northern American United States—at least, not just now." There might seem to be a contradiction here: Confederation was for defence, but would not provide additional strength. Yet to Russell, it was

> not surprising that the idea of a Confederation for the purposes of common defence ... should have arisen. It is surprising that it should have floated about for so long, and have stirred men to action so feebly. I think it is the first notion that occurs to a stranger visiting Canada and casting about for a something to put in place of the strength which distant England cannot, and Canadians will not, afford.[90]

Confederation, then, was at best a long-term development strategy ingeniously passed off as an emergency response to current crisis. Once launched, the idea seized the centre ground of political debate, and it became easier to go forward than to attempt to fall back. French Canadian Bleus would no longer be able to resist "rep. by pop." within the province of Canada after agreeing to the principle in the proposed federal legislature. As the Montreal *Gazette* remarked, it would be highly optimistic to believe "that, after an acknowledgement that Upper Canada ... is entitled to seventeen more members than Lower Canada, the agitation can ever again be quelled."[91] Joseph Cauchon's great fear was that the Lower Canada English minority would crumble under the pressure of a united upper province, preferring to see the issue settled even at the cost of privileged sectional representation: entrenchment of the equal representation of the two sections had been abolished in 1854, and a simple majority would be sufficient to redistribute ridings in favour of Upper Canada.[92] In practice, legislation would involve something much more bitter and protracted than a snap vote, but even so few could welcome a crisis which, as Bishop Laflèche put it, would end either in "la guerre civile ou la domination du Haut-Canada dans l'Union Législative."[93] It was better to settle for the local autonomy within a wider confederation which was actually on offer rather than hope to negotiate similar guarantees from an upper province which knew it had the upper hand. For his part, John A. Macdonald equally could not afford to see Confederation fail, since he needed the Maritimes to make good his relative weakness in Upper Canada: at the very least, Confederation as a policy aim was a useful basis for ministerial alliance with former opponents, such as William McDougall, in 1864-66, just as it had been for gaining A. T. Galt in 1858. While significant sections of the province of Canada found it in their interest to keep Confederation at the head of their agenda, their allies in the Maritimes could accept temporary reverses as the price of long-term success.

Recent consideration of the issue in Nova Scotia and New Brunswick challenges the pejorative view that all Maritimers were sunk in parochial lethargy, and tends rather to see objections as directed against the terms of the Quebec scheme rather than the aim of union itself, to be ultimately quietened not by "Repeal" but by "Better Terms."[94] Yet even if we embrace the traditional and more censorious view of Maritime hostility to Confederation, we can still see how pressure for the idea from Canada—with or without financial inducements—and from Britain turned it into a juggernaut which politicians had to board unless they wished to be crushed. The very breadth of the opposition coalition made it vulnerable to rupture, both in New Brunswick in 1865-66 and successively in Nova Scotia from 1866 through to 1869.

Thus once Confederation became launched as a practical issue, there is no great mystery in explaining how it managed to occupy the centre ground, marginalising its critics on all sides. The challenge to the historian is to identify the origins of that idea, which means ceasing to portray it as the necessary product of British North American circumstances. It means moving the starting point of explanation away from the perceived shortcomings of the province of Canada. It means above all abandoning Morton's "cantilever" of interlocking and equally imperative causal arguments, recognising instead the lesson which Gladstone learnt from Peel, that a scheme may be backed by different individuals for different reasons. Of course, this makes the explanation less artistically satisfying, gives it the appearance of being less scientifically watertight, less mathematically complete. It is good to note that at least one distinguished scholar has abandoned the flirtation with basic physics. "One can add up the causes of Confederation and still not get the sum of it," Peter Waite wrote in 1987.[95] Far from being an abandonment of the historian's responsibility of explanation, such a conclusion is in fact a fundamental precondition for interpreting the past in the way that the past actually happened. "One might, indeed, put together a kind of algebraic formula or polygon of forces from the many external and internal elements that converged in pressure upon British North America to unite," wrote J. B. Brebner, "but it would be an inexact thing at best."[96] In seeking to explain Canadian Confederation, it is better for historians to settle for the humility of inexact geometry than to delude themselves with the bombast of inexact science.

Notes

1. Bury's Cambridge inaugural lecture of 1903, "The Science of History," is given in H. Temperley, ed., *Selected Essays of J. B. Bury* (Cambridge, 1930), pp. 3-22, with the quoted phrase at pp. 4, 23; for G. M. Trevelyan's reference to Canada, see his *Clio, A Muse And Other Essays* (London, 1913), p. 141. I am grateful to Dr James Sturgis for discussion of the points at issue, and to Mr Louis A. Delvoie for pointing out that Bury is misquoted in E. H. Carr, *What is History?* (Harmondsworth ed., 1964), p. 57.

2. Especially in D. G. Creighton, *The Road to Confederation: The Emergence of Canada, 1863-67* (Toronto, 1964) and W. L. Morton, *The Critical Years: The Union of British North America 1857-73* (Toronto, 1964). The various textbooks cited below indicate that the consensus of explanation did not simply originate in the Centennial decade: Creighton, for instance, had been an advisor for the 1937-40 Rowell-Sirois Commission whose deliberations were influenced by the idea of a strong central government.

3. Arthur Marwick, *The Nature of History* (London, 1970), p. 99. Marwick's view is endorsed by G. Kitson Clark, *The Critical Historian* (London, 1967), pp. 19-31, but for a very different approach, see Lee Benson, *Toward The Scientific Study of History: Selected Essays* (Philadelphia, 1972). See also Carr, *What is History?*, pp. 56-86.

4. Trevely in, *Clio*, p. 147.

5. Chester Martin, *Foundations of Canadian Nationhood* (Toronto, 1955), pp. 297-98.

6. *The Canadian Encyclopedia* (3 vols, Edmonton, 1985),i, p. 399.

7. R. D. Francis, R. Jones and D. B. Smith, *Origins: Canadian History to Confederation* (Toronto, 1988), p. 378.

8. D. H. Fischer, *Historians' Fallacies: Toward a Logic of Historic Thought* (New York, 1970), pp. xxi-xxii.

9. Peter Stansky, *Gladstone: A Progress in Politics* (New York, 1979), p. 26, and cf. John Morley, *The Life of William Ewart Gladstone* (3 vols, London, 1903), i, p. 192.

10. J. M. Beck, *Joseph Howe: ii, The Briton becomes Canadian, 1848-1878* (Kingston, 1973), p. 182.

11. J. M. S. Careless, *Canada: A Story of Challenge* (Toronto, rev. ed., 1974), pp. 230, 245.

12. A. R. M. Lower, *Colony to Nation: A History of Canada* (Don Mills, rev. ed., 1964), p. 313. Lower believed that the United States constitution was drawn up at Annapolis in 1789. Ibid., p. 314.

13. W. L. Morton, *The Kingdom of Canada: A General History from Earliest Times* (Toronto, rev. ed., 1969), p. 317.

14. Donald Creighton, *John A. Macdonald* (2 vols, Toronto, 1965).

15. E. W. Watkin, *Canada and the States: Recollections 1851 to 1886* (London [1886]).

16. D. G. Creighton, *Dominion of the North: A History of Canada* (Toronto, rev. ed., 1962), esp. pp. 304-5; K. McNaught, *The Pelican History of Canada* (London, rev. ed., 1978), pp. 115, 134.

17. *The Nation* (Toronto), 26 February 1875, quoted F. H. Underhill, *The Image of Confederation* (Toronto, 1964), p. 20.

18. J. Bartle: Brebner, *Canada: A Modern History* (Ann Arbor, 1960), p. 273.

19. National Library of Wales, Harpton Court Collection, C/2028, Herman Merivale to G. C. Lewis, 23 September 1858.

20. J. L. Finlay and D. N. Sprague, *The Structure of Canadian History* (Scarborough, Ont., rev. ed., 1984), p. 170.

21. Lower, *Colony to Nation,* p. 321.

22. J. R. Colombo, ed., *Colombo's Canadian Quotations* (Edmonton, 1974), p. 381, quoting E. B. Biggar, *Anecdotal Life of Sir John A. Macdonald* (1891).

23. Morton, *Critical Years,* p. 112. Morton also damned Sandfield as "an unabashed mediocrity, reckless in speech but cautious in action" whose real offence seems to have been that he aimed "to prolong the life of the Union, and avoid disruption, or confederation." (Ibid., p. 113) Goldwin Smith, no forgiving observer, called him "a thoroughly good fellow, and honest." Goldwin Smith, *Reminiscences* (New York, 1910), p. 436. Professor Roger Hall points out that the "pawky" Sandfield won the hand of a Louisiana beauty.

24. By F. R. Scott, in a famously sardonic poem in 1957.

25. Joseph Pope, *Memoirs of the Right Honourable Sir John Alexander Macdonald* (Toronto, 1894), p. 373.

26. In a bound, Sandfield Macdonald is premier on Ontario on p. 4 of Creighton's second volume. Cf Bruce W. Hodgins, *John Sandfield Macdonald, 1812-1872* (Toronto, 1971), pp. 87-88.

27. Creighton, *Dominion of the North,* p. 290.

28. Lower, op. cit., p. 300.

29. Cf Ged Martin, "Launching Canadian Confederation: Means to Ends 1836-64," *Historical Journal,* xxvii (1984), p. 595 and n.

30. Morton, *Critical Years,* p. III.

31. Spencer Walpole, *The Life of Lord John Russell* (2 vols, London, 1889), ii, pp. 13-30, esp. p. 25.

32. Ibid., ii, p. 144. Cf Donald Southgate, *"The Most English Minister ...": The Policies and Politics of Palmerston* (London, 1966), pp. 308-10.

33. For the militia in this period, see Morton, *Critical Years,* pp. 126-28, 145; Hodgins, *Sandfield Macdonald,* pp. 70-71; Richard A. Preston, *Canada and "Imperial Defense"* (Durham, N.C., 1967), pp. 46-47, 59-62.

34. Quoted, Underhill, *Image of Confederation,* p. 19.

35. Lower, op. cit., pp. 307-8.

36. Henri Joly drew attention to the awkward discrepancy in *Parliamentary Debates on the Subject of the Confederation of the British North American Provinces* (Quebec, 1865), p. 357. [Cited as *CD*].

37. Lower, op. cit., p. 311.

38. Ibid., p. 313.

39. E.g. Thomas Scatcherd and Christopher Dunkin, *CD,* pp. 747, 508.

40. Lower, op. cit., p. 310.

41. The point was made by Henri Joly and A-A. Dorion in *CD,* pp. 356, 528.

42. Lower, op. cit., p. 315.

43. Figures quoted from British Parliamentary Papers, and given in Ged Martin, "The Case Against Canadian Confederation," fn, 86 in Ged Martin, ed., *The Causes of Canadian Confederation: Papers from a Seminar held at Edinburgh May 1988* (Fredericton, forthcoming). For contemporary doubts about trade, see *CD,* pp. 863 (J-B-E. Dorion) and 355 (Henri Joly).

44. *CD,* p. 230.

45. P. B. Waite, *Canada 1874-1896: Arduous Destiny* (Toronto, 1971), pp. 76-77.

46. Morton, *Kingdom of Canada,* p. 317.

47. Pope, *Memoirs,* P. 684.

48. Doug Owram, *Promise of Eden: The Canadian Expansionist Movement and the Idea of the West, 1856-1900* (Toronto, 1980), pp. 38-58; cf. *Weekly Globe,* 14 September 1855, cited J. M. S. Careless, *Brown of the Globe, i: The Voice of Upper Canada 1818-1859* (Toronto, 1959), p. 229.

49. Lower, op. cit., p. 295.

50. Macdonald to Watkin, 27 March 1865, in Pope, op. cit., pp. 397-98. Of course, Macdonald had some motive in talking down the value of the West, since Canada would have to purchase the land it needed for settlement.

51. Alexander Morris, *Nova Britannia* (Toronto, 1884 ed.), p. 78.

52. Letter to unnamed recipient, 13 November 1860, in Watkin, *Canada and the States,* pp. 12-15. "I hope you will not laugh at me as very visionary" began W. H. Draper when he told the parliamentary enquiry of 1857 of his hope that a transcontinental railway might be built, if not in his own lifetime, then in that of his children. British Parliamentary Papers, 1857 (2nd session), xv, q. 4102, p. 218.

53. G. P. Browne, ed., *Documents on the Confederation of British North America* (Toronto, 1969), p. 99.

54. Creighton, *Macdonald, i: Young Politician,* pp. 348-49.

55. Browne, ed., *Documents,* p. 165.

56. *CD,* p. 453 (T. C. Wallbridge).

57. e.g. J. B. B. Pouliot, MPP for Témiscouata.

58. *CD,* pp. 54-55.

59. P. B. Waite, *The Life and Times of Confederation, 1863-67* (Toronto, 1962), pp. 134-160; A. I. Silver, *The French-Canadian Idea of Confederation, 1864-1900* (Toronto, 1982), pp. 33-50.

60. Joseph Cauchon, *L'Union des Provinces de l'Amérique Britannique du Nord* (Quebec, 1865), p. 46.

61. *CD,* p. 624 (Joseph Perrault).

62. Morton *Critical Years,* p. 149.

63. This idea was reflected in a number of questions asked at the British parliamentary enquiry of 1857.

64. C. P. Stacey, "Confederation: The Atmosphere of Crisis," in Edith G. Firth, ed., *Profiles of a Province: Studies in the History of Ontario* (Toronto, 1967), pp. 73-79.

65. *British Colonist,* 7 January 1865, quoted Creighton, *Road to Confederation,* pp. 229-30.

66. Speech at Montreal, 22 October 1864, in E. Whelan, comp., *The Union of the British Provinces* (Charlottetown, 1865), pp. 122-23.

67. Printed in Paul Knaplund, *Gladstone and Britain's Imperial Policy* (London, 1927), pp. 228-42.

68. *The Times,* 11 July 1864, confirmed in an admiring leading article of 12 July.

69. G. E. Buckle, ed., *Letters of Queen Victoria,* 2nd series (London, 1926), i, pp. 248-49.

70. Newcastle's despatch of 21 August 1862 to Lord Monck is widely quoted. Cf Browne, ed., op. cit., p. 32.

71. As A-A Dorion pointed out, *CD,* p. 256-57.

72. James Hiller, "Confederation Defeated: The Newfoundland Election of 1869," in J. Hiller and P. Neary, eds, *Newfoundland in the Nineteenth and Twentieth Centuries* (Toronto, 1980), p. 83. Ct Ged Martin, "The Case Against Canadian Confederation" for similar statements in the Maritimes.

73. Dorion again, *CD,* p. 257.

74. Quoted, J. Schull, *Laurier: The First Canadian* (Toronto, 1966), p. 57.

75. Public Record Office, Co 217/235, MacDonnell to Cardwell, 22 November 1864, fos 187-212.

76. Public Record Office, Russell Papers, PRO 30/22/27, Palmerston to Russell, 29 July 1864. "There may be much to be said for the theory ... that our Colonies are an encumbrance and an expense, and that we should be better off without them, but that is not the opinion of England, and it is not mine." Even Gladstone reluctantly concluded: "If Canada desires to be British, and to fight for British connection as men fight for their country, I do not think we can shrink from the duty of helping her." Gladstone to Cardwell, private, 23 May 1865, in Knaplund, *Gladstone and Britain's Imperial Policy,* pp. 243-46.

77. Public Record Office, Russell Papers, PRO 30/22/97, Russell to Lord Lyons, copy, 20 October 1864, fos 87-88.

78. Rogers to Taylor [1865], in *Autobiography of Henry Taylor, 1800-1875* (2 vols. London, 1885), ii, pp. 241-42.

79. *Sun,* 25 November 1864. Cardwell, so often cited as the closet separatist, spoke in almost identical terms in the House of Commons on 11 March 1869. J. Mackay Hitsman, *Safeguarding Canada, 1763-1871* (Toronto, 1968), p. 214.

80. Quoted, Creighton, *Macdonald, ii: Old Chieftain,* p. 277.

81. Compare Creighton, *Road to Confederation,* p. 215 with *The Times,* 24 November 1864.

82. Goldwin Smith, "The Political Destiny of Canada," *Fortnightly Review,* cxxiv, 1 April 1877, pp. 431-59, esp. p. 458.

83. Joseph Howe, *Confederation in Relation to the Empire* (London, 1866) printed in J. A. Chisholm, ed. *The Speeches and Public Letters of Joseph Howe* (2 vols, Halifax, 1909), ii, p. 489.

84. Ged Martin, "An Imperial Idea and Its Friends: Canadian Confederation and the British, 1836-64," in G. Martel, ed., *Studies in British Imperial History: Essays in Honour of A. P. Thornton* (Houndmills, 1986), pp. 49-94.

85. Quoted, W. M. Whitelaw, *The Maritimes and Canada before Confederation* (ed. P. B. Waite, Toronto, 1966), p. 128.

86. William Annand, quoted by Waite, *Life and Times,* p. 50.

87. Saint John *Evening Globe,* quoted ibid., p. 63.

88. Speech at Halifax, Whelan, comp., *Union of the British Provinces,* p. 46.

89. *The Times,* 15 October 1864.

90. W. H. Russell, *Canada: Its Defences, Condition, and Resources* (London, 1865), pp. 311-12.

91. Montreal *Gazette,* 3 March 1865, quoted Waite, *Life and Times,* p. 155.

92. Cauchon, *L'Union des Provinces,* p. 18.

93. Laflèche to Boucher de Niverville, 2 March 1864, quoted in Walter Ullmann, "The Quebec Bishops and Confederation," *Canadian Historical Review,* xliv (1963), p. 218.

94. Phillip A. Buckner, "The Maritimes and Confederation: A Reassessment"; James L. Sturgis, "The Opposition to Confederation in Nova Scotia, 1864-1868" and B. D. Tennyson, "Economic Nationalism, Confederation and Nova Scotia," forthcoming in Ged Martin, ed., *Causes of Canadian Confederation.*

95. Peter Waite, "Between Three Oceans: Challenges of Continental Destiny (1840-1900)," in C. Brown, ed., *The Illustrated History of Canada* (Toronto, 1987), p. 314.

96. Brebne, *Canada,* p. 277.

Name Index

Adams, John, 275
Alexander, David, 400, 413
Aleyrac, Jean-Baptiste de, 178
Allen, Ethan, 259
Alston, Willis, 283
Amherst, Jeffery, 48, 173, 201-202
Andreani, Paolo, 342
Anne (Queen of England), 128, 141
Anne of Austria, 73
Antorche, Antoine, 77
Ariès, Philippe, 66
Armstrong, Lawrence, 142
Arthur, Sir George, 440
Astor, John Jacob, 318, 478
Aubin, J., 367
Auge, Étienne, 203-204
Auld, William, 340
Aylmer, Lord, 381, 385

Baby, Louis-François-Georges, 200,
    202-206, 214
Bagot, Sir Charles, 440, 445
Bailey, Jacob, 242, 246
Baldwin, Robert, 435, 445, 450, 465-
    470, 548
Baldwin, Stanley, 553
Ballenden, John, 341
Barbel, Marie-Anne, 81, 119, 121
Barclay, Robert, 306
Batt, James, 346
Bayard, James A., 280
Beaud, Michel, 227
Beauharnois de la Boische, Charles
    de, 221
Beaulac, Madame de, 80

Beaven, James, 491
Bedford, Duke of, 209
Beer, D., 443
Bégon, Michel, 111
Belle-Isle, Maréchal de, 176
Bellestre, Picotté de, 211
Benoist, Madame, 82-83
Berkley, George, 292
Bernard, J.B., 371
Bernier, Gérald, 92, 197, 224-227,
    229-230, 232
Bertrand, Joseph, 372
Biard, Pierre, 15, 20, 21, 24
Bibaud, Michel, 199
Bigge, J.T., 444-445
Bigot, François, 121-123, 152, 161,
    200-201, 218
Bird, James, 343, 347
Bismarck, Otto von, 544
Black, John, 481, 483-485, 487
Blain, Jean, 223
Blake, Edward, 435
Bleecker, Hermanus, 284
Bliss, Michael, 92, 103
Bonaparte, Napoléon, 286, 294-296,
    299, 301, 304
Bond, William, 514
Borroughs, Peter, 441
Bosher, J.R., 117
Bottum, Sarah, 259, 262
Boucher, Pierre, 81
Boucherville, Pierre Georges
    Boucher de, 368
Bougainville, Louis-Antoine de, 177-
    178, 180, 183

Bourdon, Joseph, 372
Bourgeault, Ron, 337, 345
Bourgeoys, Marguerite, 73, 74, 119-120
Bourget, Bishop Ignace, 451-456, 462
Bourlamaque, François-Charles de, 177, 182
Bowler, Arthur, 271, 291
Bowman, Elizabeth, 261
Braddock, Edward, 131, 166, 177, 179
Brant, Molly, 256-257, 264
Brassier, Gabriel-Jean, 214
Braudel, Fernand, 107, 231
Bréard, Jacques, 121
Brebner, J.B., 133, 141, 550, 565
Brewster, William, 366
Briand, Bishop Jean-Olivier, 207
Brigham, Elijah, 284
Brock, Isaac, 303, 305-306
Broglie, Maréchal de, 186
Bronson, Editha, 517
Bronson, H.F., 517
Brougham, Lord, 442, 445
Brown, Desmond, 124, 133
Brown, George, 435, 530, 535, 556-557
Brown, Jennifer, 334, 335
Brown, Thomas Storrow, 359, 374, 389
Brown, Wallace, 239-240
Brunelle, Ambrose, 373
Brunet, Jean, 118
Brunet, Michel, 91, 197, 198
Brydges, C.J., 557
Buller, Charles, 442, 445
Bumsted, Jack, 476-477
Burgoyne, John, 257-258, 264
Burwell, William A., 278
Bury, J.B., 543
Butler, John, 241

Byles, Mather, 249

Cadet, Joseph-Michel, 121-122
Cadore, Duc de, 296
Caldwell, Henry, 208-209
Calhoun, John C., 287
Campbell, Patrick, 245
Campbell-Bannerman, Sir Henry, 438
Campot, Jacques, 118
Cardwell, Edward, 541-542
Careless, J.M.S., 547
Carleton, Guy, Lord Dorchester, 206-207, 209-212, 245-246
Carleton, Thomas, 246
Carman, Bliss, 249, 393
Carnarvon, Lord, 541-542
Caron, René-Édouard, 455
Cartier, George-Étienne, 471, 530, 533-539, 548, 551-553
Cartier, Jacques, 3
Cartwright, Elizabeth, 258
Cartwright, Richard, Jr., 258
Cartwright, Richard, Sr., 244, 258
Cauchon, Joseph-Édouard, 453, 455-456, 459, 463, 557, 564
Caulfield, Thomas, 142
Cazeau, Charles-Félix, 455, 461
Champigny, Jean Bochart de, 41, 43
Champlain, Samuel de, 3, 5
Chapman, H.S., 438
Charbonneau, Hubert, 55
Charlebois, Léon, 359
Charles Emmanuel III, 176
Charlevoix, F.X., 64, 74, 79
Chartier, Abbé Étienne, 368, 372, 375, 386
Chartier de Lotbinière, Michel, 209, 214
Cherrier, Côme, 359
Choiseul, Étienne-François, duc de, 163, 186
Claus, Daniel, 257

Clay, Henry, 279, 282, 286, 304
Clay, Matthew, 285-286
Cobbett, William, 244
Cocking, Matthew, 339
Coke, Edward, 138-140
Colbert, Jean-Baptiste, 75, 94, 95, 104-106, 165
Colborne, Sir John, 450
Colen, Joseph, 345
Collins, John, 207
Collins, Kins, 234
Cook, James, 537
Copeland, Sir Reginald, 437, 444
Cornwallis, Edward, 143, 150-157
Cortés, Donoso, 454
Côté, Dr. C.H.O., 360
Cotton, Barthélemy, 103
Couagne, Madame, 81
Courson, Joseph, 455
Couture, Claude, 197, 223
Coward, J., 363
Craig, G.M., 444
Craig, James, 296, 302, 307
Craig, Robin, 404
Crampton, J.F.T., 539
Creighton, Donald, 224, 355, 530-531, 547, 549, 551
Crémazie, Jacques, 461
Cugnet, François-Étienne, 113

Daccarrette, Michel, 118, 120
Daine, Madame, 70
Dalhousie, Lord, 380
Darche, François, 374
Davidson, John, 249
Deane, Phyllis, 228
Dearborn, Henry, 305-306
Dechêne, Louise, 39-40, 48
De Lery, François-Joseph, 209
De Lery, Gaspard-Joseph Chaussegros, 209-210
De Lery, Louis-René, 210-211, 214

Delezenne, Ignace-François, 118
Delisle, Guillaume, 93
Denonville, Jacques-René, 43
Denys, Nicolas, 10, 15, 20-22
Dérigé, Louis, 363
Desandrouins, Jean-Nicolas, 168, 180
D'Eschambault, Joseph Fleury, 211
Desgenettes, Abbé, 452
Desha, Joseph, 285
Diblee, Filer, 243
Dièreville, Diere de, 13, 20, 23
Dieskau, Jean-Armand, Baron de, 168-169, 175, 177, 179
Dingman, Garnet, 258
Dobb, Maurice, 333
Dorchester, Lord (see Carleton, Guy)
Dorion, A.A., 535
Doughty, Arthur, 79
Draper, William Henry, 456, 466-467
Drucour, Augustin de Boschenry de, 168
Drummond, Lewis Thomas, 455-457
Dudouyt, Abbé, 44
Dugard, Robert, 114-116, 120-121
Dumouchelle, Joseph, 364-365
Dunn, Thomas, 205, 207
Dupanloup, Bishop, 459
Dupré, Saint-Georges, 204-206
Dupuy, Claude, 46
Durham, Lord, 391-392, 437-448

Eales, Walter, 476, 492, 493, 502
Eccles, W.J., 39-40, 114, 161-162, 174
Elgin, Lord, 446, 458, 462, 466
Ellis, Edward, 439-442
Empy, Philip, 259
Enard, Jeanne, 81
Estèbe, Guillaume, 121

Fabre, Édouard, 372, 382
Fanning, Edward, 244
Farb, Peter, 11
Fauteux, Joseph-Noel, 113
Feeny, John, 335
Ferguson, Rachel, 260
Fergusson, C. Bruce, 124-125
Ferland, J.B.A., 199
Fidler, Peter, 326, 328
Fiedmont, Louis-Thomas Jacau de, 174
Fingard, Judith, 394, 419
Finlay, Hugh, 207
Finlay, J.L., 550
Finlay, William, 348
Fischer, David Hackett, 546
Fischer, Lewis R., 394
Fish, Mary, 255
Flett, George, 487
Forbin-Janson, Bishop Charles, 451
Forest, Madame de la, 70
Fornel, Louis, 119
Fornel, Madame, 83
Foucoult, François, 120
Francheville, François Poulin de, 112, 118
Francheville, Therese, 118
Franklin, Benjamin, 116, 275, 276
Franklin, John, 326-327
Franquet, Louis, 43, 47, 64, 67, 70, 74, 80, 82, 216
Fraser, Malcolm, 205
Fraser, Simon, 244, 537
Frederick the Great, 175
Frégault, Guy, 70, 91, 160-161, 174, 197
French, Mrs. Jeremiah, 261
Frontenac, Louis de Buade, Comte de, 71, 127

Gallatin, Albert, 282
Galt, A.T., 564
Gariépy, Joseph, 360

Garneau, F.X., 199
Gaston, William, 286
Genêt, Edmond Charles Édouard, 301, 302
George I, 129, 141
Giannettino, Susan, 310, 321
Girod, Amury, 364, 373
Gladstone, W.E., 546, 559-561, 565
Glasford, Jane, 259
Glenelg, Lord, 441
Glenie, James, 246
Godet, Michel, 374
Gosford, Lord, 386-387, 389, 444
Gradis, David, 121-122
Graham, Andrew, 345-346
Graham, G.S., 404, 444
Grandmaison, Eleonore de, 81
Grant, Phoebe, 264
Grant, William, 205, 207
Gray, John, 207
Greer, Allan, 333
Gregory XVI, 452
Greville, C.C.F., 442
Griffiths, Naomi, 125, 149
Groulx, Abbé Lionel, 91, 197, 357-358
Groulx, Lionel, 530
Grundy, Felix, 279
Guertin, Catherine, 71
Guillimin, Charles, 109-110
Guinaud, Henry, 203
Guinaud, Joseph, 203
Gullison, B.F., 404
Gunn, John, 486
Gustede, Dominique Nicolas de Laas de, 188
Guy, Pierre, 203, 204

Haldimand, Frederick, 201, 206, 208, 210, 212-213, 242
Haliburton, Thomas C., 249
Hamel, M.P., 443
Hamelin, Jean, 92, 197, 231

Hankey, Robert, 203
Hargrave, James, 346
Harmon, Daniel, 315, 326
Harper, John A., 280
Harrison, William Henry, 298
Hart, Benjamin, 373
Haughey, Charles J., 554
Havy, François, 99-100, 115-116, 119-120
Hazeur, François, 109
Head, Sir Edmund, 533
Head, Sir Francis Bond, 438, 446
Hearne, Samuel, 314, 338-339, 345
Henripin, Jacques, 55
Henry, Alexander, 205, 314-315, 326-327
Henry, John, 296
Hincks, Francis, 465, 468-471, 548
Hocquart, Gilles, 96, 111-113, 115, 220, 222
Hopson, Peregrine, 157
Horsman, Reginald, 271-272
Howe, John, 277, 301
Howe, Joseph, 248, 443, 539, 546
Howick, Viscount, 438, 440-441
Howse, Joseph, 347
Hubert, Bishop Jean-François, 213, 214
Hudon, Mgr. Hyacinthe, 455
Hull, William, 272-273, 282, 286, 304-306
Hunt, George T., 1-2
Huntly, Sir Henry, 484
Huppé, Joseph, 103

Ingersoll, Charles, 287
Inglis, Bishop Charles, 246
Innis, Harold, 310, 336, 396, 400
Isham, Charles, 339

Jablow, Joseph, 322-323
Jackson, Andrew, 281
Jacobs, Wilbur R., 12

Jaenan, Cornelius, 2
Jarvis, Amelia, 478, 485
Jarvis, Edward, 477-487
Jarvis (Gray), Elizabeth, 478, 480, 482
Jarvis, Henry, 478, 484
Jarvis, Mary, 478, 480, 482, 483, 486
Jarvis, Munson (father), 478
Jarvis, Munson, 478, 481, 483-484
Jarvis, William, 484
Jauge, Simon, 203
Jefferson, Thomas, 277-278, 281, 293, 295-296, 299, 304, 547
Jobin, André, 370
Johnson, John, 244, 255-256, 259-260, 262, 264
Johnson, Mary Watts, 255-256
Johnson, Polly Watts, 261
Johnson, Richard M., 280
Johnson, William, 179, 256-257
Johnstone, Chevalier de, 185
Jordan, Jacob, 208
Joybert, Madame, 81
Juchereau, Charlotte-Françoise, 119

Kalm, Peter, 40, 43-44, 46-47, 64, 74
Kelso, J.J., 522-523
Kennedy, John F., 438
Kerber, Linda, 263
King, William Lyon Mackenzie, 435, 551
Kingwood, Mary Anne, 515
Kingwood, Sarah, 515
Knox, John, 48
Konwatsi'tsianienni (See Molly Brant)
Kosciusko, Thaddeus, 281

Labadie, Angélique, 361
Labouchere, Henry, 541
La Chesnaye, Charles Aubert de, 106-109, 118, 216

Laflèche, Bishop, 564
Lafontaine, Louis-Hippolyte, 435, 445, 449, 450, 455-470, 548
La Galissonière, Roland-Michel Barrin de, 96, 152
Lahontan, Louis-Armand, 10
La Jonquière, Jacques Pierre Taffanel, Marquis de, 132
Lalemant, Gabriel, 5
Lamennais, Jean-Marie de, 452
Lamothe, Madame, 43
La Naudière, Thomas de, 204, 206
Lanctôt, Gustave, 75
Langevin, Edmond, 461-462
Langevin, Hector, 461-462
Langevin, Jean, 461
La Pause, Chevalier Jean-Guillaume-Charles de, 177-178, 182
Laplanche, Christophe, 366
Lartigue, Bishop Jean Jacques, 368, 390, 450, 458
La Rodde, Étienne-Guillaume de Senezergues de, 170
Laslett, Peter, 66-67, 334, 489
La Tour, Françoise Marie de, 79, 81
Laurier, Wilfrid, 435, 561
Laval, François, 24, 45, 107
Lavoie, L., 366
Law, Lyman, 284
Lawrence, Charles, 132, 143, 154-155, 157-159
Leacock, Stephen, 468
Leboeuf, Marguerite, 77
Le Clercq, Chrestien, 20, 23
Lefebvre, Jean, 99, 100, 115-116, 119-120
Legueux, Barbe, 68
Le Jeune, Paul, 10
Le Loutre, Jean Louis, 131, 152-154, 157
Le Mercier, François, 168

Lemothe, Madame de, 82
Lemoyne, Madame, 83
Leroux, J., 372
Léry, Gaspard-Joseph Chaussegros de, 174
Lespérance, T., 373
Lévis, Chevalier François-Gaston de, 173, 176, 180, 185-189
Lewis, N.B., 404
Lewis, Oscar, 329
Liancourt, François, Alexandre Frédéric la Rochefoucault, 342
Lijphart, Arend, 471
Lincoln, Abraham, 547
L'Isle Dieu, Abbé, 156
Littleton, Thomas, 138
Liverpool, Lord, 296
Lompre, Jérôme, 365
Longmoor, Robert, 339
Lord, William, 425
Lotbinière, Madame, 70
Louis XIV, 41, 66, 96, 164-166
Louis XV, 163-164
Lowe, Sir H., 486
Lower, A.R.M., 547, 550, 551, 553-555
Lucas, Sir Charles, 437, 446
Ludlow, Gabriel, 244
Lunn, Jean, 112
Lusignan, Madame, 80
Lynch, Isidore, 203
Lynch, Thomas, 203
Lytton, Sir Edward George Earle Bulwer, 541, 542

MacDonagh, O., 444
Macdonald, Agnes, 517
Macdonald, John, 326
Macdonald, John Alexander, 471, 530, 533-539, 547-548, 550-552, 556, 563, 564

MacDonald, John Sandfield, 469, 471, 551-553
Macdonnell, Alexander, 469
Macdonnell, Miles, 319, 339-340, 346, 348
MacDonnell, Sir Richard, 561
MacDougall, Colonel, 552, 553
MacGregor, James, 245
Mackenzie, Alexander, 327, 336, 537
Mackenzie, Roderick, 334
Mackenzie, Simon, 207
Mackenzie, William Lyon, 358, 360, 386, 435, 498
Macleod, William C., 8
MacNutt, W.S., 247-248
Macon, Nathaniel, 283, 285, 287
Madison, James, 274, 278-279, 284, 291, 293-294, 296-299, 305
Maisonneuve, Paul de Chomedey, 65, 73
Makahonuk, Glen, 310, 332
Malartic, Anne-Joseph-Hippolyte de Maurès de, 184, 187-188
Mance, Jeanne, 73-74, 119
Manning, Helen Taft, 355
Mantoux, Paul, 227, 344
Marcel, Pierre, 178
Marchington, Philip, 244
Maria Theresa (Empress of Austria), 175
Marie de l'Incarnation (Marie Guyart Martin), 68, 73, 78, 120
Marie-Joseph-Angélique, 119
Marie-Magdelaine, 81
Marin, Madame, 70
Marston, Benjamin, 246
Marteilhe, John, 207
Marten, Humphrey, 335, 347
Martin, Calvin, 1, 10
Martin, Chester, 435-436, 545, 550, 564

Martin, Ged, 435-437, 531, 543
Marwick, Arthur, 544
Marx, Karl, 227-228, 234, 342, 344
Mascarene, Paul, 130, 142-143, 150-151, 156
Mason, George, 275
Mathias, Peter, 230
Matonabbee, 314
Matthews, Keith, 413,
Maurepas, Jean-Frédéric Phélypeaux de, 95-96
Maximilian, Prince, 328, 330
Mayhew, Henry, 424
Mazzini, Joseph, 458, 461
McClellan, Catherine, 323
McClelland, Peter, 396, 408-410
McConell, Jean, 264
McDonald, Alexander, 253
McDonald, Susannah, 253
McDonell, John, 261
McDougall, William, 564
McGee, Thomas D'Arcy, 559
McGinnis, Sarah Kast, 257-258, 262-263
McGinnis, Timothy, 257
McLachlan, James, 497
McLane, David, 302
McMaster, William, 555
McNaught, Kenneth, 549
Melbourne, Lord, 438-439, 442
Menou d'Aulnay-Charnisay, Charles, 79
Merceau, Madame de, 80
Merriman, John X., 446
Merritt, William Hamilton, 469
Metcalfe, Sir Charles, 443, 466
Meulles, Jacques de, 110, 221
Meyers, John Walden, 260
Meyers, Mary Cruger, 260
M'Gillivray, Duncan, 326-328
Miller, Morris, 286
Miquelon, Dale, 92, 197, 198, 215

Molière (Jean Baptiste Poquelin), 66
Molson, John, 372
Monet, Jacques, 436, 449
Monroe, James, 281-282, 286, 304
Montaigne, Michel Eyquem de, 32
Montals, Bishop Clausel de, 452, 456
Montcalm, Louis-Joseph, Marquis de, 121-122, 160-161, 167-172, 174-176, 178-179, 181-184, 189
Montour, Nicolas, 207
Montreuil, Chevalier Pierre-André de Gohin de, 177, 179, 185
Moore, Mary, 516
Moore, Stephen, 207
Moreau, Édouard, 368
Morgan, Edmund, 495
Morgan, Lewis H., 5, 6
Morin, Augustin-Norbert, 455-457, 461-462, 470-471, 548
Morris, James, 469
Morse, Jedediah, 277
Morton, A.S., 310
Morton, W.L., 310, 311, 547, 551, 556, 558, 565
Mountain, Bishop Jacob, 491
Munro, John, 259
Munro, Mary, 259-260
Murray, James, 173, 188, 207-209
Myatt, Joseph, 338

Neilson, John, 381, 386, 449
Nelson, Horatio, 294
Nelson, Robert, 374
Nelson, Wolfred, 358, 360, 373-374, 389-390
Newcastle, 5th Duke of, 560
Nicks, John, 338
Nicolai, Martin L., 161, 174
Nish, Cameron, 118, 197
Noble, Arthur, 131
Noel, Jan, 40, 63

Noël, S.J.R., 436, 465
Normanby, Marquis of, 441
North, Lord, 438

Odell, Jonathan, 244, 249
Ommer, Rosemary, 413
Osgood, Herbert L., 6
Osgood, T., 511
Osgoode, William, 211
Ouellet, Fernand, 92, 197, 224, 231, 355-356, 390
Owen, Wendy, 476-477

Pacaud, J.N., 371
Palmer, Bryan, 334
Palmerston, Henry Temple, 552, 560, 561
Panting, Gerry, 410, 413
Papineau, Denis-Benjamin, 455-457
Papineau, Louis-Joseph, 357-361, 365, 367, 369, 372, 374, 381, 383-384, 386, 388, 390, 449-450, 458, 461, 463
Paquet, Gilles, 231
Parent, Étienne, 388, 449, 463-464
Parker, Isabel, 261
Parker, Samuel, 329
Parkman, Francis, 1, 5, 39, 91, 160
Parmentier, Louis, 367
Parr, John, 241-242, 247
Parr, Joy, 475
Pascaud, Antoine, 216, 220
Péan, Angélique, 70, 121
Péan, Michel, 121
Peck, Catherine, 264
Peel, Robert, 388, 546, 565
Pelly, Robert Parker, 510
Peltier, Toussaint, 359
Pennisseaut, Louis, 121
Pentland, H.C., 333-334
Percival, Spencer, 296
Perkins, Bradford, 273

Perry, Oliver Hazerd, 306
Philipps, Richard, 141-142
Pie, Cardinal Louis-Édouard, 452
Pitt, William, 245
Pius IX, 458
Plessis, Parscau du, 182
Pocahontas, 314
Poisson, Mathurine, 81
Polk, James K., 445
Pompadour, Madame, 121
Pontchartrain, Jérôme Phélypeaux, Comte de, 71, 94-96
Pontleroy, Nicolas Sarrebource de, 168, 179
Porchnev, Boris, 357-358
Potter, Janice, 240, 250
Pouchet, Pierre, 179, 182, 184-185
Pratt, Julius, 273-274
Prentice, Alison, 476, 488
Prevost, George, 302-303, 307-308
Price, Benjamin, 207
Prieur, F.-X., 372
Procter, Henry, 306
Prophet, The, 298

Quincy, Josiah, 284

Ramezay, Claude de (son), 82
Ramezay, Claude de, 70
Ramezay, Jean-Baptiste Nicolas Roch de, 82, 131
Ramezay, La Gesse de, 82
Ramezay, Louise de, 82, 119
Randolph, John, 279, 280, 301
Rappaport, Roy A., 12
Ratisbonne, Théodore de, 452
Raudot, Antoine-Denis, 71
Raudot, Jacques, 45, 71, 216, 222
Ray, Arthur J., 336
Reid, S,J., 446
Rémond, Rene, 233
Renaud, F.-X., 368

Repentigny, Agathe de Saint Père, Mme de, 70, 82, 119
Repentigny, Le Gardeur de, 70, 82
Rice, Richard, 397
Rich, E.E., 336, 343, 347
Richardson, John, 233
Ridgeley, Henry, 284
Riverin, Dennis, 109
Robertson, Thomas, 282-283
Robinson, Alice, 521
Robinson, John Beverley, Jr., 243, 248
Rocheblave, Philippe de, 214
Rochembeau, Comte de, 186
Roebuck, John, 384, 438
Rogers, Robert, 180
Rogers, Sir Frederick, 561
Rooke, Patricia T., 476, 506
Roothaan, Fr. John, 452
Ross, Alexander, 329-330
Ross, Alexander, 477-487
Ross (Boyd), Anna Maria, 478, 480, 482, 485
Ross, Henrietta, 478, 481, 484-485
Ross, James, 478, 481-487
Ross, Jemima, 478, 481, 484-485, 487
Ross, Roderick, 484, 487
Ross, Sarah, 478
Ross, William, 477, 479, 481-485
Rothman, David, 511
Rousseau, Jean Jacques, 492
Rouville, Seigneuress de, 82
Ruette d'Auteuil, 71
Russell, Jonathan, 281
Russell, Lord John, 387, 441-442, 445, 552, 561
Russell, Peter E., 161
Russell, W.H., 564
Ryerson, Egerton, 442, 476, 490-501
Ryerson, Stanley, 334, 355
Ryland, Herman, 302

Sagar, Eric W., 394
Sahlins, Marshall, 324
Saint Félix, Pierre Cassagniau de, 183
Saint Germain, Vincent, 207
Saint Père, Agathe de, 82
Saint Simon, Madame, 70
Saint Vincent de Paul, 73
Saint-Vallier, Jean, 24-45
Salaberry, Charles-Michel de, 214
Salaberry, Charles René de, 308
Salée, Daniel, 224
Salisbury, Lord, 561
Saunders, John, 244, 246
Saunders, S.A., 410
Saxe, Maurice, Maréchal de, 162, 164, 176
Schnell, R.L., 476, 506
Schwartz, Mrs. Simon, 260
Schwartz, Simon, 260
Séguin, Maurice, 91, 197, 530
Selkirk, Earl of, 318-319, 340, 342
Séné, Marcel, 366
Senneterre, Maréchal de, 174
Shaw, George Bernard, 549
Sheffey, Daniel, 285
Shelburne, Lord, 208, 210, 211
Sherbrooke, John, 299, 301
Sherwood, Justus, 259
Shirley, William, 132, 150, 159
Signay, Archbishop Joseph, 450
Silver, Arthur, 557
Simcoe, John G., 247, 297, 303
Simiand, François, 100
Simpson, George, 336, 340, 341, 343
Simpson, Thomas, 346
Sissons, C.B., 495
Slobodin, Richard, 322, 323
Smith, Adam, 342, 344
Smith, Goldwin, 562
Smith, William, 244, 246
Smyth, Alexander, 272, 273, 286
Sombart, Werner, 233

Speck, Frank G., 15
Spence, Nicholas, 343
Sprague, D.N., 550
Stacey, C.P., 161, 559
Stagg, J.C.A., 274
Stanley, G.F.G., vi
Stanley, Lord, 442
Stansky, Peter, 546
Steele, Ian, 175
Stephen, James, 299, 440
Stephens, J.W., 499
Stewart, John, 486
Stone, Dothe, 254, 255
Stone, Joel, 254
Stow, Silas, 283
Strachan, John, 247, 300, 490-501
Sully, Artus de, 81
Surprenant, Jacques, 360-361
Sutherland, James, 335
Sutherland, Neil, 506, 525
Swainson, Donald, 469
Sydenham, Lord, 443, 451

Taché, Étienne-Pascal, 455-457, 552, 553
Talon, Jean, 75, 104-106, 116
Tanquay, Cyprien, 220
Ta Van, Vinh, 92, 197, 224, 229-230, 232
Taylor, John, 281
Taylor, William, 346
Tecumseh, 298, 306
Tétro, Jean Marie, 374
Têtu, J.-F., 366
Thompson, David, 326, 329-330, 336, 537
Thompson, E.P., 344-345, 348
Tilley, Samuel Leonard, 244
Tomison, William, 345, 347
Toomy, James, 346
Tough, Frank, 349
Traun, Field Marshal, 175
Trevelyan, G.M., 543, 545

Trofimenkoff, Susan, 356, 380
Trudel, Marcel, 197
Tunbridge, John, 515
Tupper, Charles, 530
Turton, Thomas, 439

Umfreville, Edward, 335, 336, 338

Van Kirk, Sylvia, 334, 338, 479
Van Rensselaer, Soloman, 305
Vauban, Sébastien Le Prestre de, 94
Vaudreuil-Cavagnal, Pierre de
    Rigaud, Marquis de, 161, 169-
    173, 181, 185
Vaudreuil, Louise-Elisabeth de
    Joybert, Marquise de, 67, 70-71
Vaudreuil, Philippe de Rigaud,
    Marquis de, 70, 71, 98, 221
Verchères, Marie-Madeleine de, 79
Veuillot, Louis, 451-452
Vézin, Olivier de, 112, 113
Vezon, Joseph Fournerie, 188
Vialars, Antoine, 203
Vialars, Daniel, 203
Victoria, Queen, 534-535, 560
Viger, Denis-Benjamin, 360-361,
    372-373, 449, 456-458, 462
Viger, Louis-Michel, 373
Villiers, Coulon de, 131

Wadin, Jean-Etienne, 207
Waiser, W.A., 349
Waite, Peter, 545, 557, 565
Wakefield, Edward Gibbon, 439,
    441, 443
Waldec, Mary 259
Wallace, Frederick William, 393,
    395, 400, 405
Wallot, Jean-Pierre, 231
Ward, Artemus, 287
Ward, J.M., 437
Washington, George, 158, 261, 275-
    276, 287
Watkin, Edward, 549, 556
Watts, Isaac, 507, 510
Wax, Murray, 16
Webster, Daniel, 286
Wellington, Duke of, 552
Wentworth, John, 244, 247
White, Alexander, 261
Wilmot, Lemuel Allen, 248
Wilson, Thomas, 287
Winslow, Edward, 245-246
Witthoft, John, 19
Wolfe, James, 160-161, 165, 167,
    171-172, 183
Wright, H., 486
Wrong, George M., 39
Wyeth, Nathaniel J., 329